Nuclear and Particle Physics

W E Burcham
and
M Jobes

Longman Scientific & Technical

Longman Scientific & Technical
Longman Group Limited
Longman House, Burnt Mill, Harlow, Essex CM20 2JE, England
and Associated Companies throughout the world

Copublished in the United States with
John Wiley & Sons, Inc., 605 Third Avenue, New York
NY 10158

First published 1995

British Library Cataloguing in Publication Data
A catalogue entry for this title is available from the British Library.

ISBN 0-582-45088-8

Library of Congress Cataloging-in-Publication data
Burcham, W. E.
Nuclear and particle physics / by W. E. Burcham and M. Jobes.
p. cm.
Includes bibliographical references and index.
ISBN 0-470-23421-0 (USA only)
1. Nuclear structure. 2. Particles (Nuclear physics)—Measurement. 3. Particle acceleration. I. Jobes, M. (Melvyn) 1938– . II. Title.
QC793.3.S8B87 1994
539.7—dc20 94-13700 CIP

Set by 16UU in Times New Roman
Produced by Longman Singapore Publishers (Pte) Ltd
Printed in Singapore

Contents

4, 5, 6

6, ...

Preface

This book is not a history of nuclear and particle physics. It does of course recognize the debt that the latter discipline owes to the former in the development of both concepts and technologies since the end of the Second World War. But it takes the point of view that advances in understanding of the fundamental nature of matter are now likely only to be found in an energy range traditionally regarded as the province of the particle physicist.

For this general reason the book is written at two levels. In Part I is presented a brief summary of the main topics normally appearing in an undergraduate course in nuclear structure physics. Much of this will even have been studied in A level courses at school and the emphasis in this part is on simplicity. In Part II, in contrast, an attempt is made to explore the fundamental symmetries of nature in detail and this requires the presentation of an adequate theoretical background, or reference to it in standard textbooks. In view of this emphasis on theory in Part II the necessary description of particle detection and acceleration techniques used in high energy physics is included briefly in Part I (chapter 2). The development attempted in Part II, however, cannot be brief and is appropriate to the latter part of an undergraduate course and also to postgraduate studies.

We have attempted to use SI units as far as possible. But complete unification of both nomenclature and units is still a distant goal. We regretfully believe that the student must become accustomed to meeting differences of convention in his reading and must make the appropriate concessions to established practice. Therefore, although the symbols J, I and P are used for angular momentum, isobaric spin and parity, the reader must be aware of the alternative symbolism I, T and π that is still much used in nuclear structure and atomic physics books and papers.

We also regret that it has not been possible, without making an already long book longer, to include an account of the many important applications of nuclear physics (and even of particle physics). The roles of nuclear fusion in stellar energy development and of nuclear fission in reactor physics are not described and there is no mention of the stimulus given to computer and superconductor technology by high energy accelerator programmes. It has been thought better to concentrate on the principles and requirements that underlie these developments.

W E BURCHAM
M JOBES
BIRMINGHAM, AUGUST 1993

Note added in proof. The results of a search for the top quark (see p. 578) in $p\bar{p}$ collisions at a centre-of-mass energy of 1.8 TeV have recently been presented by the CDF collaboration at Fermilab. The search includes standard model decays of the top quark to $ee\nu\bar{\nu}$, $e\mu\nu\bar{\nu}$ and $\mu\mu\nu\bar{\nu}$ final states as well as final states consisting of $e\nu$ + jets and $\mu\nu$ + jets. The excess of events over the expected background can be interpreted as due to $t\bar{t}$ production although the statistics are too limited to establish the existence of the top quark beyond doubt. Under the assumption that the excess is due to $t\bar{t}$ production, a constrained fit on a subset of events yields a mass of $174 \pm 10^{+13}_{-12}$ GeV/c^2 for the top quark.

W.E.B.
M.J.
BIRMINGHAM, MAY 1994

Acknowledgements

We are grateful to the following for permission to reproduce copyright material: Addison-Wesley Publishing Company, Menlo Park, California for Figs 12.24 and 12.25 from D H Perkins (1987) *Introduction to High-energy Physics* 3rd Edition and Fig. 14.38 from V D Barger and R J N Phillips (1987) *Collider Physics*; American Institute of Physics for Figs 4.11, 4.12, 5.10, 8.4, 9.13, 9.15, 9.16, 10.12, 10.13, 10.14, 10.17, 11.26, 11.27, 14.43 and 15.3 from *Physics Review Letters*, Figs 6.6, 6.7, 6.8, 6.12, 9.23, 12.8 and 12.14 from *Physical Review*, Figs 5.9 and 6.11 from *Reviews of Modern Physics* and Fig. 2.10 from *Reviews of Scientific Instruments*; Annual Reviews Inc., New York for Figs 12.15 and 12.16 from *Annual Review of Nuclear and Particle Science*; W A Benjamin, New York for Figs 3.4 and 3.6 from A Bohr and B Mottelson (1969) *Nuclear Structure I*; CERN for Figs 2.19, 2.20, 13.7 and 14.2; Institute of Physics, Bristol for Figs 12.27, 14.12, 14.13 and 14.15 from *Reports of Progress in Physics*; McGraw-Hill, New York for Figs 2.6, 2.7, 3.1(a), 3.2, 3.3 and 5.3 from R D Evans (1955) *The Atomic Nucleus*; North-Holland, Amsterdam for Figs 11.28, 12.13, 12.19, 14.24, 14.35, 14.39, 14.49, 14.59, 14.60, 14.61 from *Physics Letters*, Figs 14.54, 14.55, 14.56 and 14.57 from *Physics Reports*, and Fig. 6.22 and 14.51 from *Nuclear Physics*; Oxford University Press for Fig. 3.7 from R J Blin-Stoyle (1957) *Theories of Nuclear Moments* and Fig. 2.2 from W Heitler (1954) *The Quantum Theory of Radiation*; K P Pretzl for Fig. 2.25; Royal Society, London for Figs 6.1 and 6.2 from *Proceedings of the Royal Society*; Springer-Verlag, Berlin for Figs 13.7 and 14.45 from *Zeitschrift für Physik*; Taylor and Francis, Basingstoke for Fig. 2.15 from *Contemporary Physics*; van Nostrand Reinhold, New York for Fig. 2.9 from S A Korff (1946) *Electron and Nuclear Counters*; John Wiley and Sons Inc., New York for Fig. 5.14 and 5.15 from G C Hanna (1959) *Experimental Nuclear Physics III*; World Scientific Publishing Company, Singapore for Fig. 14.29 from *International Journal of Modern Physics* and Figs 14.47, 14.54, 14.56 and 14.57 from *Physics in Collision.*

While every effort has been made to trace the owners of copyright material, in a few cases this has proved impossible, and we take this opportunity to offer our apologies to any copyright holders whose rights we may have unwittingly infringed.

Part I *Nuclear Physics*

1 *The atomic nucleus*

Natural radioactivity · The nuclear hypothesis · The nuclear atom and nuclear properties · The evolution of nuclear physics · Units and definitions

The atomic theory was one of the great developments in physics in the nineteenth century and it provided a powerful microscopic model of the structure of matter. But little or nothing was contained in the theory in respect of the structure of the atoms themselves and it was not until the twentieth century brought the discovery of the nucleus and the concept of energy quanta that a useful atomic model could be envisaged. Nuclear physics is therefore both historically and essentially *subatomic physics*. In many nuclear phenomena the electronic environment can be disregarded, but it is nearly always present and plays an important part in the determination of nuclear properties.

In this introductory chapter we shall review the experiments that led to Rutherford's hypothesis of 1911 and we shall briefly survey the role that the nucleus plays both as the constituent of an atom and as an object in its own right. The starting point is the recognition in 1896 of a radically new behaviour of certain heavy atoms, the property of *radioactivity*.

1.1 *Natural radioactivity*[1–5]

In 1896 Henri Becquerel was studying the luminescence of uranium salts excited by ordinary light. He observed that radiations from the salts could cast shadows of opaque objects which could be recorded on a photographic plate wrapped in black paper, as in the case of the newly discovered X-rays. But unlike X-rays, the uranium shadow-casting radiation persisted even when the exciting light had been removed and he had to conclude that spontaneous emission of radiation, or *radioactivity*, was a property of the uranium atom itself. We now know that the radiations detected in these experiments were fast electrons emitted in the β decay of daughter products of the nuclide ^{238}U.

The new radiations were soon found to have the ability to discharge an electrified body and this permitted the use of the current in an ionization chamber for the quantitative assessment of radiation intensity, or *activity*. By using electrical detectors of this type in conjunction with chemical and physical procedures, Pierre and Marie Curie[2] were able to separate firstly polonium and next radium from crude uranium ores; 110 mg of radium was obtained from 10^3 kg of ore.

The work of Becquerel attracted the attention of Ernest Rutherford,[3,5] who was working on the conductivity of gases under J. J. Thomson in Cambridge. After some brief experiments with the uranium rays he turned his attention to the radiations of thorium and continued to study this substance during his tenure of the chair of physics at McGill University, Montreal (1898–1907). This was the heroic age of radioactivity, in which Rutherford, Soddy and their collaborators placed the subject on a quantitative basis.

The experiments of Curie and of Rutherford showed that radioactive radiations contained components with different powers of penetrating matter. The radiations first described were as follows.

(a) *α rays* are characterized by a positive charge and a low penetrating power of about 0.02 mm of lead. Experiments such as that of Rutherford and Royds, in which helium gas was found to appear in a tube into which α rays were being emitted, proved that the particle concerned ended its career as a helium atom. An α particle is a helium nucleus of charge $+2e$ and mass approximately $4m_p$ where m_p is the mass of the hydrogen nucleus or proton.

(b) *β rays* have a penetrating power of about 1 mm of lead. Magnetic deflection experiments showed this radiation to behave like particles with a negative specific charge e/m about equal to that of the electron; a β-particle is historically an electron, with charge $-e$ and mass m_e. For a good many years these particles were not clearly distinguished from the *internal conversion electrons* which originate in the electronic structure of the atomic system. In 1932 (see section 2.1.4, 'Pair production and annihilation', and chapter 7) the *positron*, which is the *antiparticle* of the electron, with mass m_e but charge $+e$, was discovered in the cosmic radiation and in 1934 positron-emitting radioactive elements were produced artificially. The symbols β^- and β^+ are frequently used to distinguish the two radiations in nuclear decay while e^- and e^+ are customarily used in particle physics.

In addition to these radiations we now recognize γ rays.

(c) *γ rays* are exponentially absorbed in matter and are capable of penetrating several millimetres of lead. This radiation is not deflected by magnetic fields and interacts with matter as do X-rays. γ radiation is electromagnetic and the radioactive γ rays were not always distinguished from characteristic X-radiations originating in the atomic system as a result of internal conversion or electron capture processes (chapter 5).

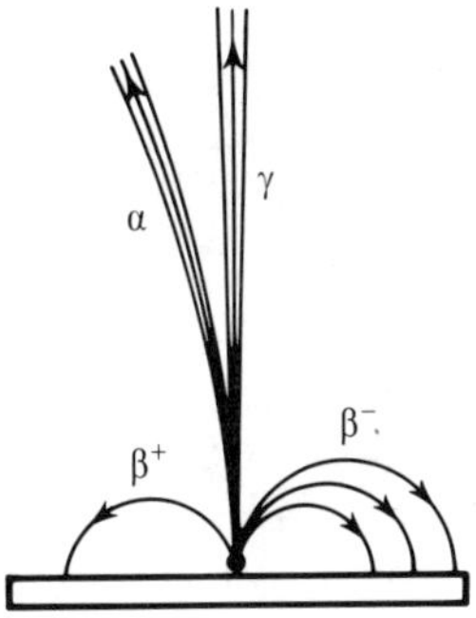

Figure 1.1
Schematic representation of the main radioactive radiations. A magnetic field is applied perpendicular to the plane of the diagram. Among the β^- rays, internal conversion electrons might also be found, and with the γ rays may also be X-rays from rearrangements of the atomic electrons.

Following Rutherford, the three main radioactive radiations are often represented schematically as shown in figure 1.1. Each exhibits an essential property of radioactivity, namely that the observed activity diminishes exponentially with time. If the activity A, as measured for instance by an ionization current, is assumed to be due to an atom by atom process, it must be proportional to the rate of decrease or of de-excitation of the number N_t of atoms present in a sample at time t and we may define it to be equal to this rate, i.e.

$$A = -\frac{dN_t}{dt} \text{ atoms s}^{-1}. \tag{1.1}$$

If the decay is really exponential

$$N_t = N_0 \exp(-\lambda t) \tag{1.2}$$

where λ is a *decay constant* and N_0 is the initial number of atoms, and then

$$A = \lambda N_t. \tag{1.3}$$

The *mean life* of the radioactive atoms is easily seen to be

$$\tau = \frac{\int_{N_0}^{0} t \, dN_t}{\int_{N_0}^{0} dN_t} = \frac{1}{\lambda} \tag{1.4}$$

and the half-value period of *halflife* $t_{1/2}$ is given by

$$\frac{N_0}{2} = N_0 \exp(-\lambda t_{1/2})$$

whence

$$t_{1/2} = \frac{\ln 2}{\lambda} = \frac{0.693}{\lambda} = 0.693\tau. \tag{1.5}$$

The decay law (1.2) may be deduced from the assumption that for a given atom the probability of decay per unit time is independent of the previous life of the atom. For such a process the probability of observing a given number of decays in a given time interval is governed by the *Poisson distribution* for random events.

Table 1.1
Part of the thorium series

Historical name	Nuclidic symbol	Halflife	
Thorium	$^{232}_{90}Th$	1.4×10^{10} a	(α)
Mesothorium 1	$^{228}_{88}Ra$	6.7 a	(β)
Mesothorium 2	$^{228}_{89}Ac$	6.13 h	(β)
Radiothorium	$^{228}_{90}Th$	1.91 a	(α)
ThX	$^{224}_{88}Ra$	3.64 d	(α)
Thoron	$^{220}_{86}Rn$*	55 s	(α)

* Each naturally occurring radioactive series contains a noble gas, historically called *radon, thoron* and *actinon.* These were understood to be isotopes of a single element that was at first called *radon* and was given the symbol Rn. The alternative name *emanation* (Em) is now often used.

Rutherford and Soddy in Montreal knew from the work of the Curies that radioactivity was connected with the appearance of new chemical substances in the radioactive sample, and after their concentrated study of the decay of thorium they proposed in 1903 the *transformation theory* of radioactivity. According to this the atoms of a radioactive substance disintegrate spontaneously, in accordance with the law (1.2), with the emission of an α or a β particle and with the formation of a new chemical atom. Ten years later, when the concept of atomic number Z as an index to the periodic table of the elements was gradually being understood, Soddy, Russell and Fajans wrote down the *displacement laws,* which describe these changes:

(a) the loss of an α particle displaces an element two places to the left in the periodic table and lowers its mass by four units ($\Delta Z = -2$, $\Delta A = -4$ using the atomic and mass numbers Z and A as defined in section 1.5.3);
(b) the loss of a β particle displaces an element one place to the right in the periodic table, but does not essentially alter the atomic mass ($\Delta Z = +1, \Delta A = 0$ for negative electron emission).

The application of these laws to the decay of the thorium atom is shown in figure 1.2. The nuclides shown in the figure are labelled with the historical name of the active element; present nuclidic designations are shown in table 1.1. It will be seen from figure 1.2 that ^{232}Th and ^{228}RdTh have the same atomic number, and therefore chemical nature, but a different mass. They are in fact *isotopes* of the element thorium; many elements have two or more stable isotopes and all elements have isotopes if unstable atoms are counted. The existence of isotopes was directly demonstrated by electromagnetic deflection by Thomson (1913) and by Aston (1919). Aston's mass spectrograph provided us with the first comprehensive table of isotopic masses. These were seen to be approximately integral multiples of the hydrogen atom mass and the nearest integer gave the mass number A; this is consistent with the modern

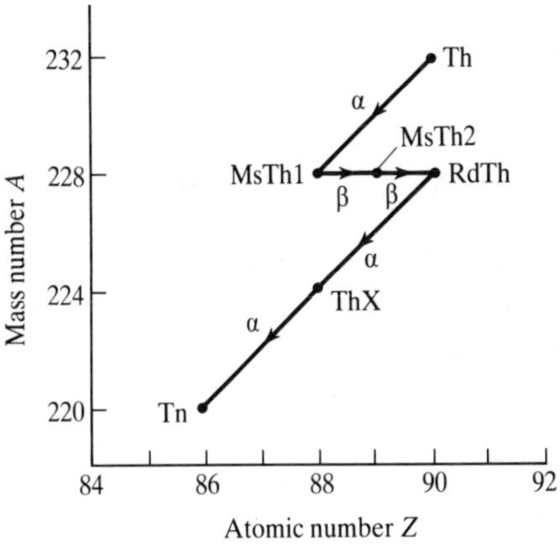

Figure 1.2 The displacement laws of radioactivity, illustrated by an A–Z plot for part of the naturally occurring theorium series. α decay changes both A and Z but β decay changes Z leaving A unaltered. See table 1.1 for modern nomenclature.

definition (section 1.5.3) because of the near equality of the proton and neutron masses.

The sequence of changes shown in figure 1.2 is the beginning of a *radioactive series*. Three such series are found in nature, deriving from long-lived parent atoms; they are the thorium series (mass number $4n$), the uranium–radium series ($4n + 2$) and the uranium–actinium series ($4n + 3$). Each of these leads through α and β emissions to a final stable isotope of lead. A fourth series (neptunium, $4n + 1$) has been prepared artificially and leads to a stable isotope of bismuth. In each series the emission of an α or β particle may be accompanied by γ radiation. The origin of this radiation was not understood until after the discovery of the nucleus, but we now recognize it to be the de-excitation spectrum of excited nuclear states, as shown in figure 1.3.

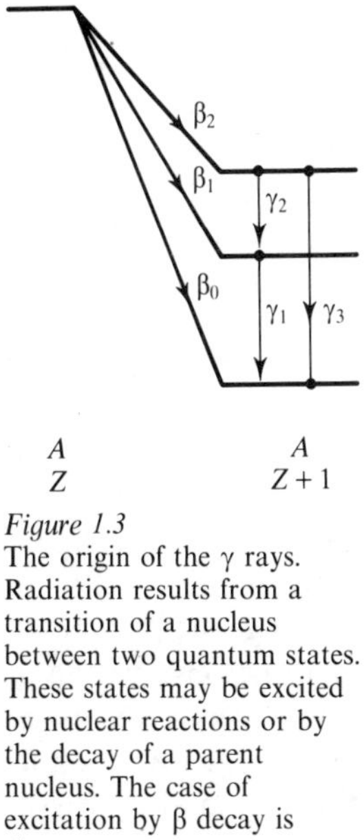

Figure 1.3
The origin of the γ rays. Radiation results from a transition of a nucleus between two quantum states. These states may be excited by nuclear reactions or by the decay of a parent nucleus. The case of excitation by β decay is shown.

The phenomena of classical radioactivity are now seen to be particular examples of general nuclear processes, which are observed abundantly in artificially produced active atoms over the whole accessible range of masses. Radioactivity had an immediate practical application to geological dating, but its outstanding importance to physics as a whole was that it gave evidence for a new group of fundamental interactions (now known as the short-range interactions, to distinguish them from electromagnetism and gravity) and that it provided the technology that led to the recognition of the atomic nucleus.

1.2 The nuclear hypothesis

During his work on the deflection of α rays in a magnetic field (1906), Rutherford noticed that the presence of a small amount of air in the vacuum apparatus affected the path of the particles, whereas it was quite difficult to achieve this with the available external electric fields. He concluded that the atom must be 'the seat of very intense electrical forces' and as soon as quantitative methods of counting α rays had been established he started an investigation of atomic structure using the deflection method.

At the time of these experiments the neutral atom was supposed, following the ideas of J. J. Thomson, to be a number of negatively charged electrons, moving in mechanically stable orbits within an equal quantity of positive electricity distributed throughout a sphere (figure 1.4(a)). With

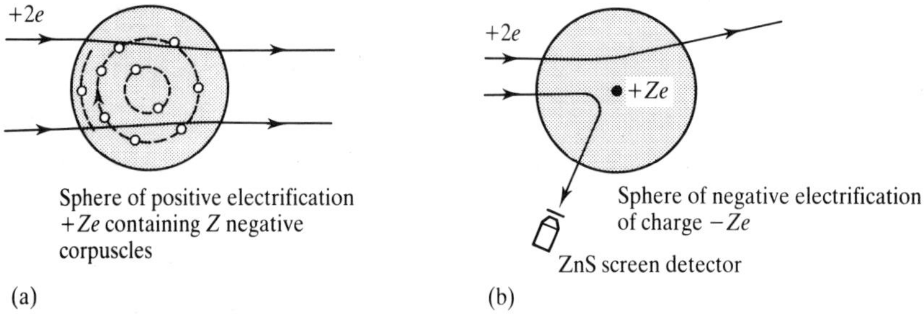

Figure 1.4
The scattering of α particles by an atom: (a) the Thomson model; (b) the Rutherford model.

such a structure, scattering of an incident charged particle would be a multiple effect due to superposition of a large number of individual encounters. The final angle of deflection of charged particles in passing through a thin foil would be small and should increase as $x^{1/2}$, where x is the thickness of the foil. Some evidence for this dependence was found for β particle scattering. Geiger, who was working at Manchester under Rutherford on the deflection of α particles by a gold foil, also observed many small-angle deflections using a scintillation detector, but Rutherford was not content with this and he asked Marsden, a student working with Geiger, to look particularly for large-angle scattering, of which there was already some evidence in the β particle work. The surprising result was found that a few α particles were scattered through large angles (figure 1.4(b)) from even the thinnest foils that could be used.

This result dominated Rutherford's thinking during the winter of 1910–11 but it was not long before he had interpreted the observation in terms of a model in which the electrons of an atom filled a sphere of atomic dimensions, approximately 10^{-10} m, but their charge was neutralized by a central positive charge on a *nucleus* of much smaller extent, approximately 10^{-14} m. Most of the atomic mass would reside in the nucleus and the incident particle would interact with the nucleus through the Coulomb repulsion between the two charges. The resulting orbit would be a hyperbola and for this a geometrical relation between the incident impact parameter and the final, asymptotic angle of deflection was easily obtained. This relation may be found as follows.

Let the hyperbolic trajectory of the incident α particle of mass m_1 and charge ze approaching a fixed charge Ze with velocity v_1 (at infinity) be

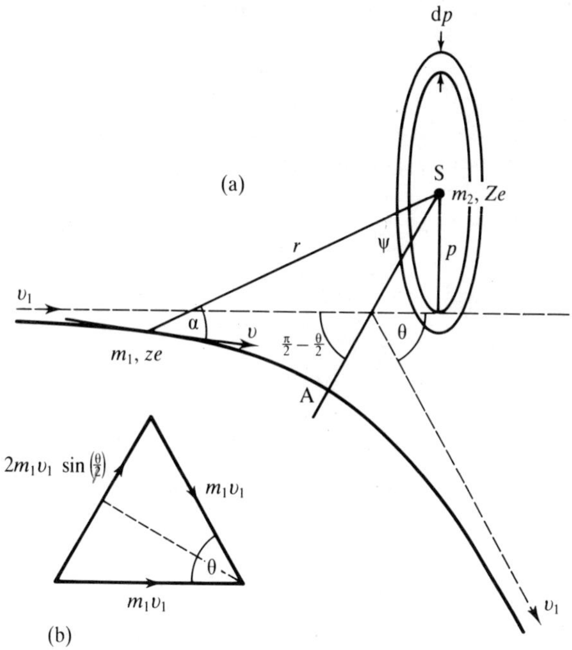

Figure 1.5
Rutherford scattering of a positively charged particle by a point nucleus: (a) particle trajectory; (b) vector diagram for momentum change.

as shown in figure 1.5(a). We assume non-relativistic conditions and an infinitely heavy scattering centre. The effect of the collision is to deviate the α particle through an angle θ without changing its energy but with a momentum change (figure 1.5(b)) of

$$q = 2m_1v_1 \sin(\theta/2) \tag{1.6}$$

in the direction of SA. This is effected by the Coulomb force, whose total impulse resolved along SA may be written

$$\begin{aligned} q &= \int_0^\infty \frac{zZe^2}{4\pi\epsilon_0 r^2} \cos\psi \, \mathrm{d}t \\ &= \int_{-\infty}^{\infty} \frac{zZe^2}{4\pi\epsilon_0 r^2} \cos\psi \frac{\mathrm{d}s}{v} \\ &= \frac{zZe^2}{4\pi\epsilon_0} \int_{-(\pi/2-\theta/2)}^{\pi/2-\theta/2} \frac{\cos\psi \, r \, \mathrm{d}\psi}{r^2 v} \frac{}{\sin\alpha} \end{aligned} \tag{1.7}$$

where α is the angle between the radius vector and the trajectory and ds is the path element. Since angular momentum must be conserved, we have

$$pv_1 = vr \sin\alpha \tag{1.8}$$

where p is the *impact parameter* for the collision, and the momentum change then becomes, after integration,

$$q = \frac{zZe^2}{2\pi\epsilon_0 p v_1} \cos\left(\frac{\theta}{2}\right). \tag{1.9}$$

Equating this to expression (1.6) gives

$$p = \frac{b}{2} \cot\left(\frac{\theta}{2}\right) \tag{1.10}$$

where

$$b = \frac{zZe^2}{2\pi\epsilon_0 m_1 v_1^2} \tag{1.11}$$

and is sometimes known as the *collision diameter*. It is easy to see that b is the closest distance of approach in a head-on collision.

In an actual experiment, we observe a number of particles within a small solid angle subtended by a suitable detector at a small target. If the target is of area A and thickness x, with N infinitely heavy nuclei per unit volume, the chance of a particle incident normally on the target finding a nucleus for an impact parameter between p and $p + \mathrm{d}p$ is

$$\frac{NAx2\pi p\,\mathrm{d}p}{A} = Nx\frac{b^2}{16}\operatorname{cosec}^4\left(\frac{\theta}{2}\right)(2\pi \sin\theta\,\mathrm{d}\theta) \tag{1.12}$$

by substitution from (1.10) and rearrangement. The particle considered will suffer a deflection between θ and $\theta + \mathrm{d}\theta$ and will leave the target within the solid angle $\mathrm{d}\Omega = 2\pi \sin\theta\,\mathrm{d}\theta$, which has been written explicitly in equation (1.12).

For n_0 incident particles and a detector subtending a solid angle $\mathrm{d}\Omega$ the number of such scattered particles observed will be

$$\mathrm{d}Y = n_0 Nx\left(\frac{zZe^2}{8\pi\epsilon_0 \mu v_1^2}\right)^2 \operatorname{cosec}^4\left(\frac{\theta}{2}\right)\mathrm{d}\Omega \tag{1.13}$$

using (1.11) and (1.12) and removing the restriction that the nucleus (mass m_2) is infinitely heavy by using the reduced mass μ $(=m_1 m_2/(m_1 + m_2))$ instead of m_1. The deflection θ then relates to the centre-of-mass system (appendix C).

Equation (1.13) makes the specific predictions that the scattered intensity is proportional to

(a) $\operatorname{cosec}^4(\theta/2)$, where θ is the angle of scattering,
(b) the thickness x of the scatterer,
(c) the square of the central nucleus charge Ze,
(d) the inverse square of the incident energy $\frac{1}{2}m_1 v_1^2$ (or strictly $\frac{1}{2}\mu v_1^2$).

Each point was verified in the careful experiments of Geiger and Marsden over the years 1911–13 and it was concluded, from a knowledge of the incident α particle energy, that the Coulomb law of force held down to an interparticle distance of at least 3×10^{-14} m. The validity of the hypothesis of a nucleus of minute dimensions and of mass considerably greater than that of the α particle seemed beyond dispute.

Today, with numerical values as given in chapter 3, we could characterize the gold nuclei studied by Geiger and Marsden as spherical objects of radius about 7×10^{-15} m and of mass about 3.3×10^{-25} kg for mass number 197. Fortunately for the development of nuclear physics, the Rutherford scattering law also follows from the full quantum mechanical calculation of charged particle scattering in a Coulomb field.

Equation (1.13) may be written in the form

$$\begin{aligned} \mathrm{d}Y &= n_0 N x \,\mathrm{d}\sigma \\ &= n_0 N x \sigma(\theta)\,\mathrm{d}\Omega \end{aligned} \tag{1.14}$$

where

$$\sigma(\theta) = \frac{\mathrm{d}\sigma}{\mathrm{d}\Omega} = \left(\frac{zZe^2}{8\pi\epsilon_0 \mu v_1^2}\right)^2 \operatorname{cosec}^4\left(\frac{\theta}{2}\right) \tag{1.15}$$

is known conventionally as the *differential cross-section.* This important quantity, determination of which is frequently an experimental object, is discussed generally in appendix B. Essentially it gives the probability of the occurrence of the process under investigation and here in particular it embodies the properties of the Coulomb interparticle interaction. For Rutherford scattering it may be seen from equation (1.6) to depend on the momentum transfer q in the collision as $1/q^4$.

1.3 The nuclear atom and nuclear properties

The nuclear atomic model arising from Rutherford's work in 1911 has had profound implications throughout physics and chemistry. In the first place the concept enables a clear distinction to be made between *atomic* and *nuclear* properties. For the former, the model concentrates on the electrons and the positive ions with which they interact and offers an explanation of chemical binding, optical and X-ray spectra and the macroscopic properties of matter in bulk. For the latter, since the nucleus is relatively inaccessible to normal disturbances (except magnetic fields) its own intrinsic properties such as radioactivity will be unaffected by the ordinary physical and chemical changes in which an atom participates. The energy carried by the radioactive radiations moreover, which is characteristic of nuclear energy changes, is larger by a factor of 10^5–10^6 than typical chemical energies.

The main link between the two types of property was provided convincingly by Moseley (1913), working in Rutherford's laboratory. He showed that the frequency of the lines of the characteristic X-ray spectrum depended regularly on the *atomic number* of the element concerned, equal to the ordinal number of the elements arranged in a sequence of increasing atomic mass value. As soon as Bohr (1913) developed his theory of spectra the atomic number used by Moseley was seen to be exactly the nuclear charge Ze expressed in units of the absolute value of the electronic charge, or alternatively the number of electrons in the neutral atom. These two quantities could be measured independently and each was found to be equal to Moseley's number.

Despite the enormously different scale of atomic and nuclear energy changes the nucleus and the electrons of an atom are tied together by the Coulomb force and the separation between nuclear and electronic phenomena is not complete. The interaction between nuclear charges and moments and the internal fields due to the electrons can give rise to *hyperfine structure effects* (appendix E), which are important in the determination of nuclear properties.

The properties of a nucleus X with which we will be concerned in this book, and especially in chapter 3, are

(a) charge Ze (where Z is the integral atomic number),
(b) mass m_x (absolute scale) or M_x (atomic scale) and mass number A equal to the integer nearest to M_x/M_H,
(c) radius R, of a spherical nucleus,
(d) angular momentum, or spin, characterized by a quantum number J which is integral or half-integral (other symbols, s, S, l, L and j, will be defined and used in specific contexts),
(e) magnetic dipole moment μ_J, for $J \geqslant \frac{1}{2}$,
(f) electric quadrupole moment Q_J, for $J \geqslant 1$,
(g) intrinsic parity P, related to spatial symmetry and usually said to be even or odd ($P = +1$ or -1),
(h) isobaric spin, related to nuclear structure symmetry and characterized by a quantum number I which is integral or half-integral,
(i) statistics, for an assembly of nuclei,
(j) lifetime against decay, if unstable.

These properties can all be measured for a nucleus in its lowest, most stable or *ground state*, but nuclei also have excited states or energy levels and indeed the sequence of such states is another important nuclear characteristic. Each excited level has its own individual set of properties; some are conventionally indicated on nuclear level diagrams as shown in figure 1.6.

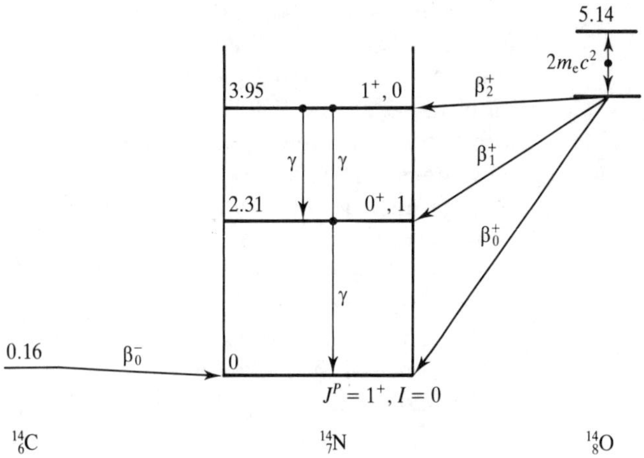

Figure 1.6 A nuclear level diagram (^{14}N) showing the labels conventionally used to describe a well-defined state. The main quantum numbers are J, I and P. Excitation energies relative to the ground state of ^{14}N are given in mega-electrovolts. Observed β decays are indicated: for the origin of the displacement of $2m_ec^2$ see section 3.2.3.

If nuclear wavefunctions are known, nuclear properties such as electromagnetic moments may be predicted by the application of suitable quantum mechanical operators and one of the aims of nuclear physics is to check whether the methods of quantum mechanics are valid in describing an object as small and as tightly bound as a nucleus. So far the techniques that have been found to work well in atomic physics have also been successful in the nuclear context.

Many of the properties are best measured, and some can only be measured, by using nuclear reactions and by applying quantum theory to the interaction process. It was Rutherford again who showed in 1919, several years before the advent of quantum mechanics, that the fast particles that had revealed the existence of the nucleus could be used to probe its structure through artificially induced transmutations. His work, even during his own lifetime, led to the development of accelerators and to the discovery of the *neutron*, which together with the proton is basic to models of nuclear structure. The neutron in turn led to the discovery of *fission* and to the building of nuclear reactors. Accelerators and reactor facilities have provided the bulk of the vast quantity of nuclear data that is now tabulated.

1.4 The evolution of nuclear physics

Nuclear physics would be a relatively barren and unattractive subject were its sole object the acquisition of data on nuclear states. The intellectual stimulus of the subject in fact is to understand how these properties arise and that means the development of techniques for handling a rather complex many-body problem. In the uranium nucleus for instance, at least 238 component particles could be interacting through force fields that are still not entirely understood except in the case of the long-range and relatively weak Coulomb force between charges. In an average nucleus the number of particles is not so large that its precise value is unimportant, as in macroscopic problems. Nor can the nuclear structure physicist anticipate the existence of a well-defined centre of force in the nucleus as in the atom, although the success of the nuclear shell model (chapter 4) means that nuclei do show a similar behaviour as a consequence of their fermion constitution.

The evolution of the subject since the 1920s has therefore been guided by the formulation of a sequence of models of nuclear structure, the more important of which are discussed in chapter 4. The models started with the pre-neutron idea of a proton plus electron structure (with grouping into α particles) and moved through *single-particle* (*atomic type*) and *liquid-drop* proposals to the more sophisticated *collective* and *unified* concepts of the 1950s. Each model has tended to concentrate on one particular aspect of nuclear behaviour, as revealed by experiment, but the latest models bring as many of the observed features as possible together into one framework. Some of the models with which experimentalists are concerned describe the properties of the nuclear ground state and the low-lying excitations that can be observed above it. Others concentrate on the higher excitations and seek to give an account of the nuclear level density using statistical methods. There is also a more fundamental approach which seeks to calculate the binding of a nucleon in infinite nuclear matter of normal nuclear density (0.16 nucleon fm^{-3}). Real nuclear properties are derived from such calculations by imposing the requirement of a finite size and therefore a finite surface.

A realistic model of interacting particles should use realistic forces to describe the basic interactions or at least effective forces in which important features of the real force are preserved. This requirement at once establishes a connection between nuclear structure physics and the scattering experiments which probe the force between neutrons and protons and reveal that it is of a range (for attraction) of about 2×10^{-15} m but is highly repulsive at interparticle distances of about 0.5×10^{-15} m, as shown in figure 3.11, p. 117, and discussed in section 3.11. An understanding of this complex short-range force connects nuclear structure physics with the nature and properties of elementary particles because the first explanation of the range of the force was given by Yukawa (1935) in terms of the exchange between neutron and proton of a particle which was subsequently identified, when in its free state, as a *pion* (section 7.4.2). The repulsive core seems to involve other particles even heavier than the pion, and the nuclear structure physicist must now recognize that not only these particles* and their excitations but also their substructures which we call *quarks* may contribute to the observable properties of a nucleus. So long, however, as we concern ourselves only with distances of greater than 1 fm and with nucleon momenta of less than the corresponding value of a few hundred MeV/c (section 1.5.1), the nucleus can safely be regarded as an assembly of nucleons interacting by pion exchange and this will be the standpoint of Part I of this book.

It is expected that if the nuclear excitation energy or the nuclear density or both can be raised sufficiently above normal, the quarks and the *gluons* that convey interquark forces may form a quark–gluon plasma, which would be a radically new state of matter with entirely novel degrees of freedom.[6] It would be distinct from 'nuclear' matter, in which nucleons are still recognized and in which the quarks are *confined* within the nucleons.

In parallel with the development of structure models there has been a similar effort to describe nuclear reaction mechanisms (chapter 6), and this has shown close connections with structure concepts at several points. Perhaps because Rutherford scattering is a simple one-particle scattering process, involving only the charge of the nucleus and not its internal constitution, the earliest theories of reactions considered an incident particle making just a few orbits about a target nucleus before stimulating a transmutation and having at all times a good chance of escaping without doing so. When experiments with slowed-down neutrons could be done this was found not to be the case for these particles and after 1936 Bohr's compound nucleus model, which has affinities with the liquid-drop structure, seemed more powerful. In the 1950s, however, experiments at higher energies began to reveal just the single-particle features expected by the earlier models and today we believe that the first stage of a nuclear interaction is often to create an unbound state of the same sort as the bound states that are described by the shell-structure model. If elastic scattering is the main outcome of the interaction we speak of an *optical model* and if inelastic effects ensue we may distinguish the two general types of reaction known as *compound nucleus* and *direct interaction* processes. In the former there is a complete amalgamation of the incident particle with the target, but in the latter only a few peripheral nucleons may be involved. In all reactions except some of those of neutrons, Coulomb effects occur and may become dominant in fields opened up by experiments with fast heavy ions. In recent years the subject has been enriched by the use of these ions and of unstable particles such as pions and kaons in transmutation processes. In all this work the object has been twofold, namely to understand the reaction mechanism itself and to use it to extract structure information from experimental results. A broad

---

* Subnuclear particles are listed and discussed in chapter 7.

view of the pattern of nuclear states that may be explored by nuclear reactions in which a particle a bombards a target nucleus X leading to a product particle b and a residual nucleus Y is given in figure 3.10, p. 114.

The development of accelerators has been a natural consequence of a desire to explore the nuclear spectrum with greater precision and to a greater extent than was possible with radioactive sources. The main types of machine were defined and constructed during the 1930s and 1940s and since then advances have been largely due to the advent of the new technologies such as cryogenics. The most successful machine for nuclear structure studies has probably been the tandem electrostatic generator (chapter 2), but in the particular field of electromagnetic response of the nucleus, electron linear accelerators, synchrotrons and microtrons have been of great importance. An important goal of much accelerator development is the probing of new types of nuclear structure or the excitation of new degrees of freedom in nuclear dynamics. There is current interest for instance in states of high angular momentum produced by heavy-ion bombardment (section 6.6.3), in regions of particle stability far removed in respect of neutron or proton number from the naturally occurring nuclei and in the states of high energy and density that could lead to excitation of the quark–gluon plasma. For such studies of extreme conditions accelerators providing heavy-ion beams with energies extending into the ultra-relativistic region and others perhaps providing beams of 'radioactive' nuclei are being increasingly demanded.

These are adventures for the nuclear physicist that may yield no more than the intellectual satisfaction of the new discovery. But within the realm of conventional nuclear physics one must recognize the enormous growth of applied nuclear science resulting from the availability of (mainly) reactor-produced isotopes and the detailed knowledge of their decay schemes that has been reached. The successful functioning of a nuclear reactor itself is critically dependent on the knowledge of the fission reactions and absorption processes occurring within it. Radioactive isotopes are also produced by accelerators and the charged particles, photons and neutrons produced by these machines are used in medical diagnosis and therapy and in a variety of studies in condensed matter physics. In an entirely different area a knowledge of nuclear reactions and of β decay processes is crucial to the understanding of energy generation processes in the Sun and stars. But to reach back to the very instant of creation in the hot big bang we must take our leave of general nuclear structure physics and enter the domain of quarks and leptons. Some aspects of their behaviour will be described in Part II of this book.

Surveys of some of the areas of current activity in nuclear structure studies and applications are to be found in references 7–9.

1.5 Units and definitions[10]

1.5.1 Units in general

Although absolute SI units are often needed in calculations, they are not convenient for discussions of nuclear properties and behaviour (and even in calculations simplifications often result from the use of dimensionless constants or variables). The following quantities therefore have special units in both nuclear and particle physics. The corresponding absolute values will be found in appendix A.

(a) *Energy* The unit of energy is the *electronvolt* (eV) which is the kinetic energy acquired by a particle with one electronic charge as a result of falling through a potential difference of 1 volt. The electronvolt itself is appropriate to atomic physics and for nuclear and particle physics the multiples 10^3, 10^6, 10^9 and 10^{12} are frequently used leading to the units keV, MeV, GeV and TeV.

(b) *Mass* In special relativity the mass m of a free particle is related to its energy E_0 at rest by the famous equation $E_0 = mc^2$ where c is the velocity of light. If the particle disintegrates spontaneously into two fragments whose combined mass is less than that of the original particle by Δm, the energy released is $\Delta E = c^2 \Delta m$. A particle in motion with velocity v has an energy $E = \gamma mc^2$ where $\gamma = (1 - v^2/c^2)^{-1/2}$ and is known as the Lorentz factor. For the particles discussed in this book the energy unit is conveniently the mega-electronvolt and the mass (MeV/c^2) may be given as the equivalent mega-electronvolt value. The conversion factor is given in section 3.2.1 and in appendix A.

The mass of a neutral atom is usually given in *atomic mass units* (amu or u, see section 3.2) and is then a mass relative to the standard ^{12}C-atom mass. It is written $M(A, Z)$ where A is the mass number and Z the atomic number (section 1.3). Conversion to energy units is straightforward (section 3.2.1 and appendix A).

(c) *Momentum* Since the Einstein equation for a particle in motion, $E^2 = m^2c^4 + p^2c^2$, shows that the momentum p multiplied by c has the dimensions of energy, it is convenient in accelerator and particle physics to express momenta in MeV/c or GeV/c.

(d) *Velocity* Velocity is conveniently expressed in units of c and is then written $\beta = v/c$.

(e) *Angular momentum* The reduced Planck quantum $\hbar = h/2\pi$ is convenient for expressing angular momentum.

(f) *Length* A useful length is the reduced Compton wavelength $\hbar/mc$ of the electron or the pion since these quantities enter many formulae. For general purposes such as describing nuclear radii and inter-nucleon distances, however, SI units are used at the submultiple level. The name *fermi* (F) is given to the femtometre (10^{-15} m), which is the appropriate unit, but in this book the abbreviation fm will be used.

(g) *Time* A unit appropriate to nuclear interactions is the reduced Compton wavelength divided by c, i.e. $t = \hbar/mc^2$, but no special name is given to this quantity.

(h) *Cross-section* This important quantity is discussed in appendix B. It could be measured in femtometres squared, but historically it has the special unit *barn* (10^{-28} m^2) and this unit, in both multiples and submultiples, is universally used. The symbol σ is always used for cross-section.

1.5.2 *Natural units (appendix F)*

For many calculations, and generally in particle physics, it is now customary to use a set of units in which $\hbar = c = 1$. Despite the considerable simplifications offered by the use of these units, physical content is sometimes obscured and in Part I of this book $\hbar$ and c will usually be retained. An indication will be given in the text in cases where for consistency with Part II it seems desirable to take $c = 1$.

1.5.3 *Specific definitions and terminology*

We collect together here some of the expressions used in this book, under the convenient assumption that a *nucleus* is a finite structure of N neutrons and Z protons constituting the centre of force in an atom. The symbols used for observable nuclear properties are given in section 1.3.

A *nuclide* is a specific nucleus with a given neutron number N and proton number (or atomic or charge number) Z. The total number of *nucleons* $N + Z$ gives the mass (or baryon) number A (or B), and each of these numbers is integral.

An *isotope* is one of a group of nuclides having the same proton number Z. The nuclides of a chemical element may be a mixture of isotopes.

An *isotone* is one of a group of nuclides having the same neutron number N.

A particle-in, particle-out *nuclear reaction* is written in general terms as

$$\mathrm{X + a \rightarrow Y + b}$$

and abbreviated X(a, b)Y; it is often said to be of the (a, b) type. The symbols used in reaction schemes are based on those for the *chemical elements*, e.g.

mass number   state of ionization

$$^{14}_{7}N^{6+}_{2}$$

atomic number   atoms per molecule

Usually only the mass number and atomic number are shown, since both the number of baryons and the total charge are taken to be conserved, e.g. for the $^{14}N(\alpha, p)^{17}O$ reaction we may write explicitly

$$^{14}_{7}N + ^{4}_{2}He \rightarrow ^{17}_{8}O + ^{1}_{1}H$$

as well as

$$^{14}_{7}N + \alpha \quad \rightarrow ^{17}_{8}O + p.$$

The formation of an excited state of a nucleus is indicated by a star, e.g. $^{17}O^*$, and the associated reaction particle may then have a suffix or a dash, e.g. p_1, p'. If the excited state is long lived it may be described as *isomeric* and is indicated by a superscript m, e.g. $^{26}_{13}Al^m$. Nuclear mass is *not* conserved (section 3.2).

In particle physics the *decay* of a particle p into products q, r, s, . . . , is written

$$p \rightarrow qrs \ldots$$

and the *interaction* between particles a and b to form products c, d, e, . . . , is written

$$ab \rightarrow cde \ldots.$$

Superscripts are used to indicate charge states.

The *becquerel* (Bq) is the unit of *activity*; one becquerel is a rate of one nuclear decay per second. It replaces the historical *curie* (Ci) which initially represented the quantity of radon in equilibrium with 1 g of radium, but was later redefined to be a rate of 3.7×10^{10} decays per second.

The stationary *states of motion* of a particle in a spherically symmetrical potential well (appendix D) are described by a wavefunction ψ_{nlm}, where n is the principal quantum number, l is the azimuthal quantum number and m is the magnetic quantum number. We use the spectroscopic convention that single-particle states with $l = 0, 1, 2, \ldots$ are known as s, p, d, . . . states. If the motion of nucleons in a complex nucleus can be adequately described in this way a nuclear state may be labelled as in atomic spectroscopy by the symbol $^{2S+1}L_J$, where S is the quantum number for the resultant intrinsic spin of the nucleons, L is the number for the resultant orbital angular momentum and J is the total angular momentum quantum number for the state. An alternative form of coupling for the angular momentum vectors will be discussed in chapter 4.

The *matrix element* of a quantum mechanical operator $\hat{O}$ between two states 1, 2 is the quantity

$$\int \psi_2^* \hat{O} \psi_1 \, d\tau$$

where τ is an element of configuration space. The squares of such matrix elements for appropriate operators determine transition probabilities. Quantum mechanical formalism helpful for Part I of this book is clearly set out in reference 11.

REFERENCES 1

1 **Rutherford E, Chadwick J and Ellis C D** 1930 *Radiations from Radioactive Substances* Cambridge University Press

2 **Curie Eve** 1938 *Madame Curie* Heinemann

3 **Eve A S** 1939 *Rutherford* Cambridge University Press

4 **Feather N** 1973 'Radioactivity' *Chambers Encyclopaedia* International Learning Systems Corporation Ltd

5 **Moon P B** 1974 *Ernest Rutherford and the Atom* Priory Press

6 **Baym G** 1985 'Major facilities for nuclear physics' *Physics Today* **38** March (40)

7 **Diamond R M and Rasmussen J O (eds)** 1981 'Proceedings of the International Conference on Nuclear Physics' *Nucl Phys* **A354**

8 **Ajzenberg-Selove F and Warburton E K** 1983 'Nuclear spectroscopy' *Physics Today* **36** November (26)

9 **Bohr A and Mottelson B R** 1973 'The many facets of nuclear structure' *Ann Rev Nucl Sci* **23** November (363)

10 *Quantities, Units and Symbols* 1975 The Royal Society

11 **Cassels J M** 1982 *Basic Quantum Mechanics* Macmillan

EXAMPLES 1

1.1 Prove the result given in equation (1.4).

1.2 Given that the probability of a radioactive decay in a small time interval Δ is $\lambda\Delta$, write down the probability that the atom concerned shall not have undergone change in a time $t = k\Delta$ and hence, by letting Δ become zero while $k\Delta$ remains finite, deduce the decay law (1.2). (Reference 1 gives the calculations.)

1.3 Write down and solve the equations that express (a) the decay of ThX chemically extracted from thorium and (b) the recovery of ThX activity in the original thorium sample as a result of the decay of RdTh (figure 1.2 and table 1.1). Draw the corresponding decay and recovery curves (which form part of the arms of Lord Rutherford of Nelson. The original work is described by Rutherford and Soddy in *Phil Mag* **4** (370), 1902.)

1.4 A finitely collimated beam of α particles ($z = 2$) having a current of 1 μA bombards a metal foil of thickness 2 g m^{-2} of an element of atomic weight 107.8. A detector of projected area 10^{-4} m^2 at a distance of 0.1 m from the foil counts at a rate of 6×10^4 particles s^{-1}. Using equations (1.14) and (1.11) calculate the collision diameter b if the angle of observation is 60°. Neglect centre-of-mass corrections. [13.1 fm]

1.5 An α particle ($A = 4$) is scattered through an angle of 56° by collision with a heavier nucleus, which moves off at an angle of 54° from the original direction of the α particle. Find the probable mass number of the struck nucleus. [$A = 12$]

1.6 Using expression (1.10) for the impact parameter in Rutherford scattering, calculate the angular momentum quantum number l of a 1 MeV proton with respect to a fixed scattering centre with $Z = 90$ for an angular deflection of 90°. [14]

2 *Experimental techniques*

The passage of charged particles and radiation through matter · Detectors for nuclear structure studies · Detectors for particle physics studies · Accelerators for nuclear structure studies · Accelerators for particle physics studies

The penetration of ionizing radiations into matter has been of theoretical interest and of practical importance for nuclear physics since the early days of the subject. The classification of the radiations from radioactive substances as α, β and γ rays was based on the ease with which their intensity could be reduced by absorbers. The range or absorption coefficient provided, and still provides, a useful method of energy determination, and the associated processes of ionization and excitation underlie the operation of nearly all present-day particle and photon detectors. In the present chapter, we start by examining the basic processes of the interaction of radiation with matter, with particular reference to nuclear detecting techniques.

Detectors for both nuclear structure and particle physics studies are then reviewed. In the latter field especially, large and complex installations are now used; no attempt has been made to describe these in detail. Accelerators are treated similarly, with attention focused mainly on general principles and references where appropriate.

2.1 *The passage of charged particles and radiation through matter*

2.1.1 *General*[1–4]

For energies up to a few hundred mega-electronvolts, the main process by which a charged particle such as a proton loses energy in passing through matter is the transfer of kinetic energy to atomic electrons through the Coulomb interaction between charges. It is useful to think of two extreme types of transfer collision – the 'heavy' type in which the electrons behave as free particles and the 'light' type in which the interaction is with the atom as a whole. Heavy collisions lead to ionization of the atom and to energetic electrons which are visible along the track of a charged particle in an expansion chamber as *δ rays*. Inhibition of this type of collision leads to the reduced energy loss observed in the phenomenon of *channelling*.[5]

In special cases, e.g. for fission fragments or other heavy ions, transfer of energy to the *nuclei* of the medium may also be important. In such cases of high charge or low velocity or both, *large-angle scattering* of the Rutherford type from nuclei may be observed, but for fast ions this is a rare event. It is consequently reasonable, at least for such particles, to define a definite *range* in matter (figure 2.1(a)).

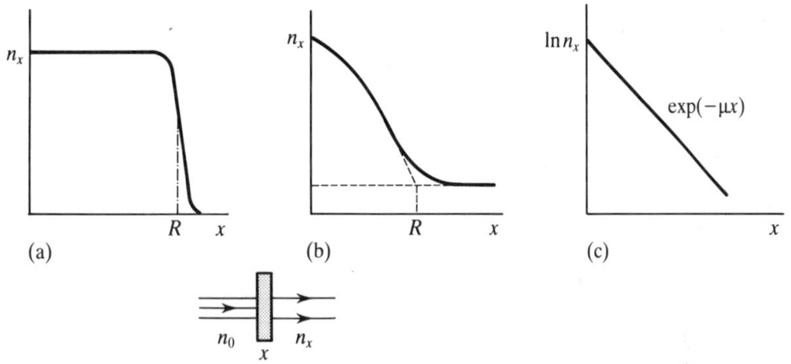

Figure 2.1 Absorption of initially homogeneous particles by matter (schematic): (a) light ions (e.g. α, p, muons), showing mean range R; (b) electrons, showing extrapolated range R; a finite level of background, often due to γ radiation, is shown; (c) photons, $E_\gamma < 10$ MeV. Absorber thicknesses x and ranges R are conveniently measured as mass per unit area of absorber and μ in (c) is then a mass absorption coefficient, with units of metres squared per kilogram.

Fast electrons also lose energy by collision with other electrons and may be scattered through angles up to 90° in such collisions. They lose very little energy to nuclei because of the disparity in mass, but can suffer large deflections of more than 90°. In all collisions in which accelerations are experienced, electrons also lose energy by the radiative process known as bremsstrahlung. Heavy particles do not radiate appreciably in this way because their accelerations are much smaller. As a result of scattering and radiative energy loss a group of initially monoenergetic electrons may traverse considerably different thicknesses of matter before being brought to rest and range can best be defined by an extrapolation process (figure 2.1(b)).

Electromagnetic radiation interacts with matter through the processes of elastic (Rayleigh and nuclear) scattering, the photoelectric effect, the Compton effect and pair production. These processes reduce the *number* of photons in a beam in proportion to the number incident on an absorber, thereby creating an exponential attenuation (figure 2.1(c)). No definition of range is appropriate, but the attenuation coefficient is energy dependent. For radiation of energy above, say 10 MeV, the electrons and positrons from the pair production processes (section 2.1.4, 'Pair production and annihilation') themselves generate bremsstrahlung and annihilation quanta and an electromagnetic shower builds up characterized by a linear dimension called the *radiation length* (section 2.1.3).

The relative importance of collision and radiative energy loss for electrons and protons in lead is shown in figure 2.2.

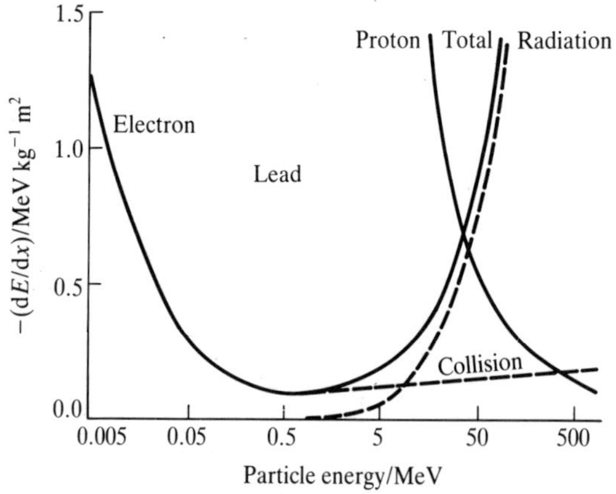

Figure 2.2
Energy loss for electrons and protons in lead as a function of kinetic energy (Heitler W 1954 *The Quantum Theory of Radiation* Clarendon).

2.1.2 *Energy loss by collision*

If a particle other than an electron, of charge ze and non-relativistic velocity v, passes through a substance in which there are N atoms of atomic number Z per unit volume, then if it is also assumed that all the Z electrons per atom are free, the energy loss per unit path length or stopping power is

$$\left(-\frac{\mathrm{d}E}{\mathrm{d}x}\right)_{\text{coll}} = \frac{1}{(4\pi\epsilon_0)^2}\frac{4\pi z^2 e^4}{m_e v^2} NZ \ln\left(\frac{2m_e v^2}{I}\right) \text{ J m}^{-1} \qquad (2.1\text{a})$$

where I is a mean excitation potential for the atoms of the substance and E is the *total* energy of the particle. The form of this equation may be obtained by a simple calculation of the impulse conveyed to an electron by the passage of the particle (see example 2.1).

If the path x is measured as mass per unit area rather than as a length, then the number density in equation (2.1a) is replaced by the inverse of the mean mass, in kilograms, of an atom of the stopping material. This in turn (see section 3.2.1) is equal to N_A/A where N_A is Avogadro's number and A is the atomic weight in kilograms (e.g. 0.012 kg for ^{12}C). If A is taken, as an approximation, to be a mass number, N_A/A must be multiplied by a factor of 10^3 because N_A is defined in terms of the mole rather than the kilomole.

Calculation of stopping power

The observed stopping power of aluminium for protons of energy 2.0 MeV is 11.2 MeV kg^{-1} m^2 (112 keV mg^{-1} cm^2).

To calculate the stopping power using formula (2.1a) we first of all replace N by N_A/A and insert values of fundamental constants. This gives, using appendix A,

$$-\frac{dE}{dx} = (9 \times 10^9)\frac{12.56 \times (1.6 \times 10^{-19})^4 \times 6 \times 10^{23} \times 13}{9.1 \times 10^{-31} \times v^2 \times 0.027} \ln\left(\frac{2m_e v^2}{I}\right)$$

in which we have inserted the atomic weight in kilograms.

The quantity $2m_e v^2/I$ may be written

$$\frac{4m_e}{m_p}\tfrac{1}{2}m_p v^2 \frac{1}{I} = 4 \times \frac{1}{1836} \times \frac{2 \times 10^6}{11 \times 13} \qquad \text{using } I = 11Z \text{ eV}$$

$$= 30.4$$

so that

$$\ln\left(\frac{2m_e v^2}{I}\right) = 3.42.$$

For v^2 we easily find the value 3.84×10^{14} m^2 s^{-2} and the stopping power is then

$$-\frac{dE}{dx} = \frac{81 \times 10^{18} \times 12.56 \times (1.6 \times 10^{-19})^4 \times 6 \times 10^{23} \times 13 \times 3.42}{9.1 \times 10^{-31} \times 3.84 \times 10^{14} \times 0.027}$$

$$= 1885 \times 10^{-15} \text{ J kg}^{-1} \text{ m}^2.$$

Converting to mega-electronvolts

$$-\frac{dE}{dx} = \frac{1885 \times 10^{-15}}{1.6 \times 10^{-13}} = 11.8 \text{ MeV kg}^{-1} \text{ m}^2$$

in satisfactory agreement with the observed value, remembering that equation (2.1a) does not contain the proper relativistic corrections.

Equation (2.1a) was presented in relativistic form by Bethe and by Bloch,[1,2] who also showed how to correct for the binding of the inner electrons in the absorber atoms. Taking x as mass per unit area the relativistic equation for a heavy particle may be written

$$\left(-\frac{\mathrm{d}E}{\mathrm{d}x}\right)_{\text{coll}} = \frac{KZ}{A}\cdot\frac{1}{\beta^2}\left\{\ln\left[\frac{2m_e c^2\beta^2 E_{\text{max}}}{I^2(1-\beta^2)}\right] - 2\beta^2\right\} \text{ J kg}^{-1}\text{ m}^2 \qquad (2.1\text{b})$$

where

$$K = \frac{1}{(4\pi\epsilon_0)^2}\frac{2\pi N_A z^2 e^4}{m_e c^2}$$

and $\beta = v/c$ is the particle velocity expressed as a fraction of the velocity of light. E_{max} is the maximum energy that may be transferred to an electron, i.e. the maximum δ ray energy, and is given by

$$E_{\text{max}} = \frac{2m_e c^2\beta^2}{1-\beta^2} = 2m_e c^2\beta^2\gamma^2 \qquad (2.1\text{c})$$

where $\gamma = (1-\beta^2)^{-1/2} = E/mc^2$ is the Lorentz factor for the particle. Formulae similar to (2.1a) and (2.1b) can be given for the collision loss for electrons, for which allowance must be made for the identity of the initial and struck particles. The total energy loss for electrons must include radiative loss (section 2.1.3).

It will be noted from equation (2.1b) that because Z/A for most materials is approximately 0.5, collision loss is roughly independent of the nature of the medium. The variation of $\mathrm{d}E/\mathrm{d}x$ with energy in the low energy ($\gamma \approx 1$) region is similar to the experimental observation for protons in aluminium, shown in figure 2.3; it will be noted that m_e is the mass of the electron, not that of the incident heavy particle. Over much of the energy range shown the collision loss varies as $1/v^2$ but at very low energies the simple theory is not valid for heavy particles because of the effect of capture and loss of electrons by the particle. In the $1/v^2$ region, $\mathrm{d}E/\mathrm{d}x$ can be used as a means of *particle identification* if the corresponding energy is known because particles of the same energy but different mass will have a different velocity.

At kinetic energies comparable with and greater than the mass of the particle ($\gamma = E/mc^2 \approx 3$ in figure 2.3) a region of nearly energy-independent collision loss, usually known as the region of *minimum ionization*, is reached. All particles of this energy suffer the same collision loss of 0.1–0.2 MeV kg^{-1} m^2 (for a single charge) and particle identification by $\mathrm{d}E/\mathrm{d}x$ is no longer possible. At higher energies still ($\gamma \approx 10$) the logarithmic term in equation (2.1b) leads to the so-called *relativistic rise* in energy loss and there is a small mass dependence for a given momentum, so that

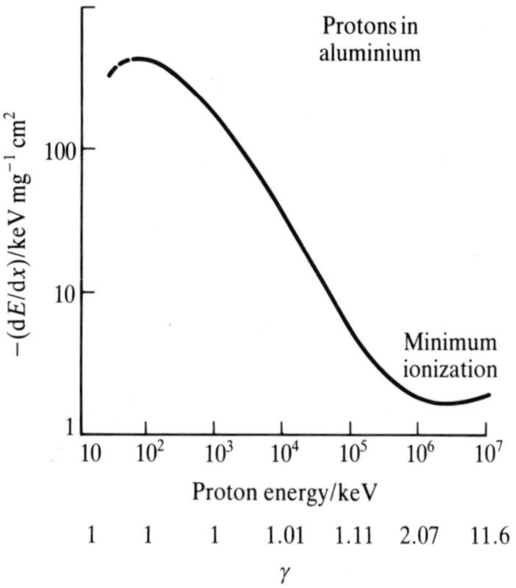

Figure 2.3 Specific energy loss, or stopping power, of aluminium for protons. The quantity $\gamma = (1 - \beta^2)^{-1/2}$ gives the mass of the particle in units of its rest mass. Note that the energy loss at minimum ionization is about 2 keV mg^{-1} cm^2.

identification again becomes possible (see figure 2.18 in section 2.3.1). At very high energies ($\gamma \approx 100$) the collision loss reaches the *Fermi plateau* value because polarization effects in the medium limit the energy transfer (section 2.3.5).

Collision loss, or ionization density, varies as z^2 and for large z the high density may result in lattice damage and storage of energy (in dielectrics) over long periods, until it is released by thermal annealing or chemical etching.

In placing equations (2.1a–c) on an absolute scale the principal uncertainty is in the atomic excitation potential I. It may be obtained from measurements of stopping power or from calculations based on an atomic model; both indicate that

$$I = kZ \text{ eV}$$

where $k \approx 11$, with some dependence on Z for very light and very heavy atoms.

Observable phenomena basically governed by the collision-loss formula for a single particle are

(a) production of ion pairs in solids, liquids and gases and of electron–hole pairs in semiconductors,
(b) production of light in scintillator materials,
(c) production of bubbles in superheated liquid,
(d) production of developable grains in a photographic emulsion or of damage trails in a dielectric.

Each of these has been made the basis of an energy-sensitive particle detector.

Collision loss of energy determines the range of a heavy charged particle in matter, at least up to energies at which nuclear interactions become important. The range is the distance in which the velocity v of a particle (of mass m and charge ze) reduces to zero and it may be estimated by changing the variable from E to v in equation (2.1a). Since in the present approximation E is the sum of a constant rest energy mc^2 and a kinetic energy $T = \frac{1}{2}mv^2$ it is straightforward to obtain

$$R = -\int_v^0 \mathrm{d}v \left(\frac{\mathrm{d}v}{\mathrm{d}x}\right)^{-1} = \frac{m}{z^2} f(v). \tag{2.2}$$

In this formula the mass and charge number of the particle are shown explicitly and the integral $f(v)$ contains other constants. This permits the range to be compared with the range R_p of a reference particle such as a proton ($z = 1$). If we choose kinetic energies so that the velocity is the same in each case it follows that

$$R(T) = \frac{m}{m_p z^2} R_p\left(\frac{Tm_p}{m}\right). \tag{2.3}$$

This shows that a deuteron has about twice the range of a proton of half the deuteron kinetic energy E.

Since energy loss is a statistical process, particles of initially homogeneous energy will exhibit a spread of energy after passage through a given thickness of matter. Similarly, for a given energy loss, the range has a spread and this is known as *straggling*. The distribution of energy loss in a thin absorber was calculated by Landau, and verified by others experimentally, to be asymmetric about the mean loss. These effects are enhanced for electrons, which may lose up to half of their energy in a single collision.

If a charged particle moves through a single crystal, it may follow certain directions defined by the crystal structure in which the electron density is especially low. The collision loss is then lower than the average loss in the other directions and the particles are said to be *channelled*.[5]

2.1.3 *Energy loss by radiation*

Electrons of kinetic energy T and total energy E ($= T + m_e c^2$) passing through a thin absorber give rise in each radiative collision to a bremsstrahlung photon of any energy between 0 and T. The process may be envisaged as in figure 2.4 in which the Coulomb field existing between

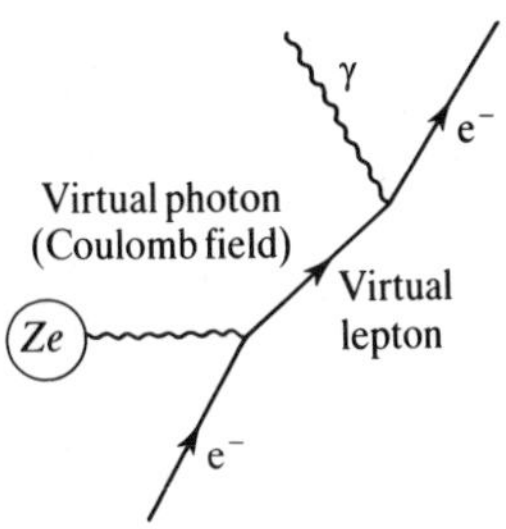

Figure 2.4
Production of bremsstrahlung by an electron in the field of a nucleus *Ze*; the virtual lepton is said to be 'off the mass shell" because the mass derived from the familiar expression $E^2 - p^2c^2$ is not that of a real particle. This and subsequent similar figures are not intended to display the precise order of events, and other diagrams showing a different order may be drawn. Time increases to the top of the page, and a fixed Coulomb field is shown as a wavy horizontal line. Rules exist for calculating cross-sections from such graphs.

the incident electron and a nucleus, or another electron of the absorbing medium, is represented by an emission of virtual photons.* The real electron makes a Compton scattering collision (section 2.1.4) with a virtual photon, creating a virtual lepton which then gives rise to a real photon, i.e. the bremsstrahlung quantum and a real electron of reduced energy. The bremsstrahlung process $e \to e' + \gamma$ cannot take place in free space because momentum and energy cannot then be conserved. Photons can, however, be emitted by electrons moving in the magnetic field of an orbital accelerator (section 2.5.1) and this emission is known as *synchrotron radiation.*

The probability of emission of a bremsstrahlung photon of energy between $h\nu$ and $h(\nu + d\nu)$ due to an electron–nucleus collision is given in reference 1 in the form

$$\phi(E, \nu)\, d\nu \propto Z^2 f(E, \nu) \frac{d\nu}{\nu}. \tag{2.4}$$

At high energies ($E > 100$ MeV) the function $f(E, \nu)$ varies only slowly with the frequency ν and we will assume this to be true in a rough approximation for lower energies as well. To this degree of approximation the energy-loss distribution $h\nu\phi(E, \nu)\, d\nu$ is constant and by integration over the frequency spectrum, neglecting screening effects, the radiative loss becomes

$$\begin{aligned}\left(-\frac{dE}{dx}\right)_{\text{rad}} &= \frac{N_A}{A}\int_0^{T/h} h\nu\phi(E, \nu)\, d\nu \\ &= \frac{N_A}{A} Z^2 \int_0^{T/h} hf(E, \nu)\, d\nu \\ &= \frac{N_A}{A} Z^2 E\bar{f}\end{aligned} \tag{2.5}$$

since the integrand varies only slowly with ν. In this formula $\bar{f}$ is a calculable function and we have written $E = T + mc^2 \approx T$ for energies well above the mass of the electron. Radiative loss is therefore proportional to the total energy E of the electron, whereas the collision loss given by the Bethe–Bloch formula (2.1b) increases only as $\ln E$. The electron energy at which the two losses are equal is the *critical energy* E_c. When radiative loss is dominant it is useful to define a *radiation length* X_0 by the

* A virtual particle is one which is emitted only because conservation of energy may be relaxed over a time given by the uncertainty relation $\Delta E \Delta t \approx \hbar$. It must disappear by re-absorption or interaction within the time Δt for energy increment ΔE so that conservation is obeyed overall.

Table 2.1
Critical energy and radiation length[1,2]

Material	E_c/MeV	X_0/kg m^{-2}
H	340	580
C	103	425
Fe	24	138
Pb	6.9	58
Air	83	365
NaI	12.5	95
Lead glass	15.8	96

equation

$$\left(-\frac{dx}{X_0}\right)=\frac{dE}{E} \tag{2.6}$$

so that X_0 is the absorber thickness over which the electron energy is reduced by a factor *e*. Table 2.1 gives critical energies and radiation lengths for a few common materials.

Classically, bremsstrahlung originates in the acceleration of a charged particle as a result of Coulomb interaction, and its intensity is therefore inversely proportional to the square of the particle mass according to Maxwell's theory. The muon has 200 times the electron mass and its radiative energy loss is therefore negligible except at very high energies. This holds *a fortiori* for all other charged particles, since they are still heavier.

All charged particles independently of their mass do, however, suffer a small electromagnetic loss in matter through *Cherenkov radiation*.[6] This depends on the gross structure of the medium through which the particle passes, and in which a macroscopic polarization is set up. If the velocity v ($=\beta c$) of the particle exceeds the velocity of light in the medium, the polarization is longitudinally asymmetric because it can only relax to symmetry on a time scale determined by this velocity. Secondary wavelets then originate along the track AB of the particle (figure 2.5) and these form a coherent wavefront propagating in a direction at angle θ with the path of the particle where

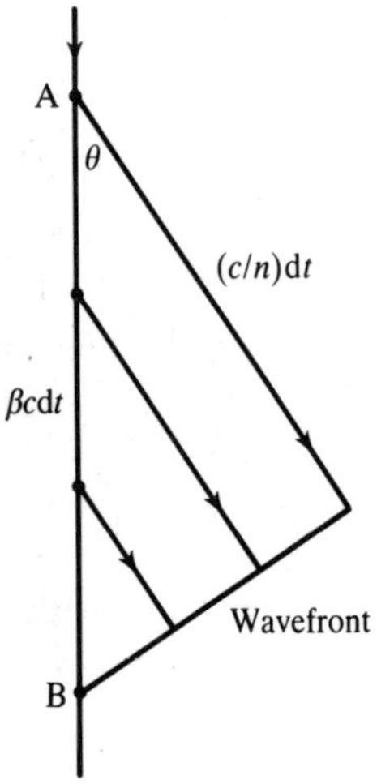

Figure 2.5
Formation of a coherent wavefront of Cherenkov radiation.

$$\cos\theta=\frac{c/n}{\beta c}=\frac{1}{\beta n} \tag{2.7}$$

n being the refractive index. The process is analogous to the formation of the bow wave of a ship. It has the important features for nuclear detectors that coherence does not appear until $\beta = 1/n$, i.e. there is a *velocity threshold* for observable radiation, and that the direction of emission is very well defined. The use of counters based on the Cherenkov effect for the identification of particles of relativistic energy is discussed in section 2.3.5.

Cherenkov loss is only about 0.1 per cent of collision loss at the ionization minimum, although it increases with energy in the region of the relativistic rise (section 2.1.2). The loss for a singly charged particle is

$$\left(-\frac{\mathrm{d}E}{\mathrm{d}x}\right)_{\mathrm{Ch}} = \frac{\pi e^2}{c^2\epsilon_0}\int\left(1-\frac{1}{\beta^2 n^2}\right)\nu\,\mathrm{d}\nu \tag{2.8}$$

where the integration extends over all frequencies for which $\beta n > 1$. Within these bands the spectral distribution of energy loss is proportional to $\nu\,\mathrm{d}\nu$, in contrast with the $\mathrm{d}\nu$ proportionality of bremsstrahlung. The difference is that bremsstrahlung originates incoherently from the incident particle itself while Cherenkov radiation arises coherently from the medium.

If a charged particle moves through an *inhomogeneous* medium, e.g. if it crosses a boundary between different media, a further small contribution to radiative loss known as *transition radiation*[7] occurs. It arises in the relativistic case because of the different extent of the electric field of the particle in the transverse plane due to different polarization effects in the two media (section 2.1.2). Transition radiation, unlike Cherenkov radiation, occurs for any velocity of the particle and it yields photons not only in the optical but also in the X-ray region.

2.1.4 *Absorption of electromagnetic radiation*[8,9]

The exponential absorption of a beam of homogeneous photons shown in figure 2.1(c) may be described by the equation

$$n_x = n_0 \exp(-\mu x) \tag{2.9}$$

where μ (m^{-1}) is the *linear attenuation coefficient* and n_0 is the initial number of photons in the beam. In a microscopic model of the absorption process a *cross-section* σ (appendix B) is ascribed to each atomic absorbing centre and if these centres have a volume density N then $\mu = N\sigma$. If x is measured in kilograms per metre squared rather than in metres, equation (2.9) becomes

$$n_x = n_0 \exp(-\mu_{\mathrm{m}} x) \tag{2.10}$$

in which the *mass attenuation coefficient* $\mu_{\mathrm{m}} = \mu/\rho = N\sigma/\rho = N_{\mathrm{A}}\sigma/A$ where ρ is the density of the absorbing material and A is the atomic weight, in kilograms, of the absorber atoms; μ_{m} is measured in metres squared per kilogram.

The total cross-section σ may be broken down into partial cross-sections as follows:

$$\sigma = \sigma_{\mathrm{PE}} + Z\sigma_{\mathrm{C}} + \sigma_{\mathrm{PP}}. \tag{2.11}$$

The individual cross-sections relate to the *photoelectric effect*, the *Compton effect* and *pair production* respectively and the factor Z embodies the assumption that all the atomic electrons contribute individually (and incoherently) to Compton scattering. This will be true if the photon energy is much greater than the K-shell ionization energy of the atom. Elastic (Rayleigh) scattering has been neglected, since it is sharply forward-peaked at mega-electronvolt energies and does not remove photons from a beam unless collimation is very fine.

The relative importance of the three absorption processes as a function of energy and of atomic number is shown in figure 2.6, and the actual

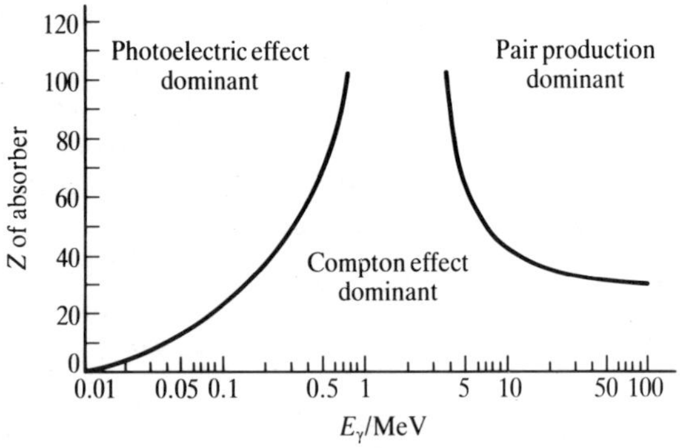

Figure 2.6
Relative importance of the three major types of γ ray interaction (Evans R D 1955 *The Atomic Nucleus* McGraw-Hill).

mass absorption coefficient μ_{m} for lead is given as a function of energy in figure 2.7. This curve shows (a) sharp peaks at energies corresponding with the atomic absorption edges and indicating the onset of increased photoelectric absorption as a new electron shell becomes available, and (b) a minimum absorption coefficient due to the compensation of photoelectric and Compton cross-sections, which fall with energy, by the pair production cross-section which rises. Both effects mean that the energy is not a single-valued function of μ_{m} throughout its range for a given absorbing material. The individual processes indicated in equation (2.11), together with elastic scattering, are all part of the total electromagnetic interaction between radiation and matter and are therefore connected. For most practical purposes, in the energy range of interest to nuclear physics, it is possible to regard them as independent, each contributing to the total cross-section to a degree determined by the quantum energy. The salient features of the processes are as follows.

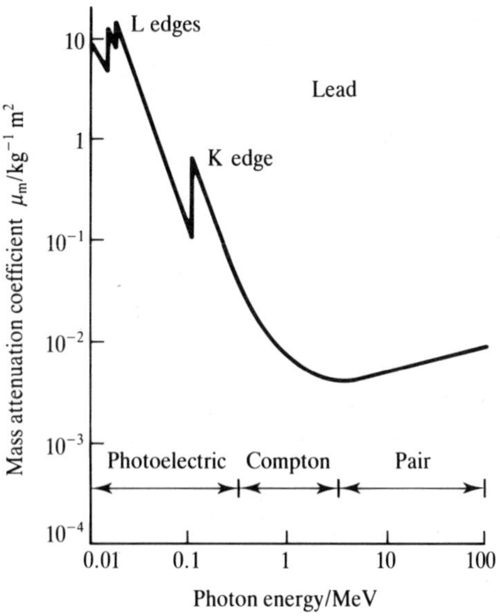

Figure 2.7
Mass attenuation coefficient for electromagnetic radiation in lead (Evans R D 1955 *The Atomic Nucleus* McGraw-Hill).

Photoelectric effect

Because of the necessity to conserve energy and momentum, a free electron cannot wholly absorb a photon. Photoelectric absorption, therefore, tends to take place most readily in the most tightly bound electronic shell of the atom available, for a particular incident photon energy, since then momentum is most easily conveyed to the atom. The kinetic energy of a photoelectron from the K-shell is

$$T = h\nu - E_K \tag{2.12}$$

where E_K is the K-ionization energy. The cross-section depends on atomic number Z and wavelength of radiation λ approximately as

$$\sigma_{PE} \approx Z^5 \lambda^{7/2}$$

in the energy range 0.1–0.35 MeV. The vacancy in the atom created by the ejection of a photoelectron leads to the emission of characteristic X-rays or of low energy photoelectrons known as *Auger electrons* from less tightly bound shells as an alternative process favoured for light atoms.

Compton effect

The scattering of photons by atomic electrons that may be regarded as free is a simple collision process. With the quantities as shown in figure 2.8(a) the law of conservation of momentum gives

$$\begin{aligned} \frac{h\nu}{c} &= \frac{h\nu'}{c}\cos\theta + p\cos\phi \\ 0 &= \frac{h\nu'}{c}\sin\theta - p\sin\phi \end{aligned} \tag{2.13}$$

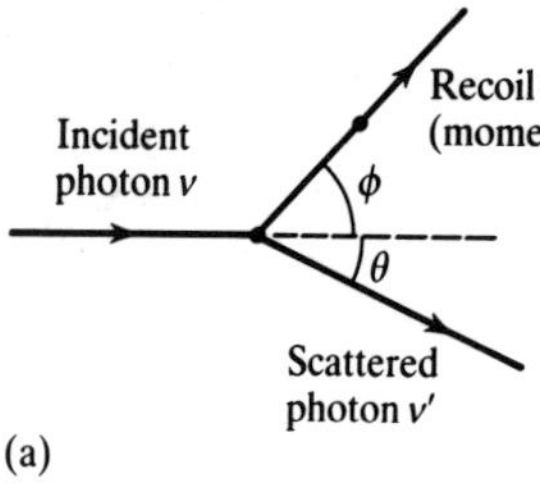

(a)

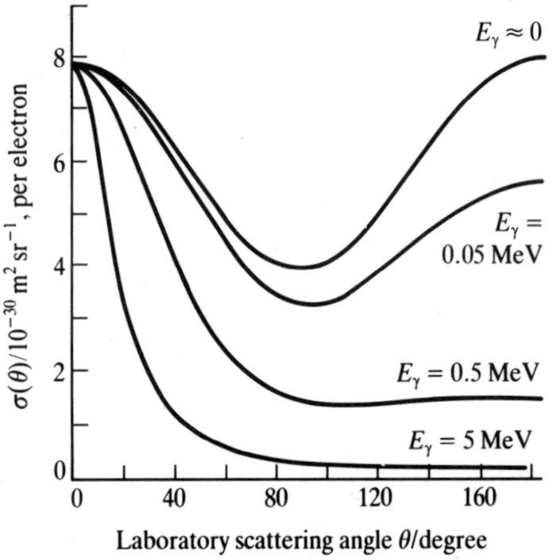

(b)

Figure 2.8 (a) Compton scattering of a photon by a free electron; (b) differential cross-section for Compton scattering, giving the *number* of photons scattered per unit solid angle at angle θ, for energies of 0–5 MeV.

where p is the momentum of the recoil electron. The law of conservation of energy gives

$$h\nu = h\nu' + T$$

where T, the kinetic energy of the electron, is related to p by the equation of special relativity theory:

$$p^2c^2 = T(T + 2m_ec^2).$$

By elimination of ϕ and p we find

$$\frac{c}{\nu'} - \frac{c}{\nu} = \lambda' - \lambda = \frac{h}{m_ec}(1 - \cos\theta) \qquad (2.14)$$

where h/m_ec is the *Compton wavelength* of the electron and is equal to 2.43×10^{-12} m. The energy of the recoil electron is $h(\nu - \nu')$; it is zero for $\theta = 0$ and is continuously distributed up to a maximum for $\theta = \pi$. Emission of the electron leaves an excited atom.

The Compton wavelength shift is independent of wavelength and of the material of the scatterer. The differential cross-section for the process is given by a formula due to Klein and Nishina, which predicts that at a given angle the cross-section decreases with increasing photon energy. The angular variation for a range of energies is shown in figure 2.8(b); in all cases there is a finite cross-section for $\theta = 0$ and equation (2.14) shows that over a small angular range about zero the wavelength is essentially unmodified.

As $h\nu/m_e c^2$ tends to zero the angular distributions shown in figure 2.8(b) become more symmetrical about 90° and finally reach the form characteristic of classical *Thomson scattering* from a free charge. However, the assumption of scattering from free electrons then becomes less tenable for matter in its normal state and coherent *Rayleigh scattering* from the bound electrons forming the atomic charge distribution takes over.

Pair production and annihilation

In 1932–3 both Anderson in the USA and Blackett and Occhialini in England were seeing the tracks of particles of electronic mass but positive charge in cloud chamber studies of the cosmic radiation at sea-level. The possibility of the existence of such *antiparticles* was being considered theoretically at the time by Dirac, who noted that the expression of special relativity $E^2 = p^2c^2 + m^2c^4$ for the square of the total energy of a particle of mass m led to the conclusion that

$$E = \pm(p^2c^2 + m^2c^4)^{1/2}. \tag{2.15}$$

This in turn suggested that electrons might occupy states of both positive energy ($E = m_e c^2$ to ∞) and of negative energy ($E = -m_e c^2$ to $-\infty$).

The difficulty that ordinary electrons should all make transitions to negative energy states was circumvented by the suggestion that normally the states are all occupied so that the restrictions offered by the Pauli principle would apply. But if an electron in a negative energy state were raised by an electromagnetic process to a positive energy level, with an expenditure of energy greater than the minimum of $2m_e c^2$ (=1.02 MeV) required, the remaining 'hole' would behave as a normal particle of equal mass but opposite charge, i.e. as an anti-electron or *positron*, as seen in the experiments. Further details of the Dirac 'hole' theory are given in section 11.4.6.

The pair production process

$$h\nu \rightarrow e^+ + e^- \tag{2.16}$$

contributes increasingly to γ ray absorption as the quantum energy rises above the threshold energy of 1.02 MeV. The process cannot take place in free space because momentum cannot be conserved (see example 2.11) but it occurs if a third electron, or better still a nucleus, is present to absorb recoil momentum. In the latter case the cross-section is proportional to the value of Z^2 for the absorber as in the case of bremsstrahlung (section 2.1.3), which is theoretically at least a similar process. The rising cross-section for each of these phenomena as quantum energy increases is ultimately limited by screening of the nuclear charge by the atomic electrons.

The positron is a stable particle like the electron but it may disappear by annihilation with an electron. The exact converse of process (2.16) is *single-quantum annihilation* which cannot take place in free space and occurs only with fairly low probability when positrons are brought to rest in matter. The more prolific *two-quantum annihilation radiation*

$$e^+ + e^- \rightarrow 2h\nu \tag{2.17}$$

is readily observed as a pair of oppositely directed 511 keV quanta, if the electron and positron are essentially at rest. This radiation contributes a soft component to a flux of γ radiation of energy above the pair production threshold. Fast-moving positrons may both radiate and annihilate in flight in a Coulomb field, yielding energetic quanta which contribute to the build-up of cosmic ray showers of the type studied by Blackett and Occhialini.

In part II of this book we shall see that not only the electron but also all fermions, e.g. the proton and neutron, have antiparticles.

2.2 *Detectors for nuclear structure studies*[10–14]

2.2.1 *Gaseous detectors*

An α particle of energy 6 MeV wholly absorbed in a gas will produce about 2×10^5 ion pairs, equivalent to positive and negative charges of 3.2×10^{-14} C. If charged electrodes are placed in the gas to form a simple ionization chamber (figures 2.9(a) and 2.9(b)) and if the chamber capacitance is 10 pF there will be a change of potential of 3.2 mV, which is a large signal in comparison with the input noise voltage of a typical amplifier. The response of such a chamber to both α and β particles, as a function of collecting voltage, is shown in figure 2.9(c). In the ionization chamber region only primary ion pairs are collected, but above the field corresponding to the voltage V_p there is ionization by collision and small primary ionizations may be multiplied with strict proportionality if the field is not too high. At higher fields still, above the voltage V_g, the

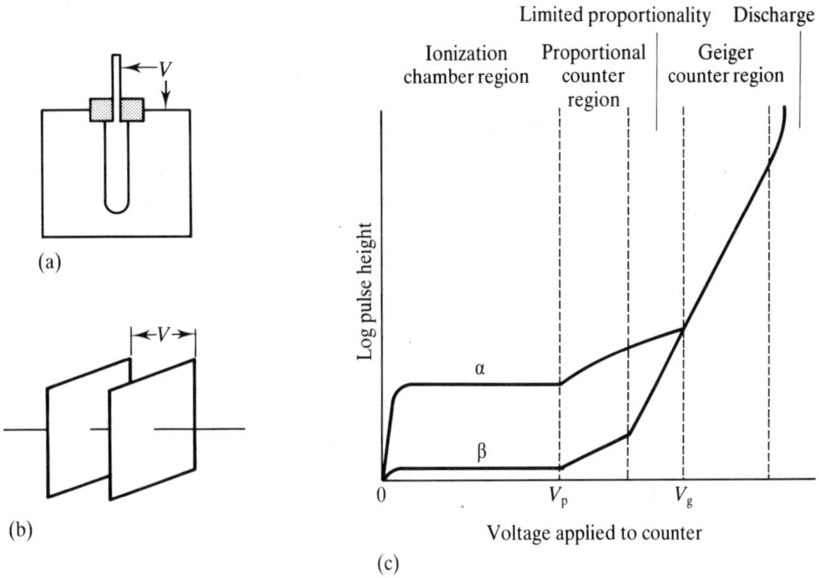

Figure 2.9 (a), (b) Simple forms of ionization chamber or counter. (c) Pulse size obtained from a counting chamber as a function of voltage applied. Curves are drawn for a heavy initial ionization, e.g. from an α particle, and for a light initial ionization, e.g. from a fast electron. For voltages less than V_p, only the primary ion pairs are collected; for $V > V_p$ ionization by collision takes place and the counter ceases to be a conventional ionization chamber. Very roughly the electric field in argon at atmospheric pressure corresponding to V_p is 10^6 V m^{-1} (from Korff S A 1946 *Electron and Nuclear Counters* van Nostrand).

ionization by collision further increases, there is propagation of the effect by ultraviolet photons and signals reach a constant amplitude at a given voltage, independent of the initial ionization. The main types of gaseous detector based on this behaviour are as follows.

Ionization chamber

These instruments have been used since the early days of radioactivity and can now be applied to both single-particle and radiation-flux detection. For measurement of the energy of a single particle which stops in the chamber, gases such as argon or argon–CO_2 mixtures which do not form negative ions are usually used. There is then a fast pulse at the anode due to electron collection and this may be rendered independent of the position of the initial track in the chamber by placing a 'Frisch' grid near the collecting electrode (figure 2.10(a)) to screen off the induction effect of the positive ions. The chamber voltage must of course ensure complete electron collection but must not lead to ionization by collision (figure 2.9). The high mobility of the electrons permits pulses of a width of approximately 1 μs to be derived from the chamber, although recovery is slower because of the low mobility of the positive ions. The resolution of an ionization chamber for α particles of energy about 4.5 MeV can be

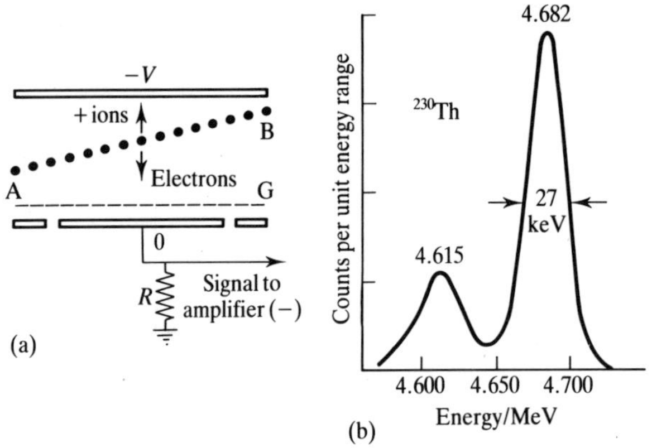

Figure 2.10 (a) Ionization chamber with Frisch grid; AB is the track of a charged particle from which ion and electron collection starts; (b) spectrum of α particles from ^{230}Th in a gridded ionization chamber. (Engelkemeir D W and Magnusson L B 1955 *Rev Sci Instrum* **26** (295).)

about 0.5 per cent as shown in figure 2.10(b). Both this energy resolution and the time resolution of the chamber are relatively poor compared with the response obtainable from semiconductor detectors (section 2.2.2, 'Semiconductor detectors').

Proportional counters

For detection of singly charged particles producing a low ionization it is often desirable, because of their high velocity, to use a detector operating in the proportional region of figure 2.9. The field necessary for ionization by collision in argon is about 10^6 V m^{-1} at atmospheric pressure and it is convenient to realize this in the wire-cylinder geometry of the counter

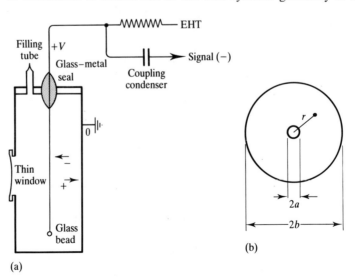

Figure 2.11
The proportional counter:
(a) construction – the glass bead prevents sparking from the end of the wire;
(b) cross-section in cylindrical geometry.

shown in figure 2.11. The field at radius r is given by

$$E = \frac{v}{r \ln(b/a)} \tag{2.18}$$

and is a maximum at the surface of the positive wire (anode) and rapidly decreases towards the cylinder (cathode). When an ionizing particle passes through the counter electrons drift towards the anode and positive ions towards the cathode. Near the wire the field becomes strong enough for gas multiplication to begin and an avalanche develops, surrounding the wire and extending about 0.5 mm along it. Because the avalanche begins close to the wire the electrons are collected in about 1 ns while the positive ions drift much more slowly. The arrival of the electrons produces only a small signal because of the presence of the positive ion space charge and the main pulse shape is governed by the movement of the ions. In a typical argon-filled counter with $a = 10$ μm, $b = 8$ mm and an operating voltage of 3 kV the total drift time is 550 μs, but the pulse height increases very rapidly at the beginning and very short signals ($\approx$30 ns) can be obtained by differentiation (figure 2.12). The total multiplication factor

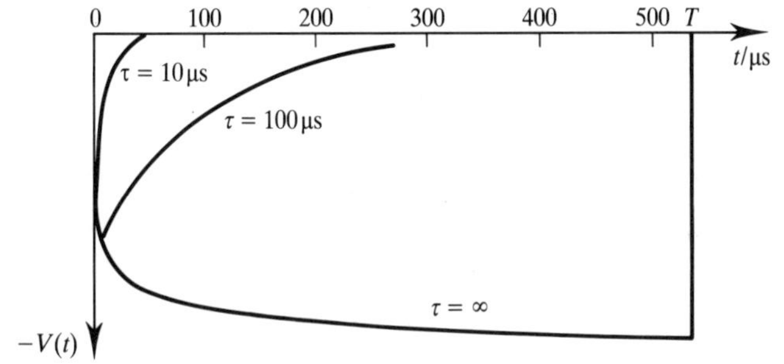

Figure 2.12 Time development of the pulse in a proportional counter. The total drift time of positive ions from anode to cathode is labelled *T*. The pulse shape for different time constants is shown.

provided by a proportional counter is usually between 10 and 10^3 and since the multiplication occurs near the wire the pulse shape is independent of the position of the primary track in the counter.

Proportional counters are very suitable for studying low energy radiations which can be wholly absorbed in the gas filling, e.g. the β particles of ^{3}H (<18 keV) or characteristic X-rays. Single-wire proportional counters may be used as detectors in the focal plane of a magnetic spectrometer and multiwire counters may be used in position sensitive detectors in both nuclear structure work (section 2.2.2 Semiconductor detectors) and particle physics experiments (section 2.3.3).

Geiger–Muller counters

The construction of a Geiger–Muller (GM) counter may be almost identical with that of the proportional counter shown in figure 2.11, but the operating conditions are those of the region $V > V_g$ (but less than the discharge threshold) in figure 2.9. The avalanche resulting from the motion of even a single electron towards the wire is much more violent than in a proportional counter and secondary ultraviolet photons are produced in sufficient number to convey the discharge down the whole length of the counter wire. This results in the availability of a constant charge for collection, independent of the magnitude and location of the initial ionization. The GM counters thus show both a threshold for operation ($V \approx V_g$) and a uniform-sized signal when operating. The filling is usually an argon–halogen mixture chosen to quench the counter discharge and terminate a signal. There are dead-time and recovery-time intervals resulting from the development and quenching of the discharge which in practice limit counting rates to perhaps a few hundred per second and even then large corrections are necessary. For this reason, and also because of its poor sensitivity as a γ ray detector, the GM counter is now little used in nuclear structure work.

2.2.2 *Solid state detectors*

The scintillation counter

The development of the modern scintillation particle-counting system from the original zinc sulphide screen viewed by a microscope, as used by Rutherford, is due first to the application of the photomultiplier as a light detector (Curran and Baker) and secondly to the discovery of scintillating materials that are transparent to their own fluorescent radiations (e.g. anthracene by Kallman and sodium iodide by Hofstadter).

The processes resulting in the emission of light when a charged particle passes through matter depend on the nature of the scintillating material. Inorganic crystals such as NaI are specially activated with impurities (e.g. thallium) to provide luminescence centres in the band gap. Electrons raised from the valence band of the crystal by Coulomb interaction may themselves excite an electron in a luminescence centre. This excitation will take place, preferentially, so that the relevant interatomic spacing in the centre is left unchanged. It is followed by a radiationless transition and then by photon emission also preserving interatomic spacing. The fluorescent radiation is of a longer wavelength than that corresponding to the absorption transition and is thus not usually re-absorbed by the scintillator. In organic scintillators molecular electrons are excited directly to one of several singlet levels and make radiationless transitions to the lowest excited singlet level. From this, fluorescent radiation to the vibrational substates of the ground state takes place, independently of the initial excitation process and without the intervention of any activator, so that the light pulse is generally faster than with inorganic materials.

The scintillators chiefly used for particle or photon detection are as follows.

(a) *Sodium iodide* (thallium activated); *bismuth germanate* Because of the high density sodium iodide is an efficient scintillator for γ ray detection. The rise time of the light pulse is about 0.06 μs and the decay time is about 0.25 μs, with a longer component of about 1.5 μs.

Even higher efficiency is obtainable with bismuth germanate (BGO) because of its higher atomic numbers and density.

(b) *Plastic and liquid scintillators* These are readily obtainable in very large volumes and can be adapted to many different geometrical arrangements, including counting of a source over a solid angle of 4π. The scintillator often contains a wavelength shifter to degrade the emitted spectrum to a wavelength that is transmitted efficiently through the crystal and that matches a photomultiplier detector. The light pulse associated with an instantaneous burst of ionization decays at first very rapidly, with a time constant of about 0.005 μs, so that these scintillators are useful for fast counting

The scintillator is placed directly on the window of a photomultiplier tube (figure 2.13), or is coupled to it via a light guide. The window is coated on the inside with a thin antimony–caesium layer from which photoelectrons are emitted with up to about 10 per cent efficiency for photons of wavelength 400–500 nm. The multiplier provides an amplification determined by the interelectrode potential difference, and the output pulse shape, before external amplification, depends on the relative

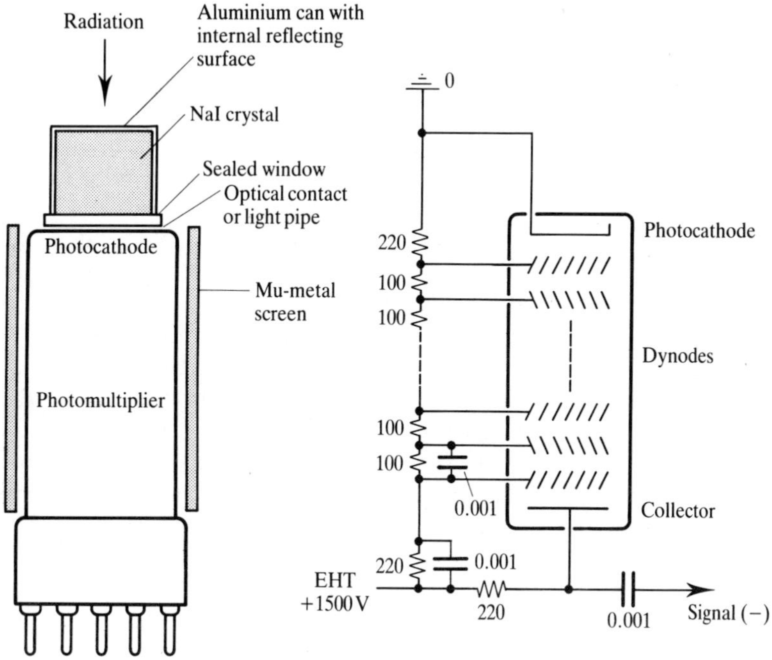

Figure 2.13
Scintillation counter, showing the circuit arrangement for supplying dynode potentials (resistances in kilo-ohms, capacitances in microfarads

magnitudes of the rise time τ_1 for the scintillator response, the decay time τ for the response and the time constant τ_a of the photomultiplier anode circuit. For $\tau_a \ll \tau_1$ the rise time of the output pulse is limited by τ_1 or by the rise time of the photomultiplier itself, while the decay time is determined by the scintillator decay time τ. This is known as the *current* mode of operation, and is used in fast timing applications with organic scintillators. If $\tau_a \gg \tau_1$, however, the current pulse is integrated and the rise time of the output pulse is determined by τ and the decay time by τ_a. This is the *voltage* mode and is especially suitable for pulse-height analysis.

If external amplification is used, the pulse shape and duration may be further controlled by differentiation and integration time constants. In particular they can be used to minimize pulse pile-up and to discriminate against circuit noise.

In the detection of γ radiation by a sodium iodide scintillator an incident photon of energy say 1 MeV interacts with an atom or an electron of the scintillator and produces photoelectrons or Compton electrons together with lower energy radiation which may itself interact similarly in the crystal. This primary process, converting photon energy into electron energy, takes place in approximately 10^{-10} s with an efficiency, as far as photon detection is concerned, determined by the absorption coefficient of the material, e.g. about 30 per cent for a cylindrical crystal of 25 mm depth × 40 mm diameter. The primary electrons excite radiation from the luminescence centres and the fluorescent radiations eject photoelectrons from the photocathode of the multiplier. When all efficiency factors are included, the 1 MeV incident photon may produce only about 2000 photoelectrons, with an associated statistical fluctuation of $\sqrt{(2000)}$, i.e. 2 per cent. The resulting spread of the final output pulse height distribution, assuming that all radiations are completely absorbed in the scintillating crystal, is further increased by variations in the dynode multiplication factor and in the efficiency of light collection over the detector volume. In practice, the pulse height distribution for a homogeneous radiation of energy $E_\gamma = 1$ MeV gives a resolution of about 10 per cent. The contribution to the resolution due to statistical fluctuations is expected to vary as $E_\gamma^{-1/2}$ and the mean pulse height is closely proportional to the energy E_γ. The spectra observed with a pulse height analyser for radiations from ^{57}Co, ^{137}Cs and ^{22}Na detected by a sodium iodide crystal are shown in figure 2.14. Their characteristic features are determined by the relative probabilities of the basic photon interaction processes in the crystal. For ^{57}Co, $E_\gamma = 122$ keV, there is a full energy peak due to the production of photoelectrons and the capture of all radiations resulting from the atomic vacancy produced. A much weaker, lower energy 'escape peak', indicating that sometimes the atomic K X-ray (26.8 keV for iodine) leaves the crystal, may also be resolved. For ^{137}Cs, with $E_\gamma = 662$ keV, a similar full energy peak appears, but there is a contribution to this from Compton scattering and below the main peak is the continuous distribution with a sharp 'Compton edge' due to recoil

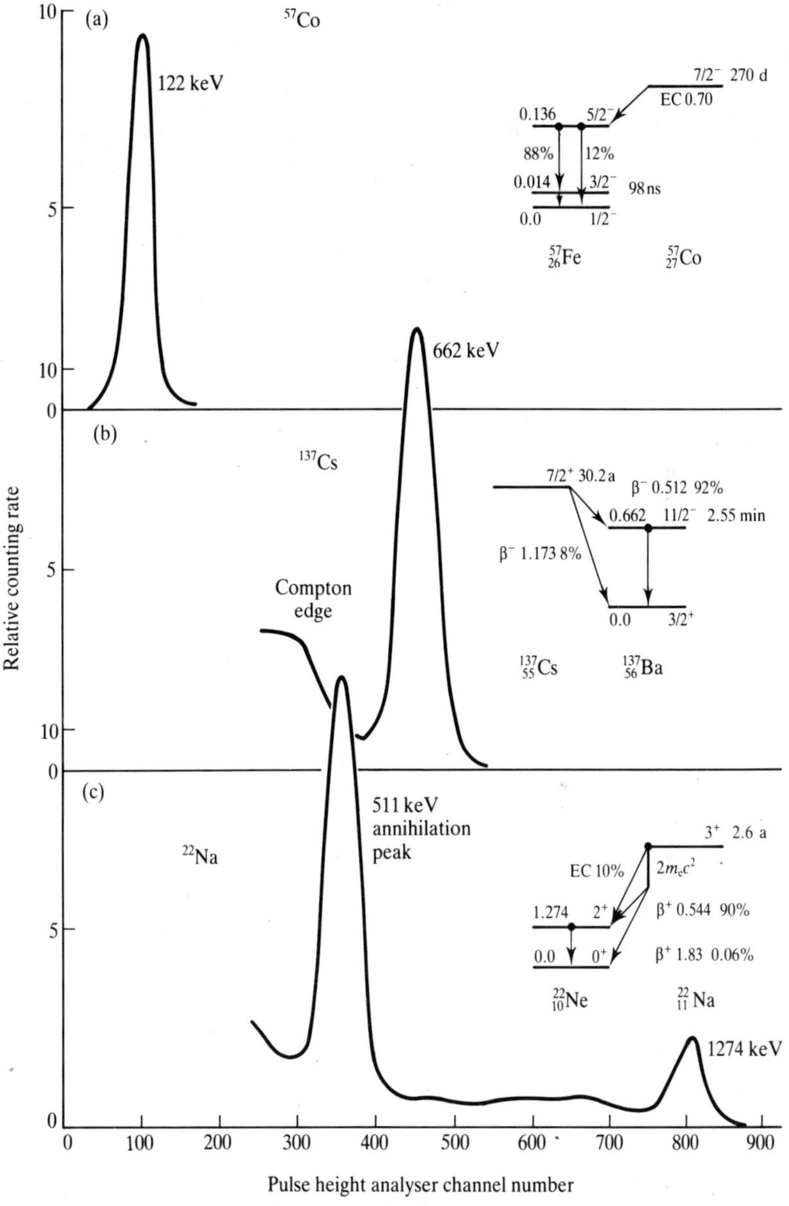

Figure 2.14 Scintillation counter: pulse height distribution for radiations from (a) ^{57}Co, (b) ^{137}Cs and (c) ^{22}Na detected in a cylindrical NaI(Tl) crystal of dimensions about 25 mm × 40 mm. In part (a) the weak 136 keV transition is not resolved; in part (b) internal conversion electrons accompany the 0.662 keV transition but the Ba X-rays of energy 32 keV are not shown. In all spectra peaks due to back-scattering of forward-going Compton-scattered photons and due to the escape of the 28.6 keV X-ray of iodine are omitted. The lifetimes shown are *halflives*, $t_{1/2}$.

electrons for which the associated Compton-scattered photon leaves the crystal. The angle dependence of the recoil electron energy leads to a peaking of the continuous distribution as a function of energy near the Compton edge.

With ^{22}Na, $E_\gamma = 1.28$ MeV, both photoelectric and Compton effects, and especially the latter, take place and in addition pair production ($\gamma \rightarrow e^+e^-$) with a threshold of 1.02 MeV occurs. If the positron produced in this last effect ultimately annihilates in the crystal the two 511 keV annihilation quanta generally produced may both be fully detected by the crystal. A pulse with height corresponding to E_γ then appears since the annihilation energy adds to the kinetic energy of the e^+e^- pair. If one annihilation quantum escapes there is a pulse at energy $E_\gamma - m_e c^2$, and if both escape there is one at $E_\gamma - 2m_e c^2$. The resulting spectrum is therefore somewhat complex even for a homogeneous photon energy. The width of the full energy peaks is seen to be approximately 10 per cent. The escape peaks for ^{24}Na may be seen in figure 2.17 on p. 48.

The main advantage of the scintillator detector is that a high efficiency coupled with moderate resolution for γ ray detection may be obtained with NaI(Tl) or BGO in a reasonably small space and at a reasonably low cost. Anticoincidence shields made of these materials are used in nuclear spectroscopic work with escape-suppressed spectrometers (section 2.2.2, 'γ ray detectors'). Organic scintillators provide excellent timing signals and can be built into the very large and complex arrays necessary for particle location and identification in high energy physics (section 2.3).

Semiconductor detectors

Solid state detectors operate essentially through the promotion of electrons from the valence band of a solid to the conduction band as a result of the entry of the particle or photon to be detected into the solid. Since the band gap in some solids is only about 1 eV, production of an electron–hole pair as part of the general energy loss by collision may require only 3–4 eV on average. The stopping of a particle of energy 1 MeV may thus produce 3×10^5 electron–hole pairs and the associated statistical fluctuation would be only 0.2 per cent, which offers a great advantage in basic resolution over the scintillation detector and indeed over the simple gas-filled ionization chamber for which an energy expenditure of 30 eV per ion is required.

The difficulty in realizing the attractive features of solid state detectors in practice has been in obtaining materials in which residual conductivity is sufficiently low to permit conduction pulses due to single particles to be distinguished above background and in which the charged carriers are not rapidly 'trapped' by impurities. This has, however, been achieved for certain *semiconductors* in the following types of detector.

Junction detectors for charged particles

In an n-type semiconductor conduction is due to the motion of electrons in the conduction band, and in p-type material the process is effectively

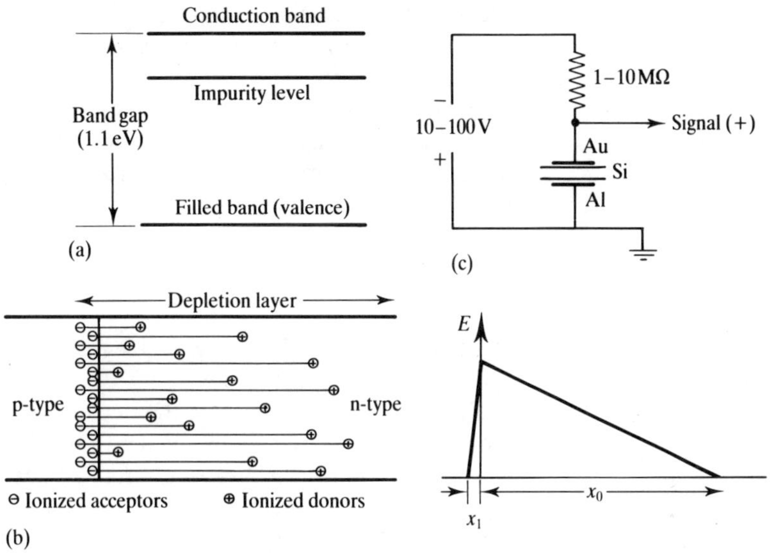

Figure 2.15 Semiconductor counter: (a) bands and impurity level in a semiconductor; (b) charge and electric field distributions in the depletion layer of a p–n junction; (c) circuit arrangement. (Dearnaley G 1967 *Contemp Phys* **8** (607).)

a motion of positive holes resulting from the rearrangement of electrons between atoms in the crystal. The two materials are prepared from an intrinsic semiconductor such as silicon by the controlled addition of electron-donating or electron-accepting elements (figure 2.15(a)). In the case of intrinsic silicon these elements could be phosphorus and indium respectively and the effect of their existence within surroundings of silicon is to produce hydrogen-like structures with their own set of energy levels, known as impurity levels. These are slightly below the conduction band and slightly above the valence band respectively, so that thermal excitation of electrons to the former and from the latter is readily possible. The corresponding conduction process is then by electrons (n type) or by holes (p type); it is assumed that all impurities are ionized.

If a junction between p- and n-type regions is formed in a crystal then conduction electrons predominate in the n region but a few will diffuse into the p region (figure 2.15(b)) where the conduction electron density is low. Similarly, holes from the p region will diffuse into the n region and the joint effect of these motions is to leave a positive space charge in the n region and a negative space charge in the p region, near the boundary. The electric field resulting from this double layer generates a potential difference between the n and the p regions and this causes a drift current of thermally excited electrons or holes in the opposite direction to the diffusion current so that a dynamical equilibrium exists in which there is no net transfer of charge. The region of the crystal occupied by space charges has lost charge carriers in comparison with the rest of the solid and is able to sustain an electric field; it is known as the *depletion layer*.

The depth x_0 of the depletion layer depends on the density of impurity centres and on any applied potential difference V (reverse bias making the n region more positive with respect to the p region). If ρ is the resistivity of the n-type region,

$$x_0 \approx (\rho V)^{1/2}. \tag{2.19}$$

For silicon of the highest practicable resistivity a depletion depth of about 5 mm may be obtained.

If a charged particle enters the depletion layer the electron–hole pairs produced are swept away by the field existing across the layer and a pulse may be detected in an external circuit. Because of the low value of the energy required to form an electron–hole pair, and because of the existence of another favourable factor (Fano factor F) which recognizes that energy losses for a particle of finite energy are not wholly independent, a resolution as good as 0.25 per cent is obtainable at 5 MeV. Figure 2.16 shows the spectrum of α particles from ^{212}Bi observed with a silicon detector of resistivity 27 Ω m.

Two types of p–n detector have been developed: the *diffused junction* detector in which a donor impurity, usually phosphorus, is introduced

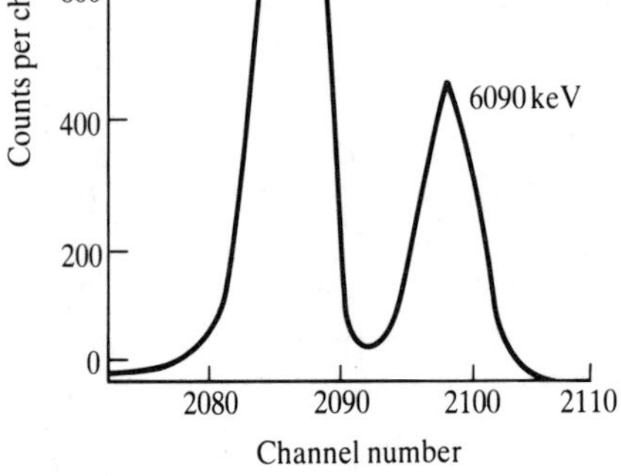

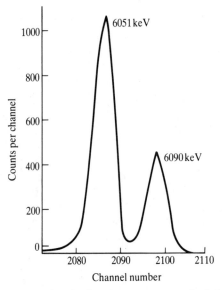

Figure 2.16 Semiconductor counter: pulse height distribution for 6 MeV α particles from ^{212}Bi (ThC) detected in a silicon surface-barrier counter 134 μm thick. The groups are of width 16 keV at half maximum intensity (England J B A, private communication).

into a p-type (boron-doped) silicon single crystal to form a depletion layer at the diffusion depth, and the *surface barrier* detector in which a p-type layer is formed on the surface of n-type silicon by oxidation. Contact is made to the detectors through a layer of gold. The counter base is often a layer of aluminium. Signals are derived from the surface barrier detector by the connections shown in figure 2.15(c). Since the depth of the depletion layer, and consequently the interelectrode capacitance, depends on the applied voltage, a charge sensitive rather than voltage sensitive pre-amplifier is used. Semiconductor counters are not themselves amplifying, and a typical output voltage might be 20 mV for a particle of energy 5 MeV.

The advantages of the silicon p–n junction as a detector of heavy particles are its excellent resolution and linearity, its small size and consequent fast response time permitting a high counting rate and the fairly simple nature of the necessary electronic circuits. The solid state counter is not actually a windowless counter because of the existence of p- or n-type insensitive layers of thickness 0.1–0.5 μm in surface-barrier and diffused-junction detectors respectively. This is not a serious drawback, although it adds to the line width, and its effect is outweighed by the overall simplicity of the counters, permitting the use of multi-detector arrays. The handling of data from such a complex system demands the availability of an on-line computer for storage of information and data processing. A special facility of high value in the use of solid state detectors is the easy construction of particle identification telescopes based on energy loss × energy product signals (see example 2.18). Counters of a length of a few centimetres may also be used as position sensitive indicators in the focal plane of a spectrometer, since it can be arranged that output pulse height depends on the distance of entry of the incident particle from the collecting electrode. A disadvantage of silicon detectors for use with heavy ions and fission fragments is that nuclear scattering by the silicon nuclei worsens resolution and gives rise to an energy defect because of the occurrence of non-ionizing transitions with large statistical fluctuations in the solid lattice. For this reason, gas-filled detectors can give a better performance in this application.

Increased sensitive volumes of semiconductor detectors can be obtained by compensating the acceptor centres in a p-type semiconductor by the controlled addition of donor impurities. The most suitable donor is lithium because this atom has a very low ionization potential in a semiconductor and also a high mobility. The lithium is 'drifted' into the bulk material from a surface layer by raising the temperature to about 420 K in the presence of an electric field. Compensated depths of about 15 mm and active volumes (in germanium) up to 100 cm^3 can be made. Large volume detectors may also be prepared from highly purified germanium (impurity concentration about 1 part in 10^{13}). The germanium (Ge(Li)) detectors must be kept at a temperature below 150 K to prevent the lithium drifting away from the counting region.

γ ray detectors

The major application of the lithium-drift technique is to the (Ge(Li)) counter, which has transformed the subject of γ ray spectroscopy. Germanium has a band gap of only 0.67 eV and must be cooled to liquid nitrogen temperature when used as a counter in order to minimize thermal excitation of electrons to the conduction band. This is an inconvenience which results in a preference for silicon counters (although these are also improved by cooling) for charged particle spectrometry. For γ ray detection, however, the higher atomic number of germanium ($Z_{Ge} = 32$, $Z_{Si} = 14$) leads to a marked improvement in efficiency as may be seen from the Z dependence of the basic processes of photoelectric, Compton and pair production absorption shown in figure 2.6. The difference between Ge(Li) and Si(Li) counters is especially marked in the energy ranges in which the photoeffect and pair production predominate because of the particular Z dependence. The Ge(Li) detector cannot yet be made as large as a sodium iodide or bismuth germanate scintillator and is less

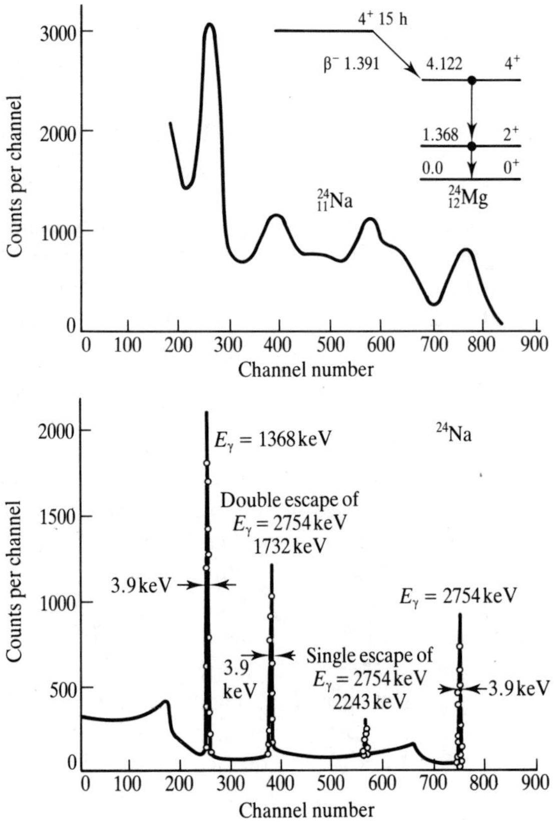

Figure 2.17 Semiconductor counter: spectrum of radiations from ^{24}Na as seen (a) in an NaI(Tl) crystal and (b) in a 30 cm^3 Ge(Li) detector. (Adapted from Orphan V J and Rasmussen N C 1967 *Nucl Instrum Meth* **48** (282)).

suitable than these when the highest efficiency is required, but its resolution is better by more than an order of magnitude and line widths of less than 1 keV have been reported. These are narrower than those observed for charged particles because there is no counter 'window' and energy loss in atomic collisions is not important.

Figure 2.17 shows a spectrum of ^{24}Na γ rays taken with a Ge(Li) detector compared with one obtained with a scintillation counter. Low energy radiations, e.g. electrons of approximately 10 keV, or characteristic X-rays may be recorded with high resolution by Si(Li) counters.

If a high resolution germanium detector is surrounded by a large sodium iodide (NaI) or bismuth germanate (BGO) scintillator operated in an 'anticoincidence' mode it is possible to veto those events in the germanium whose secondary radiations (e.g. Compton-scattered photons) give a signal in the surrounding detector. The background in the germanium spectrum of full energy events such as photopeaks is then much reduced. Such escape-suppressed spectrometers (ESS) are sometimes arranged around central BGO detectors which sense total energy and γ ray multiplicity in a nuclear cascade.[14]

Progress in nuclear spectroscopy and in the study of nuclei under extreme conditions (section 1.4) will increasingly depend upon large escape-suppressed photon detecting assemblies. The limit of detectability of rare events may be lowered by the use of multiple coincident events in high resolution detectors covering as large a solid angle as possible. In the EUROGAM assembly for use on European accelerators 45 BGO-shielded detectors surround the target and up to quadruple cascade γ ray coincidences in the germanium counters may be studied with good yield.

2.3 Detectors for particle physics studies[15]

2.3.1 General

In high energy collisions many particles can be produced and the basic aim of a detector is to identify them and to measure their momenta. If the particles are produced in a thick target a large variety of purpose-built detectors may be used but for the study of interactions with colliding beams (section 2.5.4) detectors cannot be so easily changed and tend to be large multipurpose installations. The term detector will be applied both to such installations and to the individual particle-sensitive components from which they are assembled.

In most experiments it is necessary to measure coordinates along the trajectories of charged particles. If a magnetic field is employed, the curvature of a trajectory determines the sign of charge and the momentum of the particle. For identification by mass determination (section 2.1.2), a

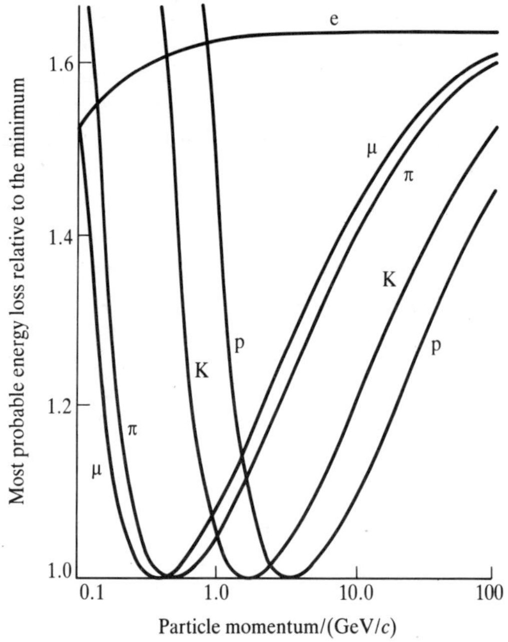

Figure 2.18
Rate of energy loss in a mixture of argon and methane, relative to the minimum, for electrons, muons, pions, kaons and protons, as a function of momentum.

simultaneous measurement of momentum and velocity, or of momentum and energy, must be made; figure 2.18 illustrates the use of the relativistic rise in collision loss for this purpose.

A complete kinematic reconstruction of an 'event' involves a determination of the energy–momentum four-vectors of any neutral particles produced as well as of charged particles. When the multiplicity of secondary particles is high the detector must be capable of separating nearby particles in space and, since the interaction rate in a practical case may be very high, the detectors may need a good time resolution. A typical apparatus in a high energy physics experiment involves many types of component detector, each performing one or more of the above tasks.

As with the nuclear structure detectors discussed in section 2.2, particle physics detectors also rely on the loss of energy of a charged particle in matter. The collision-loss phenomena listed in section 2.1.2 have led to the following general categories.

(a) Multiwire proportional counters (section 2.3.3) and streamer or spark chambers (section 2.3.4) rely on the ionization of gases. The miniature 'microstrip' silicon detectors,[15] which offer enormous advantages in complex installations needing good spatial resolution, are based on the production of electron–hole pairs in semiconductors.
(b) Scintillation counters (section 2.2.2) detect light flashes associated with primary ionization or excitation processes. They are mainly used to provide time-reference signals and triggers for other detectors in particle physics experiments, though the high photon detection

efficiency and good energy resolution of NaI(Tl) makes it ideal for use in total absorption shower counters[16] (section 2.3.6).

(c) Bubble chambers (section 2.3.2) rely on the deposition of energy along the track of a particle in a superheated liquid. Although now declining in importance they have had a highly significant as well as aesthetic role in particle physics.

(d) Nuclear emulsions record particles because of the production of developable grains along the track of the particle. They have had important applications in cosmic ray physics because of their small size and integrating property. They were used in 1947 in the discovery of the pion and of the π–μ decay sequence but they now have only somewhat special applications in particle physics, such as the decay of very short-lived particles, e.g. the B mesons (section 14.4.7).

Radiative processes such as bremsstrahlung, Cherenkov radiation and transition radiation are the basis of the detectors discussed in sections 2.3.5 and 2.3.6(a). Photons themselves and heavy neutral particles are detected by observation of the charged particles that they excite as secondary radiations in passing through matter (cf. section 2.1.4 for photons). Neutrinos can only be detected as a result of their weak interactions with nuclei.

Although traditionally the problem of particle detection has involved the characterization of stable particles,* γ, e, μ, p, n, Λ, $\Sigma, \ldots, \Lambda_c, \ldots, \pi$, K, D etc., there is now increasingly a change of emphasis. The events, particularly at colliding beam machines, have characteristic 'jet' structures caused by the fragmentation of heavy quarks and gluons and often contain energetic leptons and exhibit 'missing' energy due to escaping neutrinos. The traditional magnetic momentum analysis now has to be supplemented by precise global measurements of event structure involving determinations of energy and momentum flow among multiple jets of particles. Calorimeters (section 2.3.6) are ideally suited to this task and play an important part, for instance, in the large hybrid detectors ALEPH, DELPHI, L3 and OPAL now in use with the large electron–positron collider LEP at CERN.† The object of these installations above all is to test the predictions of the standard model of electroweak interactions and of gauge theories of the strong interaction.

2.3.2 *Bubble chambers*

In 1952 Glaser[17] showed that bubble formation could be initiated in a superheated liquid by the passage of an ionizing particle. In the super-

* The particle names and symbols used in this section will be found in chapter 7.
† CERN stands for Conseil Européen pour la Recherche Nucléaire and is used to refer to the laboratory of that organization at Geneva.

heated state at a given temperature the liquid pressure is less than the saturated vapour pressure and the liquid is therefore unstable. In order that boiling can occur in the body of the liquid, energy must be supplied and this can happen as a result of ionization along the track of a charged particle leading to a series of bubbles which define the particle trajectory. In the practical application, the liquid is prevented from boiling by the application of external pressure and becomes superheated, and therefore particle sensitive, when the pressure is suddenly reduced. In the earliest, very small, chambers very clean conditions were necessary to prevent spontaneous boiling, but soon after it had been shown by Hildebrand and Nagle[18] that liquid hydrogen could be used as the working fluid it was also discovered by Wood[19] that spontaneous boiling could be tolerated at the edges of a *large* retaining vessel. The single proton that is the hydrogen nucleus gives liquid hydrogen a great advantage over other liquids in the study of elementary particle interactions and after Wood's discovery very large metal-bodied chambers were built with optically flat glass windows for photography; figure 2.19 shows the Big European Bubble Chamber at CERN which had a total volume of 34 m^3 and incorporated provision for a magnetic field of the order of 2 T.

The detailed technical features of bubble chamber operation will not be described here but it must be noted that although the chamber expansion is phased with a pulsed accelerator cycle, it cannot be triggered by a selected event. This is because the centres on which the bubbles grow are short lived and disappear (after a trigger) before the chamber can be fully expanded. The particle beam must therefore be delivered to the chamber while it is already in its sensitive state. Despite this disadvantage the bubble chamber, with its solid angle acceptance of 4π sr, is unsurpassed in its capability for track reconstruction. In addition, the bubble density along the tracks can be used for mass identification purposes over a certain range of β values.[20] A rather special event, but one that well shows the full capabilities of the technique, is reproduced in figure 2.20.

Interactions with neutrons can be studied in chambers filled with liquid deuterium and high energy photons can be detected, through pair production, in heavy liquids such as xenon or freon. In the 'track-sensitive target'[21,22] a central liquid hydrogen section in which interactions take place is surrounded by a neon-filled section in which photons may be observed. One large chamber has been modified so that one of its cameras records events on holographic film, which greatly improves spatial resolution.

Bubble chambers have now been almost entirely replaced in high energy laboratories by purely electronic detectors. The reasons for this are that

(a) the chamber cannot be triggered,
(b) the repetition rate of 1–10 Hz is low and a pulse of charged particles must be limited so that only about 30 tracks are formed,

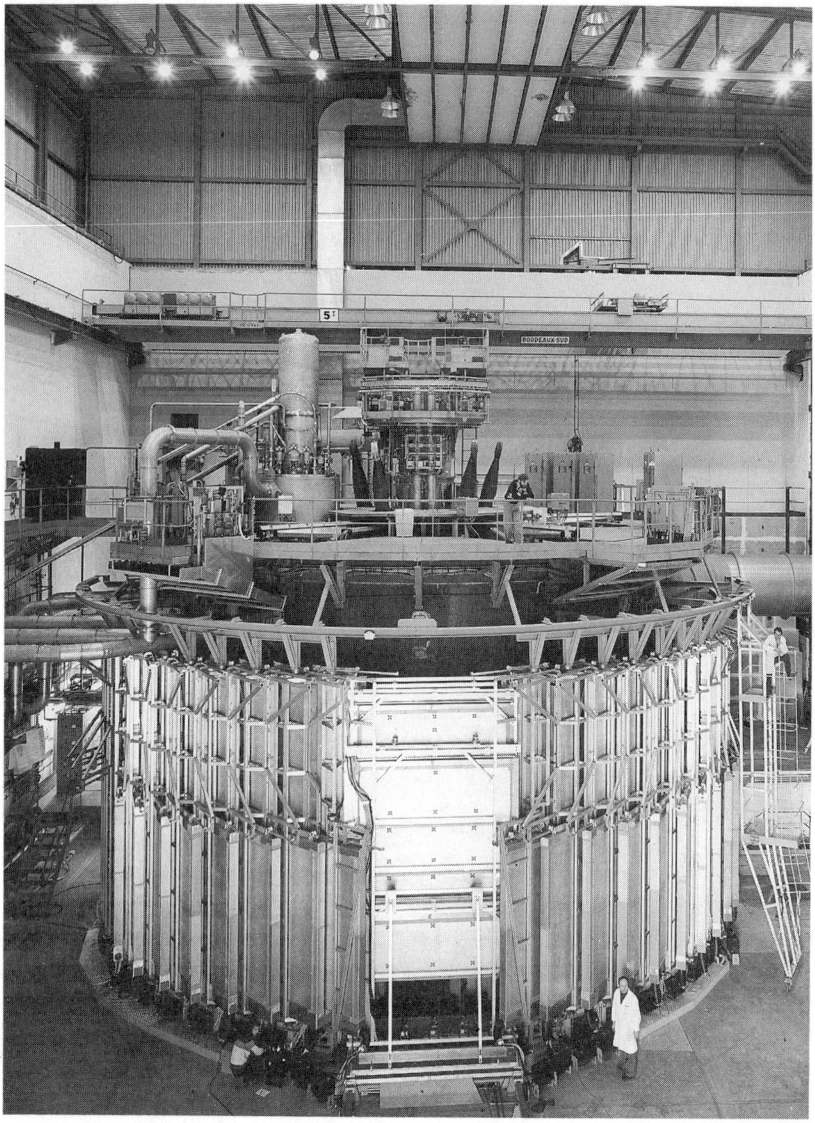

Figure 2.19
The Big European Bubble Chamber (BEBC) at CERN. (Photograph by courtesy of CERN.)

(c) event processing using views from three stereo cameras is inevitably slow, and
(d) the chambers are not suitable for use with colliding beam machines.

2.3.3 Multiwire proportional chambers and drift chambers

The simple cylindrical proportional counter described in section 2.2.1 is extensively used to determine the energy loss of a particle in matter,

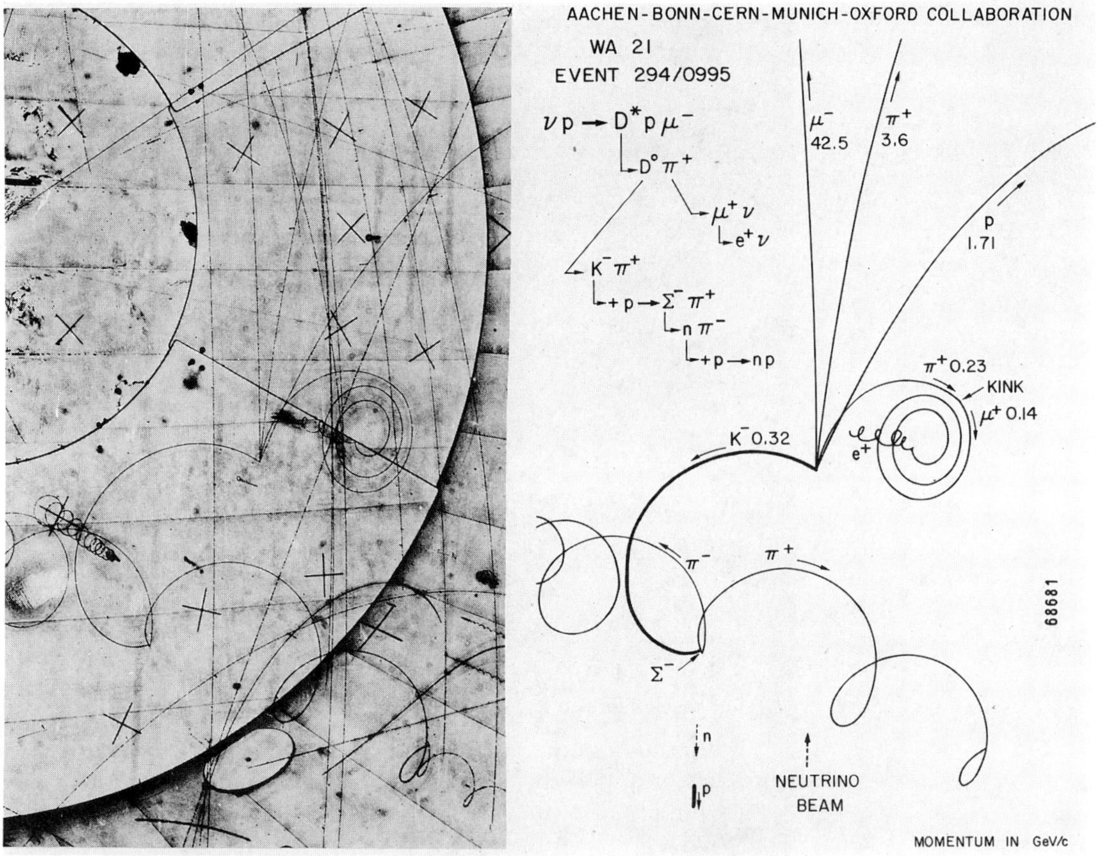

Figure 2.20 Production of a heavy charmed meson D* by a neutrino in the hydrogen-filled bubble chamber BEBC at CERN. On the left can be seen the actual photograph with the complete interpretation of the event on the right. (Photograph by courtesy of CERN.)

but its spatial resolution is clearly limited by size. Good spatial resolution, however, can be achieved with the multiwire chambers[15,23] developed by Charpak and his collaborators at CERN. These chambers have a set of thin, parallel, equally spaced anodes or 'sense' wires placed symmetrically between two cathode planes (figure 2.21(a)). The gap between the cathode planes is typically six to eight times larger than the gap between the anode wires. With the anodes earthed and a negative potential applied to the cathodes, a nearly uniform field develops in the main body of the detector away from the anode wires (figure 2.21(b)).

As discussed in section 2.2.1, the electrons from an ionizing event in the counter drift along the field lines and initiate avalanche multiplication in the high field region near the anode wire. The subsequent motion of the positive ion space charge in the field induces a negative pulse on the wire. Corresponding positive signals are produced on all other electrodes which largely compensate the negative signals produced by capacitative

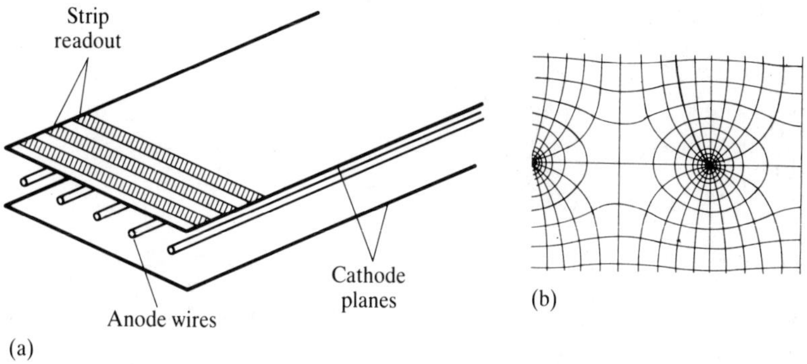

Figure 2.21 (a) Basic structure of a multiwire proportional chamber; (b) view of the electric field equipotentials and field lines around the anode wires (wire spacing 2 mm, wire diameter 20 μm).

coupling. Each sense wire therefore acts as an independent counter and the chamber as a whole is continuously sensitive. Today, track-sensitive detectors are generally multiwire structures operated in the proportional mode. They range from small high precision devices to large, multi-square-metre chambers with tens of thousands of read-out channels. A spatial resolution of approximately 0.7 mm is possible if the anode pulses are used but if the cathode plane is in strip form a determination of the centre of the cathode pulses can yield resolutions of the order of 50 μm.

The position of the primary ionization column caused by the passage of a charged particle may be determined by measuring the time for collection on the sense wire using an arrangement similar to that shown in figure 2.22. The wider anode wire spacing in such *drift chambers* leads to a decrease in the number of channels needed for operation. Spatial

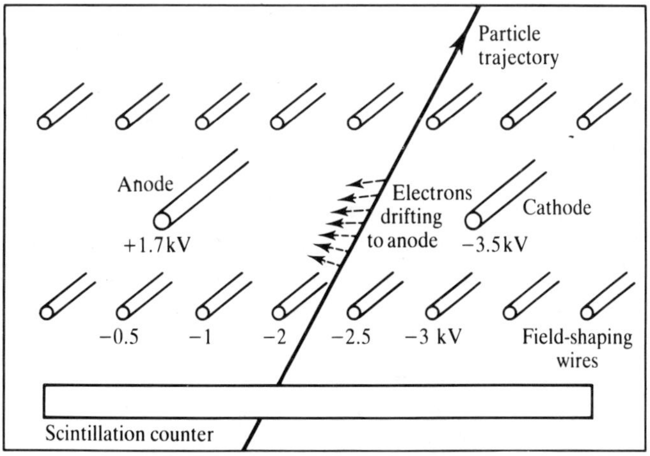

Figure 2.22 Schematic diagram showing the principles of operation of a drift chamber. The electrode configuration creates an almost uniform drift field so that the relation between track distance from the anode wire and drift time is linear.

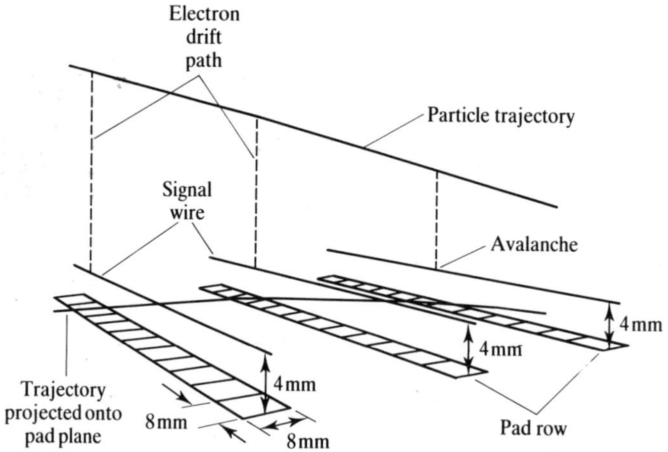

Figure 2.23
Schematic diagram showing the principles of operation of a time-projection chamber.

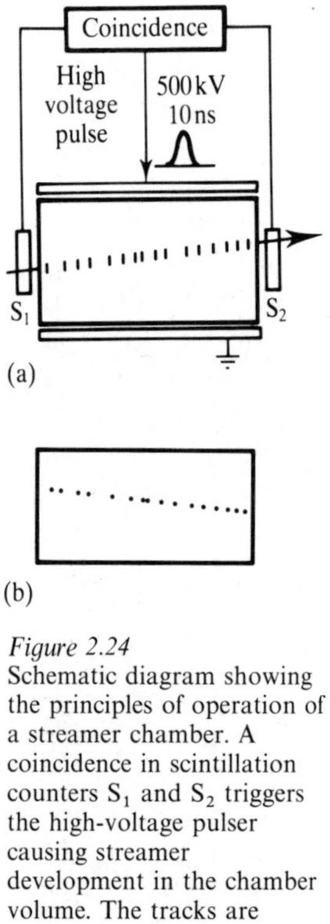

Figure 2.24
Schematic diagram showing the principles of operation of a streamer chamber. A coincidence in scintillation counters S_1 and S_2 triggers the high-voltage pulser causing streamer development in the chamber volume. The tracks are normally viewed through the transparent electrodes along a direction parallel to the electric field when they appear as a series of dots reminiscent of a bubble chamber photograph.
(a) View normal to the electric field; (b) view parallel to the electric field.

resolutions of about 100 μm are possible in such chambers, but they are only useful when detection rates are low.

The *time-projection chamber* (TPC)[24,25] is a large drift volume with a single planar multiwire chamber. Complete track images can be obtained by drifting the trajectory ionization on to the wire plane as shown in figure 2.23. Proportional wires and a segmented cathode provide coordinates perpendicular to the drift direction and time information determines the coordinates along the drift direction. Particle identification by dE/dx measurement is possible, although because of the Landau fluctuations (section 2.1.2) many independent samples of the energy loss must be made.

2.3.4 *Streamer chambers and spark chambers*

If a gaseous detector of ionization is operated above the region of proportional response shown in figure 2.9, with an amplification of perhaps 10^8, the avalanches grow into 'streamers'. These develop when the space charge in the avalanche is high enough to nullify the effect of the external field locally. Recombination of the ions and electrons can then occur and photon emission makes the streamer visible. Complete breakdown of the chamber is prevented by using a voltage pulse of short duration (≈ 10 ns) which is triggered when a charged particle passes through the chamber. A schematic diagram of a streamer chamber is shown in figure 2.24 and a photograph of a multitrack event is reproduced in figure 2.25.

If a longer pulse is applied to the chamber the streamers grow into *sparks* and such discharges between closely spaced electrodes have also been used for track recording. This detector can be triggered but because of the need to clear ions after a spark the time resolution and repetition rate are low and spark chambers are now rarely used.

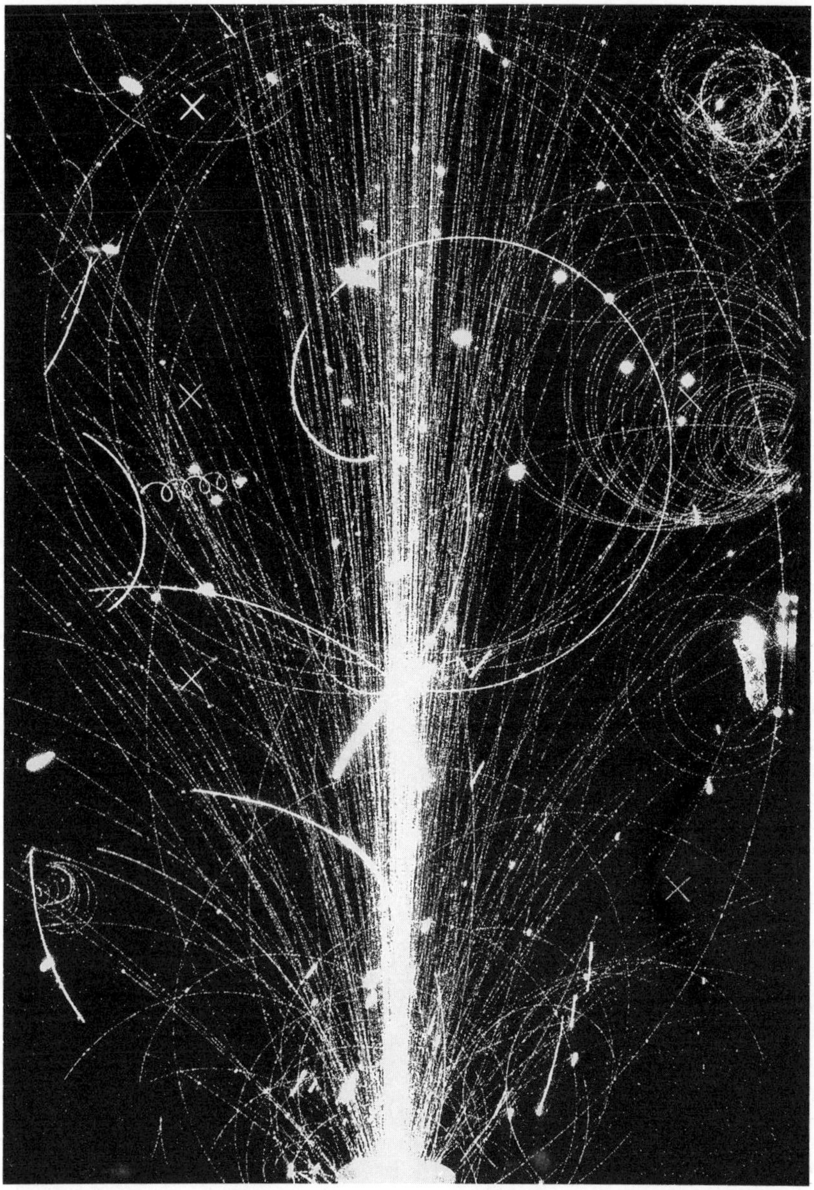

Figure 2.25 Photograph of a remarkable interaction produced by a collision of a ^{16}O nucleus on Pb and recorded by the streamer chamber of experiment NA35 at CERN. The ^{16}O nuclei were accelerated to 200 GeV/c per nucleon in the SPS (section 2.5.1), extracted and transported to a Pb target in the North Area. A total of 3.2 TeV laboratory energy was involved in this event. (Photograph by courtesy of K. P. Pretzl.)

Table 2.2
Cherenkov radiators

Radiator	$n-1$	γ_{th}
Plastic scintillator	0.58	1.3
Water	0.33	1.5
Pentane (STP)	1.7×10^{-3}	17
Helium (STP)	3.3×10^{-5}	123

2.3.5 Cherenkov and transition radiation detectors

The photons produced along the path of a charged particle in matter by the Cherenkov effect (section 2.1.3) may be detected by photomultipliers in the visible region or by multiwire proportional counters in the ultraviolet. The threshold velocity $v_{th} = \beta_{th} c$ below which no Cherenkov light is seen is determined by the refractive index n of the medium and, in the case of gases, can be conveniently varied by altering the pressure. The corresponding Lorentz factor $\gamma_{th} = (1 - \beta_{th}^2)^{-\frac{1}{2}}$, which gives the threshold energy in terms of the particle mass, is shown for a few radiating materials in table 2.2.

In figure 2.26 the angle of emission of Cherenkov radiation, given by

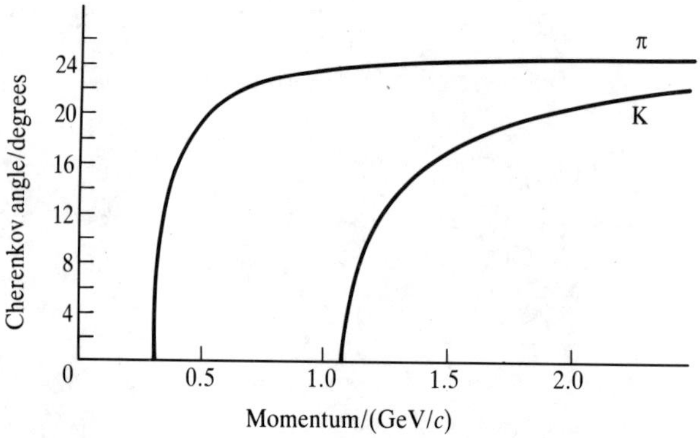

Figure 2.26
Cherenkov angle versus momentum for pions and kaons in a radiator with refractive index 1.1.

equation (2.7), is plotted against momentum for pions and kaons in a radiator with $n = 1.1$. It is evident that discrimination between the particles is also possible by angle selection and this has been used for particle identification in the region of minimum ionization where collision-loss methods fail.

Simple arrangements for identification of relativistic particles of different mass but the same momentum by the Cherenkov effect are shown in figures 2.27(a) and 2.27(b). In the threshold detector (figure 2.27(a)) the refractive index of the radiator is chosen so that the heavier particle of a possible pair has a velocity just below the threshold. In the differential counter (figure 2.27(b)) angle selection for a ring image is achieved using

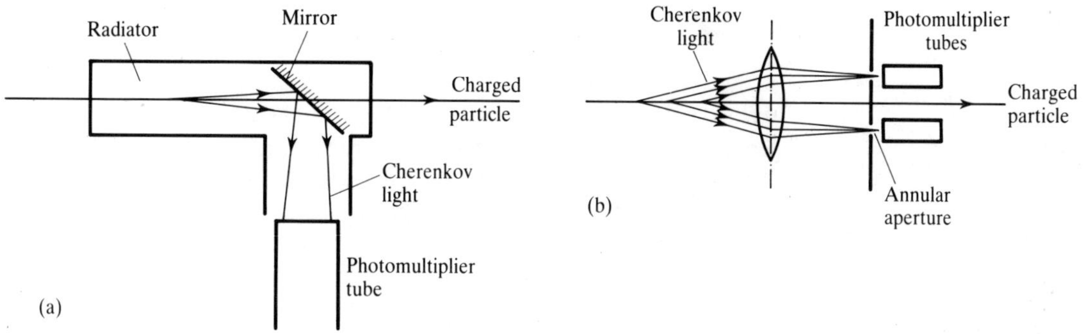

Figure 2.27
Principles of operation of (a) threshold and (b) differential Cherenkov counters.

adjustable annular apertures. Velocity resolution $d\beta/\beta$ as good as 10^{-7} has been reached[26,27] providing pion, kaon and proton separation above 100 GeV/c momentum.

Like all detectors that give a response to γ radiation, Cherenkov detectors take advantage of the fact that the electric field of a relativistic particle is concentrated in the plane perpendicular to its motion by the Lorentz transformation; the field measured in the laboratory in that plane is increased by the factor γ. As γ increases, processes can take place at greater and greater impact parameters and the energy loss increases (section 2.1.2) until polarization of the atoms of the medium inhibits the spread of the field. This saturation effect can be pushed to higher values of γ by the use of low density radiators but the energy loss is then so small that very long radiators are required. To avoid this difficulty in the ultrarelativistic region the phenomenon of transition radiation (section 2.1.3) has been exploited.

The weakness of transition radiation can be augmented by allowing particles to pass through a series of foils whose contributions add together coherently as in multiple beam interferometry. In one detector[28] a stack of 650 lithium foils 50 μm thick and 250 μm apart was used; X-ray photons were detected (figure 2.28) in a multiwire proportional counter and by selecting the frequency of the radiation it was possible to identify electrons in the energy range of a few giga-electronvolts ($\gamma > 1000$) while rejecting heavy particles ($\gamma < 100$).

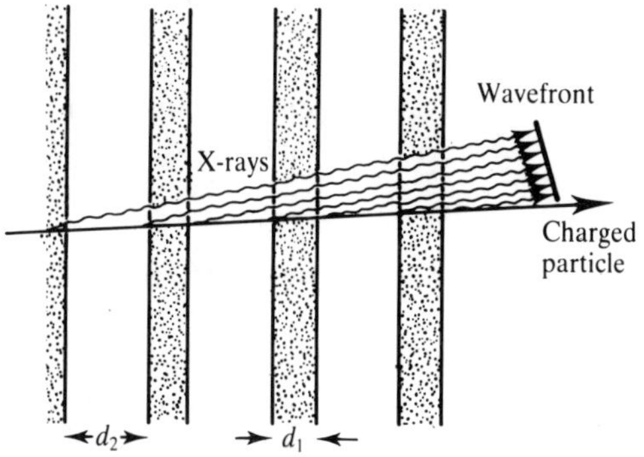

Figure 2.28
Schematic diagram showing the use of multiple-foil interference in the practical application of transition radiation.

2.3.6 Total absorption calorimeters

In the particle physics detectors so far described (sections 2.3.1–2.3.5) a particle loses only a small fraction of its total energy. In a total absorption calorimeter, however, a particle interacts and produces a cascade of shower particles in a block of dense material. If a section of the calorimeter is sensitive to scintillation light, Cherenkov radiation or ionization a signal proportional to the total energy can be received. The uncertainty in such an energy measurement arises from statistical fluctuations in the shower development and the energy resolution $\Delta E/E$ improves with increasing energy as $E^{-1/2}$.

If we assume that the rate of energy deposition is proportional to the particle energy then it is clear that the size of a calorimeter scales only logarithmically with energy, whereas a magnetic spectrometer scales as $p^{1/2}$ for a given momentum resolution $\Delta p/p$. Calorimeters can be used to detect neutral particles as well as charged particles and if the detector is segmented the position and direction of an incident particle can also be measured. In general, signals are formed on a time scale between 10 and 100 ns and may be used for real-time event selection. Identification is also possible employing the specific response of the detectors to electrons, muons and hadrons.

The main types of calorimeter are as follows.

(a) In *electromagnetic calorimeters* a shower is initiated by a high energy electron or photon and proceeds through successive processes of pair production and bremsstrahlung (sections 2.1.3 and 2.1.4). As the shower develops the number of particles increases exponentially with depth until it reaches a maximum when the particle energy is of the order of the *critical energy* E_c (section 2.1.3). The scale of longitudinal development is set by the *radiation length* (section 2.1.3). The transverse shower dimensions are determined by the radiation length and by the multiple Coulomb scattering of the low energy electrons in the shower. In *homogeneous* electromagnetic calorimeters the whole detector is sensitive. Commonly used materials are lead glass and NaI(Tl); in the former, Cherenkov radiation from electrons and positrons is detected and in the latter, scintillation light is detected. The critical energies and radiation lengths are given in table 2.1. In *heterogeneous* calorimeters there are alternate layers of passive absorber and active material such as plastic scintillator, in which about 10 per cent of the total energy is deposited.

(b) In *hadronic calorimeters* the shower development is similar in principle to the electromagnetic case but is more complex and more erratic. The scale of hadronic shower development is governed by the nuclear absorption length $\lambda = A/N_A \rho\sigma$, where A is the atomic mass number, N_A the Avogadro number, ρ the density and σ the cross-section for inelastic

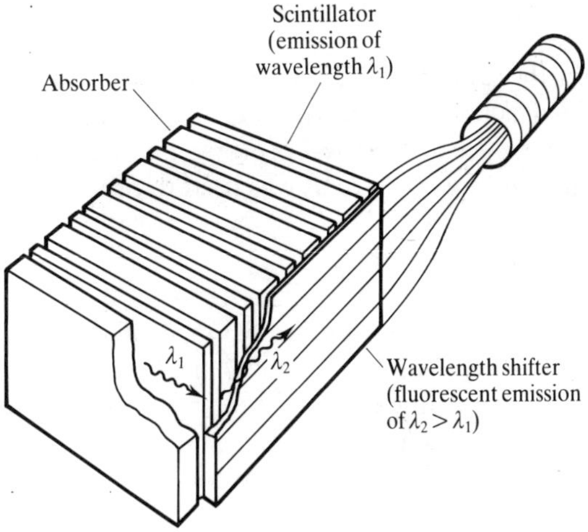

Figure 2.29
Calorimeter readout using wavelength shifters.

collisions. Materials commonly used are liquid argon, iron and uranium, with λ values for nucleons of 80.9, 17.1 and 12.0 cm, respectively. In contrast with the electromagnetic case about 30 per cent of the incident energy is dissipated in reactions which do not produce an observable signal owing to leakage of muons, neutrinos or slow neutrons for instance. These calorimeters are heterogeneous and if plastic scintillator is used as the active medium it is coupled to photomultipliers via a wavelength-shifting guide (figure 2.29).

Alternatively, direct charge collection read-out may be used with or without amplification of ionization.

2.4 *Accelerators for nuclear structure studies*[29–34]

The accelerators now used for nuclear structure studies may be classified broadly into those which develop a steady accelerating field (electrostatic generators) and those in which radiofrequency electric fields are used (linear accelerators, cyclotrons, synchrotrons, microtrons). As interest moves into the 100–1000 MeV range of energies only accelerators in the second class can be considered, and for linear accelerators and cyclotrons in particular the use of superconducting techniques to reduce radiofrequency power input then offers great advantages. In this section only the historically important low energy accelerators will be considered; high energy machines for particle physics studies will be described in section 2.5.

2.4.1 *The tandem electrostatic generator*[29,30]

In the famous 1932 experiment of Cockcroft and Walton (section 6.1.2) in which the lithium-7 nucleus was disintegrated for the first time by laboratory-accelerated protons, a transformer–rectifier–capacitance voltage-multiplying circuit was used to produce protons of velocity v given by

$$\tfrac{1}{2}m_p v^2 = eV \tag{2.20}$$

where V was the output voltage of the generator on load ($\approx$500 kV). This direct method can be used for voltages up to about 5 MV but for general nuclear structure research the most versatile and powerful accelerator is now the electrostatic generator developed by Van de Graaff in 1931. Although electrostatic generators readily accelerate electrons, those with which we are concerned in this section are to be thought of as positive ion machines.

Figure 2.30 shows the main components of a typical electrostatic generator, incorporating the tandem principle. Referring first of all to the lower half of the figure, charge is conveyed to the terminal by an insulating belt or by a 'laddertron' of conducting bars insulated from each other but forming a flexible chain. Charge is transferred to the belt or chain at the low potential end by a corona discharge from spray points or by electrostatic induction. At the terminal end the transfer process is reversed and by allowing the terminal pulley to reach a higher potential than the terminal itself, negative charge may be conveyed to the downgoing charging track. A sectionalized evacuated accelerating tube traverses the terminal and the insulating stack structure that supports it and terminates at earth potential. The stack structure itself is a series of equipotential surfaces separated by rigid insulators and connected by resistors. It provides a uniform axial field, within which the accelerating tube is contained.

Electrostatic generators are normally enclosed in a pressure vessel filled with an insulating gas such as sulphur hexafluoride, to permit the axial voltage gradient to be raised to about 2 MV m^{-1}. Pressures of up to 10 atmospheres are used in large machines.

In the early electrostatic accelerators ions were injected into the accelerating tube from a gaseous discharge tube housed in the terminal. In the tandem accelerator, however, shown in figure 2.30, the ion source is at earth potential and produces negative ions, e.g. H^-, He^-, $^{16}O^-$. These are accelerated to the terminal through an extension of the accelerating tube already mentioned. In the terminal, H^- ions for instance, are moving with a velocity v given by (2.20) and passage through a thin stripper, e.g. a carbon foil of thickness about 50 μg cm^{-2} or a tube containing gas at low pressure, removes the extra electron and a further electron as well so that a positive ion H^+ is available for acceleration to earth potential from the terminal, yielding an energy of $2eV$. Negative

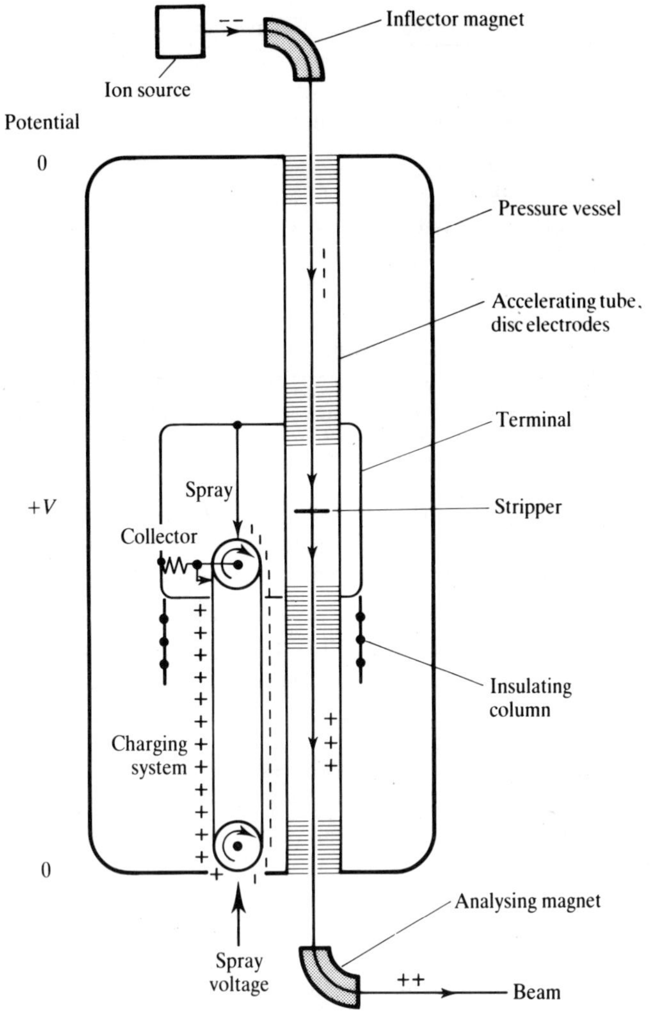

Figure 2.30 The electrostatic generator (schematic). The lower half is effectively a single-ended machine and the addition of the upper half with an extra tube and a stripper converts it to a tandem accelerator.

ions of heavier elements may be stripped to a positive charge state qe in the terminal and the final velocity in this case corresponds to acceleration through a potential $(1 + q)V$; additional strippers in the positive-ion tube can be used to increase q.

The energy of an electrostatic generator may be stabilized by controlling the charging current from an error signal derived from the accelerated beam itself. This passes through an analysing magnet (figure 2.30) and an exit slit with insulated jaws, from which a difference signal is derived if the beam deviates from the axis.

Energy definition to about 0.5 keV is possible in this way with a spread about the mean energy of not more than 1–1.5 keV even in the largest accelerators of, say, 20 MV terminal voltage supplying proton currents of, say, 10 μA. This type of performance is ideal for nuclear reaction experiments.

2.4.2 *Linear accelerators*[31]

It was recognized early that the extension of direct voltage methods to the production of very high particle energies would ultimately encounter insulation problems. The possibility of successive re-application of the same moderate electric field to a particle beam was therefore studied and led to the development of the linear accelerator.

Drift tube accelerators

The earliest heavy particle accelerators (Wideroe 1928, Sloan and Lawrence 1931, Beams and Snoddy 1934) were of this type. The principle is illustrated in figure 2.31. In the Sloan–Lawrence accelerator, operated

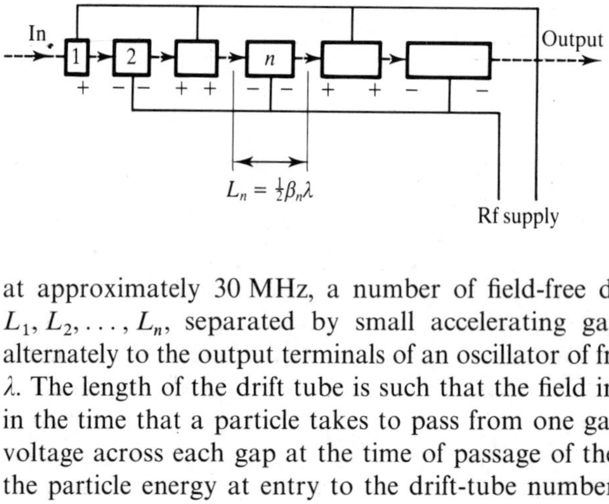

Figure 2.31
Principle of the Sloan–Lawrence linear accelerator.

at approximately 30 MHz, a number of field-free drift tubes of length $L_1, L_2, \ldots, L_n$, separated by small accelerating gaps, were connected alternately to the output terminals of an oscillator of free-space wavelength λ. The length of the drift tube is such that the field in a gap just reverses in the time that a particle takes to pass from one gap to the next. If the voltage across each gap at the time of passage of the particles is V then the particle energy at entry to the drift-tube numbered n is neV (for an assumed initial injection energy of eV) and the particle velocity is

$$v_n = \left(\frac{2neV}{m}\right)^{1/2} \tag{2.21}$$

where m is the mass of the particles being accelerated. The frequency of the oscillator is c/λ and for a time of flight of half a cycle the length of the drift tube n must therefore be

$$L_n = \frac{1}{2}\frac{v_n\lambda}{c} = \frac{1}{2}\beta_n\lambda \tag{2.22}$$

so that, for non-relativistic energies, from (2.21) and (2.22),

$$L_n \propto n^{1/2}.$$

It also follows that if the energy gain per gap is held constant the accelerator length is directly proportional to wavelength. The particles emerge in bunches corresponding closely with the times of appearance of the gap voltage V, at which resonance is possible.

The apparent requirement that the drift-tube structure should be designed for exact resonance with the accelerating beam was realized to be unnecessary following the enunciation of the principle of *phase stability* by McMillan and by Veksler in 1945 (section 2.5.1). In its application to the linear accelerator (figure 2.32(a)) this principle considers a particle that crossses a gap with a phase angle ϕ_s with respect to the accelerating voltage waveform (point A). If ϕ_s corresponds to the voltage V (equation 2.21)) for which the drift tube structure is designed, then the particle arrives at the next gap with the same phase angle. Late particles, however,

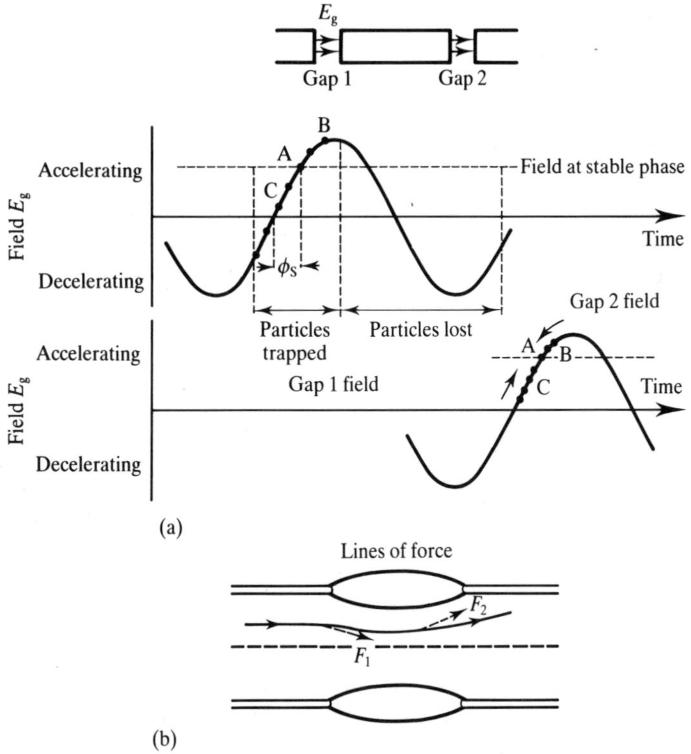

Figure 2.32 (a) Phase stability in a drift-tube ion accelerator. The dots show the phase angles with respect to the gap field of a bunch of particles of uniform velocity arriving at gap 1. At gap 2 there is increased bunching about the stable phase ϕ_s. (b) Radial defocusing of particles passing through a cylindrical gap in a field increasing with time.

($\phi > \phi_s$, points B) receive a larger acceleration in the gap, traverse the drift tube more quickly and move towards point A in phase at the next gap. Similarly, early particles ($\phi < \phi_s$, points C) will be less accelerated and will also move towards A in phase. Particles corresponding to point A thus have stable phase, and all particles with phase angles within a certain range of ϕ_s will be trapped and will oscillate about the point of stable phase. Latitude is therefore possible in the mechanical tolerances that must be applied to the drift tube structure.

The desirable feature of axial (phase) stability leads to radial instability because the stable phase point is on the rising part of the voltage wave. Figure 2.32(b) illustrates this; because the field increases as the particle traverses the gap, the defocusing force predominates. Radial stability is now generally restored by means of quadrupole magnets within the drift tubes themselves.

The original mode of excitation indicated in figure 2.31 is used only for low energy accelerators. For energies above, say, 5 MeV for protons, the availability of high powers at microwave frequencies makes it highly desirable to use the resonant cavity type of excitation introduced by Alvarez (figure 2.33). The cavity is tuned by radius rather than length

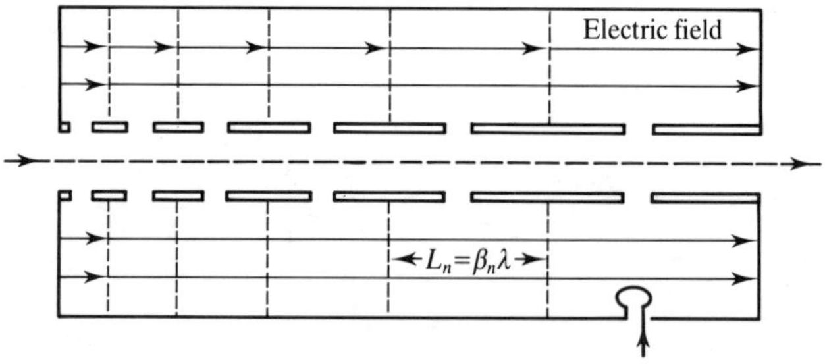

Figure 2.33
Alvarez resonant accelerator.

and is excited in the lowest longitudinal mode, with a uniform axial electric field throughout its length. The drift tubes divide the cavity into n sections and the particles traverse the successive drift tubes while the field is in the decelerating phase, receiving acceleration at the gaps. The section length L increases with particle velocity according to the equation

$$L_n = \frac{v_n \lambda}{c} = \beta_n \lambda \tag{2.23}$$

since the particles traverse one complete section in each cycle. The high radiofrequency power required to excite the cavity is not usually supplied continuously and the accelerator is operated from a pulsed transmitter with a duty cycle (on–off ratio) of about 1 per cent. A direct current injector supplies ions of energy 500–4000 keV to the main accelerator, and an improvement in intensity is sometimes obtained by incorporating a special cavity to 'bunch' the injected beam at approximately the selected stable phase angle of the main radiofrequency field.

Drift-tube accelerators have been built both for protons and for heavier ions; the principle is similar in each case. For a given structure and wavelength equation (2.23) requires that the velocity increments at each accelerating gap should be the same for each particle. A range of values of ze/m, corresponding to different heavy ions in different charge states, can therefore be accelerated by adjusting the radiofrequency voltage so that the gap field E is proportional to m/z.

The main advantages of the drift-tube accelerator as a source of heavy nuclear projectiles are the good collimation, the high homogeneity, the relatively high intensity of the beam and the possibility of extension of the machine to extremely high energies. A disadvantage for experiments requiring coincidence counting is the sharply bunched nature of the output, which increases the ratio of random to real coincidences in the counter systems. It is also difficult, though not impossible, to vary the output energy and in this and the preceding respect the linear accelerator is much inferior to the electrostatic generator, although superconducting techniques may enable it to approach continuous operation.

Waveguide accelerators

A standing-wave pattern in a cavity, such as that developed in the ion accelerator, may also be regarded as a superposition of two progressive waves moving in opposite directions. One of these waves travels with the particles and accelerates them. This suggests the feasibility of an equivalent form of accelerator in which particles are continuously accelerated by a progressive wave in a metal guide. If the particles are moving with nearly the velocity of light, the wavelength of the radiofrequency field is constant; the energy conveyed to the particles increases their total energy γm rather than accelerating them. Waveguide accelerators are especially suitable for electrons since these particles have a velocity of $0.98c$ for an energy of only 2 MeV, which may easily be provided at injection by an electrostatic accelerator.

In familiar types of waveguide the phase velocity of the travelling wave is always greater than the velocity of light but may be reduced by loading the guide with a series of diaphragms (figure 2.34). Electrons move in bunches near the peak field of the travelling wave and gain energy continuously from the wave. At velocities approaching the velocity of light

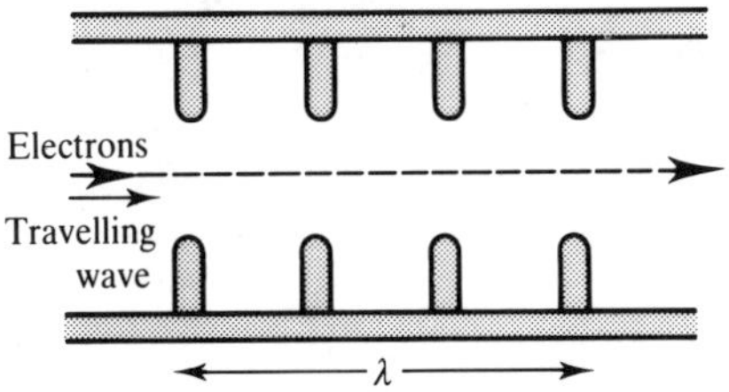

Figure 2.34
Disc-loaded circular waveguide.

radial defocusing forces vanish (since there is compensation between effects due to electric and magnetic fields in the guide) and there is no definite axial stability, so that good quality of mechanical construction is necessary. An impressive example of what can be done is the 3 km Stanford linear accelerator (SLA), which is described in section 2.5.2. The high energy electron linear accelerator has been extensively used for electron-scattering studies of nuclear sizes and excitations.

2.4.3 *The cyclotron*[32]

The cyclotron is a magnetic-resonance orbital accelerator developed by Lawrence and his collaborators at Berkeley in the 1930s. After Cockcroft and Walton's success in disintegration experiments with high velocity protons in 1932 the cyclotron rapidly became a powerful competitor in the field, with the particular advantage that it did not require generation of a high voltage.

The equations governing the orbital motion of charged particles in a cyclotron are of general application. If a particle of mass m and charge q moves with constant speed v in a plane perpendicular to the lines of force of an azimuthally uniform magnetic field of flux density B, it feels a constant force at right angles to its velocity vector and describes a circle of radius r given by

$$qvB = \frac{\gamma m v^2}{r} \tag{2.24}$$

where $\gamma = (1 - \beta^2)^{-1/2}$ with $\beta = v/c$.

The linear momentum of the particle is

$$p = \gamma m v = qBr \tag{2.25}$$

and its angular velocity is

$$\omega = \frac{v}{r} = \frac{qB}{\gamma m} \text{ rad s}^{-1}. \tag{2.26}$$

The frequency of rotation in the circular orbit, known as the *cyclotron frequency*, is

$$f = \frac{\omega}{2\pi} = \frac{qB}{2\pi\gamma m} \tag{2.27}$$

which equals 15.25 MHz per tesla for protons for $\gamma = 1$ ($f = f_0$).

If the field is uniform azimuthally, but non-uniform radially, the axial component at radius r may be written

$$B_z = B_0\left(\frac{r_0}{r}\right)^n \tag{2.28}$$

where B_0 is the flux density at a reference radius r_0, for which it is reasonable to assume that $\gamma = 1$ and the field index is

$$n = -\frac{r}{B_z}\frac{\partial B_z}{\partial r}. \tag{2.29}$$

The frequencies of axial and radial oscillation about an equilibrium orbit of radius r_0 are[32]

$$\begin{aligned} f_z &= f_0(n)^{1/2} \\ f_r &= f_0(1-n)^{1/2}. \end{aligned} \tag{2.30}$$

For the orbit to be stable n must be between 0 (radially uniform field) and 1.

The total energy of a particle occupying such a stable orbit is (setting $c = 1$ in the next three equations)

$$\begin{aligned} E &= \gamma m \\ &= (p^2 + m^2)^{1/2} \\ &= \{(qBr)^2 + m^2\}^{1/2}. \end{aligned} \tag{2.31}$$

In the non-relativistic approximation the kinetic energy T $(=E - m)$ is given by

$$T = \frac{p^2}{2m} \tag{2.32}$$

but for extreme relativistic energies

$$T = E = p. \tag{2.33}$$

To increase the particle energy it may be given a series of properly timed impulses from an electric field. Lawrence noticed that for non-relativistic motion ($\gamma = 1$) the cyclotron frequency f given by the equation (2.27) is constant and equal to f_0, i.e. the motion is *isochronous*. The electrical impulses can therefore be derived from an oscillating field of frequency f_0, in resonance with the cyclotron frequency. This is done in practice by the use of a D-shaped electrode (figure 2.35(a)) in the vacuum system in which

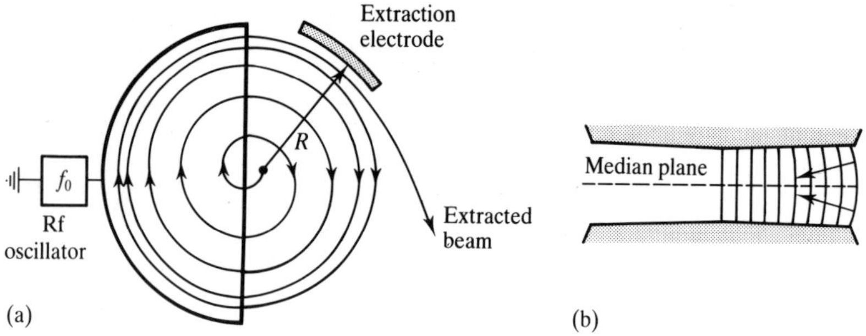

Figure 2.35 The isochronous cyclotron: (a) path of ions in a cyclotron from central ion source to extracted beam, for an azimuthally uniform field; (b) axial forces in a radially decreasing cyclotron field.

the particles move. At resonance this gives an acceleration causing an increase in orbit radii twice per revolution, at entry to and exit from the D electrode. At the maximum radius R useful in practice for acceleration, the kinetic energy is

$$T = \frac{p^2}{2m} = \frac{q^2 B_z^2 R^2}{2m} \tag{2.34}$$

and the particles may be extracted by the application of suitable deflecting fields. If *negative* ions are accelerated, extraction is simplified by the use of a stripping foil to reverse the charge and curvature in the magnetic field.

In a uniform field cyclotron, bunching of ions from the central source occurs early in the acceleration process and is maintained, at about a 10 per cent duty cycle, during the passage to maximum radius. The stability condition $0 < n < 1$ requires a radially *decreasing* magnetic field, as shown in figure 2.35(b). Unfortunately this destroys isochronism which is in any case prejudiced by the gradual increase of γ above 1 as the particle velocity increases. The ion bunch therefore gradually loses phase with respect to the accelerating field and would in the end begin to suffer deceleration. The conventional azimuthally uniform field cyclotron is therefore limited in output energy – in practice to about 30 MeV for protons.

Although it is possible because of the principle of phase stability to design a cyclotron (*synchrocyclotron*) in which synchronism at an accelerating phase can be preserved by a programmed decrease of the frequency f of the electric field, it is preferable to use a magnetic field shape that permits the radial *increase* required for isochronism, but provides some extra focusing forces. The radial variation of mean field required is found from equation (2.27) to be

$$B = \gamma B_0 = \frac{B_0}{(1 - \beta^2)^{1/2}} \tag{2.35}$$

Calculation of energy of particles in a cyclotron

Suppose that an isochronous cyclotron has a maximum radius of 0.3 m and a magnetic field at this radius of 1.6 T. Then from equation (2.34) the kinetic energy of a circulating proton at this radius would be

$$\begin{aligned} T &= \frac{q^2 B_z^2 R^2}{2m_p} \\ &= \frac{(1.6 \times 10^{-19})^2 (1.6)^2 (0.3)^2}{2 \times 1.67 \times 10^{-27}} \text{ J} \\ &= 17.65 \times 10^{-13} \text{ J} \end{aligned}$$

Converting to mega-electronvolts

$$\begin{aligned} T &= \frac{17.65 \times 10^{-13}}{1.6 \times 10^{-13}} \\ &= 11 \text{ MeV}. \end{aligned}$$

The radiofrequency voltage may be such that the proton gains on average about 50 keV of energy in each revolution. The total number of turns is then about 220. The orbit spacing decreases as the proton moves out.

and approximately this gives

$$B = B_0(1 + \tfrac{1}{2}\beta^2) = B_0\left(1 + \frac{r^2\omega_0^2}{2c^2}\right) = B_0\left(1 + \frac{2\pi^2 f_0^2 r^2}{c^2}\right). \quad (2.36)$$

The extra focusing is obtained, following a suggestion of L. H. Thomas, by introducing *azimuthal variation* into the field, also known as *sector focusing*. In such a field there are alternate high and low field regions. A closed orbit in this field is non-circular and as a particle in such an orbit crosses a sector boundary (either high → low or low → high) *radial* components of velocity arise. The field variation at the boundaries gives rise to *azimuthal* components and the new $\boldsymbol{v} \times \boldsymbol{B}$ force is axially focusing in both types of transition region. The sector focusing may be improved by using spiral instead of radial sector boundaries. Several such cyclotrons with design energies of the order of 100 MeV for protons have been built. Because of their low mass, and therefore rapidly increasing γ under acceleration, electrons cannot be accelerated in an ordinary cyclotron or even in a synchrocyclotron. Phase-stable machines with a variable magnetic field, however, can accelerate either electrons or protons, and following the development of powerful focusing techniques these *synchrotrons* have become of outstanding importance for particle physics. They are described in section 2.5.1.

2.4.4 *The microtron*[32]

The relativistic limitation of the ordinary cyclotron may also be overcome if the increase in energy at each acceleration is so large that the revolution time increases by one radiofrequency period $1/f_0$. From equation (2.27) it can be seen that this requires integral increments of γ, i.e. an energy increase of mc^2, per turn. This is practicable for electrons ($m_e c^2 = 511$ keV) and the microtron uses this principle (figure 2.36).

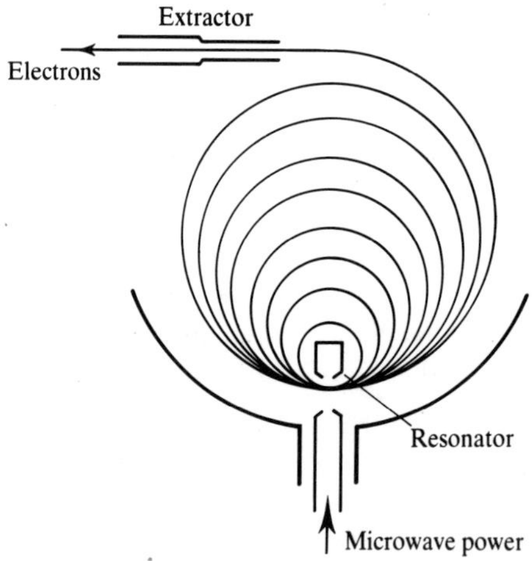

Figure 2.36
Successive electron orbits in the microtron.

Electrons pass through a cavity excited from a pulsed radiofrequency source of frequency about 3000 MHz. The corresponding magnetic field, from equation (2.27) with $\gamma = 1$, is 0.107 T and this field is maintained over a large area bounded by the cavity. After N transits the total energy has become $(N + 1)m_e c^2$ and the orbit radius is given by equation (2.24), with $q = e$, as

$$R_N = \frac{(N + 1)m_e c^2}{eBc} = \frac{(N + 1)m_e c}{eB} \tag{2.37}$$

since the electron velocity rapidly approaches the value c. The orbits are widely spaced and extraction is thus easy. There is phase stability during the acceleration and the beam is monochromatic to about 0.1 per cent.

Microtrons built with a 'race-track' geometry use a linear accelerator as the accelerating section and with superconducting techniques continuous operation is possible. Such a facility is very suitable for electron scattering experiments at energies up to 1 GeV as an alternative to a large linear accelerator since the continuous mode of operation allows the use of coincidence counting techniques.

If the electron beam from an accelerator such as the microtron is allowed to strike a heavy target, bremsstrahlung photons will be produced. With each photon there is a reduced energy electron and if the energy of this electron is determined by magnetic analysis, the energy of the associated photon is known. In this way a spectrum of '*tagged*' *photons* is provided and can be used, in coincidence with a signal from the tagging electron, for photodisintegration experiments (see also section 2.5.3).

2.4.5 New techniques

In section 1.4 it was noted that the frontier studies in nuclear structure physics relate to extremes of excitation energy, angular momentum and isobaric spin. The accelerators used or planned to attack these problems are based on the principles outlined in sections 2.4.1–2.4.4, extended to include synchrotrons (section 2.5.1) but augmented both in size and performance in comparison with earlier machines. The techniques applied to enhance performance are those developed to meet the requirements of particle physics experiments, the most important being the use of *storage rings* (section 2.5.4), the application of *electron cooling* (section 2.5.4) to stored beams and the incorporation of *superconducting elements* in accelerator structures.

Electron cooling is a method of reducing the lateral momentum of an ion beam circulating in a storage ring by letting it interact, in a straight section, with a well-defined beam of electrons of equal velocity but much lower energy. The ions impart unwanted momentum components to the electrons through the Coulomb interaction. Superconducting cavities in linear accelerators reduce dissipation and enable new machines to be planned for continuous operation, while superconducting coils in orbital accelerators enable higher fields to be obtained than with conventional magnets.

By such means, it is probable that electron machines will reach an energy of 15 GeV with continuous beam and will then be able to reveal the quark structure of the nucleons that make up nuclei. For the excitation of the quark–gluon plasma, however, heavy particles and much higher energies are necessary to create the required baryon density and temperature. Although heavy ions (e.g. ^{32}S) have reached energies of about 200 GeV per nucleon in the CERN super proton synchrotron (SPS) accelerator (section 2.5.1), it is likely that this problem will ultimately demand a heavy-ion *collider* (section 2.5.5), with cooled beams and high luminosity (appendix B), to produce energy densities even greater than the 2 GeV fm^{-3} reached at the SPS. It is not easy to be sure that a quark–gluon plasma has been reached but comparison of yields of certain particles in say p–Pb and S–Sb collisions may be definitive.

High spin states may be explored with more modest machines and here the emphasis is more on elaborate but efficient detector arrays (section 2.2.2) which permit the observation of as many radiations as possible in coincidence. The tandem Van de Graaff accelerator at Daresbury (UK), the GANIL orbital accelerator in France and the heavy-ion linear accelerator UNILAC and heavy-ion synchrotron SIS at Darmstadt (Germany) have been notable in this field.

For the study of nuclei of unusual neutron to proton ratio, an accelerator such as GANIL may be used to provide a primary heavy-ion beam which fragments in passing through a *thin* target. The required (radioactive) product is separated from unwanted fragments, focused and delivered as a usable beam. Alternatively (at Darmstadt) the radioactive beam is injected into a synchrotron/storage ring, with a cooling facility, for further acceleration. Finally, the selected beam may be allowed to interact with a suitable target to produce exotic nuclides.

In another method, a *thick* target is bombarded by a proton or heavy-ion beam and the radioactive atoms needed are collected from the target and used to form an atomic or ionic beam. At the on-line isotope separator ISOLDE at CERN many laser-spectroscopic studies of hyperfine interactions have been made using such beams. The collected radioactive ions may be further accelerated if desired for reaction studies. The use of secondary beams produced by primary interactions in a solid target in particle physics is described in section 2.5.3.

The historical evolution of accelerators for nuclear structure studies is shown in the 'Livingston chart' (see figure 2.44 on p. 86).

2.5 *Accelerators for particle physics studies* (references 32–34 and table 2.3)

The object of particle physics studies is to probe the structure of matter with the finest possible resolution, greatly exceeding that necessary to examine the properties of finite nuclei. From the de Broglie wavelength relation $\lambda = h/p$ we see that this means increasing the momentum p of the probing beam of particles as much as possible. This in turn implies that new particles not found in nature as stable entities may be created and a study of their properties has yielded vital information on the forces that hold matter together. The starting point, in the years immediately following the Second World War, was the desire to reach energies corresponding at least with the proton mass, approximately 1000 MeV, and hopefully largely in excess of this. Success soon came (1952) and subsequent technological developments, which will be briefly reviewed in this section, have brought us to energies a thousand times greater, namely

Table 2.3
The world's highest energy accelerators

		Year	Energy/GeV
Proton synchrotrons	CPS (CERN, Geneva)	1959	29
	AGS (Brookhaven, USA)	1960	30
	Serphukov, Russia	1967	70
	Fermilab main ring (FNAL, USA)	1972–82	400
	SPS (CERN, Geneva)	1976	450
	Tevatron II (FNAL, USA)	1984	800
Proton–proton collider	ISR (CERN, Geneva)	1971–83	31 + 31
Proton–antiproton colliders	Sp̄pS (CERN, Geneva)	1982	315 + 315
	Tevatron I (FNAL, USA)	1986	900 + 900
Electron synchrotrons	DESY (Hamburg)	1964	7
	Cornell (USA)	1967	12
Electron linac	SLAC (Stanford, USA)	1966	30
Electron–positron colliders	PETRA (Hamburg)	1978	23 + 23
	CESR (Cornell, USA)	1979	8 + 8
	PEP (Stanford, USA)	1980	15 + 15
	Vepp 4 (Novosibirsk, Russia)	1980	7 + 7
	SLC (Stanford, USA)	1987	50 + 50
	TRISTAN (Tsukuba, Japan)	1987	30 + 30
	BEPC (Beijing, China)	1989	2.8 + 2.8
	LEP I (CERN, Geneva)	1989	50 + 50
Electron–proton collider	HERA (Hamburg)	1992	30(e) + 820(p)

10^6 MeV ($=10^3$ GeV = 1 TeV). The rich harvest of fundamental physics that has resulted is the subject of chapters 7–15 of this book.

2.5.1 *The synchrotron*[32–34]

The construction of an isochronous cyclotron (section 2.4.3) for the multigiga-electronvolt range of energies would be prohibitively expensive. But if particles undergoing acceleration can be held under phase-stable conditions in a mean orbit of constant radius only an annular magnet is required. An accelerator of this type, named the synchrotron, was conceived by McMillan[35] and independently by Veksler.[36]

In the first synchrotrons the functions of bending and focusing of the particle beam were combined in the magnet design and the magnetic field was in principle azimuthally uniform, although for practical purposes a ring could be built up from separated sectors. In such *weak focusing*, or *constant gradient* (CG), machines beam instabilities were controlled by shaping the pole tips to give a field index n (section 2.4.3) between 0 and 1. The main components of such a synchrotron are sketched in figure 2.37. Particles are injected into the magnet ring from a linear accelerator and the magnetic field at this time is that required to maintain them on the stable orbit. An accelerating electric field is provided by radiofrequency

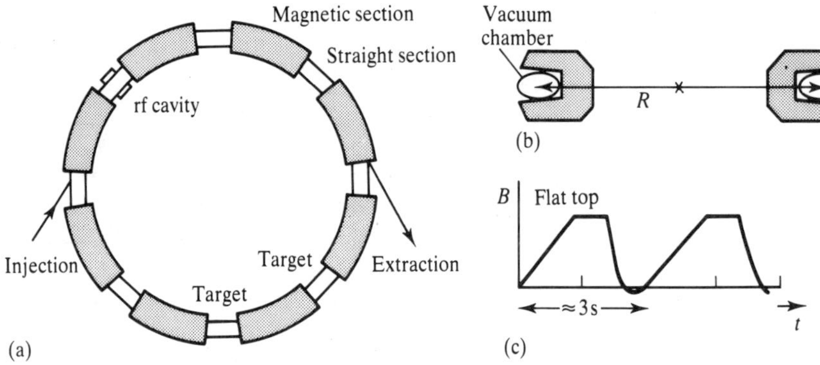

Figure 2.37 The weak-focusing proton synchrotron: (a) magnet ring; (b) cross-section through a magnetic sector; (c) magnetic field cycle, showing the flat top to give a long 'spill-time' of the extracted beam.

cavities through which the particles pass and as their momentum increases the magnetic field is increased synchronously to maintain them on an orbit of radius R. The frequency necessary at a total energy E is given by

$$f = \frac{qB}{2\pi E} = \frac{qB}{2\pi(m^2 + q^2B^2R^2)^{1/2}} \left(\rightarrow \frac{1}{2\pi R} \text{ for } E \gg m \right) \tag{2.38}$$

using equations (2.27) and (2.31). A typical magnetic field cycle is shown in figure 2.37(c). Once the particles have reached full energy they can be ejected by a pulsed extraction magnet to form an external beam, or directed to an internal target from which secondary beams of product particles may be obtained (section 2.5.3).

A major advance in accelerator design was made when Christofilos, and independently Courant, Livingston and Snyder,[37] realized that it is not necessary to render axial and radial oscillations stable simultaneously. In the *strong focusing* or *alternating gradient* (AG) synchrotron alternate magnetic field sectors have reversed gradients so that there is either axial or radial focusing in a given sector but not both together. There is, however, *net* focusing in both directions after passage through two sectors (cf. the achromatic lens combination in optics). A typical value of $|n|$ in AG synchrotrons is 300, and since this means a shorter free oscillation period the amplitude of these oscillations is reduced and a considerable spread of momentum can be accommodated in a small radial space, with consequent saving of magnet and vacuum chamber costs. In recent AG synchrotrons the bending and focusing take place in *separated* sectors.

The particle motion is phase stable in synchrotrons. In weak focusing machines a particle arriving early (B) at the accelerating gap (figure 2.38) receives a greater energy than it should and moves to a slightly greater radius, at which an orbit takes *longer* to describe. At the next transit of the accelerating cavity it has therefore moved towards the phase-stable

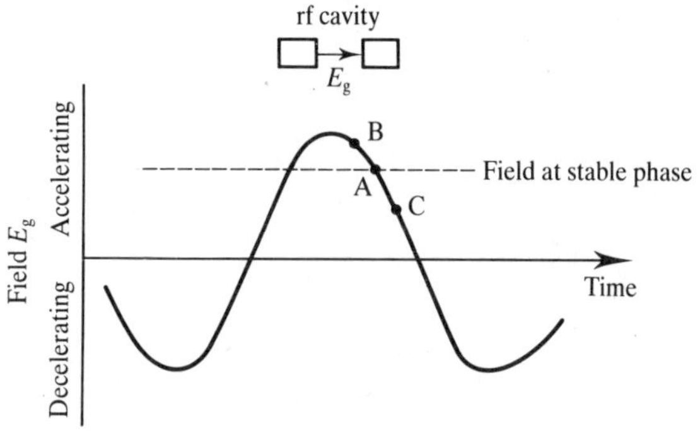

Figure 2.38
Phase stability in a weak focusing (CG) synchrotron; particles arriving at times B and C move towards time A, relative to the voltage wave, as acceleration proceeds.

point A. Similarly, late particles (C) also move towards A, which is on the *falling* part of the cavity voltage waveform, in contrast with the situation for linear accelerators (figure 2.32).

In strong focusing machines, because of the large value of n, the change of radius with momentum is rather small and the orbits for late particles at low energy may actually take a shorter time to describe. The phase-stable point is then on the *rising* part of the voltage wave, as with the linear accelerator. Above a certain energy, known as the *transition energy*, the orbit for late particles begins to take a longer time to describe than that for the synchronous beam and the phase-stable point then moves to the *falling* part of the voltage wave as for CG machines.

The first AG machine to be completed (1959) was the CERN proton synchrotron (CPS), which has a maximum proton energy of 29 GeV. A slightly larger machine, the alternating gradient synchrotron (AGS) was built at the Brookhaven National Laboratory in the USA and came into service in 1960. Each of these accelerators has played an important role in high energy physics, particularly in the discovery and characterization of resonant states, which led to the formulation of the quark model (chapter 10). The 1970s saw a tenfold increase in beam energy; in 1972 a 500 GeV machine was commissioned at Fermilab near Chicago and in 1976 the SPS, which uses the CPS as an injector, became active at CERN. This accelerator now provides protons not only for fixed target experiments but also for colliding-beam experiments (section 2.5.4); heavy ions have also been accelerated to relativistic energies (section 2.4.5). The layout of the CERN accelerator complex is shown in figure 2.39.

The highest energy orbital electron accelerators, the 7 GeV machine DESY in Hamburg and the Cornell 12 GeV synchrotron, are both AG machines. Unfortunately, extension of orbital acceleration to higher electron energies meets the severe and unavoidable problem of radiation loss (section 2.1.3). A charged particle of mass m and energy E, moving in an orbit of radius R, suffers a loss proportional to $(E/m)^4(1/R)$. This is negligible for proton machines because of the factor m^{-4}, but becomes prohibitive for high energy electron machines, unless they have a very

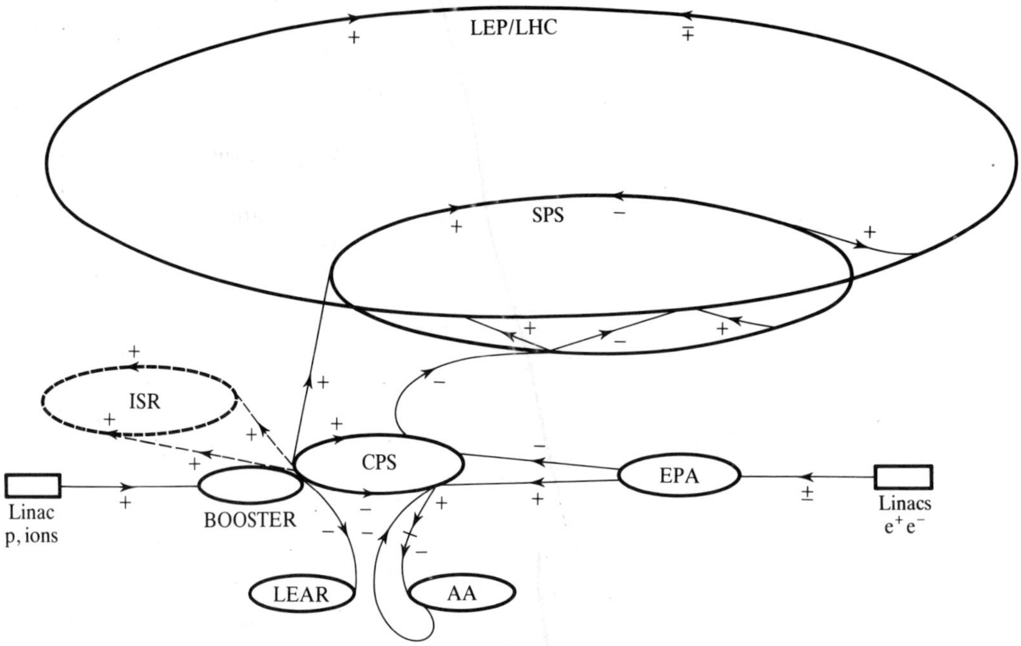

Figure 2.39 General layout of the CERN accelerators. The basic accelerator is the CPS which receives protons (or heavy ions) from one linear accelerator injector or electrons and positrons from another linac system via the electron–positron accumulator (EPA). Protons from the CPS are used to produce antiprotons which fill LEAR or the accumulator AA (section 2.5.4) from which they are redirected to the CPS. Full energy protons and antiprotons, or electrons and positrons, fill the SPS (section 2.5.1) for further acceleration. Appropriate beams from the SPS are used to fill LEP (section 2.5.4) or the LHC (section 2.5.5). The CPS and SPS beams may be extracted into external fixed-target experimental areas, not shown in the diagram. Heavy ions may be used instead of protons for ultra-relativistic experiments. In the ISR (section 2.5.4, now discontinued) and in the LHC (not completed 1993) proton beams circulate in opposite directions in separate rings.

large radius, because the necessary radiofrequency power cannot be supplied. The *synchrotron radiation* accompanying a circulating electron beam can be used as an intense spectroscopic source from the X-ray region to the infra-red.

Both electron and proton machines produce a beam in which there is bunching within pulses of a repetition rate governed by the modulation cycle.

2.5.2 The electron linear accelerator

Because of the limitation that radiation loss imposes upon orbital machines, electrons of energy above 20 GeV are mainly produced by linear accelerators (section 2.3.2). In 1962 a project to build a 3 km long waveguide accelerator to produce 15–45 GeV electrons was approved for Stanford University in the USA. This remarkable machine (the Stanford Linear Accelerator (SLA))[38] was completed in 1966, building on the experience gained with lower energy machines used for nuclear structure studies.

In the SLA power is fed into a disc-loaded waveguide of 960 sections constructed with high mechanical precision (figure 2.34) from 240 klystron amplifiers driven in synchronism from a master oscillator. Electrons are injected into a short tapered section in which the phase velocity and longitudinal accelerating field both increase and are bunched at a phase near the peak field of the travelling wave. Phase oscillations are damped owing to the rapidly increasing energy and the bunch moves through the main accelerator with essentially the velocity of light. No auxiliary focusing is needed because of the relativistic shortening of the 3 km guide in the electron frame of reference to less than 1 m. Each of the 240 klystrons feeds microwave power at 2856 MHz in pulses of 2.5 μs and 1–360 Hz repetition rate to four sections of the guide. A final electron energy of 22 GeV is obtained with an energy spread of 1.3 per cent.

In an alternative mode of operation, in which part of the klystron pulse is stored in an intermediate cavity and then suddenly discharged into the waveguide to reinforce the rest of the pulse, an energy of 35 GeV can be obtained and further extension to 50 GeV by this means has been achieved.

2.5.3 Secondary beams at fixed target accelerators[39–41]

The radiations produced by the impact of a primary beam of protons or electrons on a fixed target may themselves be used to produce further interactions in a second target, which might be a bubble chamber. The important characteristics of these secondary beams are firstly their production timing and secondly their momentum resolution and purity; requirements differ according to the nature of the final detector. Reviews of this subject will be found in the references.

For use with the bubble chamber (section 2.3.2), which cannot be triggered to record selected events, the incident secondary beam should be highly pure to keep down the number of unwanted events. To help in identification of particular final states in analyses, the momentum resolution of the secondary beam should be better than the accuracy of momentum measurement with the chamber and values of about 1 per cent have been achieved. The time duration of the incident beam should be short compared with the bubble growth time and the necessary beam spills of less than 100 μs are produced by a pulsed magnetic deflector.[42]

In contrast, beams intended for use with electronic detectors (sections 2.3.3 and 2.3.5) should have high intensity and long spill-time, which is obtained in synchrotrons by holding the magnetic field constant at the end of the accelerating cycle and turning off the radiofrequency power. The beam then drifts slowly across the primary target. The time resolution of a typical electronic detector such as a multiwire chamber may be about 30 ns and such detectors can handle up to 3×10^7 particles per second. As with bubble chambers, good momentum resolution of the secondary beam is required, but since electronic detectors can be triggered by a signal that includes particle identification, high beam purity may be unnecessary.

The minimum requirements of good momentum definition and appropriate beam spatial profile can be achieved by combinations of dipole (bending) magnets and collimators and quadrupole (focusing) magnets. Such relatively simple unseparated beams are suitable only for protons in the case of a positively charged beam and for negative pions in the case of a negative beam. For particles other than these *separated* beams are necessary.

An *electrostatic separator* is formed by two parallel plate electrodes with a uniform electric field between them. Charged particles of a given momentum but different mass have different velocities and are deflected through different angles in their passage between the plates (example 2.26). Good separation of 5 GeV/c negative kaons from negative pions has been achieved using two separators of length 10 m and a field of 5 kV mm^{-1}, but for higher momenta the length of the separator required rapidly becomes impractical and, as indeed in the case of accelerators, it becomes necessary to use time-varying fields.

In a *radiofrequency separator* a beam with a well-defined momentum enters a transversely deflecting radiofrequency cavity designed to be short enough for the difference in transit time for particles of different mass to be negligible compared with the radiofrequency period. Two such cavities, separated by a distance large compared with their length, are used and a system of quadrupole magnets focuses the particles onto the second cavity at the same angle with the axis as that with which they leave the first. The particles of different mass have a different flight time between the cavities and the phasing with the radiofrequency field can be arranged so that the unwanted particles are deflected back onto the original axis while the wanted particles receive a double deflection. A beam stopper placed on the axis then removes the unwanted component while the wanted particles pass around it. The radiofrequency cavities are generally of the disc-loaded, travelling wave type (section 2.4.2, 'Waveguide accelerators') powered by klystron oscillators with pulse lengths of a few microseconds. For effective separation the pulse length of the beam must be less than this so that radiofrequency separated beams are well matched to the fast extraction used for bubble chamber experiments.

The most commonly produced charged hadron (chapter 7) beams consist of protons and antiprotons and pions and kaons but for some experiments beams of the relatively short-lived hyperons (Σ and Ξ particles) have been produced. Through the decay of pions and kaons charged lepton (chapter 7) beams, i.e. beams of electrons, positrons or muons, have become available. Neutral beams of photons, neutrons, neutrinos, π^0 particles or K^0 particles may be defined. We select from the foregoing three types of beam which have had special significance.

Neutrino beams
Because of the low cross-section for neutrino interactions (chapter 11) experiments with these particles demand high intensities and massive detectors. The neutrinos or antineutrinos are produced by the decay of positive or negative pions, kaons and muons. If such a *positively* charged secondary hadron beam is selected from a primary target the ensuing processes may be seen from the table of particles (chapter 7) to yield neutrinos mainly of the muon type. They are produced in a long decay region followed by a massive shield to remove the remaining hadrons and the muons also produced in the hadron decays. In *wide-band* neutrino beams high intensities are achieved by accepting the parent π and K mesons over the widest possible momentum range and focusing these with a special device known as a magnetic horn.[43] In a *narrow-band* neutrino beam a momentum-selected hadron beam is used. In both cases the neutrino spectrum can be calculated from knowledge of the parent hadron intensities and their decay characteristics.

Muon beams
The muons produced, together with neutrinos, by pion and kaon decays may themselves be concentrated into a secondary beam. The pions and kaons are separated magnetically from the primary protons from an accelerator and are directed into a decay channel containing large-aperture quadrupole magnets. A hadron absorber at the end of the channel removes most of the surviving pions and kaons and the muons are then momentum selected and transported to the experimental site.

Photon beams
The photon 'tagging' system described in section 2.4.4 has also been applied in the 100 GeV energy range. In an experiment at CERN, protons from the SPS accelerator struck a beryllium target and the high energy γ radiation produced in or near the target was allowed to strike a lead converter of thickness 0.5 radiation length. Electrons from the pair production processes in the converter were then allowed to excite bremsstrahlung in a tungsten radiator and the energy of individual photons was measured by observing the momentum of the incident and scattered electron, the latter in coincidence with the photon signal.

In a novel technique used at Stanford[44] the Compton interaction (section 2.1.4, 'Compton effect') of a laser beam ($\lambda = 266$ nm, after frequency doubling) with a 30 GeV electron beam yields 180°-scattered photons of energy around 20 GeV. A photon spectrum obtained in this work is shown in figure 2.40.

2.5.4 Colliding-beam machines

If oppositely moving beams of particles of mass m and energy E collide the energy available per collision in the centre-of-mass system (appendix

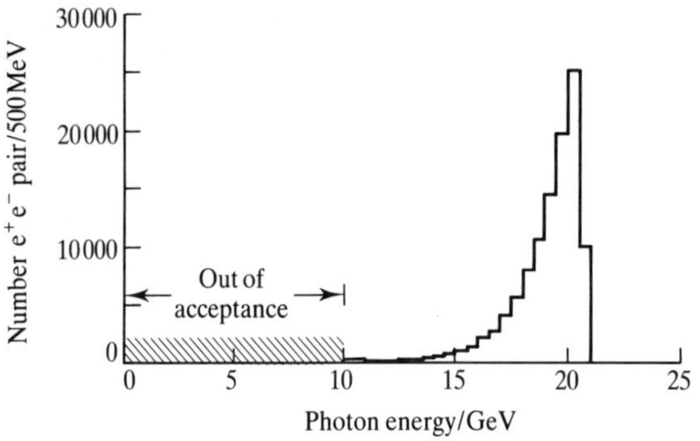

Figure 2.40
Monoenergetic photons from the scattering of ultraviolet light by 30 GeV electrons at SLAC. The energy is measured by conversion to pairs in a magnetic spectrometer.

B) is $2E$ and this may be spent in the production of new particles. But if one of the colliding particles is at rest in a fixed target the energy available is only $\sqrt{[2m(E + m)]}$ (example 2.25). A colliding-beam machine therefore is a very effective means of deploying a large amount of energy, but such machines, of course, are only practicable for stable particles such as protons, electrons and their antiparticles. Moreover, the interaction rates in colliders are much less than in fixed target installations and they cannot furnish secondary beams. Despite these drawbacks the advantage in available energy as E increases has led to major developments in this field.

The event rate in a colliding-beam machine is specified by the *luminosity* $\mathscr{L}$ (appendix B). The quality of a collider is measured by its integrated luminosity $\int \mathscr{L}\, dt$ (cm^{-2}). Thus, for example, for an integrated luminosity of 10^{35} cm^{-2} and a reaction cross-section of 1 nb ($=10^{-33}$ cm^2) 100 events will be produced in the running period. Interactions take place at intersection points around an accelerating or *storage* ring and detection equipment is built around the intersections. Examples of colliding beam installations follow.

Proton–proton and proton–antiproton colliders

In 1961 a proposal was made at CERN to accumulate many successive pulses of beam from the CPS in two *intersecting storage rings* (ISR) as shown in figures 2.39 and 2.41. Stored currents of over 50 A have been obtained in a vacuum vessel held at a pressure of a few times 10^{-12} Torr. With special focusing arrangements a luminosity of 6×10^{31} cm^{-2} s^{-1} has been reached. For 30 GeV protons in each ring the corresponding energy required for a fixed target would be 1800 GeV.

Because of the low cross-section for the production of antiprotons in proton–proton collisions the intensity of an antiproton beam injected into a storage ring will also be low. In order to reach an adequate luminosity for collisions with a proton beam the transverse oscillations (section 2.4.3) of the circulating antiprotons must be damped or 'cooled' as much as possible. In 1967 Budker suggested the 'electron cooling' system described in section 2.4.5, but for the CERN $p\bar{p}$ collider an alternative method due to Van der Meer[45] and known as 'stochastic cooling' is used.

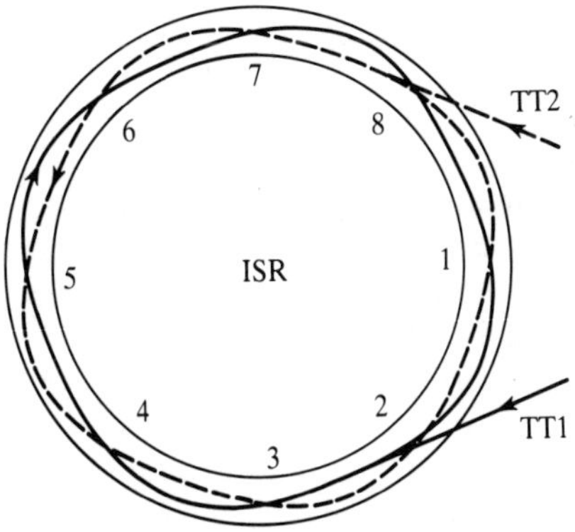

Figure 2.41 Intersecting proton beams in the ISR at CERN. The oppositely circulating beams are sent from the CPS (figure 2.39) through the transfer tubes TT1 and TT2 into high vacuum systems with a separate ring of magnets for each beam. Experiments are conducted at intersections 1–8.

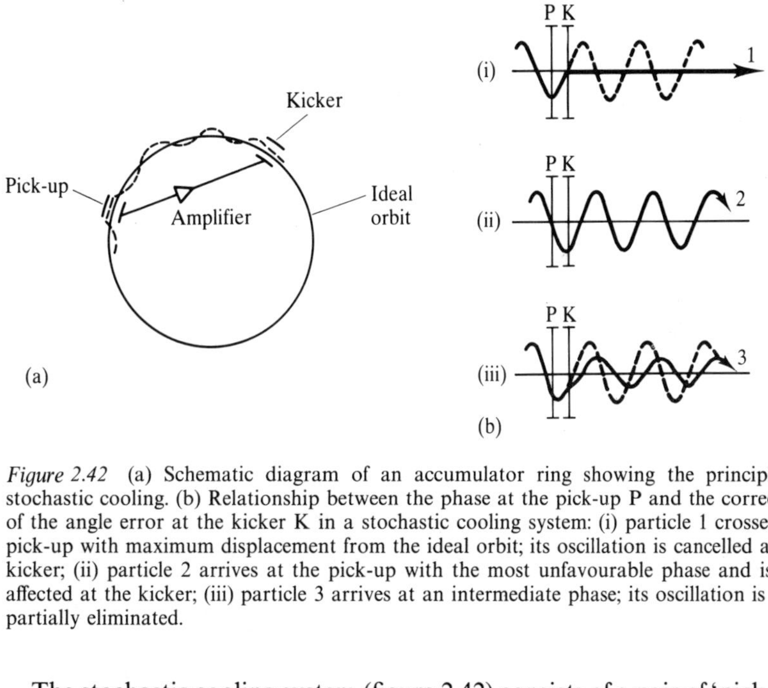

Figure 2.42 (a) Schematic diagram of an accumulator ring showing the principle of stochastic cooling. (b) Relationship between the phase at the pick-up P and the correction of the angle error at the kicker K in a stochastic cooling system: (i) particle 1 crosses the pick-up with maximum displacement from the ideal orbit; its oscillation is cancelled at the kicker; (ii) particle 2 arrives at the pick-up with the most unfavourable phase and is not affected at the kicker; (iii) particle 3 arrives at an intermediate phase; its oscillation is only partially eliminated.

The stochastic cooling system (figure 2.42) consists of a pair of 'pick-up' plates placed symmetrically about the ideal orbit and a pair of 'kicker' plates between which an electric field may be applied. The pick-up plates sense the position of a particle displaced from the central orbit and send a signal to the kicker plates to arrive there after amplification at the same time as the particle. The pick-up plates detect *position* but the kicker plates alter the *angle* of the trajectory so their separation is chosen to be a quarter of an oscillation wavelength plus an integral number of half wavelengths.

Then ideally a particle with a maximum excursion at pick-up would be brought back to the ideal orbit by the kicker as shown in figure 2.42(b). In practice, of course, the beam particles have random initial phases and the pick-up electrodes react to the instantaneous centre of charge of the beam. Individual particles in the beam pulse will be affected differently by the kicker but on average the transverse oscillation amplitude is decreased.

At the CERN collider the cooling system operates in an accumulator ring (AA, figure 2.39) which is filled over a period of 24 h with antiprotons of energy 3.5 GeV produced in the CPS. When a prescribed accumulation has been reached the stored antiprotons are transferred back to the CPS and accelerated to an energy of 26 GeV. They are then transported to the SPS and accelerated to 270 GeV. At the same time protons are also accelerated to 270 GeV in the SPS but in the opposite direction. The two beams are then available for collision experiments, of which the most exciting has been the production of the $W^{\pm}$ and Z^0 bosons (chapter 13).

In an additional facility at CERN the antiprotons are *decelerated* in the CPS from 3.5 GeV to a momentum of 0.6 GeV/c and are then injected into a low energy antiproton ring (LEAR, figure 2.39) where they are cooled and further accelerated or decelerated to provide an antiproton beam of energy between 5 and 1270 MeV. Slow extraction provides a beam of 100 per cent duty cycle which has been useful in the study of exotic atoms,* in meson spectroscopy and in the comparison of p and $\bar{p}$ masses.

Collider development has also taken place at Fermilab. By 1984 the iron-cored magnets in the synchrotron ring had been replaced by superconducting dipoles with a field of 5 T and protons had been accelerated to 1000 GeV (1 TeV). This beam has been used for fixed target experiments (*Tevatron II*) and also to provide cooled antiprotons for collider operation, with beam energies of 900 GeV (*Tevatron I*).

Electron–positron colliders

Positrons are readily produced from a high energy electron beam in a linear accelerator by allowing the electrons to strike a heavy metal target in which bremsstrahlung and pair production take place successively. The positrons may themselves be accelerated in the production linear accelerator (linac) and are then ready, with electrons from the same or another linac, to be fed to a further accelerator, and then to a storage ring or directly to the main ring.

---

* An exotic atom is one in which an electron has been replaced by a negative muon, pion, kaon, antiproton or hyperon. Because of the increased mass the new particle occupies orbits that are much smaller than the electronic orbits. Transition energies in exotic atoms are sensitive to nuclear size and to nuclear interactions. See also 'γ ray, X-ray and optical spectra' in appendix E1.

In the PETRA collider at Hamburg acceleration to 23 GeV takes place partly in a synchrotron and partly in the storage ring. At Stanford the SLA (section 2.5.2) has been used to fill the PEP storage ring directly with 15 GeV electrons and positrons. In both PETRA and PEP the circulating beams intersect at several stations around the storage ring but in the Stanford Linear Collider (SLC) counter-propagating electron and positron beams of energy 50 GeV from the SLA meet in a single pass (figure 2.43). The success of this collider depends on the production of

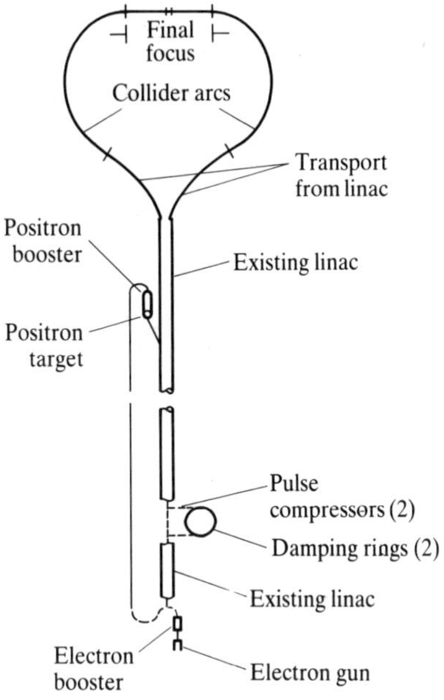

Figure 2.43
Layout of the SLAC linear collider SLC.

bunches of particles with a diameter of only a few microns at the intersection point.

Beams of 50 GeV electrons and positrons have been available since 1989 in the CERN Large Electron–Positron Collider (LEP, figure 2.39) which has an orbit circumference of 27 km to keep radiation losses down to an acceptable level. The injection system for this major installation is indicated in figure 2.39.

Electron–proton colliders

At Hamburg the collider HERA now operates with beams of electrons of energy 30 GeV and of protons of 820 GeV. This provides effectively 140 GeV for studies of lepton–quark scattering processes. If plans for the development of the CERN accelerator complex mature, energies considerably in excess of this figure may be reached.

2.5.5 *Future outlook*

The approximately exponential growth of machine energy with time is shown in the 'Livingston chart' (figure 2.44) and the highest energy accelerators now, or recently, in operation are listed in table 2.3, p. 75. In the near future it is planned to increase the energy of the LEP beams to 100 GeV (LEP II) for further searches for the top quark and the Higgs boson (chapter 13). Proton–proton colliders for 0.6 TeV + 3 TeV (UNK at Serphukov), for 8 TeV + 8 TeV (Large Hadron Collider (LHC) at CERN, figure 2.39) and for 20 TeV + 20 TeV (Superconducting Super Collider (SSC) in the USA) are projected but will only be built if funds are available.

At CERN it is hoped to study e–p collisions using LEP II and the LHC. There is the further possibility that each separated beam channel in the LHC can store relativistic heavy ions instead of protons. For a fully stripped lead nucleus a total energy of 1250 TeV would be possible. Such beams would allow the continuation of work begun in the SPS in 1986 with 3.2 TeV oxygen and 6.4 TeV sulphur beams. This work consists of seeking evidence of the quark–gluon phase of matter in which these entities are de-confined (chapter 11). The USA plans to build a relativistic heavy-ion collider with energies of 20 TeV in each beam (of gold ions).

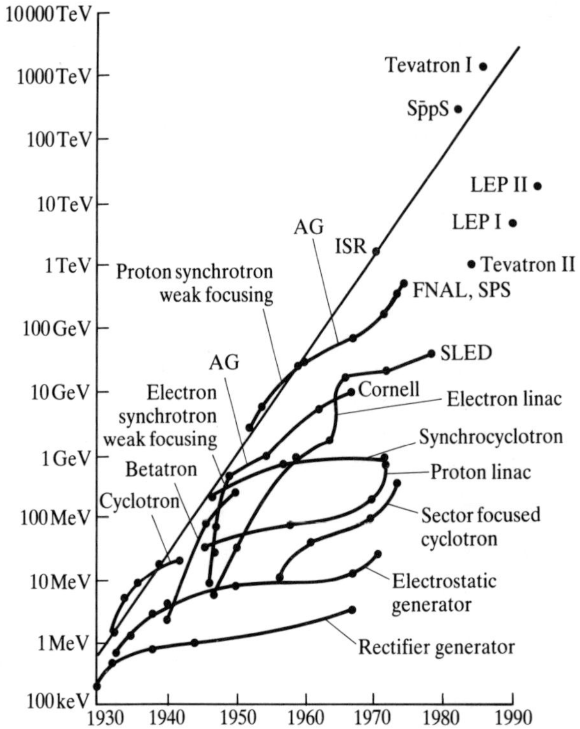

Figure 2.44
A 'Livingston chart' showing the roughly exponential growth with time of accelerator energies. The energies shown for the colliders (ISR, LEP I, LEP II, S$\bar{p}$pS and Tevatron I) are the equivalent fixed target energies.

For the more distant future, unless new methods of producing high electric fields can be discovered, progress to higher energies must be based on an extension of present methods and will therefore be limited by economic factors.

REFERENCES 2

1 **Sternheimer R M** 1961 'Interaction of radiation with matter' in Yuan L C L and Wu C S (eds) *Methods of Experimental Physics* 5 (*Part A*) Academic Press

2 **Segrè E** 1977 *Nuclei and Particles* Benjamin chs 2–4

3 **Heitler W** 1954 *The Quantum Theory of Radiation* (3rd edn) Clarendon

4 **Evans R D** 1955 *The Atomic Nucleus* McGraw-Hill

5 **Gemmel D S** 1974 'Channelling and related effects in the motion of charged particles through crystals' *Rev Mod Phys* **46** (129)

6 **Jelley J V** 1958 *Cherenkov Radiation* Pergamon

7 **Ginsburg V L and Frank I M** 1946 *Soviet Phys JETP* **16** (15)

8 **Davisson C M and Evans R D** 1952 'Gamma ray absorption coefficients' *Rev Mod Phys* **24** (79)

9 **Dyson N A** 1973 *X-rays in Atomic and Nuclear Physics* Longman

10 **England J B A** 1974 *Techniques in Nuclear Structure Physics* Macmillan

11 **England J B A** 1976 'Detection of ionizing radiation' *J Phys* **E9** (283)

12 **Siegbahn K (ed)** 1965 *Alpha, Beta and Gamma Ray Spectroscopy* North-Holland

13 **Bromley D A (ed)** 1979 'Detectors in nuclear science' *Nucl Instrum Meth* **162**

14 **Sharpey-Schafer J F and Simpson J** 1988 'Escape suppressed spectrometer arrays' *Prog Part Nucl Phys* **21** (293)

15 **Hall G** 1992 'Modern charged particle detectors' *Contemp Phys* **33** (1)

16 **Oreglia M** *et al.* 1982 *Phys Rev* **D25** (2259)

17 **Glaser D A** 1952 *Phys Rev* **87** (665)

18 **Hildebrand R H and Nagle D E** 1953 *Phys Rev* **92** (517)

19 **Wood J G** 1954 *Phys Rev* **94** (731)

20 **Chechin V A, Kotenko L P, Merson G I and Ermilova V C** 1972 *Nucl Instrum Meth* **98** (577)

21 **Leutz H** 1966 *Nucl Instrum Meth* **68** (213)

22 **Fisher C M** 1973 in Stipcich S (ed) *Proceedings of the 5th International Conference on Instrumentation for High Energy Physics, Frascati* 21 CNEN

23 **Charpak G, Bouclier R, Bressani T, Favier J and Zupancic C** 1968 *Nucl Instrum Meth* **62** (235); see also **Charpak G** 1993 *Physics Today* **46** January(17)

24 **Fancher D** *et al.* 1979 *Nucl Instrum Meth* **161** (383)

25 **Allison W W M, Brooks C B and Holmes A R** 1978 *Nucl Instrum Meth* **156** (169)

26 **Litt J and Meunier R** 1973 *Ann Rev Nucl Sci* **23** (1)

27 **Apsimon R J** *et al.* 1985 *Nucl Instrum Meth* **A241** (339)

28 **Cobb J** *et al.* 1977 *Nucl Instrum Meth* **140** (413)

29 **Allen K W** 1974 'Electrostatic accelerators' in Cerny J (ed) *Nuclear Spectroscopy and Reactions* (*Part A*) Academic Press

30 **Skorka S J** 1977 *Nucl Instrum Meth* **146** (67)

31 **Fry D W and Walkinshaw W** 1949 'Linear accelerators' *Rep Prog Phys* **12** (102)

32 **Livingood J J** 1961 *Principles of Cyclic Particle Accelerators* Van Nostrand

33 **Scharf W** 1991 *Particle Accelerators and Their Uses* Harwood

34 **Crowley-Milling M C** 1983 *Rep Prog Phys* **46** (51)

35 **McMillan E M** 1945 *Phys Rev* **68** (143)

36 **Veksler V** 1945 *J Phys USSR* **9** (153)

37 **Courant E, Livingston M S and Snyder H** 1952 *Phys Rev* **88** (1190)

38 The machine is fully described in **Crowley-Milling M C** 1983 *Rep Prog Phys* **46** (51); see also **Neal R B** 1967 *Physics Today* **20** April (27)

39 **Chamberlain O** 1960 *Ann Rev Nucl Sci* **10** (161)

40 **Sternheimer R M and Cork B** 1963 'Beam transport systems' in Yuan L C L and Wu C S (eds) *Methods of Experimental Physics 5* (*Part B*) Academic Press

41 **Sandweiss J** 1967 'Beam production at modern accelerators' in Shutt R P (ed) *Bubble and Spark Chambers III* Academic Press

42 **Rahm O C** 1961 *Rev Sci Instrum* **32** (1116)

43 **Van der Meer S** 1961 *Yellow Report* CERN/61–7

44 **Milburn R H** 1963 *Phys Rev Lett* **10** (75); see also **Arutynnian F R** *et al.* 1964 *Soviet Phys JETP* **18** (218) and **Ballam J** *et al.* 1973 *Phys Rev* **D7** (3150)

45 **Van der Meer S** 1991 *IEEE Trans Nucl Sci* **NS-28** (1994)

EXAMPLES 2

2.1 A heavy particle of charge ze and velocity v passes an electron at a perpendicular distance b from its path. Calculate the transverse momentum and energy transfer to the electron assuming that the path of the heavy particle is a straight line. Taking the number of electrons with impact parameters between b and $b + db$ in 1 m thickness of an absorber with N atoms of atomic number Z per unit volume to be $2\pi b \, db \times NZ$, show that an equation of the form (2.1a) for the stopping power follows.

2.2 Assuming that equation (2.1a) were true at low energies show that the stopping power reaches a maximum as the velocity decreases. Find the energy of protons in aluminium for which this maximum would be expected assuming $I = 150$ eV. [187 keV]

2.3 An α particle has a range of 300 μm in a nuclear emulsion. What range would you expect for (a) a ^{3}He nucleus, (b) a ^{3}H nucleus, each of the same initial velocity as the α particle? [225 μm, 900 μm]

2.4 A triton (^{3}H) of energy 5000 MeV passes through a transparent medium of refractive index $n = 1.5$. Calculate the angle of emission of Cherenkov light. [44°]

2.5 Using equation (2.8) calculate the number of photons produced per metre of air ($n = 1.000293$) by the Cherenkov effect from the path of a relativistic electron in the wavelength range $\lambda = 350$–550 nm. [27]

2.6 In an experiment with a source of X-radiation the mass attenuation coefficients μ/ρ for the elements Al, Ti and Cu are found to be 9.97, 37.7 and 9.97 m^2 kg^{-1}, respectively (the atomic numbers are 13, 22 and 29). Explain qualitatively the result for Ti.

2.7 A beam of X-radiation is attenuated by a factor of 0.64 in passing through a block of graphite of thickness 0.01 m. Assuming that the attenuation is due only to classical Thomson scattering, with a total cross-section of 6.7×10^{-29} m^2 per electron, estimate the atomic number of carbon.

2.8 Calculate for the Compton scattering of X-rays of wavelength 0.01 nm (a) the wavelength of the scattered radiation at 45°, (b) the velocity of the corresponding recoil electron and (c) the momentum transfer to the electron. [0.0107 nm, 5.3×10^7 m s^{-1}, 93 keV/c]

2.9 Calculate the energy of a 100 keV photon scattered backwards ($\theta = 180°$) from an electron of energy 1000 keV moving towards the photon. [1015 keV]

2.10 What is the energy of Compton-scattered photons at 90° when $h\nu \gg m_e c^2$? [511 keV]

2.11 By considering the conservation of four-momentum or otherwise, verify the statement (section 2.1.4, 'Pair production and annihilation') that materialization of a photon into an electron–positron pair cannot take place in free space.

2.12 Show that the threshold energy for the photoproduction of an electron–positron pair in the field of a free electron is $4m_e c^2$.

2.13 Show that in the annihilation of positrons at rest by electrons of momentum p, the angle between the two annihilation quanta is $\pi - p_{\perp r}/m_e c$ where $p_{\perp r}$ is the momentum of the electron at right angles to the line of flight of the quanta.

2.14 For the two-quantum annihilation of a fast positron of kinetic energy T by a free electron at rest, show that the energy of the forward going annihilation radiation is approximately $T + \frac{3}{2}m_e c^2$.

2.15 Calculate the electric field at the surface of the wire of a proportional counter with a wire radius of 0.1 mm and a cylinder radius of 10 mm when 1500 V is applied between the two. [3257 kV m^{-1}] Assuming that ionization by collision begins at a field of 2250 kV m^{-1} and that the electron mean free path is 5×10^{-6} m, calculate the multiplication factor. [512]

2.16 A Geiger counter is operated in a circuit which imposes a paralysis time of 300 μs after each count. What is the true rate of counting corresponding with an observed rate of 10 000 per minute? [10 526 per minute]

2.17 Calculate the energy difference between the photopeak and the high energy side of the Compton electron distribution in the pulse height spectrum from a scintillator detecting γ radiation of energy $m_e c^2$. What would the energy of the back-scattered radiation be? [170 keV, 170 keV]

2.18 In a simple heavy charged particle identification system signals from a thin counter (giving dE/dx) and stopping counter (giving $T = E - mc^2$) are multiplied. Show that the product $T(dE/dx)$ is to a first approximation independent of velocity and find the ratio of this quantity for deuterons and ^{3}He particles. [1/6]

2.19 If the terminal of a Van de Graaff generator may be regarded as a cylinder of radius r and the pressure vessel as a coaxial cylinder of radius R, the radial voltage gradient is given by

$$E_r = \frac{V}{r \ln(R/r)}$$

where V is the terminal potential. Show that for any given E_r, V is a maximum when $R/r = e$.

2.20 Calculate the velocity of a proton of energy 10 MeV as a fraction of the velocity of light [0.15]. How long would a proton take to move from the ion source to the target in a uniform 10 MV accelerating tube 3 m long? [1.4×10^{-7} s]

2.21 A belt system of total width 0.3 m charges the electrode of an electrostatic generator at a speed of 20 m s^{-1}. If the breakdown strength of the gas surrounding the belts is 3 MV m^{-1} calculate

(a) the maximum charging current, [319 μA]
(b) the maximum rate of rise of electrode potential, assuming a capacitance of 111 pF and no load current. [2.9 MV s^{-1}]

2.22 In the SLA electrons reach an energy of 20 GeV in a distance of 3 km. Assuming that increments of energy are uniform and that the injection energy is 10 MeV, find the effective length of the accelerator to an electron. [0.57 m]

2.23 Deuterons of energy 15 MeV are extracted from a cyclotron at a radius of 0.51 m by applying an electric field of 6 MV m^{-1} over an orbit arc of 90°. Calculate the equivalent reduction of magnetic field and the resulting increase in orbit radius Δr. [0.16 T, 0.053 m]

2.24 A pulse of 10^{10} particles of single charge is injected into a cyclic accelerator and is kept circulating in a stable orbit by the application of a radiofrequency field. What is the mean current when the radiofrequency is 7 MHz? [11.2 mA]

2.25 The extracted proton beam from a proton synchrotron has an energy of 28 GeV. Calculate the centre-of-mass energy in collisions with a fixed target of hydrogen. How does this compare with the energy in a collider in which each circulating proton beam has an energy of 28 GeV? What would be the energy of an equivalent fixed target accelerator?

2.26 An electrostatic separator has a uniform electric field E between the plates. If a paraxial beam of negatively charged π and K mesons with momentum p passes between the plates of the separator show that, on emerging, the angular separation between the π and K mesons is

$$\Delta\theta = \frac{eEl}{pc}\left(\frac{1}{\beta_{\mathrm{K}}} - \frac{1}{\beta_\pi}\right)$$

where l is the length of the plates and β_{K} and β_π are the relativistic velocities of the K and π mesons respectively.

For practical calculations the angular separation can be expressed as

$$\Delta\theta = 1.0 \times 10^{-6}\frac{El}{p}\left(\frac{1}{\beta_{\mathrm{K}}} - \frac{1}{\beta_\pi}\right) \text{ radians}$$

with l in metres, E in volts per metre and p in MeV/c. In a particular separator $l = 5$ m, $E = 5 \times 10^6$ V m^{-1} and the beam momentum is 3 GeV/c. Calculate the angular separation in this case. Take the masses of the π and K mesons to be 140 MeV/c^2 and 494 MeV/c^2 respectively.

2.27 A beam consists of positively charged pions, kaons and protons with momentum 10 GeV/c. Design a system of N_2-filled threshold Cherenkov counters that would *positively* identify the particles if the refractive index of N_2 gas varies with pressure p (in atmospheres) as $n = 1 + 3 \times 10^{-4}p$. Take the masses of the pion, kaon and proton to be 0.14, 0.494 and 0.938 GeV/c^2 respectively.

3 *General properties of nuclei*

Charge · Mass · Radius · Angular momentum (spin) · Magnetic dipole moment · Electric quadrupole moment · Parity · Isobaric spin (isospin) · Statistics · The nuclear level spectrum · Nuclear forces

3.1 *Charge*

The integral value of the positive nuclear charge Ze expressed in units of the electronic charge $|e|$ is implicit in the Rutherford atomic model on the assumption (well verified by experiment) that atoms are neutral. The interpretation of the charge number Z as the *atomic number* of the corresponding element in the periodic system has been discussed in section 1.3; the atomic number Z is a property of each individual nuclide, or specific nucleus, and it can be measured directly by Rutherford scattering experiments.

Charge appears to be rigorously conserved in all processes and this must be insisted upon in the interpretation of charge-changing processes such as nuclear reactions and decays. Like other similar laws, charge conservation is believed to derive from a fundamental symmetry of nature (chapter 8).

3.2 *Mass*[1]

3.2.1 *The mass tables*

The mass of an ionized atom or molecule can be measured relative to that of a chosen standard by comparing deflections in the electric and magnetic fields of a *mass spectrograph*. The work of Aston first showed that the mass of a *neutral atom* was in all cases nearly an integral multiple of the mass of the hydrogen atom and the nearest integer is the *mass number* A. According to the Rutherford model most of the neutral atom mass resides in the nucleus and A (like Z) is therefore a characteristic property of each nuclide. In the neutron–proton model of nuclear constitution (chapter 4) it is simply the number of constituent nucleons and, again like Z, it is a conserved quantity related to the general law of conservation of baryons (chapter 8).

Mass spectrographic measurements of atoms with stable nuclei have been supplemented by precision nuclear reaction studies of unstable species and relative atomic masses are in a great many cases known to an accuracy of 1 part in 10^6. By international agreement in 1961 the standard of atomic mass is one-twelfth of the mass of the neutral carbon atom ^{12}C, i.e.

$$M(12, 6) = 12.000\ldots \text{ atomic mass units (amu or u).}$$

The absolute value of the atomic mass unit is obtained by noting that for 1 mole (0.012 kg) of ^{12}C we have

$$0.012 \text{ kg} = N_A \times 12 \text{ amu (or u)}$$

where N_A is Avogadro's number. This gives

$$1 \text{ amu} = \frac{0.001}{N_A} \text{ kg} = 1.66054 \times 10^{-27} \text{ kg} = 931.494 \text{ MeV}/c^2 \quad (3.1)$$

using the conversion factor given by Einstein's relation $E_0 = mc^2$ for the rest energy of a particle of mass m and expressing the energy in mega-electronvolts (appendix A).

Neutral atom masses $M(A, Z)$ in atomic mass units are comprehensively tabulated,[1] often together with the difference between the actual measured mass and the integral mass number A expressed as an energy equivalent by use of (3.1). For most calculations of nuclear energy changes, atomic masses may be used because the initial and final atoms are neutral systems, but correction must be made (section 3.2.3) when positron (β^+) emission is involved. Nuclear energies and energy changes may often be conveniently expressed in atomic mass units as an alternative to mega-electronvolts. If the actual *nuclear mass* M_{AZ} is required it can be obtained from the equation

$$M(A, Z) = M_{AZ} + ZM_e - B(Z) \quad (3.2)$$

where M_e is the atomic mass of the electron and $B(Z)$ is the total binding energy of the atomic electrons, both expressed in atomic mass units. M_{AZ} may be placed on the absolute scale by use of the conversion factor in (3.1).

In most nuclear processes, including spontaneous decay, the mass of the final system differs from that of the initial system and there is an absorption or release of energy. The energy change is specified by a Q *value* where

$$Q = \text{kinetic energy of final system} - \text{kinetic energy of initial system.} \quad (3.3)$$

Classically the origin of a finite Q value cannot be understood but from the special theory of relativity we see that it is directly determined by the overall mass change Δm(absolute) or ΔM(amu), so that

$$Q = \Delta mc^2 \text{ joules}$$

or (3.4)

$$Q = \Delta M \text{ amu} = 931.494\Delta M \text{ MeV}.$$

Q values can be obtained directly from the mass tables[1] in atomic mass units but are normally given in mega-electronvolts. The tabulated Q values relate to transitions involving only the ground state of the product nucleus. If excited states are populated, the Q values are reduced by the corresponding excitation, and determination of these values is one of the objects of nuclear spectroscopy.

3.2.2 *Binding energy*

The reason that atomic masses are not exact multiples of the hydrogen atom mass is partly because a nucleus contains $A - Z$ neutrons as well as Z protons, but more importantly because all the nuclear constituents are held together by attractive forces. Work must be done to set the nucleons free and this work is called the *total nuclear binding energy*. It is obtained from the equation

$$B(A, Z) = ZM_{\mathrm{H}} + (A - Z)M_{\mathrm{n}} - M(A, Z) \text{ amu} \quad (3.5)$$

where M_{H} and M_{n} are the masses of the hydrogen atom and of the neutron in atomic mass units. Conversion to the energy equivalent is straightforward using (3.1). The definition (3.5) implies that a stable nucleus has a positive total *binding energy*, but a negative energy with respect to that of its uncombined constituents at infinite separation.

Before mass tables became so comprehensive (and still for experiments on highly unstable nuclei) it was helpful to have a *semi-empirical mass formula*[2,3] from which reliable predictions could be made. Such a formula

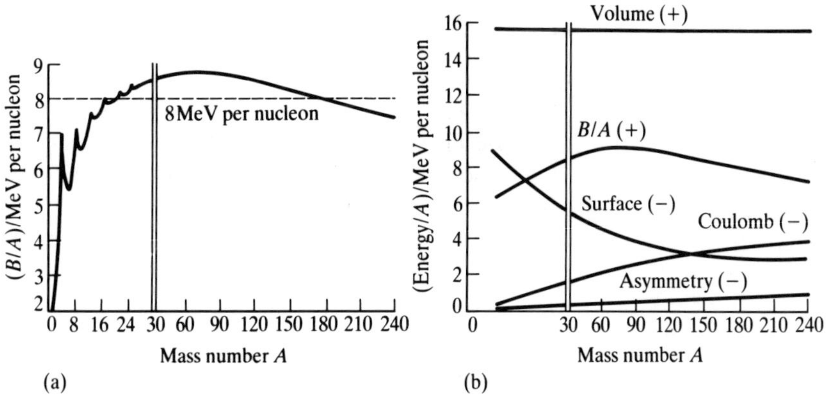

Figure 3.1 The semi-empirical mass formula. (a) General trend of observed binding energy per nucleon B/A for stable nuclei as a function of mass number A (Evans R D 1955 *The Atomic Nucleus* McGraw-Hill). (b) Semi-empirical prediction of B/A on the basis of the liquid-drop nuclear model showing contributions of volume, surface, asymmetry and Coulomb terms per nucleon. Note that since the increase in the Coulomb term is nearly balanced by the decrease in the surface term the fall-off seen in B/A effectively results from the asymmetry energy.

should in the first place predict the measured binding energies of the stable nuclei. If these are expressed as the *binding energy per nucleon*, $B(A, Z)/A$, a general dependence on A of the form shown in figure 3.1(a) is obtained. The construction of the mass formula may be understood from figure 3.1(b) in which components of the binding energy are shown separately. These are inferred from the curve of figure 3.1(a) as follows.

(a) Since the value of B/A does not vary greatly for $A > 16$ it is a good approximation to write $B \propto A$. This is characteristic of a short-range force (creating potential energy) between nucleons, and different from the expectation $B \propto \frac{1}{2}A(A-1)$ for a long-range interaction, under which all nucleon pairs would contribute. The binding energy associated in this way with each nucleon is known as the *volume energy* and is a property of infinite nuclear matter. In a real finite nucleus the volume energy is not fully developed because nucleons near the surface are less effectively bound; a *surface energy* correction varying as R^2 where R is the nuclear radius must be made.

(b) Light nuclei show enhanced stability when α particle structures with $Z = N = 2$ can be formed and several of the most stable, e.g. ^{12}C, ^{16}O, have $Z = N = A/2$. A similar tendency is seen throughout the whole range of A values; it is a quantum mechanical effect due to the fermion nature of the nucleons, which can only enter energy levels in pairs with spins opposed.

If extra nucleons of one kind are added, they must enter higher energy levels and are less tightly bound than those already present. For a given A, the most stable nucleus would have neutron and proton numbers as nearly equal as possible (apart from a Coulomb effect still to be discussed). To take account of this effect an *asymmetry energy* proportional to $(A/2 - Z)^2/A$ (see example 3.1) is included in the mass formula.

(c) The B/A value does in fact decrease from 8.7 MeV at $A = 60$ to 7.6 MeV at $A = 238$. Such an effect could be due to the mutual repulsion of the nuclear protons and it is certainly necessary to include a *Coulomb energy* in the mass formula. For Z protons within a sphere of radius R this energy is proportional to Z^2/R, or more strictly $Z(Z - 1)/R$ (see example 3.2).

In combining all these items, which are shown separately in figure 3.1(b), it is first necessary to relate R to the mass number A and this requires a model. For a spherical nucleus of constant density independent of A, like a liquid drop, we have

$$R = r_0 A^{1/3} \tag{3.6}$$

where r_0 is a constant, and the mass formula, noting that the surface, asymmetry and charge terms all *reduce* binding, or increase mass, may be written as

$$M(A, Z) = ZM_{\mathrm{H}} + (A - Z)M_{\mathrm{n}} - \alpha A + \beta A^{2/3} + \frac{\gamma(A/2 - Z)^2}{A} + \frac{\epsilon Z^2}{A^{1/3}} \tag{3.7}$$

where α, β, γ and ϵ are constants. For the binding energy per nucleon

$$\frac{B}{A} = \alpha - \frac{\beta}{A^{1/3}} - \frac{\gamma(A/2 - Z)^2}{A^2} - \frac{\epsilon Z^2}{A^{4/3}} \tag{3.8}$$

and this will give a variation with A very close to the smooth curve of figure 3.1(a) with constants derived from an empirical fit to observed masses. The set used in figure 3.1(b), due to A. E. S. Green and expressed as energy equivalents, is

$\alpha = 15.75$ MeV $\beta = 17.8$ MeV $\gamma = 94.8$ MeV $\epsilon = 0.71$ MeV.

The ϵ value corresponds with a radius parameter $r_0 = 1.22\ \mathrm{fm}^{-1}$.

The mass formula is improved by the addition of a term $\delta(A, Z)$ to describe the difference in stability between even-Z, even-N and odd-Z, odd-N nuclei of the same even A. Physically this arises because of the important *pairing force* which energetically favours the formation of pairs of like nucleons (pp, nn) with opposite intrinsic spins and linear momenta in nuclear matter. If we take δ to be zero for odd A, then empirically

$$\delta = +12A^{-1/2} \text{ MeV for } A \text{ even, } Z \text{ odd}$$

$$\delta = -12A^{-1/2} \text{ MeV for } A \text{ even, } Z \text{ even.}$$

The major deficiency of the mass formula as it stands, however, is the neglect of corrections due to the shell structure of nuclei that will be discussed in chapter 4.

3.2.3 *Stability and abundance*[4–6]

Absolutely stable nuclei are those which do not exhibit any kind of spontaneous transformation or energy change however lengthy the time of observation. A stable *particle* is one which does not decay by the strong interaction (section 7.4.2) although it may transform by β or γ emission. For nuclei, it is particularly the process of β decay (or electron capture) that determines which nuclei are now found on earth after the cosmological element formation.

The naturally occurring nuclides are conveniently displayed on a rectangular grid (Segrè chart) in order of increasing N and Z. This neutron–proton diagram, given in figure 3.2,[7] shows that many stable nuclei of low mass number have $N \approx Z \approx A/2$, but medium weight and heavy nuclei have excess neutrons, because the disruptive effect of the increasing Coulomb forces has to be balanced by additional attractive interactions (despite the increased asymmetry energy). The β-unstable nuclides form a fringe to the band of stability, but sometimes, and especially for the naturally occurring radioactive elements, the β-stable nucleus is α unstable (cf. figure 1.2).

If a third coordinate representing the atomic mass $M(A, Z)$ is added to the neutron–proton diagram a three-dimensional *mass surface* is defined. Stable nuclei group around the bottom of a valley in this surface. Intersections of the mass surface by planes of constant A pick out groups of isobars comprising both stable and unstable nuclei. Formula (3.7) shows that for A constant, $M(A, Z)$ is a parabolic function of Z (figure 3.3). For odd A one parabola is obtained but for even A there are two, separated by an energy $2\delta(A)$.

From figure 3.3 there is just one stable isobar for A odd but for even A there may be two or three stable species. Stability is reached in an isobaric sequence by spontaneous radioactive β decays which, by changing a nuclear neutron into a proton or vice versa, alter the nuclidic N/Z ratio in the direction of increasing stability. Such decay processes are indicated in the figure; electron (β^-) emission is similar to the familiar β decay of classical radioactivity while positron (β^+) emission is a process of the same sort involving the antiparticle e^+ of the electron (section 2.1.4).

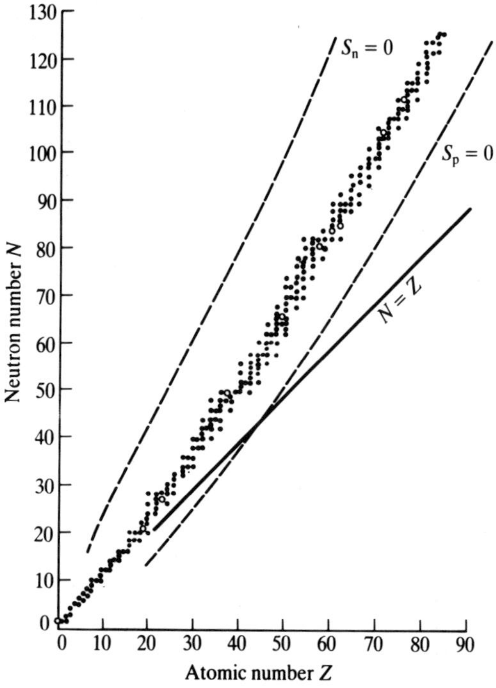

Figure 3.2 Neutron–proton diagram (Segrè chart) for the naturally occurring nuclei with $Z < 84$. The 'drip-lines' showing the limits of neutron and proton stability are rough indications only: •, stable; ○, radioactive. (Evans R D 1955 *The Atomic Nucleus* McGraw-Hill; Pearson J M 1986 *Nuclear Physics: Energy and Matter* Adam Hilger ch. II; Bohr A and Mottelson B 1969 *Nuclear Structure I* Benjamin.)

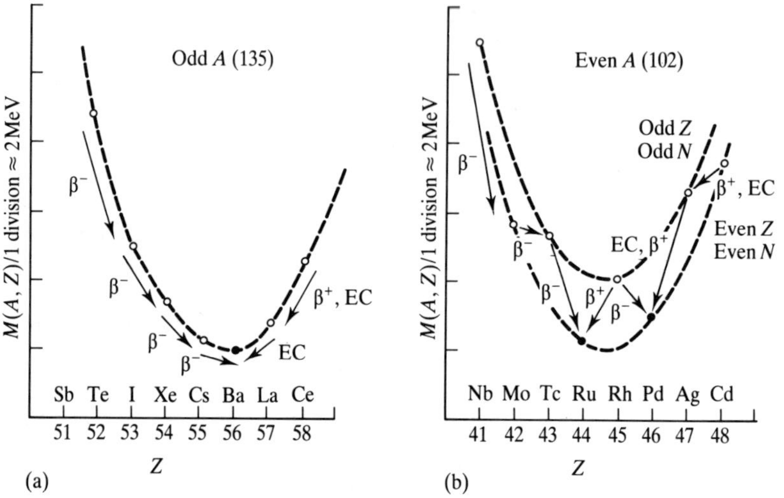

Figure 3.3 Stability of isobars, showing atomic mass plotted against atomic number (a) for odd A and (b) for even A. Electron capture is possible in all cases of positron decay and in a few cases in which β^+ emission is energetically forbidden (see equations (3.9a)). (Evans R D 1955 *The Atomic Nucleus* McGraw-Hill; Pearson J M 1986 *Nuclear Physics: Energy and Matter* Adam Hilger ch. II.)

Atomic electron capture (EC) is an alternative to β^+ decay and will be discussed in section 5.2.5.

In each spontaneous decay energy is released, not because of any disappearance of baryons ($\Delta A = 0$) but because there is a change of binding energy and therefore of mass between the initial and final systems. The Q value for β decay, as defined in section 3.2.1, is given in atomic mass units by

$$\begin{aligned} Q_{\beta^-} &= M(A, Z) - M(A, Z+1) \\ Q_{\beta^+} &= M(A, Z) - M(A, Z-1) - 2M_e \\ Q_{EC} &= M(A, Z) - M(A, Z-1) - B_e \end{aligned} \qquad (3.9a)$$

where $2M_e$, equivalent to 1.02 MeV, arises because the change of Z frees an atomic electron, of mass M_e amu, in addition to the decay positron and where B_e is the ionization energy in atomic mass units for the electron captured in the neutral atom of charge $Z - 1$. These relations assume that the mass of the neutrino or antineutrino known to be emitted in such processes is zero.

Q value equations similar to (3.9a) may be written for any postulated type of decay that is consistent with the conservation laws, e.g. for nucleon emission

$$\begin{aligned} Q_p &= M(A, Z) - M(A-1, Z-1) - M_H(= -S_p) \\ Q_n &= M(A, Z) - M(A-1, Z) - M_n(= -S_n) \end{aligned} \qquad (3.9b)$$

and similar equations may be written for the emission of complex particles.

The Q values given in equations (3.9a) and (3.9b) may be expressed in terms of binding energies by use of equation (3.5). For β decay and electron capture a term representing the difference between the neutron and proton mass then appears. For nucleon emission the Q value is equal to the difference between the total binding energy of the initial and final nuclei but for complex particles the binding energy of the particle itself must be taken into account (see example 3.4).

Absolute stability against a given process requires $Q < 0$. For heavy particles the quantity $-Q$ (in mega-electronvolts) is just the work required to detach the postulated particle from the initial nucleus with zero kinetic energy* and is known as the *separation energy* S; it is given for nucleons by equations (3.9b). Nucleon separation energies plotted as a function of N for constant Z (or Z for constant N) show an odd–even staggering effect arising from the pairing force and parametrized by the term $\delta(A)$ in the mass formula. The mass tables[1] often include lists of separation energies.

* In practice, an energy above the separation energy may be necessary in order for the particle to surmount a potential barrier; the particle is then emitted with finite kinetic energy.

The mass tables[1]

The entries in the tables are derived from mass spectrographic, decay and reaction data, adjusted by a least-squares fitting procedure; errors are about 1 part in 10^7 or better for the most stable nuclei.

To illustrate relationships in the tables consider radioactive sodium $^{24}_{11}\mathrm{Na}$ for which the table gives

$$M(A, Z) = 23.9909635 \pm 0.0000009 \text{ amu}$$

The total binding energy is given by equation (3.5) as

$$\begin{aligned} B(A, Z) &= ZM_{\mathrm{H}} + (A - Z)M_{\mathrm{n}} - M(A, Z) \\ &= 11(1.007825037) + 13(1.008664967) - 23.9909635 \\ &= 0.207755 \text{ amu} \\ &= 193522.5 \text{ keV} \qquad \text{using equation (3.1)} \end{aligned}$$

compared with $B(24, 11) = 193525.5$ keV given in the tables. $^{24}\mathrm{Na}$ decays to $^{24}\mathrm{Mg}$ (stable) by β emission and from the first of equations (3.9a) we find from the tables, for the β decay energy,

$$\begin{aligned} Q_{\beta^-} &= M(24, 11) - M(24, 12) \\ &= 5.918 \times 10^{-3} \text{ amu} \\ &= 5512.6 \text{ keV} \end{aligned}$$

which checks with the tabulated value.

In part II of the tables we find separation energies. These may be obtained from equations (3.9b) or directly from the total binding energy difference. Thus for

$$^{24}_{11}\mathrm{Na} \rightarrow {}^{23}_{11}\mathrm{Na} + \mathrm{n}$$

we get

$$\begin{aligned} S(\mathrm{n}) &= B(24, 11) - B(23, 11) \\ &= 6959 \text{ keV} \end{aligned}$$

which checks with the tabulated value.

If the Q value for the emission of a certain particle from a nucleus rises above zero, spontaneous decay becomes possible although it may be impeded by external barrier effects so that ground-state decay lifetimes are lengthened as in α and spontaneous fission decay (sections 5.3 and 5.4). This situation is reached for nucleon emission at highly abnormal N/Z ratios and the position of such nuclei on the N–Z diagram is defined by the so-called nucleon 'drip-lines'; these are sketched in figure 3.2.

For $Q > 0$ the probability of decay rapidly increases with increasing Q and for charged particles leads to the observed dependence of radioactive lifetimes on decay energy. Ultimately lifetimes against decay will become so short that the nucleus concerned can hardly be considered to exist as an observable entity; the highest atomic number so far reached via nuclear reactions is $Z = 109$.

The conditions (3.9a) simply define the area of stability against β decay on the neutron–proton diagram – they do not indicate the population of this area by the β-stable nuclides. This has been determined by the nucleosynthesis reactions of the early universe which in turn were strongly dependent on specific properties of nuclei, such as the ability to absorb neutrons of a particular energy. From observations on meteorites a standard solar system elemental abundance catalogue has been set up and nuclidic abundances have been obtained by mass spectroscopy; these are shown for even–even nuclides with $A > 50$ in figure 3.4. It seems likely that these abundances are typical of the present universe as a whole.

The main conclusions from nuclidic abundance data are the following.

(a) The elements of highest abundance in the universe are hydrogen and helium.

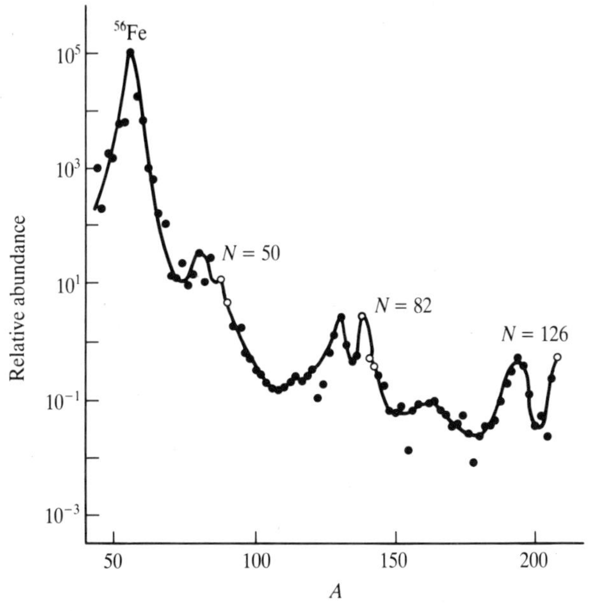

Figure 3.4 Relative abundance (number of atoms) for even-Z, even-N nuclides as a function of mass number A for $A > 50$. (Bohr A and Mottelson B 1969 *Nuclear Structure I* Benjamin.)

(b) There is a deficiency of the elements Li, Be and B in solar system abundances presumably because the corresponding nuclides are readily consumed in nucleosynthesis. The cosmic rays, however, contain larger relative quantities of these nuclei, because they can be produced by interactions in interstellar space.
(c) Beyond the light elements a marked peak in the abundance of the even-Z, even-N nuclei occurs around iron, $A = 56$ (figure 3.4), which correlates with the maximum binding energy per nucleon shown for this A value in figure 3.1(a). These are the most stable elements, and would be formed as end products of an element building stage in which thermal equilibrium was reached.
(d) Beyond the iron group, distinct peaks are seen at A values corresponding with neutron numbers $N = 50$, 82 and 126. If these nuclides are built from lighter species by successive neutron capture and β decay then such peaks will be expected when a shell closes because the next neutron is less tightly bound (chapter 4). Arguments can be given to relate the additional peaks at $A = 80$, 130 and 194 to the same shell structure.

Further evidence for shell structure in nuclei from abundance data comes from an examination of the distribution of isotopes and isotones with respect to the line of stability shown by figure 3.2. It is found that

(e) the number of stable and long-lived isotopes is greater for $Z = 20$, 28, 50 and 82 than for nearby elements;
(f) the number of stable and long-lived isotones is greater for $N = 20$, 28, 50, 82 and 126 than for nearby N values.

3.3 Radius[8]

When Rutherford and Chadwick extended α particle scattering experiments to light elements such as aluminium, deviations from the Coulomb law of scattering (equation (1.13)) were observed at a scattering angle of 135°. This was most readily interpreted to mean that at the corresponding interparticle distance the effect of non-Coulomb forces was being felt. Since the observed effect was a reduction of scattering in the first place, the new force would be attractive. It was therefore possible to think of a nuclear radius R_C at which, for an incident nuclear particle of negligible dimensions and positive charge, the potential energy, initially due only to Coulomb repulsion, drops because of the short-range attractive forces holding the nucleus together. In figure 3.5 this is shown for an idealized case; the *Coulomb barrier* defined in this way is of height

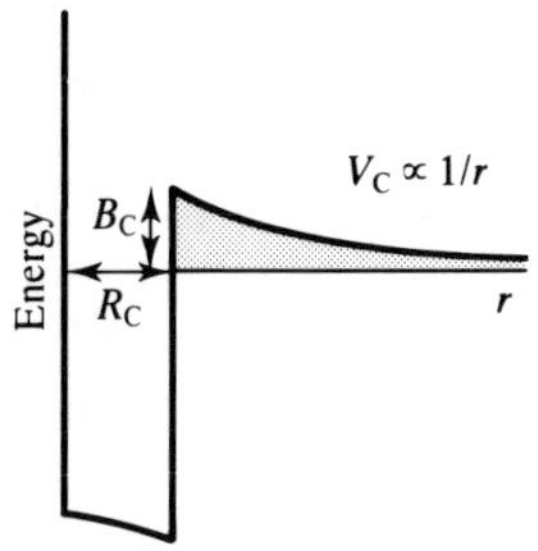

Figure 3.5
Potential well of radius R_C with Coulomb barrier (shaded) of height B_C; spherical symmetry is assumed.

B_C where

$$B_C = \frac{Z_1 Z_2 e^2}{4\pi\epsilon_0 R_C} \tag{3.10}$$

if the charges of the incident particle and nucleus are $Z_1 e$ and $Z_2 e$ respectively. For $Z_1 = 1$, $Z_2 = 92$ and $A = 238$ the R_C value given by equation (3.15) is 7.6 fm and $B_C = 17.4$ MeV. It must be remembered that the *potential well* shown in figure 3.5 is essentially three dimensional.

As already noted in section 3.2.2, a constant density model of the nucleus will require the radius R_C to vary as $A^{1/3}$ (equation (3.6)) and this uniform model is adequate, with a suitable value of r_0, for the calculation of the Coulomb term in the mass formula. It is, however, a highly inadequate representation of the density of nuclear matter near the surface of a nucleus. To make the concepts of nuclear radius and nuclear size more realistic we must consider more refined scattering experiments.

Electron scattering

If the particle approaching the nucleus is an electron there is no attractive nuclear force, but the Coulomb force itself becomes attractive. The scattering can reveal detail of the charge distribution if the reduced de Broglie wavelength of the incident electrons is less than a typical nuclear dimension, say $\lambda\!\!\!^{-} \approx 1$ fm, $E \approx 200$ MeV. The electron is not known to have any structure and behaves like a point charge. The effect of the finite size of the target is then seen directly as a reduction of the scattering at a given angle below that expected, as first calculated by Mott. In the pioneer experiments of Hofstadter and his collaborators at Stanford, using linear accelerators providing electrons with energy up to 550 MeV, the ratio of observed and calculated intensities at a given angle was expressed as the square of a form factor F. Since the electromagnetic interaction is completely known F can be given directly in terms of the nuclear charge density $\rho(r)$ on the assumption that the scattering can reasonably be described by the Born approximation of quantum mechanics. In terms of the momentum transfer q to the nucleus, as used for instance in equations (1.6)–(1.9) for α scattering,

$$F(q) = \frac{4\pi\hbar}{qZe}\int_0^\infty \rho(r)\sin\left(\frac{qr}{\hbar}\right) r\,\mathrm{d}r \tag{3.11}$$

where $q = |\boldsymbol{q}| = (2E/c)\sin(\theta/2)$, E is the total energy of the electron and θ is the angle of scattering, both in the centre-of-mass system. To simplify this and similar formulae it is usual to write the momentum transfer vector as $\hbar\boldsymbol{q}$ so that q becomes a reciprocal length and (3.11) reads

$$F(q) = \frac{4\pi}{qZe}\int_0^\infty \rho(r)\sin(qr) r\,\mathrm{d}r. \tag{3.12}$$

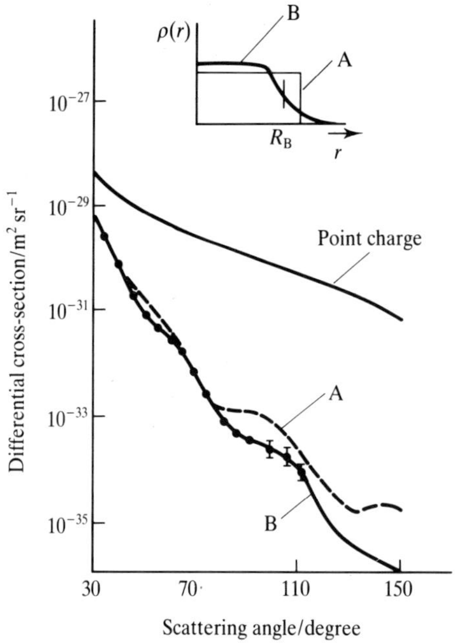

Figure 3.6 Scattering of 153 MeV electrons by gold with (inset) charge distributions that may be used to fit the data points; the 'half-way' radius is marked. (Bohr A and Mottelson B 1969 *Nuclear Structure I* Benjamin.)

Experimental data from which values of $F(q)$ may be derived are shown in figure 3.6. If a sufficiently large range of q values can be covered then $\rho(r)$ can be obtained by making a Fourier transform of $F(q)$ with respect to q. In general, however, this is not possible and a density distribution must be assumed, e.g. the Fermi function

$$\rho(r) = \frac{\rho_0}{1 + \exp(r - R_{1/2})/a}. \tag{3.13}$$

Comparison with experiment then gives best-fit values for the half-way radius $R_{1/2}$ and the surface thickness parameter a. In the inset to figure 3.6 such a distribution is shown, together with the uniform distribution of radius R_C which best fits the data points. The mean square radius for a given $\rho(r)$ is defined as

$$\langle r^2 \rangle = \frac{1}{Ze} \int r^2 \rho(r) 4\pi r^2 \, \mathrm{d}r \tag{3.14}$$

and for the density distribution (3.13) we have $\langle r^2 \rangle^{1/2} < R_{1/2} < R_C$. For a wide range of nuclei with $A > 20$, an $A^{1/3}$ dependence of $R_{1/2}$ and R_C is found.

Other methods of determining the mean square radius of the charge distribution, or its variation from one nucleus to another, are observations of

(a) energy displacements in the spectra of muonic atoms (appendix E),
(b) the Coulomb energy of mirror nuclei such as ^{13}C and ^{13}N which have the same structure except that Z and N are interchanged, and
(c) optical and X-ray isotope shifts (appendix E).

The results of all these methods are consistent with those of the electron-scattering determinations and combining all available data for the charge distribution the charge radius of a spherical nucleus may be given as

$$R_{1/2} = 1.1 A^{1/3}\ \text{fm}$$
or
$$R_C = (1.2\text{–}1.3) A^{1/3}\ \text{fm}. \tag{3.15}$$

The 'surface thickness' or radial distance between regions of 90 per cent and 10 per cent of the central density is about 2.5 fm for all nuclei (so that light nuclei are nearly all 'surface'). Non-spherical nuclei will be discussed in section 4.3. The scattering of electrons by protons is followed in detail in chapter 12.

Nucleon scattering

The density distribution of nuclear matter, $\rho_m(r)$, as distinct from that of nuclear charge, $\rho(r)$, may be studied by neutron–nucleus scattering or by proton–nucleus scattering at energies in excess of the Coulomb barrier. Despite the fact that the probe is not a point particle and that the interaction is not known, it is possible to obtain equivalent potential parameters. If the radial variation of the potential is taken to have the Fermi form of equation (3.13) with an overall negative sign, it is possible to extract from experimental results a half-way radius R_V for the matter distribution. It has the expected $A^{1/3}$ dependence and differs only slightly from the $R_{1/2}$ value for the charge distribution. For the heaviest nuclei there is some evidence for a slightly increased radius for the neutron distribution.

3.4 *Angular momentum (spin)*[9,10]

Many nuclear states, including the ground state, have a finite angular momentum specified by a quantized vector $\boldsymbol{J}$. This vector has an absolute magnitude given by the equation

$$|\boldsymbol{J}| = \sqrt{[J(J+1)]}\,\hbar \tag{3.16}$$

where J, the *nuclear spin quantum number*, is integral for nuclei of even mass number and half-integral for nuclei of odd mass number, including the neutron and proton ($J = \frac{1}{2}$). In accordance with the uncertainty principle $\boldsymbol{J}$ itself is unobservable, but its component $m_J\hbar$ along an axis of quantization may be measured and is found to have one of the $2J + 1$ values given by the inequality

$$J \geqslant m_J \geqslant -J. \tag{3.17}$$

The maximum value of the component of $\boldsymbol{J}$ is $J\hbar$ and this, or often just the quantum number J, is known as the nuclear spin. Angular momentum is conserved overall in nuclear processes (chapter 8) and J is a good quantum number for nuclear states.

If the nucleus is built up from neutrons and protons, its angular momentum $\boldsymbol{J}$ will be a vector sum of the orbital ($\boldsymbol{l}$) and spin ($\boldsymbol{s}$) angular momenta of the nucleons. It is the business of particular nuclear models to discuss the coupling of these vectors, but it is reasonable to assume that in general like nucleons try to form pairs with equal and opposite orbital and spin angular momenta. This would be consistent with the requirements of the Pauli principle (section 3.9) and would minimize potential energy for attractive forces by allowing good overlap of wave-functions. It then follows independently of specific models that even-Z, even-N nuclei have zero ground-state spin. And if all pairs of nucleons do couple to a zero resultant it also follows that the spin $\boldsymbol{J}$ of an odd-A nucleus is equal to the resultant angular momentum $\boldsymbol{l} + \boldsymbol{s}$ of the odd nucleon. The ground-state spins of a sequence of odd-mass nuclei show a jump in value as the neutron number N or proton number Z passes through the special values 20, 28, 50, 82 and 126 and the single-particle shell model (chapter 4) offers an explanation of these 'magic numbers'.

Nuclear ground-state spins are determined by the hyperfine and magnetic resonance methods outlined in appendix E.

3.5 *Magnetic dipole moment*[9,10]

A charged particle in orbital motion generates a magnetic dipole moment of a magnitude proportional to its orbital angular momentum. Furthermore, a particle with intrinsic angular momentum or spin has an intrinsic magnetic moment. This is clear for the electron and proton, from the theory of the hydrogen atom, but it is also true of the neutron because that particle does have a charge structure although it has zero total charge; it is not yet clear for the neutrino. Complex nuclei are therefore expected, as suggested by Pauli in 1924, to possess a magnetic moment in their ground and excited states, except in the case of states with total $\boldsymbol{J} = 0$.

The magnetic moment of the neutron and proton differ substantially from the value predicted by the Dirac equation (chapter 11) for a particle of spin $\frac{1}{2}\hbar$.

The nuclear magnetic moment is described by a vector $\boldsymbol{\mu}_J$ but unlike angular momentum it is not quantized and is not governed by any conservation law. The moment may be expressed in absolute units or in *nuclear magnetons*, defined as $\mu_N = e\hbar/2m_p$ in analogy with the Bohr magneton, but smaller by a factor $m_e/m_p = 1/1836$. The direction of the vector $\boldsymbol{\mu}_J$ in space is not observable, as with the angular momentum $\boldsymbol{J}$, and the observable magnetic moment is the expectation value of a vector operator $\hat{\boldsymbol{\mu}}$ in the state $(J, m_J = J)$ in which m_J has its maximum value.

The *nuclear gyromagnetic ratio* is defined as

$$\gamma_J = \frac{\mu_J}{J\hbar} \tag{3.18}$$

with all quantities in absolute units but the dimensionless nuclear *g factor* is the ratio of the nuclear moment in magnetons to the nuclear spin in units of $\hbar$. It is related to γ_J by the equation

$$g_J = \frac{\gamma_J 2m_p}{e}. \tag{3.19}$$

If the nuclear moment and spin are oppositely directed as for the neutron, μ_J, γ_J and g_J are negative. The g factor defined in (3.19) has a value of the order unity but if the magneton used is the Bohr magneton μ_B then the nuclear g factors are of the order of 1/2000. From (3.18) and (3.19) we have

$$\mu_J = \gamma_J J\hbar = g_J J\mu_N \text{ or } g_J J\mu_B. \tag{3.20}$$

In the neutron–proton nuclear model, nuclei with even Z and even N have no magnetic moment as well as no angular momentum in the ground state because of pairing of the nucleons. In a sequence of nuclei of odd mass number magnetic moments change when spin values change, e.g. at the magic numbers (section 3.4 and chapter 4). In a nucleus with just one unpaired nucleon, the magnetic moment can be predicted by a simple calculation following the derivation of the Landé g factor in atomic physics. From this the nuclear g factor is found to be

$$g_J = \left(g_l \pm \frac{g_s - g_l}{2l + 1}\right) \tag{3.21}$$

where g_l and g_s are the orbital and intrinsic spin g factors for the odd nucleon concerned (see values in appendix A), l is the orbital angular momentum quantum number and the upper sign is taken for $J = l + \frac{1}{2}$. If in a given case the nuclear spin J is known, the observed magnetic moment of an odd-mass nucleus will reliably indicate the orbital l value for the odd nucleon.

Nuclear magnetic moments may be measured by the methods listed in appendix E. They are found generally to be smaller in absolute value than the extreme *single-particle* ('*Schmidt*') *values* predicted by equations (3.20) and (3.21) as shown in figure 3.7. This has important consequences for nuclear models (chapter 4).

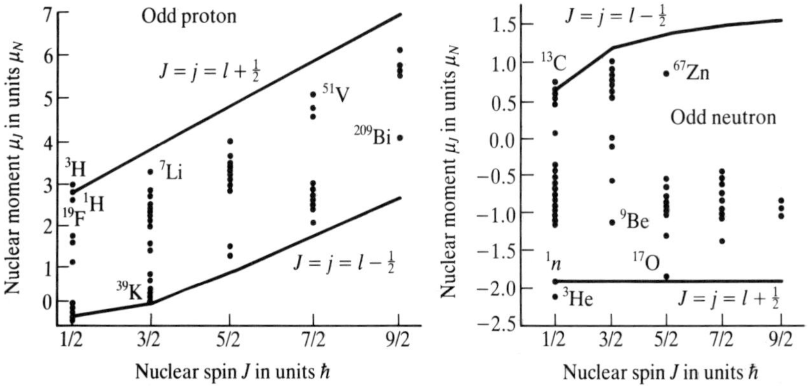

Figure 3.7 Schmidt diagrams showing magnetic moment of odd-mass nuclei as a function of nuclear spin. The lines show the magnetic moments expected for a single nucleon at the spin values $j = l \pm \frac{1}{2}$ (Blin-Stoyle R J 1957 *Theories of Nuclear Moments* Oxford University Press).

3.6 *Electric quadrupole moment*[9,10]

The distribution of charge throughout the volume of a nucleus of finite size gives rise to electric moments. The electric dipole moment can be shown (reference 11, p. 24) to vanish for a well-defined quantum mechanical state, such as a nuclear ground state. A quadrupole moment eQ exists if a nucleus is non-spherical and classically, for a nucleus with symmetry about an axis Oz' fixed in itself, the moment may be defined by the equation

$$eQ = \int \rho(3z'^2 - r'^2)\, \mathrm{d}^3r'$$

$$= \int \rho r'^2(3\cos^2\theta' - 1)\, \mathrm{d}^3r' \qquad (3.22)$$

where ρ is the charge density and d^3r' is the volume element. The integral will contain the total nuclear charge Ze and it is therefore customary to divide each side of equation (3.22) by e and to call Q the quadrupole moment. It is then measured in square metres or barns (10^{-28} m^2). The quantum expression for an observable quadrupole moment Q_J is the expectation value of a quadrupole operator (similar to (3.22)) in the state $(J, m_J = J)$ in which m_J has its maximum value. Because the axis of nuclear spin Oz' cannot be completely aligned with the space-fixed axis Oz (figure 3.8), the moment Q_J is less than the intrinsic moment Q_0 arising from the nuclear non-sphericity and it may be shown (reference 12, p. 71) that the relation between the two is

$$Q_J = \frac{2J - 1}{2(J + 1)} \cdot Q_0 \tag{3.23}$$

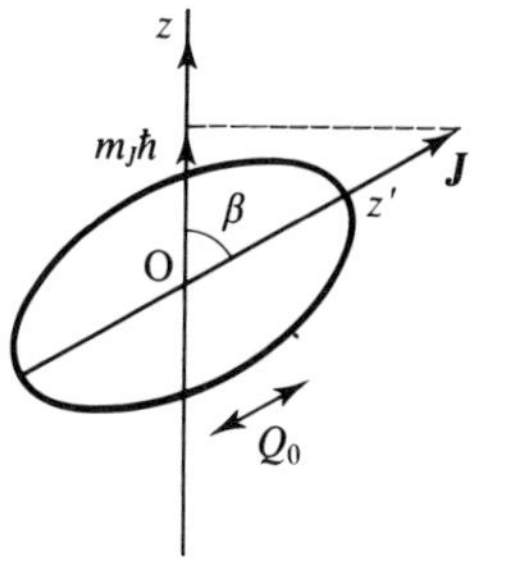

Figure 3.8
Nuclear quadrupole moment. In this diagram both the intrinsic angular momentum **J** and the intrinsic quadrupole moment Q_0 are related to the body-fixed axis Oz'. Observable values $J\hbar$ ($=m_J\hbar$) and Q_J are defined with respect to the space-fixed axis Oz.

and that Q_J exists only for states with $J \geqslant 1$. The sign of Q_J is that of Q_0, i.e. negative for an oblate nucleus and positive for a prolate (cigar-shaped) nucleus.

If the nuclear non-sphericity is due only to the orbital motion of a nucleon, *single-particle quadrupole moments* for the nucleus can be calculated. The single-proton moment is of order $\langle r^2 \rangle$ and is negative, while the single-neutron moment should be zero in a first approximation.

Measured quadrupole moments disagree with these predictions except in the case of a few odd-proton nuclei with Z values just above the magic numbers of the shell model (chapter 4) at which a spherical form is expected. The moments change in sign as Z passes through the magic numbers, but the positive moments are usually larger than expected and for the rare earth group of nuclei are very large indeed compared with the single-particle value. Morever, odd-neutron nuclei have moments that are comparable with those of the odd-proton nuclei. All this evidence suggests that many particles must contribute to the observed moments (section 4.3.2).

Quadrupole moments are determined experimentally by the methods outlined in appendix E and by nuclear reaction methods (chapter 6).

3.7 Parity

In classical physics the normal modes of oscillation of a system such as a stretched string fall into patterns of even or odd symmetry. In the even patterns the sign of a coordinate x makes no difference to the displacement y or velocity $\dot{y}$, while in the odd patterns a change of sign of x reverses both y and $\dot{y}$. In the quantum description of stationary states similar symmetries arise and the wavefunction of a particle in such a state may or may not change sign when all space coordinates are inverted

$(x \to -x, y \to -y, z \to -z)$. This transformation can be viewed alternatively as a reflection *through the origin* or as a reflection in a plane followed by a rotation of 180° about an axis perpendicular to the plane. It transforms a right-handed coordinate system into a left-handed system and is clearly a *discrete* transformation since no continuous transformation in ordinary space can link the one frame to the other. The parity operator U_P which effects the transformation evidently satisfies the equation

$$U_P^2 = 1 \tag{3.24a}$$

since if the transformation is applied twice we must obtain the identity transformation. But U_P is also unitary $(U_P^\dagger U_P = 1)$ and from (3.24a) it follows that $U^\dagger = U_P$. The operator U_P is therefore also hermitian and the parity eigenvalues are real observables.

If $|\psi(r)\rangle$ is an eigenstate of parity, then

$$U_P|\psi(r)\rangle = P|\psi(r)\rangle$$

and (3.24b)

$$U_P^2|\psi(r)\rangle = PU_P|\psi(r)\rangle = P^2|\psi(r)\rangle = |\psi(r)\rangle$$

so that $P^2 = 1$ and the parity eigenvalues P are ± 1 characterizing states $|\psi(r)\rangle$ of *even or odd parity*. The parity P is a *multiplicative* quantum number rather than *additive* as in the case of the angular momentum J, which is associated with a continuous transformation (chapter 8).

If the Hamiltonian of a system is invariant under the parity transformation, parity is conserved (chapter 8) and there is good evidence for this in electromagnetic and strong-interaction processes. Nuclear states can therefore usefully be assigned a parity P; strongly interacting *particles* can also be given a parity as an intrinsic property (section 8.6). Parity is *not* conserved in weak processes (chapter 11).

Nucleons are by convention assigned even parity and the overall parity of a nucleon in a nucleus is determined by its orbital motion. If this motion is described (in a spherical polar coordinate system) by a wavefunction containing the spherical harmonic $Y_l^m(\theta, \phi)$, the parity transformation changes θ to $\pi - \theta$ and ϕ to $\pi + \phi$. From the explicit formulae for spherical harmonics it is straightforward to show that the parity of an orbital angular momentum state is $(-1)^l$ and is independent of m. The parity of a nucleus is the product of the parities of all the neutrons and protons and, for odd mass number, is given by the parity of the unpaired particle, i.e. s, d, g, . . . states have even parity, $P = 1$, and p, f, h, . . . states have odd parity, $P = -1$.

The parity of nuclear states can be measured, relatively at least, by studying nucleon transfer collisions (chapter 6) or radiative transitions (chapter 5). The concept of parity is further discussed in section 8.6.

3.8 Isobaric spin (isospin)

The neutron and proton have a similar mass and identical spin $\frac{1}{2}\hbar$. Already in the 1930s they were found to behave similarly in scattering processes (section 3.11) and the binding energies of mirror nuclei such as ${}^{7}_{3}$Li and ${}^{7}_{4}$Be were found to be the same (after correcting for Coulomb energy). This indicated the equivalence of the (n, n) and (p, p) interactions, or in other words a *charge symmetry* of the nuclear force. It was therefore suggested by Heisenberg and others that the neutron and proton might be regarded as alternative states of the one basic particle, the *nucleon*. To quantify this proposal, Heisenberg introduced an internal degree of freedom, the *isospin* $\boldsymbol{I}$, in complete analogy with the ordinary intrinsic spin $\boldsymbol{s}$. The two orientations of the isospin $\boldsymbol{I}$ ($I = \frac{1}{2}$) in a notional isospin space, namely $I_3 = +\frac{1}{2}$ and $I_3 = -\frac{1}{2}$, would correspond with the proton and neutron respectively.

It will be emphasized in chapter 8 that for ordinary spin the absence of a preferred direction in free space renders spin-up and spin-down states indistinguishable and that this arises from the invariance of interactions under rotations, which leads in turn to the conservation of angular momentum. Similarly, in the absence of charge-distinguishing Coulomb fields, the arbitrariness of isospin 'up' or isospin 'down' in isospin space implies that the (strong) nuclear force, and therefore the nuclear Hamiltonian, is invariant under rotations in isospin space or that *isospin is conserved in the strong interactions*. It follows that I, like the angular momentum J and the parity P, is a useful quantum number for strongly interacting particles (hadrons) and for nuclear states. It has special importance for the hadrons, which will be seen to belong to isospin multiplets (sections 7.3 and 8.7). For nucleons the isospin concept leads to a useful extension of the Pauli principle (section 3.9).

The actual charge Q of a nucleon is given in units of $|e|$ by

$$Q = I_3 + \tfrac{1}{2} \tag{3.25}$$

and for a nucleus containing N neutrons and Z protons the third component of total isobaric spin would be

$$I_3 = \tfrac{1}{2}(Z - N) = \tfrac{1}{2}(2Z - A). \tag{3.26}$$

From the quantum mechanical formalism the total isobaric spin I of such a nuclear state must be greater than or equal to $|I_3|$ and a state with this I value might occur in each of the $2I + 1$ nuclei with $I_3 = I$, $I - 1, \ldots, -(I - 1), -I$. It is the essence of the isobaric spin concept to assert that such a state *will* occur in these nuclei because of the equivalence of the neutron and proton in the basic strong interaction that determines the states. Many examples of the validity of the concept are known;

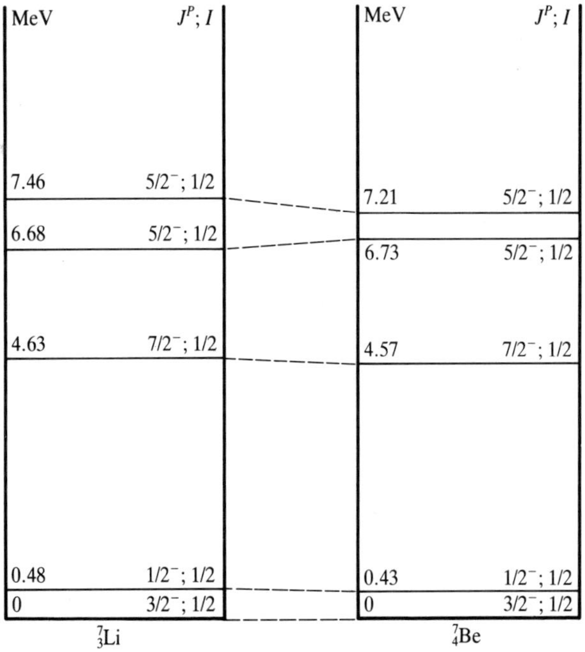

Figure 3.9 Low-lying energy levels of the mass-7 isobaric doublet, showing correspondences. The notation follows that of figure 1.6. All excited states except the first are particle-unstable and some have large widths. (Data taken from Ajzenberg-Selove F 1979 'Energy levels of light nuclei $A = 5$–10' *Nucl Phys* **A320** (1).)

figure 3.9 illustrates the resulting correspondence for the familiar isobaric doublet ^{7}Li–^{7}Be, for which we have $I = \frac{1}{2}$ and $I_3 = -\frac{1}{2}$ and $+\frac{1}{2}$, respectively.

The concept of isobaric spin is discussed further in section 8.7.

3.9 *Statistics*

Many of the statistical concepts of atomic physics are required to interpret nuclear properties. For instance, the well-known result that the number of allowed states of motion for a spinless particle in a phase space volume corresponding with a volume element $4\pi p^2\,\mathrm{d}p$ in momentum space and a volume V in ordinary space is

$$\mathrm{d}N = \frac{4\pi p^2\,\mathrm{d}p V}{h^3} \tag{3.27}$$

is much used in discussing the break-up of nuclei and particles. For particles with spin a weighting factor $2s + 1$ is also needed.

The occupation of these states by particles is governed by the necessity for ensuring indistinguishability of identical particles in an assembly. For two such particles it is known (reference 11, p. 39, and section 8.5) that the wavefunction for the pair must be either totally symmetric or totally antisymmetric under interchange. Experiment tells us that assemblies of electrons are described by antisymmetric wavefunctions since the Pauli exclusion principle applies. All available evidence indicates that protons, neutrons, muons and generally all particles and nuclei of half integral spin (i.e. of odd A) behave similarly. Such particles are known as *fermions* because their distribution between allowed states in a potential well, for instance, obeys the *Fermi–Dirac statistics*; for spin $s = \frac{1}{2}$ only $2s + 1 = 2$ identical particles can enter each spatial state characterized by the quantum numbers n, l and m (appendix D) and this is highly significant for nuclear structure in the neutron–proton model.

For two *nucleons*, regarded as identical particles, the Pauli principle may be extended by use of the isospin formalism (section 3.8). The wavefunction for the two particles has the form (section 8.7.2)

$$\Psi = \psi(\text{space})\,\chi(\text{spin})\,I(\text{isospin})$$

and for two identical fermions this must be antisymmetric with respect to interchange. The functions χ and I have the same structure and each leads to singlet and triplet terms as is well known in spectroscopy. For the two nucleons an isospin singlet ($I = 0$) is just a neutron–proton pair while an isospin triplet ($I = 1$) is a proton–proton pair, a neutron–neutron pair and a neutron–proton pair in a space–spin state permitted to (pp) and (nn). The antisymmetry requirement then leads to the states specified in spectroscopic notation as

$${}^1S_0,\ {}^3P_{0,1,2},\ {}^1D_2, \ldots$$

with $I = 1$, $I_3 = \pm 1, 0$ for (pp), (nn) and (np) and

$${}^3S_1,\ {}^1P_1,\ {}^3D_{1,2,3}, \ldots$$

with $I = 0$, $I_3 = 0$ for (np) only. Such states will be met in discussion of the two-nucleon interaction (section 3.11).

Symmetric wavefunctions must be used to describe assemblies of photons, pions, deuterons and generally all particles and nuclei of integral spin (i.e. of even A). The Pauli principle does not limit the number of identical particles which may enter a given state. The distribution is determined by the *Einstein–Bose statistics* and the particles are known collectively as *bosons*.

The connection between spin value and statistics obeyed was established empirically, but in 1940 Pauli was able to explain it theoretically. The statistics appropriate to a complex nucleus have been established in some cases by the analysis of intensity ratios in the spectra of homonuclear diatomic molecules.

Formula (3.27) and its extension to a system of n particles are discussed in section 9.3.

3.10 The nuclear level spectrum

The result of an experiment to examine the level spectrum of a nucleus of middle mass, say $A = 100$, by exciting it through the reaction X(a, b)Y might be as shown in figure 3.10. On the right-hand side of the figure

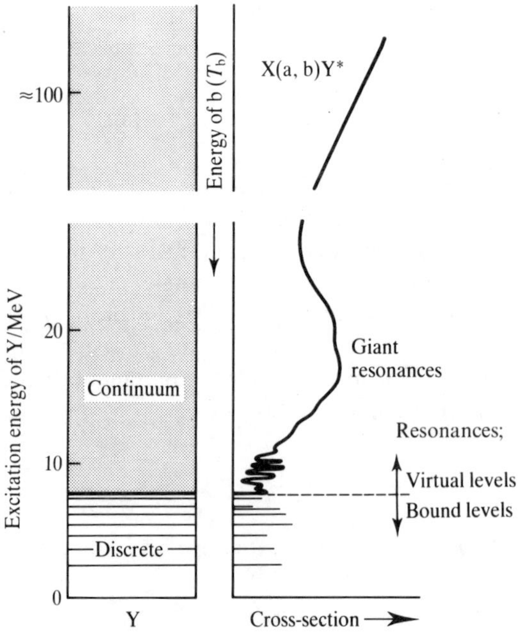

Figure 3.10
The nuclear level spectrum for a nuclide Y of $A \approx 100$, as deduced from the energy spectrum of particles b emitted in a nuclear reaction X(a, b)Y.

is shown the cross-section for the reaction as a function of the energy of the outgoing particle b and on the left-hand side is given the level structure inferred from the observed outgoing particle energies. It can be seen that there are two quite distinct regions, namely the low energy *discrete* region in which well-separated *bound* levels may be distinguished and the higher energy *continuum* region in which the levels are unbound or *virtual* and overlap considerably, although special features may still be observed.

Each excited level has its own set of the properties listed in section 1.3. For the purpose of discussing a level spectrum however, we assume a level to be mainly characterized by an excitation energy above the ground state (cf. figure 1.6), by a width Γ which is related to the lifetime τ of the level against all forms of decay by the expression*

$$\Gamma\tau = \hbar = 6.6 \times 10^{-16} \text{ eV s} \tag{3.28}$$

and by the quantum numbers for spin J, parity P and isobaric spin I, although effects exist which can cause some mixing of I values in a state of good angular momentum. There is no abrupt change of level properties, other than level density, between the discrete and continuum regions and the boundary between these regions is near the energy of excitation at which the emission of a particle becomes possible and probable. This will often be the neutron binding energy of about 8 MeV and above this energy the widths of the virtual levels increase rapidly with energy, although the discrete structure survives for the lowest virtual levels and may be seen as individual *resonances* in appropriate reactions. Below the particle separation energy the bound levels decay by emission of radiation or even by β particle emission if electromagnetic transitions are inhibited.

The theoretical description of nuclear level properties requires the formulation of a nuclear Hamiltonian and the solution of a formidable quantum mechanical many-body problem to provide a wavefunction from which properties may be calculated. This microscopic approach is impossible in practice without massive simplifications. In the discrete region of excitation these may take the form of assumptions that the motion of most of the particles may be disregarded and that the levels arise from the independent motion of a few active nucleons. Or alternatively that there is strong coupling between all the particles of the nucleus and a resulting coherent motion which leads to collective effects of rotation and vibration. At the higher energies of the continuum region detailed models of this type lose their validity and although the underlying microscopic structure must still exist the motion assumes a random or chaotic character which demands a statistical treatment.

Special states that are found mainly, though not entirely, above the neutron binding energy are the *giant resonances* and the *isobaric analogue levels*. The former may be regarded as the basic electromagnetic oscillations of the nucleus as a whole and are at an excitation that varies smoothly with mass number. The latter are structurally related to the low-lying states of an isobaric neighbour nucleus, and although they are found at high excitation because they are pushed up by the Coulomb energy they still exhibit the wide spacing characteristic of low-lying states.

Both nuclear decays (chapter 5) and nuclear reactions (chapter 6) provide information on the nuclear level spectrum and on properties of

---

* This equation means that the energy width and the mean lifetime are alternative ways of characterizing the decay probability per unit time of the excited state. The equation is consistent with the Heisenberg uncertainty principle, which relates the uncertainty in the time for which a state will survive to the uncertainty in its observable energy. For discussion see reference 11, pp. 384 and 417.

individual levels. Compilations of level schemes will be found in references 13 and 14.

3.11 Nuclear forces[15,16]

All nuclear properties reflect to some extent the properties of the strong force between nucleons that binds them together. That force in turn has its origin in the quark–gluon constitution of the nucleon (section 7.4.2) but a discussion of this fundamental strong interaction will be deferred to chapter 7. Here we will consider only the internucleon force, and that from a semi-phenomenological point of view, using data obtained from an experimental study of the two-body system. Some understanding of this force has materially aided the construction of the models (chapter 4) that attempt approximation to the complete nuclear Hamiltonian.

3.11.1 General nature of the nuclear force between nucleons

From the fact that complete nuclei exist, the force must be *attractive*, and sufficiently strong to overcome the repulsion of the Z protons contained within the nuclear volume (according to the neutron–proton model). The *range* was indicated crudely by the early α particle scattering experiments, which showed deviations of the force from pure Coulomb repulsion for light nuclei at distances of approach of the order of a nuclear radius, say 4×10^{-15} m, and the range of the internucleon force seemed likely to be smaller than this. Unfortunately, an assembly of nucleons interacting attractively by a short-range force would collapse to a size of the order of the force range. The total potential energy of a nucleus containing A nucleons would then increase as the number of interacting pairs, i.e. roughly as A^2, whereas the evidence of mass measurements (section 3.2) is that the total binding energy varies only as A. It therefore becomes necessary to postulate a force that provides *saturation*, i.e. that limits the number of attractive interactions within the nucleus.

One way of ensuring saturation is to assume that the potential energy V of a pair of nucleons due to the nuclear force has the form shown in figure 3.11. Such a potential indicates an attractive force $F = -\partial V/\partial r$ at extreme range and a repulsive force at very short distances. If the interparticle distance at the potential minimum $V = -V_0$ is r, then according to the uncertainty principle the particles must have a relative momentum of the order of $\hbar/r$. The corresponding kinetic energy is $\frac{1}{2}\hbar^2/\mu r^2$, where μ is the reduced mass ($1/\mu = 1/m_n + 1/m_p \approx 2/m_p$) of the system, assuming non-relativistic motion. If

$$V_0 > \frac{\frac{1}{2}\hbar^2}{\mu r^2} \tag{3.29}$$

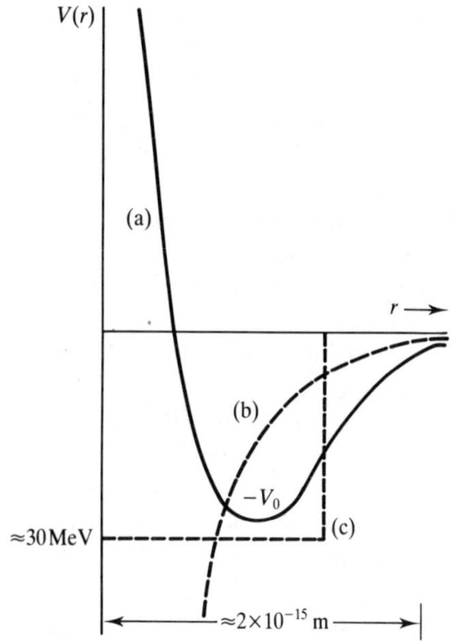

Figure 3.11
The internucleon potential: curve (a) schematic, showing the repulsive core; (b) form of the Yukawa potential; (c) square-well potential often used in calculation.

a bound state may be formed, with a negative discrete energy (section 3.11.2). If, however,

$$V_0 < \frac{\frac{1}{2}\hbar^2}{\mu r^2} \tag{3.30}$$

the total energy of the system lies in the continuum and the interaction is a scattering process (section 3.11.3).

The existence of a repulsive core creates difficulties in some nuclear calculations. It is therefore usual, at least for problems concerned only with low relative momentum, to approximate the potential by the simple spherically symmetrical form with a suitable long-range behaviour shown in figure 3.11, namely the *square well* of radius R,

$$V = \begin{cases} -V_0 & \text{for } r < R \\ 0 & \text{for } r > R \end{cases} \tag{3.31}$$

or the *Yukawa potential*

$$V = -V_0 \frac{\exp(-r/R)}{r/R}. \tag{3.32}$$

For discussion of the nucleon–nucleon system at low energies and of the average potential in nuclei it will be convenient to use the square-well approximation with a range of 1.5–2 fm and a depth of 30–60 MeV.

3.11.2 The deuteron

The deuterium nucleus ($A = 2$, $Z = N = 1$) is a bound state of the neutron–proton system, into which it may be disintegrated by irradiation with γ rays of energy above the binding energy ϵ of 2.2245 ± 0.0002 MeV. The deuteron has no excited states but it has an angular momentum of $1\hbar$ and both a magnetic dipole moment μ_d and an electric quadrupole moment. The magnetic moment is not equal to the algebraic sum of the magnetic moments of the proton μ_p and neutron μ_n, but it is sufficiently near to preclude the possibility of relative orbital motion of the two particles in a first approximation. The simplest structure to assume for the ground state of the deuteron is, therefore, a neutron and a proton in an S state of orbital motion with parallel spins, i.e. a $^3S_1$ or triplet state with even parity. The $^1S_0$ state of the deuteron, in which the proton and neutron have antiparallel spins, is unbound.

To obtain a wavefunction $\psi(r)$ for the deuteron we use the spherically symmetrical square-well potential whose radial variation is shown in figure 3.12. It is convenient to use the radial function $u = r\psi$, where r is the internucleon distance, rather than ψ itself because the Schrödinger equation then simplifies. For the wavefunction in the internal region $r < R$ we have, assuming no orbital angular momentum ($l = 0$),

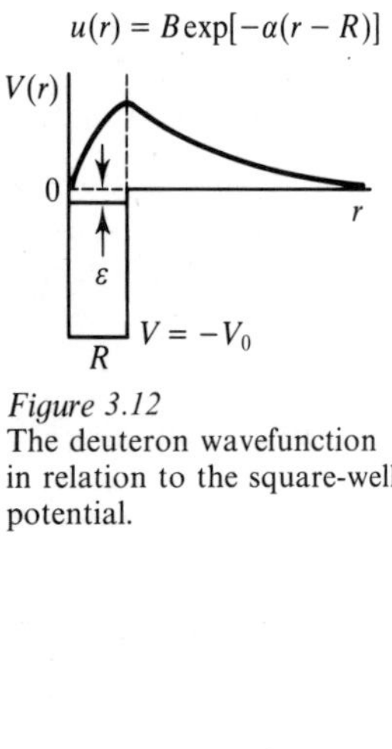

Figure 3.12
The deuteron wavefunction in relation to the square-well potential.

$$\frac{d^2u}{dr^2} + \frac{2\mu}{\hbar^2}(V_0 - \epsilon)u = 0 \tag{3.33}$$

where μ is the reduced mass of the neutron–proton system and the solution of this equation may be written (after excluding a term in $\cos(K_d r)$ which does not vanish at $r = 0$) as

$$u = \frac{A}{K_d}\sin(K_d r) \tag{3.34}$$

where

$$K_d^2 = \frac{2\mu}{\hbar^2}\cdot(V_0 - \epsilon). \tag{3.35}$$

This internal wavefunction (figure 3.12) must turn over within the radial extent R of the potential well if it is to join smoothly to an external wavefunction that dies away to zero. This latter function will be a solution, for $r > R$ (where $V = 0$), of the equation

$$\frac{d^2u}{dr^2} + \frac{2\mu}{\hbar^2}(-\epsilon)u = 0 \tag{3.36}$$

and after excluding a term that diverges as r increases this solution may be written

$$u = B\exp[-\alpha(r - R)] \tag{3.37}$$

where

$$\alpha^2 = \frac{2\mu\epsilon}{\hbar^2} = (0.232)^2\ \text{fm}^{-2}. \tag{3.38}$$

The quantity $1/\alpha = 4.31$ fm is a 'size' parameter for the deuteron.

Continuity of the functions (3.34) and (3.37) at the sharp well boundary $r = R$ is ensured by equating values of the function u and its derivative conveniently as the quantity $(1/u)(\mathrm{d}u/\mathrm{d}r)$. This gives

$$K_\mathrm{d}\cot(K_\mathrm{d}R) = -\alpha \tag{3.39}$$

and substitution from (3.35) and (3.38) leads to

$$\cot(K_\mathrm{d}R) = \frac{-\alpha}{K_\mathrm{d}} = -\left(\frac{\epsilon}{V_0 - \epsilon}\right)^{1/2} \tag{3.40}$$

which is a small quantity if V_0 is in the range 30–60 MeV.

Assuming then as a first approximation that ϵ may be neglected in comparison with V_0, we have

$$K_\mathrm{d}R = \frac{\pi}{2}$$

and, substituting from equation (3.35),

$$V_0R^2 = \frac{\pi^2\hbar^2}{8\mu} = 10^{-28}\ \text{MeV m}^2 \tag{3.41a}$$

which is a relation between the *range of the central force and the depth of the triplet well.* For a well depth of 30 MeV the well radius would be 1.83 fm.

More strictly, allowing for ϵ, equation (3.41a) should be re-written

$$V_0R^2 \geqslant \frac{\pi^2\hbar^2}{8\mu} \tag{3.41b}$$

and this is a condition for the existence of a bound state which refines that already given in equation (3.29).

The magnetic moment of the deuteron in units of the nuclear magneton $\mu_\mathrm{N} = e\hbar/2m_\mathrm{p}$ is less than the sum of the intrinsic magnetic moments of the neutron and proton, taken antiparallel for the ^{3}S configuration:

$$\mu_d = 0.857411 \pm 0.000019$$
$$\mu_n = -1.91315 \pm 0.00007$$
$$\mu_p = 2.79271 \pm 0.00002$$
$$\mu_n + \mu_p = 0.87956 \pm 0.00007.$$

The closeness of the two values confirms that the magnetic moment of the neutron is negative, but it is not possible to explain the difference if the two particles are in a pure s state of relative motion. Moreover, such a state is spherically symmetrical and has no electric moments, whereas the deuteron is known, from molecular beam magnetic resonance experiments (appendix E), to have a positive electric quadrupole moment (section 3.6) of 0.29 fm^2 corresponding with an elongation of the density distribution along the spin axis.

These facts can be explained if the deuteron wavefunction contains a small percentage (up to about 7 per cent depending on the assumed internucleon potential) of a d state component, indicating some motion of the two particles with a relative *orbital* angular momentum quantum number of 2. The d state consistent with the observed spin of the deuteron is $^3D_1$ (i.e. orbital and intrinsic spin vectors opposed). Central forces of the sort so far discussed do not mix states of different angular momentum, but a tensor force, resembling in form the classical interaction between magnetic dipoles and thus depending on the relative orientation of spin vectors, is able to do this.

3.11.3 The scattering of low energy neutrons by protons

We consider neutron energies for which only s waves, with zero orbital angular momentum in the centre-of-mass system, are needed. In this energy range, if effects due to the binding of two protons into a hydrogen molecule are excluded, the neutron-free proton total cross-section is constant at about 20.4 b over a range of several hundred electronvolts. The angular distribution of scattering in the centre-of-mass system is isotropic.

To try to explain this result by a simple extension of the theory of the triplet-state deuteron to positive energies (neglecting for the moment any effect of the singlet state), we proceed as shown in figure 3.13. The neutron wave $u_i(r)$ incident on a target proton is taken to have the simple form $\sin(kr)$ with the centre-of-mass wavenumber k given by equations (C.16) (appendix C) for equal masses, i.e.

$$k^2 = \left(\frac{2\mu}{\hbar^2}\right)\tfrac{1}{2}T_n \qquad (3.42)$$

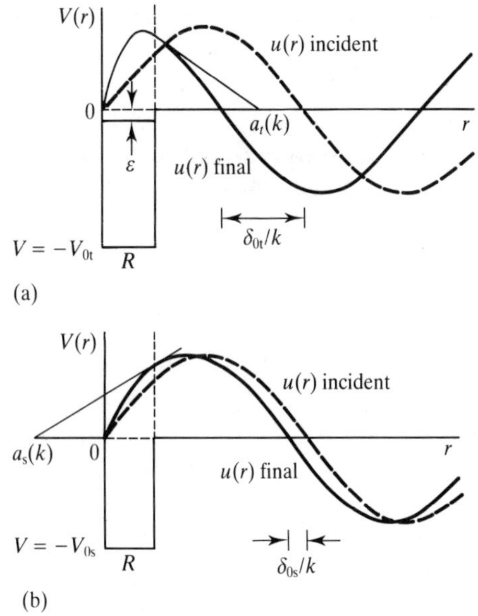

Figure 3.13 Neutron–proton scattering at low energy, showing wave amplitudes, phase shifts and scattering lengths in relation to the square-well potential for (a) the triplet (^{3}S) state and (b) the singlet (^{1}S) state.

where $\frac{1}{2}T_n$ is the centre-of-mass energy of the system for an incident neutron energy T_n. The time factor in the wavefunction is omitted since we consider only an energy-conserving steady state.

If T_n is in the electronvolt range, the wavefunction within the potential well will be very similar to that of the deuteron, equation (3.34), and the final or scattered wave profile will have to join smoothly to this function. As may be seen from figure 3.13(a), a suitable form for $r > R$ is

$$u_f(r) = \frac{C}{k}\sin(kr + \delta_0) \tag{3.43}$$

where δ_0 is the *s wave phase shift* produced by the interaction and C is a constant. Since at this point we neglect dependence of the scattering on intrinsic spin we may use the general formulae for the mutual scattering of spinless particles (section 9.2.1) to connect δ_0 with the total elastic scattering cross-section. Equation (9.21) gives us

$$\sigma_{el}^0 = \frac{4\pi}{k^2}\sin^2\delta_0 \tag{3.44}$$

and what we wish to do is to find an expression for δ_0 in terms of the parameters of the triplet well.

The simplest case is that of the zero energy limit $k \to 0$. The final wavefunction may then be written in the approximate form

$$u_f(r) \to C(r - a_t) \cos \delta_0 \tag{3.45}$$

where a_t is a quantity known as the *triplet scattering length* defined at zero energy by the equation

$$a_t = -\left(\frac{\tan \delta_0}{k}\right)_{k \to 0} \tag{3.46}$$

which follows from (3.43) and (3.45). Geometrically a_t has the meaning shown in figure 3.13(a) – the final ($k \to 0$) wavefunction is linear in r and intersects the axis of r at a distance of a_t from the origin; it is also tangential to the internal wavefunction at the boundary $r = R$. The latter condition of continuity gives the required information, since if we assume that the internal wave number is indeed that of the deuteron (K_d) we have, from (3.34) and (3.45) by equating values of $(1/u)(du/dr)$ at $r = R$,

$$K_d \cot(K_d R) = \frac{1}{R - a_t} \tag{3.47}$$

and bringing in the deuteron parameter α from equation (3.39) we find

$$a_t = R + \frac{1}{\alpha} \tag{3.48}$$

or, if the further approximation of *zero-range forces* is made,

$$a_t = \frac{1}{\alpha} = 4.3 \text{ fm}. \tag{3.49}$$

Moving now to a finite but small k, the experimental cross-section should be given by

$$\begin{aligned} \sigma^0_{el} &= \frac{4\pi}{k^2} \frac{1}{1 + \cot^2 \delta_0} = 4\pi \frac{1}{k^2 + 1/a_t^2} \\ &= \frac{2\pi\hbar^2}{\mu(\frac{1}{2}T_n + \epsilon)} = \frac{5.2}{\frac{1}{2}T_n + \epsilon} \times 10^{-28} \text{ m}^2 \end{aligned} \tag{3.50}$$

using (3.49), (3.42) and (3.38) and inserting numerical values of constants with T_n and ϵ in mega-electronvolts. This cannot be brought into agreement with the observed value of 20.4×10^{-28} m^2 by any attention to approximations.

The disagreement was explained by Wigner, who pointed out that the neutron and proton can also collide (once in every four approaches on the average) in the singlet $^1S_0$ state in which their intrinsic spins are opposed. There is no bound singlet state for the deuteron and the $^1S_0$ internal wavefunction therefore does not turn over within its potential well, like the triplet function, but behaves instead as in figure 3.13(b). If the discussion of the triplet scattering length is followed through for this case it is easily seen that the singlet scattering length a_s is *negative*, and may be very large, depending on the excitation energy of the unbound singlet state.

Introducing this contribution, the cross-section becomes, in an obvious notation,

$$\sigma_{el}^0 = \frac{4\pi}{k^2}\cdot(\tfrac{3}{4}\sin^2\delta_{0t} + \tfrac{1}{4}\sin^2\delta_{0s})$$

$$= \pi\left(\frac{3}{k^2 + 1/a_t^2} + \frac{1}{k^2 + 1/a_s^2}\right) \tag{3.51}$$

and the near zero-energy cross-section is correctly predicted with a value of $|a_s|$ of about 24 fm. The importance of this result is that it clearly establishes the *spin dependence of the internucleon force*; further analysis suggests that the singlet well is shallower but wider than the triplet. For both wells the radial parameter R is considerably less than $1/\alpha = 4.32$ fm so that there is a high probability of the neutron and proton in the deuteron being separated by more than the range of the force.

3.11.4 Further evidence and summary

Many other phenomena, which will not be described in detail here (see references 15 and 16 for a full account) give information on the internucleon force. Some of them will be mentioned briefly in the following summary of the main properties of the force, whose central potential is approximated in figure 3.11.

(a) *Short range*, $\approx$1.5–2.0 fm, with a repulsive core of radius about 0.5 fm in the ^1S state and an attractive potential outside the core in both ^1S and ^3S states (from saturation (section 3.11.1) and from high energy nucleon–nucleon scattering phase shifts).

(b) *Spin dependence* (from low energy n–p scattering (section 3.11.3), from coherent scattering of very slow neutrons by the nuclei of hydrogen molecules and from the capture of slow neutrons by protons and its inverse process of photodisintegration (section 6.6.2)).

The Pauli principle requires that two identical nucleons in an s state of relative orbital motion should have opposite spins ($^1S_0$). For the two-nucleon system this is in effect the pairing interaction that is important in complex nuclei (section 3.2.2). In the deuteron the strong attractive force between the neutron and proton in the parallel-spin ($^3S_1$) state overcomes any pairing effect that would lead to a singlet ($^1S_0$) state and produces the ground state of spin $J = 1$.

(c) *Charge symmetry* within about $\frac{1}{2}$ per cent and *charge independence* within about 1 per cent (from a comparison of scattering lengths and ranges of forces in n–p and p–p scattering and from a study of the $\pi^-d + nn$ reaction). Charge independence, however, is only valid for interaction in states of motion permitted to all three nucleon–nucleon pairs (pp, nn, np), i.e. to states with $I = 1$ in the formalism (section 3.9). In a state of $I = 0$ the space–spin part of the wavefunction is different and a different interaction would be expected. Generally it may be stated that the nuclear force depends on the total isospin of a nucleon state and not on its third component.

(d) *Exchange behaviour* (from the angular distribution of high energy neutron–proton scattering, which shows that the neutron and proton may exchange identity in the scattering process). This behaviour was originally postulated by Heisenberg in order to explain the saturation property, but this is now ascribed to a repulsive core. Exchange forces can readily describe the spin dependence property mentioned earlier.

(e) *Non-central components* (from quadrupole moment of the deuteron (section 3.11.2) and from the observation of polarization in nucleon–nucleon and nucleon–nucleus scattering). The *tensor force* (section 3.11.2) is velocity independent and cannot account for the polarization effects, which depend on velocity. They can be understood if there is a coupling between the spin and orbital motion of a nucleon in a potential field. This *spin–orbit force* in a complex nucleus may be derived from a two-body spin–orbit force between a pair of nucleons and is velocity dependent, in contrast with the tensor force.

If a π meson ($J^P = 0^-$) is actually *exchanged* between interacting nucleons, most of these properties follow directly. The repulsive core, however, requires the exchange of heavier mesons and the spin–orbit force needs a vector meson, with spin-parity 1^-. The one-pion exchange potential (OPEP) introduced by Yukawa to predict the 'long-range' properties of the nuclear force is further discussed in section 7.4.2.

The characteristics outlined above are embodied as far as possible in the effective forces used in the nuclear models to be surveyed in the next chapter.

REFERENCES 3

1 **Wapstra A H and Audi G** 1985 *Nucl Phys* **432** (1–54, 'masses', and 55–139, 'reaction and separation energies'; see also **Wapstra A H, Audi G** and **Hoekstra R** 1988 *Atomic Data and Nuclear Data Tables* **39** (281). For reaction energies see also **Gove N B** and **Wapstra A H** 1972 *Nuclear Data Tables* **A11** (127)

2 **Evans R D** 1955 *The Atomic Nucleus* McGraw-Hill

3 **Pearson J M** 1986 *Nuclear Physics: Energy and Matter* Adam Hilger ch. II

4 **Clayton D D and Woosley S E** 1974 'Thermonuclear astrophysics' *Rev Mod Phys* **46** (755)

5 **Trimble V** 1977 'The origin and abundances of the chemical elements' *Rev Mod Phys* **47** (877)

6 **Williams P M** 1978 'The evolution of the elements' *Contemp Phys* **19** (1)

7 **Bohr A and Mottelson B** 1969 *Nuclear Structure I* Benjamin

8 **de Jager C W, de Vries H and de Vries C** 1974 'Nuclear charge and magnetisation density distribution parameters from elastic electron scattering' *Atomic Data and Nuclear Data Tables* **14** (479)

9 *Nuclear Data Tables* 1969 **A5** (433), 1970 **A7** (495) and 1989 **42** (189)

10 **Siegbahn K** (ed) 1965 *Alpha, Beta and Gamma Ray Spectroscopy* North-Holland p. 1657 (see also reprint of 1979)

11 **Blatt J M and Weisskopf V F** 1952 *Theoretical Nuclear Physics* Wiley

12 **Preston M A and Bhadhuri R K** 1975 *Structure of the Nucleus* Addison-Wesley

13 *Nuclear Data Sheets* Academic Press

14 **Lederer C M and Shirley V S** 1979 *Table of Isotopes* (7th edn) Wiley

15 **Brown G E and Jackson A D** 1976 *The Nucleon–Nucleon Interaction* North-Holland

16 **Brink D M** 1965 *Nuclear Forces* Pergamon

EXAMPLES 3

3.1 The total kinetic energy of n fermions in a potential well of radius R may be taken to be proportional to $n^{5/3}/R^2$. By applying this result to the Z protons and N neutrons of a nucleus and comparing with the case $Z = N = A/2$, deduce the form of the asymmetry energy in equation (3.7).

3.2 Calculate the Coulomb potential energy of a uniform spherical charge distribution of radius R and total charge Ze $[(1/4\pi\epsilon_0)(3Z^2e^2/5R)]$ and calculate it in mega-electronvolts for $Z = 40$, $A = 90$ and $R = 1.25A^{1/3}$. [251 MeV]

3.3 Calculate the binding energy B, the binding energy per nucleon B/A and the neutron and proton separation energies S_n and S_p for ^{114}Cd given that the mass excesses (i.e. the difference between the mass in atomic mass units and the mass number A) are as follows: p, 7.29 MeV; n, 8.07 MeV; ^{114}Cd, -90.01 MeV; ^{113}Cd, -89.04 MeV; ^{113}Ag, -87.04 MeV. [972.55, 8.53, 9.04, 10.26 MeV] Compare your results with prediction from the semi-empirical mass formula with the constants given in the text.

3.4 The energy release in the reaction X(d, p)Y is Q. Show that the neutron separation energy for nucleus Y is $S_n = Q + \epsilon$ where ϵ is the binding energy of the deuteron.

3.5 The scattering of α particles through 60° by lead ($Z = 82$) begins to deviate appreciably from the predicted Coulomb value at an energy of 27 MeV. Estimate a radius for the target nuclei. (For kinetic energy T the closest distance of approach in this Coulomb scattering is $(Ze^2/4\pi\epsilon_0 T)[1 + \text{cosec}(\theta/2)]$.) [$1.3 \times 10^{-14}$ m]

3.6 Using the tabulated values of the magnetic moment of the neutron and proton, calculate the force between these two particles in a triplet state at a separation of 3×10^{-15} m and the work required, on account of this force, to bring the neutron from infinity to this distance from the proton. Assume that the spins always point along the line joining the particles. [1 N, 6267 eV]

3.7 Assuming that the zero range wavefunction $u(r) = r\psi(r) = C\exp(-\alpha r)$ is valid for the deuteron from $r = 0$ to $r = \infty$ obtain an expression for the normalization constant C. [$(\alpha/2\pi)^{1/2}$] If $\alpha = 0.232\ \text{fm}^{-1}$ find the probability that the separation of the two particles in the deuteron exceeds a value of 2 fm. Find also the average distance of interaction for this wavefunction. [0.395, 2.2 fm]

4 Nuclear models

Types of model · The nuclear shell model · The collective model · Single-particle motion in a deformed potential

4.1 Types of model[1,2]

A brief survey of the development of nuclear models was given in section 1.4 and some of the main features of the nuclear level spectrum were listed in section 3.10. It will be clear from those sections that models of nuclear structure are closely related to models which describe nuclear reactions, but it will be convenient to postpone the consideration of the unbound states that influence reactions until a later chapter (chapter 6).

The early nuclear model of an assembly of protons and electrons, possibly grouped in part into α particles and held together by the Coulomb force, was abandoned for the following reasons.

(a) The observed spin and statistics of many nuclei disagree with the model. Even-mass nuclei of odd charge, e.g. $^{2}_{1}$H, $^{14}_{7}$N, obey Bose statistics and have integral spin, contrary to the proton–electron prediction.
(b) Nuclear magnetic moments are of the order of the nuclear magneton $e\hbar/2m_p$ rather than the Bohr magneton $e\hbar/2m_e$.
(c) An electron confined within nuclear dimensions would have to move with a kinetic energy of about 20 MeV and there is no evidence that the proton–electron interaction could bind such a particle.
(d) It is no longer necessary (see chapter 5) to postulate the emission of pre-existing electrons in β radioactivity.

The discovery of the neutron in 1932 by Chadwick (chapter 6) removed the difficulties (a)–(c) and a neutron–proton assembly is now the basis of all models which attempt to interpret overall nuclear properties in terms

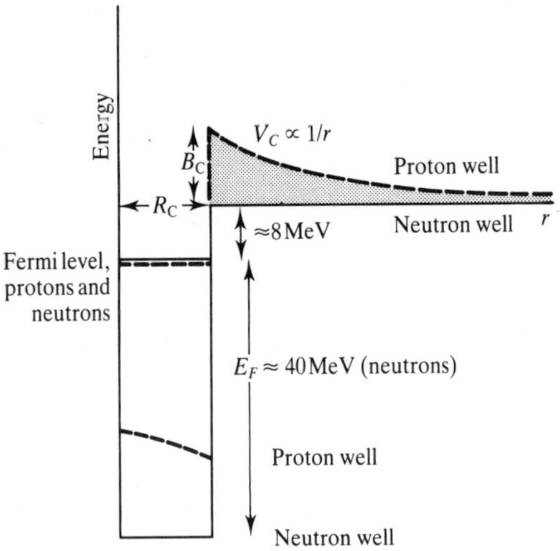

Figure 4.1 The nuclear potential well already shown in figure 3.5 is now re-drawn to separate the wells for protons and neutrons. The Fermi levels for the two-component fermion systems are at about the same energy. The radius of the wells is R_C and the Coulomb barrier height (idealized) is B_C.

of individual particle states. These states are essentially those occupied by fermions in a spherical nucleus represented by a potential well of depth approximately 50 MeV, as shown in idealized form in figure 4.1 for a nucleus of $A \approx 100$, $R_C \approx 5.2$ fm (which is sufficiently large to avoid dominance of surface effects).

There are separate distributions for neutrons and protons and the proton well is raised above the neutron well by the Coulomb potential energy. The particles fill their respective wells, in accordance with the Pauli principle, to the kinetic energy known as the Fermi energy E_F. This may be calculated easily (cf. section 3.9) for a nucleus of known volume $4\pi R_C^3/3$ and known constituent nucleon numbers; for the neutrons it is found that $E_F \approx 40$ MeV, roughly independent of A. The nuclear radius and equivalent well radius increase in accordance with equation (3.6) as nucleons are added.

The Fermi energies for neutrons and protons in a stable nucleus must be at about the same position below zero to ensure stability against mutual decay, although this may be inhibited by the Pauli principle. If the zero of energy is taken to represent a nucleon plus residual nucleus at rest at infinite separation, the position of the Fermi level gives the nucleon separation energy. This is equivalently described as the binding energy of the 'last' nucleon which is experimentally comparable with, though not identical to, the average binding energy per nucleon, $B/A \approx 8$ MeV (shown in figure 4.1). Actual effective potentials must be generated by the interactions between particles themselves. Following atomic theory it is possible to think of a self-consistent field, known as the Hartree–Fock field, in which the particles move as if under the influence of a central potential. Detailed calculations are beset with difficulties arising from the hard core of the internucleon force, but if a phenomenological potential is assumed then there is some justification for setting up a quasi-atomic or *shell model*. The shells are defined by significant gaps in the spectrum of states in the assumed potential well and the levels within each shell specify allowed states of motion for a nucleon. Nuclei of the successive existing elements arise from the filling-up of the sequence of states of the potential well with nucleons as allowed by the Pauli principle.

In its extreme form the shell model neglects interactions between nucleons and nuclear properties, including total energy, are just due to the combination of single-particle values. This *single-particle shell model* (SPSM) is especially appropriate to nuclei in which there are just a few nucleons outside a filled shell, or a few vacancies in one. Once interactions between nucleons are introduced, shell-model calculations, although more realistic, become increasingly difficult as the number of particles being considered increases. The cooperative effects then seen in nuclear properties can be described by phenomenological *collective models*. There is still an underlying microscopic shell structure and models in which both shell and collective features appear are described as *unified*. A familiar example of these is the *Nilsson model* (section 4.4) which calculates single-particle spectra for a deformed potential well. A more recent attempt (1975) to reduce the complexities of the shell model is the *interacting boson model* in which the nuclear fermions cluster into *bosons* with angular momentum 0 or 2 which then interact through a suitable force. This model describes collective effects and has proved especially useful in giving an account of spectra in the transitional region between spherical and deformed nuclei.

In all models an increase of energy of excitation above the nucleon binding energy leads to broadening and overlapping of levels and a *statistical model* is appropriate to describe the emission of unbound particles. This uses thermodynamic arguments and is parametrized by a level-density function. The 'low-temperature' limit of such models, in which very little discrete structure remains, is the *liquid-drop model*, which has already been used in discussion of the mass formula (section 3.2) and gave us our first understanding of the dynamics of nuclear fission (section 6.1.5). This model is also the basis of the simplest phenomenological collective models. We shall consider here mainly the shell and collective models and, briefly, the Nilsson model.

4.2 The nuclear shell model[3,4]

4.2.1 Empirical evidence for the regularity of nuclear properties

Discontinuities in nuclear mass are seen when accurately measured masses are compared with the predictions of a smoothly varying mass formula,

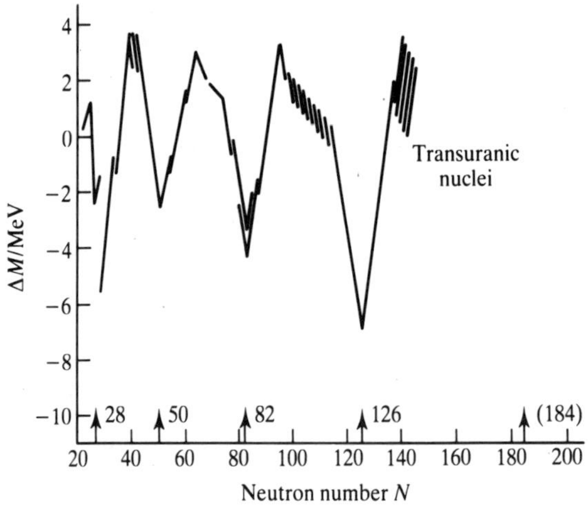

Figure 4.2
Periodicity of nuclidic masses: ΔM is the observed mass less that predicted by a smoothly varying formula (adapted from Kummel H *et al.* 1966 *Nucl Phys* **A81** (129)).

such as that based upon a liquid-drop model. Figure 4.2 shows a plot of this difference against neutron number; the discontinuities are interpreted as due to the formation of closed shells of particles. Similar breaks are seen in plots of the nucleon binding energy against neutron number and further evidence for shell structure comes from abundance data (section 3.2.3), decay energies in α and β radioactivity and thermal neutron capture cross-sections. The periodicity of nuclear spin, parity and magnetic and electric moment has already been mentioned in chapter 3. All these pieces of evidence suggest that nuclei which contain 20, 28, 50, 82 or 126 neutrons or 20, 28, 50 or 82 protons are particularly stable and that if another neutron or proton respectively, is added to the structure, it is more loosely bound.

A quite different aspect of periodicity is seen in the occurrence of *isomeric states* (section 5.1.2) in nuclides with neutron or proton numbers below but near the 'magic' values just listed. These excited states have a long lifetime because of the low energy of excitation or high spin or both.

Direct evidence for the existence of shell structure has come from nuclear reactions which pick off just one nuclear particle. Such a process is the *knock-out* reaction

$$^{12}\mathrm{C} + \mathrm{p} \rightarrow {}^{11}\mathrm{B} + \mathrm{p} + \mathrm{p} \tag{4.1}$$

produced by incident protons of energy 50–400 MeV. The outgoing proton energies are measured in coincidence and geometrical conditions can be imposed which minimize energy loss to the recoil nucleus ^{11}B. The overall loss of energy in the reaction then measures the binding of the knocked-out proton in the ^{12}C nucleus. Figure 4.3 shows some results obtained from this nucleus in the form of a scatterplot relating the energy of one proton to that of the other proton with which it is associated in the reaction. The distinct band at 45° to the axis indicates that for these

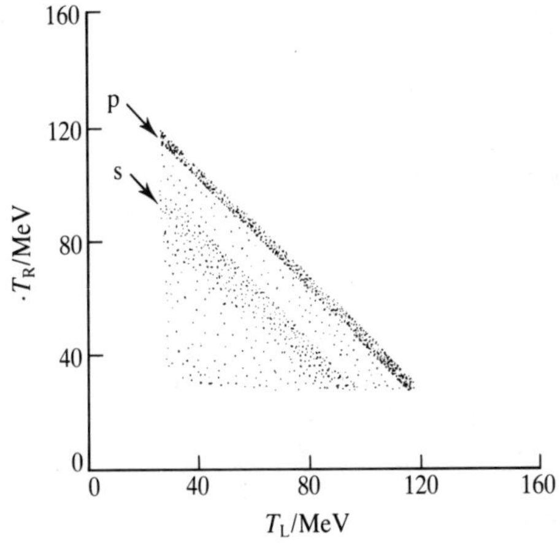

Figure 4.3 Scatterplot of the energies T_L and T_R of proton pairs from the $^{12}C(p, 2p)\ ^{11}B$ reaction observed at $\pm 42.5°$ with a beam of 160 MeV protons (adapted from Gottschalk B *et al.* 1967 *Nucl Phys* **A90** (83)).

events the sum of the proton energies is constant and this means that there is a well-defined binding energy (here approximately 16 MeV) for the struck proton; for ^{12}C this is interpreted as the energy necessary to form a hole in a shell of protons of angular momentum $l = 1$ (p shell). The figure also shows a much broader distribution, with indicated binding energies of 30–40 MeV, which may be associated with a shell of angular momentum $l = 0$ (s shell). The angular momentum assignments are those suggested by the simplest quasi-atomic model for the six protons of the ^{12}C nucleus and are confirmed by angular distribution measurements. Similar evidence for proton shell structure in nuclei has been obtained by the use of high energy electrons as probes of momentum distribution.

4.2.2 *The single-particle shell model*[3,4]

Objectives

The first objective of the model is clearly to understand how the magic stability numbers of 20, 28, 50, 82 and 126 neutrons or protons arise. To these numbers it is usual to add 2 (the α particle) and 8 (oxygen-16), although these are numbers that arise very naturally among the light nuclides because of the simple nature of $l = 0$ and $l = 1$ levels, already known in atomic physics. If a satisfactory orbital sequence can be established then the regular filling of orbits will be expected to account for the main features of the properties discussed in chapter 3.

A second objective is to ensure that the potential well adopted to account for the sequence of orbits is consistent with the observed binding energies of the single-particle levels and with the general properties of nuclear matter as determined by the internucleon interaction.

Finally, the model must indicate the directions in which it may be improved.

Sequence of levels

The starting point of all shell models is the solution of the Schrödinger equation for a particle moving in a spherically symmetrical *central* field of force, i.e. in a field in which the potential energy V of the particle with respect to the centre is a function $V(r)$ of radial distance r only. This problem is examined briefly in appendix D with specific attention to the harmonic oscillator potential. The eigenfunctions for the central potential are in general characterized by a principal quantum number n, an orbital angular momentum quantum number l and a magnetic quantum number m giving the resolved part of the angular momentum vector along the axis of the quantization.

No potential with a simple radial form produces shell closures at the magic numbers. For the pure harmonic oscillator, for instance, the level order indicated in appendix D is

$$n, l; = 1s; 2p; 2s, 3d; 3p, 4f; \ldots \tag{4.2}$$

which gives shell closures for fermions at total particle numbers

$$2, 8, 20, 40, 70, 112 \ldots \tag{4.3}$$

The average spacing of these levels can be obtained by choosing the basic oscillator frequency ω so that the expectation value or quantum mechanical average of r^2 is equal to the mean square nuclear radius. This gives

$$\hbar\omega_0 \approx 40A^{-1/3} \text{ MeV} \tag{4.4}$$

and this expression is useful in tracing the systematics of single-particle states.

A more realistic potential, which is now very widely used, follows the nuclear charge distribution, equation (3.13). This is reasonable because the strong short-range forces between neutrons and protons ensure that the total nuclear matter distribution is similar to that of the charge. The resulting central potential is said to have a *Woods–Saxon* form and is shown in figure 4.4. It is more attractive at large radii, relative to its maximum depth, than an oscillator potential of similar mean square radius and this lowers the levels of higher orbital angular momentum for a given oscillator number (appendix D). The depth of the average shell-model potential well set up in this way is found empirically to require correction for the difference between the number of neutrons and protons in the nucleus considered, in analogy with the asymmetry correction in the semi-empirical mass formula (section 3.2.2).

An essential addition to the shell-model potential, made in 1949 by Mayer and by Haxel, Jensen and Suess, is a velocity-dependent term usually known as the *spin–orbit* coupling. Such an effect has already been noted as a component of the two-nucleon interaction (section 3.11). Within the constant-density nuclear volume a force such as this may be expected to average out, but in the nuclear surface there is a density gradient and, therefore, a direction with respect to which the orbital angular momentum $\boldsymbol{r} \times \boldsymbol{p}$ of a single nucleon may be defined. It is assumed that the spin–orbit potential V_{so} depends on the relative direction of the orbital and intrinsic spin vectors and that it may be written

$$V_{\mathrm{so}}(r) = V_{ls}(r)\boldsymbol{l}\cdot\boldsymbol{s} \tag{4.5}$$

where $\boldsymbol{l}$ and $\boldsymbol{s}$ are the orbital and spin angular momenta of the nucleon considered in units of $\hbar$. The radial dependence of $V_{ls}(r)$ near the nuclear surface should be given mainly by the gradient of the nuclear density profile given in equation (3.13), as shown in figure 4.4 (inset).

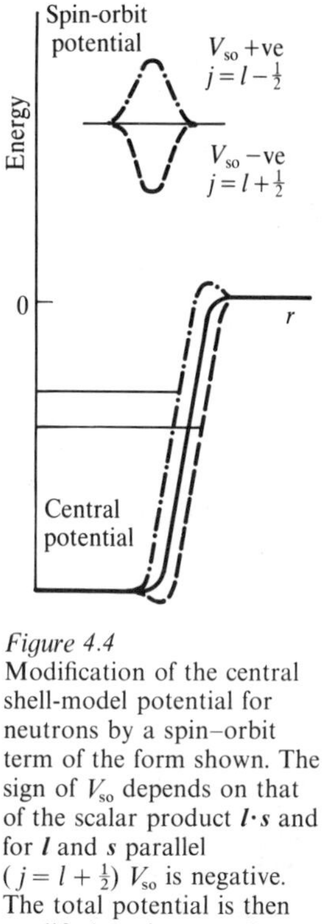

Figure 4.4
Modification of the central shell-model potential for neutrons by a spin–orbit term of the form shown. The sign of V_{so} depends on that of the scalar product $\boldsymbol{l}\cdot\boldsymbol{s}$ and for $\boldsymbol{l}$ and $\boldsymbol{s}$ parallel ($j = l + \frac{1}{2}$) V_{so} is negative. The total potential is then modified as shown and a given level is *lowered* from its energy in the unmodified well. For $j = l - \frac{1}{2}$ the level is raised. The main central potential (full line) here has the Woods–Saxon form

$V(r) = -V_0[1 + \exp(r - R)/a]^{-1}$

where R and a are shape parameters, and in this well the states of high l are already lowered in energy for a given oscillator number N.

The coupling of the vectors $\boldsymbol{l}$ and $\boldsymbol{s}$ for a nucleon ($s = \frac{1}{2}$) gives rise to doublet levels with a total angular momentum quantum number

$$j = l \pm \tfrac{1}{2} \tag{4.6}$$

and the observed energies of these two levels, in many odd-A nuclei, are related by

$$E_{(l+1/2)} - E_{(l-1/2)} = -10(2l + 1)A^{-2/3}\ \mathrm{MeV}. \tag{4.7}$$

This means that the level with the larger j is the more stable and that the doublet splitting increases with l value (example 4.5). The modification of the central potential by this spin–orbit effect is shown in figure 4.4.

With these modifications to the oscillator potential the magic numbers arise naturally, as shown in figure 4.5. First the levels of high angular momentum for a given oscillator quantum number N are lowered because of the change of well to the Woods–Saxon shape; then, as the l value of the levels increases, so does the spin–orbit spacing, equation (4.7) and the first $g_{9/2}$ level, belonging to $N = 4$, merges with the levels of oscillator number $N = 3$, of opposite parity. This is also shown in figure 4.5 in which we have departed from the spectroscopic definition of n used in equation (4.2) and simply numbered the levels of a given l value serially. This is reasonable because in the nuclear spectrum the spin–orbit coupling has an effect on energies comparable with that due to changes of radial quantum number.

A given nuclide in the N–Z chart may now be described as an assembly of N neutrons and Z protons filling levels defined by the spin–orbit coupling scheme and labelled nl_j. If there are x nucleons of a given kind, we speak of a *configuration* $(nl_j)^x$ and, for a given j, $2j + 1$ neutrons

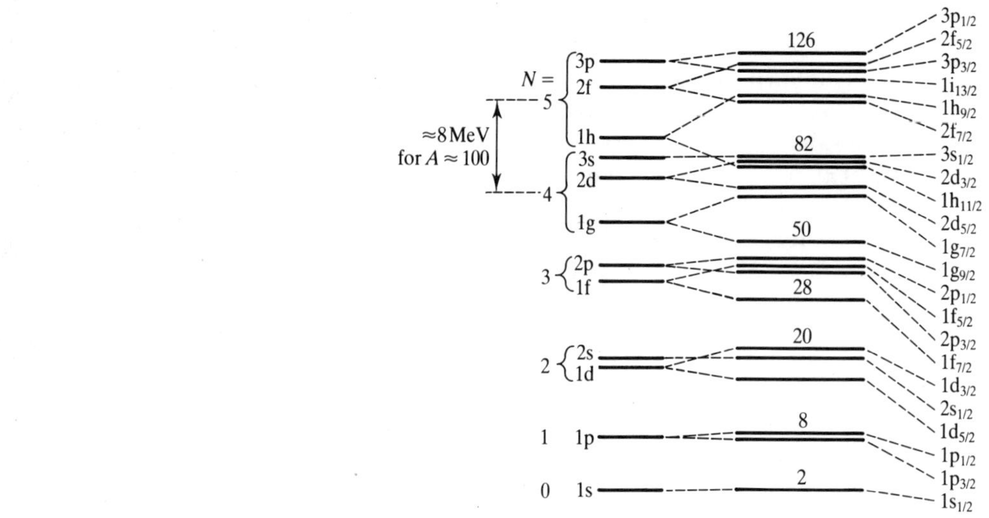

Figure 4.5 Single particle levels in a Woods–Saxon type of potential well with spin–orbit coupling. A pure harmonic oscillator potential would give equally spaced degenerate groups of levels with excitation $N\hbar\omega$ (appendix D), but a slight anharmonicity can lower the levels of high l for a given N. For $N = 4$ the additional spin–orbit effect shown in figure 4.4 is sufficient to overcome the oscillator spacing and the magic numbers result.

or protons can be accommodated without offending the Pauli principle, since m_j can run from $-j$ to $+j$. If we count occupations in this way, figure 4.5 shows that *major shell closures*, followed by a gap in the level sequence, occur at exactly the magic numbers

$$2, 8, 20, 28, 50, 82, 126. \tag{4.8}$$

Between major shells, *subshells* will be completed, with smaller energy differences. Nuclides like $^{208}_{82}Pb$, in which both neutrons and protons complete a major shell, are of *double-closed shell* type and are spherical in shape because of the occupation of all spatial states.

The importance of the SPSM is that it provides a sequence of single-particle levels, classified according to n, l and j. The nucleons forming a configuration $(nl_j)^x$ of neutrons or protons will couple through the internucleon forces to give a sequence of levels which form the spectrum of ground and excited states for a given configuration. But if x is even, and if it is recognized (section 3.4) that residual interactions not included in the shell-model potential favour the *pairing* of particles with equal and opposite m_j values, then the SPSM predicts that the resultant total angular momentum of the lowest level is zero. Even-N, even-Z nuclei therefore have $J = 0$. When x is odd the resultant is equal to the j value of the configuration. Both predictions are verified, as noted in section 3.4. Just below the major shells, e.g. at N or $Z = 50$, 82 and 126, levels of large spin difference lie close together and may form the ground and first excited state of the nucleus. This offers the explanation of a number of examples of isomerism (section 5.1.2).

In odd-mass nuclei near to double-closed shells the sequence of single-particle excited states is clearly shown experimentally. In some cases deviations from the sequence are due to the fact that promotion of a nucleon to a level which requires crossing of a major shell gap may be less favourable than breaking a pair in a low subshell and forming one in a higher subshell. A hole state rather than a particle state is then seen in spectrum. More generally, deviation of the shell-model potential from the simple central form leads to a splitting of single-particle strength over a group of levels. These may be identified experimentally by transfer reactions (section 6.5).

The shell-model potential is generated by the nucleons themselves, and is essentially a property of nuclear matter. That such a simple model, implying an apparently long mean free path for the nucleon within the Fermi distribution, should be so successful is at first sight surprising. It can only be understood by invoking the Pauli principle, which inhibits the collisions in nuclear matter which would transfer one of the colliding partners to an already occupied state.

The impressive successes of the SPSM in the prediction of nuclear properties have been described in chapter 3, but the divergences from strict single-particle behaviour are equally important. The major difficulties requiring an extension of the model are the occurrence of many states in the nuclear spectrum other than those of single-particle motion, the location of observed magnetic moments *between* the Schmidt limits and the large values of electric quadrupole moment for rare-earth nuclei, as well as the existence of this moment at all for single neutron nuclei like ^{17}O. In all these cases the single-particle predictions of the model (sections 3.4–3.6) provide a useful starting point for comparison with observation and a guide to the need for more sophisticated models.

Extension of the SPSM; approach to collectivity

In the SPSM, attention is concentrated on the main central potential and its spin–orbit modification. The central potential is certainly not a complete representation of the total interaction in the nuclear many-body system and extension of the model must be concerned with the *residual forces* between the particles of a configuration. In closed shells or subshells these forces ensure the pairing of particles with opposite angular momenta but in the open configurations which often determine the observable properties of a nucleus the effect of the residual forces must be more closely examined. The natural extension of the SPSM is therefore to the *individual particle model* (IPM) in which matrix elements of an assumed residual interaction are evaluated in a model space defined by the configuration. Calculations of this type involve the diagonalization of very large matrices.

As already noted, the short-range, attractive *pairing-force* component of the residual interaction is especially important in even-Z, even-N

nuclei with nucleon numbers near to closed shell values. For such nuclei the $J^P = 0^+$ ground-state energy is lowered by the occurrence of an especially regular collision pattern in the motion of even one neutron–neutron or proton–proton pair moving with opposite spin and orbital angular momentum. This effect creates an *energy gap* between the actual ground-state energy and that predicted from the SPSM level energies without residual interactions.

Low-lying excited states of even-Z, even-N nuclei may be formed by re-coupling the ground-state configurations to yield an angular momentum with $J > 0$. Other configurations within the same shell may lead to the same spin values. Again the residual forces cause a lowering of energies but it is not so marked as for the paired ground state. In these even–even nuclei, however, the lowest $J^P = 2^+$ state is often pushed down into the energy gap and becomes the first excited state. An alternative to this microscopic description of the first excited state is a macroscopic interpretation in terms of the *surface vibration* of a liquid drop about a spherical equilibrium state. This latter description, however, is not appropriate for high spin states in spherical nuclei. For these the required excitation energy and angular momentum may be more realistically reached by pair-configuration breaking and alignment of nucleon spins along the nuclear axis.

If there are sufficient (paired) valence nucleons outside a closed shell the longer range part of the residual interaction may lead to a distortion of the inner shell, i.e. to a change from a spherical to an ellipsoidal shape. This makes quantized macroscopic *rotation* of the nucleus possible (section 4.3.3) and also means that the valence nucleons move in a non-central field of force. In these nuclei the motion of the pairs is even more important than in spherical nuclei and their cooperative effect in lowering the energy of the ground state is known as *pair correlation.*

Both in the rotation of deformed nuclei and in the vibration of spherical ones we see an interplay between the intrinsic motion of the valence nucleons, as described by the shell model extended to include pairing, and the collective aspects of nuclear excitations. These latter aspects will now be surveyed.

4.3 The collective model[5–8]

The early development of the collective model was guided by the theory of molecular spectra in which the complex motion of a molecule is divided into components relating to the intrinsic motion of the electrons and to vibration and rotation of the molecule as a whole. For a nucleus a similar division may be made with valence nucleon motion providing the intrinsic part. For the molecule such a separation is useful because the energies associated with the different types of motion are considerably different and the motions can in a first approximation be treated independently. For the nucleus this is not always so but it is still useful to think of the motions individually.

4.3.1 *Collective vibration*

General

We confine discussion to nuclei with a spherical equilibrium shape, i.e. to those with nucleon numbers near to and including closed-shell values. If such a nucleus is described (macroscopically) as a charged drop of incompressible liquid, the simplest collective motion is a simple harmonic vibration of the surface about equilibrium. The distortion of the surface may be described by expressing the radius R as a series of spherical harmonics $Y_\lambda^\mu(\theta, \varphi)$ ($\lambda = 0, 1, 2, 3$; $|\mu| \leqslant \lambda$) multiplied by arbitrary amplitudes. The individual excursions specified by λ are said to have *multipolarity* λ and the lowest modes are called monopole, dipole, quadrupole and octupole. A possible form of each of these excursions is shown in figure 4.6.

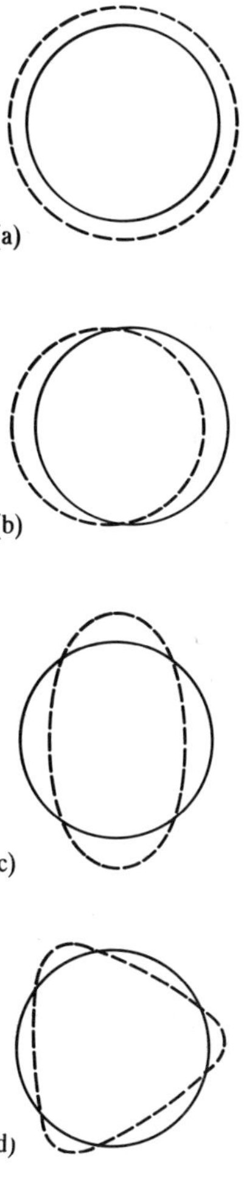

(a) (b) (c) (d)

Figure 4.6
Modes of nuclear vibration about a spherical equilibrium state (full line). The broken line shows one extreme excursion of the nuclear surface: (a) $\lambda = 0$; (b) $\lambda = 1$ (relevant to opposite motions of neutron and proton fluids); (c) $\lambda = 2$; (d) $\lambda = 3$.

The oscillator frequencies ω_λ are determined by the properties of the liquid and, if quantized, define oscillator quanta or *phonons* of energy $\hbar\omega_\lambda$, angular momentum $\lambda\hbar$ and parity $(-1)^\lambda$. The energy and J^P values of a given vibrational state are then determined by the number of phonons required to excite it and by the coupling between them. For a single phonon state the multipolarity λ becomes the number of units of angular momentum $\hbar$ characterizing the motion.

Nuclei of course are not rigid objects and if a degree of compressibility is admitted, the liquid-drop picture must be extended to include acoustic-type waves involving density fluctuations throughout the nuclear volume. Estimates of the corresponding frequencies suggest that these modes, when quantized, have a higher energy than the surface modes. The characteristics of this 'nuclear sound' are discussed in reference 9.

Nuclear vibrational modes may be given a *microscopic* interpretation[9] in terms of nucleon transitions between shell-model states (section 4.2.2). For a given angular momentum $\lambda\hbar$ and parity change it is found that many transitions group together at about the same energy; for some λ, both low energy and high energy groupings appear. The energy is roughly determined by the change in the single-particle oscillator number N and the multipolarity λ is given simply by the angular momentum change, e.g. for $\lambda = 1$ a typical transition (to an incomplete shell) is $2p_{3/2}$ ($N = 3$) $\rightarrow$ $2d_{5/2}$ ($N = 4$) (figure 4.5). It is also found, as will be discussed in section 5.1.1 for radiative transitions, that both 'electric' Eλ and magnetic Mλ transitions exist and that they have opposite parity for a given λ; we shall confine attention to the former, which relate to the motion of charge. Because nuclei contain both neutrons and protons it is also necessary to recognize the changes of isobaric spin (section 3.8) in the transition and to classify them as either *isoscalar* ($\Delta I = 0$) or *isovector* ($\Delta I = 1$). In the former, in the liquid-drop model, the neutrons and protons move together while in the latter they move in opposition.

Experimental

The identification of collective vibrational states in spherical nuclei is based on their energy, angular momentum and radiative transition strength (sections 5.1.2 and 5.1.4) in terms of what might be expected for single-particle transitions. Of outstanding significance[9–11] are the *giant resonances* at excitations of 10–20 MeV which appear as an enhancement of cross-section for reactions such as photodisintegration (section 6.6.2) and inelastic scattering of charged particles. The angular distribution of the scattered particles can be used to infer the angular momentum transfer $\lambda\hbar$, i.e. the multipolarity of the transition. Referring for convenience to figure 4.6 we may describe the observed vibrational states as follows.

(a) $\lambda = 0$ (*monopole, figure 4.6(a)*) This is a wholly radial oscillation without change of shape which may best be visualized as a 'breathing' mode and is only possible in a compressible nucleus. The giant isoscalar resonant state has $J^P = 0^+$ and is found experimentally in nuclei with A greater than about 40 at an energy

$$\mathrm{E0} \approx 80A^{-1/3}\ \mathrm{MeV}. \tag{4.9}$$

(b) $\lambda = 1$ (*dipole, figure 4.6(b)*) In the liquid-drop model the isoscalar mode of dipole oscillation is just a periodic displacement of the mass centre. The centre of charge always coincides with the centre of mass and the system has no electric dipole moment. In the isovector mode, however, the centres of charge and mass separate and a dipole moment develops. The collective isovector excitation has $J^P = 1^-$ in even–even nuclei and an energy given by

$$\mathrm{E1} \approx 77A^{-1/3}\ \mathrm{MeV} \tag{4.10}$$

which is close to that of the monopole resonance. It was the first giant resonance to be identified (1947) and is seen clearly in photoneutron production (figure 4.7). The relative motion of the neutron and proton distributions may also include a rocking or 'scissors' type of behaviour which has been interpreted as a magnetic excitation.

In the shell-model picture the giant dipole resonance is formed by a group of transitions between major shells with a change in oscillator number $\Delta N = 1$ giving a parity change as well. The excitation energy is larger than that predicted by equation (4.4) but introduction of the residual interaction between an excited particle and the hole that it leaves corrects this defect; essentially the dipole state (1^-) is pushed *upwards* by a mechanism similar to that which lowers the 0^+ state in

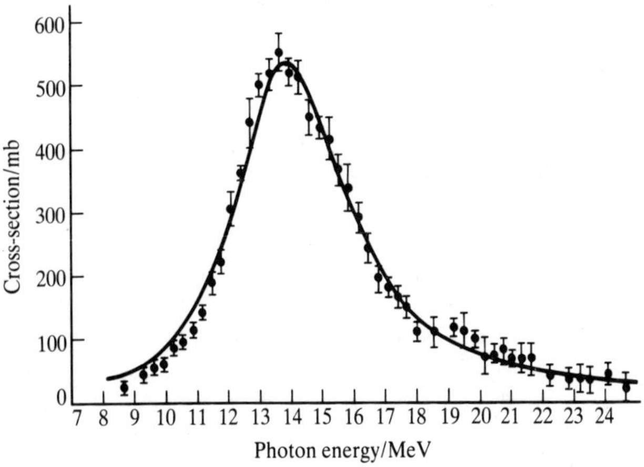

Figure 4.7 Giant resonance of photodisintegration in ^{197}Au. The yield of neutrons is shown as a function of the energy of the monochromatic photons used to produce the reaction (Fultz S C *et al.* 1963 *Phys Rev* **127** (1273)).

non-closed-shell even–even nuclei (section 4.2.2; 'Extension of the SPSM').

(c) $\lambda = 2$ (*quadrupole, figure 4.6(c)*): $\lambda = 3$ (*octupole, figure 4.6(d)*)
Allowing for the special nature of the $\lambda = 0$ and $\lambda = 1$ excitations, it will be seen that the quadrupole vibration is the fundamental mode of a spherical liquid drop as far as surface (shape) oscillation is concerned. In its extreme form this type of deformation leads to fission instability (section 5.4). The lowest vibrational state is created by just one phonon and has the energy, angular momentum and parity ($J^P = 2^+$) of that phonon. If two phonons are excited by the production reaction in an even–even nucleus, they couple together to form a triplet of states with spin-parity $J^P = 0^+$, 2^+ and 4^+ at about twice the energy of the single phonon state; this pattern is often found experimentally. In the shell-model picture the single phonon vibrations correspond with in-shell excitations and $\Delta N = 0$ leading to $J^P = 2^+$.

A giant isoscalar quadrupole resonance is found at an energy

$$E2 \approx 63A^{-1/3}\ \text{MeV} \tag{4.11}$$

corresponding roughly with excitations across two major shells and with a change in oscillator number $\Delta N = 2$. The resonance of course has $J^P = 2^+$ in even–even nuclei.

Octupole states ($J^P = 3^-$) are often seen near the two-phonon triplet in even–even nuclei, e.g. as the lowest excited state in the double closed-shell nuclei ^{16}O, ^{40}Ca and ^{208}Pb, for which no $\Delta N = 0$ quadrupole vibrations are possible because shells are filled. These states appear as a low-lying giant resonance, with $\Delta N = 1$, at an energy

$$E3 \approx 32A^{-1/3} \text{ MeV}. \tag{4.12}$$

A higher energy octupole mode with $\Delta N = 3$, $J^P = 3^-$ would be expected at about three times this energy.

Deformed nuclei

Vibrational energies are found to decrease as the number of valence neutrons outside a closed shell increases. This is because the nuclear structure is becoming less compact and the distorting effect of the intrinsic motion may then lead to a stable deformation (section 4.2.2, 'Extension of the SPSM; approach to collectivity', and figure 4.8). The collective motion then includes rotation as well as vibration about an ellipsoidal equilibrium shape. Such rotation is not possible for a spherical nucleus (or for a deformed nucleus about a symmetry axis) because different azimuthal angles cannot be distinguished quantum mechanically in these cases.

The giant dipole resonance is split into two components in a permanently deformed nucleus with axial symmetry, corresponding with oscillation in the direction of, and perpendicular to, the symmetry axis.

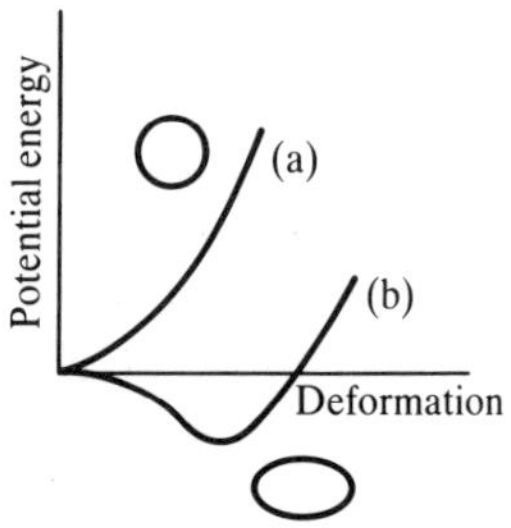

Figure 4.8
Potential energy of a nucleus as a function of deformation: curve (a), spherical shape; curve (b), deformed shape (adapted from Alder K *et al* 'Coulomb Excitation' 1956 *Rev Mod Phys* **28** (432)).

4.3.2 Collective rotation

Observation of nuclear deformation

Although the radius parameter r_0 of the nuclear charge distribution is given with fair accuracy by equation (3.15), for a wide range of nuclides there are distinct regions of the N–Z plot in which anomalies occur. The most celebrated of these was discovered by the refined techniques of *optical isotope shift* measurement (appendix E) long before accurate electron scattering data became available. It was found for nuclei in the rare-earth region that the effect of adding two neutrons to the nuclides in an isotopic sequence, e.g. $^{152}Sm \rightarrow {}^{154}Sm$, was to change the mean square of the charge radius by much more than would be expected on the basis of the $A^{2/3}$ dependence indicated by equation (3.15). Extension and refinement of such observations has confirmed the onset of a deviation of the nuclear shape from spherical symmetry at a neutron number of $N = 88$ or 90, which is entirely unconnected with the SPSM. An ellipsoidal deformation of the magnitude seen in the isotope shift work is sufficient to account for the enhanced *electric quadrupole moments* of the same nuclei. The main groups of deformed nuclei are the rare earths ($A \approx 170$), the actinides ($A > 225$) and nuclei with $A \approx 24$ in the s–d shell; these all lie near the line of stability in the N–Z diagram and are located between magic numbers. New regions of deformation removed from the line of stability have been found at $A \approx 80$, $A \approx 100$ and $A \approx 130$. In these deformed nuclei, a characteristic pattern of low-lying levels, quite different from the single-particle or vibrational sequence, is seen. They can be understood as the levels of a system in which collective rotational motion of a deformed shape is taking place. Extensive spectroscopic studies of rotational transitions have shown that for low angular momenta it is the valence nucleon configuration that determines whether the deformation is oblate (like the earth) or prolate (like a cigar). For high angular momenta, however, the collective rotational energy of the core dominates and a marked prolate shape known as a *superdeformation* may develop.

The rotational spectrum

Consider an ellipsoidally deformed nucleus (figure 4.9) in which the body-fixed symmetry axis is labelled Oz'. If the Hamiltonian of the whole system is independent of spatial orientation, then the total angular momentum $\boldsymbol{J}$ and its projection $M\hbar$ on a space-fixed axis Oz are constants of the motion.

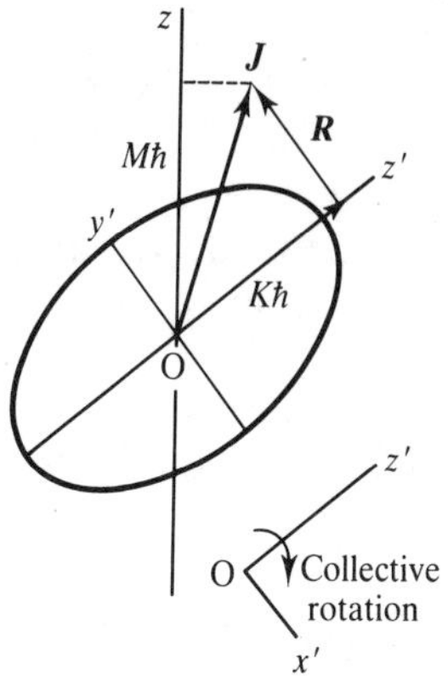

Figure 4.9
Cross-section of axially symmetric deformed nucleus, showing body-fixed axis Oz' and space-fixed axis Oz. The total angular momentum vector $\boldsymbol{J}$ is indicated; $M\hbar$ is the resolved part of $\boldsymbol{J}$ along Oz and $K\hbar$ is the resolved part along Oz'. $\boldsymbol{R}$ is the vector representing collective rotation which adds vectorially to the intrinsic angular momentum $K\hbar$ to form $\boldsymbol{J}$.

If only intrinsic and rotational motion are taking place, the total angular momentum $\boldsymbol{J}$ is a vector sum of the corresponding momenta and this addition is constrained in two ways by the circumstance of axial symmetry. First, as already noted, there is no collective rotation about the symmetry axis so that (classically) the rotation $\boldsymbol{R}$ is perpendicular to this axis. Secondly, because the Hamiltonian is invariant to the orientation of the nucleus about the symmetry axis, the component of $\boldsymbol{J}$ along the symmetry axis is a third constant of the motion. This component must be provided by the intrinsic motion of the valence nucleons about the symmetry axis and we call its resultant value $K\hbar$; it is the sum of the corresponding components $K_i\hbar$ for all the individual valence nucleons. The individual particle angular momenta are *not* constants of the motion in a non-spherical field.

If there is no angular momentum due to the intrinsic motion of the valence nucleons ($K = 0$), the spin J is due solely to the collective rotation and the rotational energy to be added to the energy determined by the intrinsic motion has the familiar value

$$E_{\text{rot}}(J) = \frac{\hbar^2}{2\mathscr{I}} J(J+1). \tag{4.13}$$

In this expression, $\mathscr{I}$ is a moment of inertia, connected with the angular momentum and angular velocity of rotation by the formula

$$\mathscr{I}\omega = |\boldsymbol{J}| = \sqrt{[J(J+1)]}\hbar. \tag{4.14}$$

When there is intrinsic angular momentum (K finite) the expression for the rotational energy becomes more complicated because of the need (a) to combine the rotational ($\boldsymbol{R}$) and intrinsic ($K\hbar$) angular momenta to yield $\boldsymbol{J}$ and (b) to consider the effect of Coriolis forces in the rotating system on the intrinsic motion. The full formulae are given in reference 6, p. 33, but an approximate expression is readily obtained from figure 4.9 which suggests that

$$|\boldsymbol{R}|^2 = |\boldsymbol{J}|^2 - K^2\hbar^2 = [J(J+1) - K^2]\hbar^2 \tag{4.15}$$

so that the rotational energy becomes

$$E_{\text{rot}}(I) = \frac{\hbar^2}{2\mathscr{I}}[J(J+1) - K^2] \tag{4.16}$$

with $J \geqslant K$.

Equations (4.13) and (4.16) show that as energy and angular momentum are supplied by a nuclear process to the collective rotation, without affecting the intrinsic motion, J increases and defines a *rotational or deformation-aligned band* of states, characterized by a specific K value, which may be half-integral or integral, including zero. In a complex nuclear spectrum of states there may be several bands including states of the same spin and it is useful in analysis to pick out from these the one of lowest energy for each spin J. These are called the *yrast* states. We comment now on three particular types of rotational band.

(a) For *even–even nuclei in their ground state* the individual particles are paired and fall alternately into states of opposite K, so that the resultant K value is zero with even parity. Because of the symmetry about a plane perpendicular to Oz', only even-J values occur (as in the case of the homonuclear diatomic molecule obeying Bose statistics) and the spin-parity values for the rotational band are

$$(K^P = 0^+) \qquad J^P = 0^+, 2^+, 4^+, 6^+ \ldots. \tag{4.17}$$

The total angular momentum arises solely from the collective rotation. Clearly defined rotational bands are found in even–even nuclei with N and Z values lying within the deformed regions of the N–Z diagram and a well-known rotational band is shown in figure 4.10. The levels of the band may be excited electromagnetically (Coulomb excitation, section 6.6.2) and decay mainly by the emission of electric quadrupole radiation (chapter 5). The ratios of excitation energies in a rotational band are (from (4.16) with $K = J_g = 0$) $E_4/E_2 = 10/3$, $E_6/E_2 = 7$, $E_8/E_2 = 12$, independently of the moment of inertia, provided that this is independent of rotational frequency.

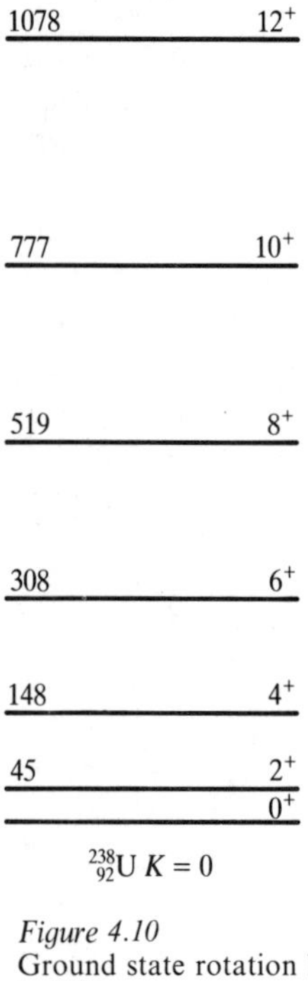

Figure 4.10
Ground state rotation band in ^{238}U.

The actual value of the effective moment of inertia $\mathscr{I}$ is model dependent. If the nucleus behaved as a rigid object of mass Am where A is the number of component nucleons of mass m then the classical rigid body value

$$\mathscr{I}_{\text{rig}} = \tfrac{2}{5}AmR^2 \tag{4.18}$$

where R is a mean radius would be found by analysis of the spacings in the rotational band. It can be shown that this rigid body value is also obtained in the shell model with wholly independent particle motion. The pairing correlation, however, inhibits this independence and the motion then exhibits a lower moment of inertia; observed values are, in fact, smaller than the rigid value by a factor of two to three for low J values.

If the data from a rotational band are analysed to determine the moment of inertia as a function of frequency of rotation, a plot of the sort shown in figure 4.11 is often obtained. This shows first an increase of $\mathscr{I}$ with ω which can be understood in terms of centrifugal stretching, but then a spectacular behaviour known as *back bending* in which there is a sharp increase in $\mathscr{I}$ towards the rigid body value. This phenomenon is connected with the Coriolis forces in the rotating system which act in opposite directions on the oppositely moving nucleons of a pair. This destroys the pair correlation step by step as the rotational frequency increases and part of the total angular momentum of the nucleus then comes from quantum mechanical alignment of the unpaired single-particle angular momentum vectors along the rotation axis. This produces a set of states known as a *rotation-aligned band* with a spacing pattern significantly different from that in the deformation-aligned band. It is the crossing of these two bands in a plot such as that of figure 4.11 that leads to the back bending appearance.

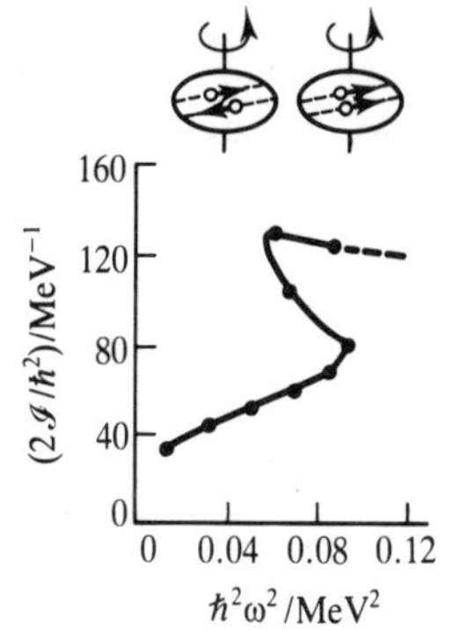

Figure 4.11
Collective moment of inertia as a function of angular velocity squared for $^{158}_{68}$Er (Grosse E *et al.* 1973 *Phys Rev Lett* **31** (840)). The insets show the alignment of a pair of nucleons at the back-bend.

(b) In *even–even nuclei with an excitation* (other than one of zero spin) from the intrinsic motion or from vibration, and in *odd-A nuclei*, K is finite and there is no need to exclude states as in the case of $K = 0$. The energy levels have spin values given by

$$(K \neq 0) \qquad J = K,\ K+1,\ K+2 \tag{4.19}$$

and these are integral for A even and half-integral for A odd. The parity is that of the intrinsic motion.

(c) In some nuclei in which normal rotational bands are found, extending to spins as high as about $40\hbar$, a small fraction of rotational excitations are found to populate a *superdeformed* band, whose levels extend to even higher spin values. An outstanding example is the even–even nucleus $^{152}_{66}$Dy in which a regular series of enhanced electric quadrupole γ ray lines (figure 4.12), observed with escape-suppressed spectrometers, is seen using the reaction ^{108}Pd(^{48}Ca, 4n)^{152}Dy. The corresponding levels have spins from $22\hbar$ to $60\hbar$ which corresponds with an excitation of about 30 MeV in the nucleus and must be close to the limit of stability against fission. The moment of inertia deduced from the lines of this band is considerably greater than that expected for a rigid spherical nucleus with $A = 152$, and suggests that the nucleus is behaving as a classical rigid ellipsoid with a deformation more than double that usually found. A ratio of two to one between the long and short axes of the ellipsoid is suggested

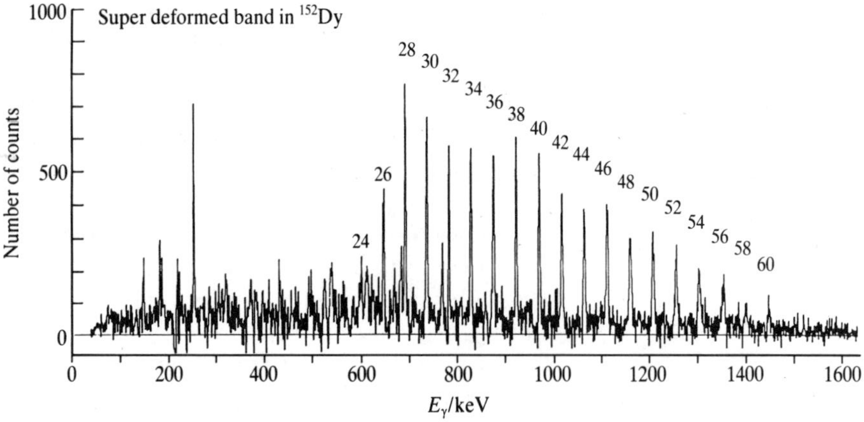

Figure 4.12 Superdeformation in $^{152}_{66}$Dy. The 'picket fence' spectrum corresponds to transitions down the superdeformed rotational band (Twin P J *et al.* 1986 *Phys Rev Lett* **57** (811); courtesy of Professor Twin and the Daresbury Laboratory).

and this is to be understood theoretically on the basis of the interplay between single-particle and collective degrees of freedom (cf. section 4.4).

Static and transition moments

If the shape of an ellipsoidal nucleus is specified by a parameter δ where

$$\delta = \frac{\Delta R}{R_0} \tag{4.20}$$

with R_0 the average nuclear radius and ΔR the difference between the major and minor axes, then the intrinsic quadrupole moment Q_0 is given by

$$Q_0 = \tfrac{4}{5} Z R^2 \delta. \tag{4.21}$$

The spectroscopically observed quadrupole moment in the state (J, K) is

$$Q_J = \frac{3K^2 - J(J+1)}{(J+1)(2J+3)} Q_0$$

which becomes, for the lowest state $K = J$ of the band, which may be the ground state,

$$Q_J = \frac{J(2J-1)}{(J+1)(2J+3)} Q_0. \tag{4.22}$$

The difference between Q_J and Q_0 arises because of averaging of the direction of the nuclear axis by the rotational motion. For $J = 0$ and $\frac{1}{2}$,

Q_J vanishes but Q_0 may still exist. The Q_0 values obtained experimentally in this way are about ten times the single-particle value (section 3.6) in the rare-earth region and suggest δ values of about 0.3.

The states of a rotational band are connected by electric quadrupole radiation in even-N, even-Z nuclei and additionally by magnetic dipole radiation for odd-mass nuclei. The radiative probability depends on Q_0^2 and the corresponding transition moments are sometimes about 100 times the single-particle value (section 5.1.2).

Magnetic moments are better predicted by the collective model than by the SPSM.

4.4 *Single-particle motion in a deformed potential*

The essential idea of the collective model is to connect the motion of the nucleons outside a closed shell with that of the remaining core. In preceding paragraphs the main concern has been to describe the resulting spectrum of collective excitations. Here we shall briefly consider a complementary problem, namely the motion of a nucleon in a deformed potential in which neither j nor l is a good quantum number.

A phenomenological potential of the form

$$V = \tfrac{1}{2}m[\omega_3^2 x_3^2 + \omega_\perp^2(x_1^2 + x_2^2)] + V_{ll}(l^2 - C_l) + V_{ls}\boldsymbol{l}\cdot\boldsymbol{s} \qquad (4.23)$$

was first used by Nilsson to calculate the single-particle energies. In this, x_1, x_2 and x_3 are Cartesian coordinates for the deformed nucleus, Ox_3 being the symmetry axis earlier lettered Oz' while ω_3 and $\omega_\perp$ are axial and transverse oscillation frequencies and differ for a non-spherical field. The term in l^2 removes the oscillator degeneracy within each major shell and the constant C_l is included to preserve the spacing between shells. The deformation of the field is proportional to $\omega_\perp - \omega_3$.

The quantum numbers used to label the states in this anisotropic oscillator field are

$N = n_3 + n_\perp$, the sum of the oscillator numbers for the two orthogonal vibrations

n_3, the oscillator number of the axial vibration

Λ, the component of the orbital angular momentum of the particle along the symmetry axis

Ω, the component of the total angular momentum j along the symmetry axis. It is the K previously used in the discussion of rotational states.

Together, N, n_3, Λ and Ω are known as *asymptotic quantum numbers* since they apply in the limit of large deformations when the conventional n, l, j, Ω scheme is invalid. States with opposite values of Ω are

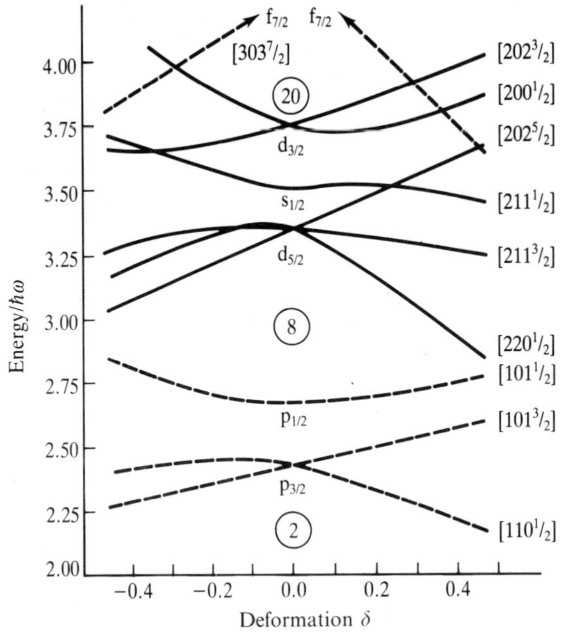

Figure 4.13 Spectrum of single-particle orbits in spheroidal potential ($N, Z < 20$, from Bohr A and Mottelson B 1975 *Nuclear Structure II* Benjamin). The level energies are in units of the oscillator spacing (equation (4.4)) and are plotted as a function of the deformation parameter δ (equation (4.20)). The individual labels are the asymptotic quantum numbers (section 4.4).

degenerate in a first approximation so that for a shell-model level of angular momentum j there are $\frac{1}{2}(2j + 1)$ Nilsson states, each containing two particles. As mentioned in the case of rotation-aligned bands, Coriolis forces remove this degeneracy and the number of states is then doubled.

A spectrum of single-particle orbits as a function of deformation is shown for $N, Z < 20$ in figure 4.13. For zero deformation one recovers the familiar magic numbers of the SPSM. More comprehensive plots of this type show new regions of stability at high (super) deformation.

For deformed nuclei the Nilsson levels should be used instead of those of the spherical shell model, and it then often happens that an apparently anomalous spin value can be understood in terms of a particular deformation. Rotational bands are built on the Nilsson states as already indicated (section 4.3.2) in discussion of the intrinsic and rotational motion.

REFERENCES 4

1 **Brown G E** 1967 *The Unified Theory of Nuclear Models and Forces* North-Holland

2 **Preston M A and Bhadhuri R K** 1975 *Structure of the Nucleus* Addison-Wesley

3 **Mayer M G and Jensen J H D** 1955 *The Elementary Theory of Nuclear Shell Structure* Wiley

4 **Elliott J P and Lane A M** 1957 'The nuclear shell model' *Encyclopedia of Physics* **39** Springer

5 **Rowe D J** 1957 *Nuclear Collective Motion* Methuen

6 **Bohr A and Mottelson B** 1975 *Nuclear Structure II* Benjamin

7 **Hodgson P E** 1987 'Superdeformed nuclei' *Contemp Phys* **28** (365)

8 **Newton J O** 1989 'Spinning nuclei' *Contemp Phys* **30** (277)

9 **Wambach J** 1991 'Nuclear sound' *Contemp Phys* **32** (291)

10 **Satchler G R** 1974 'New giant resonances in nuclei' *Physics Reports* **14C** (98)

11 **Bertrand F E** 1975 'Excitation of giant multipole resonances through inelastic electron scattering' *Ann Rev Nucl Sci* **26** (475)

EXAMPLES 4

4.1 Calculate the potential energy of a proton and an electron separated by a distance of 10^{-14} m. [0.14 MeV]

4.2 Using the relativistic relation between monentum and energy find the minimum kinetic energy of (a) an electron, (b) a proton confined within a dimension of 7×10^{-15} m (assume $\Delta p \times \Delta r = \hbar$). [28 MeV, 0.42 MeV]

4.3 Write down the expected odd-particle configuration of the following nuclei: $^{27}_{13}$Al; $^{29}_{14}$Si; $^{40}_{19}$K; $^{93}_{41}$Nb; $^{157}_{64}$Gd. [$d_{5/2}$; $s_{1/2}$; $d_{3/2} + f_{7/2}$; $g_{9/2}$; $h_{9/2}$]

4.4 Predict the spin-parity of the first excited state of the nuclei $^{31}_{14}$Si, $^{41}_{19}$K and $^{49}_{21}$Sc. [$\frac{7}{2}^-, \frac{7}{2}^-, \frac{3}{2}^-$] Comment on the fact that the observed values are $\frac{1}{2}^+, \frac{1}{2}^+, \frac{3}{2}^+$.

4.5 From the equation $\boldsymbol{j} = \boldsymbol{l} + \boldsymbol{s}$ for a single particle in an eigenstate of the operators $\hat{j}, \hat{l}, \hat{s}$, obtain the value of the quantity $(\boldsymbol{l} \cdot \boldsymbol{s})$ and show that the energy separation of a nucleon spin–orbit doublet is proportional to $2l + 1$. For the case $l = 1$, $j = \frac{3}{2}$, what is the angle between l and j? [24°]

4.6 The low-lying levels of $^{39}_{20}$Ca have spin-parity values, starting from the ground state, of $\frac{3}{2}^+, \frac{1}{2}^+, \frac{7}{2}^-$ and $\frac{3}{2}^-$. Interpret these values on the basis of the SPSM.

4.7 Calculate the ground-state magnetic moment of ^{7}Li, ^{39}K and ^{45}Sc using equations (3.20) and (3.21). The spin values are $\frac{3}{2}, \frac{3}{2}, \frac{7}{2}$ respectively. [3.79, 0.12, 5.79μ_N]

4.8 Consider two masses m bound together with an equilibrium separation R. Estimate the order of magnitude of the lowest rotational frequency of the system and compare it with the vibrational frequency due to a vibrational amplitude βR. [$\omega_v/\omega_r \approx 1/\beta^2$]

4.9 A rotational band based on the state $K = \frac{7}{2}^-$ is known in $^{179}_{74}$W. The $\frac{9}{2}^-$ state is at an excitation of 120 keV; predict the excitations of the $\frac{11}{2}^-$, $\frac{13}{2}^-$ and $\frac{15}{2}^-$ levels. [267 keV, 440 keV, 640 keV]

4.10 The nucleus $^{234}_{92}$U has levels of spin-parity 0^+, 2^+, 4^+, 6^+, 8^+ at energies of 0, 44, 143, 296 and 500 keV. Show that these form a rotational band, predict the energy of the 10^+ state [764 keV] and check the variation of the moment of inertia of the nucleus with rotational frequency. Compare the moment of inertia with the rigid body value.

4.11 Taking the nuclear density in the shell model to have the radial dependence given by the (Woods–Saxon) expression

$$\rho = \frac{\rho_0}{1 + \exp(r - R)/a}$$

obtain an expression for the spin–orbit potential V_{so}. Using the results of example 4.5, verify qualitatively the conclusions illustrated in figure 4.4.

4.12 The observed spin of $^{23}_{11}$Na is $\frac{3}{2}^+$. What are the predictions for this quantity of (a) the SPSM (figure 4.5) and (b) the Nilsson model (figure 4.13) with a deformation parameter of about $+0.1$?

5 *Decay of unstable nuclei*

Electromagnetic transitions · β decay · α decay · Spontaneous fission decay

Previous chapters have been largely concerned with the static properties of nuclei and the models that have been developed to describe them. We turn now to nuclear dynamics, which seeks to understand not only the way in which unstable nuclei *decay* into more stable systems but also the mechanism by which nuclei *interact* with one another in reaction processes.

The familiar types of decay found among the radioactive nuclei are examples of the operation of three fundamental natural forces, the strong interaction (e.g. α decay), the weak interaction (e.g. β decay) and the electromagnetic interaction (e.g. γ decay). These forces will be fully discussed in Part II of this book; here we note that (i) the strong and weak forces are of a range comparable with or less than nuclear dimensions, whereas the electromagnetic force is of infinite range, and (ii) the strength of these forces between say a pair of protons is in the following order: strong, electromagnetic, weak. Phenomenologically we observe that in α decay and in the somewhat similar fission process (section 5.4) a nucleus just divides into two parts, whereas in β and γ decay new radiations are emitted.

In nuclear reactions we need to take account chiefly of the strong and electromagnetic force, though weak reactions* such as $p + p \to d + e^+ + \nu_e$ are of extreme importance astrophysically. It will be seen in Part II that the force field for each interaction may be quantized and that a field quantum may be postulated in each case. For the strong interaction there are the gluons, for the weak interaction the vector bosons and for

---

* In order to conform with usage in Part II of this book we here give the antineutrino a suffix e to denote its association with an electron process.

the Coulomb field there is the photon. We shall start with the last, because the electromagnetic interaction is both familiar and well understood, and its expression in the formalism of quantum electrodynamics (QED) has been of great importance for the rest of physics. The formulae for decay rates contain the strength of the appropriate fundamental interaction, a nuclear *matrix element* connecting initial and final states through the interaction operator and some energy-dependent factors. If these last 'external' factors are calculated, observed lifetimes lead to useful information on the more basic quantities.

The stability convention used in particle physics (section 3.2.3) will not be rigorously applied to the β and γ decays discussed in this chapter; we shall regard all ordinary radioactive nuclei, and all excited nuclei produced in nuclear reactions, as *unstable*.

5.1 Electromagnetic transitions[1–5]

5.1.1 General properties and selection rules

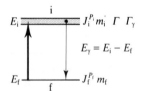

In nuclear physics the absorption or emission of radiation normally connects two nuclear levels. Both of these levels may be unstable but often the lower state is the ground state of a nucleus and then the radiative processes can be discussed in terms of figure 5.1 which indicates the relevant energies and quantum numbers as already given in part in figure 1.6.

i
E_i
$J_i^{P_i} m_i$ Γ Γ_γ
$E_\gamma = E_i - E_f$
E_f
$J_f^{P_f} m_f$
f
Excitation Decay

Figure 5.1
Emission of radiation from a level of width Γ and radiative width Γ_γ. The converse excitation between the levels is also shown.

The probability of absorption or of emission of a photon of the correct energy E_γ depends on (a) the energy E_γ itself, (b) the number of units $\hbar$ of angular momentum transferred in the process, also known as the *multipolarity*, and (c) the matrix element, which is constructed from the wavefunctions for the two levels using the appropriate electromagnetic multipole operator. Experimentally the multipolarity L is determined by conversion or angular correlation phenomena (sections 5.1.3 and 5.1.5) and the transition probability $T(L)$ may then be predicted from detailed nuclear models.

The multipolarity possible for a radiative transition is limited by *selection rules*, based on the conservation of angular momentum. With quantities as defined in figure 5.1 these rules are

$$\begin{aligned} J_i + J_f \geqslant L \geqslant |J_i - J_f| \\ m_i = M + m_f \end{aligned} \tag{5.1}$$

where $M\hbar$ is the resolved part of the photon total angular momentum $\boldsymbol{L}$. Parity is also conserved in the electromagnetic interaction to a high degree of accuracy, but a given multipole field may be of even or odd parity as shown in table 5.1. The names electric and magnetic derive from the

Table 5.1
Classification of radiative transitions

	Type of radiation		
	E1	E2 M1	E3 M2
Name	Electric dipole	Electric quadrupole Magnetic dipole	Electric octupole Magnetic quadrupole
Multipolarity	1	2,1	3,2
Parity change	Yes	No	Yes

semiclassical theory of radiation, in which a radiation field arises because of the time variation of a charge and current distribution. Monopole transitions, e.g. E0, do not exist in the real radiation field; the E0 giant resonance (chapter 4) is excited by particles or by 'virtual' photons with longitudinal field components. If $J_i = J_f = 0$ radiation as such is *strictly forbidden.*

The radiative transition probability T is the reciprocal of the mean life τ_γ of the level concerned for the emission of radiation and is connected with the radiative width Γ_γ of the upper level (figure 5.1) by the equation already introduced in section 3.10, namely

$$T = \frac{1}{\tau_\gamma} = \frac{\Gamma_\gamma}{\hbar} \tag{5.2a}$$

or

$$\tau_\gamma \Gamma_\gamma = \hbar = 6.6 \times 10^{-16}\ \text{eV s}. \tag{5.2b}$$

The total level width Γ, as used in equation (3.28), is greater than Γ_γ because of internal conversion (section 5.3.1) for bound levels and because of particle emission for unbound states.

If neither J_i nor J_f is zero, transitions of mixed multipolarity, e.g. M1 + E2, may occur. The multipole mixing ratio δ, given for example by

$$\delta^2 = \frac{\Gamma_\gamma(\text{E2})}{\Gamma_\gamma(\text{M1})} \tag{5.3}$$

can be obtained from conversion coefficients (section 5.1.3) or angular correlation experiments (section 5.1.5).

5.1.2 The lifetime–energy relation: nuclear isomerism

An expression for the radiative transition probability for a given multipolarity may be obtained both by semiclassical radiation theory, which deals with a system of oscillating charges and currents, and by use of the time-dependent perturbation theory of quantum mechanics. In both approaches simplification arises if a *long-wavelength approximation* is valid, namely that the emitted wavelength (λ) is much larger than the dimensions of the radiating system (R). If this is true, as it is in most cases in low energy nuclear physics, then the total radiative probability can be expressed in principle as a series of terms of increasing multipolarity and of diminishing intensity. For multipolarity L the transition probability is

$$T_{\mathrm{fi}}(L) = \frac{1}{\tau_\gamma} = \frac{1}{4\pi\epsilon_0} \frac{8\pi(L+1)}{L[(2L+1)!!]^2} \frac{1}{\hbar} \left(\frac{E_\gamma}{\hbar c}\right)^{2L+1} B_{\mathrm{fi}}(L) \tag{5.4}$$

where $B_{\mathrm{fi}}(L)$, sometimes written $B(L)\downarrow$ to signify an emission process, is the *reduced transition probability* and is the 'internal' factor containing nuclear information. It is essentially the square of the matrix element of the appropriate multipole operator averaged over the $2J_{\mathrm{i}} + 1$ substates m_{i} and summed over the accessible substates m_{f}. For electric transitions $B(L)$ is measured in the units $e^2\,\mathrm{fm}^{2L}$ and for magnetic transitions in $(\mu_{\mathrm{N}}/c)^2\,\mathrm{fm}^{2L-2}$, where μ_{N} is the nuclear magneton.

In some experiments such as Coulomb excitation (section 6.6.2) the upward probability $B_{\mathrm{if}}(L)$ or $B(L)\uparrow$ is measured. This has the same matrix element and is thus related to $B(L)\downarrow$ according to the definition by the formula

$$(2J_{\mathrm{i}} + 1)B_{\mathrm{fi}}(L) = (2J_{\mathrm{f}} + 1)B_{\mathrm{if}}(L). \tag{5.5}$$

For practical purposes it is convenient to introduce an estimate of the quantity B_{fi} so that a lifetime–energy relation may be established. The *Weisskopf formula* is based on the *single-particle shell model* and assumes radiation to result from the transition of a single proton from an initial orbital state to a final state of zero orbital angular momentum. The resulting reduced transition probabilities are

$$B(\mathrm{E}L) = \frac{e^2}{4\pi}\left(\frac{3R^L}{L+3}\right)^2 \quad \text{for electric radiation} \tag{5.6a}$$

and

$$B(\mathrm{M}L) = 10\left(\frac{\hbar}{m_{\mathrm{p}}cR}\right)^2 B(\mathrm{E}L) \quad \text{for magnetic radiation} \tag{5.6b}$$

where R is of the order of magnitude of the nuclear radius. The factor 10 in $B(\mathrm{M}L)$ is introduced to allow for magnetic radiation originating from reorientation of intrinsic spins. The lifetime–energy relations based on these estimates have been very widely used; they are shown in figure 5.2 for the particular case of $A = 100$. The formulae also give *single-particle radiative*

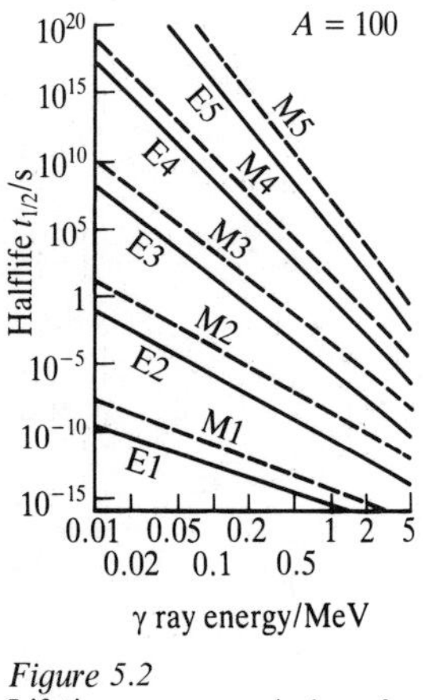

Figure 5.2
Lifetime–energy relations for γ radiation according to the single-particle formula of Weisskopf, for a nucleus of mass number $A = 100$.

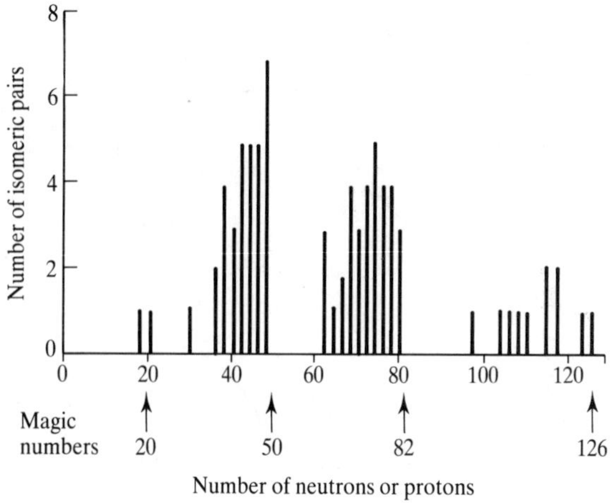

Figure 5.3 Frequency distribution of isomeric nuclei of odd A, from R. D. Evans (1955 *The Atomic Nucleus* McGraw-Hill).

widths, sometimes called 'Weisskopf units', directly, e.g.

$$\Gamma_\gamma(\mathrm{E1}) = 0.07E_\gamma^3 A^{2/3}$$
$$\Gamma_\gamma(\mathrm{M1}) = 0.021E_\gamma^3 \tag{5.7}$$
$$\Gamma_\gamma(\mathrm{E2}) = 4.9 \times 10^{-8} A^{4/3} E_\gamma^5$$

where Γ_γ is the radiative width in electronvolts, E_γ the transition energy in mega-electronvolts and A the mass number of the nucleus. If the nuclear core participates in the radiative process, collective motion of particles gives radiative widths that are much larger than the single-particle value.

Figure 5.2 shows that electromagnetic transitions of high multipolarity and low energy are relatively slow processes. Excited levels of nuclei which can only decay by such transitions may therefore have a long life on a nuclear time scale, say $t_{1/2} > 10^{-6}$ s and nuclei excited to these levels are said to be *isomeric* with respect to their ground state. Nuclear isomerism is found in groups of nuclei located just below the major shell closures at Z, $N = 50$, 82 and 126 as shown in figure 5.3. This is immediately understood on the single-particle shell model (section 4.2) because, as may be seen from figure 4.5, levels of quite different spin, such as $J = \frac{1}{2}, \frac{9}{2}$ or $\frac{3}{2}, \frac{11}{2}$, may lie quite close together for $N, Z > 20$ and may occur as low-lying states, leading to isomerism, as in ${}^{137}_{56}\mathrm{Ba}^{\mathrm{m}}$ (figure 5.4) which has 81 neutrons. Isomeric decay usually shows strong internal conversion (section 5.1.3).

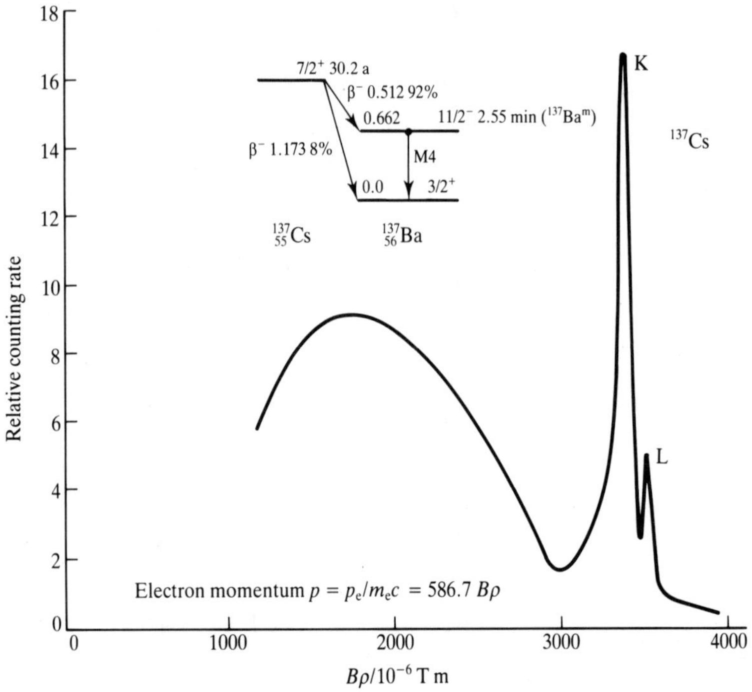

Figure 5.4 Sketch of electron spectrum seen in a simple 180° spectrometer of the β decay electrons from ^{137}Cs, together with K and L internal conversion electrons from the 0.662 MeV isomeric transition in ^{137}Ba^{m}. The decay scheme is shown, with energies in mega-electronvolts. The K and L vacancies lead to X-ray and Auger electron emission from the Ba atom.

5.1.3 Internal conversion[1–3, 6–8]

Since atomic wavefunctions have finite amplitude at or near the nucleus it is possible for nuclear excitation energy to be removed by the ejection of an atomic electron. This competing process is not sequential to γ decay but alternative to it, and if its probability per unit time is $\Gamma_e/\hbar$ then the total decay width for the transition is

$$\Gamma = \Gamma_e + \Gamma_\gamma. \tag{5.8}$$

Internal conversion electrons appear in a magnetic spectrum as homogeneous lines of kinetic energy

$$E_e = E_\gamma - B \tag{5.9}$$

where B is the binding energy of the electron ejected, and are often superimposed upon the continuous distribution arising from an associated β decay (section 5.2.1). Figure 5.4 gives a familiar example.

The *internal conversion coefficient* α for a particular transition is defined by the ratio of intensities of electrons and photons,

$$\alpha = \frac{\Gamma_e}{\Gamma_\gamma} \tag{5.10}$$

and it may be split up into partial coefficients relating to all the contributing atomic shells:

$$\alpha = \alpha_K + \alpha_L + \alpha_M + \cdots. \tag{5.11}$$

Usually K conversion is favoured because of the high K-electron density near the nucleus. The vacancy left in one of the atomic shells by the electron emission leads to characteristic X-ray or Auger electron emission (section 2.1.4) as the atom returns to its neutral state.

Extensive tables of K- and L-conversion coefficients now exist. They are especially useful in the case of heavy elements and low transition energies because then there is good discrimination between different multipolarities, although conversion coefficients decrease with increasing γ ray energy. For higher energies ($E_\gamma > 1.02$ MeV) internal conversion with the emission of a positron–electron pair is an additional mode of decay and the probability of this process *increases* with transition energy.

Internal conversion is the main mode of decay for the E0 monopole transition between states of zero spin, and in such cases (e.g. in RaC′, 1.414 MeV) we speak of *total internal conversion.*

5.1.4 Determination of transition probabilities[5,9]

If the time of formation of a nuclear excited state can be defined by an appropriate signal and if a further signal is obtained from the radiative decay itself, the probability of an interval between t and $t + \mathrm{d}t$ separating the two signals is

$$\mathrm{d}P = \mathrm{e}^{-t/\tau_\gamma} \frac{\mathrm{d}t}{\tau_\gamma}$$

where τ_γ is the radiative mean lifetime (equation (5.2)). In the *delayed coincidence* method of lifetime determination the time distribution of coincidences between a delayed start signal and the decay pulse yields τ_γ; the method has been used for τ_γ down to 10^{-11} s.

For shorter lifetimes a time scale may be set by the motion of an excited nucleus after excitation in a nuclear reaction. In the *recoil distance* method (RDM), which is usable for the range $\tau_\gamma \approx 10^{-7}$–$10^{-12}$ s, the distribution of decay points along the path of the moving nucleus is examined using

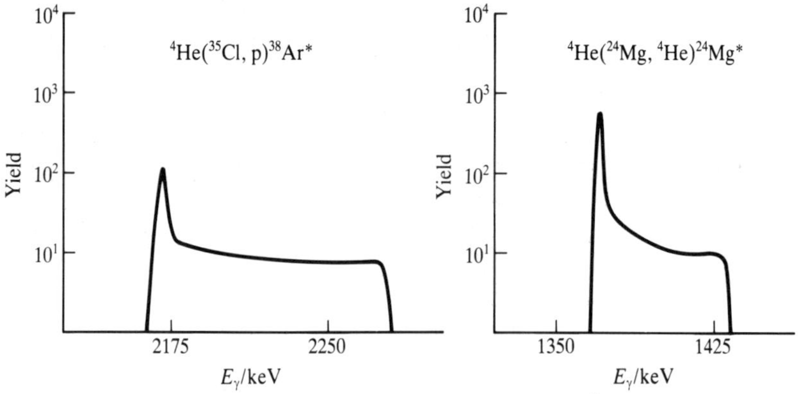

Figure 5.5 Measurement of the lifetime of the 2168 keV state in ^{38}Ar and of the 1368 keV state in ^{24}Mg by DSAM, line-shape analysis. Lifetimes of 0.72×10^{-12} s and 1.82×10^{-12} s (± 7 per cent) were deduced (adapted from Forster J S *et al.* 1974 *Phys Lett* **51B** (133)).

suitable collimating arrangements. An elegant version of this method employs a Ge(Li) detector to observe radiation emitted (a) from the moving nucleus, showing a Doppler shift of energy, and (b) from a *plunger* set at a known distance from the target, showing an unshifted line because the nucleus has been brought to rest. The lifetime is deduced from the ratio of shifted to unshifted intensity. For even shorter lifetimes, $\tau_\gamma \approx 10^{-11}$–$10^{-14}$ s, the *Doppler shift attenuation* method (DSAM) is used. In this the time scale is set by the slowing-down time α of the moving ion in an absorber; if $\tau_\gamma \approx \alpha$ the detected radiation shows a distribution of shifts from whose centroid τ_γ may be deduced using stopping-power information. For $\tau_\gamma \ll \alpha$ the full shift is found and for $\tau_\gamma \gg \alpha$ there is of course no shift at all. Detailed analysis of the Doppler-broadened line shape may be used in favourable cases, such as those shown in figure 5.5 for a transition in ^{38}Ar.

The foregoing methods all fail for $\tau_\gamma < 10^{-15}$ s but then, as equation (5.2) shows, an equivalent method of obtaining the transition probability is to measure a radiative width Γ_γ. A general method is *Coulomb excitation* (section 6.6.2) in which a nucleus is excited to the level i (figure 5.1) by the electric field of a fast charged particle, preferably a proton or heavy ion. The cross-section for the process depends on the upward transition probability (equation (5.5)) and an absolute measurement of the intensity of the radiation E_γ yields this quantity. Coulomb excitation is in principle possible using electrons but in practice it is difficult to observe as an emission process because of the presence of bremsstrahlung quanta. The *inelastically scattered electrons*, however, may be observed with good discrimination against background at large angles of scattering and peaks in their spectrum corresponding with the excitation of the lower excited levels of the target nuclei may be identified. Again the upward transition probability is found from an absolute measurement. Inelastic electron scattering, in contrast with Coulomb excitation, is able to excite monopole transitions; it is also used in particle physics to excite nucleon resonances (chapter 12).

Often the level i may be excited in a nuclear reaction by the capture of a charged particle or neutron and then the theory of resonance reactions (section 6.3.2) shows how Γ_γ may be obtained from the radiative cross-section and the variation of yield with energy. A special case arises when the exciting particle is actually a photon, originating from the downward transition i → f itself. In optics, resonant absorption of this photon, producing the upward transition f → i, is readily observed but at the much larger nuclear energies resonance is destroyed because the recoil energy conveyed freely to both source and absorber atoms is much greater than the natural line width and usually greater than the Doppler broadened width for a practical source. The recoil energy loss, which amounts overall to E_γ^2/mc^2 where m is the mass of the source and absorber atoms, can be restored by mechanical or thermal means and *nuclear resonant scattering* can then be used to obtain Γ_γ.

Recoil energy loss in a γ ray resonant scattering experiment can be eliminated in certain cases. It was discovered by Mössbauer in 1958 that the radiation from a source of ^{191}Ir contained a line of natural width $\Gamma_\gamma \approx 10^{-5}$ eV as well as the expected Doppler-broadened distribution corresponding to the source temperature. Moreover the line was *unshifted* because for photon energies less than about 200 keV the recoil energy is imparted to the source as a whole and not to an individual atom. The *Mössbauer effect*[10] has been observed in many nuclei, but the limitation to low transition energies is rather restrictive. In nuclear physics the high resolution available ($\Gamma_\gamma/E_\gamma \approx 10^{-13}$) has been exploited mainly in the measurement of nuclear moments and *isomer shifts* which arise because of the difference in mean square radius of nuclear ground and excited states. These shifts may be seen in a resonant absorption experiment if the electron density at the Mössbauer nuclei differs between source and absorber. In Mössbauer resonant scattering exact resonance can sometimes be destroyed by the Doppler shift due to motion of the source with velocities as low as a few millimetres per second.

5.1.5 *Angular correlation*[1]

The transitions shown in figure 5.1 actually take place between individual magnetic substates of the two levels i and f, but energy differences are not normally perceptible except under special conditions such as those offered by the Mössbauer effect. Each transition between substates has its own characteristic angular distribution of intensity with respect to an axis of quantization, as is clear from the semiclassical theory with its oscillating moments. If all the magnetic substates of the initial state i are

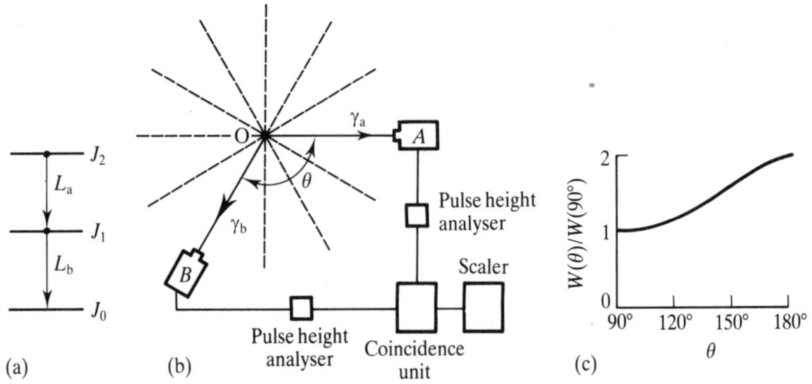

Figure 5.6
Angular correlation of successive radiations from a radioactive nucleus at O: (a) decay scheme; (b) counters; (c) correlation pattern.

equally populated in an assembly of nuclei there is random orientation effectively and an isotropic distribution of radiation intensity with respect to the axis. If on the other hand the population is rendered non-uniform, perhaps by a previous transition in cascade with the transition i → f or even by brute-force orientation, then the angular distribution is non-uniform. In a cascade an angular correlation then develops between the directions of emission of successive quanta and this is an important means of determining multipolarity.

A typical angular correlation experiment is represented in figure 5.6.

5.2 β *decay*[1–3, 11–13]

5.2.1 *General properties ('classical' period)*

In contrast with electromagnetic forces the weak forces of nuclear physics are of short range, certainly less than nuclear dimensions, and are therefore not apparent as a property of matter in bulk. Recognition of the weak interaction as a fundamental natural process had to await the advent of nuclear physics.

The main properties of nuclear β decay were established by experiments with naturally occurring radioactive elements (section 1.1). By 1934 the production of positron emitters in (α, *n*) reactions had been demonstrated by Curie and Joliot and Fermi had formulated what is still the theory of β decay, using Pauli's concept of the neutrino. The objective demonstration of the existence of this particle may be said to complete the 'classical' period of β decay studies. What followed set the nuclear process firmly within the framework of a universal weak interaction and will be examined later in chapter 11.

The emission of positive or negative electrons from nuclei and the process of electron capture determine stability limits for nuclei throughout

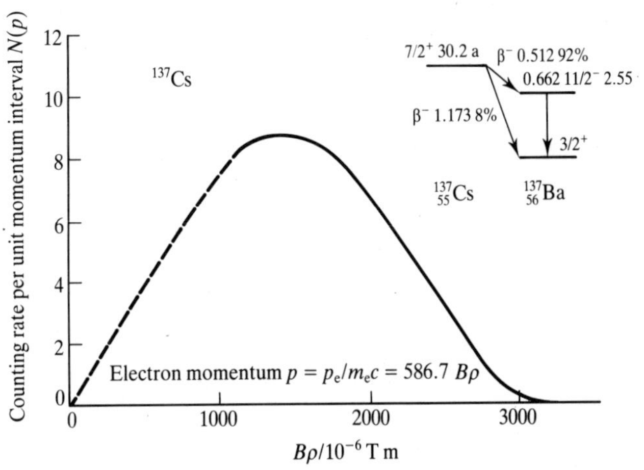

Figure 5.7 The β spectrum. The full line is the continuous electron momentum distribution obtained from figure 5.4 by removing the internal conversion lines and the yield due to the high energy transition. The ordinate $N(p)$ is proportional to the counting rate shown in figure 5.4 divided at each point by the momentum to allow for spectrometer acceptance. The Auger electron spectrum at low momenta is not shown.

the periodic system (section 3.2.3). The processes change the atomic number by ± 1, e.g. in the decay of radioactive sodium-22 ($t_{1/2} = 15.4$ h) with energy release Q (written Q_β in section 3.2.3),

$$^{22}_{11}\text{Na} \rightarrow {}^{22}_{10}\text{Ne} + \text{e}^+ + \nu_\text{e} + Q \tag{5.12}$$

stable neon is formed and the chemical identity of both the active nucleus and its decay product have been verified. For this positron emission $Q = Q_\beta = \Delta M - 2M_\text{e}$ in accordance with equation (3.9a). The decay electrons or positrons that originate in a process such as (5.12) have a *continuous distribution of energies or momenta*, as first established by Chadwick (1919) and as shown in figure 5.7. The upper limit of the energy spectrum corresponds closely with the value predicted for $Q = Q_\beta$ from the mass change (^{22}Na $\rightarrow$ ^{22}Ne in (5.12) or ^{137}Cs $\rightarrow$ ^{137}Ba$^\text{m}$ in figure 5.7) so that the mass of the neutrino (section 5.2.2) must lie within the experimental error of the best of the measurements (≈ 500 eV); a closer limit will be discussed in section 5.2.3. The homogeneous lines observed in many β spectra (and shown in figure 5.4) are due to internal conversion of γ rays present in the decay and are not directly connected with the β decay process.

The *upper limit of the spectrum* of distintegration electrons or positrons is not accurately obtainable from the direct spectrum, figure 5.7, but from an expression provided by the Fermi theory a linear plot known as the *Fermi–Kurie plot* (figure 5.8) may be obtained, using the electron kinetic energy T as a variable. This extrapolates to the upper limit which is equal to Q, apart from a small recoil correction, if the neutrino mass is zero.

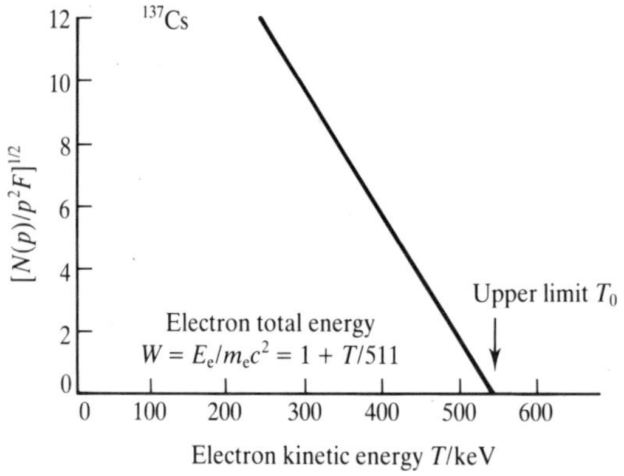

Figure 5.8 Fermi–Kurie plot to determine the endpoint of a β spectrum. The ordinate is derived from the observed N(p) (figure 5.7) by use of factors given by the Fermi theory (section 5.2.3). The abscissa is electron *kinetic* energy T ($=(W-1)m_ec^2$). An allowed-type spectrum gives a linear plot extrapolating to the upper-limit energy T_0. The ^{137}Cs decay is actually first forbidden and an energy-dependent shape correction factor should be included in an accurate evaluation.

Experimentally it is usual to measure a momentum spectrum using a magnetic spectrometer or an energy spectrum using a solid state counter, but if only the upper limit is required use may be made in suitable cases of the Q value for a nuclear reaction producing the active nucleus, e.g. (p, n) or (^{3}He, ^{3}H). The latter method agrees precisely with the spectrometer measurement if the mass of the associated neutrino (or antineutrino) is zero. Only spectrometer or energy-sensitive counter measurements give the detailed *shape* of the spectrum.

In many β decays, transitions to one or more excited states of the final nucleus take place as well as to the ground state. The Fermi–Kurie plot then deviates from a straight line but may be resolved into two or more straight lines extrapolating to different endpoints.

The lifetime, as mean life τ or halflife $t_{1/2}$, ranges from a fraction of a second to 10^6 a and is determined by conventional timing techniques, using pulsed accelerators to produce the actual nuclei in the case of very short-lived bodies. This extensive range of lifetimes may be roughly ordered by calculating a quantity known as the *comparative halflife* $ft_{1/2}$, often called the ft value. The numerical factor f is determined mainly by the energy release in the decay since this defines the accessible region of phase space for the emitted particles, but calculable Coulomb correction factors are essential. The number distribution for odd-mass β-decaying nuclei with respect to $\log(ft_{1/2})$ is shown in figure 5.9.

As will be seen in section 5.2.3 the ft value relates the experimental observables of β decay to the basic strength of the weak interaction and to the matrix element that takes account of the initial and final nuclear wavefunctions. A group in the distribution shown in figure 5.9 suggests that for the corresponding decays the nuclear matrix element is

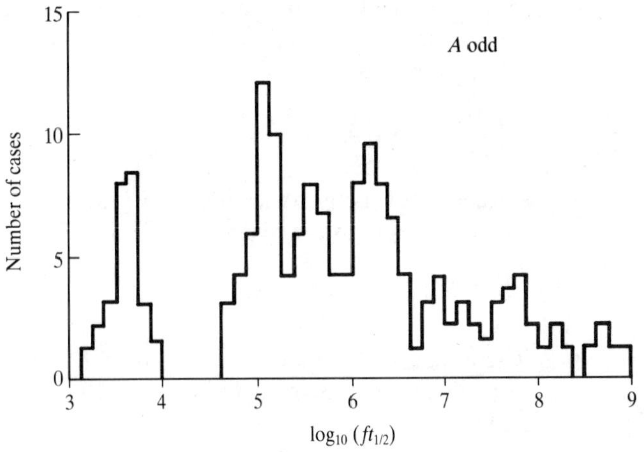

Figure 5.9
Comparative halflife for β transitions between ground states of odd-mass nuclei (from Feenberg E and Trigg G 1950 *Rev Mod Phys* **22** (399)).

independent of Z and of the energy release in the decay. A clear case arises for $\log(ft_{1/2}) \approx 3\text{–}4$ which relates to especially probable transitions known as *superallowed* transitions, in which it seems likely that there is excellent overlap between the initial and final nucleon wavefunctions. Decays of mirror nuclei (e.g. $^{13}N \rightarrow {}^{13}C$) and within isobaric triplets (e.g. $^{26}Si \rightarrow {}^{26}Al^{m} \rightarrow {}^{26}Mg$) fall into this class.

Other groupings exist, for $\log(ft_{1/2}) \approx 4\text{–}5$ and $\log(ft_{1/2}) > 6$. For the former, the transitions are *allowed* in the sense of the spin and parity changes given by selection rules (section 5.2.4) but are unfavoured with respect to the superallowed group because of poor overlap of wavefunctions. The latter are the *forbidden transitions* in the sense of the selection rules, in which there is a more drastic change of structure.

The Fermi theory shows that the grouping into allowed and forbidden transitions physically corresponds with the transport of zero and 1, 2 . . . units of orbital angular momentum by the light particles in the decay and with corresponding nuclear parity changes.

5.2.2 Neutrinos and antineutrinos

The appearance of a light neutral particle, ν_e, in a decay process such as (5.12) was Pauli's solution in 1930 to the problem of the continuous nature of the β spectrum. The energy release in a transition between two well-defined nuclear states is a definite quantity, given by the corresponding mass difference, which accords well with the upper limit of the spectrum, allowing for nuclear recoil. When a β particle is emitted with less than the maximum energy, the neutrino takes up the energy difference.

The need for such a particle, to allow conservation of energy, became apparent when Ellis and Wooster in 1928 established calorimetrically that the energy of absorbable radiation emitted in β decay agreed closely with the *mean energy* of the β spectrum. Later when the neutron–proton model of nuclear structure had been accepted it was clear that angular momentum conservation could not be satisfied in a process such as neutron decay if that were described as

$$n \to p + e^- \qquad (5.13a)$$

since each of the particles has spin $\frac{1}{2}\hbar$. Pauli's suggestion replaces (5.13a) by the scheme now written as

$$n \to p + e^- + \bar{\nu}_e \qquad (5.13b)$$

where the $\bar{\nu}_e$ here and the ν_e in (5.12) are antiparticle and particle respectively in the same way that (e^+e^-) form an antiparticle–particle pair.

The properties required of the neutrino to interpret the experimental evidence so far discussed are that it shall have

(a) zero charge
(b) zero or nearly zero mass (but see sections 5.2.3 and 15.3)
(c) half-integral angular momentum
(d) extremely small interaction with matter, because of the failure of experiments to show even the feeblest ionization caused by neutrinos passing through absorbers or track chambers.

When the further evidence of the existence of a parity-non-conserving behaviour in β decay is presented, as a general property of the fundamental weak interaction (chapter 11), it will be necessary to ascribe a new property of *helicity* to the neutrinos. This is a correlation between the spin direction of a particle with its linear momentum which makes it move like a screw; it is discussed in sections 8.12.2 and 11.2.

Fifty years after its suggestion the neutrino has become a familiar particle, with its own reactor and accelerator technology for production and massive track chambers, counters or radiochemical assemblies for detection. Before such large experiments became possible the most convincing evidence for the existence of the neutrino was that shown in figure 5.10. In this picture radioactive ${}^6_2\text{He}$ decays in a track chamber which shows both the curved track of the decay electron e^- and the heavy ionization due to the final ${}^6_3\text{Li}$ nucleus. The large angle between the tracks implies that there is a neutral third particle ($\bar{\nu}_e$) in the final state to carry away momentum.

A successful demonstration of an inverse β process using reactor antineutrinos was made in 1959 by Reines and Cowan. They sought to detect the inverse of the neutron decay (5.13) which may be written

$$\bar{\nu}_e + p \to n + e^+ + Q \qquad (5.14)$$

where comparison with (5.13) shows that the absorption of an electron

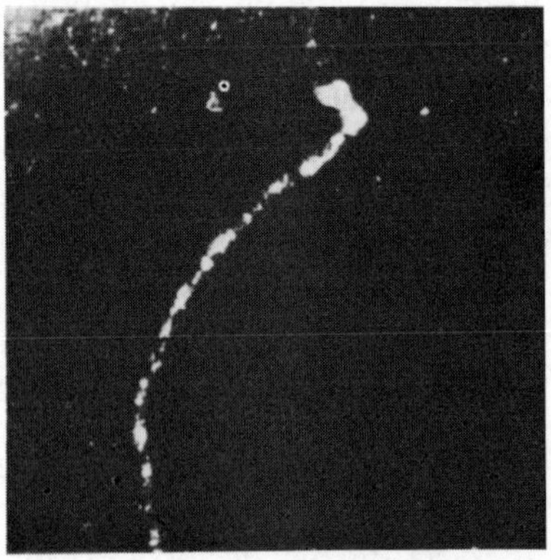

Figure 5.10
Track-chamber photograph of the β decay of ^6He showing tracks of the decay electron and recoil nucleus (Csikai J and Szalay A 1959 *Soviet Phys* **8** (749)).

has been replaced by the equivalent emission of a positron. The Q_β value is given in accordance with equation (3.9a) as $\Delta M - 2M_e = -1800$ keV. In the experiment, a large volume of liquid scintillator was exposed to the $\bar{\nu}_e$ flux and events of the type (5.14) occurring with protons of the scintillator were selected by requiring a prompt signal from the positron followed about 30 μs later by a delayed photon signal resulting from radiative capture of the slowed-down neutron in a cadmium nucleus also present in a cadmium salt in the scintillator. From the 'reactor-associated' counting rate of 36 ± 4 events per hour the cross-section for the inverse β decay was found to be

$$(11 \pm 2.6) \times 10^{-48}\ \text{m}^2.$$

The non-identity of the neutrino (ν_e) and its antiparticle ($\bar{\nu}_e$) follows because of the failure (of Davis) to observe a reaction of the type (5.14) between *antineutrinos* and the *neutrons* of a ^{37}Cl target to produce radioactive ^{37}Ar and an electron (e^-); this process requires an incident *neutrino* if light particles are to balance. It is also strongly suggested by the observed lifetime of nuclei against double β decay, e.g. $^{82}_{34}Se \rightarrow ^{82}_{36}Kr$. The experimental value of about 10^{20} a is much longer than that of 10^{16} a predicted if the two particles are identical (Section 15.3).

5.2.3 The Fermi theory of β decay

The essentials of Fermi's theory may be derived by the use of the time-dependent perturbation theory of quantum mechanics which expresses the rate of transition of a system from an initial state i to a final state f in the following form (often known as Fermi's golden rule):

$$\lambda = \frac{2\pi}{\hbar} |H_{fi}|^2 \rho(E_0). \tag{5.15}$$

In this formula λ is just the decay constant of the familiar exponential decay, the energy $|H_{fi}|$ is a matrix element connecting the basic interaction of β decay with wavefunctions describing the particles concerned in the process and $\rho(E_0)$ is the *density of states* or *phase-space* factor. This is the number of momentum states per unit energy at the energy $E = E_0$ of the final state for some assumed volume V; we shall take E to be the *total* energy of the particles. A similar formula can be used to predict the lifetime of states emitting γ radiation (section 5.1.4) for which the interaction is well understood. For β decay, Fermi proceeded in analogy with the γ decay calculation, but was unable (in 1934) to specify the interaction, which was assumed to exist only at the *point* of decay and was characterized by a strength to be extracted from experimental data. The present unification of the electromagnetic and weak interactions (chapter 13) gives a much more detailed description of the β decay matrix element, but the main conclusions of the Fermi theory are unaffected and remain essential for an understanding of the general nature of decay characteristics.

In complex nuclei β decay occurs because of the change of a neutron into a proton according to equation (5.13) or vice versa and we shall consider the former. The initial state, with wavefunction ψ_i, is a nucleus containing a number of neutrons, some or all of which are in states from which they are energetically able to transform into a proton. The final state, with wavefunction ψ_f, is a nucleus with one more proton and one less neutron than the initial state, together with an electron and an antineutrino (wavefunctions ϕ_e and $\phi_{\bar{\nu}_e}$). Fermi's assumption of a *point-like interaction* then leads to a decay matrix element, in the case of just one transforming nucleon

$$H_{fi} = G \int (\psi_f^* \phi_e^* \phi_{\bar{\nu}_e}^*) \psi_i \, d^3r \qquad (5.16)$$

where the integration for $\psi_f^* \psi_i$ is over the nuclear volume and G represents the strength of the interaction. The integration for the lepton wavefunctions is confined to the assumed final state volume V within which each is normalized by the factor $1/V^{1/2}$. Taking this normalization into account we see from equation (5.16) that because $|H_{fi}|$ is an energy, G must have the dimensions of energy × volume. It is clear from the form of the matrix element that the decay probability depends on the overlap between the initial and final wavefunctions and would be a maximum if the final proton could enter the same state of motion as the initial neutron. More generally, H_{fi} contains a summation of amplitudes for all nucleons able to transform but we shall not show this explicitly.

The formulation (5.16) will be elaborated in chapter 11 where the assumption of a point-like interaction is discarded and the matrix element is treated in a full relativistic theory. For the present, however, the simplest assumption is that all particles may be treated non-relativistically (which is *not* correct for the leptons) and that the electron and antineutrino are emitted as plane waves with spatial parts

$$\phi_e \propto \frac{\exp(i\boldsymbol{k}_e \cdot \boldsymbol{r})}{\sqrt{V}} \qquad \phi_{\bar{\nu}_e} \propto \frac{\exp(i\boldsymbol{k}_{\bar{\nu}_e} \cdot \boldsymbol{r})}{\sqrt{V}} \tag{5.17a}$$

so that the lepton part of the matrix element looks like

$$\frac{\exp[-i(\boldsymbol{k}_e + \boldsymbol{k}_{\bar{\nu}_e}) \cdot \boldsymbol{r}]}{V} = \frac{\exp[-i(\boldsymbol{k} \cdot \boldsymbol{r})]}{V} \tag{5.17b}$$

where $\boldsymbol{k} = \boldsymbol{k}_e + \boldsymbol{k}_{\bar{\nu}_e}$ and the $\boldsymbol{k}$s are de Broglie wave vectors, either for an individual particle or for the relative motion. For $r \approx R$ (the nuclear radius) $\boldsymbol{k} \cdot \boldsymbol{r}$ in β decay is normally less than about 0.1 and the exponential may be expanded either directly or in multipoles. The latter expansion shows that successive terms correspond with the emission of the electron–antineutrino pair with $l = 0, 1, 2, \ldots$ units of orbital angular momentum with respect to the nucleus (although relativistically only the total angular momentum j is meaningful). This in turn means that there is a corresponding change of angular momentum between the nuclear states i and f. Because $\boldsymbol{k} \cdot \boldsymbol{r}$ is small successive terms of the expansions decrease rapidly and it is now possible to associate $l = 0$ with allowed transitions (section 5.2.1) and $l \geqslant 1$ with the forbidden transitions of lower probability.

If we consider only the allowed transitions we take the first term of the lepton wavefunction expansion (i.e. unity) and write the remaining part of the matrix element as

$$\frac{G}{V} \int \psi_f^* \hat{\tau} \psi_i \, d^3 r = \frac{G M_{fi}}{V} \tag{5.18}$$

where M_{fi} is the (dimensionless) *nuclear matrix element* for the simple point interaction that we have assumed and $\hat{\tau}$ is an operator that changes a neutron into a proton. On the further assumption that M_{fi} is not zero because of selection rules (section 5.2.4), it remains to examine the density-of-states factor in (5.15), which will be found to determine the basic or *statistical* shape of the β spectrum.

The number of states per unit energy interval for an electron and antineutrino in a volume V may be written, using equation (3.27), as

$$\rho = \frac{1}{dE_0} \frac{d^3 p_e}{h^3} V \frac{d^3 p_{\bar{\nu}_e}}{h^3} V \tag{5.19}$$

where $d^3 p = 4\pi p^2 \, dp$. The recoil nucleus in the β decay takes up negligible energy but it absorbs momentum (figure 5.10) and as far as momenta are concerned we regard the β particle and antineutrino as independent particles. Their total energies are of course connected by the equation

$$E_0 = E_e + E_{\bar{\nu}_e} \tag{5.20}$$

in which

$$\begin{aligned} E_e^2 &= p_e^2 c^2 + m_e^2 c^4 \\ E_{\bar{\nu}_e}^2 &= p_{\bar{\nu}_e}^2 c^2 + m_{\bar{\nu}_e}^2 c^4. \end{aligned} \tag{5.21}$$

In what follows we shall assume that $m_{\bar{\nu}_e} = 0$ although it is straightforward to retain it in the formalism.

If we wish to examine the momentum spectrum of the β particles, we have to integrate over the antineutrino momenta associated with the β particle momentum p_e but subject to (5.20).* Equation (5.19) then gives, with the assumption $E_{\bar{\nu}_e} = p_{\bar{\nu}_e} c$,

$$\begin{aligned} \rho(p_e)\,\mathrm{d}p_e &= \frac{4\pi p_e^2\,\mathrm{d}p_e}{h^3} V \frac{\mathrm{d}}{\mathrm{d}E_0} \int_0^{p_{max}} \frac{4\pi p_{\bar{\nu}_e}^2\,\mathrm{d}p_{\bar{\nu}_e}}{h^3} V \\ &= \frac{16\pi^2 V^2}{h^6} p_e^2\,\mathrm{d}p_e \frac{\mathrm{d}}{\mathrm{d}E_0} \int_0^{(E_0 - E_e)/c} p_{\bar{\nu}_e}^2\,\mathrm{d}p_{\bar{\nu}_e} \\ &= \frac{16\pi^2 V^2}{h^6 c^3} p_e^2 (E_0 - E_e)^2\,\mathrm{d}p_e. \end{aligned} \tag{5.22}$$

From equations (5.15) and (5.18), the decay probability, for the emission of β particles with momentum between p_e and $p_e + \mathrm{d}p_e$, now becomes

$$\mathrm{d}\lambda(p_e) = \frac{1}{2\pi^3} \frac{G^2 |M_{fi}|^2}{\hbar^7 c^4} p_e^2 (E_0 - E_e)^2\,\mathrm{d}p_e. \tag{5.23}$$

It is usual to present this result in terms of the dimensionless variables $W = E_e/m_e c^2$ and $p = p_e/m_e c$, which are related by the equation $W^2 = 1 + p^2$, and equation (5.23) then becomes

$$\mathrm{d}\lambda(p) = \frac{1}{2\pi^3} G^2 |M_{fi}|^2 \frac{m_e^5 c^4}{\hbar^7} p^2 (W_0 - W)^2\,\mathrm{d}p. \tag{5.24a}$$

To express this result in terms of energies rather than momenta we use

* An alternative calculation of the phase-space factor using the δ function formalism (appendix I) is given by Cassels (reference 11 in chapter 1).

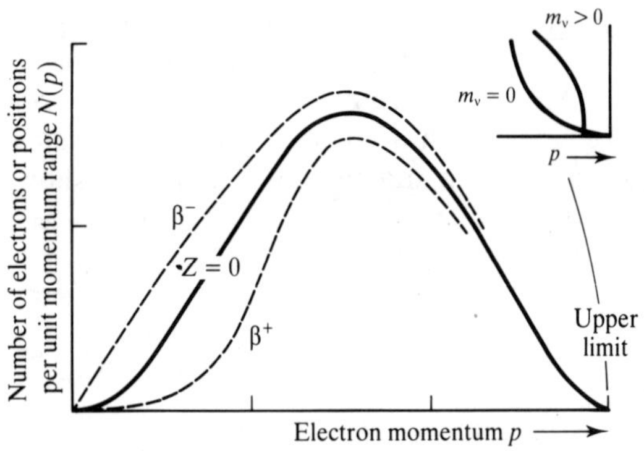

Figure 5.11 The β spectrum. The full line marked $Z = 0$ shows the momentum distribution in β decay without Coulomb correction. Introduction of the Fermi factor alters the statistical shape as shown schematically by the broken lines for electrons and positrons. The inset is an enlarged schematic version of the spectrum near the upper limit in the cases of zero and finite neutrino mass.

the relation $W\,dW = p\,dp$ and obtain

$$d\lambda(W) = \frac{1}{2\pi^3} G^2 |M_{fi}|^2 \frac{m_e^5 c^4}{\hbar^7} pW(W_0 - W)^2\,dW. \tag{5.24b}$$

From the observed rates for simple β decays it is found that $G \approx 1.4 \times 10^{-62}$ J m^3 (see section 11.6 for a fuller discussion). This quantity can also be expressed in dimensionless form by using $\hbar c$ and $\hbar/m_p c$, where m_p is the proton mass, as convenient units of energy × length and of length. We then obtain

$$G \approx 1.4 \times 10^{-62}\ \text{J m}^3 = 10^{-5}\hbar c \left(\frac{\hbar}{m_p c}\right)^2. \tag{5.25}$$

(see also example (11.10)).

The basic statistical momentum spectrum $N(p) = d\lambda/dp$ is plotted in figure 5.11 together with a magnified view of the endpoint for zero and finite $m_{\bar{\nu}_e}$. There is still discussion about the assumption $m_{\bar{\nu}_e} = 0$; it is generally agreed as a result of careful observations of the spectrum of electrons from the decay of tritium (^{3}H) that $m_{\bar{\nu}_e} \leqslant 7.3$ eV/c^2 but at least one measurement has given $m_{\bar{\nu}_e} = 35$ eV/c^2, a value which would have profound implications (section 15.3).

From equation (5.24) it can be seen that in the present approximation, for allowed transitions, the quantity used as ordinate in the Fermi–Kurie plot should be $[N(p)/p^2]^{1/2}$. This extrapolates to the total energy endpoint W_0, or if kinetic energy is used as abscissa to the upper limit $T_0 = (W_0 - 1)m_e c^2$. In fact this quantity is still not precise enough because the electron distribution is affected by the charge Ze of the final nucleus. The calculable *Fermi factor* $F(Z, p)$ (where Z is conventionally the atomic number of the final nucleus, rather than of the initial nucleus as in section 3.2.3) must be introduced into equation (5.24b) and into the Fermi–Kurie ordinate, which becomes $[N(p)/p^2F]^{1/2}$, to correct for this. The effect of F on the basic momentum spectrum is shown in figure 5.11.

The total decay probability for the β^- decay of the nucleus is obtained by integration:

$$\lambda = \int d\lambda = \frac{1}{2\pi^3} G^2 |M_{fi}|^2 f(Z, p_0) \frac{m_e^5 c^4}{\hbar^7} \tag{5.26}$$

where

$$f(Z, p_0) = \int_0^{p_0} p^2 F(Z, p)(W_0 - W)^2 \, dp. \tag{5.27}$$

This function, in terms of energy rather than momentum, is presented graphically in reference 12 and numerically in reference 13. Using the observed halflife $t_{1/2} = \ln(2/\lambda)$ we now easily find the comparative halflife for allowed β^- decays in the form

$$ft = f(Z, p_0) t_{1/2} = \frac{\text{constant}}{|M_{fi}|^2} \tag{5.28}$$

which has been discussed in section 5.2.1.

The Fermi theory sketched in this paragraph is immediately applicable to positron emission and to the nuclear capture of electrons from an atomic orbit (section 5.2.5).

5.2.4 *Selection rules for β decay*

As in the case of radiative processes (section 5.1.1) the spin change between the initial and final nuclear states in β decay is determined by the conservation of angular momentum. In the non-relativisitic approximation we have already seen that forbiddenness is related to the transport of orbital angular momentum, but the electron and (anti)neutrino each have intrinsic spin $\frac{1}{2}\hbar$ and the pair may be emitted in either a singlet ($S = 0$) or triplet ($S = 1$) state with spins antiparallel or parallel. The corresponding transitions, for all degrees of forbiddenness, are known as *Fermi type* (F) and *Gamow–Teller type* (GT). These are in principle different types of weak interaction. In addition there may be a parity change between the nuclear states and although it is now known (chapter 11) that the weak interaction does not conserve parity this applies only to the light particles, and observations confirm that the nuclear parity change is given by the assumed orbital angular momentum change. The total angular momentum change is the vector sum of the orbital change Δl and the intrinsic spin (0 or 1).

With these assumptions the non-relativistic selection rules for the nuclear quantum numbers are as follows:

Allowed transitions (no parity change, $\Delta l = 0$)

$$\Delta J = 0 \text{ (F)} \qquad \Delta J = 0, \pm 1 \text{ (GT)}$$

First forbidden transitions (parity change, $\Delta l = 1$)

$$\Delta J = 0, \pm 1 \text{ (F)} \qquad \Delta J = 0, \pm 1, \pm 2 \text{ (GT)}$$

and similarly for higher degrees of forbiddenness. When a finite transport of total angular momentum takes place, transitions between states of zero spin (e.g. 0^+) are absolutely forbidden. For states of finite spin, the selection rules permit the occurrence of mixed Fermi and Gamow–Teller transitions.

5.2.5 *Electron capture*

The overall energy release in the nuclear capture of an electron from an atomic orbit is just $m_e c^2$ or 511 keV greater than the total energy $W_0 m_e c^2$ available for the alternative process of positron decay between the same initial and final nuclei, if atomic binding is neglected. Capture can thus take place in certain cases when positron emission is energetically impossible and it is always a process competitive with the latter.

Because electron capture (EC) has a *two-body* final state, the neutrino is emitted with a unique energy and this energy determines the number of final states available. The decay probability corresponding to (5.26) includes the same nuclear matrix element as in the positron case and also a factor Z^3 arising from the wavefunction of the captured electron. Although all electrons whose wavefunctions overlap the nucleus may in principle be captured, the overlap consideration makes K capture the most probable. In general, positron emission is favoured for Z small and K capture for Z large. The capture process may be detected by the observation of X-rays resulting from the filling of the atomic vacancy. β decay of a bare nucleus into a specific electronic shell of the daughter atom, with the emission of monoenergetic antineutrinos, is in principle possible; it is the converse of electron capture in respect of the weak interaction.

5.3 α decay[1–3, 14]

5.3.1 General properties

The main properties of spontaneous α decay were established early in the history of nuclear physics by the work of Rutherford and his school on the naturally occurring radioactive elements (section 1.1). It is now known, following the development of the semi-empirical mass formula and the actual measurement of atomic masses throughout the periodic system, that most nuclei with $A > 150$ are actually unstable with respect to the emission of the tightly bound ^{4}He particle causing a change of atomic number $\Delta Z = 2$. The fact that this form of *decay*, and also the process known as spontaneous fission, are relatively rare phenomena compared with *instability* against α emission or against fission is due to the fact that these processes are always retarded by the repulsive Coulomb barrier surrounding the nucleus, as shown in figure 3.5, redrawn with additions in figure 5.12. For the lighter unstable nuclei, with one or two exceptions (e.g. ^{147}Sm), the Q value for α decay is so low that the process is effectively inhibited. For the heavier nuclei the possibility of quantum mechanical penetration (figure 5.12) explains the early difficulty that observed α particle energies were often considerably less than the barrier energy inferred from Rutherford's elastic scattering experiments.

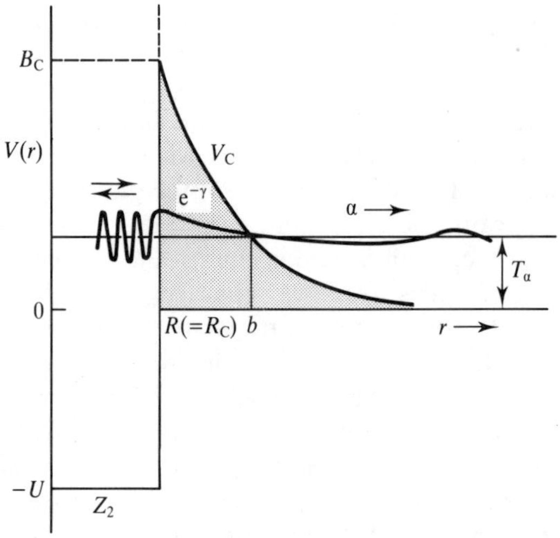

Figure 5.12 Mechanism of α decay. The wave representing the α particle has large amplitude and short wavelength within the nuclear well and is attenuated exponentially in the region of negative kinetic energy ($R < r < b$). The kinetic energy of the emitted particle is T_α; this is determined by the internal excitation in the parent nucleus, but is manifested as a result of repulsion of the particle in the Coulomb field of the final nucleus.

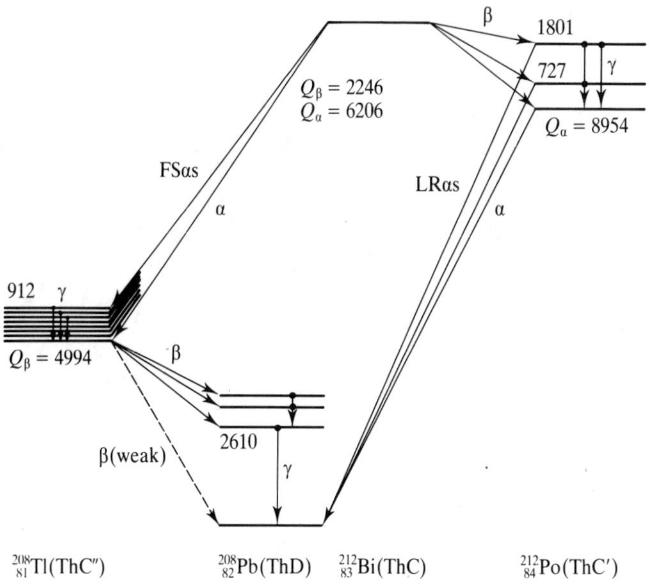

Figure 5.13 Fine-structure (FS) and long-range (LR) α particles in the naturally occurring thorium radioactive series. FS is due to levels near the ground state of a final nucleus (ThC″) and LR is due to emission from an excited state of the initial nucleus (ThC′). Partial level schemes only are shown and level energies, when entered, and Q values are in kiloelectronvolts.

In contrast with β emission, α decay is a two-body process, e.g.

$$^{238}\mathrm{Pu} \rightarrow {}^{234}\mathrm{U} + {}^{4}\mathrm{He} + Q_\alpha \qquad (t_{1/2} = 89.6 \text{ a}) \tag{5.29}$$

and the disintegration particles are emitted with a unique energy if a single final nuclear state is concerned. In some decays, including that shown in (5.29), several low-lying states of the final nucleus are accessible with reasonable probability and the α particle spectrum then shows a *branching* leading to *fine structure* of discrete groups. In other decays, α particles may be emitted from an excited state of the initial nucleus as well as from its ground state and the particles of increased energy are known for historical reasons as *long-range α particles.* Figure 5.13 illustrates these processes; in the case of the long-range particles the excited state will usually have been formed by a preceding β decay, and the 'β-delayed' α decay competes with γ emission to the ground state.

α decay energies are determined by the detailed structure of the mass surface (section 3.2) and are sensitive to shell effects. Figure 5.14 shows the dramatic effect for $A \approx 210$ of the closure of the $N = 126$ neutron shell. Extra energy is available just beyond shell closure, since two loosely bound neutrons are then removed by the emission of a tightly bound α particle. The same effect occurs for $N = 82$ and results in the appearance of α activity among the rare earths. The observed lifetimes for α decay

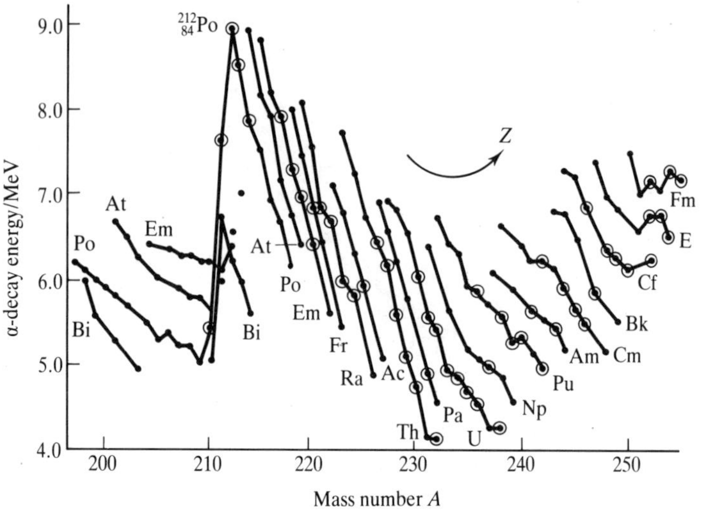

Figure 5.14 Energy release in the α decay of the heavy elements, showing the effect of neutron shell closure at $N = 126$. The nuclei ringed are stable against β decay (adapted from Hanna G C 1959 in *Experimental Nuclear Physics III*, Wiley).

through the nuclear potential barrier range from about 10^{-10} s (appropriate to the long-range particles) to 4.5×10^9 a (for ^{238}U). This large range is reminiscent of the spread of lifetimes in β decay, but it arises almost entirely because of the barrier penetration effect. Angular momentum transfer of a few units of $\hbar$, which is crucial for the β decay probability, has a relatively small effect on the penetration factor. A further difference from β decay is that α decay obeys a very simple *selection rule* – since the emitted particle has zero intrinsic spin, conservation of angular momentum only requires that for the nuclear states concerned

$$\Delta J = L$$

with a parity change $(-1)^L$ where $L\hbar$ is the orbital angular momentum removed by the particle. If an axis of quantization can be fixed for the decay the angular distribution of emitted particles is given by the quantity $[P_L(\cos\theta)]^2$.

The connection between α particle energy as measured by range in air and decay constant was studied for the three naturally occurring radioactive series by Geiger and Nuttall in 1911. Figure 5.15 is a modern version of this plot, for some even-N, even-Z nuclei only. It shows that for each Z value there is a linear dependence of $\log_{10} t_{1/2}$ on $1/T_\alpha^{\frac{1}{2}}$ where T_α is the α particle kinetic energy. Similar plots for odd-A and odd-N nuclei show hindrance factors of about 100 compared with the adjacent even–even cases.

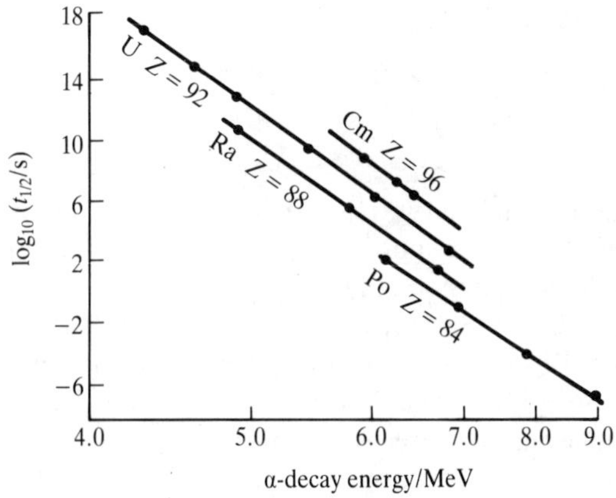

Figure 5.15 Energy–lifetime relation for even–even α emitting nuclei of indicated Z. The energy scale is linear in $1/T_\alpha^{\frac{1}{2}}$ (Hanna G C 1959 in *Experimental Nuclear Physics III*, Wiley).

5.3.2 Barrier penetration in α decay

The Coulomb potential energy of a positive point charge Z_1e at a distance r from a point nucleus of charge Z_2e is given by

$$V_C(r) = \frac{Z_1Z_2e^2}{4\pi\epsilon_0 r}. \tag{5.30}$$

In a very simple model, illustrated in figure 5.12, this electrostatic potential is terminated at a distance R_C and replaced abruptly by an attractive nuclear potential well of depth U for the point charge considered, which we will now assume to be an α particle, $Z_1 = 2$. The nuclear radius R is then taken to be R_C and the *barrier height* is

$$B_C = \frac{2Z_2e^2}{4\pi\epsilon_0 R_C}. \tag{5.31}$$

This has the value $2.4Z_2/A^{1/3}$ MeV for $R_C = 1.2A^{1/3}$ fm, i.e. 35.6 MeV for an α particle and a uranium nucleus.

We assume without discussion that the first stage of an α emission process is for this particle to exist in a quasi-stationary state of the internal potential well of the active nucleus. If the observed α particle energy (including nuclear recoil) is T_α, then the kinetic energy of the particle in the well (figure 5.12) is $U + T_\alpha$. It will make impacts on the boundary of the potential well with a frequency $f \approx v_\alpha/R_C$ and this factor will enter into the decay probability but is not sharply dependent on either v_α or R_C for the heavy nuclei. Spontaneous emission of the particle is not possible classically for $T_\alpha < B_C$ because between the points $r = R_C$ and

$r = b$, where

$$T_\alpha = \frac{2Z_2e^2}{4\pi\epsilon_0 b} \tag{5.32}$$

the kinetic energy is negative. However, as first pointed out by Gamow and by Gurney and Condon, quantum mechanical tunnelling through the potential barrier can take place and the α particle will then come out with zero kinetic energy at the radius $r = b$. It gains its final kinetic energy by repulsion as it moves away from the residual nucleus.

Solution of the Schrödinger equation for this problem provides wavefunctions that are oscillatory for $r < R_C$ and for $r > b$ as in the case of a potential well problem such as neutron–proton scattering (section 3.11). A difference in the present case is that the assumed potential boundary at $r = R_C$ causes strong reflection of the internal wave and the transmission for $T_\alpha < B_C$ is normally very small. The potential discontinuity or matching factor that arises in this way is part of the overall *transmission coefficient*. It may be calculated by imposing the normal boundary conditions on the wavefunction at $r = R_C$; the special cases of resonance that are predicted will be disregarded. In the intermediate, under-the-barrier region $R_C < r < b$, the wavenumber is imaginary and this leads to a non-oscillatory, exponentially decreasing amplitude. The decrease over the zone is given by the factor $\exp(-\gamma)$ where

$$\gamma = \frac{(2\mu_\alpha)^{1/2}}{\hbar} \int_{R_C}^{b} [V(r) - T_\alpha]^{1/2}\,\mathrm{d}r \tag{5.33}$$

where μ_α is the reduced mass of the α particle. We define the *barrier penetration factor* as the corresponding intensity ratio

$$P_0 = \exp(-2\gamma). \tag{5.34}$$

The subscript indicates that only s wave emission is considered. The factor P_0, multiplied by the potential discontinuity factor, gives the overall transmission coefficient.

Evaluation of (5.33) gives

$$\gamma = \frac{2Z_2e^2}{2\pi\epsilon_0\hbar v}\left\{\cos^{-1}\left(\frac{T_\alpha}{B_C}\right)^{1/2} - \left[\frac{T_\alpha}{B_C}\left(1 - \frac{T_\alpha}{B_C}\right)\right]^{1/2}\right\} \tag{5.35}$$

where v is the α particle velocity. In the limit of high barriers $R \to 0$ and $B_C \to \infty$ so that the expression in braces in (5.35) becomes $\pi/2$ and

$$P_0 \to \exp\left(\frac{-2Z_2e^2}{2\epsilon_0\hbar v}\right) = \exp(-2\pi\eta) \tag{5.36}$$

where the dimensionless Coulomb parameter η is given by

$$\eta = \frac{2Z_2e^2}{4\pi\epsilon_0\hbar v} \quad \text{(positive for a repulsive force).} \tag{5.37}$$

The expression (5.36) is known as the *Gamow factor*; the Coulomb parameter is large and the Gamow factor is small for particles of low velocity v in the field of nuclei of high charge Z_2e.

Use of the Gamow factor in α decay systematics provides an explanation of the observed dependence of lifetime on energy, since the decay constant λ_α $(=fP_0)$ will be sharply dependent on v_α, or more strictly on T_α/B_C, through the exponential factor. For the heavy nuclei an increase in T_α by 1 MeV decreases $\tau_\alpha = 1/\lambda_\alpha$ by a factor of about 10^5 while a 10 per cent decrease in R_C (increase in B_C) increases τ_α by a factor of 150. From (5.36) it can also be seen that for a given Z_2, i.e. for a given radioactive element rather than a series,

$$\ln \tau_\alpha = -\ln \lambda_\alpha = a + bT_\alpha^{-1/2} \tag{5.38}$$

where a and b are constant if the nuclear radius is regarded as a constant. This is of the form of the plot shown (on a large scale) in figure 5.15.

5.4 Spontaneous fission decay

The factors that make α decay an observable property of the ground states of many heavy nuclei can be evaluated for other forms of heavy particle decay, using the semi-empirical mass formula as a guide. Spontaneous nucleon decay of ground states can only be expected for nuclei very far from the line of stability and more complex particles are faced with a higher potential barrier. This, however, must be related to the energy available for the postulated decay process and to the possible effect on the barrier of nuclear shells or deformations. The emission of ^{14}C nuclei at a level of 1 in 10^9 of normal α decay events has been observed for the radium isotope $^{223}_{88}Ra$.

The binding energy per nucleon (figure 3.1) is still about 8.5 MeV at $A \approx 120$ whereas because of the increasing asymmetry energy it has dropped to about 7.5 MeV at $A = 240$. The division of a mass-240 nucleus into two equal parts would thus release 240 MeV in all and if the barrier transmission for this energy is finite the *spontaneous fission decay* of the ground state

$$C \rightarrow A + B + Q_F$$

with $Q_F \approx 200$ MeV becomes possible. In fact all conventionally stable nuclei with A greater than about 90 are unstable energetically against division into two nuclei of approximately half the original mass number, but only for $A > 230$ does the halflife, allowing for barrier penetration, become short enough to permit observation of this decay as a spontaneous mode. It exists essentially because of the delicate relation between the Coulomb and surface energy terms in the mass formula, whereby a change of shape from spherical may reduce binding sufficiently to permit the Coulomb force to push two nuclear fragments apart, after barrier penetration. In a liquid-drop model, we recognize the Coulomb effect as a reduction of the surface tension of the drop.

Spontaneous fission decay was not observed until neutron-induced fission, which takes place from an excited compound nucleus C*, had been observed and understood. This contrasts with α decay, for which the ground-state decay was observed before that from excited states produced by nuclear reactions or by β decay. Spontaneous fission increases in probability more rapidly than α decay as A increases and it may be the main mode of decay of *superheavy elements* (section 6.6.3). For nuclides near ^{238}U, however, it is a weak effect and discussion of fission phenomena will be confined to the induced process (section 6.6.3). Spontaneous fission halflives for even-Z, even-N nuclei vary between 10^6 a for ^{238}U to a few hours or less for transuranic elements such as fermium ($Z = 100$). Some of the low-lying excited states of heavy nuclei, e.g. americium, have unexpectedly short halflives, of the order of microseconds, for spontaneous fission and this has led to the discovery of structure in the fission barrier (section 6.6.2).

REFERENCES 5

1 **Siegbahn K (ed)** 1975 *Alpha, Beta and Gamma Ray Spectroscopy* North-Holland (reprinted 1979)

2 **Lederer C M and Shirley V S** 1979 *Table of Isotopes* (7th edn) Wiley

3 **Pearson J M** 1986 *Nuclear Physics: Energy and Matter* Adam Hilger ch. III

4 **Blatt J B and Weisskopf V F** 1952 *Theoretical Nuclear Physics* Wiley appendix B

5 **Hamilton W D (ed)** 1975 *The Electromagnetic Interaction in Nuclear Spectroscopy* North-Holland

6 **Pauli H C, Alder K and Steffen R M** 1975 'Theory of internal conversion' in Hamilton W D (ed) *The Electromagnetic Interaction in Nuclear Spectroscopy* North-Holland

7 **Röel F, Fries H M, Alder K and Pauli H C** 1978 'Internal conversion coefficients for all atomic shells' *Atomic Data and Nuclear Data Tables* **21** (91)

8 **Dyson N A** 1973 *X-rays in Atomic and Nuclear Physics* Longman

9 **Schwarzschild A Z and Warburton E K** 1968 'The measurement of short nuclear lifetimes' *Ann Rev Nucl Sci* **18** (265)

10 **Cranshaw T E, Dale E W, Longworth G O and Johnson C E** 1985 *Mössbauer Spectroscopy and its Applications* Cambridge University Press

11 **Morita M** 1973 *Beta Decay and Muon Capture* Benjamin

12 *Landolt-Bornstein Tables* 1969 Group I **4**

13 **Gove N B and Martin M J** 1971 'Log f tables for β-decay' *Nuclear Data Tables* **A10** (205)

14 **Rutherford E, Chadwick J and Ellis C D** 1930 *Radiations from Radioactive Substances* Cambridge University Press

EXAMPLES 5

5.1 In the ^{207}Pb nucleus the magnetic moment of the ground state is 0.59 nuclear magnetons and the halflife of the first excited state at 570 keV is 130 ps. Use this information, together with equations (3.20), (3.21) and (5.7), to deduce the single-particle character of the two states.

5.2 The isomeric state of ^{134}Cs^{m} (spin-parity 8^-) decays to the ground state (4^+) and to an excited state (5^+) by transitions of energy 137 and 127 keV. State the nature of the three transitions and estimate the relative intensity of the 137 and 127 keV radiations.

5.3 Using the Weisskopf formulae (5.4) and (5.6) for a single-proton transition deduce an expression for the E3 radiative width.

5.4 The (upward) B(E2) value for the Coulomb excitation of the 2.938 MeV state (2^+) of ^{26}Mg is 40 e^2 fm^4. Calculate the radiative lifetime if the branching ratio to the ground state is 10 per cent. [5×10^{-14} s]

5.5 In an experiment to determine the lifetime of an excited nucleus by the recoil-distance plunger method, the counting rate was found to decrease by a factor of 2 for a source displacement of 0.07 mm. If the mean lifetime of the decaying state is 7×10^{-11} s, find the velocity of recoil. [1.4×10^6 m s^{-1}]

5.6 Ions of ^{32}S of energy 150 MeV were used to excite ^{64}Zn nuclei in order to measure an excited state lifetime by the plunger technique. When the plunger was 20 mm from the target 30 per cent of detected γ rays were seen in the Doppler-shifted peak. Assuming that detection was in coincidence with back-scattered ^{32}S ions, calculate the lifetime of the state. [2.8×10^{-9} s]

5.7 Calculate the full recoil shift between the emission and absorption lines for the 411 keV level in ^{198}Hg, and the source velocity necessary to give complete overlap. [0.91 eV, 667 m s^{-1}]

5.8 The 14.4 keV γ ray transition in ^{57}Fe has been extensively studied using the Mössbauer effect (e.g. Hanna *et al.* 1960 *Phys Rev Letters* **4** (177)), and it is found that the $J = \frac{1}{2}$ ground state is split with an energy difference corresponding with a source velocity of 3.96 mm s^{-1}. If the ground-state magnetic moment is 0.0955 μ_N, calculate the internal magnetic field at the ^{57}Fe nucleus. [31.5 T]

5.9 The atomic masses of $^{74}_{32}Ge$, $^{74}_{33}As$ and $^{74}_{34}Se$ are 73.92118, 73.92393 and 73.92248. Calculate the Q values in mega-electronvolts for the possible decay schemes linking these nuclei. [$Q_{\beta^-} = 1.35$ MeV, $Q_{\beta^+} = 1.54$ MeV, $Q_{EC} = 2.56$ MeV]

5.10 Show that the relativistic expression for the ratio of nuclear recoil energy to maximum electron energy in β^- decay is $T_R/T_e = (Q + 2m_e)/(Q + 2m_R)$ where Q is the energy available for the decay products and m_R is the mass of the recoil nucleus.

5.11 Use the result of example 5.10 to infer the nuclear recoil energy in the case of electron capture, releasing energy Q_{EC}. Assume that the neutrino mass is zero.

For the decay $^{37}A \rightarrow {}^{37}Cl$, $Q_{EC} = 0.82$ MeV and $T_R = 9.7 \pm 0.8$ eV. Show that these figures are consistent with $m_{\nu_e} = 0$.

5.12 The reaction $^{34}S(p, n)^{34}Cl$ has a threshold at a laboratory proton energy of 6.45 MeV. Calculate non-relativistically the upper limit of the positron spectrum of ^{34}Cl assuming $m_e c^2 = 0.51$ MeV, $M_n - M_H = 0.78$ MeV. [4.47 MeV]

5.13 The maximum positron energy in the decay of ^{34}Cl ($t_{1/2} = 1.57$ s) is 4.47 MeV and the Fermi factor $F(Z, p)$ is equal to 0.71 over most of the spectrum. Evaluate the integrated Fermi function $f(Z, p_0)$ and the comparative halflife.

5.14 On the assumption that the nuclear matrix element for the ^{34}Cl decay (example 5.13) is given by $|M|^2 = 2$, obtain the weak interaction coupling constant G, in the units joules per cubic metre.

5.15 In a very low energy β spectrum (e.g. ^{14}C with maximum kinetic energy $T_0 = 0.156$ MeV) the energy distribution may be approximated by $d\lambda \propto T^{1/2}(T_0 - T)^2\, dT$. Show that in this case the mean kinetic energy of the spectrum is one-third of the maximum energy.

5.16 In a high energy β spectrum, with the maximum energy $E_0 \gg m_e c^2$, show that the decay constant λ is approximately proportional to E_0^5.

5.17 Investigate the stability against α decay of ^{80}Kr and ^{176}Hf, given the following atomic masses: ^{80}Kr, 79.9164; ^{76}Se, 75.9192; ^{176}Hf, 175.9414; ^{172}Yb, 171.9364; ^{4}He, 4.0026.

5.18 The Q value for the α decay of RaC(^{214}Po) is 7.83 MeV. What is the energy of the α particles emitted? [7.68 MeV]

6 *Nuclear reactions*

Historical · Formalism · Compound nucleus reactions · The optical model of particle-induced nuclear reactions · Direct reactions · Special reactions

The decay processes discussed in chapter 5 take place mainly from the ground and low-lying states of quasi-stable nuclei and the most important observable quantities are the energy and the lifetime for the decay. If the energy of the decaying system is raised above the threshold for particle emission, into the region of virtual states, β and γ decay will usually compete unfavourably with particle emission, although in section 6.6.3, 'Fission and heavy-ion reactions', we shall encounter an important example of the contrary. The lifetime then becomes extremely short, say 10^{-16} s or less, and the two processes of raising the energy and of decay from the virtual state then jointly constitute a nuclear reaction. The term also describes other and more direct processes in which the nature or excitation of a target nucleus is changed.

Interest in the nature of nuclear reactions is twofold, first because the dynamical process resulting in scattering or transmutation is a study in itself and secondly because such processes provide most of the tabulated information on nuclear properties. Progress in accelerator and detector technology has led to extensive and detailed knowledge of the level systems of a great many nuclei, a knowledge which often extends far beyond the limit of credible theoretical prediction. Naturally these two aspects of reaction studies are closely linked because it is necessary to understand reaction dynamics in order to extract reliable values for level parameters. Usually, as in the case of decay processes, theory shows how 'external' energy-dependent factors may be removed so that experimental data yield structure-dependent matrix elements.

In this chapter a brief historical account of some reaction processes will be first presented in extension of the survey given in section 1.4 and then an outline of the formalism used in interpretation will be given. Finally, a few of the well-defined areas of this very large field will be described. A full treatment of the more theoretical aspects of the subject is given in references 1 and 2.

6.1 Historical[3]

6.1.1 The disintegration of nitrogen by α particles

By 1919 many of the phenomena associated with the scattering of α particles by light nuclei had been thoroughly investigated, mainly by Rutherford and his pupils at Manchester. Among the effects observed was the production of scintillations on a zinc sulphide screen placed near an α particle source in air, but at a range greater than that of the α particles. Careful study of this phenomenon with a chamber which could be evacuated or filled with a gas led Rutherford to the conclusion that 'the nitrogen atom is disintegrated under the intense forces developed in a close collision with a swift α-particle and that the hydrogen atom which is liberated formed a constituent part of the nitrogen nucleus'. The process observed is written explicitly as

$$^{14}\mathrm{N} + \alpha \rightarrow {}^{17}\mathrm{O} + \mathrm{p} - 1.19\ \mathrm{MeV}. \tag{6.1}$$

Striking evidence for this interpretation was obtained by Blackett using a Wilson cloud chamber; figure 6.1 shows one of the pictures obtained in his experiments. This was the discovery of artificial transmutation.

Figure 6.1
Expansion chamber photograph showing ejection of a proton from a nitrogen nucleus by an α particle. (Blackett P M S and Lees D S 1932 *Proc Roy Soc* **A136** (325).)

6.1.2 The disintegration of lithium by protons

In 1932 Cockcroft and Walton, working under Rutherford in the Cavendish Laboratory, Cambridge, showed that reactions like (6.1) could be reversed by the use of artificially accelerated protons. Success was first obtained with the reaction

$$^{7}\mathrm{Li} + \mathrm{p} \rightarrow \alpha + \alpha + 17.35\ \mathrm{MeV} \tag{6.2}$$

using protons of energy as low as 125 keV and this result led in the end to an enormous development of accelerators of all kinds (sections 2.4 and 2.5). The experiment not only provided dramatic confirmation of Einstein's mass–rest-energy relation, which permitted the observed Q value to be predicted from known atomic masses, but also verified Gamow's theory of barrier penetration by particles of energy insufficient to surmount it.

6.1.3 The discovery of the neutron

Chadwick's 1932 discovery provided another example of the type of transmutation shown in (6.1), namely

$$^{9}\mathrm{Be} + \alpha \rightarrow {}^{12}\mathrm{C} + \mathrm{n} + 5.7\ \mathrm{MeV}. \qquad (6.3)$$

It was known for some years before 1932, especially from the work of Bothe and Becker, that bombardment of light elements with α particles could produce a penetrating radiation, assumed then to be γ radiation connected with the production of excited states of the residual nuclei, e.g. ^{17}O, formed in the reaction (6.1). For beryllium particularly the penetrating power of the radiation seemed exceptionally great ($\mu_m = 2 \times 10^{-3}\ \mathrm{m^2\ kg^{-1}}$ for lead). It is now clear that μ_m was impossibly low if the radiation were electromagnetic but at the time the effect of pair production in increasing absorption coefficients (see section 2.1.4) was not realized. More significant, however, was the observation by Mme Curie-Joliot and M. Joliot that the radiation from beryllium was able to eject energetic *protons* from hydrogenous material. This they ascribed to a Compton scattering of the supposed electromagnetic radiation by the target protons and from the observed range of the protons the energy of the radiation was calculated to be 35–55 MeV.

This energy seemed larger than might be expected to originate in an α particle reaction with a light element and the Compton scattering hypothesis was therefore further studied by Chadwick (1932). He found, using a simple ionization chamber and amplifier, that the beryllium radiation could produce recoil ions of many light elements as well as of hydrogen. This was most simply explained by the supposition that the radiation was not electromagnetic but was a stream of neutral particles (*neutrons*) of mass approximately equal to that of the proton. The apparatus of Chadwick is shown in figure 6.2(a). In the presence of the source assembly the pulse counting rate in the air-filled ionization chamber increased by a factor of about 40 and by a further factor when a sheet of paraffin wax was placed near the entrance to the chamber. The former increase was interpreted as due to the production of recoil nitrogen ions and the latter as due to the detection of recoil protons from the paraffin wax. The initial velocity u_p of the protons ($3 \times 10^7\ \mathrm{m\ s^{-1}}$) was deduced from their measured range (figure 6.2(b)) and the initial velocity u_N of the nitrogen recoils was found to be $4.7 \times 10^6\ \mathrm{m\ s^{-1}}$ from a separate expansion chamber study of recoil ranges made by Feather.

If the unknown radiation is assumed to consist of particles of atomic mass M_n and velocity u_n and if M_p and M_N are the atomic masses of the proton and nitrogen nucleus respectively, then it is easy to show that

$$u_p = \frac{2M_n u_n}{M_n + M_p} \quad \text{and} \quad u_N = \frac{2M_n u_n}{M_n + M_N}$$

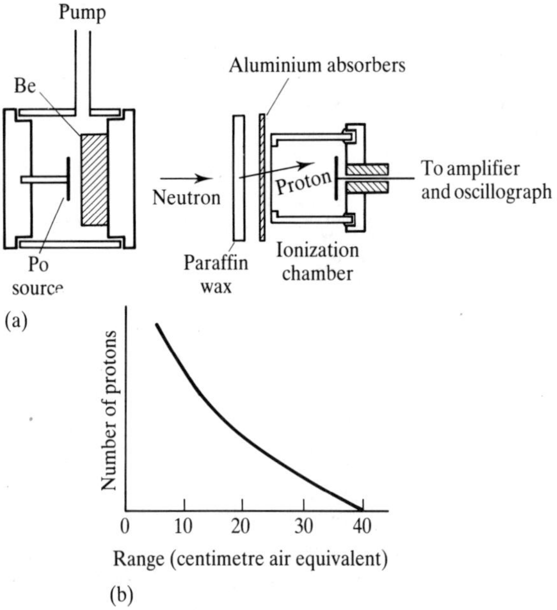

Figure 6.2 Discovery of the neutron: (a) apparatus in which the neutrons were produced by the (α, n) reaction in a block of beryllium and then ejected protons from a sheet of paraffin wax; (b) number–range curve for protons. (Chadwick J 1932 *Proc Roy Soc* **A136** (692).)

so that

$$\frac{u_p}{u_N} = \frac{3.3 \times 10^7}{4.7 \times 10^6} = \frac{M_n + M_N}{M_n + M_p}.$$

Substitution of $M_N = 14$ amu and $M_p = 1$ amu gave

$$M_n = 1.16 \text{ amu}$$

with an error of some 10 per cent. This value was soon refined, by observation of other neutron-producing reactions, to $1.005 < M_n < 1.008$ amu. This completed the proof of the existence of a neutral nuclear particle of mass closely similar to that of the proton. The whole story of the discovery of the neutron is admirably recounted in articles by Feather.[4]

6.1.4 Induced activity

An (α, n) reaction increases the proton to neutron ratio of the target nucleus in forming the final nuclear product. Although this product nucleus may be stable, it is not always so and positron decay may then ensue, e.g.

$$\begin{aligned} {}^{27}\text{Al} + \alpha &\rightarrow {}^{30}\text{P} + \text{n} - 2.69\ \text{MeV} \\ {}^{30}\text{P} &\rightarrow {}^{30}\text{Si} + e^{+} + \nu_e. \end{aligned} \tag{6.4}$$

Rutherford had always suspected that nuclear bombardment might induce activity but he looked for heavy-particle effects and artificially produced *positron* emitters, notably that shown in (6.4), were first seen in 1934 by I. Curie and F. Joliot.

Shortly after these experiments, Fermi and his group in Rome demonstrated the production of *electron* emitters by reactions of the (n, α), (n, p) and (n, γ) type, which decrease the proton to neutron ratio away from stability. In the case of aluminium the reaction is

$$\begin{aligned} {}^{27}\text{Al} + \text{n} &\rightarrow {}^{24}\text{Na} + \alpha - 3.14\ \text{MeV} \\ {}^{24}\text{Na} &\rightarrow {}^{24}\text{Mg} + e^{-} + \bar{\nu}_e. \end{aligned} \tag{6.5}$$

Fermi emphasized that neutron-induced reactions were not limited by energy loss of the incident particle in matter, or by the Coulomb barrier, and that they were to be expected for elements throughout the periodic system, including uranium. A further important discovery of the Rome group was that neutron-induced activities could often be increased by surrounding the source and target foil by hydrogenous material. This has the effect of *slowing down* the neutrons to near thermal energies so that they spend longer near the target nuclei and have a greater chance of being captured.

6.1.5 Induced fission[5,6]

Neutron-induced fission was established as an unexpected result of the search for transuranic elements in the bombardment of uranium by slow neutrons over the years 1934–9. It had been hoped to produce these elements (now familiar as neptunium and plutonium) by the succession of processes

$$\begin{aligned} {}^{238}_{92}\text{U} + \text{n} &\rightarrow {}^{239}_{92}\text{U} + \gamma \\ {}^{239}_{92}\text{U} &\rightarrow {}^{239}_{93}\text{Np} + e^{-} + \bar{\nu}_e \\ {}^{239}_{93}\text{Np} &\rightarrow {}^{239}_{94}\text{Pu} + e^{-} + \bar{\nu}_e \end{aligned} \tag{6.6a}$$

and indeed the production of 23 min ${}^{239}\text{U}$ was recognized, although accompanied by a great number of other activities. As in the early days of radioactivity, the elucidation of this complex of activities fell to the chemists, and despite the expectation that the elements produced would be either transuranic, such as Np and Pu, or more familiar bodies derived from them by α decay, e.g. radium, Hahn and Strassmann, following Curie and Savitch, were forced to conclude that there was a production of *barium* isotopes in the U + n reaction.

In 1938 Meitner and Frisch accepted these conclusions and proposed that the uranium nucleus, on absorption of a slow neutron, could assume a shape sufficiently deformed to promote *fission* into two approximately equal masses, e.g.

$$_{92}U + n \rightarrow {}_{92}U^* \rightarrow {}_{56}Ba + {}_{36}Kr + Q \tag{6.6b}$$

or to many other similar pairs each with an appropriate energy release Q. From the semi-empirical mass formula the two product nuclei, or *fission fragments*, would each have an energy of about 75 MeV and therefore an estimated range of about 30 mm of air; they would recoil after the actual fission event (or *scission* of the intermediate nucleus U) in opposite directions. Their energy is converted into available heat as they slow down in matter with a yield of 1 J for 3.2×10^{10} fission events.

Transuranic elements in the range $Z = 93$–105 have now been prepared by neutron capture processes such as (6.6) with intense beams of neutrons from nuclear reactors. They can also be made by heavy-ion bombardments of suitable targets, a process which is effectively fission in reverse. Attempts to reach superheavy nuclei with $Z \approx 114$ are in fact impeded by the occurrence of fission as a favoured decay mode of the nuclei formed.

6.2 Formalism[7]

The variables measured in nuclear reaction studies with a charged particle beam are indicated in figure 6.3, which is a sketch of a typical experimental arrangement. All measurements in practice are expressed as relative or absolute *cross-sections* σ (appendix B) and when a detector subtending a small solid angle $d\Omega$ at the target is used *differential cross-sections* $d\sigma/d\Omega$ or $\sigma(\theta)$ are obtained.

The *entrance channel* for the reaction

$$X + a \rightarrow Y + b + Q_{ab} \tag{6.7}$$

is defined by the choice of target X and projectile a, perhaps in a particular spin state. The *reaction channel* may be chosen experimentally by a *particle-identification* detector assembly, which selects particles b from the complex of reaction products. We recall (section 1.5.3) that in writing down equations such as (6.7) the mass number A and charge number Z must be conserved. Nuclear *mass* is not conserved and the change occurring as a result of the reaction determines the Q_{ab} value (section 3.2.1).

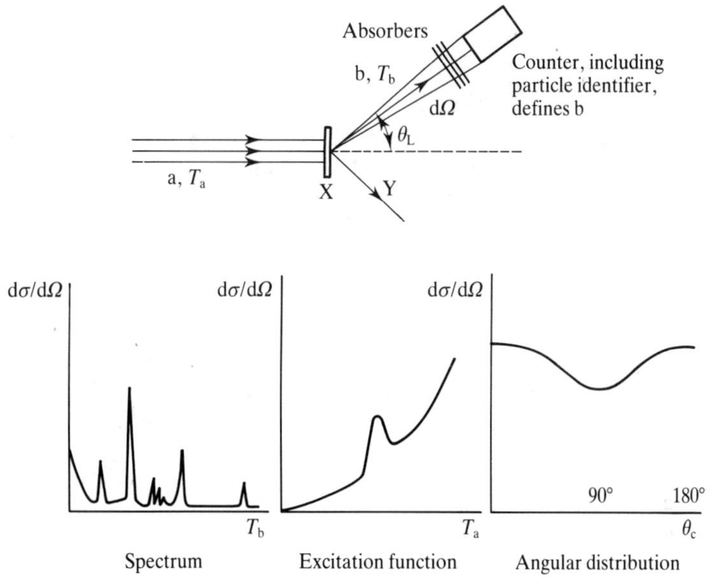

Figure 6.3 Nuclear reaction measurements. The counter, with the identifier, measures reaction yield for the process X(a, b)Y into a known solid angle at the laboratory angle θ_L, and this gives the differential cross-section $d\sigma/d\Omega$ (lab). The counter yields the *spectrum* of b directly. The variation of yield of a particular peak in the spectrum with the incident energy T_a is an *excitation function*; its variation with centre-of-mass angle θ_c is the *angular distribution*. In both cases centre-of-mass cross-sections should be used and strictly the excitation function should be plotted against channel energy, i.e. the centre-of-mass energy in the entrance channel. All scales are arbitrary. Absorbers may be used to exclude low energy particles from the counter system.

The detector is normally energy sensitive and provides at each angle $\theta_b = \theta_L$ a spectrum (figure 6.3) of particles b for each peak of which the Q value can be obtained. These Q values in turn give the excitation energies $Q^0_{ab} - Q_{ab}$ of the product nucleus Y where Q^0 is the value of Q for the ground state; these latter values are extensively tabulated (references 1 and 2 of chapter 3). For a reaction of the type (6.7) the kinetic energy of the incident and product particles is related to the Q value in mega-electronvolts by the equation

$$(m_b + m_Y)T_b - 2(m_a m_b T_a T_b)^{1/2} \cos\theta_b$$
$$= (m_Y - m_a)T_a + m_Y Q_{ab}. \tag{6.8}$$

This equation is derived (appendix C) in a non-relativistic approximation under the assumptions only of the conservation of energy and of linear momentum, which must apply whatever the detailed nature of the reaction. For high accuracy the ms should be atomic masses (and relativistic corrections should be applied) but for many purposes it is adequate to use the mass number A.

The direct yield of particle b observed over a small angular range relates to the laboratory-based system of coordinates, but for meaningful comparison with reaction theories it must be referred to the centre-of-mass system defined in the entrance channel X + a. When this has been done it is informative to consider the *excitation function*, which exhibits the dependence of $d\sigma/d\Omega$ for a selected group of particles b on the incident particle energy in the entrance channel, which is T_a reduced to allow for the centre-of-mass motion. Excitation functions (figure 6.3) locate compound nuclear levels (section 6.3) directly and may yield virtual level widths.

The *angular distribution* of the emission of the selected group of particles b in the centre-of-mass system with respect to the direction of incidence of particle a contains information on changes of angular momentum and parity between the initial (i) and final (f) states, since both these quantities are conserved in reactions governed by the strong or electromagnetic interaction.

It is not possible to give an overall formula that predicts the cross-section for all nuclear reactions in the way that the Rutherford scattering of one point charge by another may be displayed. Nuclear states are complex, many-body systems and the interactions between their constituents, and between those constituents and an incident particle, do not have a simple analytical form. Approximations are therefore nearly always essential in reaction calculations and are chosen to suit the particular process under consideration. The end product of a nuclear reaction experiment may well be the determination of a nuclear quantity such as a decay width (section 6.3) or a potential (section 6.4) which can then be analysed by microscopic theories. To extract such pieces of information from measured cross-sections known 'external' factors such as energies and momenta have to be removed; the dependence of cross-sections on these factors is often interesting in itself.

The total cross-section for the reaction X(a, b)Y between spinless particles, with neglect of centre-of-mass corrections, is shown in reference 7, p. 505, to be

$$\begin{aligned}\sigma_{ab} &= \frac{1}{\pi\hbar^4}\langle|\mathscr{H}_{fi}|^2\rangle\frac{p_b^2}{v_a v_b}\\ &= \frac{m_a m_b}{\pi\hbar^4}\langle|\mathscr{H}_{fi}|^2\rangle\frac{k_b}{k_a}\end{aligned} \tag{6.9}$$

where m_a and m_b are the masses (strictly the reduced masses) of the particles, v_a and v_b are their velocities, p_a and p_b their momenta and k_a and k_b the corresponding (reduced) wavenumbers $p/\hbar$. The quantity $|\mathscr{H}_{fi}|$, of dimensions energy × volume, contains the usually unknown nuclear factors. The formula (6.9), derived by use of Fermi's golden rule (cf. section 5.2.3), is applicable only to reactions for which resonant behaviour is not encountered and which involve transitions to a near continuum of final states; the brackets enclosing $|\mathscr{H}_{\mathrm{fi}}|^2$ indicate an average over the possible transitions. When the particles have spin, a statistical factor appears in formula (6.9) and for charged incident or emergent particles a barrier penetration factor (section 5.3.2) is included in $|\mathscr{H}_{\mathrm{fi}}|$.

If $|\mathscr{H}_{\mathrm{fi}}|$ is constant or nearly so over a certain energy range, useful results relating to the 'external' factors may be predicted. Thus in the case of the *elastic scattering* of thermal neutrons we have $v_{\mathrm{a}} = v_{\mathrm{b}} = p/m_{\mathrm{n}}$ so that the cross-section σ_{nn} in this range is energy independent. But if these same neutrons produce an exothermic reaction, e.g. the (n, α) process releasing several mega-electronvolts of energy, we have that p_{b} and v_{b} and the barrier penetration factor are practically independent of the small kinetic energy of the incident particle and $\sigma_{\mathrm{n}\alpha} \propto 1/v_{\mathrm{n}}$. This is known as the '$1/v$' law of slow neutron absorption; it was discussed by Fermi and others in the 1930s (see also example 6.10).

A formalism not involving the use of the golden rule is *partial wave analysis*. This is used extensively in part II of this book and is set out in chapter 9, where it is shown that the differential cross-section for *elastic scattering* can be written in the form

$$\frac{\mathrm{d}\sigma}{\mathrm{d}\Omega} = |f(\theta)|^2$$

in which the *scattering amplitude* $f(\theta)$ embodies *phase shifts* appropriate to the particular partial waves corresponding with discrete angular momentum about the scattering centre. These can in turn be related to a potential used to represent the interaction, as for example in neutron–proton scattering (section 3.11.3). The formalism provides a limit on the total cross-section for inelastic processes and can describe the resonant behaviour noted in compound nucleus reactions (section 6.3.2). A major application is to the theory of elastic scattering known as the optical model (section 6.4) in which the many-body problem is simplified to a one-body system with a complex interaction potential, the imaginary part representing all inelastic processes lumped together.

The elastic scattering of a particle by a fixed centre of force represented by a potential $V(r)$ can be calculated directly by the use of the *Born approximation* of quantum mechanics. This strictly applies only when the waves describing the incident particles are not strongly modified by the scattering potential and leads under these circumstances to a differential cross-section for a particle of mass m of

$$\frac{\mathrm{d}\sigma}{\mathrm{d}\Omega} = \frac{m^2}{4\pi^2\hbar^4}\left|\int V(r)\exp(\mathrm{i}\boldsymbol{q}\cdot\boldsymbol{r})\,\mathrm{d}^3r\right|^2 \tag{6.10}$$

where $\boldsymbol{q}(\times\hbar)$ is the momentum transfer in the scattering and the integration is over radial and angular variables. Under the conditions of its validity this formula is essentially equivalent to that arising from phase shift analysis.

Similar approximations have been developed[1,2] to describe inelastic processes and the predicted cross-sections have the same dependence on 'external' factors as is shown in equations (6.9) and (6.10). The 'internal' factors, however, embody assumptions about the physical nature of the process as well as the anticipated structure-dependent quantities. A brief survey of the *direct reactions* to which this type of analysis has been applied is given in section 6.5.

A simple reaction calculation

Consider the (p, α) reaction (6.2) written with the full atomic symbols

$$^{7}_{3}\mathrm{Li} + ^{1}_{1}\mathrm{H} \rightarrow ^{4}_{2}\mathrm{He} + ^{4}_{2}\mathrm{He} + Q$$

and note firstly the arithmetic addition of mass numbers and atomic numbers. Then using a table of atomic masses and the conversion factor given in equation (3.1) check the Q value shown in expression (6.2).

Next look at the intrinsic spins and parities which are $\frac{3}{2}^-$, $\frac{1}{2}^+$, 0^+ and 0^+ in order of the symbols in the equation. These must combine with the orbital angular momenta in the initial and final systems so that total angular momentum and parity are conserved between the two sides of the equation.

The final system is just two identical spinless particles in relative motion and its wavefunction must not change sign when the particles are exchanged. This means that the orbital angular momentum in this system must be even, i.e. 0, 2, 4, . . . , $\hbar$, and the parity of the system must also be even, i.e. $0^+, 2^+, 4^+, \ldots$

To reach these spin-parity values in the initial system, an odd orbital angular momentum is necessary and we could have $1^-, 3^-, 5^- \ldots$. At low bombarding energies, particles with high orbital momenta do not approach the nucleus close enough to produce the reaction, so we assume the lowest possible orbital momentum. The vector equation for addition of orbital momenta in the initial system is then (remembering that parity is *multiplicative*)

$$\tfrac{3}{2}^- + \tfrac{1}{2}^+ + 1^- \rightarrow 0^+, 1^+, 2^+, 3^+$$

of which only 0^+ and 2^+ satisfy the requirements of the final system. This scheme gives a good account of the angular distribution of the α particles, which are emitted back to back in the centre-of-mass system with equal energies. (Critchfield C L and Teller E 1941 *Phys Rev* **60** (10).)

To calculate the energy of the α particles observed at say 60° in the laboratory for 1 MeV protons we consult the mass tables for $M - A$

values and find (in kilo-electronvolts)

$$^{7}\text{Li: } 14\,908; \quad ^{1}\text{H: } 7289; \quad ^{4}\text{He: } 2425$$

so that

$$Q_{p\alpha} = 14\,908 + 7289 - 2(2425) = 17\,347 \text{ keV}$$

Then using mass numbers, equation (6.8) gives

$$(4 + 4)T - 2(1 \times 4 \times 1000T)^{1/2} \cos 60^\circ = (4 - 1)1000 + 4(17\,347)$$

or

$$8T - 63.25\sqrt{T} = 72\,388$$

giving

$$T = 9832 \text{ keV}.$$

6.3 Compound nucleus reactions[1,2,8–12]

6.3.1 The origin of the compound nucleus hypothesis

Until 1932 the only nuclear reactions studied were of the (α, p) type with light elements, as in Rutherford's original experiment. Because of low source intensities only limited data were generally obtained, but there were indeed some observations of angular distributions and excitation functions. No formal theory of reaction processes existed, though general ideas analogous to those of the single-particle shell model were often discussed. This situation did not dramatically change as a result of Cockcroft and Walton's work, for although this showed how to overcome the problem of source intensities its main contribution to reaction theory was to emphasize the role of the Gamow penetration factor in what we would now call the transition probability or cross-section (equation (6.9)).

The discovery of the neutron soon led to major advances, because the absence of Coulomb barriers for this particle made a wide range of nuclei available for the study of reactions, especially with neutrons of near thermal energy. For such particles the (n, γ) capture reaction, e.g.

$$^{107}\text{Ag} + \text{n} \rightarrow {}^{108}\text{Ag} + \gamma \tag{6.11}$$

is easily observable by detection of the activity of the product nucleus, e.g.

$$^{108}\text{Ag} \rightarrow {}^{108}\text{Cd} + \text{e}^- + \bar{\nu}_e \tag{6.12}$$

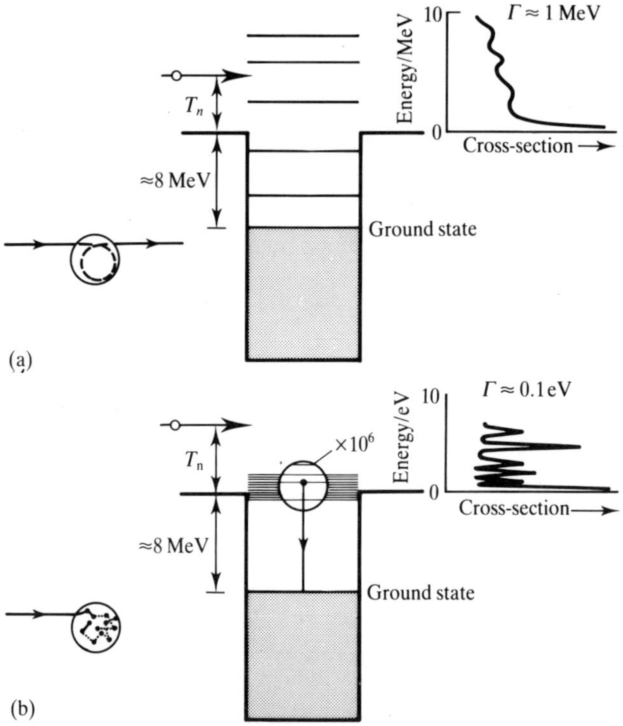

Figure 6.4 Interaction of a neutron with a nucleus. The square-well levels shown represent states of excitation of the system (neutron + nucleus) near and above the neutron binding energy of about 8 MeV: (a) potential well model; (b) compound nucleus model. (Note the different energy scales.) The appearance of levels at positive energy, $T_n > 0$, is a quantum mechanical effect arising from the potential discontinuity.

and the variation of the cross-section with energy can be studied by varying the temperature of the slowing-down medium. The first model that attempted to describe the results of such experiments was the shell model according to which the neutron would move only briefly in the potential well provided by the target nucleus and would have a high probability of emerging (figure 6.4(a)). Resonance would be observed when the incident particle created a system with an energy near one of the levels of the potential well, but the spacing of these levels would be approximately $\hbar^2/2mR^2$, i.e. about 1 MeV for $A = 100$ and m around the neutron mass. Also, the width would be large (≈ 1 MeV) because of the brief time of association ($\approx 10^{-21}$ s) of the neutron with the well. Variations of capture probability with energy in the thermal range were not likely to be produced by these resonances.

This picture is in sharp disagreement with observation at several points. Although the single-particle resonances contribute to broad structural features in scattering cross-sections as a function of energy for neutrons of a few mega-electronvolts energy, near-thermal neutrons show small scattering and large absorption for many nuclei. In particular, the work of Moon and Tillman and of Amaldi and Fermi, using reactions such as (6.11) and (6.12), established not only the existence of thermal neutrons in systems in which slowing down could take place, but also anomalies in cross-section for near-thermal energies that had to be interpreted as due to *narrow, relatively long-lived* resonant states (figure 6.4(b)).

In order to explain these observations, Niels Bohr in 1936 introduced the concept of the *compound nucleus*, which is a many-body system formed by amalgamation of the incident particle with the target nucleus, e.g. reaction (6.11) proceeds in two stages:

$$\begin{aligned} {}^{107}\mathrm{Ag} + \mathrm{n} &\to {}^{108}\mathrm{Ag}^* \\ {}^{108}\mathrm{Ag}^* &\to \text{final state} \end{aligned} \qquad (6.13)$$

where ${}^{108}\mathrm{Ag}^*$ represents a ${}^{108}\mathrm{Ag}$ nucleus plus the energy brought in by the incident neutron, which is mainly the binding energy of the neutron in ${}^{108}\mathrm{Ag}$, i.e. about 8 MeV. In such a system, which has analogies with a liquid drop, the incident particle has a short mean free path and shares the total energy with many of the internal degrees of freedom of the compound nucleus, so that it cannot be re-emitted until, as a result of further exchanges, sufficient energy is again concentrated on this or a similar particle. If the incident particle is a slow neutron, this may be a very long time, several orders of magnitude greater than the time that a fast particle takes to cross the nucleus. This slow-neutron time ($\approx 10^{-15}$ s) may be long enough to permit the electromagnetic coupling to generate the emission of a photon so that (6.13) is completed by the process

$${}^{108}\mathrm{Ag}^* \to {}^{108}\mathrm{Ag} + \gamma \qquad (6.14)$$

as shown in figure 6.4(b). This explains the predominance of the capture reaction and the suppression of elastic scattering. The sharp, closely spaced resonances display the modes of motion of the many-body system and the spacing distribution provides an excellent example of the development of chaotic features in physical interactions.

The progress of nuclear reactions such as (6.1) can be described in terms of the compound nucleus as a *two-stage process*

$$\mathrm{X} + \mathrm{a} \to \mathrm{C}^* \to \mathrm{Y} + \mathrm{b} \qquad (6.15)$$

in contrast with the *single-state process*

$$\mathrm{X} + \mathrm{a} \to \mathrm{Y} + \mathrm{b} \qquad (6.16)$$

envisaged by the single-particle shell model and leading to the same products.

The second stage of the nuclear reaction according to Bohr's suggestion is *independent* of the first. This means that the break-up of the compound nucleus into different channels Y + b, $Y_1 + b_1$ etc. should be determined only by the properties of the compound nucleus at its particular excitation and not by its mode of formation. The angle-integrated cross-section for the reaction X(a, b)Y near a compound nucleus resonance can then be written

$$\sigma_{ab} = \frac{\sigma_a \Gamma_b}{\Gamma} \tag{6.17}$$

where σ_a is the compound nucleus *formation* cross-section and Γ_b is proportional to the probability of break-up into channel Y + b. The total 'width' Γ is the sum of all partial widths, including Γ_a which measures the probability of decay back into the incident channel. In what follows we shall discuss mainly reactions induced by neutrons but charged particle processes may be similarly treated with the introduction of Coulomb penetrabilities.

6.3.2 Discrete resonances in the compound nucleus

We consider the formation of a compound nucleus by a particle of total* energy E which is near to the energy E_R of a resonance level. If the spacing D of the energy levels is large compared with their total width Γ, the formation cross-section is given by a *Breit–Wigner equation*

$$\sigma_a = \pi \lambda\!\!\!^{-2} g \frac{\Gamma_a \Gamma}{(E_R - E)^2 + \Gamma^2/4} \tag{6.18}$$

in which the statistical factor g is given by

$$g = \frac{2J + 1}{(2s_1 + 1)(2s_2 + 1)} \tag{6.19}$$

where s_1 and s_2 are the spins of the bombarding particle and the target nucleus X and J is the spin of the compound state, which is obtained as a vector sum of the spins and the incident orbital angular momentum in the collision. The form of equation (6.18) is derived from general partial wave analysis in section 9.2.3; it is similar to that of resonance formulae occurring in many other branches of physics.

---

* The total energy is indicated because of the significance of this equation in particle physics (chapter 9). It is strictly the centre-of-mass (channel) energy T^* plus mc^2. For nuclear reaction studies E is usually replaced by T^* or even by the laboratory kinetic energy T.

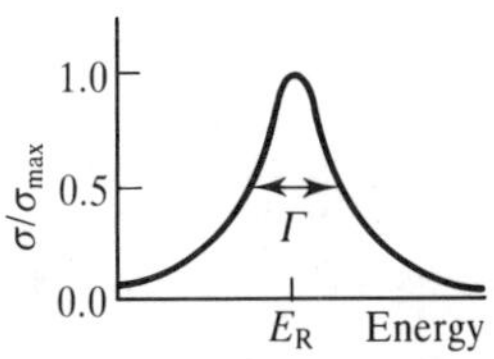

Figure 6.5
A pure Breit–Wigner cross-section curve showing the resonance energy E_R and total width Γ. The energies should be centre-of-mass values but in practice laboratory energies are often used in *nuclear* physics.

The energy variation of a cross-section following equation (6.18) is shown in figures 6.5 and 6.6(b). In the energy range considered ($D \gg \Gamma$) the independence hypothesis is reasonable and the yield of a particular *reaction* X(a, b)Y is given by (6.17) and (6.18) in the Breit–Wigner form

$$\sigma_{ab} = \pi \lambda\!\!\!^{-2} g \frac{\Gamma_a \Gamma_b}{(E_R - E)^2 + \Gamma^2/4} \tag{6.20}$$

while for *compound elastic scattering* X(a, a)X we have

$$\sigma_{aa} = \pi \lambda\!\!\!^{-2} g \frac{\Gamma_a^2}{(E_R - E)^2 + \Gamma^2/4}. \tag{6.21}$$

Experimentally, the yield of a reaction near an isolated resonance follows the Breit–Wigner form very closely but the elastic scattering is accompanied by *hard-sphere* or *potential* scattering which may be thought of as the effect of the superimposed tails of distant resonances. For charged particles there is also a Coulomb potential term. The compound and potential scattering will interfere if they evolve on a similar time scale, which can be the case when discrete resonances in light nuclei are involved. The effect of the change of sign of the real part of the compound elastic amplitude ($\propto 1/(E_R - E - i\Gamma/2)$) as the bombarding energy passes through resonance may then be clearly seen, as illustrated in figure 6.6(a).

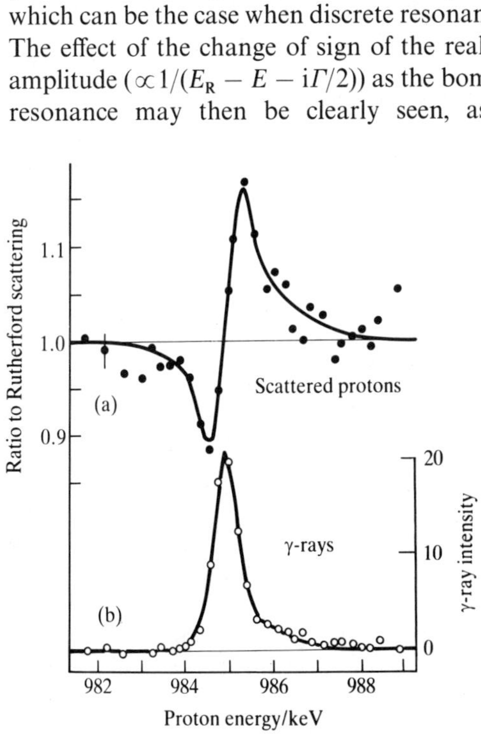

Figure 6.6 Scattering and absorption of protons at the 985 keV resonance in the $^{27}Al + p$ reaction: (a) yield of scattering protons; (b) yield of capture radiation. (Bender R S *et al.* 1949 *Phys Rev* **76** (273).) The interference in part (a) is between the nuclear and Coulomb amplitudes.

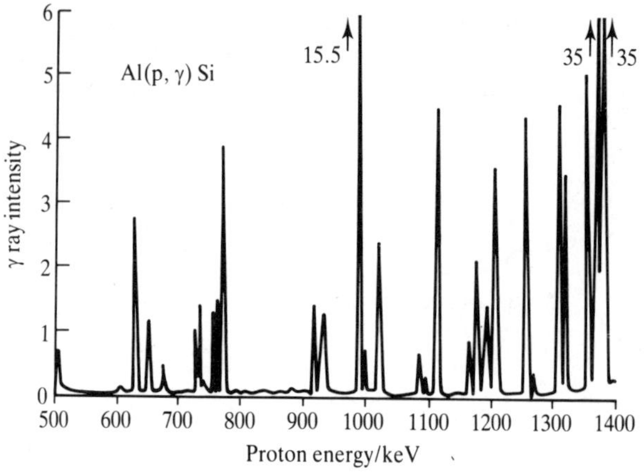

Figure 6.7
Resonant yield of γ radiation in the reaction $^{27}Al(p, \gamma)^{28}Si$. The peaks indicate virtual levels at about 12 MeV, just above the proton binding energy in ^{28}Si (Brostrom K J *et al* 1947 *Phys Rev* **71** (661)).

Resonance scattering is further discussed in chapter 9 and in reference 11 of chapter 1.

Figure 6.7 shows discrete levels at about 12 MeV excitation in the nucleus ^{28}Si, observed in the excitation function for the reaction $^{27}Al(p, \gamma)^{28}Si$; the widths are instrumental.

6.3.3 Continuum states of the compound nucleus

For compound nucleus excitations to the energy range at which the total width of levels becomes comparable with their spacing the resonances merge into a *continuum*. The cross-section for formation of the compound nucleus must now be calculated by averaging a Breit–Wigner type of cross-section over an energy interval containing many levels, and the result found for spinless particles incident as an s wave ($l = 0$) is

$$\bar{\sigma}_a = \pi\lambda\!\!\!^{-2} \cdot \frac{2\pi\bar{\Gamma}_a}{D} \tag{6.22}$$

where $\bar{\Gamma}_a$ is the mean level width over the averaging interval and D is the mean spacing of levels in this interval. The quantity $\bar{\Gamma}_a/D$ is the s wave *strength function* and is a measure of the complexity of internal motion in the compound state.

Figure 6.8
Independence assumption for the continuum region of nuclear spectra. The curves show the yield of ^{63}Zn and ^{62}Zn formed in the α particle bombardment of ^{60}Ni (full lines) and in the proton bombardment of ^{63}Cu (broken lines). The energy scales are adjusted so that the compound nucleus excitation matches in the two cases. (Ghoshal S N 1950 *Phys Rev* **80** (939).)

It is not obvious that the Bohr independence hypothesis applies to the continuum, but experimental evidence such as that shown in figure 6.8 confirms that in some cases it does, and that reaction cross-sections are described by a formula like (6.20). The decay width Γ_b must be evaluated for all transitions to available levels of the final nucleus and is thus dependent on the level density in this nucleus. If the nucleus behaves like a Fermi gas of nucleons the level density at excitation E above the ground

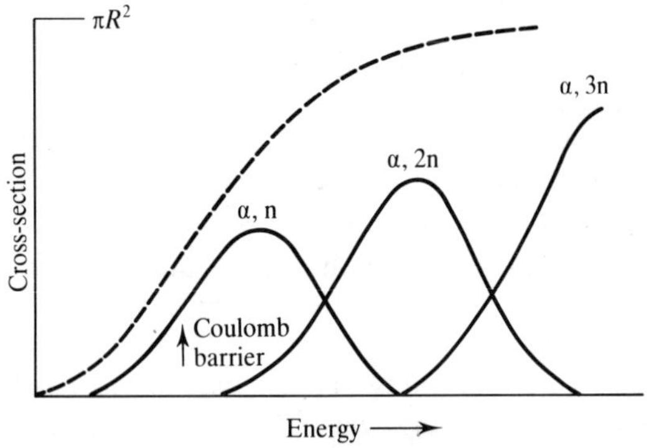

Figure 6.9 Cross-sections in the continuum theory. The figure shows the cross-sections for the X(α, *x*n) reactions and the theoretical cross-section for formation of the compound nucleus. The rise is due partly to barrier penetration and partly to the onset of new processses.

state may be written[7]

$$\omega_{\mathrm{Y}}(E) \propto \exp[2(aE)^{1/2}] \tag{6.23}$$

where a is a parameter proportional to the single-particle level spacing near the Fermi energy. From $\bar{\sigma}_{\mathrm{a}}$ and Γ_{b} the excitation function for the reaction X(a, b)Y may be calculated, with due allowance for barrier penetration factors for the incident particle and for competition between alternative channels b, c, ... The form of an excitation function for the *charged-particle* reaction (α, n) + (α, 2n) + (α, 3n) is shown in figure 6.9.

The intensity of particles b falls off at high energy of emission because it is not likely that a large amount of energy will be concentrated on one particle in the compound state. It also diminishes at low energies, partly at least because of barrier transmission effects for the low energy emitted particle. The resulting spectrum has similarities with the Maxwell distribution for the energies of the molecules of a gas. The analogy is often used to suggest that a quantity with the dimensions of energy be defined as the *nuclear temperature* and that the reaction particles b be regarded as evaporation products. The temperature, however, is simply an alternative expression for the level density of Y.

The concepts of the continuum region discussed in this section (especially that of evaporation) suggest that the emergent particles should often have an isotropic angular distribution in the centre-of-mass system. Experiment confirms this but also shows that for transitions to the lower states of Y (i.e. the higher energy emitted particles) the angular distributions have a marked forward peak. These peaks are associated with non-compound nucleus processes known as *direct interactions* (section 6.5).

6.4 The optical model of particle-induced nuclear reactions[1,2,13]

With the post-Second World War development and use of accelerators as a source of variable-energy charged particles and neutrons, nuclear reactions were studied for a wide range of incident energies E and target mass numbers A. It soon became obvious that the highly successful compound nucleus theory was unable to interpret the scattering phenomena observed with protons and neutrons of a few mega-electronvolts energy. For such neutrons for instance, with an experimental energy spread that averaged over the resonance levels of the compound nucleus, total cross-sections were expected to decrease monotonically with energy to the asymptotic value $2\pi R^2$ for a 'black' nucleus of radius R (section 9.2.1). But experimentally the total cross-section (scattering plus reaction) plotted as a function of E or A showed broad resonance features occurring at parameter values corresponding roughly with single-particle level spacings of the compound system X + a.

Other evidence for the apparent emergence of shell-model features was found at both higher and lower energies. For neutrons of approximately 100 MeV energy cross-sections fell short of the black-nucleus value, indicating a transparency of the target that could not be understood in terms of the conventional compound nucleus. Then, although slow neutron *absorption* seemed clearly to involve the compound nucleus, the (weaker) scattering of these particles showed anomalies when displayed as a function of target mass number A. These are shown in figure 6.10(a) and are found to appear when a new $l = 0$ orbit can just be bound in the compound potential well. This behaviour is contrasted in the figure with what might be expected if the scattering nucleus behaved as an impenetrable sphere (section 9.2.1) of radius $R \propto A^{1/3}$. The s wave neutron strength function, sketched in figure 6.10(b), showed corresponding features, indicating that the compound nucleus formation probability itself showed shell-model enhancement at particular mass numbers. All this evidence, together with supporting information for proton–nucleus scattering at energies above the Coulomb barrier, led to a clear requirement that an incident nucleon should have a *long mean free path* in a target nucleus, contrary to the suppositions of the Niels Bohr theory. Precisely this requirement is necessary for the shell-model description of nuclear levels. It is met theoretically by recognizing that the Pauli principle inhibits collisions with the more tightly bound nucleons because they cannot move to states that are already occupied. At higher incident energies more nucleons can interact and the mean free path is reduced, i.e. more absorption takes place. The model of nuclear reactions that results has analogies with the classical description of the refraction and absorption of light and is shown as the *optical model*.

The optical model proposes that a nuclear reaction should be determined by the solution of the Schrödinger equation for a one-body rather than a many-body problem, namely the motion of an incident particle of given

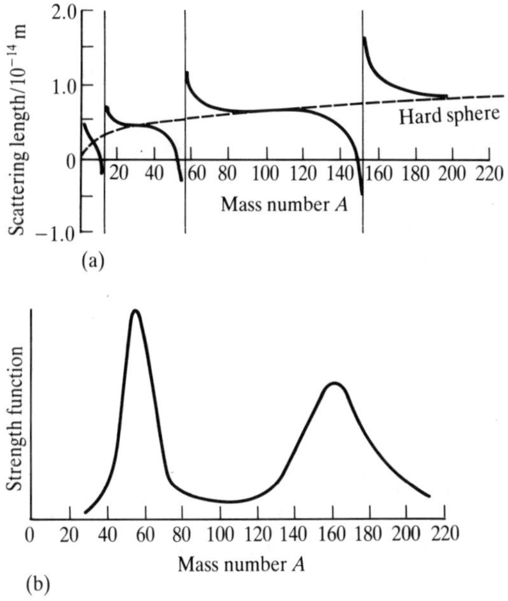

Figure 6.10 (a) Slow neutron scattering as a function of mass number showing the expectation for scattering from an impenetrable sphere and from a square-well potential (full curve). Experimental points follow the latter. The ordinate 'scattering length' is proportional to the square root of the cross-section (section 9.2.1). (b) Low energy neutron strength function, deduced from total cross-section measurements.

energy in a limited region of complex negative potential of the form

$$-[V(r) + \mathrm{i}W(r)]. \tag{6.24}$$

The real potential $V(r)$ is essentially that of the single-particle shell model (section 4.2.2) with a Woods–Saxon radial dependence. It contains the Coulomb potential in the case of charged particles and a spin–orbit term connected with polarization effects. Elastic scattering produced by $V(r)$ is evidently of single-particle type and will show broad, size-dependent resonances as the incident particle energy varies. The imaginary potential $\mathrm{i}W$ leads to a scattering amplitude that decreases with time (the sign is chosen to ensure this, otherwise a non-physical situation of continually increasing amplitude results). This term of the complex potential, therefore, represents an attenuation of the incident wave in the nucleus and determines the mean free path; it represents all reaction processes that are not associated with the prompt elastic scattering arising from the real potential V and in particular W must parametrize any elastic scattering arising through compound nucleus formation.

The course of a nuclear reaction according to these ideas may be represented as in figure 6.11. There is a preliminary or single-particle

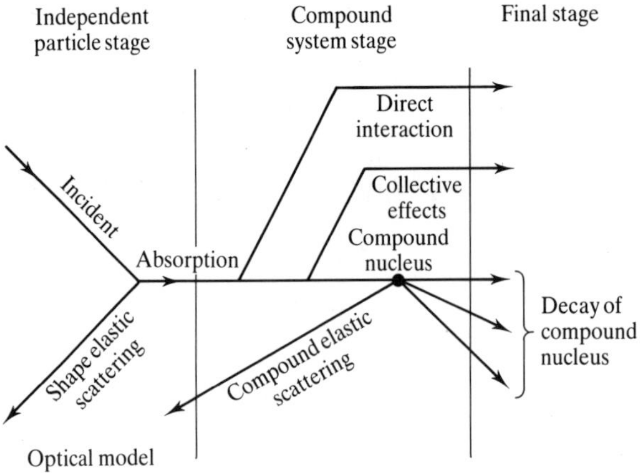

Figure 6.11
Nuclear reaction scheme according to V. F. Weisskopf (1957 *Rev Mod Phys* **29** (174)).

stage in which the interaction of the incident wave with the potential V leads to *shape-elastic* or *potential scattering*, including any shadow scattering (section 9.2.1) arising from absorption of particular partial waves. The absorption (potential W) leads to a compound system towards which the first step may be the excitation of a nucleon from the target nucleus. This creates a two-particle–one-hole (2p, 1h) state which has sometimes been called a *doorway state* since it leads both to direct interactions (section 6.5) and to further particle–hole excitations (3p, 2h; 4p, 3h etc.) which can finally create the strongly interacting many-body state that is the compound nucleus. Both the doorway state and the compound nucleus can decay back into the initial system, contributing to the total elastic scattering. Because of the complexity of motion represented by the overlapping resonance levels of a moderately heavy nucleus, *compound* elastic scattering from such a target evolves on a much longer time scale than the potential scattering and the two amplitudes are normally taken not to interfere. In fact, optical model analysis works best at energies that are high enough (say 10 MeV or above for nucleons) for the compound scattering to be disregarded in comparison with inelastic processes and certainly with shape-elastic scattering. It should not be used for light nuclei, for which sharp resonance effects may be seen. But if such resonances do appear, the energy definition of the beam must be good and this causes an uncertainty in time definition which permits interference between compound and potential amplitudes (cf. figure 6.6). Often both scattering and polarization differential cross-sections are available experimentally and the model provides the corresponding amplitudes. From W, the total reaction cross-section may be obtained. A model fit to 30.3 MeV proton–nucleus scattering is shown in figure 6.12 and the corresponding potential parameters are given in table 6.1.

The phenomenological optical model essentially provides a highly adaptable technique for describing elastic scattering and it has been used for complex particles as well as for nucleons. Following work by Greenlees,

Table 6.1
Optical model analysis of 30.3 MeV proton scattering from a range of nuclei

	^{40}Ca	^{58}Ni	^{120}Sn	^{208}Pb
V	46.1	47.0	51.1	53.4
W_V	0.4	3.4	1.2	4.0
W_S	5.96	4.4	8.7	7.6
V_{ls}	12.0	8.8	12.0	10.2

In this particular analysis, taken from the work of Greenlees G W and Pyle G J (*Phys Rev* **149** (836) 1966), the imaginary potential is split into a part W_V representing absorption over the whole nuclear volume and a surface-peaked part W_S. The value of the spin–orbit potential V_{ls} has been adjusted to allow for the use of the actual spin s in the formula for the potential rather than the spin-operator $\hat{\sigma}$.

The geometrical parameters differ for the different potentials but are approximately $R = r_0 A^{1/3}$, $r_0 = 1.25$ fm and $a = 0.65$ fm. The radial shape is thus similar to that of the charge distribution, equation (3.13).

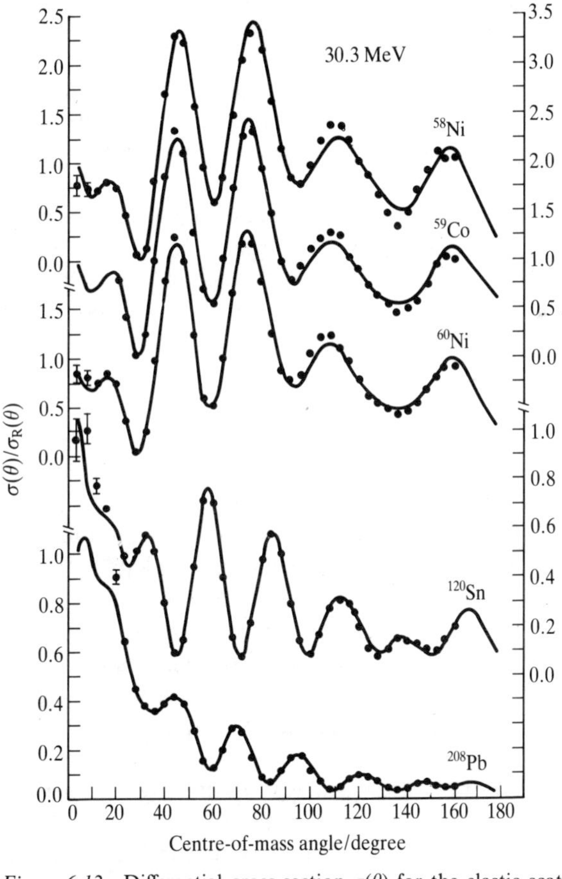

Figure 6.12 Differential cross-section $\sigma(\theta)$ for the elastic scattering of 30.3 MeV protons by nuclei shown as a ratio to the corresponding Rutherford (Coulomb) cross-section $\sigma_R(\theta)$. The points are experimental and the curves are theoretical fits. (Greenlees G W *et al.* 1968 *Phys Rev* **171** (1115).)

Pyle and Tang the number of arbitrary parameters in the potentials may be reduced by folding a suitable nucleon–nucleon potential with the matter distribution of target and projectile, if complex. (The potentials shown in table 6.1 have been extracted using the folding model.) The model gives no detail about the inelastic processes that are described by the potential iW. Of these, we have already considered compound nucleus processes and will return to these again in the discussion of heavy-ion reactions (section 6.6.3). There remains a distinct group of particle-induced inelastic phenomena already mentioned (section 6.3.3) as the *direct interactions* which we now consider.

6.5 Direct reactions[1,2,14,15]

6.5.1 Experimental characteristics

In the previous section, and especially in figure 6.11, it was seen that two types of elastic scattering take place in nuclear interactions, the shape-elastic scattering in which the incident particle rapidly senses the nuclear potential well and the much slower compound-elastic scattering which is a particular decay mode of the many-body compound state. For inelastic processes, direct reactions bear the same relation to compound nucleus reactions as does the shape-elastic scattering to the compound-elastic scattering. Essentially they evolve on the time scale of approximately 10^{-21} s set by the time that a nucleon of a few mega-electronvolts energy takes to cross an average nucleus and they excite only a few nuclear degrees of freedom.

Direct reactions are most commonly seen for incident particles with an energy of say 5 MeV per nucleon and above. These energies would excite continuum states in any compound nucleus but the outgoing particles in the reaction X(a, b)Y often have the following characteristics which are not explained by compound-nucleus theory.

(a) Emission of excess particles at high energy in comparison with the number expected according to statistical evaporation theory (section 6.3.3). These particles show resolvable structure since they lead to discrete, well-separated states of the final nucleus Y as shown in figure 3.10.
(b) Forward peaking of the higher energy particles of the spectrum in contrast with the symmetric angular distributions expected for evaporation particles, and in fact found for the lower energy particles b.
(c) Gradual and monotonic dependence of the yield of b on bombarding energy (excitation function).

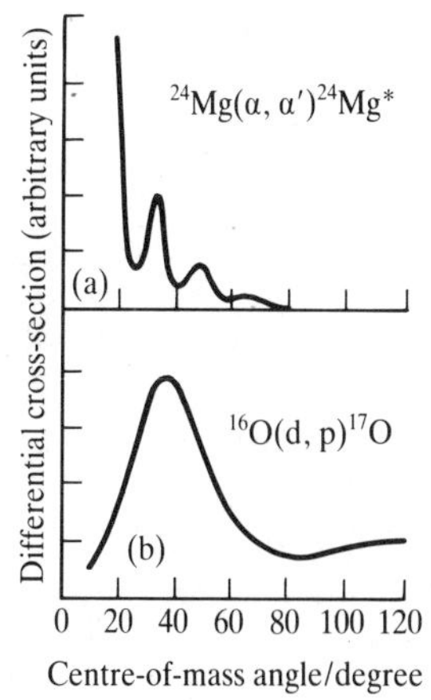

Figure 6.13
Angular distributions of direct reactions: (a) $^{24}Mg(\alpha, \alpha')^{24}Mg^*$ with 30 MeV α particles, exciting the 1.37 MeV level; (b) $^{16}O(d, p)^{17}O$ with 8 MeV deuterons. In each case the angular distribution is that of the light product particle.

These characteristics strongly suggest that the basic process at these energies is not an interaction with the target nucleus X as a whole, but with just a part of it, e.g. a single nucleon in the nuclear surface, whose emission excites particular states of the residual nucleus Y.

Examples of direct processes are

(a) direct inelastic scattering, such as the reaction

$$^{24}Mg + \alpha \rightarrow {}^{24}Mg^* + \alpha' \tag{6.25}$$

which tends to pick out *collective modes* of excitation of the residual nucleus;

(b) transfer reactions, such as the deuteron 'stripping'

$$^{16}O + d \rightarrow {}^{17}O + p \tag{6.26a}$$

$$\text{(or)} \rightarrow {}^{17}O^* + p' \tag{6.26b}$$

which select *single-particle* or *single-hole* states, including the ground state, preferentially.

Angular distributions for the two reactions (6.25) and (6.26a) are shown in figure 6.13. For each state that is excited directly, some indication of the total angular momentum may be derived from the angular distribution and the absolute value of the differential cross-section contains information on the structure (i.e. the wavefunctions) of the complex nuclei concerned.

6.5.2 Theoretical treatment

A basic consideration for the theory of direct reactions is that the occurrence of forward-peaked angular distributions means that high orbital momenta of the *incident* particle are involved since low-order partial waves give much more symmetrical distributions. This is good evidence for the peripheral or surface nature of the reactions.

The differential cross-section for the emission of particle b in the direct reaction X(a, b)Y is given in the so-called *plane-wave impulse approximation* (PWIA) as the product of a quantity related to the target structure with the cross-section for the peripheral process. For direct reactions it is the structure-dependent term that is of main interest.

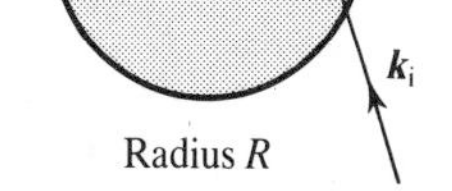

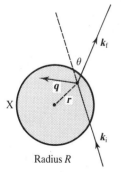

Figure 6.14
A direct inelastic scattering X(p, p′)X* in which a proton collides peripherally with a proton in the target nucleus and transfers it from an initial state ψ_i to a final state ψ_f.

Direct inelastic scattering

The most primitive approach is to represent a reaction such as X(p, p′)X* by the diagram of figure 6.14. The peripherally struck proton is transferred from a state with wavefunction ψ_i to a state ψ_f of different energy and possibly different angular momentum, leaving the rest of the nucleus unaffected in this approximation. The linear momentum transferred to the nucleus is $\boldsymbol{q}\hbar$ where, in terms of the initial and final wavenumbers of the incident particle ($k = p/\hbar$),

$$\boldsymbol{q} = \boldsymbol{k}_i - \boldsymbol{k}_f \tag{6.27}$$

$$\begin{aligned} q^2 &= k_i^2 + k_f^2 - 2k_i k_f \cos\theta \\ &= (k_i - k_f)^2 + 4k_i k_f \sin^2(\tfrac{1}{2}\theta) \end{aligned} \tag{6.28}$$

and θ is the centre-of-mass angle of scattering. For nuclear problems, q is usually expressed in reciprocal femtometres.

If ψ_i and ψ_f in this simple case represent single-particle states with orbital quantum numbers l_i and l_f and if there is no change of spin orientation in the collision, the angular momentum transfer to X is $\boldsymbol{l}$ where l is restricted by the inequality

$$l_f + l_i \geqslant l \geqslant |l_f - l_i| \tag{6.29}$$

by the need to conserve parity between initial and final states and also by the geometrical condition

$$|\boldsymbol{r} \times \boldsymbol{q}| = [l(l+1)]^{1/2} \tag{6.30}$$

where r is the position vector of the struck nucleon with respect to the nuclear centre. For peripheral reactions $r \approx R$, the nuclear radius, since collisions with smaller r are more likely to result in compound nucleus formation. The waves representing the inelastically scattered particles therefore originate on the nuclear surface at points for which the condition (6.30) is fulfilled. Interference between them creates the observed oscillatory angular distribution (cf. figure 6.13), with an angular periodicity characteristic of nuclear dimensions and of the l value for the excitation. For $r = R$, equation (6.30) can be satisfied by only one θ, which according to equation (6.28) increases with l and decreases with incident particle energy. Allowing for some spread of r values we may therefore expect a principal maximum at the angle given by

$$q(\theta) \approx \frac{[l(l+1)]^{1/2}}{R}. \tag{6.31}$$

Experimental results for light nuclei verify this prediction (see also example 6.9).

In the PWIA the structure-dependent part of the reaction matrix element is

$$\int \exp(\mathrm{i}\boldsymbol{q}\cdot\boldsymbol{r})\psi_f^* \psi_i \, \mathrm{d}^3 r \tag{6.32}$$

and this shows that the reaction picks out states ψ_f whose wavefunction overlaps strongly with ψ_i, e.g. the members of a rotational band. Such states have been excited in the inelastic scattering of electrons as well as of nuclei and heavier ions. The plane-wave theory, of course, is only a first approximation to a full theory, so since it is of the essence of a direct reaction that it does not much modify the character of the incident wave, the *Born approximation* of quantum mechanics may also be used to calculate the cross-section, as an alternative to perturbation theory. A suitable effective interaction for particle–nucleus scattering is then needed in the matrix element. In practice, most calculations are based on the *distorted-wave Born approximation* (DWBA), with potentials provided by the optical model analysis of elastic scattering. The DWBA analysis of inelastic data for a given l value determines the parameters of the nuclear model, e.g. the collective model, used to describe the excitations.

Transfer reactions

Reactions such as (d, p), (d, n), (t, d) (stripping) and (p, d), (n, d), (d, t) (pick-up) and others of this general type have angular distributions for incident energies of the order of 10 MeV or more of the type shown in figure 6.13(b). The process X(d, p)Y may also be represented by a momentum diagram such as figure 6.14, but in this case the primary process is the dissociation of the loosely bound deuteron into its component proton and neutron. This may take place outside the nucleus, in the Coulomb field, or again in the nuclear periphery; in each case the neutron moves from the projectile into the nucleus X forming the final nucleus Y with appropriate transfer of linear and angular momentum $(\boldsymbol{q}\hbar, \boldsymbol{l})$.

As with direct inelastic scattering the linear momentum transfer is given by

$$q^2 = (k_d - k_p)^2 + 4k_d k_p \sin^2(\tfrac{1}{2}\theta) \tag{6.33}$$

where the deuteron and proton wavenumbers have been used instead of k_i and k_f in figure 6.14. The angular momentum condition is the same as that given in (6.30).

The l value again determines the parity change between initial and final nuclei and limits the total angular momentum change. If the reaction amplitude arises mainly in the nuclear surface, then in (6.30) r is set equal to the nuclear radius R and the angular distribution of the observed final particle has a principal maximum at the angle for which $q \approx [l(l+1)]^{1/2}/R$. Theoretical angular distributions for the individual l values permit this quantity to be deduced from experimental results; for the stripping distribution shown in figure 6.13(b) the value $l = 2$ is indicated and this is in agreement with shell-model prediction. Pick-up reactions can be treated similarly and transfer reactions in general have provided much information on the quantum numbers of nuclear levels since the development of the theory in 1951. Nuclear structure information is contained in the differential cross-section for the reaction, e.g. at the principal maximum. The transition matrix element is now more complicated than for direct scattering since it must allow for the structure of the complex bombarding or emitted particle. Again, as with inelastic scattering, the matrix element contains an overlap integral for the initial and final states and this is normalized to unity if the target nucleus and transferred nucleon are together just equivalent to a single-particle state of the final nucleus. Generally, this is not so and if the final state of spin J_Y is formed from an initial state of spin J_X by the transfer of a particle of orbital angular momentum $\boldsymbol{l}$ and total angular momentum $\boldsymbol{j}$, the normalized differential cross-section is written, omitting isospin factors, in the form

$$\left(\frac{d\sigma}{d\Omega}\right)_{obs} = \frac{2J_Y + 1}{2J_X + 1} \sum_{l,j} S_{lj} \left(\frac{d\sigma}{d\Omega}\right)_{lj} \tag{6.34}$$

where $(d\sigma/d\Omega)_{lj}$ is the cross-section expected for the single-particle transfer (l, j) and S_{lj} is the corresponding *spectroscopic factor.*

Evaluation of the single-particle cross-section is usually carried out using DWBA codes with distorting potentials provided by optical model analysis of the related elastic scattering. In some cases more reliable values for S_{lj} can be obtained from experiments with incident particles of energy well below the Coulomb barrier, since distortions due to nuclear forces are not then present. In such experiments, however, angular distributions are no longer characteristic of the l value, but only of the Coulomb field.

A transfer calculation

In the reaction ${}^{90}_{40}Zr(d, t){}^{89}_{40}Zr$ with 21 MeV deuterons, a peak of 14 MeV tritons is observed at an angle of 23°. A rough indication of the angular momentum transfer may be obtained as follows, omitting centre-of-mass corrections.

The linear momentum of the neutron picked up from the target is vectorially related to the momenta of the incident deuteron and emitted triton. It is convenient to work in wavenumbers k because these are directly proportional to linear momenta by the relation $k = p/\hbar$. The linear momentum is therefore $\boldsymbol{q}\hbar$ where, by equations (6.27) and (6.28),

$$q^2 = k_d^2 + k_t^2 - 2k_d k_t \cos\theta .$$

For the deuteron, taking the mass to be 2 amu

$$k_d^2 = \frac{p_d^2}{\hbar^2} = \frac{2m_d E_d}{\hbar^2} = \frac{2 \times 2 \times 1.66 \times 10^{-27} \times 21 \times 1.6 \times 10^{-13}}{1.05^2 \times 10^{-68}}$$

$$= 2.02 \times 10^{30}\ m^{-2}.$$

Similarly for the triton $k_t^2 = 2.02 \times 10^{30}\ \text{m}^{-2}$ also. We then find

$$q^2 = [2.02 + 2.02 - 2 \times (2.02)^{1/2}(2.02)^{1/2} \times 0.92]10^{30}$$
$$= 0.32 \times 10^{30}\ \text{m}^{-2}$$

and $q = 0.57\ \text{fm}^{-1}$ taking $1\ \text{fm} = 10^{-15}$ m.

This linear momentum can now be used to give the angular momentum removed from the target if the location of the interaction is known. For a direct reaction we assume that this is in the low-density periphery of the nucleus so that the angular momentum is of the order l where

$$\sqrt{[l(l+1)]}\hbar \approx q\hbar R$$

if R is the nuclear radius.

The choice of radius is rather uncertain for a calculation of this sort because some correction should be made for the finite size of the deuteron at least. If we take the highest value suggested in (3.15), namely $1.3A^{1/3}$ and (arbitrarily) add 2.15 fm as half the size parameter of the deuteron (equation (3.38)) we get $R = 7.95$ fm and from the q value $l \approx 4$.

This value is in fact that required by the shell model since g-orbits are involved at the fiftieth neutron. A proper DWBA analysis of the experimental results allowing for finite size and for distortions of the representative waves would confirm this value.

Assuming $l = 4$, the shell-model prediction for the spin of the single-hole nucleus $^{89}_{40}Zr$ is $J = 9/2$.

6.6 Special reactions

We mention in this section some reaction processes with especially interesting features that do not fit neatly into preceding sections. In each of these the interplay between the nuclear and the Coulomb force is significant.

6.6.1 The excitation of isobaric analogue levels[16]

As stated in section 3.8 a level of given isobaric spin I is expected to occur in each of $2I + 1$ nuclei forming an isobaric multiplet ($I_3 = -I, \ldots, +I$). These states have now been identified in many nuclei and may be understood from a particular example, of mass 51 say.

For this mass we have a stable nuclide $^{51}_{23}V$ ($I = \frac{5}{2}$, $I_3 = -\frac{5}{2}$) which may be converted into unstable $^{51}_{24}Cr$ ($I_3 = -\frac{3}{2}$) by a *charge-exchange* direct reaction

$$^{51}_{23}V + p \rightarrow ^{51}_{24}Cr + n + Q \tag{6.35}$$

which changes a vanadium neutron into a chromium proton, with the indicated change of I_3. The ground state of ^{51}Cr presumably has $I = \frac{3}{2}$ since we need $I \geqslant |I_3|$, but among its excited states we might expect a state with the same spin and parity as the ground state of ^{51}V and with the isospin numbers $I = \frac{5}{2}$, $I_3 = -\frac{3}{2}$. This could be the analogue state in ^{51}Cr of the ^{51}V ground state if it has the same structure as this state except for a neutron–proton exchange. Production of such a state in process (6.35) should be favoured.

The experimental neutron spectrum for reaction (6.35) is given in figure 6.15 and shows just this feature; a sharp peak stands out above the mainly unresolved spectrum due to neutrons evaporated from the compound nucleus. The Q value for the production of the isobaric state in reaction (6.35) is seen from equation (3.5) to be just the difference between the binding energies of $^{51}_{23}V$ and $^{51}_{24}Cr^*$. Because of the identity of structure of these two states the binding energies differ only by their Coulomb energy so that $Q = -\Delta E_C$. The difference between this Q value and that for the ground state gives the excitation energy of the isobaric state in $^{51}_{24}Cr$ (see p. 207).

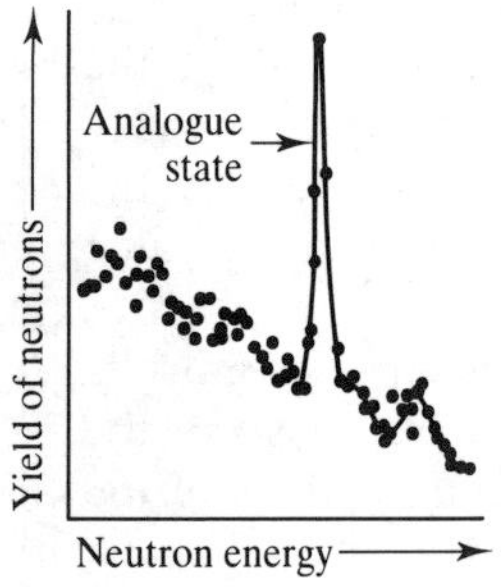

Figure 6.15
Isobaric analogue state of the target ground state, seen in the neutron spectrum for the reaction $^{51}V(p, n)^{51}Cr$ (adapted from Anderson J D and Wong C 1962 *Phys Rev Lett* **8** (442)).

In this particular example the analogue state is bound but for heavier isobaric multiplets the analogue states can be at an excitation greater than the nucleon binding energy. They may then be seen, for instance, in proton reactions as *formation* (*or isobaric analogue*) *resonances* rather than as final states. In this case they are analogous not to states of the target nucleus but to those of the nucleus formed by adding one *neutron* to it, since they exist in a compound nucleus of mass number one greater than that of the target.

6.6.2 *Electromagnetic interactions*[17]

Because the electromagnetic interaction is well understood, the nuclear reactions produced by photons, electrons and even muons have in principle a special simplicity and can sometimes be used to determine nuclear matrix elements without involving uncertain corrections. We have already commented on the elastic scattering of high energy electrons as a means of observing nuclear charge distributions (section 3.3) and it may now be noted that *inelastic scattering of electrons* provides much spectroscopic information. Although bremsstrahlung creates observational difficulties in electron experiments, it is found that groups of electrons of about 100 MeV energy, inelastically scattered from nuclei with the excitation

Excitation energy of an analogue state

For nuclei with mass number $A \approx 100$ or greater it is reasonable to use the semi-empirical mass formula (section 3.2.2) to predict the following:

(a) the excitation Δ_I of the first $I = I_0 + 1$ state in a nucleus whose ground state has $I = I_0$ (this is given immediately by the asymmetry energy term for A odd ($\delta = 0$));
(b) the binding energy displacement between states of $I = I_0 + 1$ but of different I_3, i.e. in different isobaric nuclei (this is given directly by the Coulomb energy difference ΔE_C, and is in fact equal to $-Q$ in processes such as (6.35) for the excitation of the analogue state).

For mass number $A = 51$ already discussed (section 6.6.1) these energies have been found experimentally to be $\Delta_I = 6.605$ MeV and $\Delta E_C = 8.139$ MeV but application of the mass formula to such a light nucleus is not really justified. A crude estimate of both Δ_I and ΔE_C may, however, be obtained by calculating the latter, as in the mass formula, from the potential energy of a charged sphere. This gives

$$\Delta E_C = \Delta\left[\frac{3}{5}\frac{Z(Z-1)e^2}{r_0 A^{1/3}}\frac{\mu_0 c^2}{4\pi}\right] \qquad \text{for } Z \to Z+1$$

$$= \frac{6}{5}\frac{Ze^2}{r_0 A^{1/3}}\frac{\mu_0 c^2}{4\pi}$$

$$= 8.3 \text{ MeV} \qquad \text{for } Z = 23 \text{ and } r_0 = 1.3 \text{ fm}.$$

This is the binding energy difference between the ground state ($I = \frac{5}{2}$, $I_3 = -\frac{5}{2}$) of ${}^{51}_{23}V$ and the analogue state ($I = \frac{5}{2}$, $I_3 = -\frac{3}{2}$) in ${}^{51}_{24}Cr$. To obtain the excitation of this state in ${}^{51}_{24}Cr$, i.e. the energy difference between the states $I = \frac{5}{2}, \frac{3}{2}$ for $I_3 = -\frac{3}{2}$, we have to correct for the difference between the neutron and proton mass (0.78 MeV) and for the energy displacement between the V and Cr ground states (0.75 MeV, with Cr the higher) which is shown in the mass tables. This gives

$$\Delta_I = 8.3 - 0.78 - 0.75$$

$$= 6.77 \text{ MeV}.$$

of nuclear levels, may be seen against background at large angles of scattering. By varying the scattering angle, the momentum transfer $\boldsymbol{q}\hbar$ to the nucleus may be varied independently of the energy transfer and the dependence of the scattering on $|\boldsymbol{q}|$ can be explored. Extrapolation of the observations to the 'photon point' ($q = 0$) gives the reduced probability $B(L)\uparrow$ for the excitation of a transition of multipolarity L from the ground state of the target nucleus. A special feature of this type of reaction is that the $L = 0$ monopole transitions such as $J^P = 0^+ \rightarrow 0^+$, which are strongly forbidden for real transverse photons, may be excited because of the longitudinal nature of the Coulomb field which transmits the interaction.

The transference of energy by the electromagnetic field also permits the excitation of nuclear states by positively charged particles of energy too low to surmount the nuclear Coulomb barrier. Protons or heavy ions moving in the Coulomb field at such energies describe a classical trajectory both before and after the energy transfer and the cross-section for this *Coulomb excitation* depends both on the trajectory and the reduced transition probability $B(L)\uparrow$ (section 5.1.4). The process is detected by the observation of de-excitation radiation from the upper state and is found to be especially probable for excitation of the low-lying $J = 2^+$ collective states of both spherical and deformed nuclei. Figure 6.16 shows one of the early yield curves obtained in the proton bombardment of a heavy element.

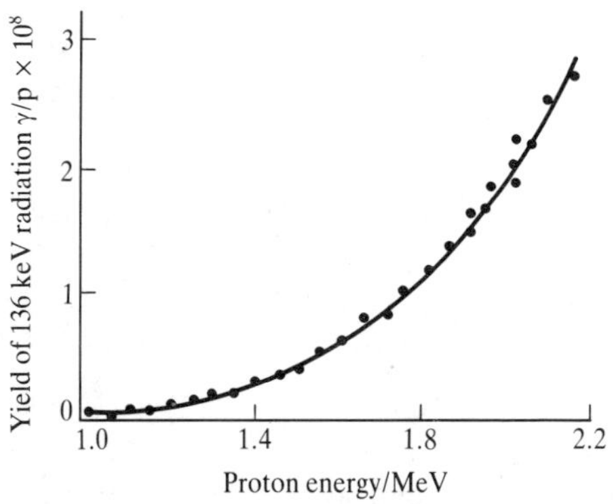

Figure 6.16 Yield of 136 keV quanta from ^{181}Ta bombarded by protons as a function of proton energy, compared with theory for E2 excitation (solid curve). (Huus T and Zupančič C 1953 (*Det Kgl Dansk Selskab* **28** (1).)

Real photons themselves, from radioactive sources, from electron bremsstrahlung or from positron annihilation, also produce nuclear effects through coupling to nuclear charge and current distributions. Among such *photonuclear reactions* the photodisintegration of the deuteron

$$\gamma + d \rightarrow n + p \tag{6.36}$$

and its inverse, neutron capture by protons

$$n + p \rightarrow d + \gamma \tag{6.37}$$

exchange energy between the neutron–proton system and the electromagnetic field. The minimum exchange is the binding energy of the deuteron and the process (6.37) gives the most accurate value of this quantity:

$$\epsilon = 2.2245 \pm 0.0002 \text{ MeV}. \tag{6.38}$$

The spins of the particles involved and the unit intrinsic spin of the photon permit the deuteron reaction (6.36) to proceed as either an M1 or an E1 transition; the former dominates near threshold.

For heavier nuclei the (γ, n) and (γ, p) photoreactions take place preferentially at energies of about 15–20 MeV because of the existence at about this excitation of the collective 1^- states which build up the giant (electric) dipole resonance. The neutron yield from the nucleus ^{197}Au excited by monochromatic photons from two-quantum annihilation of positrons is shown in figure 4.7.

6.6.3 Fission and heavy-ion reactions[18–22]

A brief account of the discovery of the fission phenomenon has been given in section 6.1.5; here it is intended to present the main experimental facts, to outline the theory of fission and to relate fission to the converse process of heavy-ion fusion. The study of heavy-ion processes has now become a major undertaking in nuclear structure laboratories.

Experimental facts (fission)

The sequence of events leading to the production of fission fragments from uranium bombardment by neutrons is shown in figure 6.17. One of

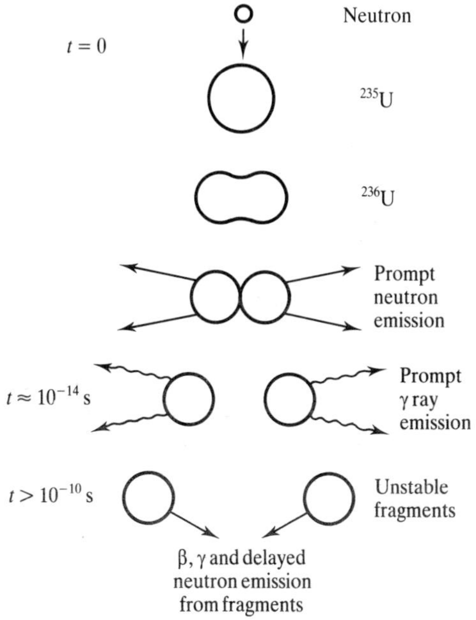

Figure 6.17
Schematic representation of the fission process in uranium. The time scale gives orders of magnitude only.

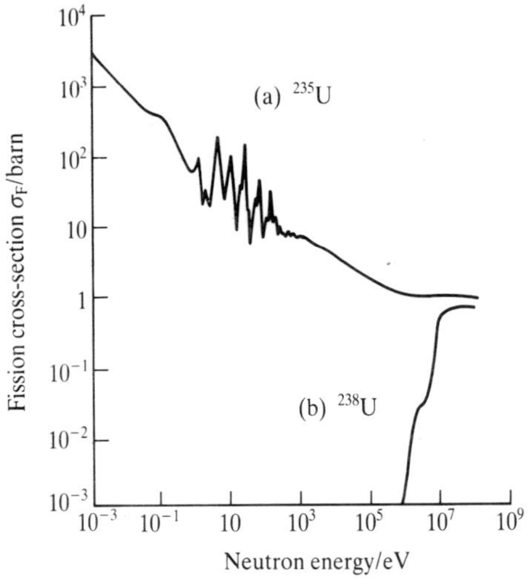

Figure 6.18
Fission cross-section, schematic, as a function of neutron energy: (a) ^{235}U; (b) ^{238}U.

the earliest theoretical proposals, rapidly verified experimentally, was that the *slow-neutron* fission of uranium should take place in the rare isotope ^{235}U. This followed from the observation that the complex of fission products did not show the particular resonance dependence on neutron energy known to be associated with the reaction $^{238}\text{U} + \text{n} \rightarrow {}^{239}\text{U}^*$. Thermal fission is also observed for other even-Z, odd-N nuclei such as ^{233}U and ^{239}Pu and the cross-section in the thermal region does indeed show its own characteristic resonances (figure 6.18(a)). The fragment pairs have an asymmetric mass distribution (figure 6.19) in which a given fission event generally yields a high mass (H) and a low mass (L) product rather than two equal masses. Conservation of linear momentum then requires the energy distribution also to be asymmetric so that the mean energies of the two groups are $\bar{E}_H = 60$ MeV and $\bar{E}_L = 95$ MeV.

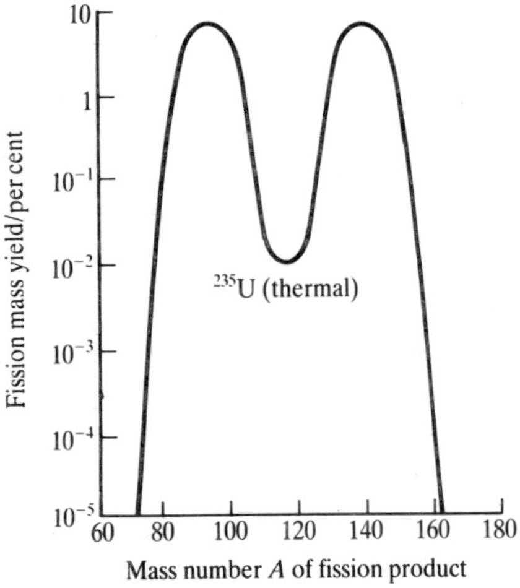

Figure 6.19
Mass distribution of fission fragments.

Fast-neutron fission is found for a number of even–even nuclei such as ^{232}Th and ^{238}U. There is a 'threshold' energy for the process, as shown in figure 6.18(b), whereas in the thermal region the main interactions are the (n, γ) capture process with a cross-section at various resonances around $\pi\lambda\!\!\!^{-2}$ and elastic scattering between resonances with the hard sphere cross-section of about $4\pi R^2$ (section 9.2.1.). Below the threshold energy fission is still possible energetically but the cross-section decreases exponentially as might be expected if the fragments have then to penetrate a Coulomb barrier. Fission is produced in many nuclei by energetic charged particles, e.g. p, d, α, and also by γ radiation. The fragment distribution for fast fission is generally more symmetric than for thermal fission.

Because the number N of neutrons in a stable nucleus increases faster than the number Z of protons as A increases, the fission fragments are initially neutron rich and very rapidly emit a small number of *prompt* neutrons. The average number per fission, ν (≈ 2.5), is an important experimental observable of the fission reactions, since these neutrons make possible the development of chain-reacting systems. The N/Z ratio of the fragments is restored to normal by sequential β decay, e.g.

$$^{140}_{54}Xe \xrightarrow{e^-} {}^{140}_{55}Cs \xrightarrow{e^-} {}^{140}_{56}Ba \xrightarrow{e^-} {}^{140}_{57}La \longrightarrow {}^{140}_{58}Ce \text{ (stable).} \quad (6.39)$$

In some of these chains one of the product nuclei may be so highly excited that neutron emission is possible. The resulting β-delayed neutrons have the halflife of the parent β emitter; they are important technically in the control of nuclear reactors.

Theory of fission

The difference between thermally fissile and fast-fissile nuclei is that in the former case an even-Z, even-N compound nucleus is formed, e.g.

$$^{235}U + n \rightarrow {}^{236}U^* \quad (6.40)$$

and in the latter an odd-Z or odd-N system is formed, e.g.

$$^{238}U + n \rightarrow {}^{239}U^*. \quad (6.41)$$

The form of the pairing energy term $\delta(A)$ in the semi-empirical mass formula (section 3.2.2) indicates that the neutron binding energy for ^{236}U is greater than for ^{239}U and the excitation of the compound nucleus for an incident thermal neutron in (6.40) is therefore greater than in (6.41). Any barrier resisting fission can be more readily overcome in the former case.

The nature of the fission barrier was discussed by Bohr and Wheeler in terms of an incompressible liquid-drop model of the nucleus, in which energies (and hence masses) are determined by the physical effects already discussed in setting up the semi-empirical mass formula. Stability against fission, when energetically possible, depends critically on the relative importance of the short-range nuclear force and the long-range Coulomb force. If a spherical, constant-density nucleus is slightly deformed in a symmetrical way, the surface energy increases, since for a sphere the ratio of surface area to volume is a minimum, and the Coulomb energy decreases. For a given A these changes are in first order proportional to the undeformed values $\beta A^{2/3}$ and $\epsilon Z^2/A^{1/3}$ shown in equation (3.7); the other terms are essentially unaltered. If the surface energy increase exceeds the electrostatic energy decrease the nucleus is stable against small deformations. By equating the two terms it can be seen that such stability is dependent on the quantity Z^2/A.

Some understanding of the general nature of the fission process may now be obtained by considering the inverse *heavy-ion* reaction in which two heavy fragments approach to form a compound nucleus by fusion (figure 6.20). If the quantity Z^2/A for this system is large, as for curve (c) of the figure, the Coulomb force is high and cannot be compensated by the nuclear force term to form even a quasi-stable state, so that a heavy nucleus of this sort is spontaneously fissionable with a very short halflife. In the other extreme, shown as curve (a) of the figure, for Z^2/A small, the two ions fuse together, with the emission of energy as radiation or as particles, to form a stable system with considerably lowered total energy. A heavy nucleus of this sort faces a formidable barrier against fission and the lifetime for such decay as a spontaneous process is very long.

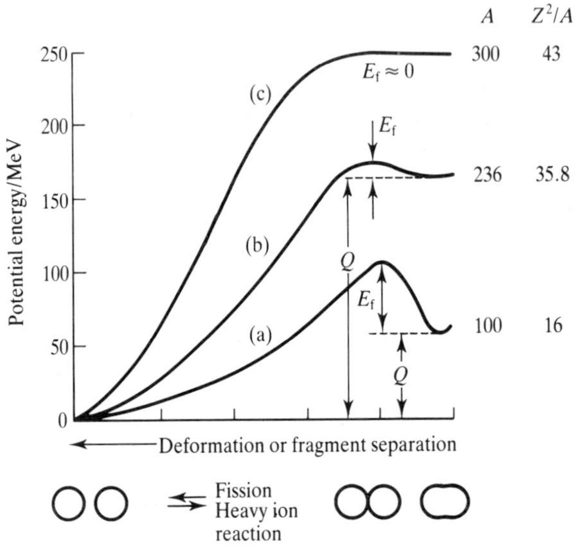

Figure 6.20 Schematic representation of fission barriers for nuclei of mass number $A \approx 100$, 236 and 300. The energy release Q relates to spontaneous fission.

The case of interest for induced fission is that shown as curve (b) of the figure, for the intermediate values of Z^2/A, when the nuclear force is sufficient to bind the two fragments together with a fission barrier E_f of a few mega-electronvolts. Bohr and Wheeler estimated the height of this barrier for the fissile nuclei and concluded that it would be about 6 MeV for $A \approx 240$. In the case of thermally fissile nuclei, equation (6.40), this energy is exceeded by the excitation energy brought to the compound system by absorption of the incident slow neutron and induced fission takes place rapidly ($\tau \leqslant 10^{-16}$ s) from states above the barrier. The fragments develop their final kinetic energy as they separate under the repulsive Coulomb force; the total energy release, including any taken by neutrons or radiation, may be calculated from the overall mass change – in equation (6.6b) for example.

The double hump[19]

It remains to account for the fission halflives of 10^{-2}–10^{-8} s which are found for excited states of some transuranic nuclei, e.g. plutonium ($Z = 94$), americium ($Z = 95$) and curium ($Z = 96$), produced in (n, γ) or other reactions. These halflives are long compared with those for over-the-barrier fission but short compared with the through-barrier spontaneous fission of ground states. The states concerned, which form what are known as *fission isomers*, are found from studies of the primary process to have an excitation of 2–3 MeV and a low spin, so that it is not obvious why they do not decay preferentially by a radiative transition, as in the case of many known isomers in lighter nuclei. Since this anomaly appears significantly in a certain range of Z values it is reasonable to ascribe it to a shell-model effect. The spherical shell-model has no magic numbers in the required range, but in a deformed potential these numbers change and lead to a bunching in energy of the shell-model orbits in the transuranic region. From the work of Strutinsky and of Nilsson it is now known that this effect can lead to a *double hump* in the potential energy curve and consequently in the fission barrier. The curve of figure 6.20(b) must then be replaced by figure 6.21 in which two stable deformations are shown, each creating a potential (I and II) with a set of energy levels.

If a nucleus like americium is excited to a level of well II, spontaneous fission (i.e. fission with barrier penetration) is impeded by a much thinner barrier than with the single-humped curve of figure 6.20(b). For fission to occur at all, of course, radiative decay to the ground state with $\tau \approx 10^{-14}$ s must be inhibited and this is so because a transition to well I requires a somewhat drastic change of nuclear deformation, which hinders the radiation. Fission from the states of well I is retarded by the *two* humps and is in fact the normal slow spontaneous process.

The important discovery of the double hump, which is not necessarily confined to fissionable nuclei, also explains some remarkable features of fission excitation functions. The first surprise is that induced fission shows sharp compound-nucleus resonances in the electronvolt–kilo-electronvolt

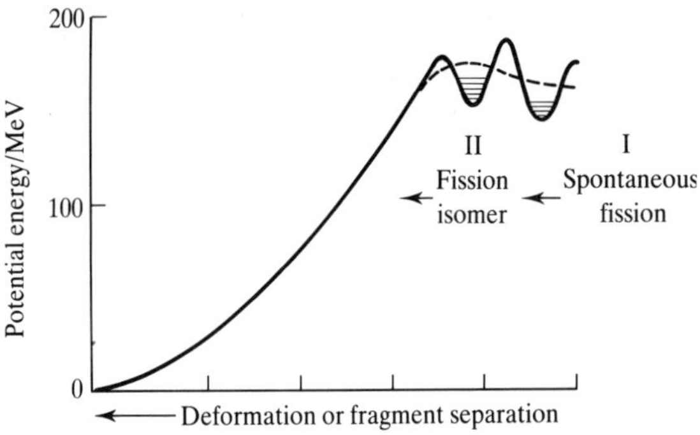

Figure 6.21 The double-humped fission barrier, arising because of shell structure. The broken line is the potential energy curve (b) in figure 6.20 appropriate to a liquid-drop model. The two potential wells I and II are not on the same energy scale as the main curve. Fission from the well I lowest state is the normal spontaneous process, but from well II it is the faster 'isomeric' decay.

energy range, corresponding to a compound nucleus excitation approximately equal to the height of the fission barrier. The explanation of this is that most of the energy is expended in producing the critical deformations, so that very few fission channels are open and the resonances of well I are not broadened. The second feature is that the excitation function for fission of some nuclei such as ^{240}Pu (figure 6.22) shows well-marked resonances *below* the threshold energy for over-the-barrier fast fission. This is due to the excitation by the incident neutrons of the closely spaced levels of well I, from which fission is hindered, and the overlap of bands of these levels with the wider and broader levels of well II, from which fission takes places, as a result of the coupling.

Experimental facts (heavy-ion reactions)

Heavy ions have characteristics which emphasize particular features of the whole range of nuclear phenomena from elastic scattering to fission and fusion. In addition, their reactions present some unique features connected with the mechanisms of energy transfer in many-body systems. Practically all available atoms may be at least partially stripped of

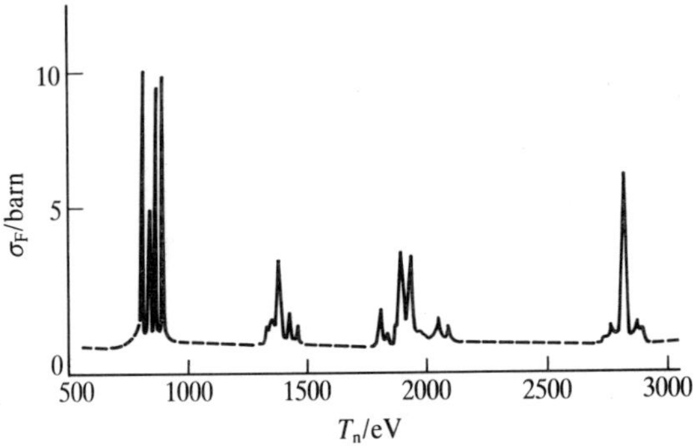

Figure 6.22
'Sub-threshold' fission cross-section of ^{240}Pu (adapted from Migneco E and Theobald J P 1968 *Nucl Phys* **A112** (603)).

electrons and accelerated in tandem electrostatic generators, cyclotrons, linear accelerators and synchrotrons usually to energies in the range 5–20 MeV per nucleon, though the injection of heavy ions into major particle physics accelerators has now yielded high relativistic energies (section 2.4.5).

The special features of heavy-ion reactions arise from (i) the high *linear momentum* of the ion for a given energy, which results in both a short de Broglie wavelength and a high *angular momentum* for a given impact parameter in a collision, and (ii) the high nuclear charge which enhances all Coulomb-dominated processes and also permits production in reactions of nuclei far removed from the line of stability. Because of the extended, complex and strongly interacting structure of a heavy nucleus, its mean free path in nuclear matter ought to be small. Processes that do not much disturb the ion should therefore be located near the nuclear surface. Deeper penetration would be expected to lead to compound nucleus formation or to fragmentation. But these ideas, based on the behaviour of light projectiles, have had to be supplemented by new mechanisms in the case of heavy ions.

The *elastic scattering* (other than compound elastic) of heavy ions is illustrated in figure 6.23. In all cases the scattering parameter kR, where k is the centre-of-mass wavenumber and R is the sum of target and ion radii, is very much greater than unity. Whether or not the diffractive-type oscillations characteristic of nuclear size appear in the angular distribution depends on the value of the Coulomb parameter η defined in equation (5.37). For large η, e.g. at low energy, pure Coulomb scattering is seen (figure 6.23(a)), whereas for low η, e.g. at high energy, the Fraunhofer diffraction pattern of a black disc of radius R is found (figure 6.23(c)). In intermediate cases in which both Coulomb and nuclear effects are present,

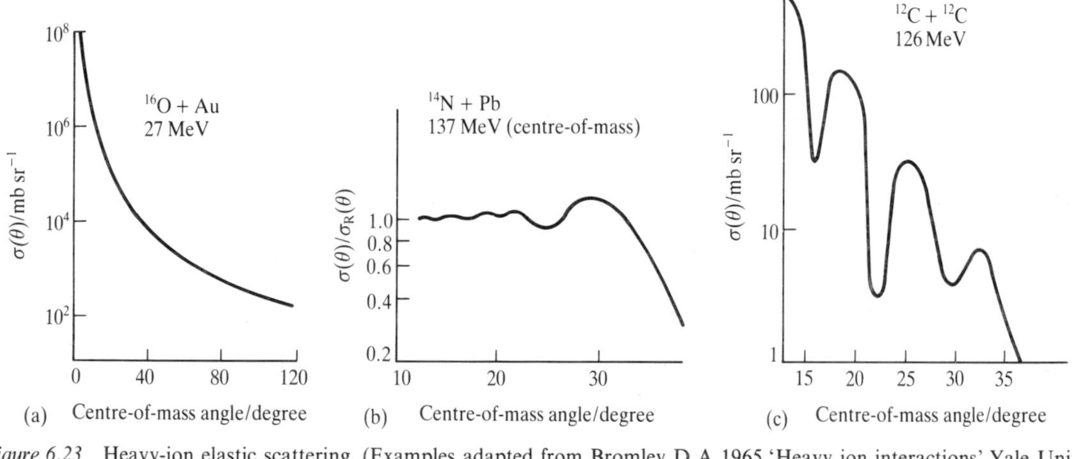

Figure 6.23 Heavy-ion elastic scattering. (Examples adapted from Bromley D A 1965 'Heavy ion interactions' Yale Univ Report 3222-32) The η values are (a) 73, (b) 27 and (c) 1.8.

a typical pattern is that of figure 6.32(b) which shows Fresnel-type diffraction peaks, superimposed on Rutherford scattering. An important parameter in many heavy-ion reactions is the *grazing angle* θ which is the deflection for the classical Coulomb trajectory which just brings the colliding nuclei into contact.

The *inelastic reactions* of heavy ions include Coulomb excitation which can be an extra-nuclear effect and is a powerful means of exciting the rotational bands of heavy nuclei. The most useful reactions for spectroscopic purposes are those of the *transfer* type provided that adequate resolution is available for the identification of final states. In these direct reactions, which may be analysed by DWBA codes, there is often high *selectivity* for states in which the transferred group has the maximum spin angular momentum allowed by the Pauli principle. A typical reaction transferring one proton is the process

$$^{48}\text{Ca} + {}^{16}\text{O} \rightarrow {}^{49}\text{Sc} + {}^{15}\text{N} \tag{6.42}$$

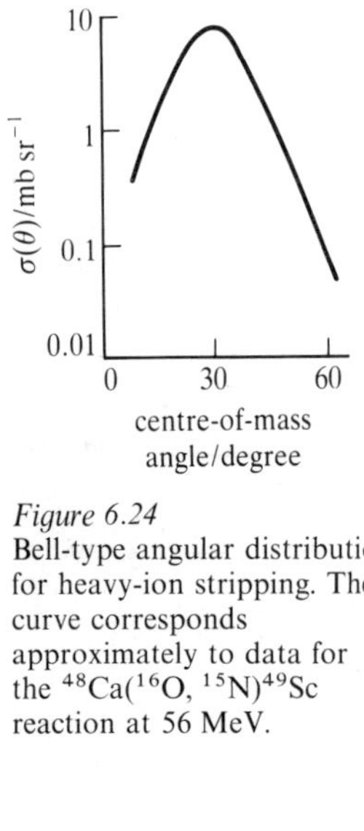

Figure 6.24
Bell-type angular distribution for heavy-ion stripping. The curve corresponds approximately to data for the ^{48}Ca(^{16}O, ^{15}N)^{49}Sc reaction at 56 MeV.

for which the angular distribution of the light product particle ^{15}N is shown in figure 6.24. This 'bell-type' curve is found for many heavy-ion reactions; it shows a maximum near the grazing angle, at which the nuclear attractive force just balances the Coulomb repulsion, because the more penetrating orbits produce yields that are strongly attenuated by absorption and the less penetrating orbits find fewer target nucleons with which to interact.

When the classical trajectory in a heavy-ion collision would indicate a deflection greater than the grazing angle, *fusion* of the two ions to form a highly excited *compound nucleus* may take place if the incident energy is greater than the barrier height. Because the heavy ion can bring in a high angular momentum the compound nucleus may be formed with a high spin, oriented at right angles to the path of the incoming ion. Emission of a reaction particle from the compound nucleus takes place with equal probability at all angles in a plane perpendicular to the nuclear spin, and if all such reaction planes (for different trajectories) are considered the centre-of-mass angular distribution for a purely compound nucleus evaporation process will have the form

$$\frac{d\sigma}{d\Omega} = \frac{d\sigma}{d\theta}\frac{d\theta}{d\Omega} = \text{constant} \times \frac{1}{\sin\theta} \tag{6.43}$$

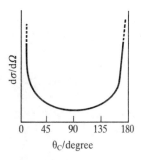

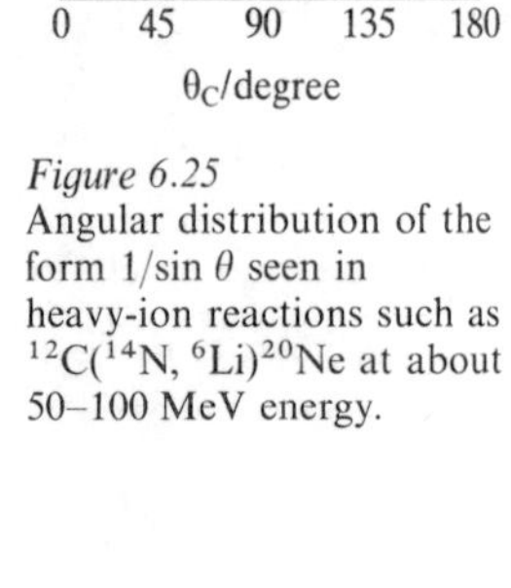

Figure 6.25
Angular distribution of the form $1/\sin\theta$ seen in heavy-ion reactions such as ^{12}C(^{14}N, ^{6}Li)^{20}Ne at about 50–100 MeV energy.

as shown in figure 6.25 for the reaction ^{12}C(^{14}N, ^{6}Li)^{20}Ne.

For heavy target nuclei the compound nucleus formed in any reaction will tend to decay by neutron rather than charged particle emission because of the Coulomb barrier; photon emission is also possible but is not favoured for excitations above the neutron binding energy. The progress of the heavy-ion–heavy-target reaction with neutron emission

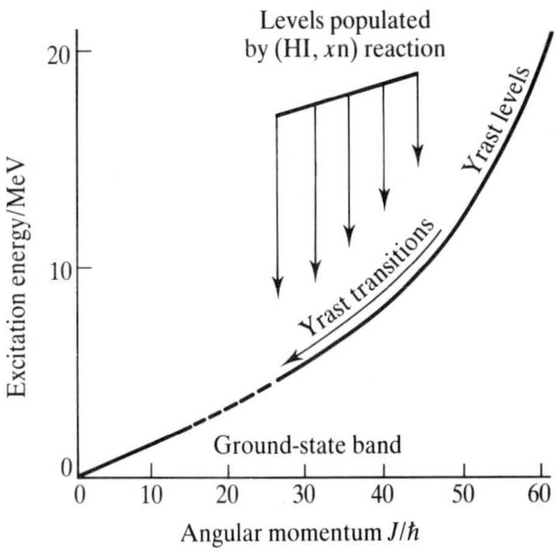

Figure 6.26 The statistical-yrast cascade in a compound nucleus of $A \approx 150$ created in a heavy-ion reaction. The transitions shown follow the emission of a small number of neutrons.

is then as shown in figure 6.26 for a compound nucleus of mass number around 150 and a final nucleus corresponding with the emission of a specific number of neutrons. The neutron emission leads to high-spin states near the neutron binding energy, at an excitation of 10–15 MeV, and there then follows the so-called 'statistical cascade' of predominantly electric dipole photon transitions. Neither the neutron nor the photon emission removes much angular momentum but finally a level is reached which lies on the so-called *yrast* line (section 4.3.2). This is the locus in an energy–angular momentum diagram such as figure 6.26 of the lowest energy level of a given spin and such levels usually de-excite by E2 radiation along the yrast line. The (HI, xn) reaction is an important means of exciting these high-spin nuclear states and of studying the phenomena of back bending and of superdeformation in collective rotational excitations (section 4.3.2).

An excited high-spin heavy compound nucleus easily enters a state of deformation from which symmetric fission is a favoured de-excitation process. Fission is an important alternative to neutron emission for target nuclei with $A \approx 200$ bombarded by ions such as ^{12}C, ^{14}N and ^{16}O. For heavier projectiles and heavy target nuclei, which have been studied with the hope of producing *superheavy* nuclei with $A \approx 300$ or greater, fission itself is less probable than the process of *deep inelastic scattering* or *incomplete fusion* which was discovered in the 1970s. In this process, the composite system does not completely fuse but separates on a short time scale compared with that for symmetric fission into two fragments similar to the initial nuclear pair. The energy spectrum of the fragment of mass comparable with the projectile shows a peak at about the Coulomb energy, as in the case of a normal fission fragment, and the mechanisms by which this fragment has lost energy to internal excitations have been discussed. It is currently throught that the two fragment nuclei must rotate in close contact while rapidly exchanging energy and mass in analogy with a classical frictional process.

REFERENCES 6

1 **Satchler G R** 1980 *Introduction to Nuclear Reactions* Macmillan

2 **Jackson D F** 1970 *Nuclear Reactions* Methuen

3 **Beyer R T** 1949 *Foundations of Nuclear Physics* Dover Publications

4 **Feather N** 1960 'A history of neutrons and nuclei' *Contemp Phys* **1** (191, 257); 1974 'Chadwick's neutron' *Contemp Phys* **15** (565)

5 **Frisch O R and Wheeler J A** 1967 'The discovery of fission' *Physics Today* **20** November (43)

6 **Segrè E** 1989 'The discovery of nuclear fission' *Physics Today* **42** July (38)

7 **Segrè E** 1977 *Nuclei and Particles* Benjamin ch. 11

8 **Bohr N** 1936 *Nature* **137** (344)

9 **Breit G and Wigner E P** 1936 *Phys Rev* **49** (519)

10 **Friedman F L and Weisskopf V F** 1955 in Pauli W (ed) *Niels Bohr and the Development of Physics* McGraw-Hill

11 **Hodgson P E** 1987 'Compound nucleus reactions' *Rep Prog Phys* **50** (1171)

12 *Nuclear Data Tables* 1973 'Neutron cross-sections (activation)' **A11** (601)

13 **Hodgson P E** 1963 *The Optical Model of Elastic Scattering* Oxford University Press

14 **Huby R** 1953 'Stripping reactions' *Prog Nucl Phys* **3** (177)

15 **Glendenning N K** 1983 *Direct Nuclear Reactions* Academic Press

16 **Wilkinson D H (ed)** 1969 *Isospin in Nuclear Physics* North-Holland

17 **Hamilton W D (ed)** 1975 *The Electromagnetic Interaction in Nuclear Spectroscopy* North-Holland

18 **Halpern I** 1959 'Nuclear fission' *Ann Rev Nucl Sci* **9** (245)

19 **Specht H J** 1974 *Rev Mod Phys* **46** (773)

20 **Bohr A and Mottelson B R** June 1979 *Physics Today* **32** June (25)

21 **Phillips W R** 1977 *Rep Prog Phys* **40** (345)

22 **Newton J O** 1989 *Contemp Phys* **30** (277)

EXAMPLES 6

6.1 Find the excitation of the compound nucleus ^{108}Ag in process (6.13) if it is produced by the absorption of a neutron of energy 1 eV. Assume that the values of $M - A$ in kilo-electronvolts for the nuclei concerned are as follows: n, 8072; ^{107}Ag; $-88\,408$; ^{108}Ag, $-87\,605$. [7269 keV]

6.2 Read through the worked example on p. 188 and write down the observable energy of the second α particle. Using equation (6.8). find the angle θ_L at which it is emitted. [8515 keV, 111.4°]

6.3 If a particle of mass m and kinetic energy T collides with a target particle of mass M show that the incoming kinetic energy available for producing internal excitation is $[M/(m + M)]T$.

Resonances are observed in the following reactions at the stated laboratory energies:

(a) $^{19}F + p \rightarrow {}^{20}Ne^*$ $\quad T_R = 340.5$ keV
(b) $^{50}V + n \rightarrow {}^{51}V^*$ $\quad T_R = 165$ eV.

The masses concerned (in atomic mass units) are ^{1}H, 1.0078; ^{19}F, 18.9984; ^{20}Ne, 19.9924; ^{50}V, 49.9472; n, 1.0087; ^{51}V, 50.9440. Calculate the energy of the compound system in each case, in mega-electronvolts. [13.16 MeV, 11.1 MeV]

6.4 In reaction (a) of example 6.3 a resonance at $T_R = 873$ keV (lab) has a total width of 5.2 keV and a width for proton re-emission of 1.1 keV. What is the resonant cross-section for α particle emission, assuming that this is the only competitive process and neglecting spin factors? [0.55 b]

6.5 The total energy of a degenerate Fermi gas may be written $E = a(kT)^2$ where T is the absolute temperature. The entropy of the gas, apart from a constant, is given by $S(E) = k\ln[\omega(E)]$. Use these formulae to show that the density of states in an excited nucleus is proportional to $\exp[2(aE)^{1/2}]$

6.6 Cadmium has a resonance for neutrons of energy 0.178 eV and the peak value of the total cross-section is about 7000 b. Estimate the contribution of scattering to the resonance. [3.37 b]

6.7 Show that in the scattering of a particle M_1 by a target nucleus M_2 the momentum transfer to the nucleus M_2 is the same in both the laboratory and centre-of-mass systems of coordinates.

6.8 The neutron separation energy for the nucleus ^{132}Xe is 8.9 MeV and the binding energy of the deuteron is 2.22 MeV. What is the Q value for the reaction $^{131}_{54}Xe(d, p)^{132}_{54}Xe$? [6.68 MeV]

Using equation (6.8) find the proton energy for the ground-state reaction at a laboratory angle of 90° for deuterons of energy 10 MeV. Find also the difference in energy between protons observed at 0° and 180°. [16.41 MeV, 0.55 MeV]

6.9 Suppose that the reaction of example 6.8 takes place in the surface of the target nucleus, for which $R = 1.2A^{1/3}$ fm. Using the single-particle shell model (chapter 4) to indicate spin and parity values, find the angle at which the maximum yield of stripped protons would be expected (neglect centre-of-mass corrections and dependence of proton energy on angle). [29°]

6.10 From equation (6.9) we may infer that the cross-section for producing particles b with velocity v_b by the reaction X(a, b)Y with particles a of velocity v_a is proportional to v_b/v_a. Use this result and the Gamow factor (5.36) to discuss the variation of the cross-section for the following general types of reaction, either near threshold or with low energy incident particles:

(a) neutron elastic and inelastic scattering,
(b) the (n, α) reaction, Q positive,
(c) the (p, n) reaction, Q negative,
(d) the (p, α) reaction, Q negative.

6.11 For a nucleus described by the semi-empirical mass formula (3.7) show that, neglecting asymmetry terms, the energy released in fission into two fragments is a maximum for equal division of the charge and mass.
Calculate the value of Z^2/A at which this division just becomes possible energetically.

6.12 Calculate the energy release in

(a) the spontaneous fission of ${}^{232}_{92}U$ to ${}^{145}_{57}La$ and ${}^{87}_{35}Br$,
(b) the neutron-induced fission of ${}^{232}_{92}U$ to ${}^{146}_{57}La$ and ${}^{87}_{35}Br$,
(c) the neutron-induced fission of ${}^{231}_{92}U$ to ${}^{145}_{57}La$ and ${}^{87}_{35}Br$.

The masses concerned (in atomic mass units) are ${}^{231}U$, 231.0363; ${}^{232}U$, 232.0372; ${}^{146}La$, 145.9255; ${}^{145}La$, 144.9217; ${}^{87}Br$, 86.9203; ${}^{1}n$, 1.0087. [182 MeV, 186 MeV, 189 MeV]

6.13 Oxygen-16 ions of energy 100 MeV are timed over a distance of 0.3 m. What timing accuracy is necessary if the mass number determination shall be accurate to ± 0.3 amu? [81 ps]

Part II *Particle Physics*

7 *Sub-nuclear physics: an overview*

Particle classification · The particle directory · Leptons and quarks: the fundamental particles · The fundamental interactions · Vacuum polarization · Towards a unification of the fundamental interactions

7.1 Particle classification

For the purposes of Part I of this book only a general classification of elementary particles such as the proton, electron, neutrino and photon into *fermions* and *bosons* was necessary (section 3.9). In sub-nuclear physics, however, a very large number of particles are encountered and it is useful further to subdivide these main groups according to the types of interaction in which they participate. All electrically charged particles, by virtue of their charge, can interact electromagnetically. With this caveat, some particles respond only to the weak force and such particles are collectively known as *leptons*. Among these are the familiar electron e^- and the neutrino ν_e*, and muon μ^- and its neutrino ν_μ and the more recently discovered τ lepton.[1] All leptons have intrinsic spin $\frac{1}{2}$ and are therefore fermions. Those particles which can participate in the strong interactions are known as *hadrons*. Unlike the leptons, which are all fermions, the hadron family contains both fermions and bosons. The hadrons with half-integer spin are also known as *baryons* amongst which the neutron and proton are the most familiar. The *mesons*, originally named because they had masses intermediate between the light or zero-mass leptons and the heavier baryons, are bosons.

---

* We shall see later that each charged lepton has a distinct neutrino associated with it which is therefore designated with the appropriate subscript ν_e or ν_μ. The τ neutrino ν_τ has not yet been observed directly.

These broad categories of particle are summarized in table 7.1.

Table 7.1
Broad classificaion of sub-nuclear particles

Fermions (half-integer spin)	Leptons (weak and electromagnetic)	
	Baryons	Hadrons (strong, weak and electromagnetic)
Bosons (integer spin)	Mesons	
	Photon (electromagnetic)	
	Z^0, $W^{\pm}$ (weak)	

All electrically charged particles can interact electromagnetically. Some hadrons decay via the weak interaction.

7.2 *The particle directory*

A list of the so-called stable particles, together with some of their properties, is given in table 7.2. By stable in this context is meant particles which are truly stable, such as the electron and its neutrino, or those which are stable against decay via the strong interactions. Those which do decay do so via the weak interaction with relatively long lifetimes, about 10^{-10} s, or via the electromagnetic interaction with much shorter lifetimes, about 10^{-16} s, such as the electromagnetic decay of the neutral pion, $\pi^0 \rightarrow \gamma\gamma$. Within the broad categories of leptons, mesons and baryons, defined in the previous section, the particles are arranged in order of increasing mass. Within each category one sees a variety of particle multiplets such as the triplet of π mesons, π^+, π^0 and π^-, with electric charge $+1$, 0 and -1 times the electron charge and roughly the same mass. There are particle doublets such as the xi or cascade particles Ξ^0 and Ξ^- and various singlets such as the neutral lambda (Λ) and the omega-minus (Ω^-) particles for which only one charge state exists. Why this is so will become apparent in due course.

One also notices in table 7.2 various adjectives like strange, charmed and bottom used in describing the hadrons. In addition to the more obvious properties such as charge, rest mass, intrinsic spin and parity, the hadrons possess these other attributes or quantum numbers, strangeness, charm and 'bottomness', in varying degrees. For the time being, let these quantum numbers merely serve as an indication of the richness of particle types in the sub-nuclear 'zoo'.

Already, on rather general grounds, this would appear to be a relatively large number of 'elementary' particles if indeed they really are elementary. In addition, to every particle there corresponds an antiparticle, although

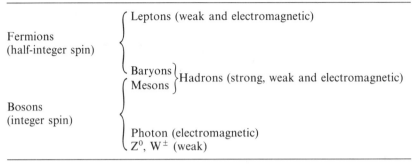

Table 7.2
Stable particle table

Particle	Spin–parity J^P	Mass/MeV	Principal decay modes	Mean lifetime/s
Leptons				
ν_e	$J = \frac{1}{2}$	$<7.3 \times 10^{-3}$	–	Stable
e	$J = \frac{1}{2}$	0.511	–	Stable
ν_μ	$J = \frac{1}{2}$	<0.27	–	Stable
μ	$J = \frac{1}{2}$	105.66	$e\nu\bar{\nu}$	2.20×10^{-6}
ν_τ	$J = \frac{1}{2}$	<35	–	Stable
τ	$J = \frac{1}{2}$	1784.1	$\mu\nu\bar{\nu}$, $e\nu\bar{\nu}$, hadrons	3.1×10^{-13}
Non-strange mesons				
$\pi^\pm$	0^-	139.57	$\mu\nu$	2.6×10^{-8}
π^0	0^-	134.97	$\gamma\gamma$	0.83×10^{-16}
η	0^-	547.5	$\gamma\gamma$, $3\pi^0$, $\pi^+\pi^-\pi^0$	$\Gamma = 1.19 \pm 0.11$ keV
Strange mesons				
$K^\pm$	0^-	493.65	$\mu\nu$, $\pi^\pm\pi^0$, 3π	1.24×10^{-8}
$K^0\bar{K}^0$	0^-	497.67	50% K_S^0, 50% K_L^0	
K_S^0	0^-		$\pi^+\pi^-$, $\pi^0\pi^0$	0.89×10^{-10}
K_L^0	0^-		$3\pi^0$, $\pi^+\pi^-\pi^0$, $\pi^\pm\mu^\mp\nu$, $\pi^\pm e^\mp\nu$	5.17×10^{-8}
Charmed non-strange mesons				
$D^\pm$	0^-	1869.3	eX, KX, K^0X, $\bar{K}^0X$	10.7×10^{-13}
$D^0\bar{D}^0$	0^-	1864.5	eX, μX, KX, K^0X, $\bar{K}^0X$	4.2×10^{-13}
Charmed strange meson				
$F^\pm$ (now $D_s^\pm$)	0^-	1971	KX, K^0X, $\bar{K}^0X$, non-$K\bar{K}X$, eX	4.5×10^{-13}
Bottom mesons				
$B^\pm$	0^-	5279	DX, $D^0/\bar{D}^0X$, D^*X, FX FD, F*D, FD*, F*D*	$(12.9 \pm 0.5) \times 10^{-13}$
$B^0\bar{B}^0$	0^-	5279		
Non-strange baryons				
p	$\frac{1}{2}^+$	938.3	–	Stable ($>10^{32}$ a)
n	$\frac{1}{2}^+$	939.6	$pe^-\bar{\nu}$	889.1 ± 2.1
Strangeness – 1 baryons				
Λ	$\frac{1}{2}^+$	1115.6	$p\pi^-$, $n\pi^0$	2.6×10^{-10}
Σ^+	$\frac{1}{2}^+$	1189.4	$p\pi^0$, $n\pi^+$	0.8×10^{-10}
Σ^0	$\frac{1}{2}^+$	1192.6	$\Lambda\gamma$	7.4×10^{-20}
Σ^-	$\frac{1}{2}^+$	1197.4	$n\pi^-$	1.5×10^{-10}
Strangeness – 2 baryons				
Ξ^0	$\frac{1}{2}^+$	1314.9	$\Lambda\pi^0$	2.9×10^{-10}
Ξ^-	$\frac{1}{2}^+$	1321.3	$\Lambda\pi^-$	1.6×10^{-10}

(*continued*)

Table 7.2 (Continued)

Particle	Spin–parity J^P	Mass/MeV	Principal decay modes	Mean lifetime/s
Strangeness – 3 baryon				
Ω^-	$\frac{3}{2}^+$	1672.4	ΛK^-, $\Xi^0\pi^-$, $\Xi^-\pi^0$	0.82×10^{-10}
Charmed baryons				
Λ_c^+	$\frac{1}{2}^+$	2282.0	ΛX, $pK^-\pi^+$, pK^0	1.9×10^{-13}
$\Sigma_c(2455)$	$\frac{1}{2}^+$	2453	$\Lambda_c^+\pi$	–
Ξ_c^+	$\frac{1}{2}^+$	2466	$\Lambda K^-\pi^+\pi^+$, $\Sigma^+K^-\pi^+$ $\Sigma^0K^-\pi^+\pi^+$, $\Xi^-\pi^+\pi^+$	$\approx 3 \times 10^{-13}$
Ξ_c^0	$\frac{1}{2}^+$	2473	$\Xi^-\pi^+$, $\Xi^-\pi^+\pi^+\pi^-$, $pK^-K^*(892)^0$	$\approx 0.8 \times 10^{-13}$
Bottom baryon				
Λ_b^0	$\frac{1}{2}^+$	≈ 5641	$J/\psi(1S)\Lambda$, $pD^0\pi^-$, $\Lambda_c^+\pi^+\pi^-\pi^-$	–
Gauge bosons				
γ	1^-	0	–	Stable
$W^\pm$	1	80.22 ± 0.26 GeV	$e\nu$, $\mu\nu$, $\tau\nu$	$\Gamma = 2.12 \pm 0.11$ GeV
Z^0	1	91.173 ± 0.020 GeV	e^+e^-, $\mu^+\mu^-$, $\tau^+\tau^-$ $\nu\bar{\nu}$, hadrons	$\Gamma = 2.487 \pm 0.01$ GeV
g (gluon)	1^-	0	–	Stable

Adapted from Particle Data Group 1992 'Review of particle properties', *Phys Rev* **D45** June. Sometimes the width Γ of a state is quoted instead of the lifetime: the width and lifetime are related through the uncertainty principle, $\Gamma \approx \hbar/\tau$ (see section 3.10). In the entries for the charmed and bottom mesons and the charmed baryons X stands for any particles consistent with the appropriate conservation laws. The spin-parity assignments for the charmed and bottom baryons are quark model predictions.

in some cases the particle and its antiparticle are indistinguishable. One can also state with confidence that new stable particles have yet to be discovered, so the list is not complete. One would expect that a truly elementary particle should have no internal structure, for if it had, the constituent parts would necessarily be 'more elementary' than the whole.

In addition to the list of stable particles, many other hadrons have been discovered in experiments using the high energy accelerators described in chapter 2. These hadrons have lifetimes of approximately 10^{-23} s, i.e. many orders of magnitude smaller than the stable particles, but in other respects they are similar to the stable particles. The extremely short lifetime is indicative of the fact that these states decay via the strong interaction. If the stable particles are considered as elementary then these new states, sometimes called resonances, could be placed on the same footing. One such state is the N(1520) where the number in brackets is the mass of the particle in mega-electronvolts and the particle symbol indicates that its basic properties are similar to the nucleon. The principal decay mode of this state is single pion emission, $N(1520) \rightarrow N\pi$, as shown

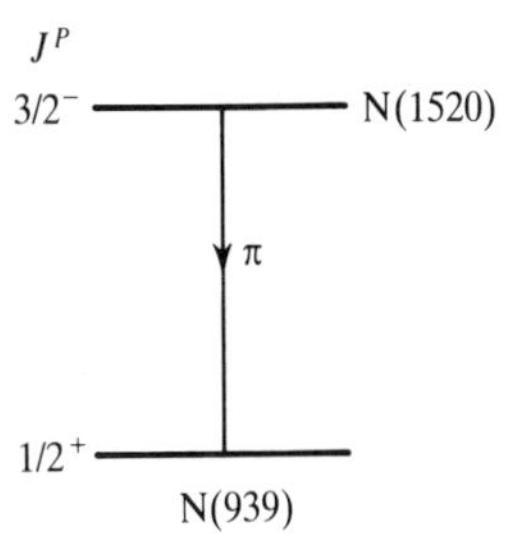

Figure 7.1
The nucleon N(939) and its first excited state N(1520).

in figure 7.1, and thus it seems more appropriate to regard the N(1520) as an excited state of the ground-state nucleon. That such an excited state exists suggests that the nucleon has some internal structure and should not be considered elementary. This viewpoint is strengthened by the parallel situation concerning the other stable baryons, the excited states of which, along with those of the nucleon, are shown in figure 7.2. Historically, the Δ(1232) was the first resonance to be discovered. It differs from the other ground states in figure 7.2 in that it decays strongly to a nucleon and a pion, $\Delta(1232) \to N\pi$, with a width of 115 MeV.* Strong decays of the other ground states are forbidden by various conservation laws. For instance, if the mass of the Σ were about 60 MeV greater than it is the Σ would be a resonant state decaying via the strong interaction to $\Lambda\pi$ with a width comparable with that of the Δ(1232). A similar situation exists in the case of the mesons. In conclusion, if we take as our definition of a fundamental or elementary particle one which is structureless and which therefore cannot exist in an excited state, then none of the hadrons is elementary.

7.3 *Leptons and quarks: the fundamental particles*

Up to the present limits of resolution, approximately 10^{-18} m, the leptons are structureless and, although specific investigations have been undertaken, none of them has been observed in an internally excited state. They are therefore regarded as fundamental particles.

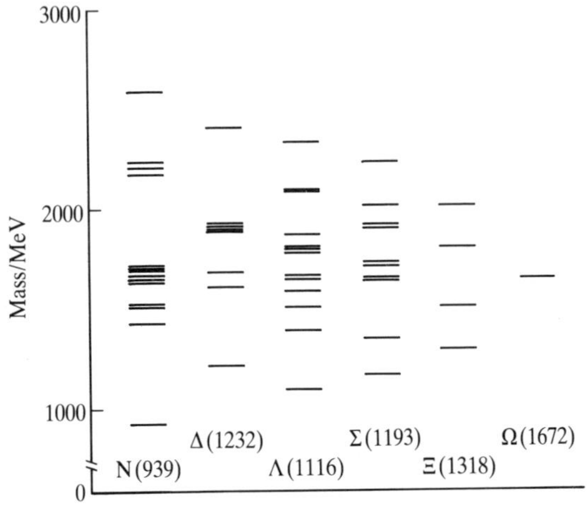

Figure 7.2
The spectrum of the strange and non-strange baryons. Only those states which are well established experimentally are shown.

* In the case of strongly decaying particles the width Γ of the state is measured directly and it is more usual to quote the width rather than the lifetime τ to which it is related by the uncertainty principle $\Gamma\tau \approx \hbar$ (see section 3.10).

In 1964 Gell-Mann[2] and Zweig, independently, suggested that the static properties of all the hadrons known at that time could be accounted for by the existence of particles known as quarks. By 1964 the strange mesons and baryons had been discovered but nothing was known about the particles labelled charmed and bottom in table 7.2. It is not necessary to consider the latter types of particle to understand the basis of the Gell-Mann–Zweig proposal but later in the book we will see how they can be incorporated into the scheme. In what follows then, we consider only the non-strange and strange mesons and baryons and, specifically, the set of $J^P = 0^-$ mesons

$$\pi^+ \ \pi^- \ \pi^0 \ \eta^0 \ \mathrm{K}^+ \ \mathrm{K}^- \ \mathrm{K}^0 \ \bar{\mathrm{K}}^0$$

and the set of $J^P = \frac{1}{2}^+$ baryons

$$\mathrm{p} \ \mathrm{n} \ \Lambda \ \Sigma^+ \ \Sigma^- \ \Sigma^0 \ \Xi^0 \ \Xi^-.$$

Before proceeding further it is necessary to discuss the concepts of baryon number, isobaric spin or isospin and strangeness.

Quite simply, each baryon is assigned a baryon number B of $+1$ and each antibaryon has $B = -1$. In all types of interaction, the baryon number is conserved so that baryons can only be created in pairs, i.e. baryon plus antibaryon. For instance, provided there is sufficient energy, the process

$$\mathrm{p} + \mathrm{p} \rightarrow \mathrm{p} + \mathrm{p} + \mathrm{p} + \bar{\mathrm{p}}$$
$$B\colon 1 + 1 \rightarrow 1 + 1 + 1 + (-1)$$

is allowed since in both the initial and final states the total baryon number, which is an additive quantum number, is 2. On the other hand a process such as

$$\mathrm{p} + \mathrm{p} \rightarrow \mathrm{p} + \bar{\mathrm{p}} + \pi^+ + \pi^+$$
$$B\colon 1 + 1 \rightarrow 1 + (-1) + 0 + 0$$

even if energetically possible, is forbidden by the conservation of baryon number. Any particle which is not a baryon has baryon number zero, so all the leptons and bosons have $B = 0$.

The concept of *isospin* was introduced in section 3.8 in connection with neutrons and protons. It was pointed out that because the strong interaction does not distinguish between the behaviour of these two particles it is useful to regard the nucleon as having an internal degree of freedom described by an isospin vector $\boldsymbol{I}$ in a fictitious space. Taking $I = \frac{1}{2}$ there would be two possible orientations of the vector with $I_3 = \pm\frac{1}{2}$ along the quantization axis corresponding to the proton and neutron respectively. The strong interaction then does not distinguish between these two orientations of the isospin vector. Since this is a general property of the strong interactions the concept of a conserved isospin $\boldsymbol{I}$ extends to all particles which can interact strongly, i.e. the hadrons. All hadrons belong to isospin multiplets. As in the case of an ordinary spin s for which there are $2s + 1$ different orientations of the spin vector, so for an isospin I there are $2I + 1$ different orientations of the isospin vector corresponding to the different particles in the isospin multiplet. The three charge states of the pion imply that $I_\pi = 1$ and $I_3 = +1, 0, -1$ for the π^+, π^0 and π^- respectively. The η^0 has no charged partners and is thus an isospin singlet with $I = 0$ and $I_3 = 0$. There is evidently a relation between the charge Q, expressed in units of $|e|$, where e is the charge of the electron, and the third component of isospin. For the π and η mesons this is simply

$$Q = I_3 \tag{7.1}$$

but this relation does not hold for the nucleon. In this case (cf. equation (3.25))

$$Q = I_3 + \frac{B}{2} \tag{7.2}$$

where B is the baryon number, and since for the mesons $B = 0$ this more general relation remains valid.

Lack of space prevents us from describing in detail the fascinating story surrounding the discovery and elucidation of the role of the so-called strange particles. Their existence was totally unexpected and originally their properties strange. The Λ^0 is one such particle which can be copiously produced for instance in collisions between negative pions and protons:

$$\pi^- + \mathrm{p} \rightarrow \Lambda^0 + \cdots. \tag{7.3}$$

The cross-section for this process is typical of that for a strong interaction. On the other hand, the 'reverse' process

$$\Lambda^0 \rightarrow \mathrm{p} + \pi^- \tag{7.4}$$

has a rate which is characteristic of a weak interaction. This apparently strange behaviour, production via the strong interaction and decay via the weak, is neatly accommodated in the hypothesis of 'associated production' put forward by Pais.[3] Gell-Mann[4] and Nishijima[5] introduced a 'strangeness' quantum number S which was assumed to be conserved in the strong interaction but not in the weak. The Gell-Mann–Nishijima scheme modified equation (7.2) to incorporate the strange particles. Accordingly

$$Q = I_3 + \frac{B + S}{2}. \tag{7.5}$$

Equation (7.5) is satisfied for the proton and pion provided both have strangeness $S = 0$. The Λ^0 with $I = I_3 = 0$ and $B = 1$ must have strangeness $S = -1$. Conservation of strangeness then prohibits the decay (7.4) via the strong interaction but allows the decay to proceed weakly. In the process (7.3) the Λ^0 must be produced in association with a particle with strangeness $S = +1$. In order to satisfy the conservation of charge and baryon number this particle must be a meson; the K^0 is a suitable candidate. According to (7.5) I_3 for the K^0 is $-\frac{1}{2}$ and in fact the K^0 and K^+ mesons form an isospin doublet: the antiparticles $\bar{K}^0$ and K^- also form an isospin doublet. We leave it as an exercise for the reader to show that the sigma baryons Σ have $S = -1$ and the cascade baryons Ξ have $S = -2$. The combination $B + S$ is known as the hypercharge, Y, and strange baryons are sometimes called hyperons.

The proposal of Gell-Mann and Zweig was that the hadrons are composite objects being bound states of spin $\frac{1}{2}$ fermions called quarks. To accommodate the rich spectrum of hadrons they introduced three types or flavour of quark, 'up', 'down' and 'strange'. The up and down quarks, u and d, form an isospin doublet with the u quark having $I_3 = +\frac{1}{2}$ and the d quark $I_3 = -\frac{1}{2}$. The strange or s quark is an isospin singlet with strangeness -1. The u and d quarks have strangeness 0. In their scheme, the baryons are bound states of three quarks and the most democratic way to produce a baryon number $B = 1$ is to assign each quark flavour a baryon number $B = \frac{1}{3}$. The properties of the quarks are summarized in table 7.3.

An important consequence of the choice of $B = \frac{1}{3}$ for the quarks is that they have fractional electric charge. Application of the Gell-Mann–Nishijima formula (7.5) gives the values of Q shown in table 7.3. For each quark there exists a corresponding antiquark for which the conserved quantities, charge, baryon number and strangeness, have the opposite sign. Consequently the values of I_3 also have the opposite sign. The properties of the antiquarks are summarized in table 7.4.

Within this framework a quark–antiquark bound state most economically produces the required $B = 0$ for mesons.

Table 7.3
Properties of the quarks proposed by Gell-Mann and Zweig

Flavour	I	I_3	S	B	Q
u	$\frac{1}{2}$	$+\frac{1}{2}$	0	$\frac{1}{3}$	$+\frac{2}{3}$
d	$\frac{1}{2}$	$-\frac{1}{2}$	0	$\frac{1}{3}$	$-\frac{1}{3}$
s	0	0	-1	$\frac{1}{3}$	$-\frac{1}{3}$

Table 7.4
Properties of the antiquarks

Flavour	I	I_3	S	B	Q
$\bar{u}$	$\frac{1}{2}$	$-\frac{1}{2}$	0	$-\frac{1}{3}$	$-\frac{2}{3}$
$\bar{d}$	$\frac{1}{2}$	$+\frac{1}{2}$	0	$-\frac{1}{3}$	$+\frac{1}{3}$
$\bar{s}$	0	0	+1	$-\frac{1}{3}$	$+\frac{1}{3}$

Table 7.5
Summary of the quantum numbers of the $J^P = 0^-$ mesons and the $J^P = \frac{1}{2}^+$ baryons

Meson	I	I_3	S	B	Y	Baryon	I	I_3	S	B	Y
K^+	$\frac{1}{2}$	$+\frac{1}{2}$	+1	0	+1	p	$\frac{1}{2}$	$+\frac{1}{2}$	0	1	+1
K^0	$\frac{1}{2}$	$-\frac{1}{2}$	+1	0	+1	n	$\frac{1}{2}$	$-\frac{1}{2}$	0	1	+1
π^+	1	+1	0	0	0	Σ^+	1	+1	−1	1	0
π^0	1	0	0	0	0	Σ^0	1	0	−1	1	0
π^-	1	−1	0	0	0	Σ^-	1	−1	−1	1	0
η^0	0	0	0	0	0	Λ^0	0	0	−1	1	0
$\bar{K}^0$	$\frac{1}{2}$	$+\frac{1}{2}$	−1	0	−1	Ξ^0	$\frac{1}{2}$	$+\frac{1}{2}$	−2	1	−1
K^-	$\frac{1}{2}$	$-\frac{1}{2}$	−1	0	−1	Ξ^-	$\frac{1}{2}$	$-\frac{1}{2}$	−2	1	−1

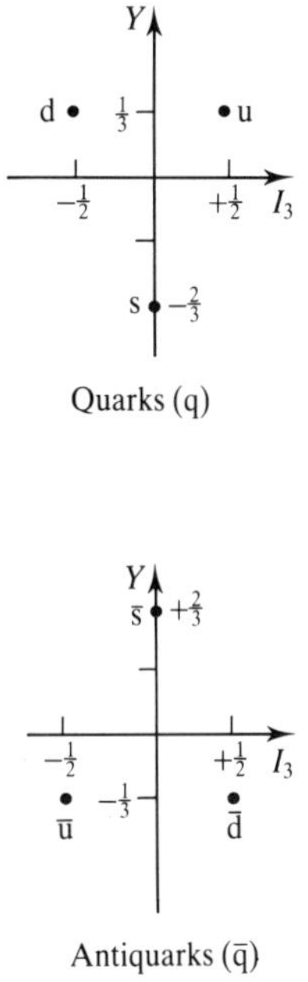

Figure 7.3
The basic quark and antiquark triplets.

It is sometimes convenient to visualize the properties of the quarks and antiquarks by plotting the hypercharge $Y = B + S$ against the third component of isospin I_3 as shown in figure 7.3.

In order to see how successfully the quark model reproduces the properties of the hadrons we summarize in table 7.5 the quantum numbers of the octet of $J^P = 0^-$ mesons and the octet of $J^P = \frac{1}{2}^+$ baryons.

The plots of hypercharge versus I_3 for these mesons and baryons are shown on the left-hand side of figure 7.4 while on the right-hand side are the quark flavour contents of the particles. The reader may readily verify the agreement between the properties of the physical particles and those predicted from the quark flavour assignment. Additionally, the quark spins may be coupled appropriately to give the correct spin-parity for the meson and baryon states. In the case of the mesons the quark–antiquark pair are bound with zero relative orbital angular momentum and spins antiparallel to give a total spin of zero. The negative parity is guaranteed by the opposite intrinsic parity of fermion and antifermion. (In the case of integer spin bosons the intrinsic parity of particle and antiparticle are the same.) The situation regarding the baryons is only slightly more complicated. The $\frac{1}{2}^+$ baryons are the lowest-lying, i.e. lightest, baryons and it is reasonable to assume that the relative orbital angular momenta l and l' in the three-quark system depicted in figure 7.5 are both equal to zero. Two of the individual quark spins can be coupled to give a resultant of zero so that the net spin-parity of the states is simply that of the unpaired quark, namely $\frac{1}{2}^+$. It is clear that by introducing orbital angular momentum into the quark systems a whole series of hadrons with different J^P values can be constructed from only three quark flavours.

An interesting and very important situation arises in the baryon spectrum when the quark spins are aligned, again with $l = l' = 0$, to give

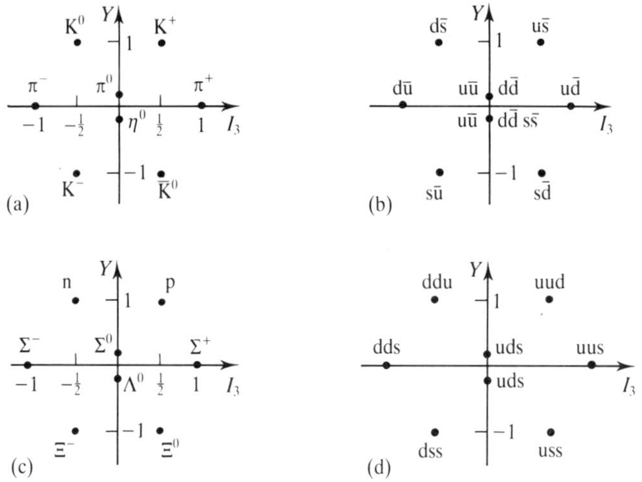

Figure 7.4
(a) The octet of 0^- mesons; (b) quark flavour assignments for the 0^- mesons; (c) the octet of $\frac{1}{2}^+$ baryons; (d) quark flavour assignments for the $\frac{1}{2}^+$ baryons.

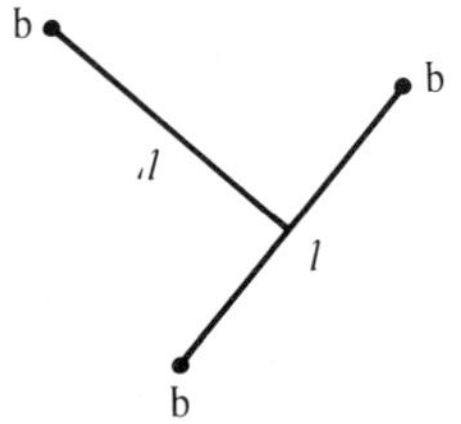

Figure 7.5
Orbital angular momentum in a three-quark system. l is the relative orbital angular momentum between two of the quarks and l' that between the di-quark system and the remaining quark.

$J^P = \frac{3}{2}^+$. There are ten $J^P = \frac{3}{2}^+$ baryons known in nature and these states are shown in figure 7.6 together with the flavour content of each state. When one focuses attention on either the $\Delta^{++}(1232)$ state with quark content uuu or the Ω^- state with three s quarks an apparent problem arises. The problem stems from the principle of indistinguishability of identical particles. Given a system of identical particles, either bosons or fermions, interchange of any pair of particles in the system can only multiply the wavefunction of the system by $+1$ or -1. For a second interchange of the two particles must result in a reversion to the original system. For bosons the factor is $+1$ and the wavefunction is symmetric with respect to particle interchange, while for fermions the factor is -1 and the wavefunction is antisymmetric, or, in other words, identical fermions must obey the Pauli exclusion principle. This appears not to be so in the case of the $\Delta^{++}(1232)$ and Ω^-, in which three identical spin $\frac{1}{2}$ quarks, whose spatial positions are on average the same, occupy the same spin state. Many ideas were put forward to explain this conflict but the simplest one has stood the test of time. In addition to flavour, quarks

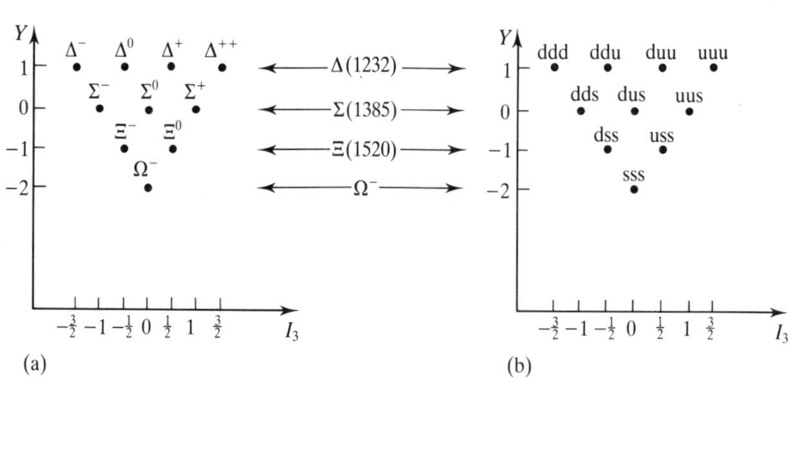

Figure 7.6
(a) The $\frac{3}{2}^+$ baryon decuplet and (b) its quark flavour content.

have another internal degree of freedom or quantum number, 'colour'. This has nothing to do with the ordinary notion of colour and may be thought of as a property somewhat akin to electric charge, except that there are three types of 'strong charge', or colour, compared with just one type of electric charge. The three colours are conventionally chosen as red, green and blue, and each quark can exist with equal probability in any of these states. The assertion is made that every hadron is a colour singlet, i.e. has no net colour or is 'white'. Then, in the $\Delta^{++}(1232)$, the three u quarks are no longer identical but instead are $u_R u_G u_B$. Since red + green + blue ≡ white, the $\Delta^{++}(1232)$ is a colour singlet as required. If this condition were not imposed there would be a proliferation of hadrons which is not observed experimentally. Just as both signs of electric charge exist so there are complementary colours, cyan, magenta and yellow or 'anti-red' $\bar{R}$, 'anti-green' $\bar{G}$ and 'anti-blue' $\bar{B}$. The antiquarks are assigned these anti-colours and colour singlets can be constructed from equal mixtures of the three colour states, as in the $\Delta^{++}(1232)$, equal mixtures of anti-colour ($\bar{R}\bar{G}\bar{B}$) or equal mixtures of colour and anti-colour, $R\bar{R}$, $G\bar{G}$ or $B\bar{B}$. These constructions produce baryons, antibaryons and mesons respectively.

According to the present available evidence, quarks are structureless particles and, along with the leptons, are considered to be elementary.

7.4 The fundamental interactions

The four fundamental interactions known in nature, namely the gravitational, electromagnetic, weak and strong interactions, at first sight appear to be totally unrelated, but as our subject develops we will see that not only are there striking similarities between them but that it may be possible to embrace them within a single unified theory. Although complete unification may be a long way off, important steps, which are outlined below, have already been taken towards this ultimate goal.

In 1928, Dirac[6] formulated a relativistic quantum wave equation for the electron, thus bringing together two of the essential ingredients of modern theoretical physics, special relativity and quantum mechanics, in a single theory. The complete unification of special relativity and quantum mechanics is possible only within the framework of a quantum field theory. The development of such a theory began in the late 1920s with the work of Dirac, Heisenberg and Pauli and is a general formalism which can in principle be applied to all four fundamental interactions. In the late 1940s Feynman, Schwinger, Dyson and Sin-itiro Tomonaga, working independently, developed the theory of quantum electrodynamics (QED), a field theory which permitted calculations to be made which agreed with experimental results to an unprecedented degree of accuracy. Over 50 years ago Fermi[7] proposed a theory of the weak

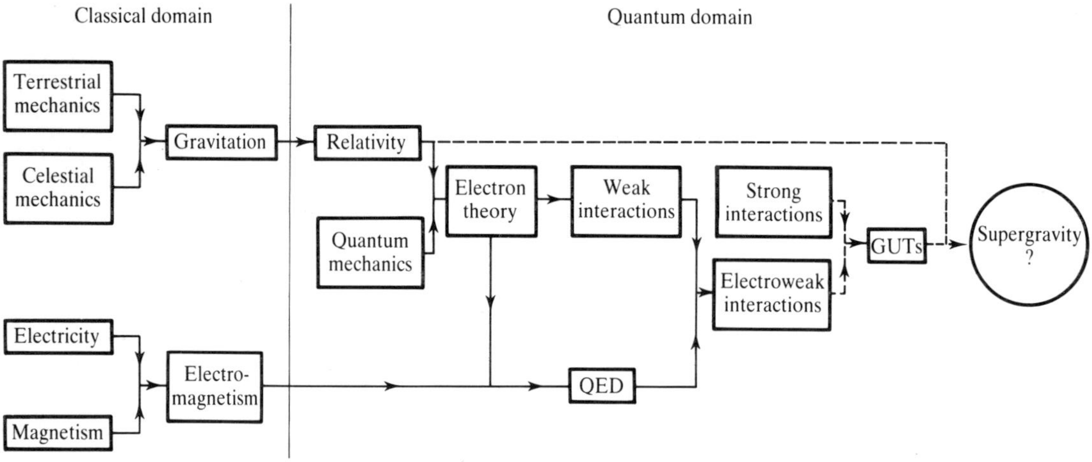

Figure 7.7 Block diagram showing the progress towards unification of the fundamental forces. The broken lines indicate steps which have yet to be completed.

interactions (section 5.2.3) which, although not quite capable in its original form of accommodating the full range of weak interaction phenomena which were later discovered, nonetheless provided a framework which is readily recognizable in the modern theory of the weak interactions. A major step along the road to unification was made by Glashow, Weinberg and Salam[8] when they unified the weak and electromagnetic interactions. Just as the photon, the quantum of the electromagnetic field, transmits the electromagnetic force between electrically charged particles, so the weak force is transmitted via the exchange of massive 'intermediate bosons', the W^+, W^- and Z^0. The 'standard theory' of the electroweak interactions, like QED, belongs to the class of theories known as gauge field theories, and the four field quanta, the γ, W^+, W^- and Z^0, are known as gauge bosons. They are all spin 1 particles and should be added to the quarks and leptons in the list of fundamental particles. It is now known that the strong interactions can also be described by a quantum gauge theory known as quantum chromodynamics (QCD) in which colour, introduced in the last section, plays a central role. Indeed, there are so-called grand unified theories (GUTs) which, although not entirely satisfactory, are a first step towards the unification of the strong, weak and electromagnetic interactions: the ultimate goal is to include gravitation. A field theoretical approach is necessary because of the need to include the possibility that particles can be created and destroyed; 'action at a distance' is achieved through the exchange of particles, the field quanta or gauge bosons referred to above. The various stages in the process of unification of the fundamental interactions are summarized in figure 7.7.

As was implicit in the previous sections in this chapter, it is a common belief that the interactions are describable by a limited number of

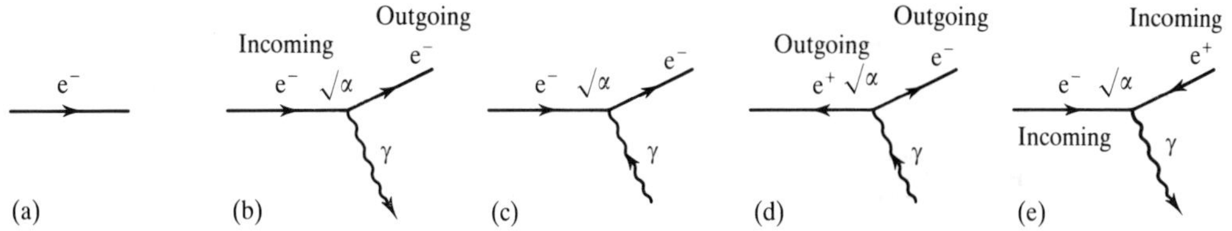

Figure 7.8 The basic Feynman diagrams of quantum electrodynamics: (a) a free electron; (b) photon emission; (c) photon absorption; (d) pair production; (e) e^+e^- annihilation.

fundamental particles interacting according to the general principles of quantum mechanics and relativity. These interactions or 'couplings' have a strength, or probability of occurrence, which is characterized by a 'coupling constant' and these span many orders of magnitude, ranging from about 10^{-39} for the gravitational interaction, which is by far the weakest, to about 1 for the strong interactions.

7.4.1 The electromagnetic coupling

The fundamental particles which couple to the electromagnetic field are the charged leptons and, by virtue of their electric charge, the quarks. By way of illustration let us consider the electron and the photon.

Following the approach due to Feynman a free non-interacting electron is represented as a line (figure 7.8(a)). There is some probability, given by the square of the amplitude for the process, that an electron emits a photon and this coupling of the electron to the electromagnetic field is represented by figure 7.8(b) in which the photon is shown as a wavy line. One can think of the incoming electron being absorbed at the vertex, where the outgoing electron and photon are created. This Feynman diagram, as it is called, represents the basic electromagnetic process $e^- \rightarrow e^-\gamma$ and the amplitude for this process is proportional to the charge on the electron, or more precisely to $\sqrt{\alpha}$ where α, the fine-structure constant, is given by

$$\alpha = \frac{e^2}{4\pi\varepsilon_0\hbar c} \approx \frac{1}{137}.$$

This is a small number and indicates that electromagnetic interactions are relatively weak. In Feynman diagrams of this sort it is possible to change the direction of the arrows provided that the particle is replaced by its antiparticle. Thus figure 7.8(c) represents the reverse process $e^-\gamma \rightarrow e^-$, corresponding to the absorption of a photon by the incoming electron. (The photon and its antiparticle are indistinguishable.) Similarly, by reversing the arrow on the incoming electron and changing it to the antiparticle, the positron, we arrive at figure 7.8(d), which represents electron–positron pair production. Finally, if all the arrows in figure 7.8(d) are reversed we get figure 7.8(e) which corresponds to electron–positron annihilation. The coupling is the same in each diagram. In the mathematical treatment the interaction is described by a Lagrangian L and in fact each of the diagrams in figure 7.8 represents one term in the Lagrangian. On the understanding that diagrams 7.8(c), 7.8(d) and 7.8(e) follow from 7.8(b) only the latter is included in the Lagrangian.

Of course none of the processes 7.8(b)–7.8(e), as they stand, conserves energy and momentum and they are called *virtual* processes. According to the uncertainty principle, however, energy conservation can be violated for a short time so that in the presence of a second electron for instance, the photon in figure 7.8(b) can be absorbed and energy and momentum conserved in the overall process. The corresponding Feynman diagram is shown in figure 7.9(a) which represents one contribution to the elastic scattering of one electron by another via virtual photon exchange. The coupling at the second vertex is again $\sqrt{\alpha}$. The amplitude for this process is essentially the product of three factors: (i) the amplitude that the incoming electron emits a photon at vertex 1, (ii) an amplitude that the photon propagates from the space–time point 1 to the space–time point vertex 2, the photon 'propagator', and (iii) the amplitude that the photon is absorbed by the second incoming electron at vertex 2. The amplitude for the overall process is thus proportional to α and is described as a first-order process. Other more complicated diagrams can contribute to the process $e^-e^- \to e^-e^-$; for instance by combining figure 7.8(b) with figure 7.8(d) one gets the second-order diagram, with an amplitude proportional to α^2, shown in figure 7.9(b). Each vertex contributes a factor $\sqrt{\alpha}$ to the amplitude. Proceeding in this fashion one can construct diagrams proportional to α^3, α^4 and so on, and indeed the total amplitude for the process $e^-e^- \to e^-e^-$ is an infinite sum of diagrams of increasing order, and hence decreasing amplitude, because $\alpha \ll 1$. Perturbation theory can be used to calculate the total amplitude, and hence the cross-section for the process $e^-e^- \to e^-e^-$, to any degree of accuracy required. All of this is known as quantum electrodynamics. There are precise rules, the so-called Feynman rules, for calculating the contribution to the amplitude for each diagram. The enumeration of the Feynman rules is beyond the scope of this book but we will nevertheless make frequent use of Feynman diagrams in our description of the interactions involving sub-nuclear particles.

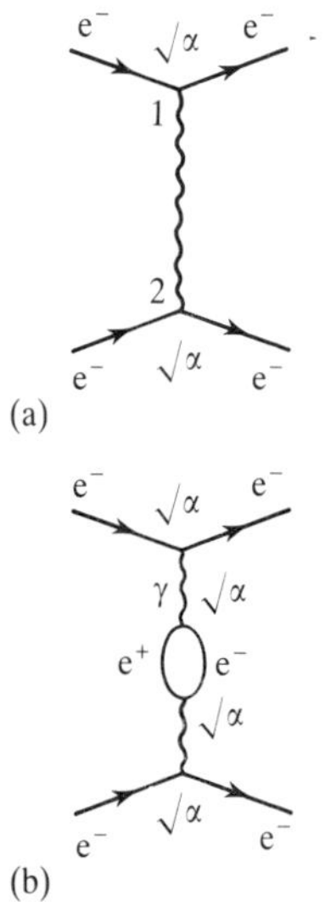

Figure 7.9
Feynman diagrams for electron–electron scattering: (a) a first-order process; (b) a second-order process.

7.4.2 The strong coupling

In section 1.4 it was pointed out that a short-range attractive force is required to bind the nucleons inside a nucleus. In 1935 Yukawa proposed, in analogy with QED, that the nuclear force was due to the exchange of a particle with non-zero mass: a meson. He envisaged the fundamental coupling shown in figure 7.10(a) and, following the argument used in the

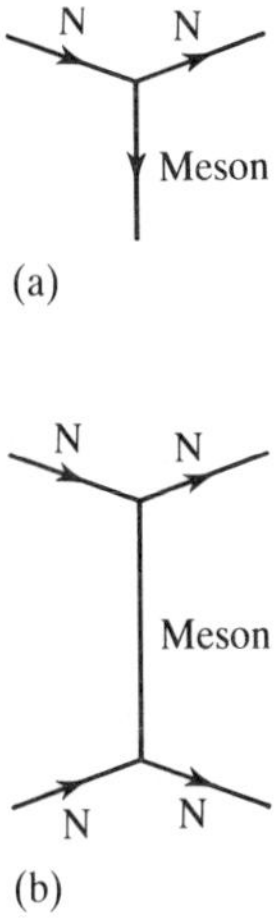

Figure 7.10
Yukawa's scheme for the strong interaction. He proposed (a) that the fundamental coupling was between the nucleon and a meson and (b) that the nucleon–nucleon force was produced by virtual meson exchange.

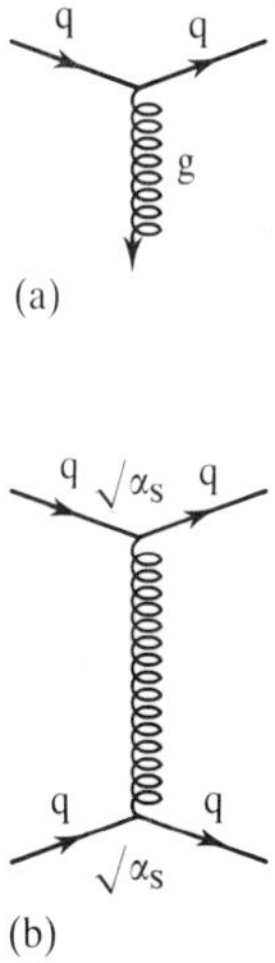

Figure 7.11
(a) The basic strong coupling between coloured quarks and gluons and (b) a Feynman diagram for quark–quark scattering via the exchange of a virtual intermediate gluon.

previous section, that the interaction between two nucleons would proceed via the exchange of a virtual intermediate meson (figure 7.10(b)).* A simple calculation based on the uncertainty principle shows that for a range of 1.4×10^{-15} m for the strong force the exchanged meson must have a mass of about 140 MeV/c^2. (For an explanation of the system of units commonly employed in elementary particle physics see section 1.5 and appendix F.) This is in contrast to the infinite range of the electromagnetic force which is due to the fact that the mass of the photon is zero.

As pointed out in section 7.3 neither the nucleon nor the mesons are in fact fundamental particles so that figure 7.10 does not represent the basic strong coupling. We recall that the hadrons are composite objects consisting of quarks which carry, in addition to electric charge, a 'strong charge', or colour, which plays a role in the strong interactions analogous to the role of electric charge in the electromagnetic interactions. We neglect, for the time being, the fact that there are three colours. The field quanta, or gauge bosons, of the strong interactions are called gluons which, like the quarks, carry colour. The fundamental coupling for the strong interactions is then between quarks and gluons (figure 7.11(a)) with a strength proportional to $\sqrt{\alpha_s}$, where α_s is the strong coupling constant, and a quark–quark interaction proceeds via the exchange of a virtual intermediate gluon (figure 7.11(b)). The gluons have zero mass and this would appear to contradict the fact that the strong or colour force is a short-range force. We return to this point in section 7.5.

The analogy with the electromagnetic interactions is not as close as would appear from the discussion so far. The photon does not carry electric charge whereas the gluons are coloured. This implies that when two quarks interact, there is a flow of colour between them. In the electromagnetic interactions electric charge is conserved not only in the overall process but at each vertex in a Feynman diagram. Similarly, the colour quantum number must be conserved at each vertex in the strong interaction diagrams. This implies that the gluons are in fact bi-coloured. To be specific let us assume that the incoming quark in figure 7.11(a) is red. It cannot get rid of its colour simply by emitting a red gluon since conservation of colour would then imply that the outgoing quark is colourless and colourless quarks do not exist. If on the other hand it gets rid of its redness by emitting a red–anti-blue gluon, colour can be conserved if the outgoing quark is blue, as shown in figure 7.12(a). We recall that in a Feynman diagram if the direction of a line is reversed the particle must be replaced by its antiparticle. The same is true for colour:

* It is perhaps more readily acceptable that a *repulsive* force can arise from the exchange of a particle. In quantum field theory an *attractive* force can also arise from the same mechanism because the impulse of the exchanged particle is not necessarily in its direction of motion.

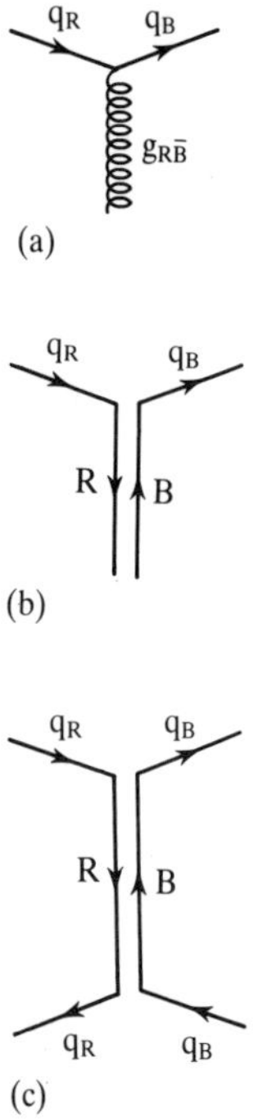

Figure 7.12
(a) A basic colour interaction. The incoming red quark q_R is absorbed at the vertex and a bi-coloured gluon $g_{R\bar{B}}$ and a blue quark q_B are created. Colour is conserved at the vertex.
(b) The flow of colour in (a).
(c) A colour flow diagram for a quark–quark interaction.

on reversing a colour line we replace it by its anti-colour and arrive at the colour flow diagram (figure 7.12(b)). The colour flow diagram corresponding to the quark–quark interaction of figure 7.11(b) is shown in figure 7.12(c), where it can be seen that the net result is that the quarks have exchanged colour.

Our specific choice of colour in the above discussion was quite arbitrary: with three colours and three anti-colours there are nine different bi-coloured combinations consisting of a colour and an anti-colour, namely

$$R\bar{R},\ R\bar{G},\ R\bar{B},\ G\bar{R},\ G\bar{G},\ G\bar{B},\ B\bar{R},\ B\bar{G},\ B\bar{B}.$$

The colour wavefunctions of the gluons can in general be linear combinations of these states and the totally symmetric combination $R\bar{R} + G\bar{G} + B\bar{B}$ is a colour singlet, i.e. it is colourless, and therefore plays no part in the strong interactions. Thus, in contrast to the electromagnetic case in which there is only one type of field quantum, the photon, there are eight coloured gluons. Furthermore, since the gluons themselves are coloured they can couple to each other and the Feynman diagrams for colour interactions may contain triple gluon vertices as shown in figure 7.13.

7.4.3 *The weak coupling*

The nuclear β decay discussed in section 5.2 is the best known example of a weak interaction. At a fundamental level neutron decay (equation (5.13b)) must require the quark change $d \rightarrow u + e^- + \bar{\nu}_e$ in which a down quark in the neutron changes flavour to become an up quark in the proton. The reader may be puzzled to see leptons apparently coupling to quarks, the fundamental particles involved in the strong interactions, in view of the statement in section 7.1 that the leptons can interact only via the weak interactions or, in the case of the charged leptons, via the electromagnetic interactions. The solution to the apparent paradox may be understood with the aid of figure 7.14. At the top vertex the incoming d quark in the neutron is absorbed and a u quark is emitted along with a weak gauge boson, in this case the W^-. The amplitude for this process is proportional to $\sqrt{\alpha_W}$; in analogy with the strong and electromagnetic processes $\sqrt{\alpha_W}$ may be thought of as a 'weak charge'. The W^- then propagates to the bottom vertex where it is absorbed and an electron and antineutrino are emitted. In this two-stage process, the leptons couple to the weak gauge boson and not directly to the quarks. Implicit in this viewpoint is the assumption that the quarks carry a weak charge in addition to the electric charge and colour or strong charge. The amplitude for the overall process is proportional to α_W. The mass of the W^- is roughly 100 times the mass of the proton, implying that the range of the weak interaction is extremely short.

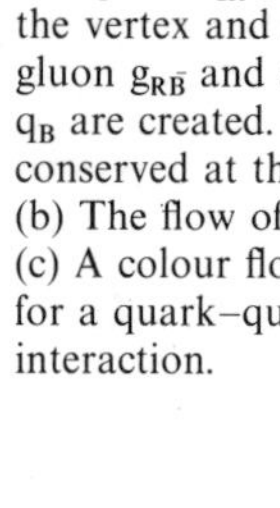

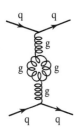

Figure 7.13
A quark–quark interaction showing three-gluon couplings.

7.5 Vacuum polarization*

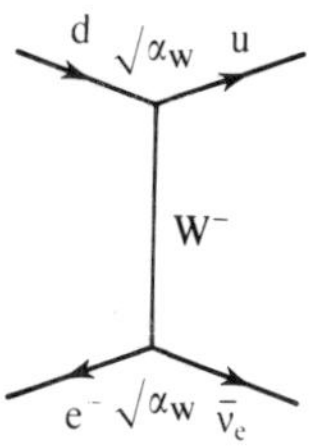

Figure 7.14
Feynman diagram for the β decay of a d quark.

It has tacitly been assumed above that the charge on the electron, the colour charge and the weak charge, or equivalently the 'fine-structure constants' α, α_s and α_W, are in fact constants. More properly, however, they should be regarded as functions of distance because of an effect which, because of analogy with the electrostatics of dielectrics, has become known as vacuum polarization.

To see this we recall that if a medium containing molecules with a permanent electric dipole moment is introduced into an electric field, that field is reduced within the dielectric by a factor ϵ, where ϵ is the dielectric constant. If the field is due to a pair of charges $\pm q$ placed within the medium (figure 7.15), the molecules will align along the field direction and produce a screening or reduction in the effective value of the two charges. In the immediate vicinity of the charges the effective charge is the bare charge q reduced by the induced 'surface' charge. The electrostatic potential energy may be written

$$V = \frac{1}{4\pi\epsilon_0\epsilon(r)}\frac{q^2}{r} \tag{7.6}$$

because over short distances the dielectric constant is a function of r. For values of r much larger than the molecular diameter d, $\epsilon(r) \to \epsilon$, the dielectric 'constant', while for $r \ll d$, $\epsilon(r) \to 1$. The effective charge $q/\sqrt{[\epsilon(r)]}$ varies with distance as shown in figure 7.16. For distances small

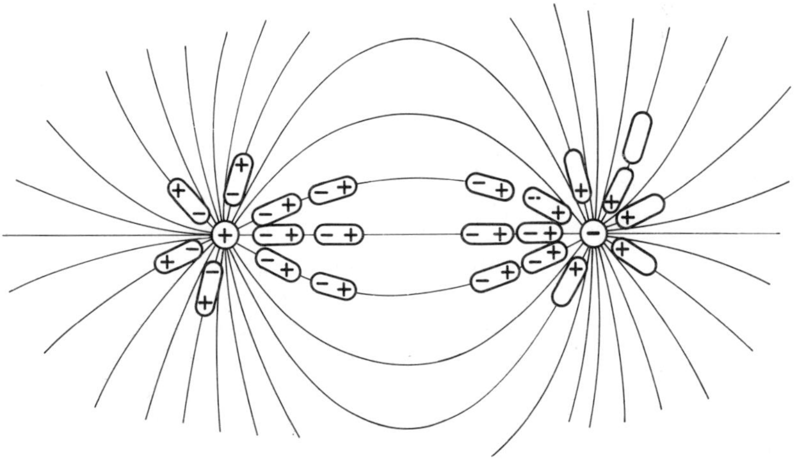

Figure 7.15
Schematic representation of macroscopic charge screening in a dielectric medium.

* A very readable and authoritative account of the vacuum in particle physics has been given by Aitchison.[9]

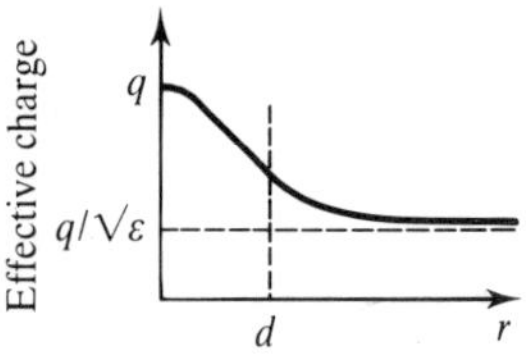

Figure 7.16
Sketch of the effective charge as a function of separation distance. d is the molecular diameter.

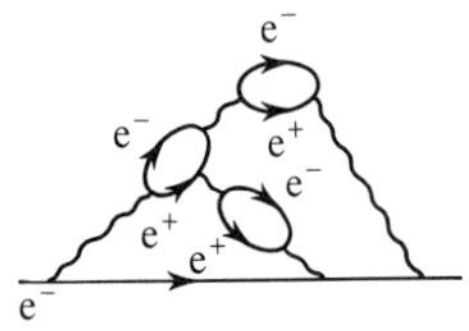

(a)

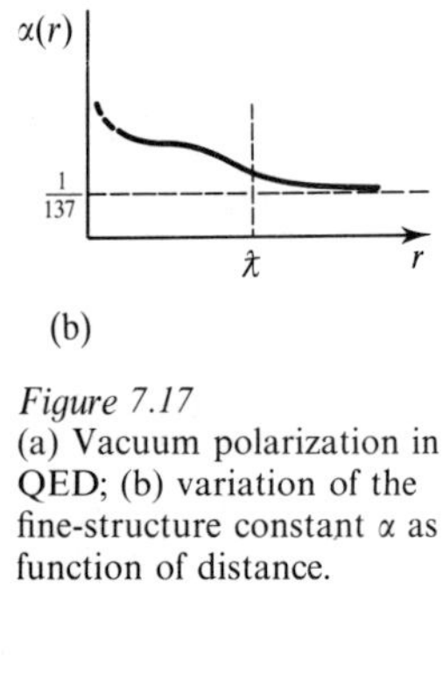

(b)

Figure 7.17
(a) Vacuum polarization in QED; (b) variation of the fine-structure constant α as a function of distance.

compared with the molecular diameter the screening effect diminishes; the effective charge increases and approaches the value of the full bare charge q. Screening effects similar to the above are evident when one considers the charge on the electron. As discussed in section 7.4.1, QED shows us that the electron can appear in many guises; it can spontaneously emit a photon which may materialize into an electron–positron pair, the electron and positron may emit further photons and so on. The electron is thus surrounded by a fluctuating 'cloud' of virtual electron–positron pairs with 'radius' of the order of the Compton wavelength, $\lambda\!\!\!^{-} = \hbar/mc$, as shown in figure 7.17(a). Because of Coulomb attraction, the positrons will on average be closer to the bare electron, and therefore the 'vacuum' will be polarized. At distances large compared with the Compton wavelength the effective charge is that which is normally quoted as the charge on the electron $e = 1.602 \times 10^{-19}$ coulomb, corresponding to a value for the fine-structure constant α of $e^2/4\pi\epsilon_0\hbar c \approx 1/137$. In analogy with the macroscopic effect discussed above, as the charge is probed at increasingly shorter distances the effective charge increases, corresponding to an increase in the fine-structure constant, as shown in figure 7.17(b). The effect is small, about 1 per cent, but nevertheless detectable. It must be noted that because the photon carries no charge there is no direct photon–photon coupling in QED. This leads to what is known as an *Abelian* field theory.

Vacuum polarization also affects the values of the strong and weak charges but in a crucially different way. The difference stems from the fact that the field quanta, the gluons and the weak bosons, themselves carry colour and weak charge respectively, unlike the photon which has no electric charge. As pointed out in section 7.4.2, the gluons can couple together and the same is true of the weak bosons. This coupling leads to what are known as *non-Abelian* field theories. The bare colour charge of a quark is modified by vacuum polarization described in QCD by diagrams like those shown in figure 7.18. If the polarization were described only by diagrams of the type shown in figure 7.18(a) the behaviour of $\alpha_s = e_s^2/4\pi\epsilon_0^s\hbar c$, as a function of distance, would be a replica of the electromagnetic case. Here, e_s is the strong charge and ϵ_0^s is the dielectric constant of the vacuum in response to the strong interactions. It was discovered independently by Gross and Wilczek[10] and by Politzer[11] that diagrams of the type shown in figure 7.18(b), which include gluon self-coupling vertices, have an 'anti-screening' effect. Roughly speaking, as we saw in section 7.4.2, the gluons tend to carry colour away from a quark or dilute the colour charge, so that in contrast to the electromagnetic case the colour charge decreases as it is probed to shorter and shorter distances. In fact, provided the total number of quark flavours u, d, s . . . is not too large, the strong coupling constant α_s approaches zero as $r \to 0$. This is known as 'asymptotic freedom' and implies that at very small distances, which would be achieved using a high energy probe, the quarks behave as free particles. The behaviour of α_s as a function of distance is shown schematically in

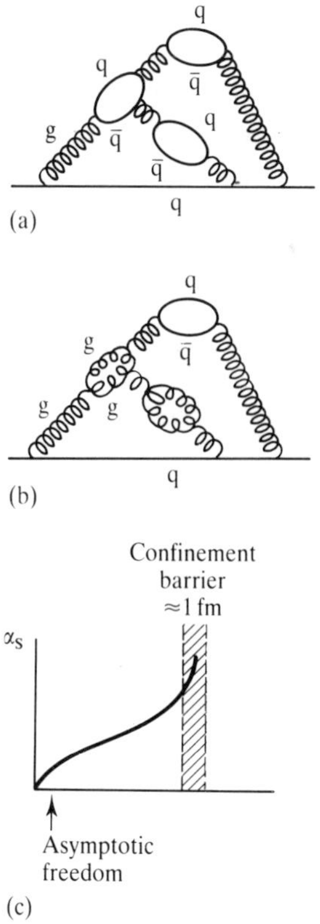

Figure 7.18
Vacuum polarization in QCD: (a) a contribution from $gq\bar{q}$ coupling; (b) a contribution including triple-gluon coupling; (c) variation of α_s with distance.

figure 7.18(c). One important consequence of asymptotic freedom is that, at least at high energies, perturbative methods can be used in the evaluation of QCD diagrams since $\alpha_s < 1$. The situation regarding the weak coupling constant, $\alpha_W = e_W^2/4\pi\epsilon_0^W \hbar c$, where now e_W is the weak charge and ϵ_0^W is the dielectric constant for the vacuum response to the weak force, is similar to the above with the gluons replaced by the weak gauge bosons. When defined in this way the relative values of the coupling constants, at distances which can be probed with today's high energy accelerators (see chapter 2), i.e. 10^{-15}–10^{-18} m, are $\alpha_W \approx 4\alpha$, $\alpha_s \approx 100\alpha$. The reader may be surprised to see that the weak coupling constant is larger than the electromagnetic coupling constant since, for example, the decay rate for a typical weak process $\pi^- \to \mu^- \bar{\nu}_\mu$ is much slower than that for the electromagnetic process $\pi^0 \to \gamma\gamma$ (see table 7.2). The apparent weakness of the weak interaction is in fact due to the extremely short range of the force caused by the very large mass of the weak bosons.* In section 7.4.2 it was stated that the gluons, like the photon, have zero mass and yet the range of the strong interaction is extremely short, of the order of 10^{-15} m. The explanation of this apparent contradiction is almost certainly connected with the variation of α_s with distance. Specifically, let us consider the colour force between a quark and an antiquark, bound by gluon exchange as in a meson. If, as indicated in figure 7.18(c), α_s increases with increasing distance, no finite amount of energy supplied to the system can liberate the quark or antiquark, or for that matter, the gluons; as the separation distance increases the colour force between the quark and antiquark becomes stronger. As indicated above this effect is due to the intrinsic non-linear character of QCD caused by the gluon self-coupling. Through the coupling of gluons to one another the colour field lines of force between the quark and antiquark are compelled to form a 'tube' as though there were attractive forces between the field lines, as shown in figure 7.19. This is in marked contrast to the Coulomb field; there is no self-interaction between the photons which prevents the field lines from spreading out. As the quark–antiquark distance r increases the potential energy of the system increases in proportion to r and so the quarks and gluons can never be freed. This 'infra-red slavery', as it is called, is believed to give rise to the total confinement of quarks and gluons inside hadrons, which, we recall, are 'colour neutral' or singlets. If one continues to stretch the colour flux tube there comes a point, beyond the 'confinement barrier' (see figure 7.18(c)), at which it is energetically

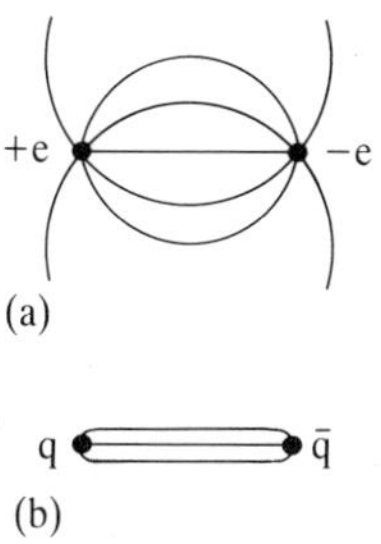

Figure 7.19
Lines of force for (a) a Coulomb field and (b) a colour field.

* In section 7.4.1 it was pointed out that the amplitude for a particular process depends not only on the coupling constants at the vertices but also on the propagator for the virtual exchanged particle. Crudely speaking this is $(p^2 - m^2)^{-1}$ where p is the four-momentum of the exchanged particle and m is its mass. For values of $p^2 \ll m^2$ this is approximately $1/p^2$ for electromagnetic interactions ($m_\gamma = 0$) and approximately $1/m_W^2$ for the weak interactions.

Table 7.6
Some basic characteristics of the electromagnetic, strong and weak interactions

Interaction	Field quanta	Basic coupling: Quarks	Basic coupling: Leptons	Coupling constants	Range/m	Typical reaction time/s	Typical cross-section/mb
Electromagnetic	γ	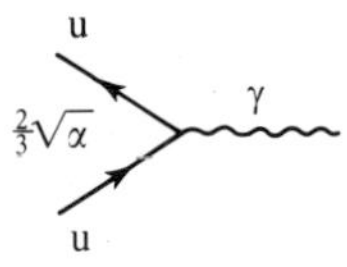 u, u, γ, $\frac{2}{3}\sqrt{\alpha}$	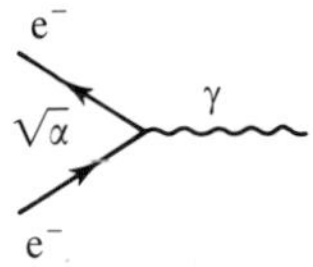 e^-, e^-, γ, $\sqrt{\alpha}$	$\alpha \approx 1/137$	∞	10^{-16} or less	10^{-3}
Strong	Gluons	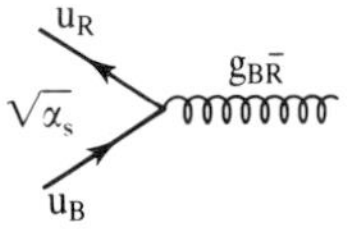 u_R, u_B, $g_{B\bar{R}}$, $\sqrt{\alpha_s}$		$\alpha_s \approx 100\alpha$	10^{-15}	10^{-23}	10
Weak	$W^{\pm}, Z^0$	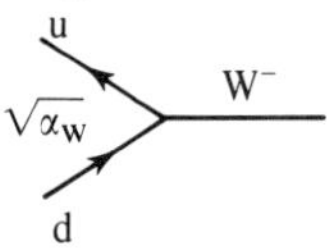 u, d, W^-, $\sqrt{\alpha_W}$	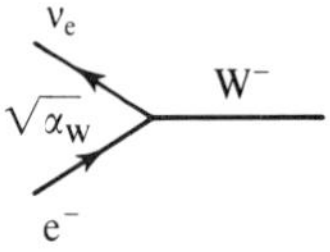 ν_e, e^-, W^-, $\sqrt{\alpha_W}$	$\alpha_W \approx 4\alpha$	10^{-18}	10^{-12} or more	10^{-11}

more favourable to rupture the tube. In doing so, another quark–antiquark pair, a meson, is created.* This gives rise to the so-called bag model of hadrons. The quarks in a hadron are confined to a 'bag' with a radius of the order of 1 fm, the confinement barrier, and the colour content of the quarks is such that the bag is colour neutral. This bag model of the hadrons then implies that if two protons, for instance, are to interact via the strong or colour force, since the bags have no net colour they must overlap before the quarks in one bag can experience the colour force due to the quarks in the other. The range of the interaction is then roughly equal to the bag radius.

Thus we see that colour, which was originally introduced to explain a statistics problem associated with the quark content of the baryons, plays a fundamental role in sub-nuclear physics. We present in table 7.6 the basic characteristics of the fundamental interactions, as modified by the existence of vacuum polarization.

7.6 Towards a unification of the fundamental interactions

In the discussion so far, the three quarks with flavours up, down and strange, together with the six leptons (e, ν_e), (μ, ν_μ) and (τ, ν_τ), have been

* This is rather like attempting to isolate the poles in a bar magnet by cutting it in half.

considered as the fundamental particles; they are all spin $\frac{1}{2}$ fermions. Their various interactions have been described in the context of quantum field theories in which the spin 1 gauge bosons γ and $W^{\pm}$, Z_0 and the eight coloured gluons are the carriers of the electromagnetic, weak and strong force respectively.

Listed among the stable particles in table 7.2 are states labelled 'charm' and 'bottom', which, like the other hadrons, are composites of quarks but with the new flavours charm (c) and bottom (b). A sixth quark flavour, top (t), is confidently expected to exist. At the present time, therefore, there appear to be 12 fundamental fermions, the six quarks and the six leptons, which can be arranged into three 'generations' of increasing mass:

$$\begin{pmatrix} \mathrm{u} \\ \mathrm{d} \\ \mathrm{e} \\ \nu_e \end{pmatrix} \begin{pmatrix} \mathrm{c} \\ \mathrm{s} \\ \mu \\ \nu_\mu \end{pmatrix} \begin{pmatrix} (\mathrm{t}) \\ \mathrm{b} \\ \tau \\ \nu_\tau \end{pmatrix}.$$

The parentheses around the top quark indicate that as yet it has not been discovered experimentally. The parallelism between the quarks and leptons is striking; the distinct generations appear to be replicas of one another. The electromagnetic and weak interactions of the quarks and leptons are similar in many respects. For instance, the annihilation process $u\bar{u} \rightarrow e^+e^-$ can proceed by either of the mechanisms shown in figure 7.20. Does this imply some fundamental link between the quarks and leptons? The notion of a multiplet implies that transitions can take place between members of the multiplet. Does the above electroweak connection imply that the quarks and leptons legitimately belong to the same multiplet? If so this would be tantamount to a unification of the weak and electromagnetic interactions; the quarks and leptons would be sources of a single unified electroweak field. Can the strong interaction field be related to this electroweak field? In other words can the electroweak and strong fields be combined into one 'grand unified field'?

Figure 7.20
Feynman diagrams for the annihilation processes
(a) $u\bar{u} \rightarrow \gamma \rightarrow e^+e^-$ and
(b) $u\bar{u} \rightarrow Z^0 \rightarrow e^+e^-$.

The steps towards this grand unification began long ago in the classical domain (see figure 7.7) when Newton unified celestial and terrestrial mechanics; the same gravitational laws explained both sets of phenomena. Maxwell unified electricity and magnetism; if the electric and magnetic charges were distinct the force on a particle with electric charge e_E and magnetic charge e_M, say, would be

$$\boldsymbol{F} = e_E \boldsymbol{E} + e_M \boldsymbol{v} \wedge \boldsymbol{B}.$$

The unification is brought about through the realization that $e_E = e_M = e$, the 'electromagnetic' charge. Maxwell's theory is a relativistic theory and the unification introduces a scale, the velocity of light c, which governs

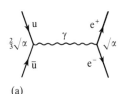

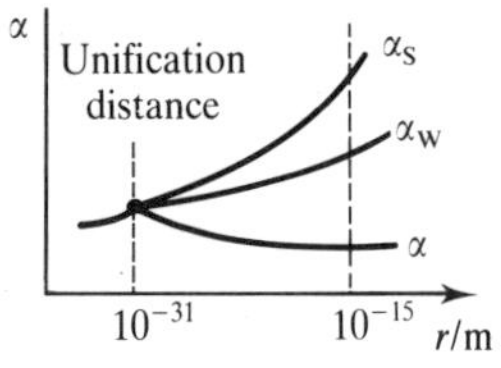

Figure 7.21
Schematic representation of the variation of the fine-structure constants showing convergence towards a single value at the 'grand unification distance' $r \approx 10^{-31}$m.

the relative strength of the two interactions. At low velocities the 'electric' force dominates but at high velocities the electric and magnetic forces are comparable. In the quantum domain we have seen that the strong, weak and electromagnetic fine-structure constants have a functional dependence on distance. At short distances, or equivalently, high energies, the electromagnetic coupling increases in strength while the strong and weak coupling decreases in strength. It is conceivable that at some unifying energy scale, or interparticle separation, the three become equal as indicated in figure 7.21. Detailed calculations show that the change in α is extremely slow at short distances, in fact logarithmic, and the unification scale is $r \approx 10^{-31}$ m. At this distance the quarks and leptons would be the sources of the 'grand unified field' mentioned earlier. As with the other fields, which are distinct at the distances which can be achieved with today's accelerators, the particles will interact through the exchange of field quanta, spin 1 X bosons. The range of the interactions implies that $M_X \approx 10^{15}$ GeV, an extremely high mass. Such ultra-high energies would be commonplace in the earliest epoch, after the 'big bang', when the universe was extremely hot and dense, but are utterly unattainable in the laboratory. However, an important feature of grand unification is that the quarks and leptons would belong to one 'super-multiplet' and therefore transitions could take place between them since they would all couple to the X bosons. This has the important and dramatic implication that baryon number would not be conserved and the proton would be unstable. A possible mechanism for the decay $p \rightarrow e^+\pi^0$ is shown in figure 7.22 in which an X boson is exchanged between an up and down quark in the proton to produce a positron and a π^0. The proton of course is known to have a lifetime which is many orders of magnitude bigger than the age of the universe; detailed calculations show that the proton lifetime is greater than 10^{31} years. This seems extremely long in the context of a unified theory which puts the quarks and leptons on the same footing but it can be qualitatively understood in the same way that at low energies the weak interactions are understood to be much weaker than the electromagnetic interactions, even though $\alpha_W \approx 4\alpha$. The weak interactions are inhibited by the high mass of the W and Z bosons. Analogously, the proton decay is inhibited by the extreme mass of the X boson. It is clear that proton decay experiments are of vital significance for the ideas of grand unification.

What about gravity? Because the gravitational force is so weak compared with the other three forces it can safely be neglected in most considerations concerning elementary particles. But, as we have seen, the

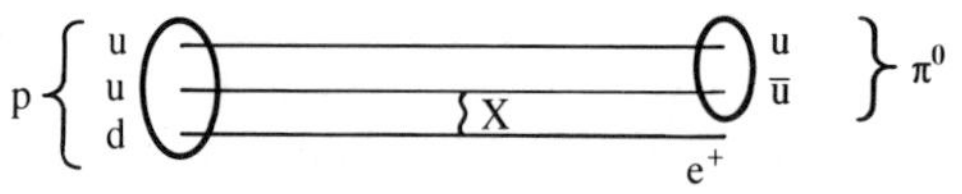

Figure 7.22
A possible mechanism for the decay $p \rightarrow \pi^0 e^+$.

relative strengths of these forces depend on the distance or, equivalently, the energy. This is also true of the gravitational force – except that in this case the strength increases as some power of the energy rather than logarithmically. Gravitational effects must be taken into account when the energy is of the order of the Planck mass, m_P, which is given by the expression

$$m_P = \sqrt{\left(\frac{\hbar c}{G}\right)} \approx 10^{19}\ \text{GeV}$$

where G is Newton's gravitational constant. Since this is much greater even than the grand unification mass scale, $M_X \approx 10^{15}$ GeV, gravity can normally be safely neglected. Attempts are being made, however, to incorporate gravitation into the scheme of unification. One such attempt, known as supergravity, embraces the Einstein gravitational field equations and the field equations of the strong and electroweak interactions in the same theory. The quantum of the supergravity field is the spin 2 graviton, which is placed in the same multiplet as certain fermions and bosons of lower spin. Such a theory takes us well beyond our present knowledge of the quarks and leptons, but whether or not it forms the basis of the unification of the four fundamental interactions it is the cherished belief that a single unified theory can be constructed.

REFERENCES 7

1 **Perl M L** *et al.* 1975 *Phys Rev Lett* **35** (1489)

2 **Gell-Mann M** 1964 *Phys Lett* **8** (214)

3 **Pais A** 1952 *Phys Rev* **86** (663)

4 **Gell-Mann M** 1956 *Nuovo Cimento* Suppl **4** (2848)

5 **Nishijima K** 1955 *Prog Theor Phys* (Kyoto) **13** (285)

6 **Dirac P A M** 1928 *Proc Roy Soc* **A117** (610)

7 **Fermi E** 1934 *Zeit Physik* **88** (161)

8 **Weinberg S** 1967 *Phys Rev Lett* **19** (1264); see also **Salam A** 1968 in Svartholm N (ed) *Elementary Particle Theory; Relativistic Groups and Analyticity* (8th Nobel Symposium) Almqvist and Wiksell

9 **Aitchison I J R** (1985) *Contemp Phys* **26** (333)

10 **Gross D J and Wilczek F** 1973 *Phys Rev Lett* **30** (1343)

11 **Politzer H D** 1973 *Phys Rev Lett* **30** (1346)

EXAMPLES 7

7.1 If a resonance has $I = \frac{3}{2}$, $B = 1$ and $S = 0$, what are its charge states?

7.2 The Σ baryon exists in three charge states: +, 0 and −. Show that the Σ has strangeness $S = -1$.

7.3 Use the Gell-Mann–Nishijima formula to verify the charges of the quarks and antiquarks given in tables 7.3 and 7.4.

7.4 What values of electric charge are possible for (a) a baryon and (b) a meson in the quark model?

7.5 (a) The Λ^0 is an isosinglet baryon with strangeness $S = -1$. What is its quark content?
(b) The Ξ baryons form an isospin doublet with $S = -2$. What charge states are possible?
(c) Determine the quark content of the K^+, K^0 ($S = +1$) and K^-, $\bar{K}^0$ ($S = -1$) mesons.

7.6 The Σ^0 hyperon decays to $\Lambda^0 + \gamma$ with a mean lifetime of 7.4×10^{-20} s. Estimate its width.

7.7 The long-range part of the strong force between two nucleons can be ascribed to the exchange of a pion. A crude estimate of the range can be obtained using the uncertainty principle $\Delta E\, \Delta t \approx \hbar$. Show that the range R and mass m of the exchanged meson are related by $R \approx \hbar/mc$ and hence that, for $m = 140$ MeV/c^2, the range is approximately 1.4 fm.

7.8 Draw a Feynman diagram showing the mechanism for μ^- decay.

8 *Symmetry transformations and conservation laws*

8.1 *Introduction*

The intimate connection between symmetry and conservation laws is perhaps nowhere so evident as in elementary particle physics; indeed the ideas of unification, briefly sketched in chapter 7, are based upon symmetry principles. The symmetries we shall deal with fall into two broad categories. The first are space–time symmetries which arise due to the existence of *equivalent* space–time frames of reference in which the laws of physics can be formulated and in which they have equal validity. Examples are translations and rotations in space. Symmetries belonging to the second category are known as internal symmetries of which isospin is an example; we shall meet others such as charge conjugation and SU(3) symmetry in due course. We shall call a symmetry transformation one which connects equivalent frames of reference.

Perhaps the most economical way to appreciate the connection between a symmetry transformation and an associated conservation law is to compare the Schrödinger and Heisenberg approaches to quantum mechanics. In the former the dynamical state of a system is represented by a wavefunction or state vector $|\psi(t)\rangle$ which evolves in time and dynamical variables are represented by operators. In the Heisenberg approach the state vectors are considered fixed while the dynamical variables evolve in time. If a system is prepared at time t_0 in the state $|\psi(t_0)\rangle$ then at some later time t the state will evolve to $|\psi(t)\rangle$. Formally, this is written

$$|\psi(t)\rangle = U(t, t_0)|\psi(t_0)\rangle. \tag{8.1}$$

The evolution operator $U(t, t_0)$ is subject to the initial condition $U(t_0, t_0) = 1$. If we postulate that the principle of linear superposition is maintained in the evolution of the system then $U(t, t_0)$ must be a linear operator. On comparing equation (8.1) with the time-dependent Schrödinger equation

$$\mathrm{i}\hbar \frac{\partial}{\partial t}|\psi(t)\rangle = H|\psi(t)\rangle \tag{8.2}$$

where H is the Hamiltonian of the system, we deduce that

$$U(t, t_0) = \exp\left[\frac{-\mathrm{i}H(t - t_0)}{\hbar}\right]. \tag{8.3}$$

Evidently $U(t, t_0)$ is a unitary operator since its adjoint $U^\dagger$ is equal to its inverse U^{-1}, or $U^\dagger U = UU^\dagger = 1$. We note that the transformation (8.1) preserves the norms of the state vectors, i.e. if $|\psi(t_0)\rangle$ is normalized then so is $|\psi(t)\rangle$; probability is conserved.

Let us now consider how a dynamical variable D evolves when the state vectors evolve according to (8.1). We are specifically interested in conserved quantities. If D is a constant of the motion its expectation value at any time t will be the same as that at time t_0. To admit the possibility of a time dependence we add a subscript 0 when the expectation value is determined in the initial state. In order to avoid cumbersome equations we omit the time dependence of the evolution operator. Then,

$$\langle\psi(t)|D|\psi(t)\rangle = \langle\psi(t_0)|U^\dagger DU|\psi(t_0)\rangle = \langle\psi(t_0)|D_0|\psi(t_0)\rangle.$$

The last equality is tantamount to the Heisenberg description in which the time dependence has been transferred from the state vectors to the dynamical variables. It follows that

$$U^\dagger DU = D_0$$

or, since U is unitary,

$$D = UD_0U^\dagger. \tag{8.4}$$

If D is indeed a conserved quantity we must have $\mathrm{d}D/\mathrm{d}t = 0$ for all t.

On differentiating (8.4) and using the explicit form (8.3) for $U(t, t_0)$ we obtain

$$\frac{\mathrm{d}D}{\mathrm{d}t} = \frac{1}{\mathrm{i}\hbar}[H, D] + \frac{\partial D}{\partial t} \tag{8.5}$$

where $[H, D] = HD - DH$ is the commutator of D with the Hamiltonian. If D does not depend explicitly on the time, $\partial D/\partial t = 0$ and then *D is a conserved quantity if it commutes with the Hamiltonian*, i.e. if $[H, D] = 0$. In order to make the connection with a symmetry transformation we observe that if $HD = DH$ then

$$D^\dagger H D = H \tag{8.6}$$

if D is unitary. If the Hamiltonian is invariant under the transformation generated by D then D is a conserved quantity. We now consider some specific examples.

8.2 *Translations in space*

The operator corresponding to an infinitesimal translation ϵ along the x axis is $D(\epsilon) = (1 + \epsilon\, \partial/\partial x)$. Its effect on a state vector $|\psi(x)\rangle$ is

$$D(\epsilon)|\psi(x)\rangle = \left(1 + \epsilon\frac{\partial}{\partial x}\right)|\psi(x)\rangle = |\psi(x)\rangle + \epsilon\frac{\partial}{\partial x}|\psi(x)\rangle = |\psi(x+\epsilon)\rangle.$$

The operator corresponding to the x component of momentum is $p_x = -\mathrm{i}\hbar\, \partial/\partial x$, so that

$$D(\epsilon) = 1 + \mathrm{i}\frac{\epsilon p_x}{\hbar}$$

or, generalizing to three dimensions,

$$D(\boldsymbol{\varepsilon}) = 1 + i\frac{\boldsymbol{\epsilon}\cdot\boldsymbol{p}}{\hbar}. \tag{8.7}$$

A finite translation $\boldsymbol{r}$ can be generated by successive application of the operator in (8.7), giving

$$D(\boldsymbol{r}) = \underset{\substack{\boldsymbol{\epsilon}\to 0\\ n\to\infty}}{\mathrm{Lt}}\left(1 + \mathrm{i}\frac{\boldsymbol{\epsilon}\cdot\boldsymbol{p}}{\hbar}\right)^n = \exp\left(\mathrm{i}\frac{\boldsymbol{r}\cdot\boldsymbol{p}}{\hbar}\right) \tag{8.8}$$

where $n\boldsymbol{\epsilon} \to \boldsymbol{r}$ as $n \to \infty$ and $\boldsymbol{\epsilon} \to 0$.

The transformation generated by D is a symmetry transformation since it connects equivalent frames: the laws of physics must be independent of the origin of a reference frame. The linear momentum $\boldsymbol{p}$ is the *generator* of translations and its conservation results from a symmetry of space: space is homogeneous. Alternatively, momentum conservation may be viewed as a symmetry of the system, for if the Hamiltonian of the system is invariant under the transformation D, the dynamical variable corresponding to D, the linear momentum in the present case, is conserved. The unitary operators (8.8) form a *representation* of the translation symmetry group and since the operators commute the group is Abelian.

8.3 Rotations in space

For rotations of the frame of reference, or equivalently the rotation of a physical system within a fixed frame, the commutative law is generally not obeyed and the rotation group is non-Abelian. If we assume Cartesian axes for the frame the coordinate transformation resulting from an infinitesimal rotation ϵ around the z axis is

$$x \to x' = x + \epsilon y \qquad y \to y' = y - \epsilon x \qquad z \to z' = z \tag{8.9}$$

and the unitary operator $D(\epsilon)$ transforming the state function is

$$\begin{aligned} D(\epsilon)|\psi(x, y, z)\rangle &= |\psi(x + \epsilon y, y - \epsilon x, z)\rangle \\ &\approx |\psi(x, y, z)\rangle + \epsilon\left(y\frac{\partial}{\partial x} - x\frac{\partial}{\partial y}\right)|\psi(x, y, z)\rangle \\ &= \left(1 - \mathrm{i}\frac{\epsilon L_z}{\hbar}\right)|\psi(x, y, z)\rangle \end{aligned} \tag{8.10}$$

where L_z is the z component of the orbital angular momentum $\boldsymbol{L}$ of the system. As in the case of a translation a finite rotation ϕ can be generated by successive operations and

$$D(\phi) = \underset{\substack{\epsilon \to 0 \\ n \to \infty}}{\mathrm{Lt}} \left(1 - \mathrm{i}\frac{\epsilon L_z}{\hbar}\right)^n = \exp\left(-\mathrm{i}\frac{\phi L_z}{\hbar}\right). \tag{8.11}$$

Generally, a rotation θ about an axis specified by a unit vector $\boldsymbol{n}$ is generated by the operator

$$D(\theta) = \exp\left(-\mathrm{i}\theta\frac{\boldsymbol{n}\cdot\boldsymbol{L}}{\hbar}\right) \tag{8.12}$$

where now the angular momentum $\boldsymbol{L}$ is the generator of the transformation.

Since the laws of physics must be independent of the orientation of the coordinate axes in space the frames of reference linked by the rotation operators are equivalent and the rotations form a symmetry group. The conservation of angular momentum can thus be regarded as being due to the isotropy of space. Alternatively, it can be regarded as a symmetry of the system; if the Hamiltonian of the system is invariant under rotations, angular momentum is conserved.

The state functions so far used have been scalar functions corresponding to scalar fields. If we extend the formalism to general fields for which angular momenta $\boldsymbol{J}$ are defined as the generators of rotations by equation (8.12) with $\boldsymbol{L} \to \boldsymbol{J}$, then for a vector field, such as that of electromagnetic radiation,

$$\boldsymbol{J} = \boldsymbol{L} + \boldsymbol{s} \tag{8.13}$$

where $\boldsymbol{s}$ is interpreted as an *intrinsic spin* associated with the field. For a vector field the field quanta have spin quantum number $s = 1$; the spin of the photon for instance is 1. For a scalar field $s = 0$.

The rotation (translation) group has the property that finite rotations (translations) can be generated as the product of successive infinitesimal rotations (translations). The group is then completely defined by consideration of infinitesimal transformations and such groups are known as Lie groups. The Lie algebra of the rotation group is based on the commutation relations for the angular momentum operators

$$[J_j, J_k] = \mathrm{i}\epsilon_{jkl}J_l \tag{8.14}$$

where $\epsilon_{jkl} = +1\ (-1)$ if j, k, l are cyclic (anticyclic) and $\epsilon_{jkl} = 0$ otherwise. The coefficients ϵ_{jkl} are known as the *structure constants* of the rotation group. The commutation relations (8.14) result from the fact that rotations in space do not commute.

An operator that commutes with all the generators of a group is called a *Casimir operator*, or invariant. For the rotation group the total angular momentum operator

$$J^2 = J_x^2 + J_y^2 + J_z^2 \tag{8.15}$$

is the only Casimir operator:

$$[J^2, J_i] = 0 \qquad \text{for } i = x, y, z. \tag{8.16}$$

We can therefore construct simultaneous eigenstates $|j, m\rangle$ of J^2 and *one* of the generators, conventionally J_z. The labels j and m are the quantum numbers of the total angular momentum and the component along the

z axis. The eigenvalue equations are

$$J^2|j, m\rangle = j(j+1)|j, m\rangle$$
$$J_z|j, m\rangle = m|j, m\rangle \tag{8.17}$$

with $m = -j, -j+1, \ldots, j-1, j$. The quantum number j can have one of the values $0, \frac{1}{2}, 1, \frac{3}{2}, \ldots$.

It is convenient to form linear combinations of the other generators, J_x and J_y, which have useful commutation relations with J_z. For the rotation group these are

$$J_+ = J_x + iJ_y$$

the 'raising operator', and

$$J_- = J_x - iJ_y$$

the 'lowering operator', which satisfy the commutation relations

$$[J_z, J_\pm] = \pm J_\pm. \tag{8.18}$$

Consider a state $|j, m\rangle$, i.e. a state with total angular momentum j and component m along the quantization axis. From (8.18) we have

$$\begin{aligned} J_z J_-|j, m\rangle &= (J_- J_z - J_-)|j, m\rangle \\ &= J_-(J_z - 1)|j, m\rangle \\ &= (m-1)J_-|j, m\rangle. \end{aligned}$$

Thus

$$J_z[J_-|j, m\rangle] = (m-1)[J_-|j, m\rangle]. \tag{8.19}$$

Equation (8.19) is an eigenvalue equation showing that the new state $J_-|j, m\rangle$ is an eigenstate of J_z with eigenvalue $m-1$. It is for this reason that J_- is called a lowering operator. Similarly, the state $J_+|j, m\rangle$ is an eigenstate of J_z with eigenvalue $m+1$. Thus we can write

$$J_-|j, m\rangle = C_-|j, m-1\rangle$$
$$J_+|j, m\rangle = C_+|j, m+1\rangle$$

with the conditions that $C_- = 0$ for $m = -j$ and $C_+ = 0$ for $m = j$. The values of C_+ and C_-, up to an arbitrary phase, can be determined as follows. We have

$$J_-J_+|j, m\rangle = J_-C_+(m)|j, m+1\rangle = C_-(m+1)C_+(m)|j, m\rangle.$$

In order to preserve the normalization of the states $|j, m\rangle$ with different m values we must have $C_-(m+1) = C_+(m)$. Then

$$J_-J_+|j, m\rangle = C_+^2(m)|j, m\rangle.$$

From the definitions of J_+ and J_- and the commutation relations (8.14) we obtain

$$J_-J_+ = J^2 - J_z(J_z + 1)$$

so

$$C_+ = [j(j+1) - m(m+1)]^{1/2}.$$

Similarly

$$C_- = [j(j+1) - m(m-1)]^{1/2}.$$

In summary,

$$J^2|j, m\rangle = j(j+1)|j, m\rangle$$

$$J_z|j, m\rangle = m|j, m\rangle$$

$$J_\pm|j, m\rangle = [j(j+1) - m(m \pm 1)]^{1/2}|j, m \pm 1\rangle. \tag{8.20}$$

The relations (8.20) define the matrix elements of the angular momentum operators in a basis in which J^2 and J_z are diagonal. Since all the operators in (8.20) are diagonal in j, matrices for each j are generally written with the rows labelled with m and the columns with m'. The matrix elements are

$$\langle j, m|J^2|j, m'\rangle = j(j+1)\delta_{mm'}$$

$$\langle j, m|J_z|j, m'\rangle = m\delta_{mm'}$$

$$\langle j, m|J_\pm|j, m'\rangle = [j(j+1) - m(m \pm 1)]^{1/2}\delta_{m,m'\pm 1}. \tag{8.21}$$

The set of states $|j, m\rangle$ with $|m| \leqslant j$ are said to form a *multiplet*. For a given j there are $2j + 1$ states corresponding to the $2j + 1$ different m values or different orientations of j. For $j = 0$, $\frac{1}{2}$ and 1 the multiplets are a singlet, doublet and triplet respectively.

The sum of two angular momenta, $\boldsymbol{J} = \boldsymbol{J}_1 + \boldsymbol{J}_2$, is also an angular momentum satisfying the commutation relations (8.14). It may be described in terms of the basis $|j_1m_1\rangle|j_2m_2\rangle$ or alternatively in terms of $|jm\rangle$. These two bases are connected by a unitary transformation

$$|jm\rangle = \sum_{m_1m_2} C^{jm}_{m_1m_2}|j_1m_1\rangle|j_2m_2\rangle \tag{8.22}$$

where the vector addition or Clebsch–Gordan coefficients can be calculated

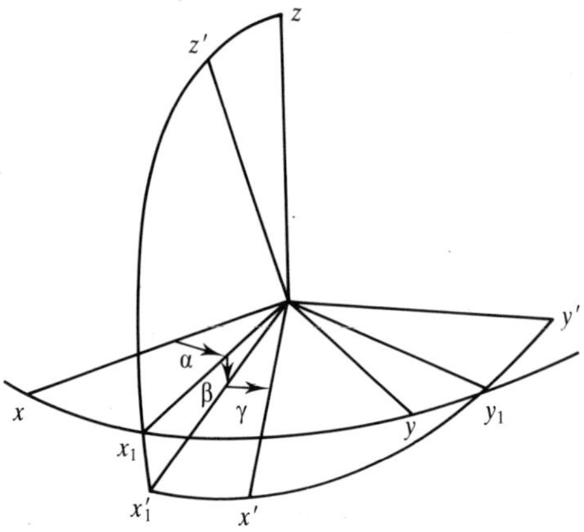

Figure 8.1
Definition of the Euler angles.

by using the raising or lowering operators but for convenience are tabulated in appendix G.

In all the foregoing angular momentum equations we have measured the angular momentum in units of $\hbar$; the absolute value of an angular momentum $\boldsymbol{j}$ is $\sqrt{[j(j+1)]}\hbar$.

Finally in this section we consider representations of the rotation group. A general rotation is normally specified in terms of the Euler angles (see figure 8.1.), which are defined by three successive rotations:

(a) a rotation through an angle α about the z axis generated by the unitary operator $D(\alpha) = \exp(-\mathrm{i}\alpha J_z)$;
(b) a rotation through β about the new y axis y_1 generated by $D(\beta) = \exp(-\mathrm{i}\beta J_{y_1})$;
(c) a rotation through γ about the z' axis and generated by $D(\gamma) = \exp(-\mathrm{i}\gamma J_{z'})$.

These rotations are anticlockwise when looking along the rotation axis towards the origin and the three rotations together have taken us from the original axes labelled xyz to the final axes $x'y'z'$. The unitary operator for this arbitrary rotation is thus

$$D(\alpha, \beta, \gamma) = \exp(-\mathrm{i}\gamma J_{z'}) \exp(-\mathrm{i}\beta J_{y_1}) \exp(-\mathrm{i}\alpha J_z). \tag{8.23}$$

This expression is inconvenient because it refers to different coordinate frames but a little thought shows that the same transformation of axes results from first a rotation γ about the *original* z axis followed by a rotation β about the *original* y axis and finally a rotation α about the *original* z axis. We therefore arrive at the important result

$$D(\alpha, \beta, \gamma) = \exp(-\mathrm{i}\alpha J_z) \exp(-\mathrm{i}\beta J_y) \exp(-\mathrm{i}\gamma J_z) \tag{8.24}$$

which now refers only to the original coordinate axes.

As usual we choose a set of basis vectors $|jm\rangle$ which are simultaneously eigenstates of J^2 and J_z. Since J^2 is invariant under a rotation the matrix of D in this representation is diagonal in j. We therefore confine ourselves to the matrix elements

$$D^{(j)}_{mm'}(\alpha, \beta, \gamma) = \langle jm|D(\alpha, \beta, \gamma)|jm'\rangle$$
$$= \exp(-\mathrm{i}\alpha m)d^{(j)}_{mm'}(\beta)\exp(-\mathrm{i}\gamma m') \qquad (8.25)$$

where

$$d^{(j)}_{mm'}(\beta) = \langle jm|\exp(-\mathrm{i}\beta J_y)|jm'\rangle. \qquad (8.26)$$

Explicit calculations of some of these matrix elements are given in appendix H. The matrix $D^{(j)}$ has dimension $(2j + 1)$ and is said to be the $(2j + 1)$-dimensional irreducible representation of the rotation group. The lowest dimension non-trivial representation of the rotation group $D^{(1/2)}$ is the *fundamental* representation in the sense that all higher dimension representations can be constructed from it. An example of the use of these rotation matrices is given in section 14.3.8.

8.4 The group SU(2)

Because of its importance in the description of both spin and isospin we review here the main properties of the special unitary group in two dimensions, SU(2).

For a spin $\frac{1}{2}$ particle the discussion of section 8.3 makes it clear that there are two eigenstates $|s, m_s\rangle$ of the commutating operators s^2 and s_z and that these have $m_s = \pm\frac{1}{2}$, namely spin 'up' and spin 'down'. If there is no preferred direction in space, so that all frames of reference that differ only by a rotation of axes are equivalent, these states are indistinguishable. They may be connected by the raising and lowering operators $s_\pm = s_x \pm \mathrm{i}s_y$ and if the eigenstates are written in the form of column vectors $\binom{1}{0}$, $\binom{0}{1}$ these operators have the simple matrix form

$$s_+ = \begin{pmatrix} 0 & 1 \\ 0 & 0 \end{pmatrix} \qquad s_- = \begin{pmatrix} 0 & 0 \\ 1 & 0 \end{pmatrix} \qquad (8.27)$$

from which we may conclude that the spin component matrices are

$$s_x = \begin{pmatrix} 0 & 1/2 \\ 1/2 & 0 \end{pmatrix} \qquad s_y = \begin{pmatrix} 0 & -\mathrm{i}/2 \\ \mathrm{i}/2 & 0 \end{pmatrix} \qquad s_z = \begin{pmatrix} 1/2 & 0 \\ 0 & -1/2 \end{pmatrix}. \qquad (8.28)$$

These are just the *Pauli matrices* σ divided by 2.

The set of all unitary 2×2 matrices is known as the group U(2). A general spin state

$$|\psi\rangle \equiv \begin{pmatrix} a \\ b \end{pmatrix} = a\begin{pmatrix} 1 \\ 0 \end{pmatrix} + b\begin{pmatrix} 0 \\ 1 \end{pmatrix}$$

is transformed into $|\psi'\rangle$ under the action of the unitary operator $U: |\psi\rangle \rightarrow |\psi'\rangle = U|\psi\rangle$. Since U is unitary, $UU^\dagger = U^\dagger U = 1$, probability is preserved under the transformation. Then,

$$\det(UU^\dagger) = (\det U)(\det U^\dagger) = (\det U)(\det U)^* = |\det U|^2 = 1$$

so that

$$\det U = \exp(\mathrm{i}\theta)$$

where θ is real. This overall phase factor is relatively uninteresting: it corresponds to a global rotation of the state $|\psi\rangle$. The smaller group of transformations, with $\det U = 1$, is known as the special,* or unimodular, unitary group in two dimensions, SU(2). Now, for any hermitian matrix X, say,

$$\det[\exp(\mathrm{i}X)] = \exp[\mathrm{i}\,\mathrm{Tr}(X)]$$

where the trace, $\mathrm{Tr}(X)$, is the sum of the diagonal elements. If the unitary matrix $\exp(\mathrm{i}X)$ is unimodular, $\mathrm{Tr}(X) = 0$. The Pauli spin matrices are hermitian and traceless and the set of matrices

$$U_i(\theta) = \exp(-\tfrac{1}{2}\mathrm{i}\sigma_i\theta) \qquad \text{with } i = x, y, z \tag{8.29}$$

form a representation of the group SU(2). The group of phase transformations mentioned above, U(1), and the group SU(2) are subgroups of U(2) and the relation between these groups is written $\mathrm{U(2)} = \mathrm{SU(2)} \otimes \mathrm{U(1)}$. The Pauli matrices (cf. (8.28)) form the fundamental, two-dimensional representation of SU(2). The algebra of the group is just the algebra of the generators, $J_i = \frac{1}{2}\sigma_i$, summarized in the commutation relations

$$\left[\frac{\sigma_i}{2}, \frac{\sigma_j}{2}\right] = \mathrm{i}\epsilon_{ijk}\frac{\sigma_k}{2}. \tag{8.30}$$

As before (equation (8.14)) the constants ϵ_{ijk} are the structure constants of the group.

Higher dimensional representations can be formed from the fundamental representation. For example, two spin $\frac{1}{2}$ particles can couple to

* The special requirement is equivalent to choosing the phase $\theta = 0$.

give a total of four states which we write symbolically as $|\uparrow\rangle|\uparrow\rangle$, $|\downarrow\rangle|\downarrow\rangle$, $|\uparrow\rangle|\downarrow\rangle$ and $|\downarrow\rangle|\uparrow\rangle$. The total spin can have the values 1 and 0 only, and these four states reduce to a triplet ($s = 1$) and a singlet ($s = 0$). Specifically

$$\begin{aligned}
|1, 1\rangle &= |\tfrac{1}{2}, \tfrac{1}{2}\rangle|\tfrac{1}{2}, \tfrac{1}{2}\rangle & & |\uparrow\rangle|\uparrow\rangle \\
|1, 0\rangle &= \frac{1}{\sqrt{2}}(|\tfrac{1}{2}, \tfrac{1}{2}\rangle|\tfrac{1}{2}, -\tfrac{1}{2}\rangle + |\tfrac{1}{2}, -\tfrac{1}{2}\rangle|\tfrac{1}{2}, \tfrac{1}{2}\rangle) & & \frac{1}{\sqrt{2}}(|\uparrow\rangle|\downarrow\rangle + |\downarrow\rangle|\uparrow\rangle) \\
|1, -1\rangle &= |\tfrac{1}{2}, -\tfrac{1}{2}\rangle|\tfrac{1}{2}, -\tfrac{1}{2}\rangle & & |\downarrow\rangle|\downarrow\rangle \\
|0, 0\rangle &= \frac{1}{\sqrt{2}}(|\tfrac{1}{2}, \tfrac{1}{2}\rangle|\tfrac{1}{2}, -\tfrac{1}{2}\rangle - |\tfrac{1}{2}, -\tfrac{1}{2}\rangle|\tfrac{1}{2}, \tfrac{1}{2}\rangle) & & \frac{1}{\sqrt{2}}(|\uparrow\rangle|\downarrow\rangle - |\downarrow\rangle|\uparrow\rangle).
\end{aligned} \tag{8.31}$$

This decomposition has led to an *irreducible* representation and in the notation of group theory is written

$$2 \otimes 2 = 4 = 3 \oplus 1.$$

This combination of representations is a simple example of equation (8.22) – the factors $1/\sqrt{2}$ are Clebsch–Gordan coefficients. This procedure can be generalized to higher dimensions and the results[1] adhere to the familiar rule that the coupling of two irreducible representations with angular momenta j_1 and j_2 yields representations with j given by

$$|j_1 - j_2| \leqslant j \leqslant j_1 + j_2. \tag{8.32}$$

8.5 Systems of identical particles

Before discussing an important example of the SU(2) group, isospin, we would like to introduce a fundamental and far-reaching symmetry connected with the behaviour of systems of identical particles under particle interchange.

If a system consists of identical particles the principle of indistinguishability asserts that there is no measurement which can be made which will distinguish a system of these particles from one in which two (or more) of them have been interchanged. For simplicity, consider a system of two identical particles, labelled with the collective quantum numbers ξ_1 and ξ_2, say. We write the state vector as $|\xi_1\xi_2\rangle$. On interchange of the two particles, the state vector can at most be multiplied by a phase factor which is unobservable in any measurement. Then,

$$|\xi_2\xi_1\rangle = e^{i\alpha}|\xi_1\xi_2\rangle$$

and, on a second interchange,

$$|\xi_1\xi_2\rangle = e^{i\alpha}|\xi_2\xi_1\rangle = e^{2i\alpha}|\xi_1\xi_2\rangle.$$

Consequently,

$$e^{2i\alpha} = 1 \qquad e^{i\alpha} = \pm 1.$$

Then, on interchange we have

$$|\xi_2\xi_1\rangle = \pm|\xi_1\xi_2\rangle. \tag{8.33}$$

Systems for which the state vector does not change sign are said to be symmetric with respect to particle interchange; those which change sign are antisymmetric. The principle is readily extended to systems containing any number of identical particles. The conditions (8.33) can be satisfied in a manner reminiscent of the equation for the coupling of two angular momentum states. The composite state vector $|\xi_1\xi_2\rangle$ can be written in terms of the individual particle state vectors $|\xi_1\rangle$ and $|\xi_2\rangle$; then

$$|\xi_1\xi_2\rangle = \frac{1}{\sqrt{2}}(|\xi_1\rangle|\xi_2\rangle + |\xi_2\rangle|\xi_1\rangle) \tag{8.34}$$

is symmetric and

$$|\xi_1\xi_2\rangle = \frac{1}{\sqrt{2}}(|\xi_1\rangle|\xi_2\rangle - |\xi_2\rangle|\xi_1\rangle) \tag{8.35}$$

is antisymmetric.

We recall that identical fermions obey the Pauli exclusion principle; no two identical fermions can exist in the same quantum state. If $|\xi_1\rangle = |\xi_2\rangle$ then, in equation (8.35), $|\xi_1\xi_2\rangle$ vanishes, whereas in equation (8.34) it does not. Consequently, a state consisting of identical fermions must be described by an antisymmetric state function. Identical bosons on the other hand are described by symmetric state functions.

8.6 Parity

The parity transformation introduced in section 3.7, unlike translation and rotation in space, is a discrete transformation. No sequence of continuous changes can convert a left-handed frame of reference to a right-handed one. If, however, this is a symmetry transformation in the sense that the Hamiltonian of a system is invariant under the transformation then we recognize parity P as a conserved quantity and the basis of a good quantum number. As already pointed out in section 3.7 it is *multiplicative* rather than additive as for the continuous transformations. Some of the uses of parity in complex systems such as nuclei have already been explored in Part I of this book, which accepts that nucleons are conventionally assigned even parity. Here we examine the question of the parity of such single particles, which we take to be an intrinsic property.

Hadrons were seen in chapter 7 to be composite objects and if the internal motion in such an object has a definite reflection symmetry it seems reasonable to assign an *intrinsic* parity which is quite separate from that appropriate to spatial motion of the hadron as a whole. For instance, the lowest-lying mesons, the pions, are considered to consist of a quark–antiquark pair (figure 8.2) in a state of relative orbital angular momentum $L = 0$. Since parity is multiplicative the overall parity is given by $(-1)^L$ times the intrinsic parities of quark and antiquark. We will see quite generally in chapter 11 that the intrinsic parity of a fermion and antifermion are opposite and it follows that the intrinsic parity of the pion is odd ($P = -1$). Such particles, with $J^P = 0^-$, are described as *pseudoscalar* because they behave as scalars under coordinate rotation but have a wavefunction which changes sign on reflection. A *scalar* particle has zero spin and even parity $J^P = 0^+$. We note that this argument is assigning an *absolute* intrinsic parity to the pion.

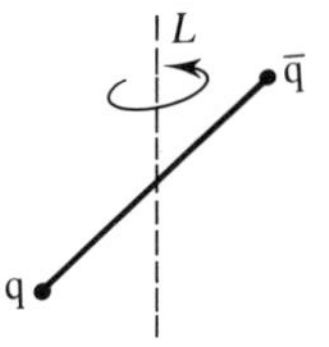

Figure 8.2
A quark–antiquark system with relative orbital angular momentum L.

The intrinsic parity of the pion was measured long before the invention of quarks. In the experiments of Panofsky *et al.*[2] and later Chinowski and Steinberger,[3] in which negative pions were stopped in deuterium, the reaction

$$\pi^- + d \rightarrow n + n$$

was observed, whereas

$$\pi^- + d \rightarrow n + n + \pi^0$$

was not. Later studies of the mesonic X-rays emitted showed that the capture takes place from an atomic S state of deuterium and it is assumed that the deuterium nucleus has $J^P = 1^+$ (section 3.11.2). Since the pion has spin 0 the total angular momentum in the initial state is $J = 1$. The only properly antisymmetrized state for two neutrons with a total angular momentum equal to one is the $^3P_1$ state with odd parity (regardless of the intrinsic parity of the neutron). Since the reaction is a strong interaction the conservation of parity requires an odd intrinsic parity for the π^-. It is a general result of quantum field theory that if the negative pion has odd parity then so does the positive pion. This is true of all bosons; the parity of the particle and its antiparticle are the same, in marked contrast to the situation concerning fermions and antifermions.

The intrinsic parity of the π^0 can be determined in principle from measurements on the two-photon decay mode, $\pi^0 \to \gamma\gamma$. A classical electromagnetic wave is transverse, the $\boldsymbol{E}$ and $\boldsymbol{B}$ fields are perpendicular to the direction of propagation of the wave. So, we suppose that a (real) photon has associated with it a polarization vector $\boldsymbol{\epsilon}$ which is perpendicular to the photon momentum $\boldsymbol{k}$; $\boldsymbol{\epsilon}\cdot\boldsymbol{k} = 0$. The following argument, due to Yang,[4] shows how the scalar or pseudoscalar nature of the π^0 can be determined. In the decay of a spin 0 pion, at rest, into two photons (figure 8.3) the photons must be collinear and the two-photon wave function must be a scalar under rotations ($J = 0$). The only vectors in the problem are the polarization vectors $\boldsymbol{\epsilon}_1$ and $\boldsymbol{\epsilon}_2$ of the two photons and their relative momentum vector $\boldsymbol{k}$. From these we can form the scalar quantities

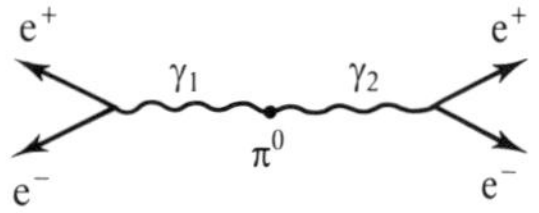

Figure 8.3
The decay $\pi^0 \to 2\gamma \to 2(e^+e^-)$ viewed in the π^0 rest frame.

$$\boldsymbol{\epsilon}_1\cdot\boldsymbol{\epsilon}_2 \quad \text{and} \quad (\boldsymbol{\epsilon}_1 \wedge \boldsymbol{\epsilon}_2)\cdot\boldsymbol{k}. \tag{8.36}$$

The former is even under the parity transformation while the latter is odd. Conservation of parity in the electromagnetic decay requires that only one of the possibilities (8.36) is allowed. Thus by measuring the relative orientation of the polarization vectors of the two photons the intrinsic parity of the π^0 can be determined. The cross-section for electron–positron pair production is sensitive to the photon polarization vector and by measuring the relative orientation of the two production planes ($\boldsymbol{k}_{e^-} \wedge \boldsymbol{k}_{e^+}$) that of the polarization vectors may be ascertained. This is an extremely difficult experiment but it was shown by Kroll and Wada[5] that the correlation between the production planes persists in the so-called double Dalitz decay mode

$$\pi^0 \to (e^+ + e^-) + (e^+ + e^-)$$

in which the virtual photons are internally converted into pairs. If ϕ is the relative orientation of the planes the frequency distribution has the theoretical expectation

$$F(\phi) = 1 + \alpha\cos(2\phi) \qquad \text{for a scalar } \pi^0$$

and

$$F(\phi) = 1 - \alpha\cos(2\phi) \qquad \text{for a pseudoscalar } \pi^0.$$

The results of Plano *et al.*[6] are given in figure 8.4 and they show that the intrinsic parity of the π^0 is odd, like that of the π^+ and π^-.

The situation regarding the parity of the nucleons is not as clear cut as for the pions: the neutron and proton are arbitrarily assigned positive intrinsic parity. Since to a very high degree of accuracy baryon number is conserved, the intrinsic parities of the baryons in the initial state of a reaction will always be the same as in the final state, regardless of the assigned intrinsic parity. This is not so for pions for which no such conservation law holds.

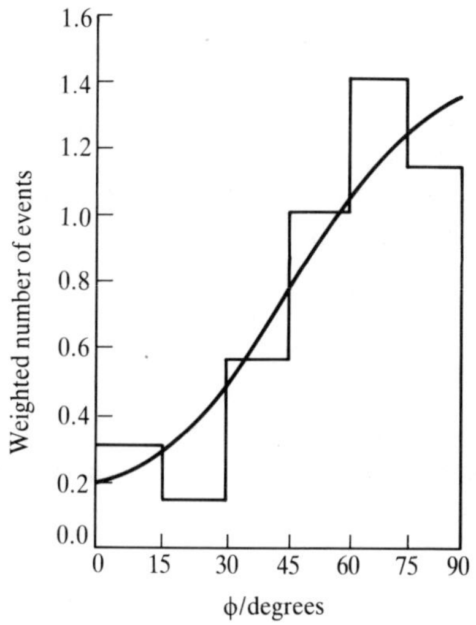

Figure 8.4 Plot of the weighted number of events as a function of the angle between the planes of polarization. Each event is weighted by the square of the correlation coefficient α for that event. The curve is a fit to the data and is given by $F(\phi) = 1 - (0.75 \pm 0.42)\cos(2\phi)$, consistent with expectations for a pseudoscalar π^0. (After Plano R *et al.* 1959 *Phys Rev Lett* **3** (525).)

The intrinsic parity of other stable baryons must be determined by some process (a) which is parity conserving and (b) in which the particle in question is either created or destroyed. Since parity is violated in the weak interactions the decay modes

$$K^0 \rightarrow \pi^+\pi^- \qquad \text{and} \qquad \Lambda^0 \rightarrow p\pi^-$$

cannot be used to determine the intrinsic parities of the K^0 meson and the Λ^0 hyperon. However, in the strong associated production process

$$\pi^- + p \rightarrow K^0 + \Lambda^0$$

the *relative* parity of the K^0 and Λ^0 can be determined. The intrinsic parity of the Λ^0 is conventionally assumed to be the same as that of the proton. Then, a detailed analysis of the angular momentum states involved in the interaction yields the result that the K^0 has odd intrinsic parity. From the rule that for bosons the parity of the particle and its antiparticle are the same, the $\bar{K}^0$ also has odd intrinsic parity. It turns out that all the *stable* mesons have odd intrinsic parity and all the stable baryons have even intrinsic parity. This does not mean, however, that *all* mesons and *all* baryons adhere to this pattern. We will see in chapter 9 that some meson *resonances* have even intrinsic parity and some baryon *resonances* have odd intrinsic parity.

8.7 *Isospin: an example of the SU(2) group*

8.7.1 *Introduction*

The concept of isospin was introduced in section 3.8 and used in sections 3.9, 3.11.4 and 7.3 without explicit development of the formalism. In terms of the arguments presented earlier in this chapter, however, it is a quantity governed by the transformations of the group SU(2).

As in the case of ordinary spin we use the two commuting variables, the isospin I (as I^2) and its third component I_3, to label states. The two possible orientations of the isospin $I = \frac{1}{2}$, corresponding to the proton and neutron, are represented by column vectors $\binom{1}{0}$ and $\binom{0}{1}$. Isospin raising and lowering operators can be constructed by forming linear combinations of the other components I_1 and I_2 of I. Then

$$I_+ = I_1 + \mathrm{i}I_2 \qquad \text{and} \qquad I_- = I_1 - \mathrm{i}I_2$$

and the matrix elements of the four isospin operators $\hat{I}^2$, $\hat{I}_3$, $\hat{I}_+$ and $\hat{I}_-$ with respect to the states $|I, I_3\rangle$ as a basis are given by

$$\begin{aligned}
\langle I, I_3'|\hat{I}^2|I, I_3\rangle &= I(I+1)\delta_{I_3,I_3'} \\
\langle I, I_3'|\hat{I}_3|I, I_3\rangle &= I_3\delta_{I_3,I_3'} \\
\langle I, I_3'|\hat{I}_\pm|I, I_3\rangle &= [I(I+1) - I_3(I_3 \pm 1)]^{1/2}\delta_{I_3',I_3\pm 1}
\end{aligned} \tag{8.37}$$

in complete analogy with equations (8.21).

The fundamental, two-dimensional representation of the isospin rotation group is based on the three matrices

$$\tau_1 = \begin{pmatrix} 0 & 1 \\ 1 & 0 \end{pmatrix} \qquad \tau_2 = \begin{pmatrix} 0 & -\mathrm{i} \\ \mathrm{i} & 0 \end{pmatrix} \qquad \tau_3 = \begin{pmatrix} 1 & 0 \\ 0 & -1 \end{pmatrix} \tag{8.38}$$

which are identical to the Pauli spin matrices but in order to stress that we are dealing with the isospin SU(2) group we have labelled them τ_i, $i = 1, 2, 3$. These operate on the isospin doublet $\binom{1}{0}$ and $\binom{0}{1}$, corresponding to the states $|\frac{1}{2}, \frac{1}{2}\rangle$ and $|\frac{1}{2}, -\frac{1}{2}\rangle$ respectively. As before, the algebra of the group is just the algebra of the generators, $I_i = \frac{1}{2}\tau_i$, summarized in the commutation relations

$$\left[\frac{\tau_i}{2}, \frac{\tau_j}{2}\right] = \mathrm{i}\epsilon_{ijk}\frac{\tau_k}{2}. \tag{8.39}$$

The matrices

$$U_i(\theta) = \exp(-\tfrac{1}{2}\mathrm{i}\tau_i\theta) \qquad \text{with } i = 1, 2, 3 \tag{8.40}$$

form the fundamental representation of the isospin rotation group. Other representations of the SU(2) group, the one-, three-, four- etc. dimensional representations, corresponding to $I = 0, 1, \frac{3}{2}, \ldots,$ can be constructed from the fundamental representation.

Again, the rules for the coupling of two isospins, I' and I'' say, are identical to those for the coupling of two angular momenta. If $I = I' + I''$, the possible values of I are restricted to

$$|I' - I''| \leqslant I \leqslant I' + I''$$

and for a given I

$$I_3 = I'_3 + I''_3.$$

The coupling involves the Clebsch–Gordan coefficients in exactly the same way as in the coupling of angular momentum states, thus

$$|I, I_3\rangle = \sum_{I'_3 I''_3} C^{II_3}_{I'_3 I''_3} |I', I'_3\rangle |I'', I''_3\rangle. \tag{8.41}$$

The basis states are now vectors in isospin space but otherwise equation (8.41) is identical to equation (8.22).

8.7.2 The extended Pauli principle

Let us re-examine the concept of the charge independence of the nucleon–nucleon force in the light of the isospin formalism introduced above. If we regard the neutron and proton as identical particles, as far as the strong interactions are concerned, the wavefunction for two nucleons may be written symbolically (see section 3.9.1) as

$$\Psi = \psi(\text{space})\chi(\text{spin})I(\text{isospin})$$

and for two 'identical' fermions this must be antisymmetric with respect to interchange of the two nucleons. The isospin states may be written down with the aid of equation (8.41). For two nucleons, with $I = \frac{1}{2}$, the total isospin can be 1 or 0. The $I = 1$ triplet is

$$|1, 1\rangle = |\tfrac{1}{2}, \tfrac{1}{2}\rangle|\tfrac{1}{2}, \tfrac{1}{2}\rangle \equiv |p\rangle|p\rangle$$

$$|1, 0\rangle = \frac{1}{\sqrt{2}}(|\tfrac{1}{2}, \tfrac{1}{2}\rangle|\tfrac{1}{2}, -\tfrac{1}{2}\rangle + |\tfrac{1}{2}, -\tfrac{1}{2}\rangle|\tfrac{1}{2}, \tfrac{1}{2}\rangle) \equiv \frac{1}{\sqrt{2}}(|p\rangle|n\rangle + |n\rangle|p\rangle)$$

$$|1, -1\rangle = |\tfrac{1}{2}, -\tfrac{1}{2}\rangle|\tfrac{1}{2}, -\tfrac{1}{2}\rangle \equiv |n\rangle|n\rangle$$

and the $I = 0$ singlet is

$$|0, 0\rangle = \frac{1}{\sqrt{2}}(|\tfrac{1}{2}, \tfrac{1}{2}\rangle|\tfrac{1}{2}, -\tfrac{1}{2}\rangle - |\tfrac{1}{2}, -\tfrac{1}{2}\rangle|\tfrac{1}{2}, \tfrac{1}{2}\rangle) \equiv \frac{1}{\sqrt{2}}(|p\rangle|n\rangle - |n\rangle|p\rangle).$$

The factors $1/\sqrt{2}$ are the appropriate Clebsch–Gordan coefficients. It is evident that the triplet states are symmetric with respect to interchange of the two nucleons while the singlet state is antisymmetric. There is no *a priori* reason why the force between two nucleons should be the same in the $I = 1$ state and the $I = 0$ state. Indeed the antisymmetry of the wavefunction I, required by the extended Pauli principle, implies that ψ(space)χ(spin) is symmetric for $I = 0$ (antisymmetric) and antisymmetric for $I = 1$ (symmetric). Because of the different space–spin wavefunctions one would expect that the force between two nucleons in the $I = 1$ state would differ from that in the $I = 0$ state. Charge independence of the nucleon–nucleon force (section 3.11.4) then applies only to the isospin triplet state and states that the pp, np and nn force depends on the total isospin but not the third component, provided that the nucleon pairs are in the same antisymmetric spin and orbital angular momentum states. There is no corresponding argument for two nucleons in an $I = 0$ state because there is only one charge state.

8.7.3 Some consequences of isospin conservation

Perhaps the most obvious consequence of isospin conservation in the strong interactions is that, as already mentioned in sections 3.8 and 7.3, all hadrons belong to isospin multiplets. We note from table 7.2 that the masses of particles in a given multiplet are very nearly the same (approximately 4 per cent difference for the pion triplet). Now the mass of a particle may be regarded as an eigenvalue of its Hamiltonian evaluated in the particle rest frame and the Hamiltonian may be written

$$H = H_\mathrm{S} + H_\mathrm{E} + H_\mathrm{W}$$

where S, E and W represent the strong, electromagnetic and weak interactions of the particle. Since the strong interactions conserve isospin the part of the mass arising from H_S will be constant within a multiplet. Unfortunately, the electromagnetic contribution cannot yet be calculated but it seems certain to be greater than that of the weak interaction and is probably responsible for the multiplet mass splitting.

It was stated in chapter 7 that the difference between the so-called stable hadrons and the resonances is that the latter decay via the strong interactions whereas the former are either genuinely stable or decay with much slower rates via the electromagnetic or weak interactions. Again, since isospin is conserved in the strong interactions, the relative decay rates of a resonance, into channels involving particles in the same isospin multiplets, will depend only on the isospin coupling rules (equation (8.41)), i.e. they will depend on the ratios of the appropriate Clebsch–Gordan coefficients. To make this statement more concrete consider the decay of the $\Delta^+(1232)$, i.e. the singly charged pion–nucleon resonance with mass 1232 MeV. Generally the rate of decay is given by 'Fermi's golden rule' as

$$\Gamma \propto |\langle f|H|i\rangle|^2 \rho(E) \tag{8.42}$$

where $\langle f|H|i\rangle$ is the matrix element for the decay from the initial state $|i\rangle$ to the final state $|f\rangle$ and the statistical factor $\rho(E)$ is the density of states or 'phase space' available for the reaction at the energy E. There are four different charge states of the $\Delta(1232)$ and therefore the isospin is $I = \frac{3}{2}$. The resonance decays into a pion, with $I = 1$, and a nucleon, with $I = \frac{1}{2}$. The possible decay channels of the $\Delta^+(1232)$ are

$$\Delta^+(1232) \to \mathrm{p}\pi^0 \qquad \text{and} \qquad \Delta^+(1232) \to \mathrm{n}\pi^+$$

and since isospin is conserved the $\mathrm{N}\pi$ final states must have $I = \frac{3}{2}$; the $I = \frac{1}{2}$ combination is forbidden. The matrix elements $\langle f|H|i\rangle$ will be the product of an amplitude, $A_{3/2}$ say, which is independent of the particular final state, and the appropriate Clebsch–Gordan coefficients for the coupling of the $I = \frac{1}{2}$ nucleon states and the $I = 1$ pion states to give the $I = \frac{3}{2}$ Δ state. Considering first the decay $\Delta^+(1232) \to \mathrm{p}\pi^0$ and labelling states as $|I, I_3\rangle$ we have

$$\begin{aligned} \Delta^+(1232) &= |\tfrac{3}{2}, \tfrac{1}{2}\rangle \\ \mathrm{p} &= |\tfrac{1}{2}, \tfrac{1}{2}\rangle \\ \pi^0 &= |1, 0\rangle. \end{aligned}$$

With reference to the tables of Clebsch–Gordan coefficients in appendix G for the coupling $\frac{1}{2} \otimes 1$ we see that

$$|\tfrac{3}{2}, \tfrac{1}{2}\rangle = \sqrt{\tfrac{2}{3}}|\tfrac{1}{2}, \tfrac{1}{2}\rangle|1, 0\rangle.$$

Therefore,

$$\Gamma[\Delta^+(1232) \to \mathrm{p}\pi^0] \propto \tfrac{2}{3}|A_{3/2}|^2 \rho(E).$$

Turning to the second channel, $\Delta^+(1232) \to \mathrm{n}\pi^+$, we have

$$\begin{aligned} \mathrm{n} &= |\tfrac{1}{2}, -\tfrac{1}{2}\rangle \\ \pi^+ &= |1, 1\rangle \end{aligned}$$

and the appropriate Clebsch–Gordan coefficient in this case is $\sqrt{(1/3)}$.

Therefore,

$$\Gamma[\Delta^+(1232) \to n\pi^+] \propto \tfrac{1}{3}|A_{3/2}|^2\rho(E).$$

Since the masses of the particles involved in the two decay channels are essentially the same, the phase space factor $\rho(E)$ is the same in each case and so the ratio of the decay rates is

$$\frac{\Gamma[\Delta^+(1232) \to p\pi^0]}{\Gamma[\Delta^+(1232) \to n\pi^+]} = 2.$$

Similar relationships hold for cross-sections of *reactions* involving members of the same isospin multiplets. As an illustration consider the π, N, K and Σ multiplets, with $I = 1, \frac{1}{2}, \frac{1}{2}$ and 1 respectively, and specifically the reactions

$$\pi^- p \to K^0\Sigma^0 \qquad \text{(i)}$$

$$\pi^- p \to K^+\Sigma^- \qquad \text{(ii)}$$

$$\pi^+ p \to K^+\Sigma^+. \qquad \text{(iii)}$$

The cross-sections σ are proportional to the square of the matrix element, or amplitude, connecting the initial and final states,

$$\sigma \propto |\langle f|H|i\rangle|^2\rho(E)$$

where, as before, the factor $\rho(E)$ is the phase space available for the reaction. Both the initial and final states involve particles with $I = \frac{1}{2}$ and $I = 1$ and therefore the total isospin can in general be $I = \frac{1}{2}$ or $I = \frac{3}{2}$. Since isospin is conserved in these strong interactions there are two channels with two independent amplitudes, one corresponding to $I = \frac{1}{2}$, $A_{1/2}$ say, and the other corresponding to $I = \frac{3}{2}$, $A_{3/2}$. We can think of the operator H as consisting of two independent parts,

$$H = H_{1/2} + H_{3/2}$$

where $H_{1/2}$ causes transitions in the $I = \frac{1}{2}$ channel and $H_{3/2}$ in the $I = \frac{3}{2}$ channel. Then,

$$\sigma = K|\langle f|H_{1/2} + H_{3/2}|i\rangle|^2 \qquad (8.43)$$

where K is a constant at a given energy E. (Again, since the masses of the particles in a given isospin multiplet are very nearly the same, the phase space factors for a particular incident energy are equal to a good approximation.) In order to calculate relations between cross-sections for the different processes we must write each initial and each final state in terms of the total isospin with the aid of the tables of Clebsch–Gordan coefficients. We have

$$|\pi^-\rangle|p\rangle = |1, -1\rangle|\tfrac{1}{2}, \tfrac{1}{2}\rangle = \sqrt{\tfrac{1}{3}}|\tfrac{3}{2}, -\tfrac{1}{2}\rangle - \sqrt{\tfrac{2}{3}}|\tfrac{1}{2}, -\tfrac{1}{2}\rangle$$
$$|\pi^+\rangle|p\rangle = |1, 1\rangle|\tfrac{1}{2}, \tfrac{1}{2}\rangle = |\tfrac{3}{2}, \tfrac{3}{2}\rangle$$
$$|K^0\rangle|\Sigma^0\rangle = |\tfrac{1}{2}, -\tfrac{1}{2}\rangle|1, 0\rangle = \sqrt{\tfrac{2}{3}}|\tfrac{3}{2}, -\tfrac{1}{2}\rangle + \sqrt{\tfrac{1}{3}}|\tfrac{1}{2}, -\tfrac{1}{2}\rangle$$
$$|K^+\rangle|\Sigma^-\rangle = |\tfrac{1}{2}, \tfrac{1}{2}\rangle|1, -1\rangle = \sqrt{\tfrac{1}{3}}|\tfrac{3}{2}, -\tfrac{1}{2}\rangle - \sqrt{\tfrac{2}{3}}|\tfrac{1}{2}, -\tfrac{1}{2}\rangle$$
$$|K^+\rangle|\Sigma^+\rangle = |\tfrac{1}{2}, \tfrac{1}{2}\rangle|1, 1\rangle = |\tfrac{3}{2}, \tfrac{3}{2}\rangle.$$

Using these isospin states* we may now calculate the cross-sections for the processes (i)–(iii).

(i) $\pi^- p \to K^0\Sigma^0$ On inserting the initial and final states into equation (8.43) we obtain

$$\sigma = K|(\sqrt{\tfrac{2}{3}}\langle\tfrac{3}{2}, -\tfrac{1}{2}| + \sqrt{\tfrac{1}{3}}\langle\tfrac{1}{2}, -\tfrac{1}{2}|)H_{1/2} + H_{3/2}(\sqrt{\tfrac{1}{3}}|\tfrac{3}{2}, -\tfrac{1}{2}\rangle - \sqrt{\tfrac{2}{3}}|\tfrac{1}{2}, -\tfrac{1}{2}\rangle)|^2.$$

Remembering that $H_{1/2}$ and $H_{3/2}$ act only on $I = \frac{1}{2}$ and $I = \frac{3}{2}$ states respectively, we have

$$\sigma = K\tfrac{2}{9}|A_{3/2} - A_{1/2}|^2$$

where $A_{3/2}$ and $A_{1/2}$ are the two (complex) amplitudes

$$A_{3/2} = \langle f|H_{3/2}|i\rangle \qquad \text{and} \qquad A_{1/2} = \langle f|H_{1/2}|i\rangle.$$

(ii) $\pi^- p \to K^+\Sigma^-$ In this case,

$$\sigma = K|(\sqrt{\tfrac{1}{3}}\langle\tfrac{3}{2}, -\tfrac{1}{2}| - \sqrt{\tfrac{2}{3}}\langle\tfrac{1}{2}, \tfrac{1}{2}|)H_{1/2} + H_{3/2}(\sqrt{\tfrac{1}{3}}|\tfrac{3}{2}, -\tfrac{1}{2}\rangle - \sqrt{\tfrac{2}{3}}|\tfrac{1}{2}, -\tfrac{1}{2}\rangle)|^2$$
$$= K\tfrac{1}{9}|A_{3/2} + 2A_{1/2}|^2.$$

(iii) $\pi^+ p \to K^+\Sigma^+$ Since both initial and final states are pure $I = \frac{3}{2}$ in this case, we have

$$\sigma = K|\langle\tfrac{3}{2}, \tfrac{3}{2}|H_{1/2} + H_{3/2}|\tfrac{3}{2}, \tfrac{3}{2}\rangle|^2$$
$$= K|A_{3/2}|^2.$$

Thus, the conservation of isospin implies that the cross-sections for these processes are in the ratios

$$\sigma_{(i)}: \sigma_{(ii)}: \sigma_{(iii)} = \tfrac{2}{9}|A_{3/2} - A_{1/2}|^2 : \tfrac{1}{9}|A_{3/2} + 2A_{1/2}|^2 : |A_{3/2}|^2.$$

* A little thought and/or experience allows the individual particle isospin states to be written down immediately. Alternatively, application of the Gell-Mann–Nishijima relation, equation (7.5), gives the I_3 values.

8.8 Charge conjugation

The charge conjugation operation, like the parity transformation, is a discrete symmetry operation. It consists of changing particle to antiparticle in any process while maintaining the dynamical variables, momentum, spin etc., unchanged. If a process and its charge conjugate behave in the same way, or satisfy the same physical laws, the process is said to be charge conjugation invariant. Alternatively, C or C-parity is said to be conserved in the process. If we specify a state by $|A, p, \sigma \ldots\rangle$ where A stands for the additive quantum numbers such as charge Q, baryon number B, lepton number L, strangeness S, etc. and p and σ represent the dynamical quantities such as momentum and spin, then the charge conjugation operation C changes the sign of the additive quantum numbers, if non-zero, and leaves p, σ, etc. unchanged. A second application of the charge conjugation operator must return the system to its original state so that, as in the case of parity, if a system is an eigenstate of C its eigenvalue is either $+1$ or -1. That is,

$$C|A, p, \sigma\rangle \to |\bar{A}, p, \sigma\rangle = e^{i\alpha}|A, p, \sigma\rangle$$

$$C^2|A, p, \sigma\rangle = C|\bar{A}, p, \sigma\rangle = e^{2i\alpha}|A, p, \sigma\rangle = 1|A, p, \sigma\rangle.$$

Therefore, $e^{i\alpha} = \pm 1$ and $C|A, p, \sigma\rangle = \pm 1|A, p, \sigma\rangle$. We use the notation $\bar{A}$ to signify the change particle $\to$ antiparticle under charge conjugation.

The observation that, under charge conjugation, $Q \to -Q$, $B \to -B$, $L \to -L$, $S \to -S$, etc. imposes severe restrictions on the possible eigenstates of C. We recall that in order that C be a constant of the motion it must commute with the Hamiltonian of the system, $[H, C] = 0$. Now, Q, B and L are all conserved quantities and, at least as far as the strong interactions are concerned, so is the strangeness S. They all commute with the Hamiltonian but none of them commute with C. For example, consider a state with $B = 1$ and $Q = L = S = 0$. If we introduce a 'baryon number operator' $\hat{B}$, which counts the number of baryons, then

$$\hat{B}|B = 1\rangle = +1|B = 1\rangle.$$

Now,

$$C\hat{B}|B = 1\rangle = +1C|B = 1\rangle = +1|B = -1\rangle.$$

On the other hand,

$$\hat{B}C|B = 1\rangle = \hat{B}|B = -1\rangle = -1|B = -1\rangle$$

hence

$$C\hat{B} \neq \hat{B}C,$$

i.e. B and C do not commute. A similar argument applies for operators corresponding to Q, L and S and we are thus led to the important conclusion* that a state can be an eigenstate of C only if it has $Q = B = L = S = 0$. The neutral pion satisfies this condition so that the π^0 and its antiparticle are indistinguishable. On the other hand, the K^0 and its antiparticle the $\bar{K}^0$ are distinct, they are not eigenstates of C because the strangeness quantum number S is non-zero.

Of course while not many isolated particles are eigenstates of C, *systems* of particles can be if they have $Q = B = L = S = 0$. For instance, a proton–antiproton system in a state of definite orbital angular momentum l and spin s is an eigenstate of C, which we now show. With reference to figure 8.5 let us assume that initially the antiproton has spatial coordinate $\boldsymbol{x}_1$ and is in a spin state σ_1 with the proton at $\boldsymbol{x}_2$ in a spin state σ_2. We have

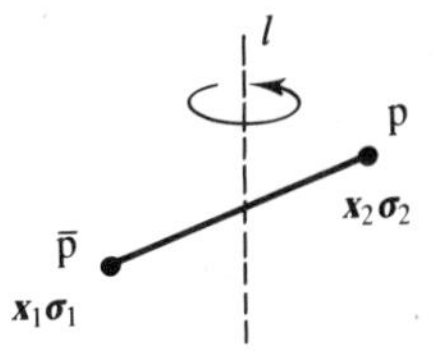

Figure 8.5
A proton–antiproton system with relative orbital angular momentum l.

$$C|\bar{p}\boldsymbol{x}_1\sigma_1 p\boldsymbol{x}_2\sigma_2\rangle = |p\boldsymbol{x}_1\sigma_1\bar{p}\boldsymbol{x}_2\sigma_2\rangle. \tag{8.44}$$

Equation (8.44) is not an eigenvalue equation but we can make it into one by interchanging the space and spin coordinates. The proton and antiproton both have spin $\frac{1}{2}$ and we have already seen that when two spin $\frac{1}{2}$ particles couple to give a total spin $s = 1$ or $s = 0$ the triplet $s = 1$ state is symmetric with respect to interchange of the spin coordinates and the singlet $s = 0$ state is antisymmetric. Thus on interchange of spin co-ordinates a factor $(-1)^{s+1}$ is introduced. Interchange of space coordinates is just the parity transformation which, for the system under consideration, gives a factor $(-1)^l$ from the orbital motion and another factor -1 from the opposite intrinsic parities of the proton and antiproton. Therefore, on interchange we have

$$C|\bar{p}\boldsymbol{x}_1\sigma_1 p\boldsymbol{x}_2\sigma_2\rangle = (-1)^{s+1}(-1)^{l+1}|\bar{p}\boldsymbol{x}_1\sigma_1 p\boldsymbol{x}_2\sigma_2\rangle \tag{8.45}$$

which is an eigenvalue equation, with eigenvalue equal to $(-1)^{l+s}$.

Both the strong and the electromagnetic interactions are invariant under charge conjugation but, as was the case with parity, the weak interactions are not. We shall see in chapter 11 that although the weak interactions violate P and C separately, to a very good approximation they are invariant under the combined operation CP.

8.9 *Time reversal*[7]

The time reversal transformation should not be regarded as a running of time backwards into the past. Classically we may think of a collision

* To the list of additive quantum numbers should be added the further quark flavours or quantum numbers charm, bottom and top.

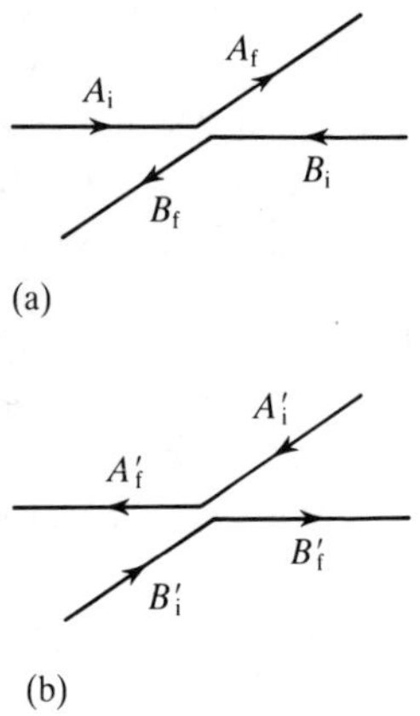

Figure 8.6
(a) A collision between two molecules and (b) the time-reversed process.

between two molecules A and B (figure 8.6(a)) with initial and final velocities A_i, B_i, A_f, B_f. The time-reversed process would be that shown in figure 8.6(b) with A_f and B_f reversed to A'_i and B'_i leading to final velocities A'_f and B'_f which are the reverse of A_i and B_i. In a gas the probabilities of the two processes shown in figures 8.6(a) and 8.6(b) would be equal and the process is described as time-reversal invariant. This is known as the principle of *microscopic reversibility*.

To describe the time reversal transformation in quantum mechanical terms we must recall that there are two types of observables. First, there is the probability that, having prepared a system in the state $|\psi\rangle$, it will be found on measurement to be in the state $|\phi\rangle$, given by $|\langle\phi|\psi\rangle|^2$. Secondly, there are the expectation values of dynamical quantities D in the state $|\psi\rangle$, i.e. $\langle D\rangle = \langle\psi|D|\psi\rangle$. In the symmetry transformations we have discussed so far the transformation operators have all been unitary, i.e. if under the transformation U

$$|\psi\rangle \rightarrow |\psi'\rangle = U|\psi\rangle$$

then the 'overlap' $\langle\phi\,|\,\psi\rangle \rightarrow \langle\phi'\,|\,\psi'\rangle = \langle\phi U^\dagger\,|\,U\psi\rangle = \langle\phi\,|\,\psi\rangle$ provided $U^\dagger U = 1$. The expectation values transform as

$$\begin{aligned}\langle\psi'|D'|\psi'\rangle &= \langle\psi U^\dagger|D'|U\psi\rangle \\ &= \langle\psi|U^\dagger D' U|\psi\rangle \\ &= \langle\psi|D|\psi\rangle\end{aligned}$$

again, provided that U is unitary.

This is not the case with time reversal. Let U be a unitary operator which changes t to $-t$. A system is time reversal invariant if U commutes with the Hamiltonian of the system, i.e. if

$$U^\dagger H U = H. \tag{8.46}$$

If the system is in a state $|\psi\rangle$ the time development is given by the Schrödinger equation

$$H|\psi\rangle = \mathrm{i}\hbar\frac{\partial}{\partial t}|\psi\rangle. \tag{8.47}$$

Now,

$$UH|\psi\rangle = U\mathrm{i}\hbar\frac{\partial}{\partial t}|\psi\rangle = -\mathrm{i}\hbar\frac{\partial}{\partial t}(U|\psi\rangle)$$

since U changes t to $-t$. Since $UH = HU$ we have

$$H(U|\psi\rangle) = -\mathrm{i}\hbar\frac{\partial}{\partial t}(U|\psi\rangle). \tag{8.48}$$

Thus, if $|\psi'\rangle = U|\psi\rangle$, we see that $|\psi'\rangle$ does not satisfy the Schrödinger equation. Instead it satisfies

$$H|\psi'\rangle = -i\hbar \frac{\partial}{\partial t} |\psi'\rangle.$$

We note, however, that $|\psi\rangle$, the solution to the Schrödinger equation, is not an observable and the symmetry can be restored by defining an operator $T = UK$, where the operator K carries out complex conjugation on anything that stands to the right of it. If we operate on (8.47) with T we have, since the Hamiltonian is real,

$$TH|\psi\rangle = HT|\psi\rangle = -i\hbar T \frac{\partial}{\partial t} |\psi\rangle = i\hbar \frac{\partial}{\partial t} (T|\psi\rangle).$$

Thus the state $T|\psi\rangle$ is a solution to the Schrödinger equation, i.e. if $|\psi(t)\rangle$ is a solution to the Schrödinger equation then so is $|\psi^*(-t)\rangle$. The operator T has been called 'antilinear' by Wigner, i.e.

$$T(C_1|\psi\rangle + C_2|\phi\rangle) = C_1^* T|\psi\rangle + C_2^* T|\phi\rangle$$

and 'antiunitary'

$$\langle\psi' \mid \phi'\rangle = \langle\psi T^\dagger \mid T\phi\rangle = \langle\psi \mid \phi\rangle^* = \langle\phi \mid \psi\rangle.$$

We note, however, that since

$$|\langle\psi' \mid \phi'\rangle| = |\langle\phi \mid \psi\rangle| = |\langle\psi \mid \phi\rangle|$$

the operator T leaves the physical content of quantum mechanics unchanged. Thus the quantum mechanical equivalent of the classical time reversal transformation is $t \to -t$ and complex conjugation, $i \to -i$. Under this transformation the quantum mechanical principle of microscopic reversibility holds.

Since, under time reversal, $\boldsymbol{x} \to \boldsymbol{x}$, $\boldsymbol{p} \to -\boldsymbol{p}$ and $i \to -i$, the basic commutation relation

$$[x_i, p_j] = i\hbar\delta_{ij}$$

still holds. The orbital angular momentum commutation relations are also preserved since $\boldsymbol{L} \to -\boldsymbol{L}$ and $i \to -i$, then

$$[L_i, L_j] = i\hbar\epsilon_{ijk} L_k.$$

In table 8.1 we list the transformation properties of some common variables under time reversal.

Table 8.1
The transformation properties of some common variables under time reversal

Variable	Behaviour
Position	$\boldsymbol{r} \to \boldsymbol{r}$
Momentum	$\boldsymbol{p} \to -\boldsymbol{p}$
Angular momentum	$\boldsymbol{L} \to -\boldsymbol{L}$
Spin	$\boldsymbol{S} \to -\boldsymbol{S}$
Electric field E	$\boldsymbol{E} \to \boldsymbol{E}$
Magnetic field B	$\boldsymbol{B} \to -\boldsymbol{B}$

We end this section on time reversal with a brief discussion of an important class of experiments which test the validity of time reversal invariance in electromagnetic interactions and, as it turns out, invariance under the parity transformation. These are experiments designed to measure the electric-dipole moments of particles. The orientation of a particle can be specified by the orientation of its spin with respect to some axis. If we choose a z axis so that the spin is aligned along it, the electric-dipole moment μ_e is given by

$$\mu_e = \int \rho z \, d\tau. \tag{8.49}$$

In this expression z is measured from the centre of mass of the particle, ρ is the electric charge density and $d\tau$ is a volume element. If the particle possesses a net electric charge, the existence of an electric-dipole moment implies that the centre of charge and the centre of mass do not coincide. If, on the other hand, the particle is electrically neutral, a non-zero electric-dipole moment can arise if there is an asymmetry in the charge distribution with a net positive charge in one 'hemisphere' and a corresponding net negative charge in the other. If the particle is assumed to possess a magnetic-dipole moment μ_m, then in the presence of an electromagnetic field the interaction Hamiltonian is

$$H_{int} = \mu_m \boldsymbol{\sigma} \cdot \boldsymbol{B} + \mu_e \boldsymbol{\sigma} \cdot \boldsymbol{E} \tag{8.50}$$

where $\boldsymbol{\sigma}$ is the particle spin. Under time reversal T we have

$$\boldsymbol{\sigma} \cdot \boldsymbol{B} \xrightarrow{T} \boldsymbol{\sigma} \cdot \boldsymbol{B} \quad \text{and} \quad \boldsymbol{\sigma} \cdot \boldsymbol{E} \xrightarrow{T} -\boldsymbol{\sigma} \cdot \boldsymbol{E} \tag{8.51a}$$

and under the parity transformation

$$\boldsymbol{\sigma} \cdot \boldsymbol{B} \xrightarrow{P} \boldsymbol{\sigma} \cdot \boldsymbol{B} \quad \text{and} \quad \boldsymbol{\sigma} \cdot \boldsymbol{E} \xrightarrow{P} -\boldsymbol{\sigma} \cdot \boldsymbol{E}. \tag{8.51b}$$

In (8.51a) the negative sign arises because of the behaviour of spin under time reversal (**E** remains unchanged), whereas in (8.51b) the negative sign arises because under the parity transformation the spin remains unaltered but $\boldsymbol{E}$ changes sign. The magnetic interaction is unchanged by either P or T. The existence of a particle with an electric-dipole moment would then be evidence for the violation of time reversal invariance and parity conservation in the electromagnetic interactions.

A description of the experiments to measure the electric-dipole moments of particles is given in the review article by Ramsey.[8] The most sensitive tests of P and T violation are measurements of the electric-dipole moment of the neutron and the current experimental limit is[9]

$$\mu_e < 1.2 \times 10^{-25} e \text{ cm}.$$

If the neutron possesses an electric-dipole moment at all, it is exceedingly small. With one very important exception, the weak decays of the K mesons, to which we shall return in chapter 11, all interactions are time reversal invariant.

8.10 The CPT theorem

There are no fundamental reasons why the forces in nature should be invariant under the transformations C, P and T separately, but taken together the combined operation of time reversal, space inversion and charge conjugation appears to be a fundamental symmetry transformation which has important and very general consequences. The CPT theorem[10–12] is based on very general assumptions of quantum field theory and relativity and states that any Hamiltonian which is invariant under proper Lorentz transformations is also invariant under the combined operation CPT, whether or not it is invariant under C, P or T separately.

The consequences of the CPT theorem are that the masses and lifetimes of particle and antiparticle should be exactly the same. No exception to this prediction has ever been found. Another consequence of the theorem is that if any individual or pair of symmetries is violated there must be a compensating asymmetry in the other operations, or operation, so that exact symmetry under CPT is upheld. As mentioned above, we shall see in chapter 11 that the weak interactions violate C and P separately but in general they are invariant under the combined operation of C and P. In the weak decays of the K^0 mesons a small but definite CP violation is evident but this is accompanied by a corresponding violation of T invariance so that CPT invariance is respected even in these decays.

8.11 G-parity

We recall that eigenstates of the charge conjugation operator must have $Q = B = L = S = 0$ so that, although particles such as the π^0, η^0, γ and neutral, particle–antiparticle combinations such as e^+e^- and $\bar{p}p$ systems can be eigenstates of C, the number of eigenstates of C is somewhat restricted by the above condition. It was pointed out by Lee and Yang[13] that a useful conservation law for the strong interactions can be set up by combining the operation of charge conjugation with a rotation in isospin space. We will see that this removes the restriction that Q must be zero.

A rotation θ about an axis defined by a unit vector $\hat{\boldsymbol{n}}$ in isospin space is given by

$$R(\theta) = \exp(-\mathrm{i}\boldsymbol{\tau}\cdot\hat{\boldsymbol{n}}\theta) \tag{8.52}$$

where $\boldsymbol{\tau}$ is the isospin operator. For an isospin doublet, for example, τ_1, τ_2 and τ_3 are just the Pauli matrices. The operation G is defined as a rotation π about the y or 2 axis in isospin space followed by charge conjugation

$$G = C\exp(-\mathrm{i}\tau_2\pi). \tag{8.53}$$

Consider the triplet of π mesons π^+, π^0, π^-. Charge conjugation has the effect of transforming $\pi^+ \to \pi^-$, $\pi^- \to \pi^+$ and $\pi^0 \to \pi^0$. The π^0 is an eigenstate of C with eigenvalue $+1$. For the charged pions we can have

$$C|\pi^+\rangle = \pm 1|\pi^-\rangle \qquad \text{and} \qquad C|\pi^-\rangle = \pm 1|\pi^+\rangle; \tag{8.54}$$

there is an arbitrary phase.

It follows from the commutation relations that the isospin operators have the same algebraic properties as the ordinary angular momentum operators. Under a rotation π about the y axis an angular momentum state $|j, m\rangle$ transforms as

$$\exp(-\mathrm{i}J_y\pi)|j, m\rangle = (-1)^{j-m}|j, -m\rangle.$$

Similarly, for rotations in isospin space we have

$$\exp(-\mathrm{i}\tau_2\pi)|I, I_3\rangle = (-1)^{I-I_3}|I, -I_3\rangle.$$

Thus, for a rotation π about the 2 axis in isospin space we have

$$R_2(\pi)|\pi^+\rangle = |\pi^-\rangle \qquad R_2(\pi)|\pi^-\rangle = |\pi^+\rangle$$

and

$$R_2(\pi)|\pi^0\rangle = (-1)|\pi^0\rangle.$$

For the neutral pion the G-parity is therefore unambiguously equal to -1. Since the strong interactions conserve isospin and are invariant under the charge conjugation operation, one might expect that the G-parity of the charged pions is the same as that of the neutral pion. In order to ensure this the phases in the charge conjugation operation (8.54) on the π^+ and π^- are chosen so that

$$C|\pi^{\pm}\rangle = (-1)|\pi^{\pm}\rangle.$$

Then, under the G-transformation

$$G|\pi^{+,-,0}\rangle = (-1)|\pi^{+,-,0}\rangle \tag{8.55}$$

so that the G-parity of the pion is -1. G-parity is a multiplicative quantum number and the G-parity of a system of n pions is $(-1)^n$. G-parity is a good quantum number for non-strange mesons and is conserved in the strong interactions. Its conservation leads to selection rules, for instance, in nucleon–antinucleon annihilation into pions. The $\mathrm{N\bar{N}}$ system can have isospin $I = 0, 1$ and the G-parity of an $\mathrm{N\bar{N}}$ system in a state with relative orbital angular momentum l and total spin s is

$$G(\mathrm{N\bar{N}}) = (-1)^{I+l+s}.$$

Thus, if $I + l + s$ is even (odd) annihilation is possible only into an even (odd) number of pions.

8.12 The electromagnetic field[14,15]

We summarize in this section some of the properties of the electromagnetic field that are important in both nuclear and particle physics. The basic equations can be found in the references quoted.

8.12.1 Gauge invariance and Maxwell's equations

The classical electromagnetic field is described by Maxwell's equations in terms of the vectors $\boldsymbol{E}$, the electric component of the field, and $\boldsymbol{B}$, the magnetic component, together with ρ the charge density and $\boldsymbol{j}$ the current density. The equation of continuity

$$\frac{\partial \rho}{\partial t} + \nabla \cdot \boldsymbol{j} = 0 \tag{8.56}$$

expresses the fact that electric charge is conserved and since the equation can be applied to an arbitrarily small volume this is a *local* conservation. The vectors $\boldsymbol{B}$ and $\boldsymbol{E}$ may be derived from vector and scalar potentials $\boldsymbol{A}$ and ϕ obeying the equations

$$\begin{aligned} \boldsymbol{B} &= \nabla \wedge \boldsymbol{A} \\ \boldsymbol{E} &= -\nabla\phi - \frac{\partial \boldsymbol{A}}{\partial t}. \end{aligned} \tag{8.57}$$

These equations, however, do not uniquely define the potentials and it is straightforward to show that $\boldsymbol{B}$ and $\boldsymbol{E}$ are invariant under the *gauge transformation*

$$\begin{aligned} \boldsymbol{A} \rightarrow \boldsymbol{A}' &= \boldsymbol{A} + \nabla\psi \\ \phi \rightarrow \phi' &= \phi - \frac{\partial \psi}{\partial t} \end{aligned} \tag{8.58}$$

where ψ is an arbitrary scalar function. If we further specify $\boldsymbol{A}$ and ϕ by use of the *Lorentz gauge*

$$\nabla \cdot \boldsymbol{A} = -\frac{\partial \phi}{\partial t} \tag{8.59}$$

then both $\boldsymbol{A}$ and ϕ can be seen to obey *wave equations*:

$$\begin{aligned} \nabla^2 \boldsymbol{A} - \frac{\partial^2 \boldsymbol{A}}{\partial t^2} &= -\boldsymbol{j} \\ \nabla^2 \phi - \frac{\partial^2 \phi}{\partial t^2} &= -\rho. \end{aligned} \tag{8.60}$$

The similarity between these equations is obvious and it can be shown[14] that both ρ and $\boldsymbol{j}$, and ϕ and $\boldsymbol{A}$, are four-vectors which we write

$$\begin{aligned} j_\mu &= (\rho, \boldsymbol{j}) \\ A_\mu &= (\phi, \boldsymbol{A}). \end{aligned} \tag{8.61}$$

If we introduce the d'Alembertian operator

$$\Box^2 = \frac{\partial^2}{\partial t^2} - \nabla^2$$

the wave equations (8.60) become

$$\Box^2 A_\mu = j_\mu. \tag{8.62}$$

Since $\Box^2$ is an invariant and A_μ and j_μ are four-vectors, the Maxwell equations expressed in the form (8.62) are the same in any frame of reference. In four-vector notation the Lorentz condition is simply $\nabla_\mu A_\mu = 0$ which means that the four-divergence of the four-potential A_μ is zero.

8.12.2 Polarization and photon spin

An alternative to the Lorentz gauge for specifying $\boldsymbol{A}$ is the Coulomb gauge defined by

$$\nabla \cdot \boldsymbol{A} = 0. \tag{8.63}$$

This is convenient for discussing propagation of electromagnetic waves in free space, for which we take $\rho = \boldsymbol{j} = 0$ and set $\phi = 0$. The wave equation for a classical free photon field then becomes

$$\Box^2 \boldsymbol{A} = 0 \tag{8.64}$$

which has a solution

$$\boldsymbol{A} = \boldsymbol{\epsilon} A_0 \exp[\mathrm{i}(\boldsymbol{k} \cdot \boldsymbol{r} - \omega t)] \tag{8.65}$$

where $\boldsymbol{\epsilon}$ is a unit vector in the direction of $\boldsymbol{A}$ and is known as the polarization vector and A_0 is an amplitude. The vector $\boldsymbol{k}$ is the propagation vector. By taking the divergence of $\boldsymbol{A}$ and using the Coulomb gauge we find that

$$\boldsymbol{\epsilon} \cdot \boldsymbol{k} = 0, \tag{8.66}$$

i.e. the polarization vector is orthogonal to the propagation vector. Since in free space,

$$\boldsymbol{E} = -\frac{\partial \boldsymbol{A}}{\partial t} = \mathrm{i}\omega \boldsymbol{A}$$

the polarization vector is in the direction of $\boldsymbol{E}$. In contrast,

$$\boldsymbol{B} = \nabla \wedge \boldsymbol{A} = \mathrm{i}\boldsymbol{k} \wedge \boldsymbol{A}$$

and therefore, $\boldsymbol{E}$, $\boldsymbol{B}$ and $\boldsymbol{k}$ are mutually orthogonal – electromagnetic waves are transverse waves. If we consider propagation along the z axis both A_z and ϵ_z are zero and

$$\begin{aligned} A_x &= \epsilon_x A_0 \exp[\mathrm{i}(kz - \omega t + \delta)] \\ A_y &= \epsilon_y A_0 \exp[\mathrm{i}(kz - \omega t)] \end{aligned} \tag{8.67}$$

where δ is a phase difference. If A_x and A_y are in phase, $\delta = 0$ and the wave is plane polarized, while for $\delta = \pi/2$ and equal amplitudes the wave is circularly polarized. By convention, if the electric vector, or equivalently the polarization vector, rotates in a clockwise (anti-clockwise) direction when viewed along the direction of propagation, the wave is said to be right (left) circularly polarized. In terms of ϵ_x and ϵ_y a state of right-circular polarization is written

$$\epsilon_R = -\frac{1}{\sqrt{2}}(\epsilon_x + i\epsilon_y) \tag{8.68}$$

and a state of left-circular polarization is written

$$\epsilon_L = \frac{1}{\sqrt{2}}(\epsilon_x - i\epsilon_y). \tag{8.69}$$

Conversely, states of linear polarization can be considered as superpositions of right- and left-circular polarization states.

In section 8.3 it was stated that the spin of the photon, the quantum of a *vector* field, is 1. In addition, because the vector potential (equation (8.65)) plays the role of the wavefunction of the photon, and because it is a *polar* vector, i.e. one that changes sign under spatial inversion, it is commonly stated that the intrinsic parity of the photon is negative. These statements are deserving of further discussion but this we defer until the next section.

Here, we consider the transformation properties of the states of circular polarization. Specifically, consider the effect on ϵ_R of a rotation θ about the propagation axis, the z axis. Under the transformation

$$\epsilon_x \to \epsilon'_x = \epsilon_x \cos\theta + \epsilon_y \sin\theta$$

$$\epsilon_y \to \epsilon'_y = -\epsilon_x \sin\theta + \epsilon_y \cos\theta.$$

Therefore,

$$\begin{aligned}\epsilon_R \to \epsilon'_R &= -\frac{1}{\sqrt{2}}[\epsilon_x \cos\theta + \epsilon_y \sin\theta + i(-\epsilon_x \sin\theta + \epsilon_y \cos\theta)] \\ &= -\frac{1}{\sqrt{2}}(\epsilon_x + i\epsilon_y)\exp(-i\theta) = \epsilon_R \exp(-i\theta).\end{aligned} \tag{8.70}$$

Similarly,

$$\epsilon_L \to \epsilon'_L = \frac{1}{\sqrt{2}}(\epsilon_x - i\epsilon_y)\exp(+i\theta) = \epsilon_L \exp(+i\theta). \tag{8.71}$$

We recall from section 8.3 that for a rotation θ about the z axis a state

$|\psi\rangle$ transforms to $|\psi'\rangle = \exp(-\mathrm{i}\theta J_z)|\psi\rangle$. On comparing this result with equations (8.70) and (8.71) we are led to the conclusion that a right-circularly polarized wave corresponds to a photon with a component of angular momentum along the direction of propagation of $+1$ and a left-circularly polarized wave corresponds to a photon with component -1. The *helicity* λ of the photon is defined as the projection of the angular momentum along the direction of motion of the photon,

$$\lambda = \frac{\boldsymbol{J}\cdot\boldsymbol{k}}{|\boldsymbol{k}|}; \tag{8.72}$$

$\lambda = +1$ corresponds to right-circular polarization and $\lambda = -1$ to left-circular polarization. Since there can be no component of *orbital* angular momentum along the direction of motion, the helicity must arise from the projection of the intrinsic spin of the photon:

$$\lambda = \frac{\boldsymbol{s}\cdot\boldsymbol{k}}{|\boldsymbol{k}|}.$$

The possible helicities $\lambda = \pm 1$ therefore imply that the intrinsic spin of the photon is $s = 1$.

8.12.3 Angular momentum, parity and C-parity of the photon

The spin of the photon is different in character from the spin of a particle with non-zero rest mass. The latter is defined as the total angular momentum in the rest system of the particle and clearly such a system does not exist for the photon. For a particle with mass and spin 1, for example, there are three possible spin components, $+1$, 0 and -1, along a specified axis. This is in marked contrast to the non-existence of a helicity zero state for a photon, which stems from the ultra-relativistic nature of the photon and corresponds to the non-existence of a polarization component in the direction of propagation; the polarization vector is always perpendicular to the propagation vector. This statement is true only for *real* photons travelling with the speed of light; *virtual* photons can be considered to have a mass and in such cases a longitudinal polarization, and hence helicity zero state, is possible.

For a particle with spin, moving slowly compared with the speed of light, the wavefunction may be expressed as the product of a spin function and a function, depending on the coordinates, which determines the orbital angular momentum state of the particle. These two functions can vary arbitrarily and independently. In the case of a photon the polarization vector plays the role of a spin and in the wavefunction

$$\boldsymbol{A} = \boldsymbol{\epsilon} A_0 \exp[\mathrm{i}(\boldsymbol{k}\cdot\boldsymbol{r} - \omega t)]$$

the spatial part and the spin part are not independent, because of the transversality condition $\boldsymbol{\epsilon}\cdot\boldsymbol{k} = 0$. Nevertheless, it is a matter of *convention* to regard the photon as a spin 1 particle with negative intrinsic parity. This is not to say that in radiative transitions one unit of angular momentum and parity are always carried away by the photon. Indeed the multipole fields referred to in section 5.1.1 are single-photon states with a definite total angular momentum j and definite parity; an electric 2^j-pole photon, labelled E_j, is one in a state with angular momentum j and parity $(-1)^j$ while a magnetic 2^j-pole photon M_j has parity $(-1)^{j+1}$. That the different types of radiation have opposite parity is due to the fact that $\boldsymbol{E}$ is a *polar* vector while $\boldsymbol{B}$ is an *axial* vector, i.e. one that does not change sign under spatial inversion.

Intrinsic spin is also an axial vector while momentum is a polar vector; therefore helicity, being a scalar product of the two, is a pseudoscalar. Any process, therefore, in which there is a non-zero value of the net helicity necessarily violates parity conservation. We shall see in chapter 11 that the neutrino, which we assume to be a massless particle like the photon, appears in nature only in one helicity state, $\lambda = -1$; a neutrino with helicity $+1$ does not exist. It is this fact which shows that parity conservation does not hold in weak interactions involving neutrinos. The parity conserving electromagnetic processes require the existence of photons in both helicity states.

Finally in this section, we make some brief remarks concerning the C-parity of the photon. Since photons are produced by the motion of charges, i.e. currents, which clearly change sign under the charge conjugation operation, it seems plausible that the photon has $C = -1$. The basic electromagnetic interaction between an electron and the electromagnetic field has a Hamiltonian of the form

$$H \approx j_\mu A_\mu \tag{8.73}$$

and since both j_μ and A_μ change sign the electromagnetic interactions are invariant under the charge conjugation operation. Since, like parity, the C-parity of a system is a multiplicative quantum number, a system containing n photons has $C = (-1)^n$. The electromagnetic decay of the π^0,

$$\pi^0 \rightarrow 2\gamma$$

is therefore allowed but the triple-photon decay

$$\pi^0 \rightarrow 3\gamma$$

is forbidden by C-parity conservation.

8.13 Summary

In this chapter we have demonstrated the intimate connection between a symmetry transformation and a conservation law. In short, if a transformation connects two *equivalent* frames of reference the dynamical variable which generates the transformation is a conserved quantity. Equivalently, if the operator corresponding to a dynamical variable commutes with the Hamiltonian of a system, the dynamical variable is a constant of the motion. Both continuous and discrete transformations have been considered; among the former, invariance under spatial translations and rotations leads to the universal conservation laws of momentum and angular momentum respectively. Completely analogous to rotations in ordinary space are rotations in isospin space. As far as the strong interactions are concerned the Hamiltonian is invariant under rotations in isospin space; the amplitude for a reaction depends on the magnitude of the isospin but not on its specific orientation in isospin space.

The discrete transformations, charge conjugation, parity and time reversal, are linked via the CPT theorem in the sense that if in an interaction any two, for example, are violated, the third must be violated in a compensating way so that the interaction is invariant under the combined operation CPT.

In chapter 7 the strangeness quantum number S was introduced. It is related to the charge, baryon number and third component of the isospin through the Gell-Mann–Nishijima relation

$$Q = I_3 + \frac{B + S}{2}.$$

Since Q, I_3 and B are all conserved in the strong and electromagnetic interactions then so is the strangeness S. For completeness we recall (see chapter 7) that to each lepton e, μ, τ ... is assigned a lepton number $L_e, L_\mu, L_\tau \ldots$ depending on the lepton type, and these are separately conserved in all interactions.

Finally, in table 8.2, we summarize the invariance properties of the strong, electromagnetic and weak interactions.

Table 8.2
Summary of the invariance properties of the strong, electromagnetic and weak interactions √, conserved; ×, violated

Transformation	Conserved quantity	Strong	Electro-magnetic	Weak
Spatial translation	Momentum p	√	√	√
Spatial rotation	Angular momentum J	√	√	√
Rotation in isospin space	Isospin I	√	×	×
Spatial inversion	Parity P	√	√	×
Particle–antiparticle conjugation	C-parity	√	√	×
Time reversal	–	√	√	×
CPT	–	√	√	√

REFERENCES 8

1 **Gottfried K** 1966 *Quantum Mechanics I: Fundamentals* Benjamin

2 **Panofsky W K H, Aamodt R L and Hadley J** 1951 *Phys Rev.* **81** (565)

3 **Chinowski W and Steinberger J** 1954 *Phys Rev* **95** (1561)

4 **Yang C N** 1950 *Phys Rev* **77** (242)

5 **Kroll N M and Wada W W** 1955 *Phys Rev* **98** (1355)

6 **Plano R, Prodell A, Samios N, Schwartz M and Steinberger J** 1959 *Phys Rev Lett* **3** (525)

7 **Davies P C W** 1974 *The Physics of Time Asymmetry* Surrey University Press

8 **Ramsey N F** 1982 *Ann Rev Nucl Part Sci* **32** (211)

9 **Particle Data Group** 1992 'Review of particle properties' *Phys Rev* **D45**

10 **Pauli W** 1955 in Pauli W (ed) *Niels Bohr and the Development of Physics* Pergamon

11 **Ludus G and Zumino B** 1957 *Phys Rev* **106** (385)

12 **Streater R F and Wightman A S** 1964 *PCT, Spin and Statistics and All That* Benjamin

13 **Lee T D and Yang C N** 1956 *Nuovo Cimento* **3** (749)

14 **Feynman R P, Leighton R B and Sands M** 1964 *The Feynman Lectures on Physics* Addison-Wesley

15 **Jackson J D** 1962 *Classical Electrodynamics* Wiley

EXAMPLES 8

8.1 The time evolution of a state vector is formally written as $|\psi(t)\rangle = U(t, t_0)|\psi(t_0)\rangle$. Using the time-dependent Schrödinger equation show that $U(t, t_0) = \exp[-iH(t - t_0)/\hbar]$.

8.2 Verify equation (8.5).

8.3 Show that $R(\epsilon) = 1 - i\epsilon L_z$, where L_z is the operator corresponding to the z component of angular momentum ($\hbar = 1$), generates an infinitesimal rotation ϵ about the z axis. A finite rotation θ can be generated by repeated application of $R(\epsilon)$ such that $R(\theta) = \text{Lt}(1 - i\epsilon L_z)^n$, where $n\epsilon \to \theta$ as $n \to \infty$ and $\epsilon \to 0$. Show that $R(\theta) = \exp(-i\theta L_z)$.

8.4 Using the angular momentum states $|j, m\rangle$ as a basis determine the matrix representations of the operators J^2, J_x, J_y and J_z for the cases $j = \frac{1}{2}$ and $j = 1$.

8.5 The orbital angular momentum l and the spin s of an electron in a hydrogen atom (say) can couple to give two values of the total angular momentum $j = l \pm \frac{1}{2}$. Thus, the P states can have $j = \frac{3}{2}$ (a quartet) or $j = \frac{1}{2}$ (a doublet). The state $|j, m\rangle = |\frac{3}{2}, \frac{3}{2}\rangle$ is uniquely defined in terms of the states

$|l, m_l\rangle|sm_s\rangle$ as $|\frac{3}{2}, \frac{3}{2}\rangle = |1, 1\rangle|\frac{1}{2}, \frac{1}{2}\rangle$. Use the angular momentum lowering operators $J_- = L_- + S_-$ to obtain the other three states in the quartet. Check your answers by looking up the appropriate Clebsch–Gordan coefficients (appendix G).

8.6 The rotation matrices have elements

$$d^{(j)}_{mm'}(\beta) = \langle j, m| \exp(-i\beta J_y)|j, m'\rangle.$$

Calculate these elements for $j = \frac{1}{2}$.

8.7 The spherical harmonics $Y_l^m(\theta, \phi)$ are defined in terms of the associated Legendre polynomials $P_l^m(\cos\theta)$ through the equation

$$Y_l^m(\theta, \phi) = \left[\frac{2l+1}{4\pi}\frac{(l-m)!}{(l+m)!}\right]^{1/2} P_l^m(\cos\theta)\exp(im\phi).$$

Given that the associated Legendre polynomials are polynomials in even (odd) powers of $\cos\theta$ if $l - |m|$ is even (odd), show that the parities of the spherical harmonics are $(-1)^l$.

8.8 Given that the K and π mesons have spin 0 show that one of the weak decay processes $K^+ \to \pi^+\pi^0$ and $K^+ \to \pi^+\pi^+\pi^-$ must violate parity conservation.

8.9 The matrices

$$\tau_1 = \frac{1}{2}\begin{pmatrix} 0 & 1 \\ 1 & 0 \end{pmatrix} \quad \tau_2 = \frac{1}{2}\begin{pmatrix} 0 & -i \\ i & 0 \end{pmatrix} \quad \tau_3 = \frac{1}{2}\begin{pmatrix} 1 & 0 \\ 0 & -1 \end{pmatrix}$$

are, apart from the factor $\frac{1}{2}$, the Pauli spin matrices. Show by explicit matrix multiplication that they satisfy the usual commutation relations for angular momenta. Construct raising and lowering operators $\tau_\pm = \tau_1 \pm i\tau_2$ and show that they have appropriate properties by examining their effect on the I spin states $\binom{1}{0}$ and $\binom{0}{1}$, representing the proton and neutron respectively.

8.10 The Δ(1232) is a resonance with $I = \frac{3}{2}$. What is the predicted branching ratio for $(\Delta^0 \to p\pi^-)/(\Delta^0 \to n\pi^0)$? What would this ratio be for a resonance with $I = \frac{1}{2}$?

8.11 Express the ratio of the cross-sections for the reactions $K^-p \to \pi^-\Sigma^+$ and $K^-p \to \pi^+\Sigma^-$ in terms of the two possible I spin amplitudes.

8.12 Determine the ratio of the cross-sections for the reactions $\pi^-p \to \pi^-p$ and $\pi^-p \to \pi^0 n$ on the assumption that the two I spin amplitudes are equal in magnitude but differ in phase by 45°.

8.13 Show that the C-parity of a $\pi^+\pi^-$ system with relative orbital angular momentum l is $(-1)^l$. Use the conservation of angular momentum and parity to determine the possible angular momentum states involved in the annihilation process $p\bar{p} \to \pi^+\pi^-$. Express your answer in spectroscopic notation. Does charge conjugation invariance impose any further restrictions on the allowed angular momentum states?

8.14 The Maxwell equations are (i) $\nabla \cdot \boldsymbol{E} = \rho$, (ii) $\nabla \cdot \boldsymbol{B} = 0$, (iii) $\nabla \wedge \boldsymbol{E} + \partial \boldsymbol{B}/\partial t = 0$ and (iv) $\nabla \wedge \boldsymbol{B} - \partial \boldsymbol{E}/\partial t = \boldsymbol{j}$.

(a) Use them to derive the equation of continuity

$$\frac{\partial \rho}{\partial t} + \nabla \cdot \boldsymbol{j} = 0.$$

(b) Justify the introduction of *arbitrary* potentials $\boldsymbol{A}$ and ϕ such that

$$\boldsymbol{B} = \nabla \wedge \boldsymbol{A} \qquad \text{and} \qquad \boldsymbol{E} = -\nabla\phi - \frac{\partial \boldsymbol{A}}{\partial t}$$

and show that $\boldsymbol{E}$ and $\boldsymbol{B}$ are invariant under the gauge transformation

$$\boldsymbol{A} \to \boldsymbol{A}' = \boldsymbol{A} + \nabla\psi \qquad \phi \to \phi' = \phi - \frac{\partial \psi}{\partial t}$$

where ψ is an arbitrary scalar function.

(c) Using the Lorentz gauge $\nabla \cdot \boldsymbol{A} = -\partial\phi/\partial t$, show that $\boldsymbol{A}$ and ϕ satisfy the wave equations

$$\nabla^2 \boldsymbol{A} - \frac{\partial^2 \boldsymbol{A}}{\partial t^2} = -\boldsymbol{j}$$

$$\nabla^2 \phi - \frac{\partial^2 \phi}{\partial t^2} = -\rho.$$

You may find the identity

$$\boldsymbol{a} \wedge \boldsymbol{b} \wedge \boldsymbol{c} = \boldsymbol{b}(\boldsymbol{a} \cdot \boldsymbol{c}) - (\boldsymbol{a} \cdot \boldsymbol{b})\boldsymbol{c}$$

which is valid for arbitrary vectors $\boldsymbol{a}$, $\boldsymbol{b}$ and $\boldsymbol{c}$, helpful.

8.15 State which of the following processes are allowed and which are forbidden. If allowed, state which interaction is responsible; if forbidden give reasons.

(a) $\Xi^0 \to \Sigma^0\gamma$
(b) $\mu^- + p \to \Lambda^0 + \nu_\mu$
(c) $\Sigma^+ \to \Lambda^0\mu^+\nu_\mu$
(d) $K^- + d \to \pi^+ + \Sigma^-$
(e) $K^+ \to \pi^0 e^+ \nu_e$.

9 *Hadron spectroscopy*

Introduction · Formation experiments · Phase space considerations · Production experiments

9.1 Introduction

In section 7.2 we gave a brief description of the particle 'directory' in which the hadrons were subdivided into 'stable' particles (table 7.2) and resonances (figure 7.2), the only distinction being that the latter can decay via the strong interactions with lifetimes of the order of 10^{-23} s while the former are either truly stable or decay via the weak or electromagnetic interactions, and therefore have much longer lifetimes. The discovery of a large number of resonant states and the determination of their quantum numbers such as spin, parity, isospin, strangeness etc. had a major influence on the search for an underlying symmetry scheme which would explain the hadron spectrum. In this chapter we outline the techniques used to identify the resonances and determine their quantum numbers.

Baryon resonances are readily excited in *formation* experiments in which mesons (π or K) interact with target nuclei at relatively low energies. The scattering cross-section is measured at a series of energies and if the total centre-of-mass energy sweeps through the mass of a resonance the cross-section will vary according to the Breit–Wigner formula (sections 6.3.2 and 9.2.3) and will in general show a peak with an energy width dependent on the lifetime of the resonant state. Quantum numbers such as baryon number, isospin and strangeness may be ascribed by application of the conservation laws appropriate to the strong interaction but spin and parity values require an analysis of the differential cross-section for the scattering (section 9.2).

Meson (and baryon) resonances can be observed in *production* experiments. These are performed at a fixed incident energy, which is higher than in formation experiments, and the cross-section for the production of a particular multiparticle final state is given by Fermi's golden rule (section 5.2.3). Resonance production in a selected group of final state particles can be seen as an enhancement of the *effective mass* M of the selected group; the mass is given by the relativistic expression ($c = 1$)

$$M^2 = \left(\sum_i E_i\right)^2 - \left(\sum_i \boldsymbol{p}_i\right)^2 \tag{9.1}$$

where E_i and $\boldsymbol{p}_i$ are the total energy and (vector) momentum of the ith particle in the group. In principle, spin-parity values may be obtained by analysing the angular distribution of the particles in their rest system.

9.2 Formation experiments

9.2.1 The partial wave formalism

For simplicity we consider the scattering of spinless particles and neglect the Coulomb interaction. The more common case of scattering of a spin 0 particle by a spin $\frac{1}{2}$ particle (e.g. π–p scattering) is a little more complicated but follows a similar pattern.

The scattering of two particles (masses m_1 and m_2) is described by the Schrödinger equation

$$i\hbar \frac{\partial \psi}{\partial t}(\boldsymbol{r}, \boldsymbol{R}, t) = \left[-\frac{\hbar^2}{2M} \nabla_R^2 - \frac{\hbar^2}{2\mu} \nabla_r^2 + V(r) \right] \psi(\boldsymbol{r}, \boldsymbol{R}, t) \tag{9.2}$$

where the relative and centre-of-mass coordinates are defined by

$$\boldsymbol{r} = \boldsymbol{r}_1 - \boldsymbol{r}_2$$

$$M\boldsymbol{R} = m_1 \boldsymbol{r}_1 + m_2 \boldsymbol{r}_2 \qquad (M = m_1 + m_2)$$

and μ is the reduced mass. We have assumed that the potential is static and depends only on the relative coordinates of the interacting particles. The operators ∇_R^2 and ∇_r^2 imply differentiation with respect to centre-of-mass and relative coordinates respectively. Equation (9.2) can be separated in a straightforward manner to give

$$\psi(\boldsymbol{r}, \boldsymbol{R}, t) = u(\boldsymbol{r})v(\mathrm{R}) \exp\left[-\frac{i(E_r + E_R)t}{\hbar} \right] \tag{9.3a}$$

$$-\frac{\hbar^2}{2\mu}\nabla_r^2 u(\boldsymbol{r}) + V(r)u(\boldsymbol{r}) = E_r u(\boldsymbol{r}) \tag{9.3b}$$

$$-\frac{\hbar^2}{2M}\nabla_R^2 v(\boldsymbol{R}) = E_R v(\boldsymbol{R}) \tag{9.3c}$$

where E_r is the total energy in the centre-of-mass system and E_R is the energy associated with the motion of the centre of mass. Equation (9.3c) implies that the centre of mass of the two particles moves like a free particle with mass M and energy E_R. Equation (9.3b), which describes the relative motion of the two particles, has the same form as the equation which describes the scattering of a particle with reduced mass μ and energy E_r by a fixed scattering potential $V(r)$. It is this energy which is available for excitation or production of new particles and so equation (9.3b) forms our starting point for the partial wave formalism.

We assume that the potential $V(r)$ is of short range so that at large distances $V(r) \to 0$ and $u(\boldsymbol{r})$ satisfies the free particle wave equation

$$\nabla^2 u(\boldsymbol{r}) + k^2 u(\boldsymbol{r}) = 0 \tag{9.4}$$

with $k^2 = 2\mu E_r/\hbar^2$. Let us further assume that the incident particles are prepared in a state of definite momentum $\boldsymbol{p} = \hbar\boldsymbol{k}$ and that the beam propagates along the positive z axis. This initial state is then described by a plane wave

$$u_i = \exp(ikz) \tag{9.5}$$

as shown in figure 9.1(a). After the collision, in addition to the plane wave there must be an outgoing spherical wave originating at the scattering centre as shown in figure 9.1(b). The asymptotic form of the final state wavefunction may then be written as

$$u_f \to \exp(ikz) + \frac{\exp(ikr)}{r} f(\theta, \phi). \tag{9.6}$$

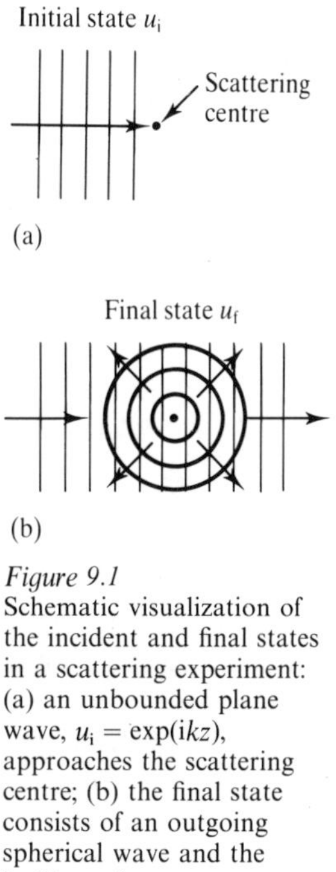

Figure 9.1
Schematic visualization of the incident and final states in a scattering experiment: (a) an unbounded plane wave, $u_i = \exp(ikz)$, approaches the scattering centre; (b) the final state consists of an outgoing spherical wave and the incident plane wave,

$u_f \to \exp(ikz) + r^{-1}\exp(ikr)f(\theta, \phi)$.

The second term in equation (9.6) corresponds to the outgoing spherical wave; it represents a particle moving radially outward from the scattering centre. The angles θ and ϕ are the usual polar and azimuthal angles of the momentum vector in a spherical polar coordinate system. The amplitude of the spherical wave can in principle depend on θ and ϕ; the dependence on r^{-1} ensures that the flux through a thin spherical shell at a distance r is independent of r.

A straightforward calculation of particle flux using the final state wavefunction u_f gives rise to interference terms between the incident plane wave and the outgoing spherical wave which are not present in practice.

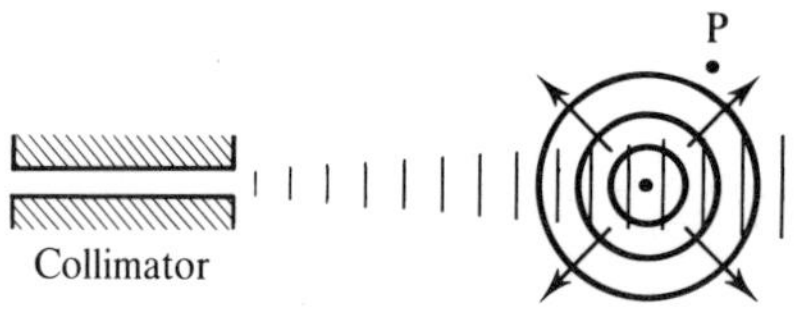

Figure 9.2 Schematic diagram showing the practical realization of a scattering experiment. The use of a collimator ensures that the incident beam is no longer unbounded as in figure 9.1 and the incident wave and scattered wave are effectively isolated. The contribution to the scattered intensity at the observation point P comes only from the outgoing spherical wave.

This is because in most experimental arrangements the incident and scattered particles are separated from each other by collimators. This difference between the theoretical situation, in which the incident plane wave is unbounded (figure 9.1), and a typical experimental situation is shown schematially in figure 9.2. In the practical case the incident beam is no longer infinite in extent but can be considered to be made up of a superposition of infinite plane waves whose propagation vectors differ slightly in magnitude and direction. Provided that the collimating apertures are not so small that diffraction effects become important, the angular spread of the incident beam is negligible; it is of the order of λ/d where λ is the wavelength associated with the incident particles and d is the width of the aperture. Since the function f in (9.6) varies only slowly with angle it is essentially unaffected by the small directional variation of the incident propagation vectors and in practice, if the scattered intensity is measured at the point of observation P, it is the spherical wave only that makes a contribution and this is virtually unchanged from that which appears in equation (9.6). Similarly, the incident flux (particles per unit area per unit time) arises from the plane wave term alone because at distances far enough from the scattering centre the second term in (9.6) becomes negligible.

The incident flux is obtained directly from the probability current density (example 9.3)

$$\boldsymbol{j}(\boldsymbol{r}, t) = \frac{\hbar}{2im}\left(\psi^*\nabla\psi - \psi\nabla\psi^*\right) \tag{9.7}$$

and substitution of the first term of (9.6) into (9.7) yields a flux v. For the scattered particles, substitution of the second term of (9.6) gives a flow of $v|f(\theta, \phi)|^2 \, \mathrm{d}\Omega$ through an area subtending a solid angle $\mathrm{d}\Omega$ at the origin. From the definition of a differential cross-section (appendix B) it follows that

$$\frac{\mathrm{d}\sigma(\theta, \phi)}{\mathrm{d}\Omega} = \frac{\text{flow per unit time and solid angle}}{\text{incident flux}} = |f(\theta, \phi)|^2.$$

We note that, since the *scattered* wave is given by

$$u_{sc} = u_f - u_i = \frac{\exp(ikr)}{r} f(\theta, \phi) \tag{9.8}$$

the quantity $f(\theta, \phi)$ is known as the *scattering amplitude.*

It is apparent that in the description so far, even in the practical case of a collimated incident beam, the position of a particle with respect to the x and y axes cannot be specified completely and the angular momentum $l\hbar$ with respect to the scattering centre can have many values. It is therefore convenient to replace the plane wave by an equivalent series of spherical waves each of which represents a particle with a definite angular momentum about the scattering centre and with no component of angular momentum in the direction of incidence. Alternatively, since we are considering the scattering of a spinless particle by a central potential, there must be axial symmetry, which leads us to the expectation that the only spherical harmonics which can appear in the problem are those with no ϕ dependence, namely $Y_l^0(\theta)$.

The expansion of $\exp(ikz) = \exp(ikr \cos \theta)$ in spherical harmonics is[1]

$$\exp(ikz) = \sum_{l=0}^{\infty} \sqrt{[4\pi(2l + 1)]}\, i^l j_l(kr)\, Y_l^0(\theta) \tag{9.9}$$

confirming that the incident wave decomposes into angular momentum states with $m = 0$ only. We require the asymptotic form of this expansion, for which we need the asymptotic behaviour of the spherical Bessel function

$$j_l(kr) \xrightarrow[kr \to \infty]{} \frac{1}{kr} \sin\left(kr - \frac{l\pi}{2}\right). \tag{9.10}$$

It is also convenient to write the spherical harmonic $Y_l^0(\theta)$ as

$$Y_l^0(\theta) = \left(\frac{2l + 1}{4\pi}\right)^{1/2} P_l(\cos \theta) \tag{9.11}$$

where $P_l(\cos \theta)$ is a Legendre polynomial. Then

$$\exp(ikz) \to \frac{1}{kr} \sum_l (2l + 1) i^l P_l(\cos \theta) \sin\left(kr - \frac{l\pi}{2}\right) \tag{9.12}$$

$$= \frac{1}{kr} \sum_l (2l + 1) i^l P_l(\cos \theta) \times \frac{\exp[i(kr - l\pi/2)] - \exp[-i(kr - l\pi/2)]}{2i}. \tag{9.13}$$

Inspection of this last formula shows the plane wave can be considered as a series of spherical waves $\exp[-i(kr - l\pi/2)]$ each of definite angular momentum $l\hbar$ (partial waves) converging on the scattering centre together with a coherent superposition of diverging waves $\exp[i(kr - l\pi/2)]$. This situation represents an *undisturbed* incident plane wave. If now we consider an interaction with the scattering centre, causality requires that only the outgoing waves can be affected. The interaction potential may modify the outgoing waves in phase only or in amplitude and phase. In the former case we have *elastic scattering* with a certain angular distribution and in the latter case there are *inelastic processes* in addition. The steady state wavefunction when the interaction takes place may therefore be written

$$u_f = \frac{1}{kr}\sum_{l=0}^{\infty}(2l+1)i^l P_l(\cos\theta)a_l \times \frac{\exp[i(kr - l\pi/2)] - \exp[-i(kr - l\pi/2)]}{2i} \tag{9.14}$$

where a_l is a complex constant representing the effect of the scattering centre on the lth partial wave. The real part of a_l gives the change in amplitude and the imaginary part the change in phase. In accordance with equation (9.8) we can obtain an expression for the scattering amplitude, and hence the differential cross-section, by subtracting the incident wave u_i, in the form given by equation (9.13), from (9.14) and comparing coefficients of $\exp(ikr)$. The result is

$$f(\theta) = \frac{1}{2ik}\sum_{l=0}^{\infty}(2l+1)(a_l - 1)P_l(\cos\theta) \tag{9.15}$$

where use has been made of the identity $i^l = \exp[i(l\pi/2)]$. As expected, the scattering amplitude has no ϕ dependence. The differential cross-section is

$$\frac{d\sigma(\theta)}{d\Omega} = |f(\theta)|^2 = \frac{1}{k^2}\left|\sum_{l=0}^{\infty}(2l+1)\left(\frac{a_l - 1}{2i}\right)P_l(\cos\theta)\right|^2. \tag{9.16}$$

This expression refers to particles which are elastically scattered. The total cross-section for elastic scattering may be obtained by integration of (9.16);

$$\sigma_{el} = \int\frac{d\sigma(\theta)}{d\Omega}\,d\Omega = \int|f(\theta)|^2\,d\Omega = \frac{\pi}{k^2}\sum_{l=0}^{\infty}(2l+1)|1 - a_l|^2. \tag{9.17}$$

The last result follows from the orthonormality of the Legendre polynomials

$$\int P_l P_{l'}\, d\Omega = \frac{4\pi\delta_{ll'}}{2l+1} \tag{9.18}$$

where $\delta_{ll'}$ is the Kronecker δ symbol.

The change in amplitude and phase of the outgoing waves is commonly parametrized in terms of an inelasticity parameter η_l and a real phase shift δ_l. Then,

$$a_l = \eta_l \exp(2i\delta_l) \qquad \text{with } 0 \leqslant \eta_l \leqslant 1. \tag{9.19}$$

In the situation in which there is *elastic scattering* only, there must be no loss of incident particles and therefore $\eta_l = 1$. Substitution in equation (9.15) gives

$$f(\theta) = \frac{1}{k} \sum_{l=0}^{\infty} (2l+1) \frac{\exp(2i\delta_l) - 1}{2i} P_l(\cos\theta). \tag{9.20}$$

The association of δ_l with a phase shift becomes evident on substituting $a_l = \exp(2i\delta_l)$ in (9.14). The exponential term becomes

$$\frac{\exp[i(kr - l\pi/2 + 2\delta_l)] - \exp[-i(kr - l\pi/2)]}{2i}$$

so that $2\delta_l$ is the phase shift of the outgoing lth partial wave.

Again, substitution of $a_l = \exp(2i\delta_l)$ in (9.17) gives for the total elastic cross-section

$$\sigma_{\text{el}} = \frac{4\pi}{k^2} \sum_{l=0}^{\infty} (2l+1) \sin^2 \delta_l. \tag{9.21}$$

Since the scattering is elastic only, this also corresponds to the total scattering cross-section. It is apparent from (9.21) that the elastic cross-section associated with any particular l value or partial wave becomes a maximum if the phase shift δ_l passes through $\pi/2$; this condition is called a *resonance*. For a given partial wave, or angular momentum state, then, the maximum possible cross-section allowed by unitarity, or conservation of probability, is

$$\sigma_{\text{el}}^{\max} = \frac{4\pi}{k^2}(2l+1) \qquad \sigma_{\text{inel}} = 0. \tag{9.22}$$

If the scattering centre is a *hard sphere* of radius R and if we consider the simple case of *low* incident energy ($kR \ll 1$) so that only $l = 0$ waves are involved then the corresponding phase shift may be obtained from equation (9.14) by imposing the requirement that the wave amplitude shall vanish on the surface of the sphere. This gives, with $\eta_l = 1$ for elastic scattering,

$$\exp(2i\delta_0) = \exp(-2ikR)$$

so that $\delta_0 = -kR$ and, from (9.21), taking $\sin \delta_0 \approx \delta_0$,

$$\sigma_{el} = 4\pi R^2.$$

This is the cross-section for the potential scattering referred to in section 6.3.2.

We turn now to the case in which the scattering process changes both the amplitude and the phase of the outgoing wave, i.e. there is some *inelastic* scattering. The inelastic cross-section is obtained by computing the *net* flow of particles associated with the wave u_f. This gives, using (9.14),

$$\sigma_{inel}^{max} = \frac{\pi}{k^2} \sum_{l=0}^{\infty} (2l+1)(1 - |a_l|^2)$$

$$= \frac{\pi}{k^2} \sum_{l=0}^{\infty} (2l+1)(1 - \eta_l^2). \tag{9.23}$$

The *total cross-section* is given by the sum of the elastic and inelastic cross-sections

$$\sigma_{tot} = \sigma_{el} + \sigma_{inel} = \frac{2\pi}{k^2} \sum_{l=0}^{\infty} (2l+1)(1 - \mathrm{Re}\, a_l). \tag{9.24}$$

The maximum inelastic cross-section for a given partial wave is when $\eta_l = 0$ and then

$$\sigma_{inel}^{max} = \frac{\pi}{k^2}(2l+1). \tag{9.25}$$

Notice that when the absorption or inelastic scattering has its maximum possible value there is still some elastic scattering with a maximum cross-section given by

$$\sigma_{el}^{max} = \sigma_{inel}^{max} = \frac{\pi}{k^2}(2l+1). \tag{9.26}$$

It is thus possible to have elastic scattering without inelastic scattering, but if absorption takes place in a particular partial wave there must be some associated elastic scattering in the same partial wave: this is known as diffraction scattering.

Diffraction scattering is well marked in the classical or *high energy limit* ($kR \gg 1$) when the scatterer is completely absorbing for all partial waves up to the value $l = kR$ (*black disc*). Putting $a_l = 0$ for $0 \leqslant l \leqslant kR$ and $a_l = 1$ for $l > kR$ in (9.17) and (9.23) gives

$$\sigma_{\mathrm{el}} = \sigma_{\mathrm{inel}} = \frac{\pi}{k^2} \sum_{0}^{kR} (2l + 1) = \pi(R + \lambda\!\!\!^{-})^2$$

so that the total cross-section is $2\pi(R + \lambda\!\!\!^{-})^2 \approx 2\pi R^2$, in contrast with the classical expectation of πR^2. Physically it arises because of the need to create a 'shadow' behind the absorber; the diffraction scattering which thus arises has an angular distribution determined by the value of $1/kR = \lambda\!\!\!^{-}/R$.

9.2.2 *The optical theorem*

The total cross-section is related to the imaginary part of the forward scattering amplitude, a relationship known as the optical theorem. Previously we obtained for the scattering amplitude the expression

$$f(\theta) = \frac{1}{2\mathrm{i}k} \sum_{l=0}^{\infty} (2l + 1)(a_l - 1) P_l(\cos\theta).$$

For forward scattering $\theta = 0$ and since $P_l(1) = 1$ we have

$$\begin{aligned} \operatorname{Im} f(0) &= \operatorname{Im}\left[\frac{1}{2k} \sum_{l=0}^{\infty} (2l + 1)\mathrm{i}(1 - a_l)\right] \\ &= \frac{1}{2k} \sum_{l=0}^{\infty} (2l + 1)(1 - \operatorname{Re} a_l). \end{aligned}$$

If we compare this expression with that for the total cross-section (9.24) we obtain the optical theorem:

$$\sigma_{\mathrm{tot}} = \frac{4\pi}{k} \operatorname{Im} f(0). \tag{9.27}$$

9.2.3 *The partial wave amplitude and the Breit–Wigner formula*

Let us define a partial wave amplitude

$$T_l(E) = \frac{\eta_l \exp(2\mathrm{i}\delta_l) - 1}{2\mathrm{i}} \tag{9.28}$$

and consider the behaviour of this amplitude as the energy E varies. For purely elastic scattering $\eta_l = 1$ and the partial wave amplitude may be written

$$T_l(E) = \exp(\mathrm{i}\delta_l) \sin \delta_l = \frac{1}{\cot \delta_l - \mathrm{i}}. \tag{9.29}$$

We have already seen in section 9.2.1 that the resonance condition is achieved as $\delta_l \to \pi/2$, so that near the resonant energy $\cot \delta_l \approx 0$. If E is the total energy of the colliding particles in the centre-of-mass system and E_R is the value of E at resonance, then in the neighbourhood of the resonance $\cot \delta_l$ can be expanded in a Taylor series to give

$$\cot[\delta_l(E)] = \cot[\delta_l(E_\mathrm{R})] + (E_\mathrm{R} - E)\left\{\frac{\mathrm{d}}{\mathrm{d}E} \cot[\delta_l(E)]\right\}_{E=E_\mathrm{R}} + \cdots. \tag{9.30}$$

At resonance $\cot[\delta_l(E_\mathrm{R})] = 0$ and if we define the quantity Γ through the relationship

$$\frac{2}{\Gamma} = \left\{\frac{\mathrm{d}}{\mathrm{d}E} \cot[\delta_l(E)]\right\}_{E=E_\mathrm{R}} \tag{9.31}$$

then

$$T_l(E) = \frac{1}{(2/\Gamma)(E_\mathrm{R} - E) - \mathrm{i}} = \frac{\Gamma/2}{(E_\mathrm{R} - E) - \mathrm{i}\Gamma/2}. \tag{9.32}$$

For a given value of l the elastic partial wave cross-section (9.17) can be written

$$\sigma_\mathrm{el}(E) = \frac{4\pi}{k^2}(2l + 1)|T_l(E)|^2 \tag{9.33}$$

and on substituting (9.32) into (9.33) we arrive at the celebrated Breit–Wigner resonance formula already used in section 6.3.2

$$\sigma_\mathrm{el}(E) = \frac{4\pi}{k^2}(2l + 1)\frac{\Gamma^2/4}{(E_\mathrm{R} - E)^2 + \Gamma^2/4}. \tag{9.34}$$

Equation (9.34) is specific to the case of spin-0–spin-0 scattering. The general case in which both the incident particle and the target particle have spin is treated in detail in reference 2. In this general case

$$\sigma_{el}(E) = \frac{4\pi}{k^2} g(J) \frac{\Gamma^2/4}{(E_R - E)^2 + \Gamma^2/4} \tag{9.35}$$

where the statistical weight for the channel spin J is

$$g(J) = \frac{2J + 1}{(2s_1 + 1)(2s_2 + 1)} \tag{9.36}$$

where s_1 and s_2 are the spins of the incident and target particles respectively.

Returning to the case of spin-0–spin-0 scattering, at an energy $E = E_R$ the elastic cross-section has its maximum value (equation (9.22))

$$\sigma_{el}^{max} = \frac{4\pi}{k^2}(2l + 1)$$

so that at any other energy

$$\frac{\sigma_{el}(E)}{\sigma_{el}^{max}} = \frac{\Gamma^2/4}{(E_R - E)^2 + \Gamma^2/4}. \tag{9.37}$$

At energies $E = E_R \pm \Gamma/2$ it is evident that $\sigma_{el}(E)/\sigma_{el}^{max} = \frac{1}{2}$ so that Γ is the full width at half maximum of the Breit–Wigner resonance shape. As pointed out already in chapter 7, the full width is related to the lifetime of the state through the uncertainty principle, $\Gamma\tau \approx \hbar$. For resonances decaying via the strong interactions the lifetimes are of the order of 10^{-23} s so that widths of 100 MeV or so are typical.

The above formulae are readily generalized to the case in which some inelastic scattering is present for which $\eta_l < 1$. The total width Γ of a resonance is the sum of the elastic (Γ_{el}) and inelastic (Γ_{in}) widths,

$$\Gamma = \Gamma_{el} + \Gamma_{in}$$

and the *elasticity* of a resonance is defined as

$$x = \frac{\Gamma_{el}}{\Gamma}.$$

The quantity

$$1 - x = \frac{\Gamma_{in}}{\Gamma}$$

is called the inelasticity. The probability of *formation* of the resonance in the elastic channel is proportional to x. The probability of *decay* into the elastic channel is also proportional to x while the probability of decay into any inelastic channel is proportional to $1 - x$. The elastic, inelastic and total cross-sections will therefore be proportional to x^2, $x(1 - x)$ and x respectively, or equivalently to Γ_{el}^2, $\Gamma_{\text{el}}\Gamma_{\text{in}}$ and $\Gamma_{\text{el}}\Gamma$. In summary, the non-relativistic generalizations of the Breit–Wigner resonance formula are

$$\sigma_{\text{el}}(E) = \frac{\pi}{k^2} g(J) \frac{\Gamma_{\text{el}}^2}{(E_{\text{R}} - E)^2 + \Gamma^2/4} \tag{9.38}$$

$$\sigma_{\text{in}}(E) = \frac{\pi}{k^2} g(J) \frac{\Gamma_{\text{el}}\Gamma_{\text{in}}}{(E_{\text{R}} - E)^2 + \Gamma^2/4} \tag{9.39}$$

$$\sigma_{\text{tot}}(E) = \frac{\pi}{k^2} g(J) \frac{\Gamma_{\text{el}}\Gamma}{(E_{\text{R}} - E)^2 + \Gamma^2/4}. \tag{9.40}$$

Let us now consider the behaviour of the partial wave amplitude (9.28) in the vicinity of a resonance for both elastic and inelastic scattering. We use the symbol α to denote the elastic channel and β to denote an inelastic channel. Following convention, the amplitude is written as $T_{\alpha\alpha}$ for elastic scattering, e.g. $\text{K}^-\text{p} \to \text{K}^-\text{p}$, and as $T_{\alpha\beta}$ for inelastic scattering, e.g. $\text{K}^-\text{p} \to \Sigma^-\pi^+$. Then (9.28) becomes

$$T_{\alpha\alpha} = \frac{\eta_l \exp(2\text{i}\delta_l) - 1}{2\text{i}}.$$

The Breit–Wigner approximation for the elastic amplitude in the new notation becomes

$$T_{\alpha\alpha} = \frac{\Gamma_\alpha/2}{(E_{\text{R}} - E) - \text{i}\Gamma/2} = \frac{x_\alpha}{\epsilon - \text{i}} \tag{9.41}$$

where we have written the elastic width as Γ_α and the elasticity as $x_\alpha = \Gamma_\alpha/\Gamma$, where as before the total width is the sum of the partial widths

$$\Gamma = \sum_\gamma \Gamma_\gamma.$$

Furthermore, we have introduced the symbol $\epsilon = \cot \delta_l = 2(E_{\text{R}} - E)/\Gamma$. From (9.41) we note that

$$u = \text{Re}\, T_{\alpha\alpha} = \frac{x_\alpha \epsilon}{\epsilon^2 + 1}$$

and

$$v = \text{Im}\ T_{\alpha\alpha} = \frac{x_\alpha}{\epsilon^2 + 1}.$$

When ϵ is eliminated from these equations it is found that

$$u^2 + \left(v - \frac{x_\alpha}{2}\right)^2 = \left(\frac{x_\alpha}{2}\right)^2$$

which is the equation of a circle with centre $(0, x_\alpha/2)$ and radius $x_\alpha/2$. When the only channel open is the elastic channel the scattering is perfectly elastic, $x_\alpha = 1$, and the radius of the circle is $\frac{1}{2}$, the so-called *unitarity* circle.

The Breit–Wigner approximation for the amplitude for the inelastic process leading from the channel α to the channel β is

$$T_{\alpha\beta} = \frac{\sqrt{(x_\alpha x_\beta)}}{\epsilon - \text{i}}. \tag{9.42}$$

In this case the amplitude lies on a circle with centre $(0, \sqrt{(x_\alpha x_\beta)}/2)$ and radius $\sqrt{(x_\alpha x_\beta)}/2$.*

It is the aim of a partial wave analysis to determine, from the experimental differential cross-sections at different energies, the behaviour of the partial wave amplitudes as a function of energy and to look for resonant behaviour in particular partial waves. The results of a partial wave analysis are frequently presented in the form of an Argand diagram, i.e. a plot of Im T versus Re T as a function of the energy. For a resonant partial wave, $\epsilon = 0$ at the resonant energy $E = E_{\text{R}}$; the amplitude is purely imaginary and for a perfectly elastic resonance the representative point on the Argand diagram has coordinates (0, 1) as shown in figure 9.3(a). At energies $E < E_{\text{R}}$, ϵ is positive and for $E > E_{\text{R}}$ it is negative. The point (0, 0) on the Argand diagram corresponds to $\delta_l = 0, \pi \ldots.$ If we assume that $\delta_l \to 0$ as $E \to 0$, or, in practice, for values of E well below the resonant energy, the representative point starts at (0, 0) and as the energy increases towards E_{R} moves around the unitarity circle in an *anticlockwise* direction. This property of the Breit–Wigner amplitude is a consequence of causality which restricts the amplitude to the form $(\cot \delta_l - \text{i})^{-1}$ and excludes the complex conjugate amplitude, which

* Strictly, (9.42) should be written $T_{\alpha\beta} = \pm\sqrt{(x_\alpha x_\beta)}/(\epsilon - \text{i})$, the sign being determined by the relative signs of the coupling of the elastic and inelastic channels to the resonant eigenstate, so that for an inelastic channel $T_{\alpha\beta}$ may be confined to the lower half-plane.

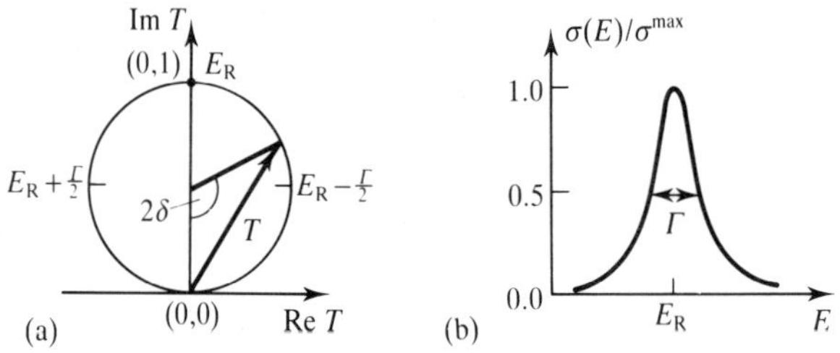

Figure 9.3 (a) An Argand diagram for a perfectly elastic resonance. When the imaginary part of the scattering amplitude T is plotted against the real part, the representative point moves around the unitarity circle in an anticlockwise direction as the energy increases. (b) The elastic cross-section showing the Breit–Wigner resonance shape.

would give the same cross-section but which would traverse the circle in a clockwise direction. This behaviour is known as the Wigner condition. Also shown in figure 9.3(b) is the corresponding behaviour of the elastic cross-section (9.37). The behaviour of the elastic amplitudes for isolated Breit–Wigner resonances with elasticities $x = 0.8$ and 0.4 are shown in figure 9.4. It should be noted that for $x > 0.5$ the phase shift passes through $\pi/2$ at resonance, as in the previous case discussed, but for $x < 0.5$ the phase shift passes through 0 at resonance.

In practice, a resonant partial wave amplitude does not always follow the idealized behaviour described above. In particular, if the amplitude contains a resonant contribution together with a non-resonant elastic background the characteristic circular motion of the amplitude in the Argand diagram may be shifted, rotated and distorted.

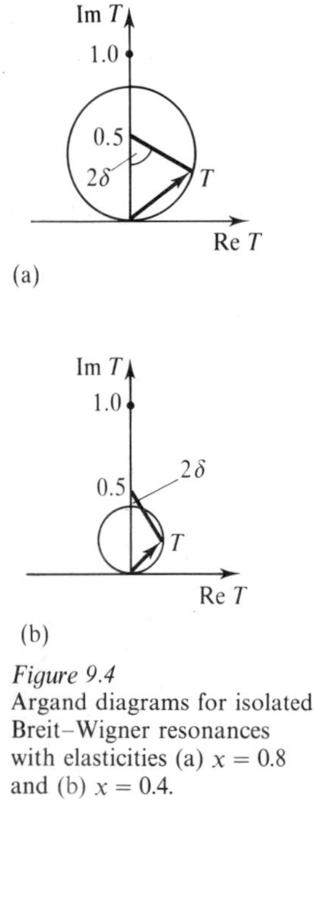

Figure 9.4
Argand diagrams for isolated Breit–Wigner resonances with elasticities (a) $x = 0.8$ and (b) $x = 0.4$.

9.2.4 Some examples of baryon resonances

At laboratory kinetic energies below 300 MeV, pion–nucleon scattering is dominated by the formation of the $\Delta(1232)$ resonance, the first resonant state to be discovered. The total cross-sections for π^+p and π^-p scattering are shown in figure 9.5. Large enhancements are seen in both cross-sections at an incident pion energy of 190 MeV, which corresponds to a total centre-of-mass energy of 1232 MeV or, equivalently, to a resonance mass of 1232 MeV/c^2. For pion–nucleon resonances the only possible values of the I spin are $\frac{1}{2}$ and $\frac{3}{2}$. Since the third component of I spin in the π^+p channel is $\frac{3}{2}$, the I spin of the $\Delta(1232)$ must be $\frac{3}{2}$. Confirmation of this assignment is given by the ratio (3:1) of the cross-sections in the π^+p and π^-p channels.

The spin of the $\Delta(1232)$ can be determined by application of the partial wave formalism developed in section 9.2.3.

However, in the present case of spin-0–spin-$\frac{1}{2}$ scattering each partial wave with a definite orbital angular momentum l has two values of J, namely $J = l \pm \frac{1}{2}$. During the collision there is some probability that the

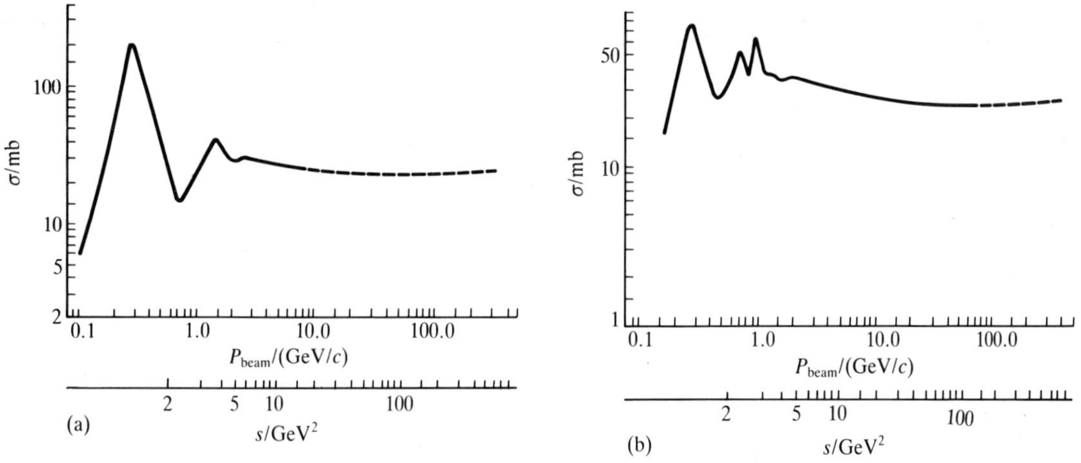

Figure 9.5 The total cross-sections for (a) π^+p and (b) π^-p scattering.

spin orientation may change but, since J_z must be conserved, any change in the z component of spin must be compensated by a corresponding change in the z component of the orbital angular momentum m. A 'spin-flip' interaction is therefore characterized by the appearance in the outgoing wave of a Legendre polynomial with non-zero m, i.e. an associated Legendre polynomial. The associated Legendre polynomials differ from the Legendre polynomials in their angular dependence and consequently the presence of spin affects the angular distribution of the scattered particles. Furthermore, since the spin-nonflip and spin-flip states are orthogonal, they will not interfere and the spin-flip states give rise to an *additional* contribution to the intensity of the scattered particles. Now, instead of the single amplitude, $f(\theta)$, there are two, a spin-nonflip amplitude

$$g(\theta) = \frac{1}{k} \sum_l [(l+1) T_{l^+} + l T_{l^-}] P_l^0(\cos\theta) \tag{9.43}$$

and a spin-flip amplitude

$$h(\theta) = \frac{1}{k} \sum_l (T_{l^+} - T_{l^-}) P_l^1(\cos\theta). \tag{9.44}$$

T_{l^+} and T_{l^-}, the partial wave amplitudes for $J = l + \frac{1}{2}$ and $J = l - \frac{1}{2}$ respectively, have the same form as T_l in equation (9.28) and the differential cross-section now becomes

$$\frac{d\sigma}{d\Omega} = |g(\theta)|^2 + |h(\theta)|^2.$$

If we take the range of the π–N interaction as $R \approx 1/m_\pi$ then the values of orbital angular momentum which contribute to the scattering will be $l \approx kR = k/m_\pi$, so that for incident pion energies up to 300 MeV only S and P waves need to be considered. Then, equations (9.43) and (9.44) for the spin-nonflip and spin-flip amplitudes become

$$g(\theta) = \frac{1}{k}\left[T_{0,1/2} + (2T_{1,3/2} + T_{1,1/2})\cos\theta\right]$$

$$h(\theta) = \frac{1}{k}(T_{1,3/2} - T_{1,1/2})\sin\theta.$$

In these expressions the notation T_{lJ} has been used for the partial wave amplitudes and the explicit expressions for the Legendre polynomials, $P_0^0(\cos\theta) = 1$, $P_1^0(\cos\theta) = \cos\theta$ and $P_1^1(\cos\theta) = -\sin\theta$ have been inserted. The differential cross-section may then be written

$$\frac{d\sigma}{d\Omega} = |g(\theta)|^2 + |h(\theta)|^2$$

$$= \frac{1}{k^2}\left(|T_{0,1/2} + (2T_{1,3/2} + T_{1,1/2})\cos\theta|^2 + |T_{1,3/2} - T_{1,1/2}|^2\sin^2\theta\right) \tag{9.45}$$

which is of the form

$$\frac{d\sigma}{d\Omega} = \frac{1}{k^2}(A_0 + A_1\cos\theta + A_2\cos^2\theta) \tag{9.46}$$

with the identification

$$A_0 = |T_{0,1/2}|^2 + |T_{1,3/2} - T_{1,1/2}|^2 \tag{9.47a}$$

$$A_1 = 2\,\mathrm{Re}\,T^*_{0,1/2}(2T_{1,3/2} + T_{1,1/2}) \tag{9.47b}$$

$$A_2 = 3|T_{1,3/2}|^2 + 6\,\mathrm{Re}(T^*_{1,3/2}T_{1,1/2}). \tag{9.47c}$$

The expressions (9.47) show that the constant term in the differential cross-section has contributions from both S and P waves, the term in $\cos\theta$ is an interference term between the S and P waves while the quadratic term has a contribution from P waves only.

In essence, a partial wave analysis consists of determining the coefficients A_0, A_1 and A_2, or equivalently the partial wave amplitudes T_{lJ}, as a function of energy from the experimentally determined differential cross-sections. Figure 9.6 shows the differential cross-sections obtained by Bussey *et al.*[3] for π^+p elastic scattering as a function of energy. The

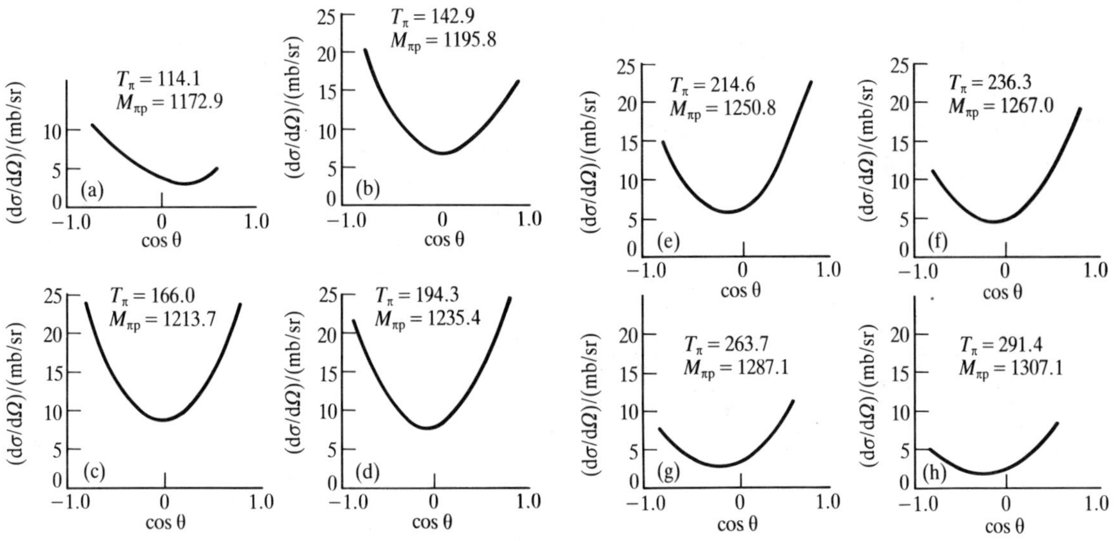

Figure 9.6 Differential cross-sections for π^+p elastic scattering at various incident pion energies. (After Bussey P J *et al.* 1973 *Nucl Phys* **B58** (363).)

asymmetry in the differential cross-section at the lowest energy shows that even at this energy the P wave amplitude is significant. As the energy sweeps through the resonant energy the distributions become symmetric about $\theta = \pi/2$ and above resonance interference is again evident. Figure 9.7(a) shows a typical variation of the coefficients A_0, A_1 and A_2 with energy. At resonance the values of these coefficients are very nearly 1, 0 and 3 respectively, i.e. the differential cross-section is

$$\frac{d\sigma}{d\Omega} = \frac{1}{k^2}(1 + 3\cos^2\theta). \tag{9.48}$$

This is precisely the form expected for the production in πp collisions of a $J^P = \frac{3}{2}^+$ state, which decays by pure P wave.

The notation $L_{2I,2J}$, where L is the orbital angular momentum, I is the I spin and J is the spin, is commonly used to describe π–N partial wave amplitudes. Figure 9.7(b) shows the Argand diagram for the P_{33} partial wave. It follows the unitarity circle, i.e. the P_{33} wave is perfectly elastic ($\eta = 1$). The phase shift passes through $\pi/2$ at the resonant energy 1232 MeV and at this energy the cross-section has its maximum value allowed by unitarity, i.e.

$$\sigma_{\max}^{\text{el}} = \frac{2\pi}{k^2}(J + \tfrac{1}{2}) = \frac{8\pi}{k^2}$$

for a $J = \frac{3}{2}$ resonance, as shown in figure 9.7(c).

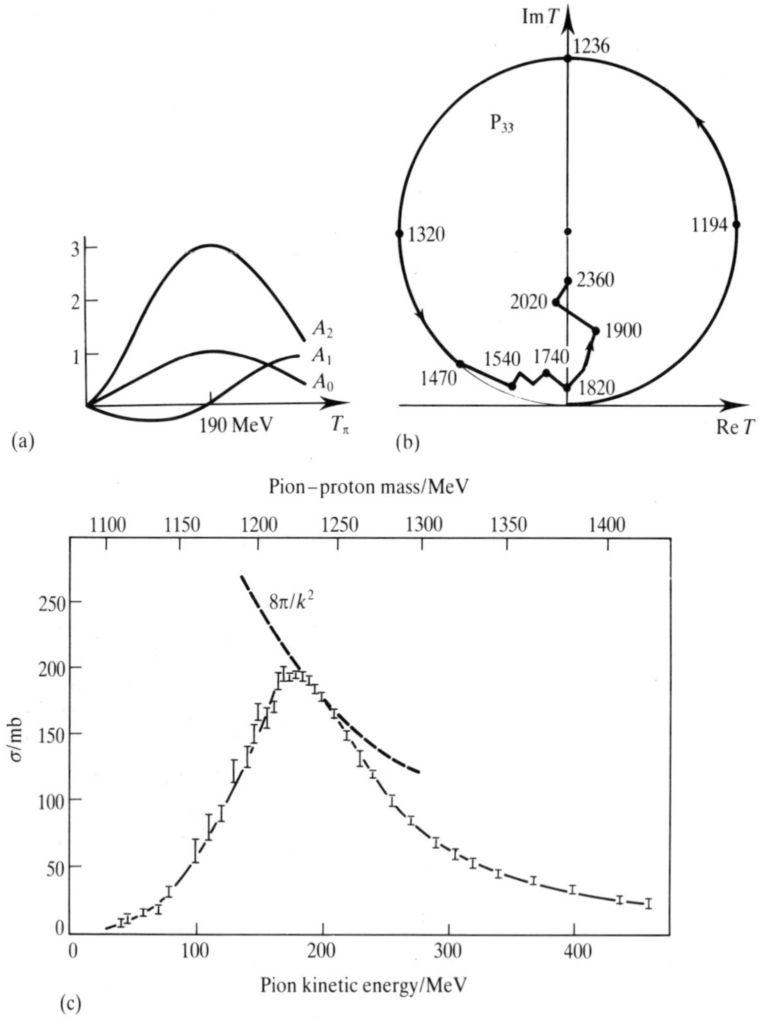

Figure 9.7 (a) Typical variation of the coefficients A_i in a fit of the differential cross-section to the formula $d\sigma/d\Omega = \Sigma A_n \cos^n \theta$; (b) Argand diagram for the perfectly elastic $\Delta(1232)$; (c) the total cross-section for π^+p scattering in the vicinity of the $\Delta(1232)$. The unitarity limit for a $J = \frac{3}{2}$ resonance $\sigma_{max} = 8\pi/k^2$ is also shown.

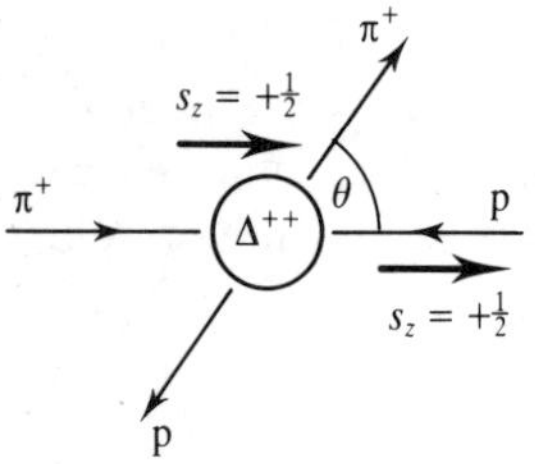

Figure 9.8
Formation and decay of the $\Delta^{++}(1232)$ viewed in the rest system of the resonance.

We now show that (9.48) is the expected angular distribution for the decay of a $J^P = \frac{3}{2}^+$ $\Delta(1232)$ produced in π^+p collisions. Let us take the direction of the incident π^+ in the centre-of-mass system as the quantization or z axis, and assume that the proton initially has its spin pointing in this direction. Since there can be no component of orbital angular momentum along the direction of incidence and because the z component of angular momentum must be conserved, the $\Delta^{++}(1232)$ must also have $s_z = +\frac{1}{2}$, i.e. the Δ^{++} is produced in the angular momentum state $|\frac{3}{2}, \frac{1}{2}\rangle$ (figure 9.8). Total angular momentum can be conserved in the decay either by P wave ($l = 1$) or D wave ($l = 2$) emission since the proton spin can couple to either of these to give a total angular momentum of $\frac{3}{2}$. Conservation of parity in the decay, however, rules out the possibility of D wave emission. For P wave decay then, the spatial wavefunction of the final state πp system must contain spherical harmonics with $l = 1$. Since the z component of the total angular momentum in the final state must be $+\frac{1}{2}$, the overall wavefunction must be

$$\psi(\theta, \phi) = \sqrt{\tfrac{1}{3}}Y_1^1(\theta, \phi)|\tfrac{1}{2}, -\tfrac{1}{2}\rangle + \sqrt{\tfrac{2}{3}}Y_1^0(\theta, \phi)|\tfrac{1}{2}, \tfrac{1}{2}\rangle \tag{9.49}$$

where the coefficients $\sqrt{\frac{1}{3}}$ and $\sqrt{\frac{2}{3}}$ are the Clebsch–Gordan coefficients for the coupling of an angular momentum $l = 1$ and a spin $s = \frac{1}{2}$ (the proton spin) to the state $|J, J_z\rangle = |\frac{3}{2}, \frac{1}{2}\rangle$. Since

$$Y_1^0 = \sqrt{\left(\frac{3}{4\pi}\right)} \cos\theta \qquad \text{and} \qquad Y_1^1 = -\sqrt{\left(\frac{3}{8\pi}\right)} \sin\theta \, e^{i\phi}$$

the decay angular distribution is

$$\frac{d\sigma}{d\Omega} = |\psi(\theta, \phi)|^2 = \frac{1}{8\pi}(1 + 3\cos^2\theta). \tag{9.50}$$

In obtaining (9.50) from (9.49) we have made use of the orthonormality of the spin states $|\frac{1}{2}, \frac{1}{2}\rangle$ and $|\frac{1}{2}, -\frac{1}{2}\rangle$ so that in forming $|\psi(\theta, \phi)|^2$ the cross-terms disappear. Furthermore, explicit calculation, or parity conservation, shows that the same angular distribution results if the proton is initially in the state $|s, s_z\rangle = |\frac{1}{2}, -\frac{1}{2}\rangle$. Equation (9.50) has the same form as the differential cross-section (9.48).

As already indicated, a π^+p system can have $I = \frac{3}{2}$ only and consequently only $I = \frac{3}{2}$ resonances can be excited in π^+p formation experiments. In figure 9.5 structure in the π^+p total cross-section can be seen at centre-of-mass energies above the Δ(1232) resonance which suggests that there may be other, higher mass Δ resonances. This is indeed the case, but carc must be taken in interpreting a bump in a total cross-section as a resonance. As the incident energy increases, more and more partial waves are brought into play and it is possible for non-resonant amplitudes to conspire to give structure in a total cross-section. Correspondingly, it is possible that in the presence of other non-resonant partial waves, a resonant partial wave may not be evident as a bump in a total cross-section. Many higher mass Δ resonances, i.e. resonances with baryon number $B = 1$, strangeness $S = 0$ and I spin $I = \frac{3}{2}$, have been identified in partial wave analyses,* although at energies above about 2 GeV the

* For detailed properties and full lists of references on these and all other particle states the reader is referred to the 'Review of particle properties' by the Particle Data Group.[4]

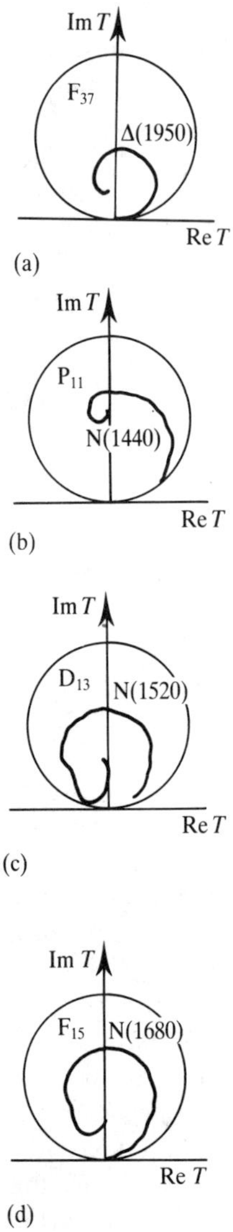

Figure 9.9
Argand diagrams for various inelastic πN resonances: (a) the F_{37} Δ(1950); (b) the P_{11} N(1440); (c) the D_{13} N(1520); (d) the F_{15} N(1680).

π^+p total cross-section is rather featureless. As an example the Argand diagram for the Δ(1950), a resonance in the F_{37} partial wave, is shown in figure 9.9(a). These partial wave analyses are similar in principle to that outlined above for low energy π^+p scattering but are in practice much more complicated because of the presence of many more partial waves.

A comparison of the total cross-section for π^-p scattering with that for π^+p scattering shows that in addition to the $\Delta^0(1232)$ there is structure in $\sigma_{tot}(\pi^-p)$ which is not present in $\sigma_{tot}(\pi^+p)$. This is because in the π^-p channel there are $I = \frac{1}{2}$ amplitudes in addition to the $I = \frac{3}{2}$ amplitudes. The decomposition of a π^-p system into I spin states $|I, I_3\rangle$ is

$$|\pi^-p\rangle = \sqrt{\tfrac{1}{3}}|\tfrac{3}{2}, -\tfrac{1}{2}\rangle - \sqrt{\tfrac{2}{3}}|\tfrac{1}{2}, -\tfrac{1}{2}\rangle \tag{9.51}$$

where, as usual, the factors $\sqrt{\frac{1}{3}}$ and $\sqrt{\frac{2}{3}}$ are Clebsch–Gordan coefficients. Thus, in terms of I spin the amplitude for elastic π^-p scattering may be written

$$\langle\pi^-p|T^I_{lJ}|\pi^-p\rangle = \langle\pi^-p|\tfrac{1}{3}T^{3/2}_{lJ} + \tfrac{2}{3}T^{1/2}_{lJ}|\pi^-p\rangle. \tag{9.52}$$

For each partial wave T_{lJ}, which is unique in the case of π^+p scattering but which strictly should have been written $T^{3/2}_{lJ}$, there are two partial wave amplitudes for each value of l and J in the case of π^-p scattering, one for each of the possible I spin values. Then, for low energy π^-p elastic scattering, with S and P waves only, the differential cross-section is obtained from that for π^+p scattering (equation (9.45)) by the replacement of the amplitudes T_{lJ} with $\frac{1}{3}(T^{3/2}_{lJ} + 2T^{1/2}_{lJ})$. The additional structure in $\sigma_{tot}(\pi^-p)$ can then be interpreted as due to the formation of resonances with $I = \frac{1}{2}$, which, since in addition have $B = 1$, $S = 0$ like the nucleon, are labelled N, with the mass of the resonance inserted, as usual, in brackets. As in the case of the $I = \frac{3}{2}$ Δ resonances, many $I = \frac{1}{2}$ nucleon resonances have been identified in phase shift analyses. As examples, we show in figures 9.9(b)–9.9(d) the Argand diagrams for the well-established P_{11} N(1440), the D_{13} N(1520) and the F_{15} N(1680) elastic amplitudes. Unlike the P_{33} Δ(1232) amplitude which, as we have seen, is perfectly elastic and follows the unitarity circle, these amplitudes are inelastic ($\eta < 1$) and lie well inside the unitarity circle. Because of the higher centre-of-mass energies involved in the formation of these resonances, various inelastic channels such as $\Delta\pi$ and $N\rho$ are open. Then, in addition to the possibility of formation *and* decay via the elastic channel, decay to the final states $\Delta\pi$ and $N\rho$ is also possible.

In this section we have illustrated the partial wave formalism through its application to low energy πN scattering. The technique is readily extended to other channels and in particular $\bar{K}N$ formation experiments have proved fruitful in the determination of the quantum numbers of baryon resonances with non-zero strangeness. In this case the initial state has conserved quantum numbers $B = 1$ and $S = -1$ and, since the interacting particles can couple to give either $I = 0$ or $I = 1$, both Λ ($I = 0$) and Σ ($I = 1$) resonances are produced. The KN channel is not so fruitful; the quantum numbers in the initial state are $B = 1$ and $S = +1$ and strangeness $+1$ baryons do not exist.

9.3 Phase space considerations

Fermi's golden rule states that the probability per unit time that a transition will take place from an initial state $|i\rangle$ to a final state $|f\rangle$ is

$$W = \frac{2\pi}{\hbar}|M_{fi}|^2\rho(E) \tag{9.53}$$

where M_{fi} is the matrix element for the transition and $\rho(E)$ is the density of states available at the energy E, or the phase space factor.

In general the matrix element may be unknown; in the extreme case of a constant matrix element the transition rate, and indeed the momentum distributions of the final state particles, are governed by the phase space factor. It is important therefore to be able to compute the latter. In principle, any deviations from phase space provide information about the matrix element.

The state of motion of a single particle, with a momentum whose magnitude is in the range 0–p, confined to a region of space of volume V, can be specified by a 'point' (x, y, z, p_x, p_y, p_z) in the six-dimensional phase space. The limits within which momentum and position can be simultaneously specified are governed by the uncertainty principle with the result that there is an elementary volume or cell in phase space of size h^3 within which states of motion cannot be distinguished. The number N_1 of distinguishable states of motion available to the single particle, then, is given by the total volume of phase space divided by the volume of the elementary cell, i.e.

$$\begin{aligned} N_1 &= \frac{1}{h^3}\int \mathrm{d}x\,\mathrm{d}y\,\mathrm{d}z\,\mathrm{d}p_x\,\mathrm{d}p_y\,\mathrm{d}p_z \\ &= \frac{V}{h^3}\int \mathrm{d}^3p. \end{aligned} \tag{9.54}$$

For a system of n particles the number of final states N_n is the *product* of the number of final states available to each particle, i.e.

$$N_n = \left(\frac{V}{h^3}\right)^n \int \prod_{i=1}^{n} \mathrm{d}^3p_i. \tag{9.55}$$

For particles with spin s_i this should be multiplied by $\prod_{i=1}^{n}(2s_i + 1)$ but it is convenient to include the spin factor and the constant volume factors in the normalization of the integral and conventionally these are omitted in the definition of the phase space factor. The density of final states $\rho(E)$ is defined as the number of momentum states per unit energy interval, so

$$\rho_n(E) = \frac{dN_n}{dE} = \frac{d}{dE}\int \prod_{i=1}^{n} d^3p_i. \tag{9.56}$$

The integration is performed over all possible values of the individual particle momenta. Because of momentum conservation not all of these are independent but are in fact constrained by the conservation equation

$$\sum_{i=1}^{n} \boldsymbol{p}_i - \boldsymbol{P} = 0 \tag{9.57}$$

where $\boldsymbol{P}$ is the total momentum. This restriction can be accommodated by integrating over all particles except the nth so that the expression for $\rho_n(E)$ becomes

$$\rho_n(E) = \frac{d}{dE}\int \prod_{i=1}^{n-1} d^3p_i. \tag{9.58}$$

Using the properties of the Dirac δ function (see appendix I and example 9.7) this can be expressed in a more symmetric form with respect to the n particles:

$$\rho_n(E) = \int \prod_{i=1}^{n} d^3p_i\delta\left(\sum_{i=1}^{n} \boldsymbol{p}_i - \boldsymbol{P}\right)\delta\left(\sum_{i=1}^{n} E_i - E\right) \tag{9.59}$$

where $\boldsymbol{P}$ is the total momentum and E is the total energy of the n particles. The δ functions embody the constraints imposed on the integral by momentum and energy conservation.

This expression for the density of states factor is not Lorentz invariant while of course the transition rate

$$W = \frac{2\pi}{\hbar}|M_{fi}|^2\rho_n(E)$$

must be independent of the frame in which it is measured; in this expression the matrix element M_{fi} must therefore also be non-invariant. The following plausibility argument indicates how M_{fi} and $\rho_n(E)$ have to be modified to obtain the relativistically invariant quantities $\mathscr{M}_{fi}$ and $R_n(E)$.

Suppose, for simplicity, a single particle of mass m moves with energy E in a region of space of volume V, and is described by the wavefunction ψ. The usual normalization of the wavefunction, $\int |\psi|^2 \, dV = 1$, implies that the particle density is $1/V$ for an observer at rest with respect to the system. If, on the other hand, the system moves at high speed v with respect to the observer, the volume element will contract along the direction of motion by a factor $\gamma = (1 - v^2/c^2)^{-1/2}$, i.e., in the moving system $dV' = dV/\gamma$, and the particle density apparently increases to γ/V. If, however, the wavefunction is suitably renormalized by the substitution $\psi' \to \sqrt{\gamma}\psi$, then

$$|\mathscr{M}_{fi}|^2 = |M_{fi}|^2 \prod_{j=1}^{n} 2E_j \prod_{i=1}^{n} 2E_i$$

where the index j represents the particles in the initial state and the transition rate is given by

$$W = \frac{2\pi}{\hbar} \frac{|\mathscr{M}_{fi}|^2}{\prod_{j=1}^{n} 2E_j} R_n(E)$$

with

$$R_n(E) = \frac{\rho_n(E)}{\prod_{i=1}^{n} 2E_i}.$$

Thus, explicitly, the Lorentz invariant phase space is given by

$$R_n(E) = \int \prod_{i=1}^{n} \frac{d^3 p_i}{2E_i} \, \delta\left(\sum_{i=1}^{n} \boldsymbol{p}_i - \boldsymbol{P}\right) \delta\left(\sum_{i=1}^{n} E_i - E\right). \tag{9.60}$$

A calculation of the Lorentz invariant two-body phase space for particles with masses m_1 and m_2 and momenta $\boldsymbol{p}_1$ and $\boldsymbol{p}_2$ in the centre-of-mass system is straightforward (example 9.8). The result is

$$R_2(E) = \frac{\pi p_1}{E} \tag{9.61}$$

where p_1 has the value

$$p_1 = \frac{\{[E^2 - (m_2 - m_1)^2][E^2 - (m_2 + m_1)^2]\}^{1/2}}{2E}. \tag{9.62}$$

Thus, we see that for a given total energy E the two-body phase space factor is just a number. This is also true in general for the n-body phase space $R_n(E)$ which depends only on the total energy E and the masses of the n particles in the final state. A knowledge of this number is necessary in order to evaluate cross-sections and relative yields (cf. section 8.7.3).

In the general case of three unequal mass particles the Lorentz invariant three-body phase space may be written

$$R_3(E) = \int \frac{4\pi p_3^2 \, \mathrm{d}p_3}{2E_3} \times \frac{\pi\{[E^2 + m_3^2 - 2EE_3 - (m_2 - m_1)^2][E^2 + m_3^2 - 2EE_3 - (m_2 + m_1)^2]\}^{1/2}}{2(E^2 + m_3^2 - 2EE_3)} \tag{9.63}$$

which is an elliptic integral. Frequently, however, what is required is not the value of $R_3(E)$ integrated over all the variables but rather a differential spectrum $\mathrm{d}R_3/\mathrm{d}p_3$ say. In the present case this is

$$\frac{\mathrm{d}R_3}{\mathrm{d}p_3} = \frac{\pi^2 p_3^2}{E_3} \times \frac{\{[E^2 - 2EE_3 + m_3^2 - (m_2 - m_1)^2][E^2 - 2EE_3 + m_3^2 - (m_2 + m_1)^2]\}^{1/2}}{E^2 - 2EE_3 + m_3^2}. \tag{9.64}$$

In a search for resonance production it is more appropriate to use a differential mass spectrum, or invariant mass distribution, than a momentum distribution. The invariant mass distribution $\mathrm{d}R_3/\mathrm{d}M_{12}$ for example may be derived from equation (9.64) using the identity

$$\frac{\mathrm{d}R_3}{\mathrm{d}M_{12}} = \frac{\mathrm{d}R_3}{\mathrm{d}p_3} \frac{\mathrm{d}p_3}{\mathrm{d}M_{12}}$$

with the result

$$\frac{\mathrm{d}R_3}{\mathrm{d}M_{12}} = \frac{\pi^2}{2M_{12}E^2} \times \{[M_{12}^2 - (m_2 - m_1)^2][M_{12}^2 - (m_2 + m_1)^2] \times [E^2 - (M_{12} - m_3)^2][E^2 - (M_{12} + m_3)^2]\}^{1/2} \tag{9.65}$$

(see example 9.9).

In our considerations so far we have dealt only with one-dimensional

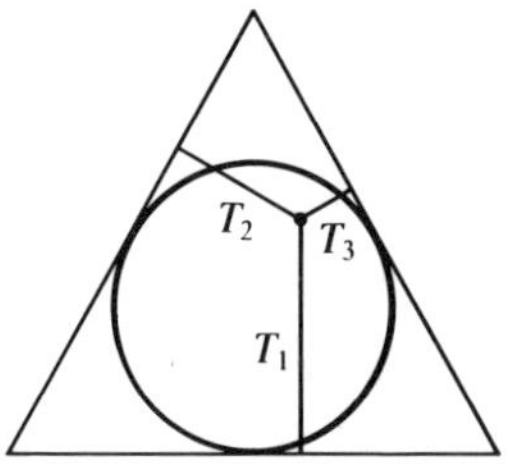

(a)

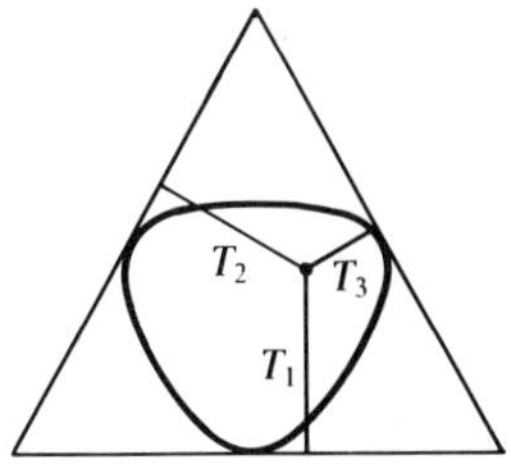

(b)

Figure 9.10
Dalitz plot for the three-body decay of a particle. The height of the equilateral triangle is made proportional to the Q value of the decay. Each event is represented by a point whose perpendicular distances from the sides of the triangle are proportional to the kinetic energies T_i of the final state particles. (a) In the non-relativistic case the points are confined to the interior of the inscribed circle and (b) for the relativistic case they are confined to the interior of the inscribed shape.

distributions such as dR/dp and dR/dM. Correlations between different physical variables are often important but these will not be evident in a one-dimensional distribution. For this reason a variety of two-dimensional plots are often used to display experimental results. One of the most widely used is the Dalitz[5] plot, of which various forms exist. A Dalitz plot may be used to study the characteristics of a three-body system produced in a process such as $K^+p \rightarrow K^0p\pi^+$, or the three-body decay of a resonant state such as the classic example of the decay of the ω meson, $\omega \rightarrow \pi^+\pi^-\pi^0$, which we will discuss further in section 9.4. For the latter type of process use is made of the fact that the sum of the perpendicular distances from the sides of an equilateral triangle to a point inside the triangle is equal to the height of the triangle. The Q value of the decay is given by

$$Q = m_\omega - 3m_\pi = \sum_{i=1}^{3} T_i$$

where m_ω and m_π are the masses of the ω and π respectively and T_i is the kinetic energy of the ith pion in the ω rest system. Thus, if the height of the triangle is made equal to Q, each decay can be represented by a point with the perpendicular distances to the sides of the triangle given by T_i, as shown in figure 9.10. For three equal mass particles moving with non-relativistic velocities, conservation of energy and momentum restricts the points to the interior of the inscribed circle, figure 9.10(a). In the relativistic case, which has been treated by Fabri,[6] the points are restricted to the interior of the inscribed shape shown in figure 9.10(b), which in the ultra-relativistic case becomes a triangle.

A different type of Dalitz plot is used to study a three-body final state produced in a scattering process. If we label the final state particles 1, 2 and 3 then the kinetic energies of any two particles, say 1 and 2, are chosen to specify the final state and the Dalitz plot is a plot of T_1 against T_2 as shown in figure 9.11(a).

The kinetic energy of particle 1 is linearly related to the square of the

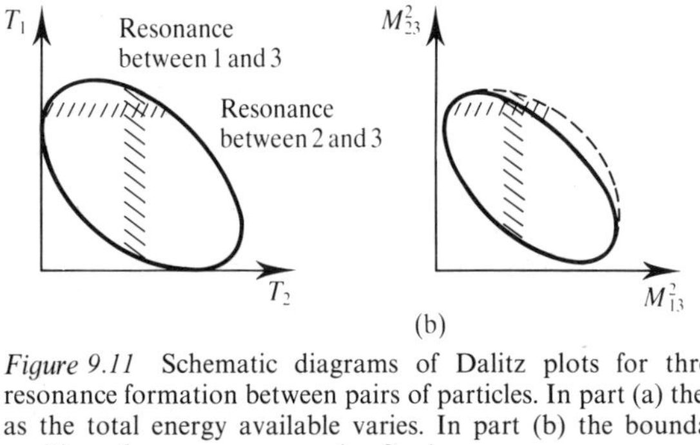

(b)

Figure 9.11 Schematic diagrams of Dalitz plots for three-body final states showing resonance formation between pairs of particles. In part (a) the position of a resonance varies as the total energy available varies. In part (b) the boundary of the plot varies but the position of a resonance remains fixed.

effective mass of particles 2 and 3 through the relation

$$T_1 = \frac{(E - m_1)^2 - M_{23}^2}{2E} \tag{9.66}$$

where E is the total energy in the centre-of-mass system, m_1 is the mass of particle 1 and M_{23} is the invariant mass of particles 2 and 3. A more widely used form of Dalitz plot is one in which the square of the invariant mass of one pair of particles is plotted against the invariant mass squared of another pair, as shown in figure 9.11(b).

Each type of Dalitz plot described above has the important property that equal areas in the plot correspond to equal volumes in the Lorentz invariant three-body phase space R_3, i.e.

$$\mathrm{d}R_3 \propto \mathrm{d}T_1\,\mathrm{d}T_2 \propto \mathrm{d}M_{23}^2\,\mathrm{d}M_{13}^2. \tag{9.67}$$

In the absence of final state interactions the density of points in the Dalitz plot will therefore be uniform. In general, the density of points is proportional to the square of the invariant matrix element for the reaction. If a resonance occurs between particles 2 and 3 say, there will be an increased density of points in a band at fixed T_1 in the Dalitz plot in figure 9.11(a), or fixed M_{23}^2 in figure 9.11(b). The boundary of the Dalitz plot is fixed by momentum conservation and the total energy available to the system. The disadvantage of the type of Dalitz plot shown in figure 9.11(a) is that the position of a resonance on the plot varies with the total energy available, thus making it difficult to combine the results of experiments performed at different energies if the data are presented in this form. A plot of the squared effective masses overcomes this difficulty; an increase in the total energy simply changes the contour of the plot but does not alter the position of a resonance. This is shown schematically in figure 9.11(b).

We end this section with a proof of (9.67). As we saw earlier, the Lorentz invariant three-body phase space is given by

$$R_3 = \int \frac{\mathrm{d}^3p_1\,\mathrm{d}^3p_2\,\mathrm{d}^3p_3}{8E_1E_2E_3}\,\delta(\boldsymbol{p}_1 + \boldsymbol{p}_2 + \boldsymbol{p}_3)\delta(E_1 + E_2 + E_3 - E)$$

which, when integrated over $\boldsymbol{p}_3$, gives

$$R_3 = \int \frac{1}{8E_1E_2E_3}\,p_1^2\,\mathrm{d}p_1\,\mathrm{d}\Omega_1\,p_2^2\,\mathrm{d}p_2\,\mathrm{d}\Omega_2\delta(E_1 + E_2 + E_3 - E)$$

where $\mathrm{d}\Omega_1 = \mathrm{d}(\cos\theta_1)\,\mathrm{d}\phi_1$ and $\mathrm{d}\Omega_2 = \mathrm{d}(\cos\theta_2)\,\mathrm{d}\phi_2$, θ_i and ϕ_i being the spherical polar angles specifying the directions of particles 1 and 2. Instead of the polar angle θ_2 it is convenient to introduce the angle θ_{12}, the angle

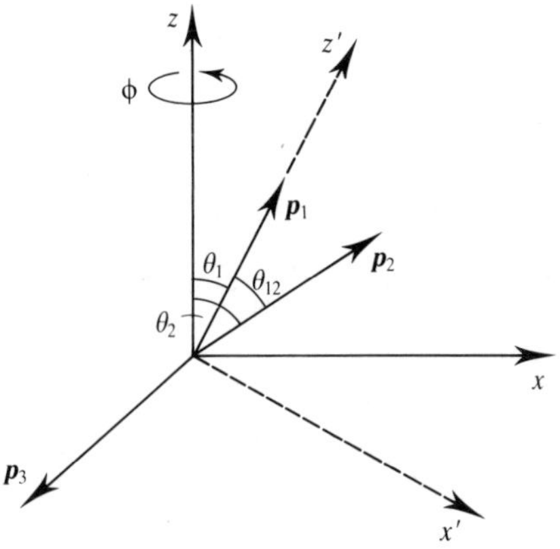

Figure 9.12
Definition of the angles used in the integration of R_3. $\boldsymbol{p}_1$, $\boldsymbol{p}_2$ and $\boldsymbol{p}_3$ are the momenta of the three particles in the centre-of-mass system.

between $\boldsymbol{p}_1$ and $\boldsymbol{p}_2$ as shown in figure 9.12. The conservation of momentum restricts the three momenta $\boldsymbol{p}_1$, $\boldsymbol{p}_2$ and $\boldsymbol{p}_3$ to lie in a plane, which without loss of generality we choose to be the z–x plane. For a given orientation of $\boldsymbol{p}_1$ we can choose the z axis to be along $\boldsymbol{p}_1$ and then

$$\int \mathrm{d}\Omega_2 = \int \mathrm{d}(\cos\theta_2)\,\mathrm{d}\phi_2 = \int \mathrm{d}(\cos\theta_{12})\,\mathrm{d}\phi_2.$$

Then

$$R_3 = \int \frac{1}{8E_1E_2E_3}\,p_1^2\,\mathrm{d}p_1\,\mathrm{d}\Omega_1\,p_2^2\,\mathrm{d}p_2\,\mathrm{d}(\cos\theta_{12})\,\mathrm{d}\phi_2\delta(E_1+E_2+E_3-E)$$

which, when integrated over all space angles except θ_{12}, becomes

$$R_3 = \int \frac{\pi^2}{E_1E_2E_3}\,p_1^2\,\mathrm{d}p_1\,p_2^2\,\mathrm{d}p_2\,\mathrm{d}(\cos\theta_{12})\delta(E_1+E_2+E_3-E).$$

For fixed $\boldsymbol{p}_1$ and $\boldsymbol{p}_2$ the angle between $\boldsymbol{p}_1$ and $\boldsymbol{p}_2$ is given by momentum conservation by the relation

$$p_3^2 = p_1^2 + p_2^2 + 2p_1p_2\cos\theta_{12}$$

from which it follows that

$$p_3\,\mathrm{d}p_3 = p_1p_2\,\mathrm{d}(\cos\theta_{12}).$$

On substitution for $\mathrm{d}(\cos\theta_{12})$ the expression for R_3 becomes

$$R_3 = \pi^2 \int \frac{p_1\,dp_1\,p_2\,\mathrm{d}p_2\,p_3\,\mathrm{d}p_3}{E_1E_2E_3}\,\delta(E_1+E_2+E_3-E).$$

Since, for an individual particle, $p^2 = E^2 - m^2$, we have $p\,\mathrm{d}p = E\,\mathrm{d}E = E\,\mathrm{d}T$, so that

$$R_3 = \pi^2 \int \mathrm{d}T_1\,\mathrm{d}T_2\,\mathrm{d}T_3\,\delta(E_1 + E_2 + E_3 - E).$$

Integration over T_3 gives the required result,

$$\mathrm{d}R_3 \propto \mathrm{d}T_1\,\mathrm{d}T_2.$$

Finally, equation (9.66) yields, on differentiation

$$\mathrm{d}T_1 \propto \mathrm{d}M_{23}^2$$

and similarly

$$\mathrm{d}T_2 \propto \mathrm{d}M_{13}^2$$

and therefore

$$\mathrm{d}R_3 \propto \mathrm{d}M_{23}^2\,\mathrm{d}M_{13}^2.$$

9.4 Production experiments

Many years of experimentation have shown that there are precisely nine mesons with spin-parity 0^-. The well-known π and K mesons, together with the I spin singlet η and $\eta'(958)$ states, form a nonet of pseudoscalar mesons. In SU(3) these nine states are further subdivided into an octet and singlet (section 10.3). Meson states with higher spins, $J^P = 1^-, 2^+$ for example, repeat this multiplet structure. In the baryon sector the octet of $\frac{1}{2}^+$ stable baryons is accompanied by a decuplet of $\frac{3}{2}^+$ baryons, the I spin quartet of Δ(1232) resonances, the Σ(1385) triplet, the Ξ(1530) doublet and the Ω^-. The quark model (chapter 10) successfully accounts for the observed multiplet structure in the hadron spectrum. In the present section we describe some of the techniques used in the analysis of production experiments to determine the quantum numbers of resonant states.

The η meson

The η was first observed[7] in an exposure of the Lawrence Radiation Laboratory 72 inch deuterium-filled bubble chamber to a beam of 1.23 GeV/c π^+ mesons. The three-pion invariant mass distribution (figure 9.13(a)) for the reaction $\pi^+ \mathrm{d} \to \mathrm{pp}\pi^+\pi^-\pi^0$ clearly shows η and ω meson production. The Dalitz plot for a compilation[8] of decays $\eta \to \pi^+\pi^-\pi^0$

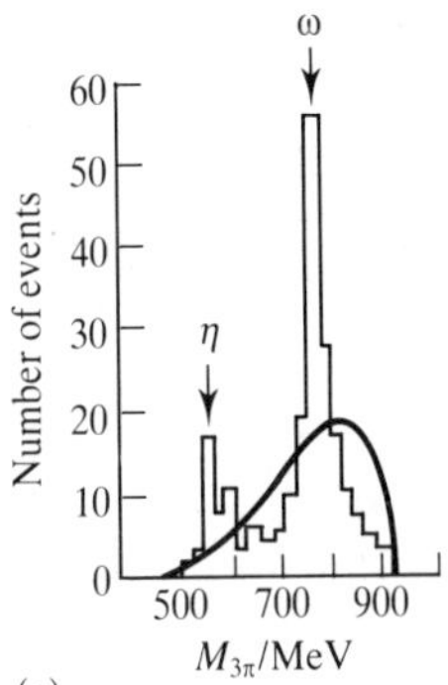

(a)

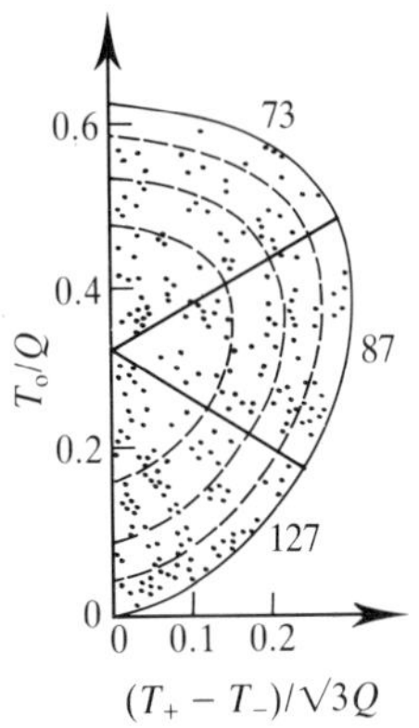

(b)

Figure 9.13
(a) Invariant mass distribution of the three-pion system in the reaction $\pi^+ d \to pp\pi^+\pi^-\pi^0$. The solid curve is the phase space prediction. (After Pevsner A *et al.* 1961 *Phys Rev Lett* **7** (421).) (b) Dalitz plot for the decay $\eta \to \pi^+\pi^-\pi^0$. Normalized Dalitz plot variables T_0/Q and $(T_+ - T_-)/\sqrt{3}Q$, where T_0, T_+ and T_- are the kinetic energies of the π^0, π^+ and π^- respectively, have been used. The plot has been folded about the T_0/Q axis. (After Alff C *et al.* 1962 *Phys Rev Lett* **9** (325).)

(figure 9.13(b)) has a distribution of events which is compatible only with the spin-parity assignment 0^- for the η meson.

In addition to the decay mode $\eta \to \pi^+\pi^-\pi^0$, several others have been seen, the most dominant of which, together with the branching fractions, are

$$\eta \to \begin{cases} \pi^+\pi^-\pi^0 & 23.6 \pm 0.6 \text{ per cent} \\ \pi^0\pi^0\pi^0 & 31.9 \pm 0.4 \text{ per cent} \\ \gamma\gamma & 38.9 \pm 0.5 \text{ per cent} \\ \pi^+\pi^-\gamma & 4.88 \pm 0.15 \text{ per cent} \end{cases}$$

The decay $\eta \to 2\gamma$ is clearly electromagnetic and because the branching fractions of the other decay modes are comparable with that for $\eta \to 2\gamma$, these too can be assumed to be electromagnetic. This assumption is consistent with the measured width $\Gamma_\eta = 1.19 \pm 0.11$ keV, which corresponds to a lifetime of roughly 10^{-18} s and is supported below by an argument based on *G*-parity. Since electromagnetic decays are invariant under charge conjugation and the *C*-parity of the photon is -1, the η has *C*-parity $+1$ so that, like the π^0, the η^0 and its antiparticle are indistinguishable.

Historically, the decay $\eta \to \pi^+\pi^-\pi^0$ has in fact proved to be important in testing *C* invariance in electromagnetic interactions. If the decay is invariant under charge conjugation there should be no asymmetry between the π^+ and π^- in the η decays, i.e. the Dalitz plot should be symmetric about the vertical axis. (In figure 9.13(b) the Dalitz plot has been folded about this axis, on the assumption that the decay is *C* invariant.) It is usual to define the asymmetry as

$$A = \frac{N_+ - N_-}{N_+ + N_-}$$

where N_+ is the number of events in which the π^+ has greater energy than the π^- in the η rest system and N_- is the number of events in which the π^- has the greater energy. Charge conjugation invariance implies that A should be zero. In an analysis of over 220 000 events Layter *et al.*[9] obtained the value $A = -0.0005 \pm 0.0022$ and thus found no evidence for *C*-violating effects.

We recall (section 8.11) that both *C* and *G* (charge conjugation followed by a rotation of π about the 2 axis in *I* spin space) are conserved quantities in the strong interactions. Since *C* is conserved in both strong and electromagnetic interactions it follows that if *G* is violated in a process that is not weak then *I* spin is not conserved or, in other words, the process takes place via the electromagnetic interaction. The η meson has no charged partners and therefore it follows that the *G*-parity of the η is also $+1$. The *G*-parity of a system of *n* pions is $(-1)^n$ and thus the decay

$\eta \to \pi^+\pi^-\pi^0$ violates G-parity and is therefore electromagnetic. This conclusion can equally well be reached by the observation that the decay $\eta \to \pi^0\pi^0\pi^0$ does not conserve I spin; the I spin of a three-pi-zero system is necessarily greater than or equal to 1.

In summary, the quantum numbers $I^G J^{PC}$ of the η meson are 0^+0^{-+}.

The ρ(770)

The ρ meson has a mass and width of 768.1 ± 0.5 MeV and 151.5 ± 1.2 MeV respectively and decays to two pions with a branching fraction of essentially 100 per cent. It exists in three charge states ρ^+, ρ^- and ρ^0 and therefore has $I = 1$.

The very large width and hence very short lifetime of the ρ meson means that the decay $\rho \to \pi\pi$ is a strong interaction. The conservation of G-parity therefore implies that $G(\rho) = +1$. Since $G = \exp(\mathrm{i}\pi I_2)C$, it follows that $C(\rho) = -1$. Furthermore, the charge conjugation operation C on a $\pi^+\pi^-$ system is equivalent to a spatial inversion, and therefore $C = (-1)^l$, where l is the relative orbital angular momentum between the π^+ and π^-; l must therefore be odd. Conservation of angular momentum and parity in the decay $\rho \to \pi\pi$ therefore implies that the ρ meson must have a spin-parity in the series $1^-, 3^- \ldots$. Which of these possibilities is the correct one may be determined by analysing the angular distribution of the pions in the dipion rest frame as outlined below.

The dominant mechanism for ρ production in the reaction $\pi^-\mathrm{p} \to \mathrm{p}\pi^-\pi^0$, for example, is single pion exchange as shown in figure 9.14(a), so that ρ production can be viewed as the result of scattering of the incident π^- and the exchanged pion π^0_{ex}. This scattering process is conventionally analysed in the ρ rest frame (figure 9.14(b)) in which the z axis is chosen as the direction of the incident pion and the y axis is defined as the normal to the scattering plane

$$y = \frac{\boldsymbol{p}_{\mathrm{in}} \times \boldsymbol{p}_{\mathrm{out}}}{|\boldsymbol{p}_{\mathrm{in}} \times \boldsymbol{p}_{\mathrm{out}}|}$$

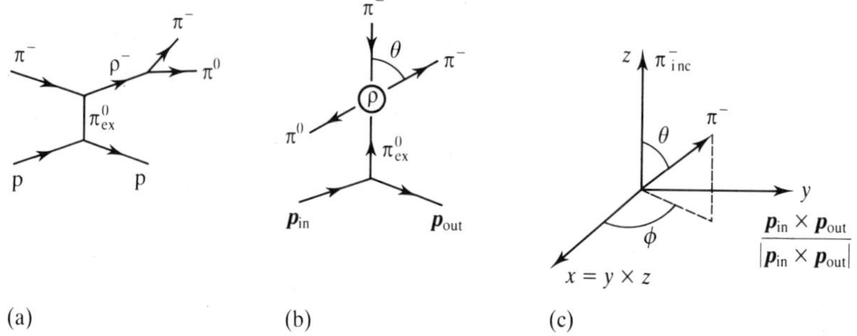

Figure 9.14
Production and decay of the ρ meson: (a) the pion exchange graph; (b) the configuration in the ρ rest system; (c) the Gottfried–Jackson coordinate system.

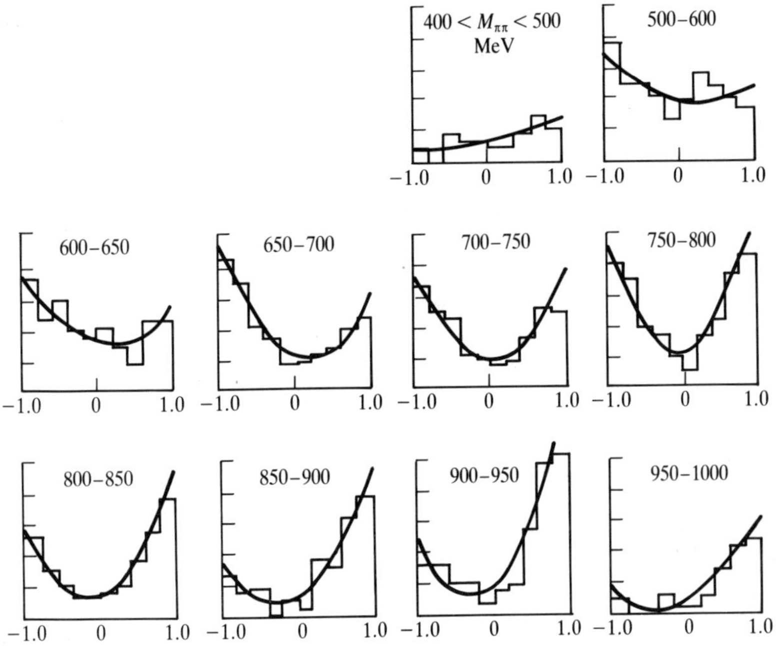

Figure 9.15 The $\pi^-\pi^0$ angular distribution in the dipion rest system, for the reaction $\pi^-p \to p\pi^-\pi^0$, as a function of $\pi^-\pi^0$ invariant mass. (After Walker W D *et al.* 1967 *Phys Rev Lett* **18** (630).)

where $\boldsymbol{p}_{\text{in}}$ and $\boldsymbol{p}_{\text{out}}$ are the momenta of the proton in the inital and final states respectively. The x axis is given by $\boldsymbol{x} = \boldsymbol{y} \wedge \boldsymbol{z}$ (figure 9.14(c)). This frame of reference is known as the Gottfried–Jackson frame. The partial wave formalism developed in section 9.2.1 for the scattering of spinless particles is applicable here. Figure 9.15 shows the distributions in $\cos\theta$, where θ is the π–π scattering angle in the dipion rest system, as a function of the dipion effective mass (total energy in the dipion rest system), obtained by Walker *et al.*[10] These angular distributions are adequately described by an expression of the form

$$I(\theta) = A_0 + A_1 \cos\theta + A_2 \cos^2\theta. \tag{9.68}$$

As expected for the scattering of spinless particles the distributions are isotropic in the azimuthal angle ϕ. The partial wave expansion equation (9.16), using S and P waves only, gives

$$\begin{aligned} I(\theta) &= \frac{1}{k^2}|T_0 + 3T_1 \cos\theta|^2 \\ &= \frac{1}{k^2}(|T_0|^2 + 6 \operatorname{Re} T_0 T_1^* \cos\theta + 9|T_1|^2 \cos^2\theta) \end{aligned} \tag{9.69}$$

which has the same form as equation (9.68). Here T_l is the amplitude for the lth partial wave.

Since pions are bosons the overall wavefunction of the π^-–π^0 system

$$\Psi = \psi(\text{space})I(I \text{ spin})$$

must be symmetric with respect to exchange of the two pions. A $\pi^-\pi^0$ system can have either $I = 1$ or $I = 2$ and, using the table of Clebsch–Gordan coefficients for the coupling of two $I = 1$ particles, the $I = 1$ state is

$$|1, -1\rangle = \frac{1}{\sqrt{2}}(|\pi^0\rangle|\pi^-\rangle - |\pi^-\rangle|\pi^0\rangle)$$

which is antisymmetric, and the $I = 2$ state is

$$|2, -1\rangle = \frac{1}{\sqrt{2}}(|\pi^0\rangle|\pi^-\rangle + |\pi^-\rangle|\pi^0\rangle)$$

which is symmetric. The symmetry requirement therefore means that P wave scattering takes place in the $I = 1$ state and S wave scattering in the $I = 2$ state. The ρ meson, with $I = 1$, is therefore a P wave π–π resonance with $J^P = 1^-$. If the S wave amplitude is predominantly real, the asymmetry term will vanish at the resonance mass, where T_1 becomes purely imaginary, and should change sign on passing through the resonant energy. This is borne out by the experimental results in figure 9.15. In conclusion, the ρ meson has $I = 1$, $G = 1$, $C = -1$ and $J^P = 1^-$.

The ω(783)

The ω meson was first observed by Maglic *et al.*[11] in a bubble chamber study of the annihilation process

$$\bar{p} + p \to \pi^+ + \pi^+ + \pi^- + \pi^- + \pi^0.$$

Figure 9.16 shows the three-pion effective mass distributions for various charge states. The neutral combinations $\pi^+\pi^-\pi^0$ show a narrow resonance centred at a mass of 787 MeV/c^2, which is absent in all other charge combinations with $|Q| \geqslant 1$. The ω meson therefore has I spin 0. The decay $\omega \to \pi^+\pi^-\pi^0$ proceeds via the strong interaction and therefore the ω has G-parity $(-1)^3 = -1$.

Because the determination of the spin-parity of the ω meson is a classic of its kind we describe in some detail how the analysis[12] of the distribution of events in the decay Dalitz plot led to the assignment $J^P = 1^-$.

We first note that since the I spin of the ω is $I_\omega = 0$ its isospin wavefunction Φ_ω must be a scalar. The only way to construct an isoscalar

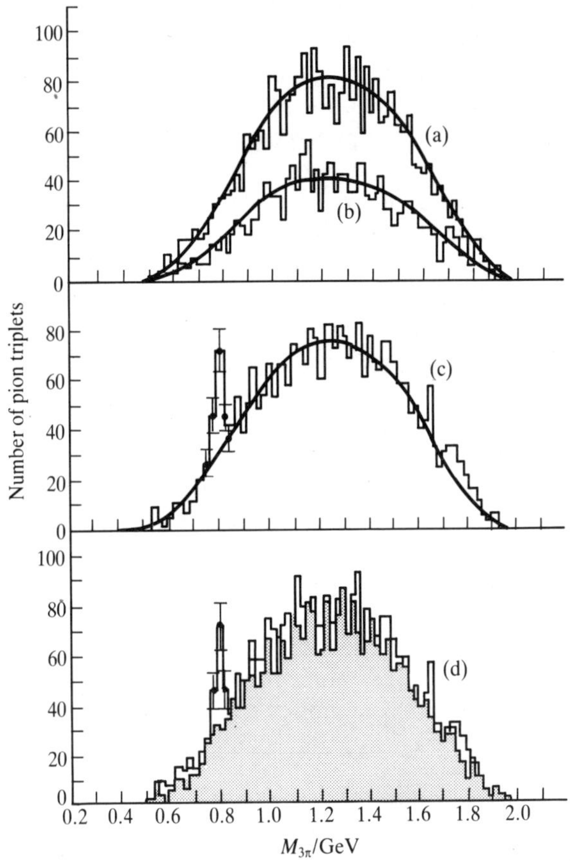

Figure 9.16 Three-pion invariant mass distributions from the annihilation process $\bar{p}p \to \pi^+\pi^+\pi^-\pi^-\pi^0$: curve (a), $\pi^+\pi^+\pi^-$ and $\pi^+\pi^-\pi^-$ combinations; curve (b), $\pi^+\pi^+\pi^0$ and $\pi^-\pi^-\pi^0$ combinations; curve (c), $\pi^+\pi^-\pi^0$ combinations. In (d) the combinations (a) and (b) (shaded) are contrasted with (c). The ω meson appears only in the neutral charge state $\pi^+\pi^-\pi^0$. (After Maglic B C *et al.* 1961 *Phys Rev Lett* **7** (178).)

from the isovector wavefunctions $\boldsymbol{\Phi}_1$, $\boldsymbol{\Phi}_2$ and $\boldsymbol{\Phi}_3$ of the three pions is to form a triple product:

$$\Phi_\omega = \boldsymbol{\Phi}_1 \cdot (\boldsymbol{\Phi}_2 \times \boldsymbol{\Phi}_3) = \boldsymbol{\Phi}_2 \cdot (\boldsymbol{\Phi}_3 \times \boldsymbol{\Phi}_1) = \boldsymbol{\Phi}_3 \cdot (\boldsymbol{\Phi}_1 \times \boldsymbol{\Phi}_2). \quad (9.70)$$

These triple products are antisymmetric with respect to interchange of any two pions. The total wavefunction for three bosons

$$\Psi_{\text{tot}} = \Phi(I \text{ spin})\, \psi(\text{space})$$

is required by Bose–Einstein statistics to be symmetric under interchange of any two particles and therefore the spatial wavefunction must be antisymmetric. This will influence the distribution of events in the Dalitz

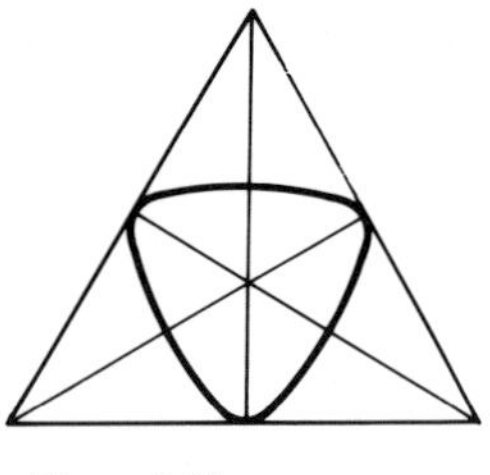

Figure 9.17
The ω decay Dalitz plot showing the symmetry axes.

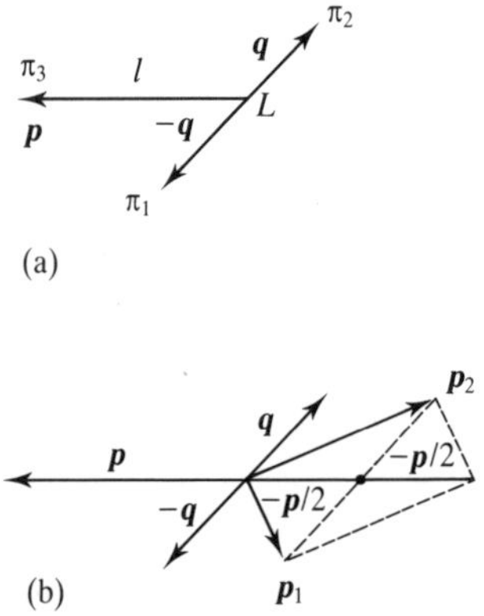

Figure 9.18
Definition of the variables used in the analysis of ω decay. (a) In the dipion system π_1 and π_2 have momenta $-\boldsymbol{q}$ and $\boldsymbol{q}$ respectively and the relative orbital angular momentum is L. The third pion π_3 has momentum $\boldsymbol{p}$ and orbital angular momentum l with respect to the dipions in the three-pion rest system. (b) Non-relativistic transformation to the overall three-pion rest system

plot. The type of Dalitz plot used is the conventional one for studying the three-body decay of a resonance (figure 9.17). Since the spatial wavefunction is totally antisymmetric the matrix element squared must be symmetric under the interchange of any pair of pions and therefore the density of points must be invariant under a reflection through any of the symmetry axes of the Dalitz plot shown in figure 9.17. This observation is borne out by the experimental results and means that the Dalitz plot can be folded about these axes thereby concentrating all the events in one sextant. The statistical accuracy of the analysis is thereby increased.

We turn now to an evaluation of the general forms of the matrix element $M(p_i, E_i)$, in terms of the momenta and energies of the three pions, for different values of the ω spin-parity. In this context we note that a scalar meson with $J^P = 0^+$ cannot decay via a parity-conserving strong interaction to three pseudoscalar mesons. We consider three possible spin-parity assignments for the ω, namely pseudoscalar 0^-, vector 1^- and axial vector 1^+. We will construct the matrix elements initially in terms of the variables shown in figure 9.18(a) in which we envisage a dipion system π_1 and π_2 with a relative orbital angular momentum L in the dipion rest frame and a single pion π_3. The single pion and the dipion system are assumed to have a relative angular momentum l in the overall three-pion rest system. The momentum $\boldsymbol{q}$ is the momentum in the dipion rest system and $\boldsymbol{p}$ is the momentum of π_3 in the three-pion rest system. In the non-relativistic limit the spin J of the ω meson is $\boldsymbol{J} = \boldsymbol{l} + \boldsymbol{L}$.

Pseudoscalar ω, $J^P = 0^-$

Since the intrinsic parity of the three pions is $(-1^3) = -1$ the matrix element for the decay of a pseudoscalar meson must have the properties of a scalar. Bearing in mind that we must construct a matrix element which is antisymmetric with respect to interchange of any two pions we write

$$M(0^-) \approx \boldsymbol{p} \cdot \boldsymbol{q}.$$

This matrix element is odd under the interchange of π_1 and π_2 for then $\boldsymbol{q} \to -\boldsymbol{q}$. Our aim is to recast this in a form which is symmetric in the labels of all three pions and which is written in terms of variables in the three-pion rest system. With reference to figure 9.18(b) and using the non-relativistic expression for the kinetic energy, the total energies of π_1 and π_2 are

$$E_1 = \frac{1}{2m}\left(-\frac{\boldsymbol{p}}{2} - \boldsymbol{q}\right)^2 + m$$

$$E_2 = \frac{1}{2m}\left(-\frac{\boldsymbol{p}}{2} + \boldsymbol{q}\right)^2 + m$$

from which it follows that

$$M(E_1 - E_2) = \boldsymbol{p}\cdot\boldsymbol{q}.$$

The matrix element for the decay of a 0^- ω is then of the form

$$M(0^-) \approx (E_1 - E_2)(E_2 - E_3)(E_3 - E_1)$$

This matrix element, and hence the density of points in the Dalitz plot, will vanish whenever two of the pions have equal energies, i.e. along the symmetry lines and in particular at the centre of the Dalitz plot where all three pions have the same energy (figure 9.19).

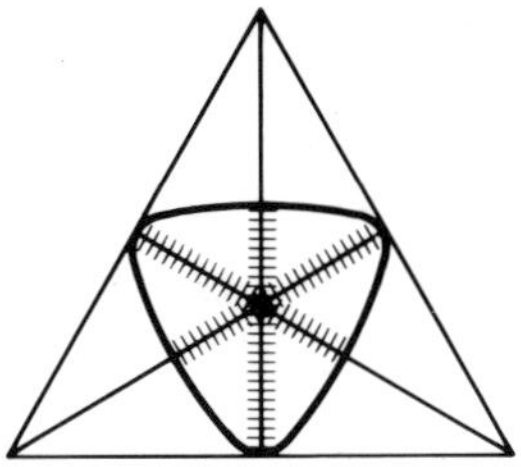

Figure 9.19
Schematic diagram showing where the density of points will vanish for a $J^P = 0^-$ ω meson.

Vector ω, $J^P = 1^-$
In this case, taking into account the negative intrinsic parity of the three-pion system, the matrix element must have the properties of an axial vector, i.e. one that does not change sign under a parity transformation. The simplest possibility for the orbital angular momenta are $L = l = 1$ and the matrix element will be of the form

$$M(1^-) \approx \boldsymbol{p} \wedge \boldsymbol{q}.$$

Using the fact that $\boldsymbol{p}_3 \equiv \boldsymbol{p}$, $\boldsymbol{p}_1 = -(\boldsymbol{p}/2) + \boldsymbol{q}$, $\boldsymbol{p}_2 = -(\boldsymbol{p}/2) - \boldsymbol{q}$ and symmetrizing with respect to the labels of the three pions we have

$$M(1^-) \approx \boldsymbol{p}_1 \wedge \boldsymbol{p}_2 + \boldsymbol{p}_2 \wedge \boldsymbol{p}_3 + \boldsymbol{p}_3 \wedge \boldsymbol{p}_1.$$

In marked contrast to the case above for a pseudoscalar ω, the matrix element in this case vanishes whenever the pions are collinear. The density of points should therefore approach zero around the boundary of the Dalitz plot as shown schematically in figure 9.20.

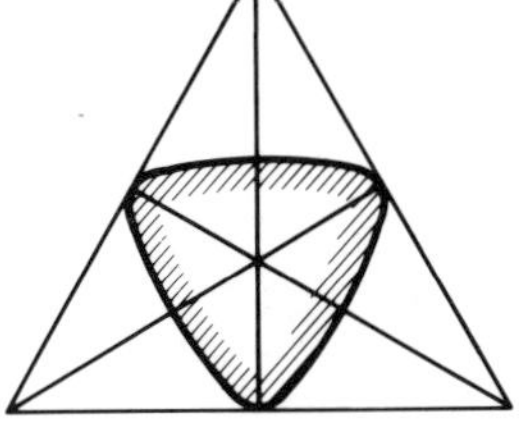

Figure 9.20
The density of points in the Dalitz plot vanishes around the boundary if the ω has $J^P = 1^-$.

Axial vector ω, $J^P = 1^+$
The matrix element in this case must have the properties of an ordinary or polar vector. The simplest configuration is that in which $l = 0$ and $L = 1$ and the matrix element can be written in the form

$$M(1^+) \approx E_3\boldsymbol{q}.$$

Since $\boldsymbol{q} = \frac{1}{2}(\boldsymbol{p}_1 - \boldsymbol{p}_2)$ the matrix element, when symmetrized with respect to the labels of the three pions, becomes

$$M(1^+) \approx E_3(\boldsymbol{p}_1 - \boldsymbol{p}_2) + E_2(\boldsymbol{p}_3 - \boldsymbol{p}_1) + E_1(\boldsymbol{p}_2 - \boldsymbol{p}_3).$$

This matrix element vanishes whenever $E_1 = E_2 = E_3$, i.e. at the centre

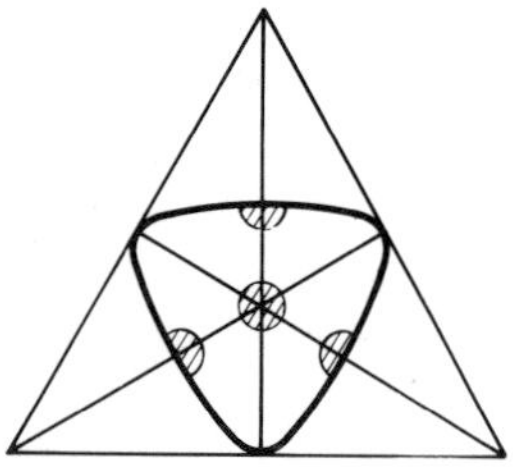

Figure 9.21
Regions of vanishing density for $J^P = 1^+$.

of the Dalitz plot, and whenever two pions have the same momenta which occurs in the regions shown in figure 9.21. The above general arguments display only the gross features of the variation of the density of points on the Dalitz plot. The detailed variation for different spin-parities is illustrated in the isometric drawings of figures 9.22(a)–9.22(c) for 0^-, 1^- and 1^+ mesons respectively. Because the resonance has a finite width, the Q value of the decay, and hence the boundary of the Dalitz plot, varies from event to event. For this reason, normalized variables T_i/Q are used as Dalitz plot variables. The height above the plane is proportional to the matrix element squared, $|M|^2$, and the maximum height above the plane is chosen as 1. Contours of equal $|M|^2$ are shown at 0.2 intervals. For a comparison of these $|M|^2$ distributions with the experimental results, both the results and $|M|^2$ have been folded about the symmetry lines of the Dalitz plot.

Figure 9.23(a) shows this folded Dalitz plot for events in the ω peak. The

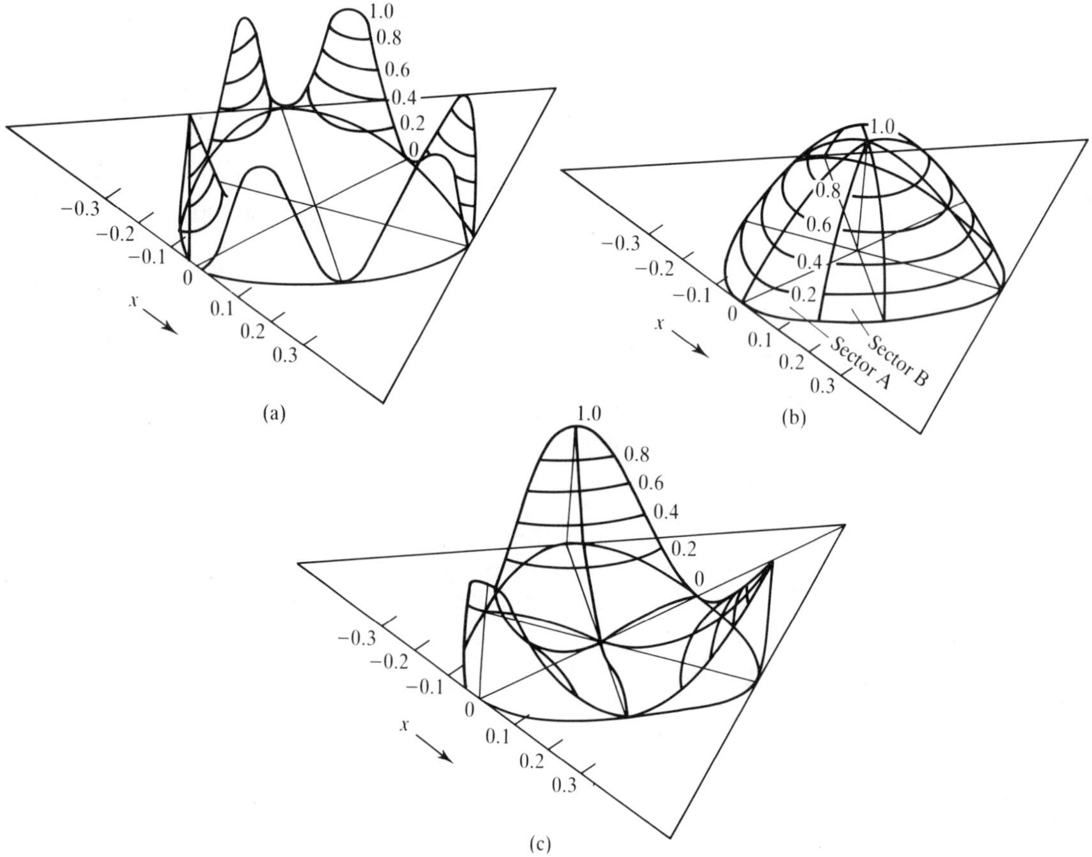

Figure 9.22 Isometric drawings showing the detailed density distributions in the Dalitz plot for (a) a 0^-, (b) a 1^- and (c) a 1^+ ω meson.

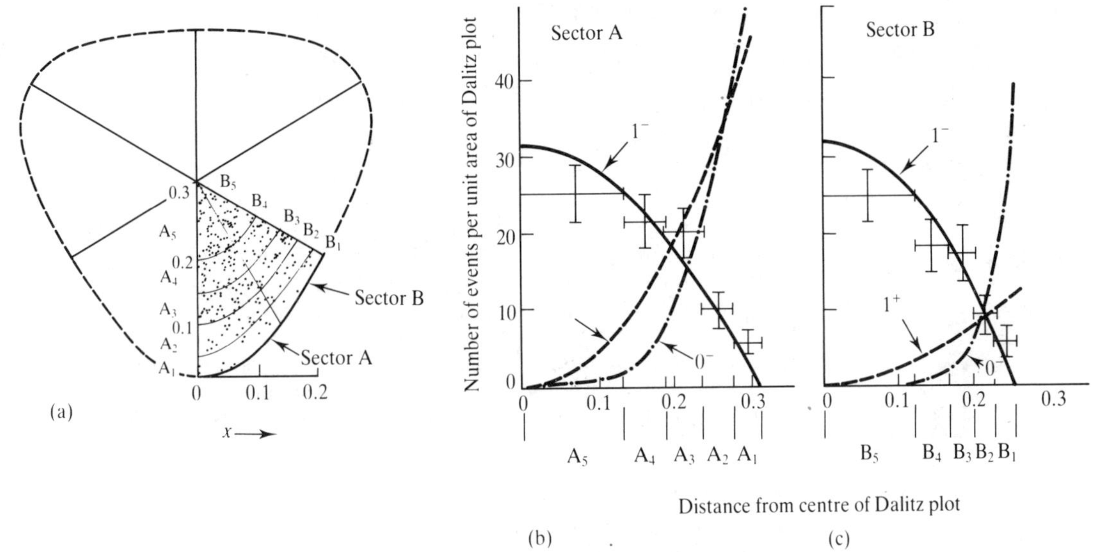

Figure 9.23 (a) Distribution of events in the folded Dalitz plot for events in the ω peak; (b), (c) distribution of events in the subsectors A_i and B_i with the theoretical expectations for $J^P = 0^-$, 1^- and 1^+. (After Stevenson M L *et al.* 1962 *Phys Rev* **125** (687).)

contours on the figure are formed by projecting the contours of the isometric drawing, for the case of a 1^- meson, onto the plane of the Dalitz plot. Since the matrix elements show considerable 'azimuthal' variation, the folded area was arbitrarily divided into two sectors A and B. The contours in turn divide each sector into five subsectors $A_1, \ldots, A_5$, $B_1, \ldots, B_5$. The number of events per unit area within $A_1, \ldots, A_5$, $B_1, \ldots, B_5$ are shown in figures 9.23(b) and 9.23(c). The curves are the predictions for the three J^P values considered and it is clear from the comparison with the data that the ω meson has $J^P = 1^-$.

REFERENCES 9

1 **Watson G N** 1944 *Theory of Bessel Functions* Macmillan

2 **Blatt J M and Weisskopf V F** 1952 *Theoretical Nuclear Physics* Wiley

3 **Bussey P J** *et al.* 1973 *Nucl Phys* **B58** (363)

4 **Particle Data Group** 1992 'Review of particle properties' *Phys Rev* **D45**

5 **Dalitz R H** 1953 *Phil Mag* **44** (1068)

6 **Fabri E** 1954 *Nuovo Cimento* **11** (479)

7 **Pevsner A** *et al.* 1961 *Phys Rev Lett* **7** (421)

8 **Alff** *et al.* 1962 *Phys Rev Lett* **9** (325)

9 **Layter J G** *et al.* 1972 *Phys Rev Lett* **29** (316)

10 **Walker W D** *et al.* 1967 *Phys Rev Lett* **18** (630)

11 **Maglic B C** *et al.* 1961 *Phys Rev Lett* **7** (178)

12 **Stevenson M L** *et al.* 1962 *Phys Rev* **125** (687)

EXAMPLES 9

9.1 A resonance has a mass of 1232 MeV/c^2 and is produced in a πp formation experiment. Determine the kinetic energy of the incident pion (in the laboratory system) at which resonance occurs.

9.2 Calculate the minimum kinetic energy of a K^+ meson in the laboratory system required to produce a ϕ meson in the reaction $K^+p \to K^+p\phi$. Take the masses of the K^+, p and ϕ to be 0.493, 0.938 and 1.020 GeV/c^2 respectively.

9.3 Use the time-dependent Schrödinger equation for a free particle to derive the continuity equation $\partial\rho/\partial t + \nabla\cdot\boldsymbol{j} = 0$, where $\rho = \psi\psi^*$ is the probability density and $\boldsymbol{j} = (\hbar/2\mathrm{i}m)(\psi^*\nabla\psi - \psi\nabla\psi^*)$ is the probability current density. What is the probability current density for a plane wave?

9.4 Show that the energy distribution of protons projected from a thin hydrogenous target by a homogeneous beam of neutrons is uniform up to the maximum available energy T_0 provided that the interaction only involves S waves.

9.5 Calculate the S wave phase shift for the elastic scattering of a particle of mass m and kinetic energy T ($\ll mc^2$) scattered by a square potential well of depth U and radius R.

9.6 Consider the scattering of a spinless particle when no inelastic reactions are possible. Assuming that only S and P waves contribute to the scattering, write down an explicit expression for the scattering amplitude $f(\theta)$ in terms of the partial wave amplitudes T_0 and T_1. Hence derive the corresponding expression for the differential cross-section $\mathrm{d}\sigma/\mathrm{d}\Omega$. Express this in terms of the phase shifts δ_0 and δ_1 and discuss the possibility of determining δ_0 and δ_1 from measurements of $\mathrm{d}\sigma/\mathrm{d}\Omega$.

9.7 Use the properties of the Dirac δ function (appendix I) to show that the n-body density of states factors

$$\frac{\mathrm{d}}{\mathrm{d}E}\int\prod_{i=1}^{n-1}\mathrm{d}^3p_i \quad \text{and} \quad \int\prod_{i=1}^{n}\mathrm{d}^3p_i\,\delta\left(\sum_{i=1}^{n}\boldsymbol{p}_i - \boldsymbol{P}\right)\delta\left(\sum_{i=1}^{n}E_i - E\right)$$

are equivalent.

9.8 Show that the Lorentz invariant two-body phase space for particles with masses m_1 and m_2 and momenta $\boldsymbol{p}_1$ and $\boldsymbol{p}_2$ in the centre-of-mass system is

$$R_2(E) = \frac{\pi p_1}{E}$$

where

$$p_1 = \frac{\{[E^2 - (m_2 - m_1)^2][E^2 - (m_2 + m_1)^2]\}^{1/2}}{2E}$$

9.9 Using equation (9.64) and the identity

$$\frac{dR_3}{dM_{12}} = \frac{dR_3}{dp_3}\frac{dp_3}{dM_{12}}$$

obtain an expression for the invariant mass distribution dR_3/dM_{12} in terms of M_{12}, E, m_1 and m_2 only. Write a computer program to evaluate dR_3/dM_{12} as a function of M_{12} for two pions produced in a $\pi\pi$N final state in which the total centre-of-mass energy is 2.0 GeV.

9.10 (a) Show that a pseudoscalar meson ($J^P = 0^-$) cannot decay to two pseudoscalar mesons without violating parity conservation.
(b) Show that a scalar meson ($J^P = 0^+$) cannot decay via a parity-conserving strong interaction into three pseudoscalar mesons.

9.11 The ϕ meson has $I = 0$ and can decay to K^+K^-. Show that it has G-parity $(-1)^J$ where J is its spin. If the decay modes $\phi \to \pi^+\pi^-\pi^0$ and $\phi \to \pi^+\pi^-$ have partial widths of 2.4×10^{-2} and 10^{-4} respectively show that the spin-parity must belong to the series 1^-, 3^- etc.

9.12 I spin conservation predicts that the ratio of the decay rates

$$R = \frac{\Gamma(\phi \to K^0\bar{K}^0)}{\Gamma(\phi \to K^+K^-)}$$

is unity, whereas the experimental ratio is $R_J \approx 0.7$. The difference can be accounted for by a centrifugal barrier factor such that

$$R_J = R\left(\frac{p_0}{p_+}\right)^{2J+1}$$

where $p_0(p_+)$ is the momentum of the neutral (charged) kaon in the ϕ rest system and J is the spin of the ϕ. Taking the masses of the ϕ, K^+ and K^0 to be 1020, 493.6 and 497.7 MeV/c^2 respectively show that $J = 1$ is preferred to $J = 3$.

9.13 In certain regions of phase space the reaction $\pi^-p \to \pi^-p\pi^+\pi^-$ proceeds via double resonance production, $\pi^-p \to \Delta^0(1232)\rho^0(770)$. The resonance decays are parity-conserving strong decays, $\Delta^0 \to p\pi^-$ and $\rho^0 \to \pi^+\pi^-$. Assuming that the production mechanism is single pion exchange determine the angular distributions of the decay products in the resonance rest systems. The spin-parities of the π, p, Δ and ρ are 0^-, $\frac{1}{2}^+$, $\frac{3}{2}^+$ and 1^- respectively.

9.14 Repeat the analysis for the production and decay of the $\Delta(1232)$ in example 9.13 assuming the Δ has $J^P = \frac{3}{2}^-$. What conclusions can be drawn concerning the possibility of determining the parity of a resonance by measuring the angular distribution of its decay products?

10 The quark model

SU(3) · Quarks · Mesons in the quark model · Baryons in the quark model · Hadron masses in the quark model · Baryon magnetic moments · Heavy-meson spectroscopy

As we saw in chapter 8 the isospin symmetry of the strong interactions leads naturally to the observation that all hadrons belong to I spin multiplets. In the absence of symmetry-breaking effects there is a degeneracy in the mass of the members of a multiplet. The electromagnetic interaction does not respect isospin symmetry and through it the degeneracy is removed with resulting mass differences of a per cent or so. The isospin operators commute with the strong interaction Hamiltonian H and therefore with other operators which also commute with H, in particular the angular momentum and parity operators. Consequently, all members of an isospin multiplet have the same spin-parity.

In the last chapter we discovered that there are larger groups of mesons and baryons with the same spin-parity, these groups containing I spin multiplets with different values of the strangeness quantum number. The observed regularities in the hadron spectrum led to the search for a higher symmetry, i.e. a symmetry higher than the SU(2) group of which isospin is an example, which would explain the existence of these larger groups of particles. A higher symmetry will involve a further additive quantum number, in addition to I and I_3, which is conserved in the strong interations but not necessarily in the weak and electromagnetic interactions. The strangeness S is such a quantum number but the hypercharge* Y, the sum of strangeness and baryon number, is found to be more convenient. The appropriate mathematical group is then SU(3).

* The name hypercharge arises because it is twice the average charge of an I spin multiplet, as can be seen from the Gell-Mann–Nishijima relation $Q = I_3 + Y/2$.

In this chapter we show how, in spite of the fact that the symmetry is quite badly broken, SU(3) and the associated quark model give a good description of the observed hadron spectrum.

10.1 SU(3)

10.1.1 The SU(3) generators

In the extension of SU(2) to SU(3) the basic doublet of SU(2) is replaced by a triplet

$$\varphi \equiv \begin{pmatrix} \varphi_1 \\ \varphi_2 \\ \varphi_3 \end{pmatrix}$$

and this basic triplet is assumed to transform as

$$\varphi \to \varphi' = U\varphi \tag{10.1}$$

where the matrices U are arbitrary, unitary, unimodular 3×3 matrices, a canonical representation of which is

$$U \equiv \exp(-\tfrac{1}{2}\mathrm{i}\theta\hat{\boldsymbol{n}}\cdot\boldsymbol{\lambda}). \tag{10.2}$$

The eight generators* $\frac{1}{2}\lambda_j$ play an analogous role to the three Pauli matrices in SU(2) and the standard form, which was introduced by Gell-Mann,[1] is

$$\lambda_1 = \begin{pmatrix} 0 & 1 & 0 \\ 1 & 0 & 0 \\ 0 & 0 & 0 \end{pmatrix} \quad \lambda_2 = \begin{pmatrix} 0 & -\mathrm{i} & 0 \\ \mathrm{i} & 0 & 0 \\ 0 & 0 & 0 \end{pmatrix} \quad \lambda_3 = \begin{pmatrix} 1 & 0 & 0 \\ 0 & -1 & 0 \\ 0 & 0 & 0 \end{pmatrix}$$

$$\lambda_4 = \begin{pmatrix} 0 & 0 & 1 \\ 0 & 0 & 0 \\ 1 & 0 & 0 \end{pmatrix} \quad \lambda_5 = \begin{pmatrix} 0 & 0 & -\mathrm{i} \\ 0 & 0 & 0 \\ \mathrm{i} & 0 & 0 \end{pmatrix} \quad \lambda_6 = \begin{pmatrix} 0 & 0 & 0 \\ 0 & 0 & 1 \\ 0 & 1 & 0 \end{pmatrix}$$

$$\lambda_7 = \begin{pmatrix} 0 & 0 & 0 \\ 0 & 0 & -\mathrm{i} \\ 0 & \mathrm{i} & 0 \end{pmatrix} \quad \lambda_8 = \frac{1}{\sqrt{3}}\begin{pmatrix} 1 & 0 & 0 \\ 0 & 1 & 0 \\ 0 & 0 & -2 \end{pmatrix}. \tag{10.3}$$

* In SU(n) there are $n^2 - 1$ generators of the group.

Table 10.1
The structure constants of SU(3)

$f_{123} = 1$
$f_{147} = f_{246} = f_{257} = f_{345} = f_{516} = f_{637} = \frac{1}{2}$
$f_{458} = f_{678} = \sqrt{3}/2$

As in SU(2), the generators satisfy the commutation relations

$$[\tfrac{1}{2}\lambda_i, \tfrac{1}{2}\lambda_j] = \mathrm{i} f_{ijk} \tfrac{1}{2}\lambda_k \qquad (10.4)$$

where the structure constants f_{ijk}, which are easily obtained by explicit calculation, have the values given in table 10.1. The f_{ijk} are antisymmetric under the interchange of any two indices. These matrices form a *three-dimensional* representation of SU(3). Among the eight generators of the SU(3) group we note that only λ_3 and λ_8 are diagonal. In SU(2) the states in a given I spin multiplet were labelled with the eigenvalues of the diagonal matrix $\frac{1}{2}\tau_3$. In a search for a higher dimensional representation of the hadronic states it is appropriate to label the states by quantum numbers associated with the eigenvalues of λ_3 and λ_8. Apart from an extra row and column of zeros the matrices λ_i, $i = 1, 2, 3$, are just the Pauli matrices, i.e.

$$\lambda_i = \begin{pmatrix} & & \vdots & 0 \\ & \tau_i & \vdots & \\ & & \vdots & 0 \\ \cdots & \cdots & \cdots & \cdots \\ 0 & 0 & \vdots & 0 \end{pmatrix} \qquad (i = 1, 2, 3)$$

and therefore λ_1, λ_2 and λ_3 are associated with the I spin operators which form an SU(2) subgroup of SU(3): in particular λ_3 is associated with I_3 and linear combinations of λ_1 and λ_2 are formed to produce I spin step operators. The eigenvalues of λ_8 are related to the hypercharge Y. In SU(3) the states in a multiplet are labelled with the eigenvalues of I_3 and Y. Accordingly, the states in SU(3) multiplets will occupy sites on a two-dimensional grid in I_3–Y space, in contrast to the one-dimensional SU(2) multiplets.

As in the case of SU(2) we generalize (10.4) by defining the generators as $F_i \equiv \frac{1}{2}\lambda_i$; the F_i will then satisfy the commutation relations

$$[F_i, F_j] = \mathrm{i} f_{ijk} F_k. \qquad (10.5)$$

The study of SU(3) amounts essentially to finding higher dimensional $N \times N$ matrices F_i which satisfy (10.5) and which transform N-dimensional states according to

$$\varphi \to \varphi' = (1 - \mathrm{i}\theta\hat{\boldsymbol{n}}\cdot\boldsymbol{F})\varphi. \qquad (10.6)$$

These states belong to N-dimensional multiplets of SU(3).

To facilitate the search for these multiplets we form linear combinations of the non-commuting operators to produces step operators. Specifically, we define

$$\left.\begin{aligned} I_\pm &= F_1 \pm \mathrm{i}F_2 \\ I_3 &= F_3 \\ V_\pm &= F_4 \pm \mathrm{i}F_5 \\ U_\pm &= F_6 \pm \mathrm{i}F_7 \\ Y &= \frac{2}{\sqrt{3}} F_8 . \end{aligned}\right\} \tag{10.7}$$

10.1.2 The representations of SU(3)

The operators $U_\pm$ and $V_\pm$ are called 'U spin' and 'V spin' operators. We shall have particular use for the U spin operators later in this chapter.

We begin with the fundamental triplet. An examination of the matrix representations of the commuting operators

$$I_3 = \begin{pmatrix} \frac{1}{2} & 0 & 0 \\ 0 & -\frac{1}{2} & 0 \\ 0 & 0 & 0 \end{pmatrix} \qquad Y = \begin{pmatrix} \frac{1}{3} & 0 & 0 \\ 0 & \frac{1}{3} & 0 \\ 0 & 0 & -\frac{2}{3} \end{pmatrix}$$

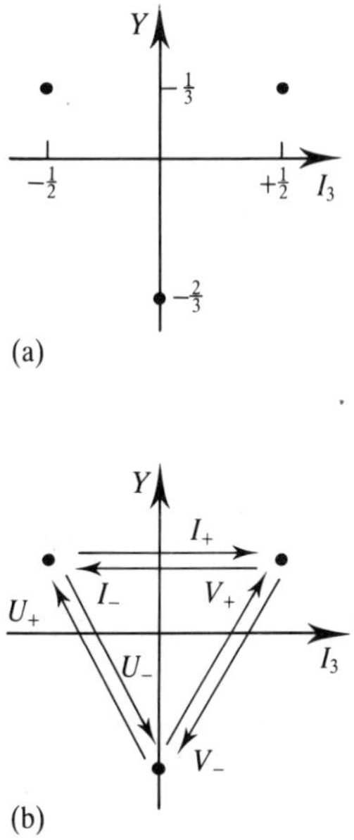

Figure 10.1
(a) The fundamental triplet of SU(3); (b) the action of the step operators $I_\pm$, $U_\pm$ and $V_\pm$ on the fundamental triplet.

shows that the fundamental triplet is described by the three eigenvectors

$$\begin{pmatrix} 1 \\ 0 \\ 0 \end{pmatrix} \quad \begin{pmatrix} 0 \\ 1 \\ 0 \end{pmatrix} \quad \begin{pmatrix} 0 \\ 0 \\ 1 \end{pmatrix} .$$

These are simultaneously eigenstates of I_3 and Y with eigenvalues (I_3, Y) of $(\frac{1}{2}, \frac{1}{3})$, $(-\frac{1}{2}, \frac{1}{3})$ and $(0, -\frac{2}{3})$, i.e. the fundamental triplet consists of an I spin doublet with $Y = \frac{1}{3}$ and an I spin singlet with $Y = -\frac{2}{3}$. The weight diagram – a plot of Y against I_3 – for the fundamental triplet is shown in figure 10.1(a).

In order to proceed further we require the commutation relations between the step operators defined in (10.7) and I_3 and Y. They are

$$[I_3, I_\pm] = \pm I_\pm \qquad [I_3, U_\pm] = \mp\tfrac{1}{2}U_\pm \qquad [I_3, V_\pm] = \pm\tfrac{1}{2}V_\pm$$

and

$$[Y, I_\pm] = 0 \qquad [Y, U_\pm] = \pm U_\pm \qquad [Y, V_\pm] = \pm V_\pm . \tag{10.8}$$

We know from our study of I spin that the state $I_+|I, I_3\rangle$, for example, is an eigenstate of I^2 and I_3 with eigenvalue $I_3' = I_3 + 1$, i.e. I_+ is the raising operator for I spin. From the commutation relation $[I_3, U_\pm] = \mp\frac{1}{2}U_\pm$ we have

$$\begin{aligned} I_3 U_\pm|I, I_3\rangle &= (U_\pm I_3 \mp \tfrac{1}{2}U_\pm)|I, I_3\rangle \\ &= U_\pm(I_3 \mp \tfrac{1}{2})|I, I_3\rangle \\ &= (I_3 \mp \tfrac{1}{2})U_\pm|I, I_3\rangle \end{aligned}$$

and therefore the operator $U_+(U_-)$ lowers (raises) the eigenvalue of I_3 by $\frac{1}{2}$. In a similar fashion, using $[Y, U_\pm] = \pm U_\pm$, it can be shown that $U_+(U_-)$ raises (lowers) the eigenvalue of Y by one. The overall effect of the commutation relations (10.8) can be summarized by the statements

$I_\pm$ induces the changes $\Delta Y = 0$, $\Delta I_3 = \pm 1$

$U_\pm$ induces the changes $\Delta Y = \pm 1$, $\Delta I_3 = \mp\frac{1}{2}$

$V_\pm$ induces the changes $\Delta Y = \pm 1$, $\Delta I_3 = \pm\frac{1}{2}$

and the action of these step operators on the fundamental triplet is shown in figure 10.1(b).

A particular representation, or multiplet, of SU(3) is completely specified when it is known which sites in the Y–I_3 plane are occupied and the multiplicity at each site is known, i.e. the number of states with a particular weight. A weight diagram contains precisely this information. As in SU(2) all states in an irreducible representation can be generated from a particular state by repeated application of the step operators. Before discussing the actual multiplets which occur in SU(3) we list some of their general properties.[2]

(a) The multiplets have hexagonal symmetry so that in general the boundary is a six-sided non-reentrant figure; in some cases it may be triangular.
(b) Every possible site on and inside the boundary is occupied by at least one state.
(c) The multiplicity of weights on layer 1, the boundary (see figure 10.2), is one, that on layer 2 is two in general, and so on until all sites have been accounted for. If a triangular layer is reached the multiplicity ceases to increase thereafter so that all sites on and inside a triangular layer have the same multiplicity.

It is convenient to have a shorthand notation which will succinctly describe the character of a particular SU(3) representation. If, starting from the state with the highest weight (maximum I_3 value), p applications of V_- (U_+ and I_+) and q applications of I_- (V_+ and U_-) are required to generate the boundary the multiplet is simply denoted as (p, q). Thus,

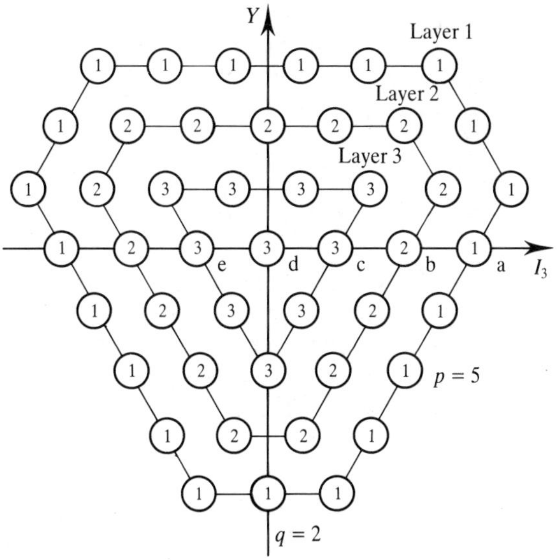

Figure 10.2
Weight diagram of a general SU(3) multiplet showing the multiplicity at each site.

for example, the fundamental triplet shown in figure 10.1 is denoted by (1, 0) and the multiplet in figure 10.2 by (5, 2). It can be shown[2] that the total number of states or the dimensionality of a multiplet $\boldsymbol{n}(p, q)$ is

$$\boldsymbol{n}(p, q) = \tfrac{1}{2}(1 + p)(1 + q)(2 + p + q)$$

so that the dimensionality of the (5, 2) representation is **81**. Sometimes multiplets are labelled simply by their dimensionality, e.g. **3** for the fundamental triplet and **81** for the (5, 2) representation.

It is clear that in the irreducible representations of SU(3) there can, in general, be a degeneracy of states with a particular weight (I_3, Y) so that an additional quantum number is required to distinguish between them. To be a good quantum number it must commute with both I_3 and Y. The square of the total I spin, $I^2 = \frac{1}{2}(I_+I_- + I_-I_+) + I_3^2$, has this property so that its eigenvalues can be used in conjunction with I_3 and Y to specify the states uniquely. Effectively, the degeneracy arises because for a given weight (I_3, Y) states from different I spin multiplets can contribute to the multiplicity of the weight. By way of illustration, consider the states with $Y = 0$ in figure 10.2, i.e. the states that sit on the I_3 axis. In essence these states form a *reducible* I spin multiplet. Seven of these states belong to an $I = 3$ multiplet, five to a multiplet with $I = 2$ and the remainder form an I spin triplet.

Before we attempt to combine multiplets in SU(3) we would like to make a remark concerning the fundamental representation. Apart from the SU(3) singlet (0, 0), the fundamental representation (1, 0) with dimensionality **3** is the simplest. Unlike the situation in SU(2), where the fundamental nucleon doublet $\binom{p}{n}$ with dimensionality **2** and its conjugate

$\bar{\mathbf{2}}$, $\binom{-\bar{n}}{p}$, transform in the same way (see example 10.1), the conjugate representation $\bar{\mathbf{3}}$ in SU(3), denoted by (0, 1), does not transform in the same way as the **3** representation. The weight diagrams of these *inequivalent* representations of SU(3) are shown in figure 10.3.

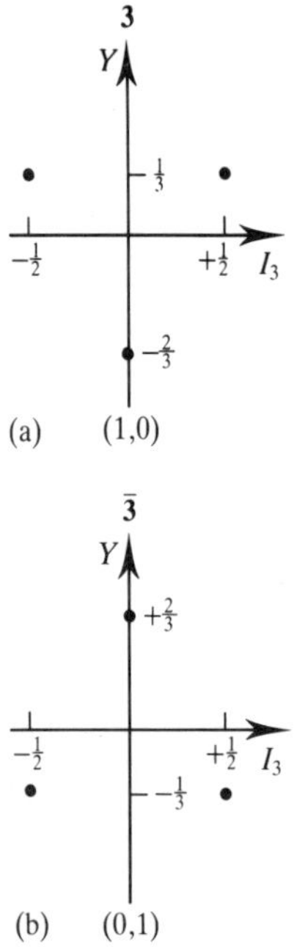

Figure 10.3
The fundamental triplet **3** and the conjugate triplet $\bar{\mathbf{3}}$ in SU(3).

10.1.3 Products of representations

The simplest way to obtain products of representations in SU(3) is to use a graphical technique. Any required reduction can be carried out by making use of the general properties of irreducible representations introduced in the last section. To illustrate the procedure we consider the product $\mathbf{3} \otimes \bar{\mathbf{3}}$. A superposition of the weight diagram of figure 10.3(b) on each weight in figure 10.3(a) yields the result shown on the left in figure 10.4. We note that the weights on the boundary of the product representation have unit multiplicity in accord with the properties of irreducible representations. The multiplicity at the centre of the representation, layer 2 in the notation of the last section, is, however, three and for an irreducible representation it ought to be two. To conform with the properties of irreducible representations the nonet must reduce to an octet and a singlet as shown in figure 10.4. The octet (1, 1) consists of two I spin doublets with $Y = +1$ and $Y = -1$ and an I spin triplet and a singlet both with $Y = 0$: the SU(3) singlet is also an I spin singlet with $Y = 0$. In the notation of group theory the product is written

$$\mathbf{3} \otimes \bar{\mathbf{3}} = \mathbf{8} \oplus \mathbf{1}. \tag{10.9}$$

As a second example we derive the results $\mathbf{3} \otimes \mathbf{3} = \mathbf{6} \oplus \bar{\mathbf{3}}$. In this case the superposition technique yields the nonet of states with the configuration shown on the left in figure 10.5. In this case there are three sites on the boundary which are doubly occupied. Again, to conform with the requirement of unit multiplicity on the boundary the nonet must reduce to a sextet (2, 0) and the conjugate triplet (0, 1).

Finally, we consider the product of three SU(3) triplets, $\mathbf{3} \otimes \mathbf{3} \otimes \mathbf{3}$. We

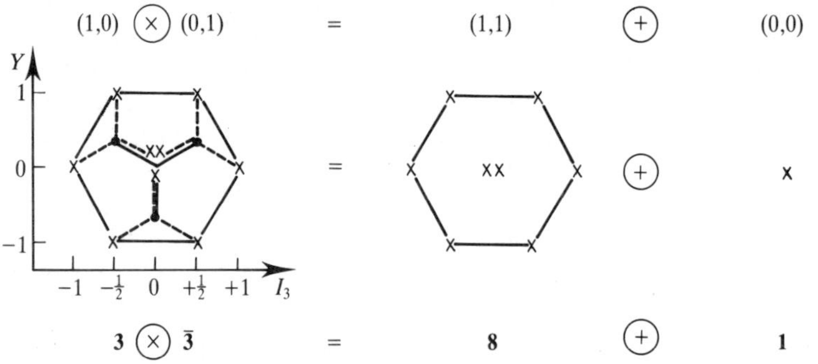

Figure 10.4
Graphical technique illustrating the reduction of the product $\mathbf{3} \otimes \bar{\mathbf{3}}$.

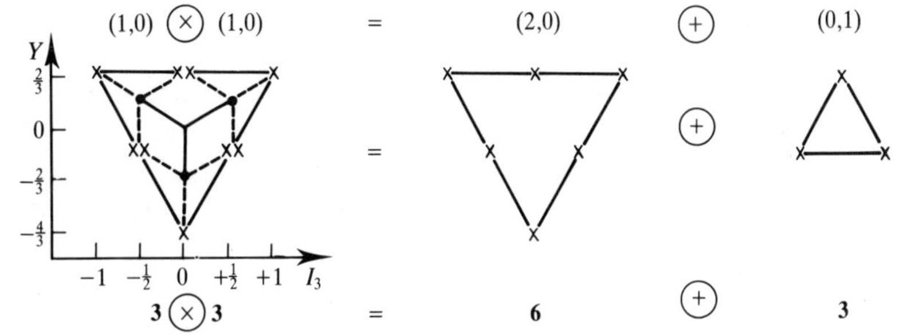

Figure 10.5
Reduction of the product $\mathbf{3} \otimes \mathbf{3}$.

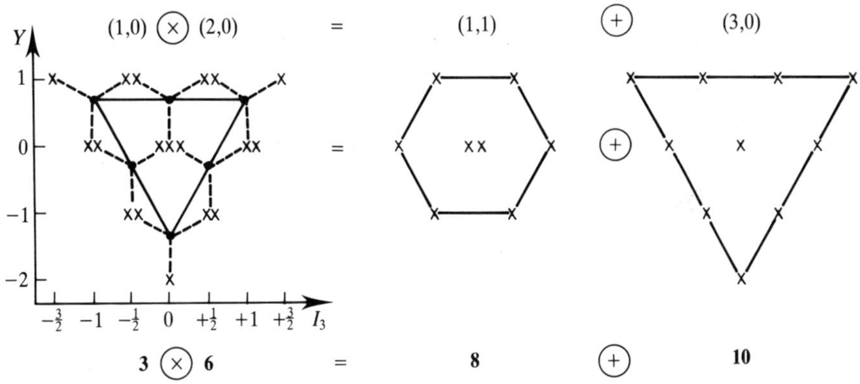

Figure 10.6
Reduction of the product $\mathbf{3} \otimes \mathbf{6}$.

have, from the last example,

$$\mathbf{3} \otimes \mathbf{3} \otimes \mathbf{3} = \mathbf{3} \otimes (\mathbf{6} \oplus \bar{\mathbf{3}}) = \mathbf{3} \otimes \mathbf{6} \oplus \mathbf{3} \otimes \bar{\mathbf{3}}. \tag{10.10}$$

We already know that $\mathbf{3} \otimes \bar{\mathbf{3}} = \mathbf{8} \oplus \mathbf{1}$, therefore we consider the product $\mathbf{3} \otimes \mathbf{6}$. Again, the superposition technique yields the weight diagram on the left of figure 10.6 which is clearly reducible. The reduction is effected by removing one of the states from each site on the boundary with multiplicity two. By the rule that all inner sites of an irreducible representation must be occupied, and that successive inner layers have a multiplicity which increases by one, we see that we must also remove two of the states from the site which has a multiplicity three. This procedure produces an octet (1, 1) and a decuplet (3, 0) both of which are irreducible. Thus $\mathbf{3} \otimes \mathbf{6} = \mathbf{8} \oplus \mathbf{10}$ and, finally,

$$\mathbf{3} \otimes \mathbf{3} \otimes \mathbf{3} = \mathbf{1} \oplus \mathbf{8} \oplus \mathbf{8} \oplus \mathbf{10}. \tag{10.11}$$

We note that the decuplet consists of an $I = \frac{3}{2}$ quartet with $Y = 1$, a triplet with $I = 1$ and $Y = 0$, a $Y = -1$ I spin doublet and an I spin singlet with $Y = -2$.

10.2 Quarks

The simplest and most elegant SU(3) scheme which successfully describes the observed hadron spectrum is the quark model proposed by Gell-Mann[3] and independently by Zweig.[4] They introduced a triplet of quarks with baryon number $B = \frac{1}{3}$ and proposed that the fundamental SU(3) triplet consists of a doublet of strangeness 0 quarks with $I = \frac{1}{2}$, the *up* quark u ($I_3 = +\frac{1}{2}$) and the *down* quark d ($I_3 = -\frac{1}{2}$), and an I spin singlet, the *strange* quark s with strangeness -1. The conjugate triplet $\bar{\mathbf{3}}$ consists of antiquarks with opposite sign of the additive quantum numbers I_3, B and S. The quantum numbers of the quarks and antiquarks are summarized in table 10.2. Note in particular the fractional charges $+\frac{2}{3}$ and $-\frac{1}{3}$ of the quarks. Furthermore, the eigenvalues of I_3 and Y of the quark triplet are precisely those of the diagonal generators given in section 10.1.2.

The weight diagrams for the fundamental quark and antiquark triplets are shown in figure 10.7.

10.3 Mesons in the quark model

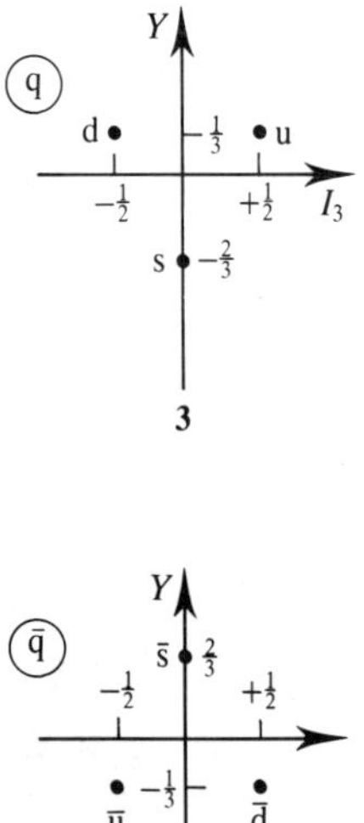

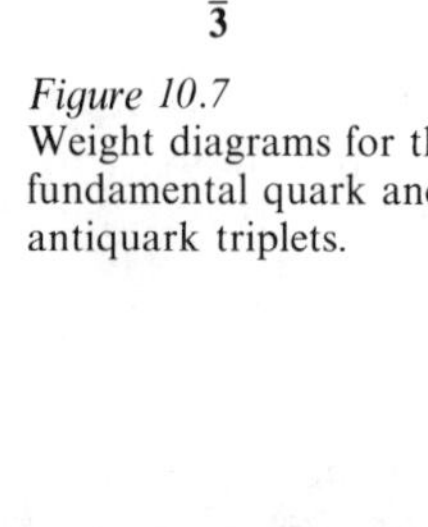

Figure 10.7
Weight diagrams for the fundamental quark and antiquark triplets.

The most economical way to construct mesons in the quark model is to form $q\bar{q}$ combinations by taking the direct product of the fundamental $\mathbf{3}$ and $\bar{\mathbf{3}}$ representations. The nonet of states is obtained in the usual way by superimposing the antiquark weight diagram on each site of the quark weight diagram and, in accordance with the properties of irreducible representations, the nonet reduces to an octet and a singlet as shown in figure 10.8. The quark content of the states on the boundary of the octet is unambiguous and is indicated in the figure. The unitary singlet with $Y = 0$ and $I = 0$ contains all the quarks on an equal footing and the normalized singlet state is therefore

$$\{\mathbf{1}, |0, 0\rangle\} = \frac{1}{\sqrt{3}}(u\bar{u} + d\bar{d} + s\bar{s}). \tag{10.12}$$

The notation on the left-hand side of (10.12) is $\{n, |I, I_3\rangle\}$ where n is the dimensionality of the representation. Equation (10.12) is seen as a natural extension from SU(2) to SU(3) if we make the substitution $\mathrm{p} \to \mathrm{u}$, $\mathrm{n} \to \mathrm{d}$, $\bar{\mathrm{p}} \to \bar{\mathrm{u}}$ and $\bar{\mathrm{n}} \to \bar{\mathrm{d}}$ (see example 10.2). Of the two states at the centre of the octet, one belongs to an I spin triplet and the other is an I spin singlet: both have $I_3 = 0$. We can write down the quark wavefunction of the $I_3 = 0$ triplet state immediately,

$$\{\mathbf{8}, |1, 0\rangle\} = \frac{1}{\sqrt{2}}(u\bar{u} - d\bar{d}). \tag{10.13}$$

Table 10.2
Quantum numbers of the light quarks and antiquarks

Flavour	Spin	Charge	I_3	Baryon number	Strangeness	Hypercharge
u	$\frac{1}{2}$	$+\frac{2}{3}$	$+\frac{1}{2}$	$\frac{1}{3}$	0	$\frac{1}{3}$
d	$\frac{1}{2}$	$-\frac{1}{3}$	$-\frac{1}{2}$	$\frac{1}{3}$	0	$\frac{1}{3}$
s	$\frac{1}{2}$	$-\frac{1}{3}$	0	$\frac{1}{3}$	-1	$-\frac{2}{3}$
$\bar{u}$	$\frac{1}{2}$	$-\frac{2}{3}$	$-\frac{1}{2}$	$-\frac{1}{3}$	0	$-\frac{1}{3}$
$\bar{d}$	$\frac{1}{2}$	$+\frac{1}{3}$	$+\frac{1}{2}$	$-\frac{1}{3}$	0	$-\frac{1}{3}$
$\bar{s}$	$\frac{1}{2}$	$+\frac{1}{3}$	0	$-\frac{1}{3}$	$+1$	$+\frac{2}{3}$

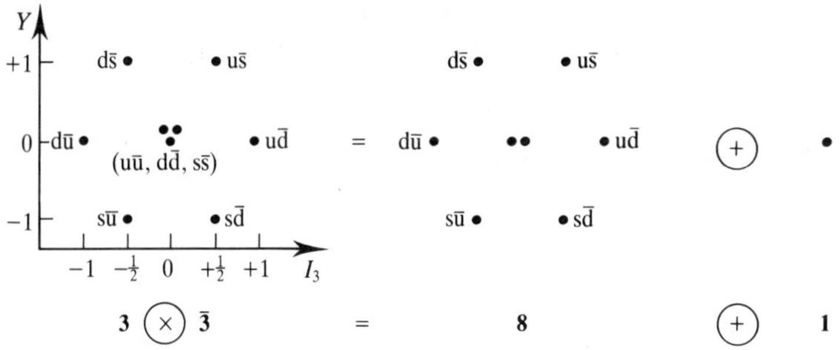

Figure 10.8
The nonet of $q\bar{q}$ states reduces to an octet and a singlet.

Alternatively, the state (10.13) may be obtained by using the I spin lowering operator on the $|1, 1\rangle$ state, i.e. $|-u\bar{d}\rangle$. We note that since the s and $\bar{s}$ quarks are I spin singlets they cannot couple to give an $I = 1$ state. They can, however, couple to give an $I = 0$ state so that the $I = 0$ state at the centre of the octet will be a linear combination of $u\bar{u}$, $d\bar{d}$ and $s\bar{s}$. The properly normalized state, which is orthogonal to both (10.12) and (10.13), is

$$\{\mathbf{8}, |0, 0\rangle\} = \frac{1}{\sqrt{6}}(u\bar{u} + d\bar{d} - 2s\bar{s}). \tag{10.14}$$

The quark model therefore predicts that mesons should belong to SU(3) octets and singlets. In the octets there are two I spin doublets with $Y = +1$ and $Y = -1$ which are particle and antiparticle, and an I spin triplet and an I spin singlet both with $Y = 0$. The unitary singlet is of course an I spin singlet. This is precisely the hypercharge I spin structure which is observed amongst the known mesons.

Let us now check that the other quantum numbers such as spin-parity and C-parity, where appropriate, agree with the experimentally observed values. Recall that the quarks are spin $\frac{1}{2}$ fermions so that in a $q\bar{q}$ state the spins may couple to give a total spin $S = 0$ or 1. If the quark–antiquark pair have relative orbital angular momentum L the total angular momentum will be the vector sum $\boldsymbol{J} = \boldsymbol{L} + \boldsymbol{S}$. The parity of the

Table 10.3
The possible J^P values of meson states arising from the coupling of quark–antiquark spin and relative orbital angular momentum

Orbital angular momentum L	Quark spins: Singlet $S = 0$	Quark spins: Triplet $S = 1$
0	0^-	1^-
1	1^+	$0^+\ 1^+\ 2^+$
2	2^-	$1^-\ 2^-\ 3^-$

states will be $(-1)^{L+1}$ where the factor $(-1)^L$ arises from the orbital motion and the factor -1 is due to the opposite intrinsic parities of quark and antiquark. The possible J^P values of the meson states formed from the coupling of quark–antiquark spin and orbital angular momentum are shown in table 10.3. The pseudoscalar and vector mesons appear as $q\bar{q}$ states with $L = 0$ and total quark spin 0 and 1 respectively, and the 2^+ tensor nonet results from the orbital excitation ($L = 1$) of the spin-triplet $q\bar{q}$ state. In figure 10.9 we show the SU(3) multiplets for the 0^-, 1^- and 2^+ mesons.

C-parity is a good quantum number only for states with $Q = B = S = 0$ where here S is the strangeness quantum number, and is therefore applicable only to the unitary singlets and to the two states at the centres of the octets. The argument which leads to the determination of C for

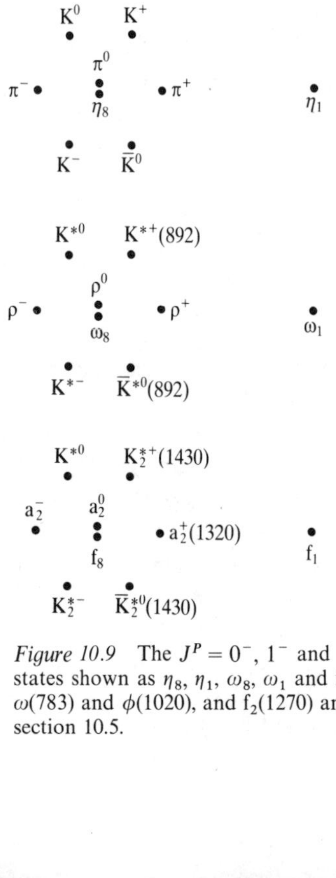

Figure 10.9 The $J^P = 0^-$, 1^- and 2^+ mesons arranged in SU(3) octets and singlets. The states shown as η_8, η_1, ω_8, ω_1 and f_8, f_1 are mixtures of the physical states η and $\eta'(958)$, $\omega(783)$ and $\phi(1020)$, and $f_2(1270)$ and $f_2'(1525)$. Mixing in the meson nonets is discussed in section 10.5.

Table 10.4
Quark model assignments of the pseudoscalar, vector and tensor mesons

$^{2S+1}L_J$	J^{PC}	$u\bar{u}$, $d\bar{d}$, $s\bar{s}$ $I=0$	$u\bar{d}$, $u\bar{u}$, $d\bar{d}$ $I=1$	$u\bar{s}$, $d\bar{s}$ $I=\frac{1}{2}$
$^1S_0$	0^{-+}	η, $\eta'(958)$	π	K
$^3S_1$	1^{--}	$\phi(1020)$, $\omega(783)$	$\rho(770)$	$K^*(892)$
$^3P_2$	2^{++}	$f'_2(1525)$, $f_2(1270)$	$a_2(1320)$	$K_2^*(1430)$

a $p\bar{p}$ state has already been given in section 8.8: for a $q\bar{q}$ state the argument is identical so that $C = (-1)^{L+S}$ where S is the total spin of the $q\bar{q}$ system and L the relative orbital angular momentum. We are thus led to the quark model assignments of the pseudoscalar, vector and tensor mesons shown in table 10.4.

10.4 Baryons in the quark model

The quark model description of baryons is more complicated than for mesons. All hadrons must be colour singlets and in section 10.3 it was tacitly assumed that in each $q\bar{q}$ pair the colour–anti-colour combinations yielded colour-singlet mesons. Since quarks have $B = \frac{1}{3}$ the simplest way to construct baryons from the basic quark triplet is to form qqq states. The quark *content* of these states is unambiguous but in order to explain the observed baryon spectrum we need to consider the *symmetry* of the quark *wavefunctions*. The overall wavefunctions

$$\Psi = \psi(\text{space})\phi(\text{flavour})\chi(\text{spin})\xi(\text{colour})$$

must be antisymmetric. Each quark flavour comes in three colours, red, green and blue (RGB), which form a fundamental triplet of the SU(3) colour group, SU(3)$_c$, which, unlike SU(3) flavour symmetry, is assumed to be exact. The SU(3)$_c$ singlet wavefunction for baryons

$$\xi = \frac{1}{\sqrt{6}}\{|RGB\rangle + |GBR\rangle + |BRG\rangle - |GRB\rangle - |BGR\rangle - |RBG\rangle\} \quad (10.15)$$

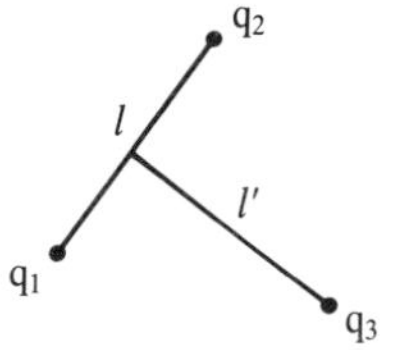

Figure 10.10
Relative orbital angular momenta in a three-quark system.

is antisymmetric in the exchange of any two quark colours. Its inclusion in the overall wavefunction Ψ guarantees antisymmetry provided $\psi(\text{space})\phi(\text{flavour})\chi(\text{spin})$ is symmetric.

Let us focus on the lowest-lying baryon multiplets, the $J^P = \frac{1}{2}^+$ octet and the $\frac{3}{2}^+$ decuplet. The relative orbital angular momenta l and l' in these three-quark states (figure 10.10) are assumed to be zero and therefore $\psi(\text{space})$ is symmetric. In the direct product of the SU(3) flavour and the SU(2) multiplets we therefore require symmetric combinations. In SU(3) we have

$$\mathbf{3} \otimes \mathbf{3} \otimes \mathbf{3} = \mathbf{10}_S \oplus \mathbf{8}_{M_S} \oplus \mathbf{8}_{M_A} \oplus \mathbf{1}_A \tag{10.16}$$

and in SU(2) the direct product of three spin doublets is

$$\mathbf{2} \otimes \mathbf{2} \otimes \mathbf{2} = \mathbf{4}_S \oplus \mathbf{2}_{M_S} \oplus \mathbf{2}_{M_A}. \tag{10.17}$$

The subscripts denote the symmetry of the wavefunctions. For example, the direct product of three flavour triplets leads to a symmetric decuplet, two octets of mixed symmetry M_S and M_A and an antisymmetric singlet. In the mixed symmetry octets S (A) implies that the wavefunctions are symmetric (antisymmetric) with respect to interchange of the first two quark flavours. The symmetry properties of the multiplets become apparent only on examination of the wavefunctions of the states (see examples 10.4–10.7).

In order to determine the nature of the baryon multiplets predicted by the quark model with spin, SU(6), we must combine the SU(3) flavour multiplets with the SU(2) spin multiplets. In the direct product $(\mathbf{10}_S \oplus \mathbf{8}_{M_S} \oplus \mathbf{8}_{M_A} \oplus \mathbf{1}_A) \otimes (\mathbf{4}_S \oplus \mathbf{2}_{M_S} \oplus \mathbf{2}_{M_A})$ the only symmetric combination is the **56** representation $(\mathbf{10}, \mathbf{4}) \oplus (\mathbf{8}, \mathbf{2})$. The notation here is $(\boldsymbol{n}_{SU(3)}, \boldsymbol{n}_{SU(2)})$ where $\boldsymbol{n}$ is the dimensionality. The quark model with spin therefore successfully predicts a decuplet of $\frac{3}{2}^+$ and an octet of $\frac{1}{2}^+$ baryons. These multiplets and their quark content are shown in figure 10.11.

Having successfully assigned the low-lying mesons and baryons to

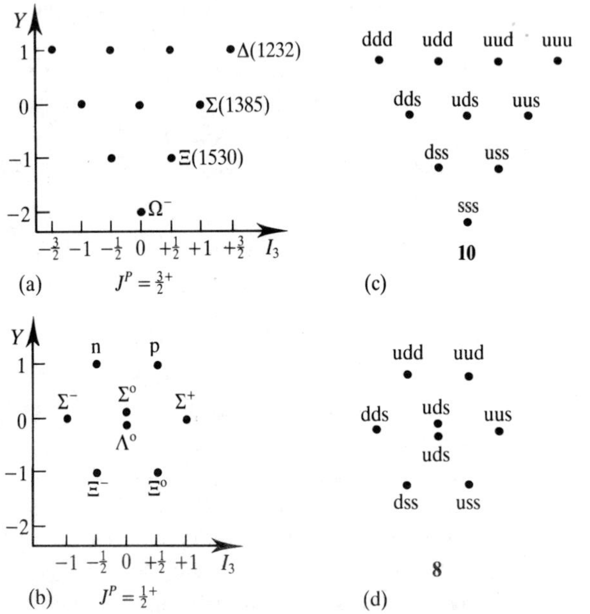

Figure 10.11
(a) The $\frac{3}{2}^+$ baryon decuplet and (b) the $\frac{1}{2}^+$ baryon octet. (c), (d) The quark content of the decuplet and octet states respectively.

multiplets of SU(3) it is natural to investigate the quark model further by examining its predictive power and comparing with experiment.

10.5 Hadron masses in the quark model

It is clear from the mass splittings in the multiplets that although flavour SU(3) describes the hadron spectrum very well, it is not an exact symmetry. If it were, the states in a given multiplet would be degenerate.

In an attempt to explain the mass splitting Gell-Mann proposed that the strong interaction Hamiltonian, H, consists of two parts – a 'very strong' interaction which is assumed to be exactly SU(3) invariant and described by a Hamiltonian H_0, plus a 'medium strong' interaction described by a Hamiltonian H', which is assumed to give deviations from exact symmetry. H_0 will therefore commute with all the SU(3) generators,

$$[H_0, F_i] = 0 \qquad (i = 1, 2, \ldots, 8) \tag{10.18}$$

while the symmetry-breaking part of the Hamiltonian will have non-zero commutation relations with some of the F_i,

$$[H', F_i] \neq 0. \tag{10.19}$$

Since isospin and hypercharge are conserved in the strong interaction, it follows that

$$[H', Y] = [H', I_3] = [H', I_\pm] = 0. \tag{10.20}$$

Gell-Mann proposed that H' should transform like one of the SU(3) generators and, since F_8 – the hypercharge – is the only generator that commutes with I_3, I_+ and I_- and, of course, with itself, he suggested that H' should transform like the hypercharge.

In order to make quantitative statements concerning the mass splitting it is convenient to work with U spin. In section 10.1.2 we saw that the U spin shift operators relate multiplet members with different hypercharge and I spin, i.e. members with different masses. From inspection of any of the multiplets it is apparent that

$$Y = U_3 + \tfrac{1}{2}Q. \tag{10.21}$$

Since all members of a U spin multiplet have the same electric charge it follows that Q commutes with all the U spin operators:

$$[U, Q] = 0. \tag{10.22}$$

In other words, the hypercharge, and consequently the symmetry-breaking part of the Hamiltonian H', transforms as a linear superposition of the third component of a vector in U spin space and a U spin scalar. Thus we may write

$$H' = H'_{\mathrm{v}} + H'_{\mathrm{s}} \tag{10.23}$$

where v and s stand for vector and scalar respectively. The mass of a particular U spin state $|U, U_3\rangle$ is then given by

$$\begin{aligned}\langle U, U_3|H|U, U_3\rangle &= \langle U, U_3|H_0 + H'_{\mathrm{v}} + H'_{\mathrm{s}}|U, U_3\rangle \\ &= m_0 + m_{\mathrm{v}} + m_{\mathrm{s}}.\end{aligned} \tag{10.24}$$

The contribution m_0 to the mass arising from the 'very strong' part of the interaction is the same for all members of a multiplet. In a given U spin multiplet m_{s} is the same for all members while m_{v} is proportional to U_3.

When equation (10.24) is applied to the U spin quartet of negatively charged $\frac{3}{2}^+$ baryons (see appendix J) we obtain the mass relation (example 10.8)

$$m_\Sigma - m_\Delta \approx m_\Xi - m_\Sigma \approx m_\Omega - m_\Xi \approx 150 \text{ MeV}.$$

Since the quark content of the Δ, Σ, Ξ and Ω is ddd, dds, dss and sss respectively, the near equality of the mass differences suggests that in some sense the mass of the strange quark is about 150 MeV greater than the mass of the d and u quarks. The much smaller mass difference between members of I spin multiplets suggests that $m_{\mathrm{u}} \approx m_{\mathrm{d}}$.

For the neutral members of the $\frac{1}{2}^+$ baryon octet the relation

$$\tfrac{1}{2}m_{\mathrm{n}} + \tfrac{1}{2}m_{\Xi^0} = \tfrac{1}{4}m_{\Sigma^0} + \tfrac{3}{4}m_{\Lambda^0} \tag{10.25}$$

holds (see example 10.9). This is an example of the Gell-Mann–Okubo mass formula and, on substituting the measured mass values, is found to be accurate to about 1 per cent.

Since the SU(3) couplings are the same for any octet one might expect the results for the baryon octet to apply without change to the meson octets. Thus, for example, for the pseudoscalar mesons one might predict

$$\tfrac{1}{2}(m_{\mathrm{K}^0} + m_{\bar{\mathrm{K}}^0}) = \tfrac{1}{4}m_{\pi^0} + \tfrac{3}{4}m_{\eta^0}. \tag{10.26}$$

The masses of the K^0 and $\bar{\mathrm{K}}^0$ are equal by the *CPT* theorem so that one expects

$$m_{\eta^0} = \tfrac{1}{3}(4m_{\mathrm{K}^0} - m_{\pi^0}). \tag{10.27}$$

On substituting $m_\eta = 549$ MeV, $m_K = 498$ MeV and $m_\pi = 135$ MeV into equation (10.27) one finds a discrepancy of about 12 per cent. It is found that the mass formula works better for mesons if the square of the particle mass is used rather than the mass.* The Gell-Mann–Okubo mass formula for the pseudoscalar mesons then becomes

$$m_{\eta^0}^2 = \tfrac{1}{3}(4m_{K^0}^2 - m_{\pi^0}^2). \tag{10.28}$$

The discrepancy in this case is still about 7 per cent. However, it is found that the η^0 is not a 'wholly octet' state: because of SU(3)-breaking the physical η^0 and η' are mixtures of the SU(3) octet and singlet states.

The Gell-Mann–Okubo formula (10.28) assumes no mixing between the SU(3) octet and singlet states. In the presence of mixing we can write

$$\begin{aligned} \eta' &= \eta_1 \cos\theta + \eta_8 \sin\theta \\ \eta &= -\eta_1 \sin\theta + \eta_8 \cos\theta \end{aligned} \tag{10.29}$$

where η' and η denote the physical states, η_1 and η_8 the singlet and octet states and θ the mixing angle in the pseudoscalar nonet. The physical states η' and η are related to the SU(3) singlet and octet states by a rotation through the angle θ. For small θ the parametrization (10.29) implies that the η' is largely a singlet state and the η largely an octet state. We assume that the matrix elements of the Hamiltonian, or the mass-matrix elements, are quadratic in the mass rather than linear. With respect to η_1 and η_8 base states we have

$$H\begin{pmatrix}\eta_1\\ \eta_8\end{pmatrix} = \begin{pmatrix} M_{11}^2 & M_{18}^2 \\ M_{18}^2 & M_{88}^2 \end{pmatrix}\begin{pmatrix}\eta_1\\ \eta_8\end{pmatrix} \tag{10.30}$$

with $M_{88}^2 = \tfrac{1}{3}(m_K^2 - m_\pi^2)$, in analogy with equation (10.28). Diagonalization of the mass matrix (see example 10.13) leads to

$$\tan^2\theta = \frac{M_{88}^2 - m_\eta^2}{m_{\eta'}^2 - M_{88}^2}. \tag{10.31}$$

Similar expressions hold for the vector- and tensor-meson nonets in which there is ϕ–ω and f_2'–f_2 mixing respectively. The mixing angles are $\theta_P \approx -11°$, $\theta_V \approx 40°$ and $\theta_T \approx 32°$. Equation (10.31) does not determine the sign of the mixing angle: it is negative (positive) according to whether the mass of the mainly octet member is less than (greater than) that of the mainly singlet member.

---

* Some justification for this derives from the Dirac equation (section 11.4.3) which describes the relativistic motion of spin $\tfrac{1}{2}$ fermions and leads to fermion propagators which depend on the fermion *mass*. Mesons on the other hand are described by the Klein–Gordon equation (section 11.4.1) which leads to meson propagators dependent on *mass squared*.

By introducing the mixing angle θ we have obtained consistency between the observed masses of the mesons, but this would be only of passing interest if no other consequences resulted from the concept of mixing. Important predictions concerning the dominant decay modes of the isoscalar states result from the observation that the 1^- and 2^+ nonets are very nearly 'ideally mixed'. The singlet and octet wavefunctions for the isoscalar states are

$$\{\mathbf{1}, |0, 0\rangle\} \equiv \psi_1 = \frac{1}{\sqrt{3}}(u\bar{u} + d\bar{d} + s\bar{s})$$

$$\{\mathbf{8}, |0, 0\rangle\} \equiv \psi_8 = \frac{1}{\sqrt{6}}(u\bar{u} + d\bar{d} - 2s\bar{s}).$$

In general, the octet–singlet mixing is parametrized by the equations

$$m_1 = \psi_1 \cos\theta + \psi_8 \sin\theta$$

$$m_8 = -\psi_1 \sin\theta + \psi_8 \cos\theta$$

where m_1 denotes the physical, mainly singlet meson and m_8 the physical, mainly octet meson. If $\sin\theta = 1/\sqrt{3}$, we have

$$m_1 \approx u\bar{u} + d\bar{d}$$

$$m_8 \approx s\bar{s}$$

and the nonet is said to be ideally mixed in the sense that the singlet state consists only of $u\bar{u}$ and $d\bar{d}$ quarks and the octet state of $s\bar{s}$ quarks. Ideal mixing occurs for $\theta \approx 35°$: this is approximately the case for the 1^- and 2^+ nonets but not for the pseudoscalar nonet. We would therefore expect that the mainly singlet members of these nonets should decay predominantly to pseudoscalar mesons consisting of u and d quarks (pions) and the mainly octet members to strange pseudoscalar mesons (kaons). This is borne out by the observed branching fractions, $B(\varphi \to \mathrm{K}\bar{\mathrm{K}}) \approx 84$ per cent and $B(\omega \to \pi^+\pi^-\pi^0) \approx 89$ per cent, for the 1^- isoscalars, and $B(\mathrm{f}_2' \to \mathrm{K}\bar{\mathrm{K}}) \approx 71$ per cent and $B(\mathrm{f}_2 \to \pi\pi) \approx 85$ per cent for the 2^+ isoscalars. In contrast, the branching fraction for the decay $\varphi \to \pi^+\pi^-\pi^0$, which is favoured over the $\mathrm{K}\bar{\mathrm{K}}$ decay mode by phase space considerations, is only about 2 per cent. We return to the suppression of this decay mode in section 10.7.2.

So far in this section we have obtained mass *relations* between members of various $\mathrm{SU(3)_{flavour}}$ multiplets, but have said nothing concerning the value of m_0 in equation (10.24) – the common mass which all members of a specific multiplet would have if $\mathrm{SU(3)_{flavour}}$ were an exact symmetry. Why is m_0 different for different multiplets? Why is it, for example, that the mass of the K^+, with quark content $\mathrm{u}\bar{\mathrm{s}}$, is less than that of the

$K^{*+}(892)$ which has the same quark content? Similarly, why is the Δ^+ (uud) heavier than the proton (uud)? The pseudoscalar and vector meson octets differ in the relative orientation of the quark spins: they are antiparallel in the 0^- octet and parallel in the 1^- octet. The spins of the three quarks in the baryon octet couple to give $J^P = \frac{1}{2}^+$ while in the $\frac{3}{2}^+$ decuplet they are parallel. It seems likely, therefore, that if we view hadrons as bound states of *interacting* quarks, the mass differences between multiplets and, indeed, between members of the same multiplet, can be attributed to a spin–spin interaction.

The currently accepted theory of interacting quarks is quantum chromodynamics (QCD) in which coloured quarks interact via the exchange of coloured gluons. Like the photon in QED the gluons are massless and at short distances the QCD potential has the form of the QED Coloumb potential,

$$V(r) \approx -\frac{\alpha_s}{r} \tag{10.32}$$

where α_s is the strong coupling constant. In QED, the spin–spin interaction gives rise to hyperfine splitting[5] in which

$$\Delta E_{\text{hfs}} = \tfrac{2}{3}\boldsymbol{\mu}_1 \cdot \boldsymbol{\mu}_2 |\psi(0)|^2. \tag{10.33}$$

In units in which $\hbar = c = 1$, the magnetic moment μ_i of a particle with electric charge e_i, spin $\boldsymbol{s}_i$ and mass m_i is given by

$$\mu_i = \frac{e_i}{m_i}\boldsymbol{s}_i. \tag{10.34}$$

Hence,

$$\Delta E_{\text{hfs}} = \frac{8\pi\alpha}{3}|\psi(0)|^2 \frac{\boldsymbol{s}_1 \cdot \boldsymbol{s}_2}{m_1 m_2} \tag{10.35}$$

where we have used the relation $e_1 e_2 = e^2 = 4\pi\alpha$, α being the fine-structure constant. In equations (10.33) and (10.35) $\psi(0)$ is the value of the wavefunction $\psi(r_1, r_2)$ at zero separation. To obtain the analogous result for QCD we have to replace the electric charges e_1 and e_2 by the appropriate colour charges (see appendix M). For mesons and baryons this amounts to the substitutions

$$\alpha \to \begin{cases} \frac{4}{3}\alpha_s & (q\bar{q}) \\ \frac{2}{3}\alpha_s & (qq) \end{cases}$$

so,

$$\Delta E_{\text{hfs}} = \frac{32}{9}\pi\alpha_s|\psi(0)|^2 \frac{\boldsymbol{s}_1 \cdot \boldsymbol{s}_2}{m_1 m_2} \tag{10.36}$$

for mesons, and

$$\Delta E_{\rm hfs} = \frac{16}{9}\pi\alpha_{\rm s}|\psi(0)|^2 \sum_{i<j} \frac{\boldsymbol{s}_i\cdot\boldsymbol{s}_j}{m_i m_j} \tag{10.37}$$

for baryons. We therefore construct a simple model in which hadron masses are supposed to arise from a sum of constituent quark masses and hyperfine interactions. Thus, for mesons

$$m(q_1\bar{q}_2) = m_1 + m_2 + a\frac{\boldsymbol{s}_1\cdot\boldsymbol{s}_2}{m_1 m_2} \tag{10.38}$$

and for baryons

$$m(q_1q_2q_3) = m_1 + m_2 + m_3 + a' \sum_{i<j} \frac{\boldsymbol{s}_i\cdot\boldsymbol{s}_j}{m_i m_j}. \tag{10.39}$$

We will regard the constants a and a' and the quark masses as free parameters and attempt to explain the hadron mass spectrum with a consistent set of values.

By way of illustration we calculate baryon masses and leave meson masses as an exercise (example 10.14). In terms of the spins of the constituent quarks the baryon spin $\boldsymbol{J}$ is given by

$$J^2 = (\boldsymbol{s}_1 + \boldsymbol{s}_2 + \boldsymbol{s}_3)^2 = s_1^2 + s_2^2 + s_3^2 + 2(\boldsymbol{s}_1\cdot\boldsymbol{s}_2 + \boldsymbol{s}_1\cdot\boldsymbol{s}_3 + \boldsymbol{s}_2\cdot\boldsymbol{s}_3)$$

hence,

$$\sum_{i<j} \boldsymbol{s}_i\cdot\boldsymbol{s}_j = \tfrac{1}{2}[j(j+1) - \tfrac{9}{4}] = \begin{cases} +\tfrac{3}{4} & \text{for } j = \tfrac{3}{2} \text{ (decuplet)} \\ -\tfrac{3}{4} & \text{for } j = \tfrac{1}{2} \text{ (octet).} \end{cases} \tag{10.40}$$

Consider first the octet baryons. For the nucleon we have (equating the masses of the u and d quarks)

$$m_{\rm N} = 3m_{\rm u} - \frac{3}{4}\frac{a'}{m_{\rm u}^2}. \tag{10.41}$$

In the evaluation of the Σ and Λ masses we have to take into account the fact that $m_{\rm s} > m_{\rm u}, m_{\rm d}$ in the calculation of the hyperfine splitting term. The Σ and Λ have isospin $I = 1$ and 0 respectively. Since the strange quark has $I = 0$, the u and d quarks must be in an $I = 1$ combination (symmetric) in the Σ and $I = 0$ (antisymmetric) in the Λ. Therefore, in the Σ the spins of the u and d quarks must couple to give spin 1 (symmetric) and in the Λ they must give spin 0 (antisymmetric) in order that the spin/flavour wavefunctions be symmetric: the antisymmetric colour wavefunction guarantees overall antisymmetry. Thus, for the Σ we have

$$J_{ud}^2 = (\boldsymbol{s}_u + \boldsymbol{s}_d)^2 = s_u^2 + s_d^2 + 2\boldsymbol{s}_u\cdot\boldsymbol{s}_d = 2$$

and

$$\boldsymbol{s}_u\cdot\boldsymbol{s}_d = \tfrac{1}{4}.$$

For the Λ, $J_{ud} = 0$ and

$$\boldsymbol{s}_u\cdot\boldsymbol{s}_d = -\tfrac{3}{4}.$$

Hence,

$$m_\Lambda = m_u + m_d + m_s + a'\left(\frac{\boldsymbol{s}_u\cdot\boldsymbol{s}_d}{m_u m_d} + \frac{\boldsymbol{s}_u\cdot\boldsymbol{s}_s}{m_u m_s} + \frac{\boldsymbol{s}_d\cdot\boldsymbol{s}_s}{m_d m_s}\right)$$

$$= 2m_u + m_s + a'\left[\frac{\boldsymbol{s}_u\cdot\boldsymbol{s}_d}{m_u^2} + \frac{1}{m_u m_s}(\boldsymbol{s}_u\cdot\boldsymbol{s}_s + \boldsymbol{s}_d\cdot\boldsymbol{s}_s)\right].$$

Noting that $\boldsymbol{s}_u\cdot\boldsymbol{s}_s + \boldsymbol{s}_d\cdot\boldsymbol{s}_s = \boldsymbol{s}_1\cdot\boldsymbol{s}_2 + \boldsymbol{s}_1\cdot\boldsymbol{s}_3 + \boldsymbol{s}_2\cdot\boldsymbol{s}_3 - \boldsymbol{s}_u\cdot\boldsymbol{s}_d = -\tfrac{3}{4} + \tfrac{3}{4} = 0$, we have, finally,

$$m_\Lambda = 2m_u + m_s - \frac{3}{4}\frac{a'}{m_u^2}. \tag{10.42}$$

A similar calculation yields

$$m_\Sigma = 2m_u + m_s + \frac{a'}{4}\left(\frac{1}{m_u^2} - \frac{4}{m_u m_s}\right). \tag{10.43}$$

The Ξ mass is obtained from equation (10.43) by the interchange u $\leftrightarrow$ s, hence

$$m_\Xi = m_u + 2m_s + \frac{a'}{4}\left(\frac{1}{m_s^2} - \frac{4}{m_u m_s}\right). \tag{10.44}$$

In the case of the $\tfrac{3}{2}^+$ decuplet, the quark spins are aligned such that each pair combines to give spin 1. Thus, for example,

$$J_{12}^2 = (\boldsymbol{s}_1 + \boldsymbol{s}_2)^2 = s_1^2 + s_2^2 + 2\boldsymbol{s}_1\cdot\boldsymbol{s}_2$$

and

$$\boldsymbol{s}_1\cdot\boldsymbol{s}_2 = \tfrac{1}{2}[j(j+1) - s_1(s_1+1) - s_2(s_2+1)] = \tfrac{1}{4}.$$

Hence, for all states in the decuplet,

$$\boldsymbol{s}_1\cdot\boldsymbol{s}_2 = \boldsymbol{s}_1\cdot\boldsymbol{s}_3 = \boldsymbol{s}_2\cdot\boldsymbol{s}_3 = \tfrac{1}{4}.$$

Table 10.5
Quark model predictions for the masses of the $\frac{3}{2}^+$ baryons

Baryon	Coefficient of m_u or m_d	Coefficient of m_s	ΔE_{hfs}	Predicted mass/ (GeV/c^2)	Observed mass/ (GeV/c^2)
N	3	0	$-3a'/4m_u^2$	0.939	0.939
Λ	2	1	$-3a'/4m_u^2$	1.114	1.116
Σ	2	1	$(3a'/4m_u^2) - (a'/m_u m_s)$	1.179	1.192
Ξ	1	2	$(a'/4m_s^2) - (a'/m_u m_s)$	1.327	1.318
$\Delta(1232)$	3	0	$3a'/4m_u^2$	1.239	1.232
$\Sigma(1385)$	2	1	$(a'/4m_u^2) + (a'/2m_u m_s)$	1.381	1.385
$\Xi(1530)$	1	2	$(a'/4m_s^2) + (a'/2m_u m_s)$	1.529	1.533
Ω^-	0	3	$3a'/4m_s^2$	1.682	1.672

(After Gasiorowicz S and Rosner J L 1981 *Am J Phys* **49** (954).)

Table 10.6
Current and constituent masses of the u, d and s quarks

Quark	Current mass/(MeV/c^2)	Constituent mass /(MeV/c^2)	
		Mesons	Baryons
u	5.6 ± 1.1 }	310	363
d	9.9 ± 1.1 }		
s	199 ± 33	483	538

The current masses are evaluated at a scale of 1 GeV/c^2.

It is then a simple matter to calculate the masses of the decuplet members using equation (10.39). The results, for constituent masses $m_u = m_d = 0.363\ \mathrm{GeV}/c^2$, $m_s = 0.538\ \mathrm{GeV}/c^2$ and $a'/m_u^2 = 0.2\ \mathrm{GeV}/c^2$, are given in table 10.5.

In spite of the simplicity of the model and the fact that effects such as variation in $|\psi(0)|^2$, different binding energies and different kinetic energies have been neglected, the agreement between the predicted and observed masses is impressive. The effective or constituent masses of the light quarks, as they appear in mesons and baryons, are summarized in table 10.6. That the effective masses in baryons appear to be about 50 MeV/c^2 greater than in mesons may be attributable to small differences in binding effects.

The constituent masses of the quarks are quite distinct from the 'current' quark masses which appear in the QCD Lagrangian describing the interactions between quarks and gluons. These are quark masses free of the dynamical effects experienced in hadrons. The $SU(3)_{flavour}$ symmetry of strong interactions arises because the current quark masses are small compared with typical hadronic mass scales. To the extent that quark masses may be neglected, the strong interactions are flavour independent: the u, d, s, . . . , quarks experience the same strong interactions. The symmetry breaking appears in the Lagrangian through terms of the form

$$L = m_u u\bar{u} + m_d d\bar{d} + m_s s\bar{s} + \cdots \tag{10.45}$$

where m_f is the current mass of the quark with flavour f. In section 10.7 we shall discover that, in addition to the light quarks u, d and s, much heavier quarks (charm c and bottom b) exist. The specific pattern of quark masses appearing in nature is a mystery: the standard model of Glashow, Weinberg and Salam (chapter 13) has nothing to say on this matter. In the study of 'ordinary' hadrons the effect of c and b quarks may safely be neglected. Consistent values for the light quark masses have been obtained from consideration of the pseudoscalar-meson masses, baryon masses and the decay $\eta \to 3\pi$. For example, the symmetry-breaking term in the Lagrangian (10.45) has been used to compute ratios of masses of the pseudoscalar mesons:[6]

$$\frac{m_d}{m_u} = \frac{m_{K^0}^2 - m_{K^+}^2 + m_{\pi^+}^2}{2m_{\pi^0}^2 + m_{K^+}^2 - m_{K^0}^2 - m_{\pi^+}^2} \approx 1.8$$

$$\frac{m_s}{m_d} = \frac{m_{K^0}^2 + m_{K^+}^2 - m_{\pi^+}^2}{m_{K^0}^2 - m_{K^+}^2 + m_{\pi^+}^2} \approx 20.$$

When combined with an estimate of the strange quark mass from the Λ–N mass difference, $m_s \approx 150\ \mathrm{MeV}/c^2$, one obtains $m_u \approx 4.2\ \mathrm{MeV}/c^2$, and $m_d \approx 7.5\ \mathrm{MeV}/c^2$. The current quark masses shown in table 10.6 are taken from the 'Review of particle properties'.[7]

We shall see in chapter 14 that the mass scale characteristic of the strong interactions has a value $\Lambda_{QCD} \approx 0.2$ GeV. The masses of the u and d quarks are negligible in comparison and it is this which results in the (accidental) isospin symmetry of the strong interactions discussed in section 8.7. The mass of the s quark is comparable with Λ_{QCD} and as a result $SU(3)_{flavour}$ is only an approximate symmetry.

10.6 Baryon magnetic moments

As a further example of the predictive power of the quark model we consider the magnetic dipole moments of the $\frac{1}{2}^+$ octet baryons. In this ground-state octet the quarks have zero relative orbital angular momentum so the net magnetic moment of a baryon is simply the vector sum of the dipole moments of the constituent quarks, $\boldsymbol{\mu} = \boldsymbol{\mu}_1 + \boldsymbol{\mu}_2 + \boldsymbol{\mu}_3$. It is a matter of convention that when one speaks of the magnetic moment of a particle, rather than the vector $\boldsymbol{\mu}$, one means the *maximum observable component* of the magnetic moment μ_z, which, for a positively charged particle, corresponds to a spin orientation 'along' the positive z axis. For a point-like spin $\frac{1}{2}$ particle of charge e and mass m the magnetic moment is

$$\mu = \frac{e}{2m}. \tag{10.46}$$

Thus, for the structureless spin $\frac{1}{2}$ quarks, the magnetic moments are

$$\mu_u = \frac{2}{3}\frac{e}{2m_u} \qquad \mu_d = -\frac{1}{3}\frac{e}{2m_d} \qquad \mu_s = -\frac{1}{3}\frac{e}{2m_s}. \tag{10.47}$$

In order to calculate the magnetic moments of the ground-state baryons we need the quark wavefunctions for the baryons with spin component $s_z = +\frac{1}{2}$. In section 10.4 we saw that the ground-state baryons belong to a **56** of SU(6) and that the totally symmetric octet arises from the linear combination

$$\sqrt{\tfrac{1}{2}}[(\mathbf{8}_{M_S}, \mathbf{2}_{M_S}) + (\mathbf{8}_{M_A}, \mathbf{2}_{M_A})]. \tag{10.48}$$

The explicit wavefunction for a spin-up proton, for example, is

$$|p\uparrow\rangle = \sqrt{\tfrac{1}{2}}(p_{M_S}\chi_{M_S} + p_{M_A}\chi_{M_A}) \tag{10.49}$$

where p_{M_S}, p_{M_A} are the flavour wavefunctions. The spin wavefunctions χ_{M_S} and χ_{M_A} have the same form as p_{M_S} and p_{M_A} with the replacement $u \to \uparrow$ and $d \to \downarrow$. Explicitly

$$|p\uparrow\rangle = \sqrt{\tfrac{1}{2}}\{\sqrt{\tfrac{1}{6}}[(ud + du)u - 2uud]\sqrt{\tfrac{1}{6}}[(\uparrow\downarrow + \downarrow\uparrow)\uparrow - 2\uparrow\uparrow\downarrow] + \sqrt{\tfrac{1}{2}}[(ud - du)u]\sqrt{\tfrac{1}{2}}[(\uparrow\downarrow - \downarrow\uparrow)\uparrow]\} \tag{10.50}$$

or

$$|p\uparrow\rangle = \sqrt{\tfrac{1}{18}}(2u\uparrow u\uparrow d\downarrow - u\downarrow u\uparrow d\uparrow - u\uparrow u\downarrow d\uparrow + 2d\downarrow u\uparrow u\uparrow - d\uparrow u\uparrow u\downarrow - d\uparrow u\downarrow u\uparrow + 2u\uparrow d\downarrow u\uparrow - u\downarrow d\uparrow u\uparrow - u\uparrow d\uparrow u\downarrow). \tag{10.51}$$

The proton magnetic moment is given by

$$\begin{aligned}\mu_p &= \langle p\uparrow|\mu_1 + \mu_2 + \mu_3|p\uparrow\rangle \\ &= 3 \times \tfrac{1}{18}[4\mu_u + 4\mu_u - 4\mu_d + (-\mu_u + \mu_u + \mu_d) + (\mu_u - \mu_u + \mu_d)] \\ &= \tfrac{1}{3}(4\mu_u - \mu_d).\end{aligned} \tag{10.52}$$

The magnetic moment of the neutron is obtained from (10.52) by interchanging u and d, so

$$\mu_u = \tfrac{1}{3}(4\mu_d - \mu_u). \tag{10.53}$$

Similar calculations can be performed for the other octet members. Using

Table 10.7
Comparison between the predicted and observed magnetic dipole moments of the $\frac{1}{2}^+$ baryons

Baryon	Dipole moment	Predicted/μ_N	Observed/μ_N
p	$\frac{1}{3}(4\mu_u - \mu_d)$	2.79	2.793
n	$\frac{1}{3}(4\mu_d - \mu_u)$	-1.86	-1.913
Λ	μ_s	-0.58	-0.613 ± 0.004
Σ^+	$\frac{1}{3}(4\mu_u - \mu_s)$	2.68	2.42 ± 0.05
Σ^0	$\frac{1}{3}(2\mu_u + 2\mu_d - \mu_s)$	0.82	
Σ^-	$\frac{1}{3}(4\mu_d - \mu_s)$	-1.05	-1.157 ± 0.025
Ξ^0	$\frac{1}{3}(4\mu_s - \mu_u)$	-1.40	-1.250 ± 0.014
Ξ^-	$\frac{1}{3}(4\mu_s - \mu_d)$	-0.47	-0.679 ± 0.031

the constituent quark masses in table 10.6 we obtain the quark magnetic moments, in nuclear magnetons,

$$\mu_u = 1.863$$

$$\mu_d = -0.931$$

$$\mu_s = -0.582.$$

These values lead to the predicted moments for the baryons shown in table 10.7. The agreement between the predicted and measured magnetic moments is good for the p, n and Λ but less so for the other members of the octet. This may not be too surprising in view of the crudeness of the model. Here, we have dealt exclusively with the so-called valence quarks which endow the hadrons with their static properties. In chapter 12 we shall see that hadrons have much more complicated structures than implied in this chapter: small contributions to the magnetic moments should arise from the 'sea' of quark–antiquark pairs which exist in baryons in addition to the valence quarks.

10.7 *Heavy-meson spectroscopy*

In addition to the three light quarks u, d and s, which we have discussed so far in this chapter, two other much heavier quarks, charm c and bottom or beauty b, are known to exist. They were first discovered as 'hidden' flavours in the ψ (psi) and Υ (upsilon) mesons which are respectively $c\bar{c}$ and $b\bar{b}$ bound states. Although on vastly different energy scales, the observed spectroscopic levels in the ψ and Υ systems are very similar to the observed level scheme in the e^+e^- system (positronium). The close agreement between theoretical predictions based on simple potential models and experimental observations of the level spacings in the ψ and Υ systems strongly supports the validity of the quark model.

10.7.1 Charmonium states

Charmonium is the name given to the series of ψ mesons first observed in 1974 in e^+e^- collisions at the Stanford Linear Accelerator Center (SLAC) by Augustin *et al.*[8] using the e^+e^- collider (SPEAR). At the same time the lowest-lying state, called J by the experimenters and subsequently known as J/ψ, was discovered in collisions of 28 GeV protons on a beryllium target at the Brookhaven alternating-gradient synchrotron (AGS) by Aubert *et al.*[9]

The mass of the J/ψ is about 3.1 GeV and in the SLAC experiment it was observed as a large, narrow peak in the cross-sections for hadronic, $\mu^+\mu^-$ and e^+e^- final states when the total centre-of-mass energy was scanned in small steps around 3.1 GeV. A second resonance, the ψ', with mass 3.7 GeV, was also discovered in this first SPEAR experiment. In the fixed-target experiment at the AGS the J/ψ was produced in the inclusive reaction

$$p + Be \to J/\psi + \text{anything}$$

and detected through its decay $J/\psi \to e^+e^-$. The e^+e^- pairs were detected in coincidence in a double-armed magnetic spectrometer and the J/ψ appeared as a sharp peak in the invariant mass distribution of the electron–positron pairs. The SLAC measurements in the vicinity of the J/ψ and ψ' are shown in figures 10.12 and 10.13, respectively, and the mass spectrum showing J/ψ production in the Brookhaven experiment is shown in figure 10.14.

The natural width of the J/ψ is actually much smaller than the observed experimental widths, the latter being dominated by the uncertainty in the circulating-beam energies in the SPEAR storage ring and by the momentum resolution in the Brookhaven experiment. Figure 10.12(a) shows the total cross-section for hadron production as a function of centre-of-mass energy in the SLAC experiment. The observed width of the J/ψ, 2.6 MeV, is consistent with that expected from the energy spread of the e^+ and e^- beams in the SPEAR storage ring so the natural width of the J/ψ resonance must be much smaller. Figures 10.12(b) and 10.12(c) show the corresponding cross-sections for the $\mu^+\mu^-$ and e^+e^- final states in the angular range $|\cos\theta| \leqslant 0.6$, where θ is the angle between the outgoing positively charged lepton and the incident positron. The cross-sections in figure 10.12 were fitted simultaneously[10] to obtain the mass and the partial widths Γ_h, Γ_μ and Γ_e for hadrons, muons and electrons respectively. The total width Γ was assumed to be the sum of these partial widths. The data in figure 10.12 have not been corrected for radiative effects. Radiative corrections were therefore incorporated into the fitting procedure in which the energy resolution function of the beam, assumed to be Gaussian, was convoluted with a Breit–Wigner cross-section. The parametrization of the Breit–Wigner formula, used by Boyarski *et al.*[10] and appropriate for the

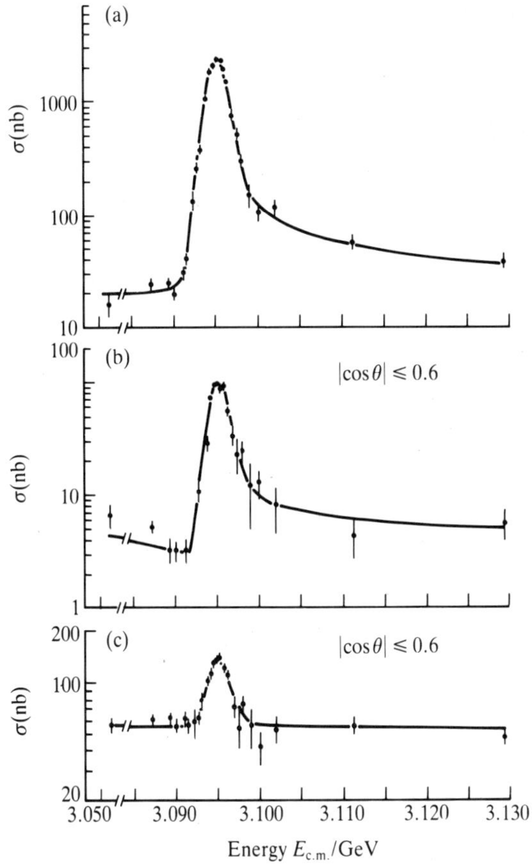

Figure 10.12 Cross-sections as a function of centre-of-mass energy E_{cm} in the vicinity of the J/ψ(3095) for (a) $e^+e^- \rightarrow$ hadrons, (b) $e^+e^- \rightarrow \mu^+\mu^-$ and (c) $e^+e^- \rightarrow e^+e^-$. The curves are fits to the data. (After Augustin J E *et al.* 1974 *Phys Rev Lett* **33** (1406).)

formation of the ψ in the reaction $e^+e^- \rightarrow \psi$ followed by decay into channel x, is

$$\sigma_x(\sqrt{s}) = \pi \frac{2J+1}{s} \frac{\Gamma_e \Gamma_x}{(\sqrt{s}-m)^2 + \Gamma^2/4}. \tag{10.54}$$

Here, J is the spin of the ψ, Γ_e and Γ_x are the partial widths for the electron channel and the channel x respectively and Γ is the total width. The centre-of-mass energy is denoted by $\sqrt{s}$ and m is the mass of the ψ. The main results of the fit were $m = 3.095 \pm 0.004$ GeV, $\Gamma_e = \Gamma_\mu = 4.8 \pm 0.6$ keV, $\Gamma_h = 59 \pm 14$ keV and $\Gamma = 69 \pm 15$ keV. The equality of the partial widths Γ_e and Γ_μ is expected from μ–e universality but the most remarkable result is the extremely small total width Γ which is several orders of magnitude smaller than one might naively expect for a hadronic state of such high

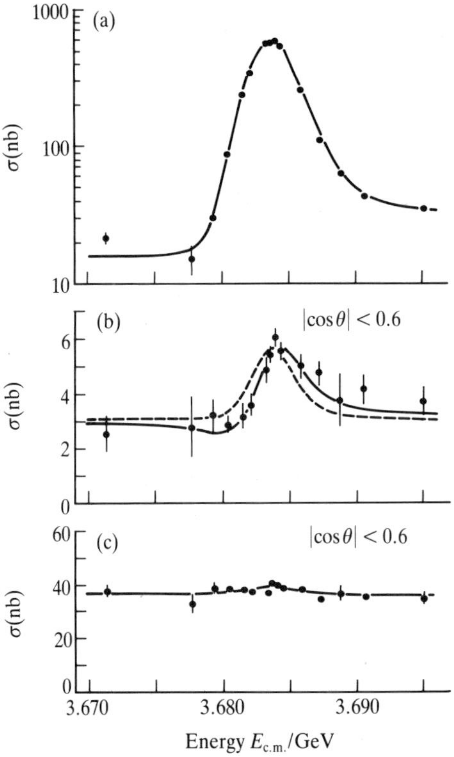

Figure 10.13 Cross-sections as a function of centre-of-mass energy E_{cm} in the vicinity of the $\psi(3685)$ for (a) $e^+e^- \to$ hadrons, (b) $e^+e^- \to \mu^+\mu^-$ and (c) $e^+e^- \to e^+e^-$. The solid curves are fits to the data. The broken curve in (b) corresponds to no interference. (After Boyarski A M *et al.* 1975 *Phys Rev Lett* **34** (1357).)

mass. A similar analysis[11] for the ψ', or $\psi(3685)$, gave $\Gamma_e = 2.1 \pm 0.3$ keV and $\Gamma \approx 228 \pm 56$ keV.

The spin and parity of the J/ψ have been determined both by the study of interference effects and by the measurement of the angular distributions of the leptons from J/ψ decays. In the vicinity of the J/ψ resonance there are two amplitudes which contribute to the process $e^+e^- \to \mu^+\mu^-$, namely direct resonance production (figure 10.15(a)) and the pure QED process (figure 10.15(b)). If the resonance has the same quantum numbers as the photon, $J^P = 1^-$, the amplitudes of these two processes should interfere. Interference is more easily studied in the $\mu^+\mu^-$ channel than in the e^+e^- because in the latter case most of the cross-section in the angular range $|\cos\theta| < 0.6$ arises through the exchange of 'spacelike' photons (figure 10.16(a)), whereas the $\mu^+\mu^-$ final state can be reached only through 'timelike' photons (figure 10.16(b)). Interference effects are thus much smaller in the e^+e^- channel than in the muon channel. Because the interference effects are quite small Boyarski *et al.*[10] chose to investigate the ratio of the yield of muon pairs to that of electron pairs, $\sigma_{\mu\mu}/\sigma_{ee}$,

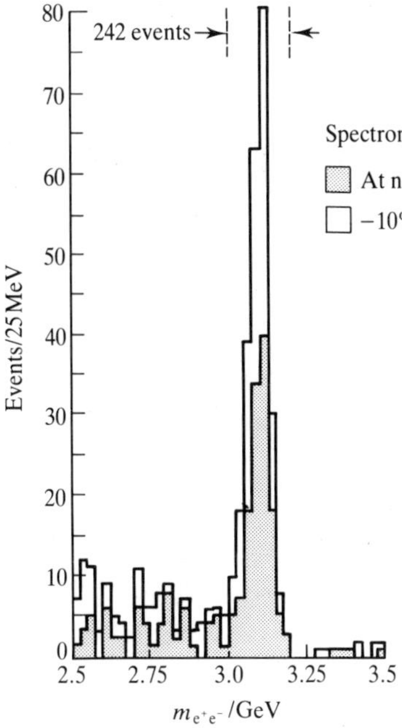

Figure 10.14
Electron–positron mass spectrum from the reaction $p + Be \rightarrow e^+e^- + X$. (After Aubert J J *et al.* 1974 *Phys Rev Lett* **33** (1404).)

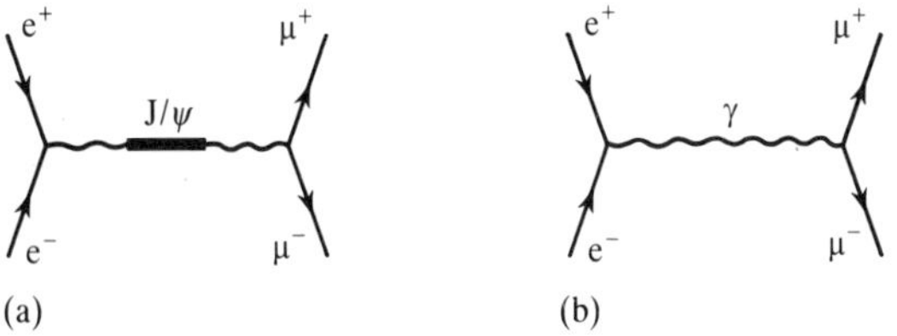

Figure 10.15
Feynman diagrams for (a) direct J/ψ production $e^+e^- \rightarrow J/\psi \rightarrow \mu^+\mu^-$ and (b) the pure QED process $e^+e^- \rightarrow \mu^+\mu^-$.

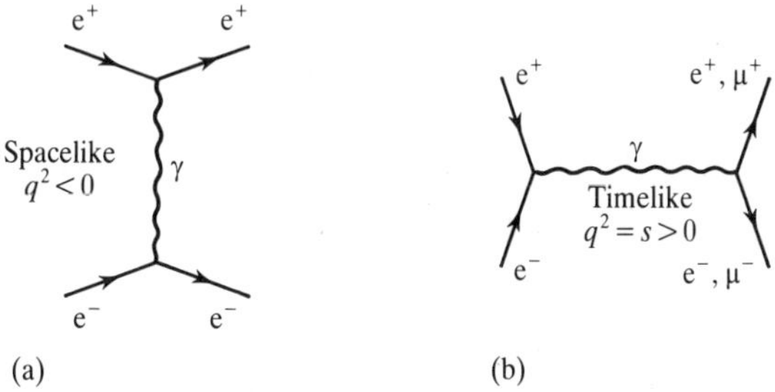

Figure 10.16
Electron–positron scattering via the exchange of (a) spacelike and (b) timelike photons.

as a function of centre-of-mass energy, in order to minimize systematic errors due to normalization. This ratio, for the detected angular range $|\cos\theta| < 0.6$ is shown in figure 10.17. Also shown for comparison are the corresponding results[11] for the ψ'. The solid curves are the predicted results for maximum interference, i.e. $J^P = 1^-$, while the broken curve is the expectation for no interference which would result, for example, if the spin-parity of the $\psi(\psi')$ were $0^\pm$ or 1^+. The spin-parity $J^P = 1^-$ is clearly preferred for both the ψ and ψ'. This interference is also evident in the

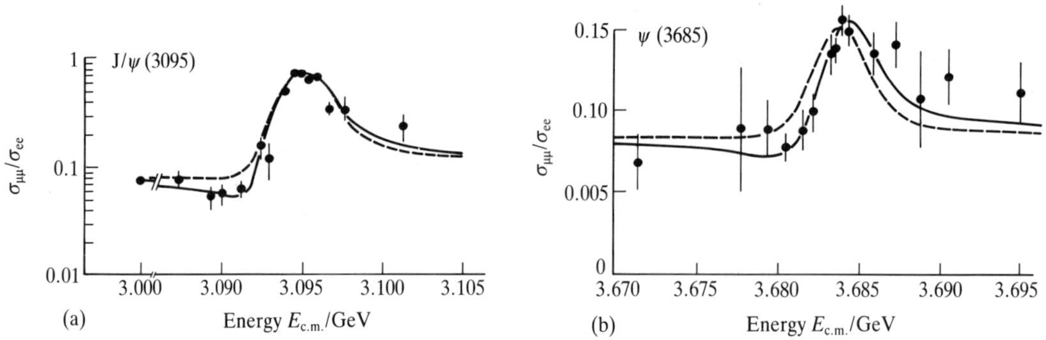

Figure 10.17 The ratio of muon pair to electron pair production in the vicinity of (a) the J/ψ(3095) and (b) the ψ(3685): ———, expected interference; -----, no interference.

asymmetrical shape of the J/ψ and ψ′ peaks in the $\mu^+\mu^-$ cross-sections in figures 10.12(b) and 10.13(b) respectively. Additional support for the $J^P = 1^-$ assignments arises from the forward–backward asymmetry for the process $e^+e^- \to \mu^+\mu^-$ in the vicinity of the resonances. In each case the asymmetry is consistent with zero, as expected for $J^P = 1^-$: a non-zero asymmetry would be expected for an axial vector meson with $J^P = 1^+$.

The charge conjugation parity C of both the J/ψ(3097) and the ψ(3685) must be -1 because of the following simple argument. Any eigenstate of C and P which decays to $\mu^+\mu^-$ is unaltered by the combined operation CP. Such eigenstates must therefore have $C = P$. The observed interference effects and forward–backward asymmetries unambiguously demand a negative intrinsic parity for both J/ψ(3097) and ψ(3685) and therefore each has $C = -1$.

Finally, we turn to the I spin and G-parity assignments of the J/ψ(3097). We recall from section 8.11 that the pion has $G = -1$ and a state which decays to n pions has G-parity $(-1)^n$. An analysis of the hadronic decays of the J/ψ shows that although decay to an odd number of pions is much more frequent than decay to an even number, both types of decay occur. One might conclude therefore that the J/ψ is not an eigenstate of G. Contributions to the hadronic decay of the J/ψ arise from both mechanisms shown in figure 10.18. The direct decays (figure 10.18(a)) are G-parity conserving while the electromagnetic decays (figure 10.18(b)) are not: the latter can give rise to final states with either even or odd numbers of pions. The dominance of the decay to odd numbers of pions arises from the direct channel and implies that $G = -1$ for the J/ψ(3097).

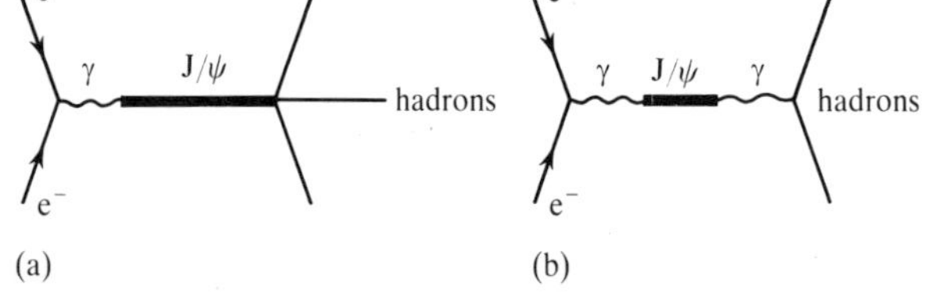

Figure 10.18
Possible mechanisms for the decay J/ψ → hadrons: (a) direct and (b) electromagnetic decays.

Table 10.8
Main properties of the 1S and 2S states, J/ψ(3097) and ψ(3685), of the charmonium system

State	Mass/MeV	Width Γ/keV	J^{PC}	I^G	Principal decay modes	Fraction Γ_i/Γ
J/ψ(1S) or ψ(3097)	3096.93 ± 0.09	68 ± 10	1^{--}	0^-	Hadrons	$(86.0 \pm 2.0) \times 10^{-2}$
					Virtual $\gamma \to$ hadrons	$(17.0 \pm 2.0) \times 10^{-2}$
					e^+e^-	$(6.9 \pm 0.9) \times 10^{-2}$
					$\mu^+\mu^-$	$(6.9 \pm 0.9) \times 10^{-2}$
ψ(2S) or ψ(3685)	3686.00 ± 0.10	243 ± 43	1^{--}	0^-	J/ψ(1S) anything	$(57 \pm 4) \times 10^{-2}$
					$\gamma\chi_{c0}(1P)$	$(9.3 \pm 0.8) \times 10^{-2}$
					$\gamma\chi_{c1}(1P)$	$(8.7 \pm 0.8) \times 10^{-2}$
					$\gamma\chi_{c2}(1P)$	$(7.8 \pm 0.8) \times 10^{-2}$
					$\gamma\eta_c(1S)$	$(2.8 \pm 0.6) \times 10^{-3}$
					e^+e^-	$(8.8 \pm 1.3) \times 10^{-3}$
					$\mu^+\mu^-$	$(7.7 \pm 1.7) \times 10^{-3}$

The I spin of the J/ψ(3097) can be determined by considering the decays $J/\psi \to 3\pi$. The existence of this decay mode implies that $I \leqslant 3$. We recall that for a neutral meson $G = C(-1)^I$ and, since both G and C are negative, I must be even, i.e. $I = 0$ or 2. The $I = 2$ assignment is ruled out by the observation that the 3π decay mode proceeds predominantly via $\rho\pi$. Experimentally, the three charge states $\rho^+\pi^-$, $\rho^0\pi^0$ and $\rho^-\pi^+$ occur with equal probability, as expected for $I = 0$. An I spin analysis of the dominant decay mode of the ψ', $\psi' \to J/\psi$ + anything, strongly favours the $I = 0$ assignment for the ψ'.

In summary, the important properties of the J/ψ(3097) and ψ(3685) are given in table 10.8.

10.7.2 *The J/ψ width and the OZI rule*

The extremely narrow widths of the J/ψ(3097) and ψ(3685), 68 ± 10 and 243 ± 43 keV respectively, cannot be explained in terms of the light quarks, u, d and s, and their antiquarks: other vector mesons such as the $\rho(770)$ and the $\omega(783)$, which are bound states of light quarks, have widths of the order of 150 and 8 MeV respectively. Some time before the discovery of the J/ψ and ψ(3685) a new flavour of quark had in fact been postulated by Glashow, Iliopoulos and Maiani[12] to explain the non-existence of strangeness-changing neutral currents (see section 13.6.2). This new flavour they called charm, C, which, like strangeness, is conserved in strong and electromagnetic interactions. It was postulated that the J/ψ and ψ(3685) are bound states $(c\bar{c})$ of these charmed quarks. If this is indeed the case, the high masses of these states implies that the charmed quark itself must be heavy with a constituent mass $m_c \approx m_{J/\psi}/2 \approx 1.5\ \text{GeV}/c^2$.

It should be noted that these $c\bar{c}$ states, charmonium, have charm quantum number $C = 0$ (hidden charm). The acid test of the charm hypothesis is that particles with $C \neq 0$ (open charm) should exist, with quark combinations such as $c\bar{d}$, $c\bar{u}$, etc. Such mesons have since been discovered: the lowest lying of these are the pseudoscalar mesons D^+ ($=c\bar{d}$) and D^0 ($=c\bar{u}$) and their antiparticles D^- ($=\bar{c}d$) and $\bar{D}^0$ ($=\bar{c}u$). One might, therefore, expect the J/ψ to decay via the charm-conserving strong decay $J/\psi \to D\bar{D}$ with a width typical of the strong interactions, i.e. several mega-electronvolts. Such a decay, although allowed by the conservation laws, is energetically forbidden: the masses of the D mesons are

$$m_{D^0} = 1864.5 \pm 0.5 \text{ MeV} \qquad m_{D^+} = 1869.3 \pm 0.5 \text{ MeV}$$

and consequently $m_{J/\psi} < 2m_D$. It follows that the J/ψ can decay only into states containing the light quarks, u, d, s, and their antiquarks, but the problem of the narrow width remains.

The way out of the dilemma is through the Zweig rule, or, more correctly, the OZI rule (Okubo,[13] Zweig[14] and Iizuka[15]). The rule was invented to explain the suppression of the 3π decay mode of the φ meson relative to the $K\bar{K}$ mode. Experimentally,

$$\frac{\Gamma(\phi \to 3\pi)}{\Gamma(\phi \to K\bar{K})} \approx 0.18$$

even though phase space considerations favour the 3π mode. The OZI rule postulates that hadronic decays described by *disconnected* quark flow diagrams are suppressed relative to those described by connected diagrams. In the case of the φ meson, a bound state of $s\bar{s}$ quarks, the decay $\phi \to K\bar{K}$ can proceed via the connected diagram shown in figure 10.19(a), whereas the decay $\phi \to 3\pi$ can proceed only via the disconnected diagram shown in figure 10.19(b).

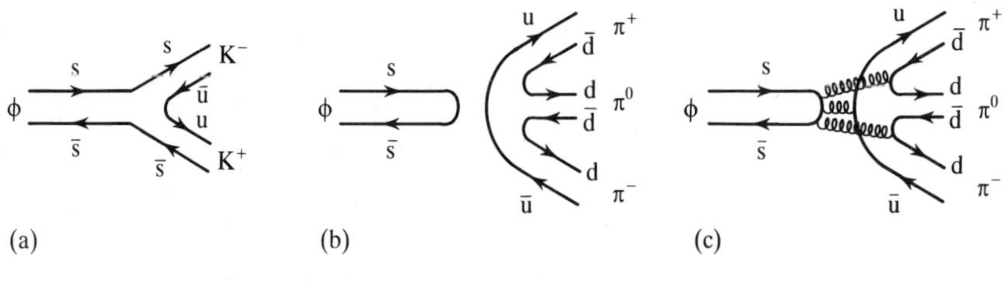

Figure 10.19
(a) OZI-allowed decay $\phi \to K\bar{K}$; (b) OZI-forbidden decay $\phi \to \pi^+\pi^-\pi^0$; (c) OZI-forbidden decay showing the three-gluon coupling.

In the latter case, the coupling between the initial and final state quarks is provided by a triplet of gluons (figure 10.19(c)), a triplet being necessary in order to preserve the colour singlet nature of the hadrons. The rate for gluon emission is governed by the strong coupling constant α_s so that the amplitude for figure 10.19(c) is proportional to $(\alpha_s)^3$ whereas that for figure 10.19(a) is proportional to α_s. The strong coupling constant at the mass of the φ meson has a value $\alpha_s \approx 0.5$, hence the suppression of the

3π mode relative to the $K\bar{K}$ mode. The fact that the width $\Gamma(\phi \to K\bar{K})$ is only about 5 MeV is due to the very limited available phase space: the $K\bar{K}$ threshold is just below the ϕ mass.

As we indicated in chapter 7 and will see in more detail in chapter 14, the strong coupling constant α_s *decreases* with increasing energy. At the mass of the J/ψ, $\alpha_s \approx 0.19$, so that the suppression of the 'OZI-forbidden' decays is expected to be even greater for the J/ψ than for the ϕ. Figure 10.20(a) shows the 'OZI-allowed' decay $J/\psi \to D\bar{D}$ while figure 10.20(b) shows the 'OZI-forbidden' decay $J/\psi \to \pi^+\pi^-\pi^0$. As pointed out earlier, the lightest charmed meson, D^0, has a mass of 1865 MeV so that both the J/ψ and the $\psi(3685)$ are below the threshold for $D^0\bar{D}^0$ decay. These states are therefore so narrow because they can decay only through 'OZI-suppressed' channels.

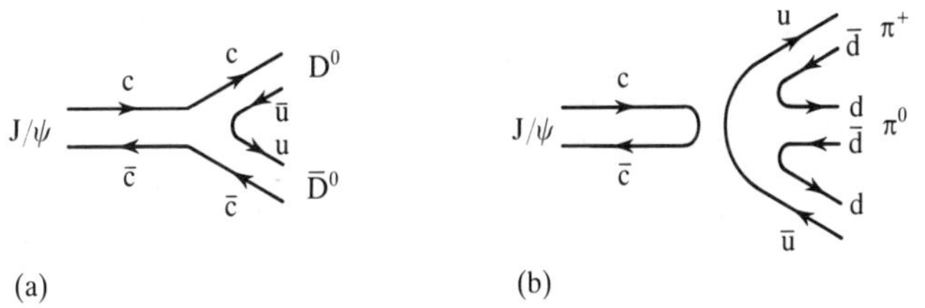

Figure 10.20
(a) OZI-allowed decay $J/\psi \to D^0\bar{D}^0$ (energetically forbidden); (b) OZI-forbidden decay $J/\psi \to \pi^+\pi^-\pi^0$.

10.7.3 Bottomonium states

A few years after the discovery of the narrow charmonium states, other narrow states in the mass range 9.0–10.5 GeV were discovered at FNAL[16,17] in the collisions of 400 GeV protons with Cu and Pt targets. The inclusive di-muon spectrum from the reaction

$$p + \text{nucleus} \to \mu^+\mu^- + \text{anything}$$

is shown for $m_{\mu^+\mu^-} > 6$ GeV in figure 10.21. There is clear evidence for at least two states superimposed on an exponentially falling continuum. These states, called upsilon (Υ), are bound states of quarks which are even heavier than the charmed quarks. The new flavour is called bottom, b, and, as for the charmed quarks, a whole new spectroscopy of $b\bar{b}$ states, bottomonium, has since been discovered. As with charmonium the Υ states are readily produced, with better experimental resolution, in e^+e^- collisions and, one year after their discovery, the Υ states were observed and extensively studied at the DORIS storage ring in Hamburg and the Cornell storage ring, CESR, where a total of four Υ states were clearly identified. These are the lowest-lying triplet S states of the $b\bar{b}$ system. Figure 10.22 shows the total cross-section for the production of hadrons

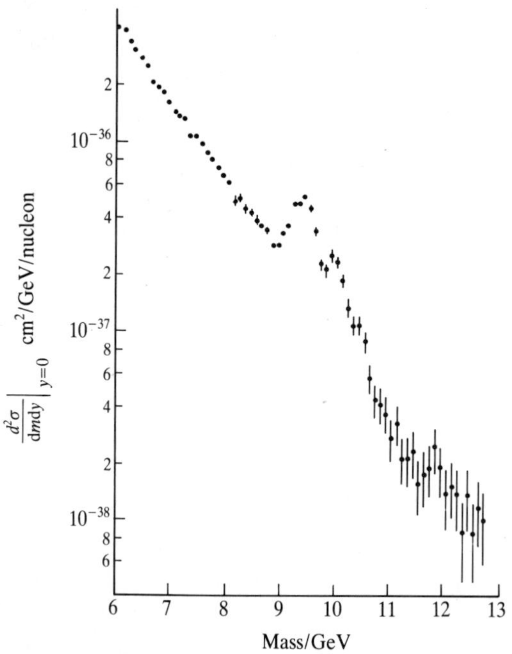

Figure 10.21
Di-muon mass spectrum from the reaction p + nucleus $\rightarrow \mu^+\mu^- X$, for $m_{\mu^+\mu^-} > 6$ GeV.

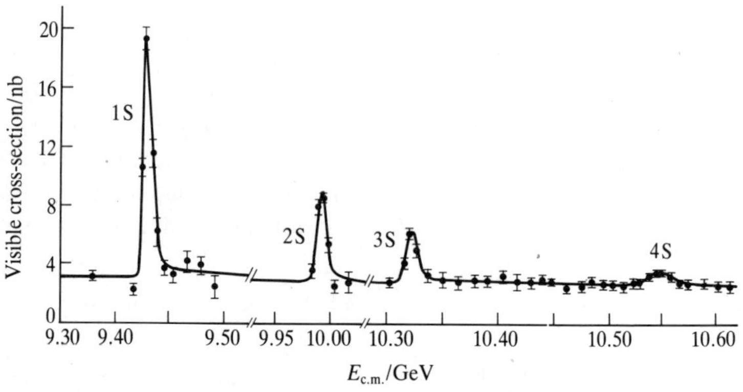

Figure 10.22 Total cross-section for $e^+e^- \rightarrow$ hadrons showing the 1S, 2S, 3S and 4S upsilon states. The masses of these states are 9460, 10 023, 10 355 and 10 580 MeV with total widths of 52 keV, 43 keV, 24 keV and 24 MeV respectively.

in e^+e^- collisions obtained by the CLEO group at Cornell. It should be noted that the first three states are narrow while the fourth is a broad resonance, its increased width arising from the energetically allowed strong decay to $B\bar{B}$ mesons. The narrow widths of the $\Upsilon(1S)$, $\Upsilon(2S)$ and $\Upsilon(3S)$, which are below the $B\bar{B}$ threshold, is due to the fact that these states can decay to hadrons only via OZI-suppressed modes.

10.7.4 Leptonic widths of vector mesons

The leptonic decays of vector mesons proceed via a single virtual photon, as depicted in figure 10.23. Assuming the $q\bar{q}$ system to be non-relativistic, the leptonic width is given to a good approximation[18] by the expression

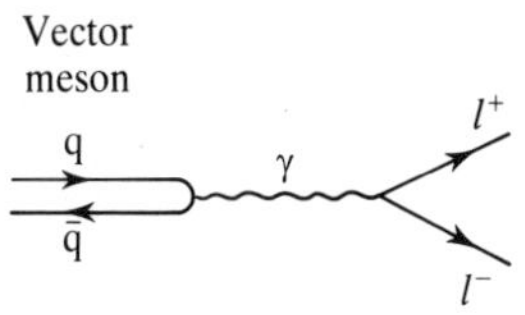

Figure 10.23
Leptonic decay of a vector meson via a virtual intermediate photon.

$$\Gamma_{v\to e^+e^-} \approx \frac{16\pi\alpha^2 Q^2}{m_v^2}|\psi(0)|^2 \tag{10.55}$$

where m_v is the mass of the vector meson, Q is the charge of the appropriate quark (in units of the charge of the electron) and $\psi(0)$ is the quark wavefunction at the origin. This expression can be understood qualitatively as follows. The amplitude for the process in figure 10.23 is proportional to the product of the coupling strengths at the two vertices and the photon propagator. The coupling strength at the quark–photon vertex is

$$\sqrt{\alpha}(\Sigma_i w_i Q_i)$$

where Q_i is the charge of quark i, w_i is the appropriate weight for that quark in the meson concerned and α is the electromagnetic coupling strength. The vertex factor at the photon–lepton vertex is simply $\sqrt{\alpha}$. The photon propagator is approximately q^{-4}, with $q^2 = m_v^2$, and the phase space factor is q^2. The wavefunction $\psi(0)$ is the amplitude for the quark and antiquark to interact with the photon at a point in space–time – the origin of their relative coordinates. On squaring the amplitude and multiplying by the phase space factor for the two-body final state (q^2) equation (10.55) is obtained.

It is quite remarkable that for the $^3S_1$ vector mesons, ρ, ω, ϕ, J/ψ and Υ, ranging in mass from 0.76 GeV to 10 GeV, the ratio $(\Gamma_{v\to e^+e^-})/Q^2$ is very nearly constant, as shown in table 10.9. Two important consequences follow from this result. First, the c and b quarks have been assumed to have charge $Q = +\frac{2}{3}$ and $-\frac{1}{3}$ respectively. In this case the pattern of charge is repeated throughout the different quark generations, (u, d), (c, s) and ((t), b), suggesting that the partner of the b quark, called top (t), which

Table 10.9
Leptonic widths of the vector mesons

State	$\Gamma_{e^+e^-}$/keV	Quark content	Q^2	$\Gamma_{e^+e^-}/Q^2$
ρ	6.77 ± 0.32	$\sqrt{\frac{1}{2}}(u\bar{u} - d\bar{d})$	$\{1/\sqrt{2}[\frac{2}{3} - (-\frac{1}{3})]\}^2 = \frac{1}{2}$	13.5 ± 0.6
ω	0.60 ± 0.02	$\sqrt{\frac{1}{2}}(u\bar{u} + d\bar{d})$	$[1/\sqrt{2}(\frac{2}{3} - \frac{1}{3})]^2 = \frac{1}{18}$	10.8 ± 0.4
ϕ	1.37 ± 0.05	$s\bar{s}$	$(\frac{1}{3})^2 = \frac{1}{9}$	12.3 ± 0.5
J/ψ	4.72 ± 0.35	$c\bar{c}$	$(\frac{2}{3})^2 = \frac{4}{9}$	10.6 ± 0.8
Υ	1.34 ± 0.04	$b\bar{b}$	$(-\frac{1}{3})^2 = \frac{1}{9}$	12.1 ± 0.4

The ratio $\Gamma_{e^+e^-}/Q^2$ is approximately constant.

has yet to be discovered, is likely to have charge $+\frac{2}{3}$. Secondly, the near constancy of the ratio $(\Gamma_{\mathrm{v}\to e^+e^-})/Q^2$ suggests that the quark wavefunction is given by

$$|\psi(0)|^2 \propto m_{\mathrm{v}}^2.$$

This observation can be used as input to determine the form of the potential in which the quarks are bound.

10.7.5 The quarkonium model

If the ψ and Υ states are $c\bar{c}$ and $b\bar{b}$ bound states respectively, it should be possible to predict the energy levels of the states provided the potential $V(r)$, in which the quarks move, is known. The basis of the quarkonium model is the e^+e^- system, positronium, which, like quarkonium, is a bound state of a fermion and an antifermion. The potential in this case is the familiar Coulomb potential, $V(r) = -(\alpha/r)$.

The energy levels of positronium are shown in figure 10.24. For easy comparison with the ψ and Υ systems we have separated the states according to their quantum numbers J^{PC}. We recall that for an electron–positron system with spin S and relative orbital angular momentum L, the parity P is $(-1)^{L+1}$ and the C-parity is $(-1)^{L+S}$.

In the case of quarkonium the exact form of the potential is not known but, by using general arguments, a potential can be found which fits the experimental data on the charmonium and bottomonium systems very well. First, the c and b quarks are heavy ($m_c \approx 1.5$ GeV/c^2, $m_b \approx 5$ GeV/c^2)

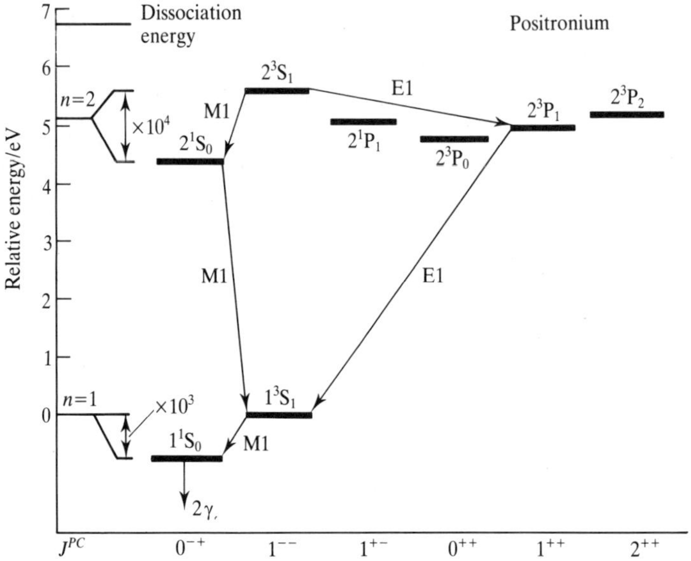

Figure 10.24
Energy levels of positronium showing fine and hyperfine splitting.

so that a non-relativistic theory can be used with the expectation that relativistic corrections should be small. In analogy with the Coulomb force, which is mediated by a single photon, the $q\bar{q}$ force should, at least at small distances, be dominated by single-gluon exchange and have the same form as the Coulomb potential, $V(r) \underset{r\to 0}{\approx} -\alpha_s/r$, where α_s is the strong coupling constant. Secondly, quarks are *confined* in hadrons so that at large distances the potential must reflect the fact that quarks cannot appear as free particles. Various forms of the confining potential have been suggested, e.g. linear, $V(r) \approx r$, and logarithmic, $V(r) \approx \ln r$. Both of these are consistent with the observation made at the end of the last section concerning the leptonic widths of vector mesons, namely, $|\psi(0)|^2 \approx m_v^2$. Thus, either

$$V(r) = -\frac{4}{3}\frac{\alpha_s}{r} + \frac{r}{a^2} \tag{10.56}$$

with $a \approx 2\ \text{GeV}^{-1}$, or

$$V(r) = -\frac{4}{3}\frac{\alpha_s}{r} + k \ln r \tag{10.57}$$

with $k \approx 0.7$ give results which are consistent with the experimental data.

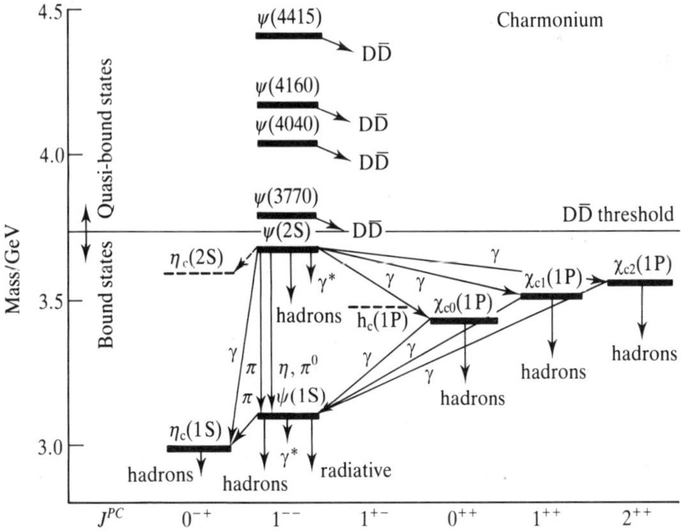

Figure 10.25 The charmonium system. Uncertain states and transitions are shown by broken lines. Transitions denoted γ^* refer to decay processes involving intermediate virtual photons, including decays to e^+e^- and $\mu^+\mu^-$. Singlet states are called η_c and h_c and triplet states ψ and χ_{cJ}. States are labelled nL in sequence, nS, nP so that, for example, the triplet state $\chi_{c0}(1P)$ would be $2\ ^3P_0$ in the conventional notation used in the positronium diagram (figure 10.24).

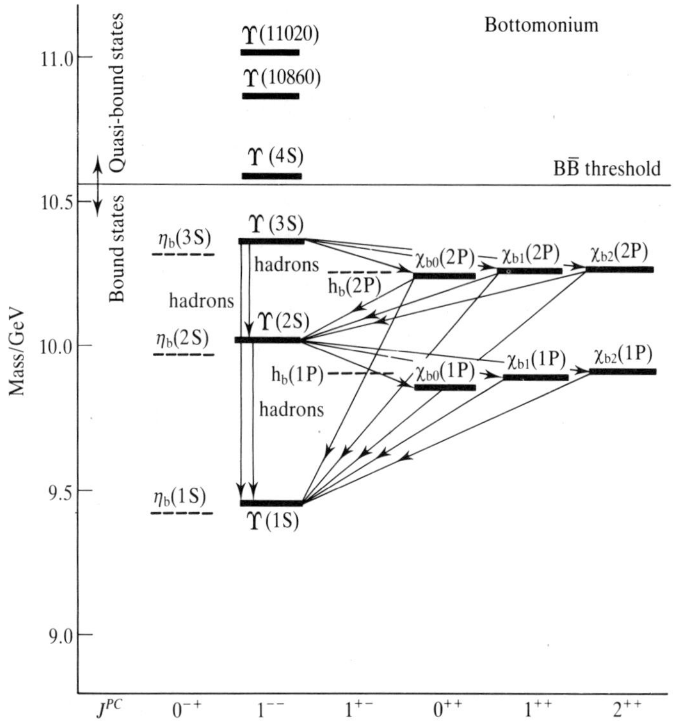

Figure 10.26 The bottomonium system. Uncertain states are shown by broken lines. The numbering and labelling convention is the same as that used in the charmonium diagram (figure 10.25). Singlet states are called η_b and h_b and triplet states ϒ and χ_{bJ}. For example, the state $h_b(1P)$ means $1\,^1P_1$ with $n = 1, L = 1, S = 0, J = 1$ and $PC = +-$. In conventional spectroscopic notation this state would be labelled $2\,^1P_1$.

The factor $\frac{4}{3}$ is a colour factor which takes account of the fact that quarks and gluons are coloured whilst the observable hadrons are colour singlets.

Figures 10.25 and 10.26 show the current experimental status of the charmonium and bottomonium systems. The obvious similarity with the positronium system lends strong support to the validity of the quarkonium model.

Finally, we note that the mass differences between the lowest-lying members of the ψ and ϒ systems are very similar:

$$[m_{\psi(2S)} - m_{\psi(1S)}] \approx 589 \text{ MeV}.$$

and

$$[m_{\Upsilon(2S)} - m_{\Upsilon(1S)}] \approx 563 \text{ MeV}$$

This observation favours a logarithmic QCD potential[19] but evidence based on an application of the string model to the spin–mass-squared relation for baryon resonances supports a linear potential.

REFERENCES 10

1 **Gell-Mann M** 1962 *Phys Rev* **125** (1067)

2 **Gasiorowicz S** 1966 *Elementary Particle Physics* Wiley

3 **Gell-Mann M** 1964 *Phys Lett* **8** (214)

4 **Zweig G** 1964 CERN Reports TH.401 and TH.412; see also **G. Zweig** 1965 in Zichichi A (ed) *Symmetries in Elementary Particle Physics* Academic Press

5 **Kuhn H G** 1969 *Atomic Spectra* Longman p. 338

6 **Weinberg S** 1977 *N.Y. Acad Sci* **II** 38 (185)

7 **Particle Data Group** 1990 'Review of particle properties' *Phys Lett* **B239** (see also 1992 'Review of particle properties' *Phys Rev* **D45**)

8 **Augustin J E** *et al.* 1974 *Phys Rev Lett* **33** (1406)

9 **Aubert J J** *et al.* 1974 *Phys Rev Lett* **33** (1404)

10 **Boyarski A M** *et al.* 1975 *Phys Rev Lett* **34** (1357)

11 **Lüth V** *et al.* 1975 *Phys Rev Lett* **35** (1124)

12 **Glashow S L, Iliopoulos J and Maiani L** 1970 *Phys Rev* **D2** (1285)

13 **Okubo S** 1963 *Phys Lett* **5** (165)

14 **Zweig G** 1964 Unpublished, CERN Preprints TH401 and TH412

15 **Iizuka J** 1966 *Suppl Prog Theor Phys* **37–8** (21)

16 **Herb S W** *et al.* 1977 *Phys Rev Lett* **39** (252)

17 **Innes W R** *et al.* 1977 *Phys Rev Lett* **39** (1240)

18 **Appelquist T, Barnett R M and Lane K** 1978 *Ann Rev Nucl Part Sci* **28** (387)

19 **Quigg C and Rosner J L** 1977 *Phys Lett* **71B** (153) and **72B** (462)

EXAMPLES 10

10.1 A general SU(2) transformation, i.e. a rotation of the axes through an angle α in isospin space about the direction $\hat{\boldsymbol{n}}$, specified by the angles (θ, ϕ) in spherical polar coordinates, is given by

$$|\psi\rangle \to |\psi'\rangle = \exp\left(-\mathrm{i}\frac{\alpha}{2}\hat{\boldsymbol{n}}\cdot\boldsymbol{\tau}|\psi\rangle\right)$$

where the components of $\boldsymbol{\tau}$ are the Pauli matrices. By expanding the exponential, collecting terms in even and odd powers of α and using the fact that $(\hat{\boldsymbol{n}}\cdot\boldsymbol{\tau})^2 = \mathbf{1}$, the unit matrix, show that

$$\exp\left(-\mathrm{i}\frac{\alpha}{2}\hat{\boldsymbol{n}}\cdot\boldsymbol{\tau}\right) = \mathbf{1}\cos\left(\frac{\alpha}{2}\right) - \mathrm{i}\,\hat{\boldsymbol{n}}\cdot\boldsymbol{\tau}\sin\left(\frac{\alpha}{2}\right).$$

Hence show that, under a rotation α about the 2 axis in isospin space, the nucleon doublet $|\psi\rangle \equiv \binom{p}{n}$ transforms as

$$p \to p' = p\cos\left(\frac{\alpha}{2}\right) - n\sin\left(\frac{\alpha}{2}\right)$$

$$n \to n' = p\sin\left(\frac{\alpha}{2}\right) + n\cos\left(\frac{\alpha}{2}\right).$$

Apply charge conjugation to these equations to show that the doublet $|\bar{\psi}\rangle \equiv \binom{\bar{n}}{\bar{p}}$ does *not* transform in the same way as the nucleon doublet (**2**). Show, however, that if we define the conjugate doublet $\bar{\mathbf{2}}$ as $|\bar{\psi}\rangle \equiv \binom{-\bar{n}}{\bar{p}}$, this does transform identically to the **2**.

10.2 Defining the conjugate antinucleon doublet as in example 10.1 has the advantage that the N and $\bar{\mathrm{N}}$ doublets can be combined using conventional Clebsch–Gordan coefficients. By coupling the N and $\bar{\mathrm{N}}$ doublets, and assuming the $\mathrm{N\bar{N}}$ pairs are in singlet spin states with relative orbital angular momentum 0, determine the *G*-parity of the isospin triplet and singlet states. Write down the quantum numbers $I^G J^P$ of these states and identify them with physical particles.

10.3 Write down the matrix representations of the SU(3) operators $I_\pm$, I_3, $V_\pm$, $U_\pm$ and Y and verify the commutation relations given in equations (10.8). Hence, show that the step operators $U_\pm$ and $V_\pm$ induce the changes $\Delta Y = \pm 1$, $\Delta I_3 = \mp\frac{1}{2}$ and $\Delta Y = \pm 1$, $\Delta I_3 = \pm\frac{1}{2}$ respectively.

10.4 The fundamental quark triplet may be regarded as a V spin doublet $\binom{u}{s}$ and a V spin singlet d, or as a U spin doublet $\binom{d}{s}$ and a U spin singlet u. Show that $V_-|u\rangle = |s\rangle$ and $U_+|s\rangle = d$.

10.5 The direct product of two quark triplets gives rise to a sextet and an antitriplet (see figure 10.5). Determine the quark *wavefunctions* of these nine states.

10.6 The decomposition of the product of three quark triplets is $\mathbf{3} \otimes \mathbf{3} \otimes \mathbf{3} = (\mathbf{6} \oplus \bar{\mathbf{3}}) \otimes \mathbf{3} = \mathbf{10}_\mathrm{S} \oplus \mathbf{8}_{\mathrm{M_S}} \oplus \mathbf{8}_{\mathrm{M_A}} \oplus \mathbf{1}_\mathrm{A}$. Determine the normalized quark wavefunctions of (i) the *uud* and (ii) the *uds* states in the decuplet, the $\mathrm{M_A}$ octet and the $\mathrm{M_S}$ octet. (iii) What is the wavefunction of the unitary singlet state?

10.7 Show that the direct product of three spin doublets decomposes according to $\mathbf{2} \otimes \mathbf{2} \otimes \mathbf{2} = (\mathbf{1}_\mathrm{A} \oplus \mathbf{3}_\mathrm{S}) \otimes \mathbf{2} = \mathbf{4}_\mathrm{S} + \mathbf{2}_{\mathrm{M_S}} + \mathbf{2}_{\mathrm{M_A}}$ and write down explicit wavefunctions for the quartet and mixed-symmetry doublets.

10.8 Apply equation (10.24) to the U spin quartet of negatively charged $\frac{3}{2}^+$ baryons and show that

$$m_\Sigma - m_\Delta \approx m_\Xi - m_\Sigma \approx m_\Omega - m_\Xi.$$

10.9 The neutral members of the $J^P = \frac{1}{2}^+$ baryon octet form a U spin triplet, n, $\frac{1}{2}(\Sigma^0 + \sqrt{3}\Lambda^0)$, Ξ^0 with $U_3 = +1$, 0 and -1 respectively. Use equation

(10.24) to obtain the mass relation

$$\tfrac{1}{2}m_n + \tfrac{1}{2}m_{\Xi^0} = \tfrac{1}{4}m_{\Xi^0} + \tfrac{3}{4}m_{\Lambda^0}.$$

10.10 The negatively charged $\frac{3}{2}^+$ baryons Δ^-, $\Sigma^-(1385)$, $\Xi^-(1530)$ and Ω^- form a U-spin quartet, the neutral $\frac{1}{2}^+$ baryons n, Λ^0, Σ^0 and Ξ^0 a U-spin triplet (see example 10.9) and the negatively charged 0^- mesons π^- and K^- a U-spin doublet. Assuming U-spin conservation determine the amplitudes for the decays

$$\begin{array}{ll} \Delta^- \to n\pi^- & \Xi^-(1530) \to \Xi^0\pi^- \\ \Sigma^-(1385) \to nK^- & \Xi^-(1530) \to \Sigma^0 K^- \\ \Sigma^-(1385) \to \Sigma^0\pi^- & \Xi^-(1530) \to \Lambda^0 K^- \\ \Sigma^-(1385) \to \Lambda^0\pi^- & \Omega^- \to \Xi^0 K^-. \end{array}$$

10.11 Use the fact that the photon is a U-spin scalar to establish a relationship between the amplitudes for the electromagnetic decays $\pi^0 \to \gamma\gamma$ and $\eta^0 \to \gamma\gamma$.

10.12 Use U-spin conservation to obtain the amplitudes for the processes

$$\begin{array}{l} \pi^- p \to K^+\Sigma^-(1385) \\ \pi^- p \to \pi^+\Delta^- \\ K^- p \to K^+\Xi^-(1530) \\ K^- p \to \pi^+\Sigma^-(1385). \end{array}$$

10.13 Octet-singlet mixing in the pseudoscalar nonet can be expressed as

$$\begin{pmatrix} \eta' \\ \eta \end{pmatrix} = R \begin{pmatrix} \eta_1 \\ \eta_8 \end{pmatrix}$$

where η' and η denote the physical states, η_1 and η_8 the singlet and octet states and R is the rotation matrix

$$\begin{pmatrix} \cos\theta & \sin\theta \\ -\sin\theta & \cos\theta \end{pmatrix}.$$

With respect to the η_1 and η_8 base states the mass matrix (see equation 10.30) is

$$\begin{pmatrix} M_{11}^2 & M_{18}^2 \\ M_{18}^2 & M_{88}^2 \end{pmatrix}$$

By diagonalizing this matrix show that the mixing angle is given by

$$\tan^2\theta = \frac{M_{88}^2 - m_\eta^2}{m_{\eta'}^2 - M_{88}^2}.$$

10.14 Meson masses in the quark model are predicted to be the sum of constituent quark masses and a hyperfine interaction:

$$m(q_1\bar{q}_2) = m_1 + m_2 + a\frac{\boldsymbol{s}_1 \cdot \boldsymbol{s}_2}{m_1 m_2}$$

where s_1 and s_2 are the spins of the constituent quarks with masses m_1 and m_2. Assuming $m_u = m_d = 0.310\ \text{GeV}/c^2$, $m_s = 0.483\ \text{GeV}/c^2$ and $a/m_u^2 = 0.64\ \text{GeV}/c^2$ obtain the masses of the pseudoscalar and vector mesons and compare them with the measured values.

10.15 Obtain an explicit quark wavefunction for the Λ^0 with spin component $s_z = +\frac{1}{2}$. Hence, show that the quark model predicts that the magnetic moment of the Λ^0 is μ_s, the intrinsic magnetic moment of the s quark.

10.16 The J/ψ resonance is produced in an electron–positron collider in which the energy in each circulating beam is 1.5 GeV. The integrated cross-section for J/ψ production followed by decay into the e^+e^- channel may be written

$$\int \sigma(E)\,dE = 4\pi\lambda\!\!\!^{-2} \frac{2J+1}{(2s_1+1)(2s_2+1)} \int_0^\infty \frac{\Gamma_e^2/4}{(E-E_R)^2 + \Gamma^2/4}\,dE$$

where E is the centre-of-mass energy, $\lambda\!\!\!^{-} = \hbar/p$ where p is the centre-of-mass momentum, J is the spin of the resonance and s_1 and s_2 are the spins of the colliding particles. E_R is the energy at the resonance peak, Γ_e is the partial width for decay into the e^+e^- channel and Γ is the total width of the resonance. Assuming that the J/ψ can be produced in all possible helicity states show that

$$\int \sigma(E)\,dE = \frac{3\pi^2}{2}\lambda\!\!\!^{-2}\left(\frac{\Gamma_e}{\Gamma}\right)^2 \Gamma.$$

(*Hint*: The integration is most easily performed by making the substitution $\tan\theta = 2(E - E_R)/\Gamma$.)

If the integrated cross-section is 870 nb MeV and the branching fraction Γ_e/Γ is 0.07, determine the total width.

11 *Weak interactions*

11.1 *Introduction*

The two lightest charged leptons, the electron and the muon, have been known to physicists for roughly a century and a half-century respectively. In weak interactions each charged lepton has a neutrino associated with it. In section 5.2.2 evidence was presented to show that the neutrino associated with the electron, ν_e, is distinct from its antiparticle, the antineutrino $\bar{\nu}_e$. In the early 1960s, experiments performed at Brookhaven and CERN produced conclusive evidence that a neutrino ν_μ, quite distinct from the electron neutrino, is associated with the muon. In essence, this assertion was based on the observation that muon neutrinos ν_μ, produced in the decay of π mesons

$$\pi^+ \to \mu^+ + \nu_\mu$$

subsequently gave rise to the production of muons via the reaction

$$\nu_\mu + n \to p + \mu^-$$

but no reactions occurred in which electrons were observed, i.e. there were no interactions of the type

$$\nu_\mu + n \to p + e^- .$$

These observations are formalized by the introduction of a lepton number L_e for the electron family and L_μ for the muon family and the requirement that L_e and L_μ are separately conserved. The lepton numbers are assigned as follows:

	e^-	ν_e	e^+	$\bar{\nu}_e$
$L_e =$	$+1$	$+1$	-1	-1

$= 0$ for all other particles

	μ^-	ν_μ	μ^+	$\bar{\nu}_\mu$
$L_\mu =$	$+1$	$+1$	-1	-1

$= 0$ for all other particles

These conservation laws explain why the decays

$$\mu^\pm \to e^\pm + \gamma$$

and

$$\mu^\pm \to e^\pm + e^+ + e^-$$

for instance, have never been observed.

The newest member of the lepton family, the τ lepton, was first observed in 1975 by Perl *et al.*[1,2] at the SLAC e^+e^- collider, SPEAR. The analysis of the e^+e^- annihilations was complicated by the presence of a large hadronic background but 24 events were found in which the only charged particles produced were a high energy electron and a high energy muon with a substantial 'missing' or undetected energy. These events were attributed to the process

$$e^+ + e^- \to \tau^+ + \tau^-$$
$$\tau^- \to \mu^- + \bar{\nu}_\mu + \nu_\tau$$
$$\tau^+ \to e^+ + \nu_e + \bar{\nu}_\tau$$

with the neutrinos carrying away the missing energy. The reaction occurred only above the threshold energy of 3.56 GeV, corresponding to a mass of 1.78 GeV/c^2 for the τ lepton. The *direct* observation of τ neutrinos through their interactions with matter has not yet been observed. As in the case of the electron and muon families, a τ

lepton number L_τ, which again is separately conserved, is assigned as follows:

$$\begin{array}{lcccc} & \tau^- & \nu_\tau & \tau^+ & \bar{\nu}_\tau \\ L_\tau = & +1 & +1 & -1 & -1 \\ & = 0 \text{ for all other particles} \end{array}$$

In section 11.3.2 it will be shown that neutrinos and antineutrinos differ in the value of their helicity, the component of spin along the direction of motion, but it should be noted that this distinction holds only if the neutrinos have zero mass. Indeed, if neutrinos have non-zero mass, lepton number conservation will no longer be valid: the phenomenon of neutrino 'oscillations' could then occur with the decay of one neutrino type into another (see section 15.3). In the absence of strong evidence to the contrary we assume in this chapter that the neutrino masses are zero.

Three different types of weak interaction are known experimentally – leptonic, semi-leptonic and non-leptonic. Examples of the former are muon decay

$$\mu^- \to e^- + \bar{\nu}_e + \nu_\mu$$
$$\mu^+ \to e^+ + \nu_e + \bar{\nu}_\mu$$

and the τ lepton decay given above; only leptons are involved. Semi-leptonic weak interactions involve the hadrons, strange and non-strange, as well as the leptons. The β decay of the neutron

$$n \to p + e^- + \bar{\nu}_e$$

is an example. Note that since the neutron is heavier than the proton, the decay

$$p \to n + e^+ + \nu_e$$

is energetically forbidden for free protons – it can occur of course if the proton is bound in a nucleus. The β decay of the Λ^0

$$\Lambda^0 \to p + e^- + \bar{\nu}_e$$

and pion decay

$$\pi^+ \to \mu^+ + \nu_\mu \qquad \pi^- \to \mu^- + \bar{\nu}_\mu$$

are further examples of semi-leptonic weak interactions. The non-leptonic weak interactions involve hadrons only. Examples are

$$K^+ \to \pi^+\pi^0 \qquad K^+ \to \pi^+\pi^+\pi^-$$

and

$$\Lambda^0 \to p\pi^- \qquad \Lambda^0 \to n\pi^0.$$

These non-leptonic decays of the Λ^0 account for essentially 100 per cent of the decay rate; the branching fraction for the decay $\Lambda^0 \to p + e^- + \bar{\nu}_e$ is $(8.35 \pm 0.14) \times 10^{-4}$. Note that there is a change of strangeness $|\Delta S| = 1$ in these decays but this does not imply that weak interactions between non-strange hadrons do not exist. Rather, only in those cases in which the strong interaction is forbidden – strangeness-changing interactions – can the non-leptonic interaction be observed experimentally with relative ease.

11.2 *Parity violation*

The most striking difference between the weak interactions and the strong and electromagnetic interactions is that the former violate parity conservation while the latter conserve parity. Until the early 1950s it was common belief that all interactions were invariant under spatial inversion but the so-called τ–θ puzzle* cast doubt on this assumption as far as the weak interactions are concerned. The τ and θ mesons were originally thought to be different particles with weak decay modes $\theta \to 2\pi$ and $\tau \to 3\pi$. Since the pion has spin-parity 0^- it is clear that the spin-parity of the θ must belong to the series $0^+, 1^-, 2^+, \ldots$ etc., if the decay conserves parity. The spin-parity of the τ meson was determined from an analysis of the decay Dalitz plot and found to be 0^- and thus the τ meson appeared to be a different particle from the θ meson. The puzzle was that measurements of the masses and lifetimes of the τ and θ showed them to be equal within experimental errors and this degeneracy made it unlikely that the τ and θ were in fact different particles.

In 1956 Lee and Yang[3] resolved the paradox by suggesting that the τ and θ were different decay modes of the same particle (the K meson) and that parity was *not* conserved in the weak interactions. These 2π and 3π decay modes of the K meson can in retrospect be regarded as evidence for the breakdown of parity conservation, but at the time so little was known about these strange particles that evidence for parity violation was

* τ meson is an old-fashioned name for one of the decay modes of what is now called the K meson and should not be confused with the more recently discovered τ lepton.

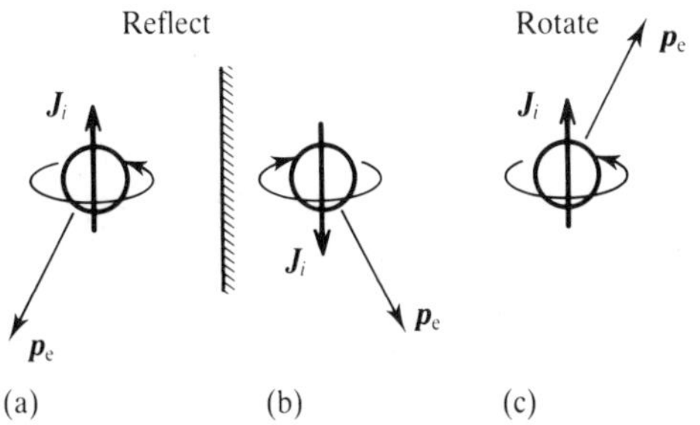

Figure 11.1 Schematic diagram showing parity violation in the β decay of aligned nuclei: (a) electrons emitted preferentially in a direction opposite to the nuclear spin J_i; (b) the system reflected in a plane; (c) rotation through 180° about an axis perpendicular to the plane and electrons now emitted preferentially in a direction along the nuclear spin.

sought in other weak interactions, in particular nuclear β decay. After their study of earlier work on β decay Lee and Yang concluded that no experiment had been performed which was sensitive to parity violating effects and they pointed out that in order to detect parity violation one would have to observe a *pseudoscalar* quantity.* In β decay experiments one suitable pseudoscalar is $\boldsymbol{J}_i \cdot \boldsymbol{p}_e$ where $\boldsymbol{J}_i$ (an axial vector) is the spin of the parent nucleus and $\boldsymbol{p}_e$ (a polar vector) is the electron momentum. An asymmetry in the angular distribution of the electrons measured with respect to the nuclear spin direction, i.e. a net value of the pseudoscalar $\boldsymbol{J}_i \cdot \boldsymbol{p}_e$, would constitute unequivocal proof of parity violation in the decay. This can be understood pictorially with the aid of figure 11.1. Imagine a β active source in which the spins of the parent nuclei are aligned and suppose that the electrons are emitted preferentially in a direction *opposite* to the direction of the nuclear spin as shown in figure 11.1(a). We recall that the parity operation can be envisaged as a reflection in a plane (figure 11.1(b)) followed by a 180° rotation about the normal to that plane (11.1(c)). Notice that in this parity transformation the polar vector (electron momentum) has changed sign whereas the axial vector (nuclear spin) has not. More importantly, we see in 11.1(c), the parity reflected system, that the electrons are emitted preferentially *along* the direction of the nuclear spin. The system is thus not invariant under the parity operation, i.e. parity is violated.

Another pseudoscalar quantity which has particular relevance to the study of β decay is the helicity of a particle; if parity is conserved the expectation value of the helicity must be zero (see example 11.1). Conversely, if a non-zero expectation value of helicity is observed in an interaction, parity must be violated in that interaction.

* A pseudoscalar is an observable which is invariant under rotation but which changes sign under spatial inversion (the parity operation); the scalar product of a polar vector and an axial vector is an example of a pseudoscalar. A scalar quantity on the other hand is invariant under both rotation and spatial inversion.

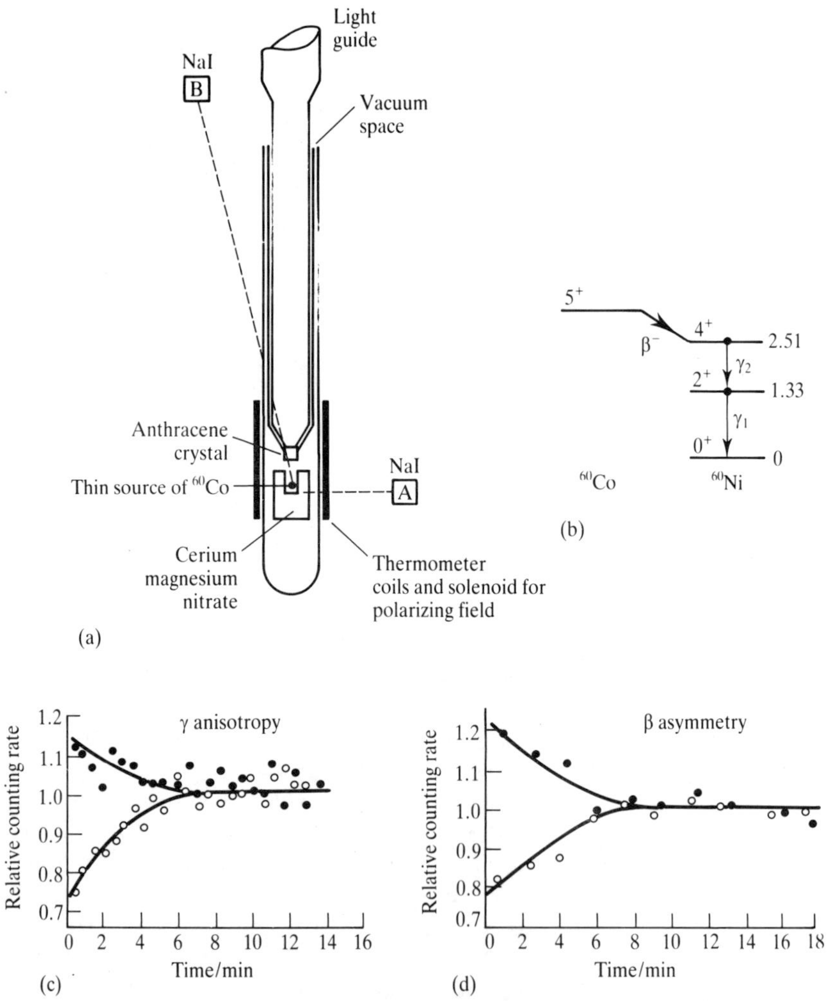

Figure 11.2 (a) Apparatus; (b) decay scheme of ^{60}Co (Gamow–Teller decay); (c) γ ray anisotropy obtained from counter A (●) and counter B (○) at different times as the crystal warms up; the difference between the curves measures the net polarization of the nuclei; (d) β ray asymmetry shown by the counting rate in the anthracene crystal for two directions of polarizing field (●, down ↓; ○ up ↑) (Wu C S *et al.* 1957 *Phys Rev* **105** (1413)).

11.3 Experimental verification of parity violation

11.3.1 The ^{60}Co experiment

Parity non-conservation was first established by measuring the angular distribution of electrons, emitted in the decay of ^{60}Co, relative to the orientation of the nuclear spin. Figure 11.2(a) shows the experimental arrangement used by Wu *et al.*[4] A source of ^{60}Co which decays according to the scheme shown in figure 11.2(b) was incorporated into a crystal of cerium magnesium nitrate. If a relatively small external magnetic field, ≈ 0.05 T, is applied to this paramagnetic salt the orientation of the *electronic* moments produces a strong local field of 10–100 T which, through the hyperfine coupling, will polarize the ^{60}Co nuclei if the sample is cooled to a temperature of about 0.01 K. The technique, first proposed by Gorter[5] and Rose,[6] achieves this low temperature through adiabatic demagnetization. The polarization was monitored by observing the anisotropy of the γ ray emission in the decay of ^{60}Ni to its ground state. For E2 transitions an angular distribution of the form $W(\theta) = \sum_{n=0}^{2} a_{2n} \times \cos^{2n}\theta$ is expected and a convenient measure of the nuclear polarization is the γ anisotropy coefficient $[W(\pi/2) - W(0)]/W(\pi/2)$. The γ rays were detected by the equatorial sodium iodide detector A and the polar detector B in figure 11.2(a) and the observed γ anisotropy is shown in figure 11.2(c). An anthracene scintillation counter was used to measure the intensity of β emission as a function of the direction of alignment (i.e. the direction of polarizing field), and the result shown in figure 11.2(d) was obtained. The asymmetry of β emission and the anisotropy of γ emission both disappeared as the crystal warmed up because of equalization of the population of magnetic substates.

The demonstration of β asymmetry in this experiment provided dramatic confirmation of the suggestion of Lee and Yang that parity might not be conserved in weak interactions. A similar confirmation for another weak decay process, the $\pi \to \mu \to e$ decay sequence, to which we will return in section 11.3.3, was almost simultaneously forthcoming. An asymmetric angular distribution always involves interference between amplitudes of opposite symmetry. The β asymmetry therefore means that the transition between the ground state of ^{60}Co and the second excited state of ^{60}Ni (both of definite parity) can take place by emission of an electron–antineutrino pair in both odd and even parity states and that the two corresponding amplitudes interfere, leading to an angular distribution of electron emission of the form $a + b\cos\theta$ with respect to the nuclear axis. That this asymmetry confirms the violation of parity conservation has already been explained in section 11.2.

11.3.2 Measurement of the neutrino helicity

The conjecture of Lee and Yang and its confirmation by Wu *et al.* was followed by a period of intense experimental and theoretical activity aimed at understanding the detailed nature of the weak interaction. Of paramount importance in this work was the measurement of the helicity of the neutrino by Goldhaber, Grodzins and Sunyar.[7] Here we give a simplified description of this classic experiment; for more details the reader is referred to the review article by Grodzins.[8]

The metastable state of ^{152}Eu decays about 24 per cent of the time by

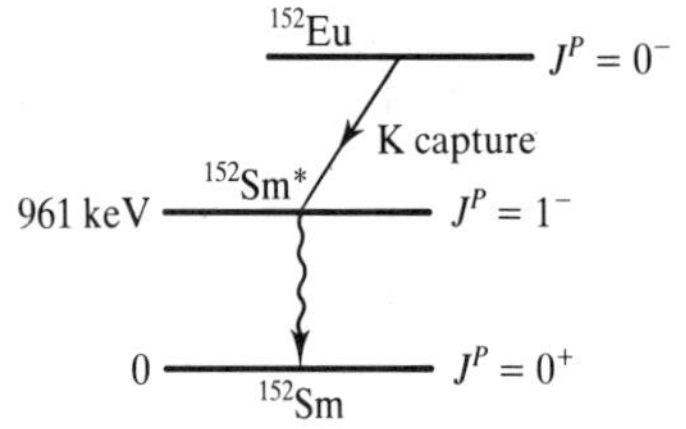

Figure 11.3
Simplified decay scheme of ^{152}Eu.

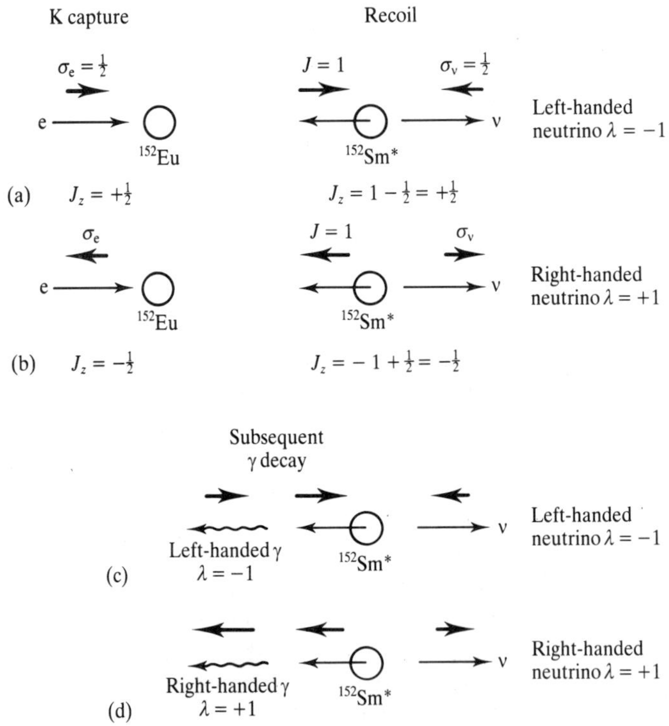

Figure 11.4 Schematic diagram, based on angular momentum conservation, showing the handedness of the particles involved in the K capture decay of ^{152}Eu: (a) production of left-handed neutrinos; (b) production of right-handed neutrinos. The subsequent decay of ^{152}Sm* illustrated in (c) and (d) shows that the forward-emitted γ rays have the same handedness as the neutrino.

K electron capture to an excited state of ^{152}Sm which in turn decays to the ground state of samarium by the emission of a 961 keV γ ray. (The lifetime of the excited state is extremely short, $\approx 10^{-14}$ s.) Furthermore, since K capture is a two-body process, the emitted neutrino has a unique energy, $E_\nu \approx 900$ keV in this case, i.e. close to the γ ray energy, an important consideration in this experiment. A simplified decay scheme of ^{152}Eu is shown in figure 11.3; note in particular the spin-parities of the levels involved. Conservation of angular momentum requires that the recoiling samarium nucleus (^{152}Sm*) has the same 'handedness' as the neutrino as depicted in figures 11.4(a) and 11.4(b), regardless of whether the neutrino has helicity $+1$ or -1. The problem of measuring the neutrino helicity (an extremely difficult one because of the very low interaction cross-section of neutrinos with matter) can thus be transferred to a measurement of the helicity of the recoiling $^{152}Sm^*$ nucleus. Since the lifetime of the 1^- level is only about 10^{-14} s the γ decay retains a knowledge of the nuclear recoil and again, by angular momentum conservation, γ rays emitted *in the direction of recoil* have the same helicity as the $^{152}Sm^*$ nucleus, and hence the same helicity as the neutrino as shown in figures 11.4(c) and 11.4(d). Thus the neutrino helicity can be inferred from a measurement of the helicity of the forward-produced γ rays, i.e. γ rays emitted in the direction of recoil of the $^{152}Sm^*$ nucleus. The experimental problem is thus to measure the γ ray helicity. This can be done relatively simply by examining the transmission of the γ rays through magnetized iron. The dominant interaction with matter of γ rays of energy 961 keV is the Compton effect and the method relies on the fact that the cross-section for Compton scattering is spin dependent. The formulae are somewhat complicated and can be found for instance in reference 8, but the main result is that the transmission is greatest when the photon spin is parallel to the electron spin. Of course, as indicated above, it is only those γ rays emitted in the opposite direction to the neutrino which have the same helicity as the neutrino and the ingenious method devised by Goldhaber *et al.* to select these γ rays was to make use of resonant scattering. In the emission of a γ ray from an excited state with energy of excitation E_0 a momentum E_0/c must be imparted to the emitting nucleus and consequently the energy of the γ ray is reduced by an amount $E_0^2/2Mc^2$ where M is the mass of the nucleus. Similarly, on absorption, an extra energy $E_0^2/2Mc^2$ must be supplied to counteract the nuclear recoil. This energy, $\Delta E = E_0^2/Mc^2$, lost by recoil in emission and absorption, is in general much greater than the level width so that resonant absorption will take place only if extra energy, equal to the energy lost, is supplied to the emitted γ rays. In the experiment under consideration, it is precisely those γ rays emitted in the direction of recoil of the $^{152}Sm^*$ nucleus, i.e. opposite to the neutrino direction, which have the correct energy to undergo resonant absorption. A simple calculation (see example 11.2) shows that the resonance condition is $E_\nu \cos\theta = E_0$ for a γ ray emitted at an angle θ with respect to the $^{152}Sm^*$ recoil direction. Thus for γ rays emitted opposite to the neutrino direction the requirement that $E_\nu \approx E_0$ becomes apparent. Thermal motion gives rise to a spread in energies so that the resonance condition can be met in practice.

The experimental arrangement used by Goldhaber *et al.* is shown in figure 11.5. The scatterer was in the form of a ring of samarium oxide and the γ rays were detected with an NaI(Tl) detector which was shielded from the direct radiation by 12 in. of lead. The helicity of the γ rays was analysed by transmission through fully magnetized iron. With the field direction as shown in figure 11.5 the γ ray energy spectrum shown in figure 11.6 was obtained. The presence of full energy peaks at 961 and

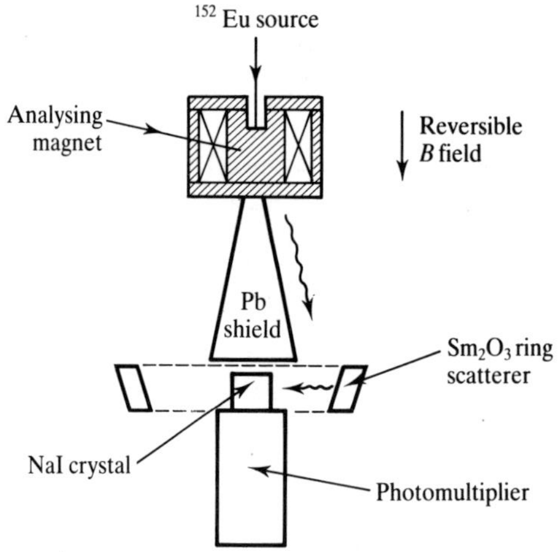

Figure 11.5 Experimental arrangement used by Goldhaber *et al.* to measure the circular polarization of resonantly scattered γ rays. With the field direction as shown left-handed γ rays are preferentially transmitted (Goldhaber M *et al.* 1958 *Phys Rev* **109** (1015)).

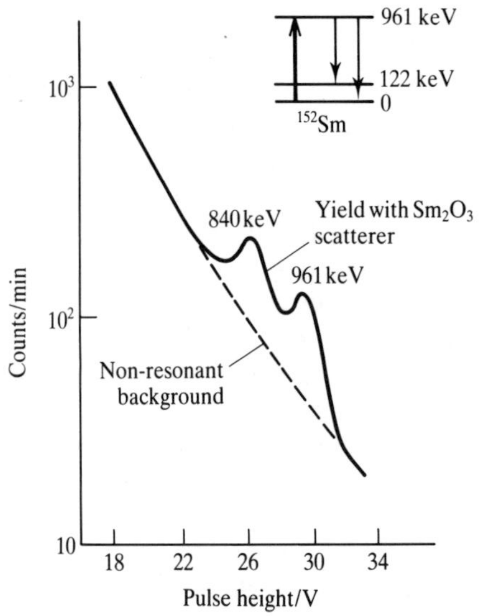

Figure 11.6 Pulse height spectrum of resonantly scattered γ rays from the decay of ^{152}Sm* (upper curve). Non-resonant background is indicated by the lower curve. The energy levels of ^{152}Sm are shown in the inset.

837 keV indicates that resonant scattering has taken place and since, with the field direction indicated, γ rays with helicity $\lambda = -1$ are preferentially transmitted, the neutrino must have helicity -1. Two full energy peaks are observed in the energy spectrum of the scattered radiation because the decay scheme is slightly more complex than indicated in figure 11.3 and is shown as an inset in figure 11.6. After

resonant absorption de-excitation of the 961 keV level can take place either by a direct transition to the ground state or via an intermediate level at 122 keV.

We note that the observation of a definite helicity of the neutrino in K capture is evidence for parity violation in the decay as indicated in section 11.2.

The helicity of the antineutrino has been inferred to be positive from the asymmetry measurements in the decay of polarized neutrons,[9] a result which is supported by later measurements. The neutrino and antineutrino are thus distinguished from each other by their helicities: the neutrino has helicity -1 while the antineutrino has helicity $+1$; the parity violation is said to be maximal.

11.3.3 Parity violation in the $\pi \to \mu \to e$ *decay sequence*

Following the proposal of Lee and Yang,[3] Garwin, Lederman and Weinrich[10] confirmed that parity is violated in the successive decays $\pi^+ \to \mu^+ + \nu_\mu$, $\mu^+ \to e^+ + \nu_e + \bar{\nu}_\mu$. If parity violation is maximal, as in the case of β decay, then in the decay of stopped pions the muons will be polarized along the direction of motion as indicated in figure 11.7(a). Maximal parity violation implies that the muon neutrino ν_μ is left handed (helicity $= -1$) and since the pion has spin 0 and there can be no component of orbital angular momentum along the line of flight of the muon, conservation of angular momentum requires that the μ^+ must be polarized with helicity -1.

In the experiment of Garwin *et al.* the muons were brought to rest, without loss of polarization, in a carbon absorber. In the subsequent decay the positron energy spectrum was strongly peaked near the maximum allowed value ($m_\mu/2$) as shown schematically in figure 11.7(b). The most

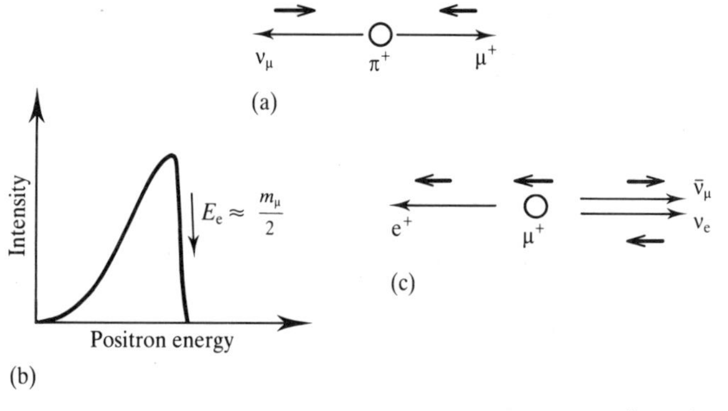

Figure 11.7 (a) Sketch showing polarization in the decay $\pi^+ \to \mu^+\nu_\mu$. Particle spins are shown by short arrows. (b) Sketch of the positron energy spectrum for the decay $\mu^+ \to e^+\nu_e\bar{\nu}_\mu$. The spectrum is strongly peaked towards the kinematically allowed maximum. (c) Particle polarizations in the most likely configuration in the decay $\mu^+ \to e^+\nu_e\bar{\nu}_\mu$.

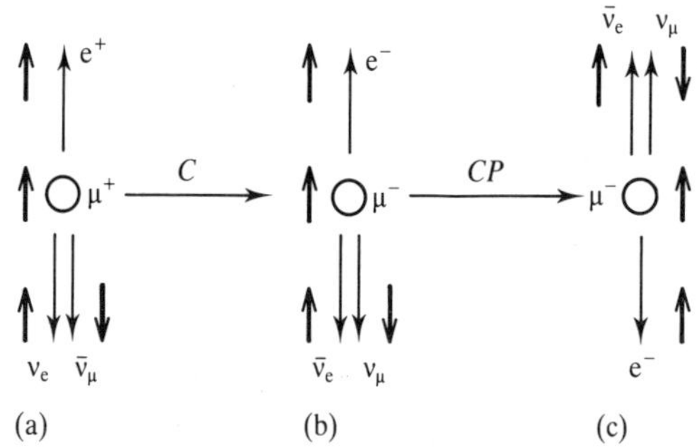

Figure 11.8
Sketch showing C violation and CP conservation in the decay $\mu^+ \to e^+\nu_e\bar{\nu}_\mu$.

probable decay configuration is therefore that shown in figure 11.7(c) and, if parity is maximally violated, the particle helicities will be as indicated. One thus expects an asymmetry in the angular distribution of the positron with respect to the spin direction of the muon, with more positrons being emitted parallel to the muon spin direction, i.e. opposite to the incident muon direction. Experimentally the angular distribution was of the form $I(\theta) = 1 - \frac{1}{3}\cos\theta$ where θ was measured with respect to the line of flight of the incident muon. Not only does this asymmetry confirm parity violation in the decay processes but in addition the form of the distribution is precisely that required by the so-called V–A interaction discussed in section 11.5.5.

The weak interactions, in addition to violating parity also violate charge conjugation invariance, as can be seen by a consideration of the most probable configuration (figure 11.8(a)), in muon decay. Figure 11.8(b) shows the result of the charge conjugation operation on this configuration. The neutrinos ν_μ and $\bar{\nu}_e$ have helicities which do not occur in nature, thus the decay is not invariant under the charge conjugation operation. However, if this is followed by the parity transformation, the configuration in figure 11.8(c) results and in this case the particle helicities are precisely as expected. Thus, although the interaction separately violates P and C, it is invariant under the combined operation CP. This is true of most weak interactions but in the very important case of the decays of the neutral K mesons there is good evidence for the existence of a small CP-violating amplitude. We defer discussion of this phenomenon until section 11.13.4.

In this chapter so far we have learned two crucial experimental facts about the weak interactions, namely that parity is violated and that the neutrino (antineutrino) has negative (positive) helicity. In chapter 5 we outlined the Fermi theory of β decay and discussed the transition rate mainly in terms of the density of states factor. We now proceed to investigate what restrictions are imposed on the matrix element by the fact that parity is violated in the weak interactions and the violation is maximal, giving rise to neutrinos and antineutrinos of definite handedness. Since the particles involved often have relativistic velocities – neutrinos always travel with the velocity of light – our starting point must be a relativistic wave equation.

11.4 Relativisitic quantum mechanics

11.4.1 The Klein–Gordon equation

A relativistic wave equation may be constructed by making the usual association, $E = i\hbar(\partial/\partial t)$ and $\boldsymbol{p} = -i\hbar\nabla$, between the dynamical variables and operators and using the relativistic energy–momentum relation $E^2 = p^2 + m^2$ $(c = 1)$. The resulting equation

$$\left(\nabla^2 - \frac{m^2}{\hbar^2}\right)\phi = \frac{\partial^2\phi}{\partial t^2} \tag{11.1}$$

is known as the Klein–Gordon equation. By judicious manipulation of equation (11.1) we obtain (see example 11.4)

$$\frac{\partial}{\partial t}\left[i\left(\phi^*\frac{\partial\phi}{\partial t} - \phi\frac{\partial\phi^*}{\partial t}\right)\right] + \boldsymbol{\nabla}\cdot\left[\frac{1}{i}(\phi^*\nabla\phi - \phi\nabla\phi^*)\right] = 0 \tag{11.2}$$

which has the form of the continuity equation $\partial\rho/\partial t + \boldsymbol{\nabla}\cdot\boldsymbol{j} = 0$, if we define

$$\rho = i\left(\phi^*\frac{\partial\phi}{\partial t} - \phi\frac{\partial\phi^*}{\partial t}\right) \quad \text{and} \quad \boldsymbol{j} = \frac{1}{i}(\phi^*\nabla\phi - \phi\nabla\phi^*).$$

The probability current density $\boldsymbol{j}$ is essentially the same as in the non-relativistic case, but a problem arises when we attempt to interpret ρ as a probability density. A probability density must be positive definite. If, as in example 11.4, we calculate ρ for a plane wave solution of the Klein–Gordon equation, we obtain $\rho = 2|N|^2E$, where E is the particle energy and N is a normalization constant. The problem arises because the energy eigenvalues of the Klein–Gordon equation are $E = \pm(p^2 + m^2)^{1/2}$. The negative energy solutions originally caused a problem but it was subsequently shown that they can be interpreted in terms of antiparticles, which certainly exist in nature, and may be regarded as support for this approach. However, since ρ has the same sign as E, the negative energy solutions present a problem in the interpretation of ρ as a (matter) probability density. We therefore follow the course of history and proceed to a discussion of the Dirac equation. In order to facilitate this discussion we first introduce the notation commonly used in relativistic quantum mechanics.

11.4.2 *Relativistic notation*

It is well known that space–time coordinates (ct, x, y, z) in a stationary reference frame are related to those, (ct', x', y', z'), in a frame moving with uniform velocity v in the direction of the positive z axis by the Lorentz transformation

$$\begin{pmatrix} ct' \\ x' \\ y' \\ z' \end{pmatrix} = \begin{pmatrix} \gamma & 0 & 0 & -\beta\gamma \\ 0 & 1 & 0 & 0 \\ 0 & 0 & 1 & 0 \\ -\beta\gamma & 0 & 0 & \gamma \end{pmatrix} \begin{pmatrix} ct \\ x \\ y \\ z \end{pmatrix} \tag{11.3}$$

where $\beta = v/c$ and $\gamma = (1 - \beta^2)^{-1/2}$. The four-vector (ct, x, y, z) is often written as x^μ, with the understanding that $x^0 = ct$, $x^1 = x$, $x^2 = y$ and $x^3 = z$, and (11.3) can be written in the shorthand notation

$$x'^\mu = \sum_\nu \Lambda^\mu_\nu x^\nu \qquad (\mu, \nu = 0, 3). \tag{11.4}$$

Any set of four quantities which transform according to (11.4) is by definition a *contravariant* four-vector. A *covariant* four-vector, written with the index in the lower position, has the same time component as the contravariant vector but the space components have the opposite sign. Thus x_μ is a covariant vector with $x_0 = ct$, $x_1 = -x$, $x_2 = -y$ and $x_3 = -z$. The two are related through the metric tensor $g_{\mu\nu}$, with components $g_{00} = 1$, $g_{ii} = -1$ for $i = 1, 2, 3$ and $g_{\mu\nu} = 0$ for $\mu \neq \nu$, i.e.

$$(g_{\mu\nu}) = \begin{pmatrix} 1 & 0 & 0 & 0 \\ 0 & -1 & 0 & 0 \\ 0 & 0 & -1 & 0 \\ 0 & 0 & 0 & -1 \end{pmatrix}. \tag{11.5}$$

Then,

$$x_\mu = \sum_\nu g_{\mu\nu} x^\nu$$

$$x^\mu = \sum_\nu g^{\mu\nu} x_\nu$$

with $g^{\mu\nu}$ defined by the relation

$$\sum_{\mu} g^{\mu\nu} g_{\mu\sigma} = \delta^{\nu}_{\sigma}$$

where the Kronecker symbol

$$\delta^{\nu}_{\sigma} = \begin{cases} 1 & \text{for } \sigma = \nu \\ 0 & \text{otherwise.} \end{cases}$$

Thus, the raising or lowering of the indices of a four-vector changes the sign of the space components but leaves the time component unchanged.

A Lorentz invariant may be formed from the scalar product of two four-vectors and, in particular, the scalar product of x_μ with itself is

$$\sum_{\mu\nu} g^{\mu\nu} x_\nu x_\mu = \sum_{\mu} x^\mu x_\mu = c^2 t^2 - \boldsymbol{x}\cdot\boldsymbol{x}. \tag{11.6}$$

Similarly, for the energy–momentum four-vector of a free particle $p^\mu = (E/c, p_x, p_y, p_z)$ we have

$$\sum_{\mu\nu} g^{\mu\nu} p_\nu p_\mu = \sum_{\mu} p^\mu p_\mu = \frac{E^2}{c^2} - \boldsymbol{p}\cdot\boldsymbol{p} = m^2 c^2 \tag{11.7}$$

where m is the rest mass of the particle. Henceforth, we revert to natural units in which the speed of light $c = 1$. In addition, we will use Greek letters for indices which run from 0 to 3 and Latin letters for those which run from 1 to 3 and use the convention that repeated indices imply a summation over all possible values so that the Lorentz transformation for a contravariant vector (11.4) will simply be written

$$x'^\mu = \Lambda^\mu_\nu x^\nu. \tag{11.8}$$

The corresponding transformation law for a covariant four-vector is

$$\Lambda^\mu_\nu x'_\mu = x_\nu. \tag{11.9}$$

In what follows we shall need to differentiate with respect to the space–time coordinates. It can be shown that since x^μ is a contravariant vector $\partial/\partial x^\mu$ is a covariant vector and to stress this it is written with a lower index,

$$\partial_\mu \equiv \left(\frac{\partial}{\partial x^0}, \nabla\right) = \left(\frac{\partial}{\partial t}, \nabla\right) \tag{11.10}$$

where ∇ is the three-dimensional gradient operator. On the other hand,

$$\partial^\mu \equiv \left(\frac{\partial}{\partial x_0}, -\nabla\right) = \left(\frac{\partial}{\partial t}, -\nabla\right) \tag{11.11}$$

is a contravariant vector. It follows that, in this notation,

$$\partial_\mu \partial^\mu = \frac{\partial^2}{\partial t^2} - \nabla^2 = \Box^2 \tag{11.12}$$

is the d'Alembertian operator. Note that in constructing a Lorentz invariant the upper and lower indices must balance. The condition that an equation be Lorentz covariant is that on the two sides of the equation the unrepeated upper and lower indices must balance separately and repeated indices must appear once as an upper and once as a lower index.

11.4.3 The Dirac equation

In 1928 Dirac[11] succeeded in finding a form of the equation

$$i\hbar \frac{\partial}{\partial t} \psi(\boldsymbol{x}, t) = H\psi(\boldsymbol{x}, t) \tag{11.13}$$

which satisfied Lorentz covariance and avoided the problem of negative probability densities encountered with the Klein–Gordon equation. Dirac argued that the symmetry between energy and momentum required by special relativity dictates that since the Hamiltonian H is linear in E it must be linear in $\boldsymbol{p}$. Equivalently, since (11.13) is linear in the time derivative, the Hamiltonian must be linear in the space derivatives. Equation (11.13) may therefore be written in the general form

$$i \frac{\partial \psi}{\partial t}(\boldsymbol{x}, t) = \left[-i\left(\alpha_1 \frac{\partial}{\partial x^1} + \alpha_2 \frac{\partial}{\partial x^2} + \alpha_3 \frac{\partial}{\partial x^3} \right) + \beta m \right] \psi(\boldsymbol{x}, t) \tag{11.14}$$

where we have used natural units with $\hbar = c = 1$. Here m is the rest energy of the particle.

We shall see that the coefficients α_i and β cannot simply be numbers and Dirac proposed that (11.14) be regarded as a matrix equation with the wavefunction ψ written as a column matrix with n components,

$$\psi = \begin{bmatrix} \psi_1 \\ \psi_2 \\ \vdots \\ \psi_n \end{bmatrix}$$

and the coefficients α_i and β as $n \times n$ matrices. Equation (11.14) becomes in effect n coupled first-order equations. For (11.14) to be a suitable relativistic equation the correct energy–momentum relation, $E^2 = p^2 + m^2$, must hold for a free particle and therefore each component of ψ must satisfy the Klein–Gordon equation,

$$-\frac{\partial^2\psi}{\partial t^2} = (-\nabla^2 + m^2)\psi.$$

With

$$\alpha_1 \frac{\partial}{\partial x^1} + \alpha_2 \frac{\partial}{\partial x^2} + \alpha_3 \frac{\partial}{\partial x^3}$$

written as $\boldsymbol{\alpha}\cdot\boldsymbol{\nabla}$ the Dirac equation becomes

$$\mathrm{i}\frac{\partial\psi}{\partial t} = (-\mathrm{i}\boldsymbol{\alpha}\cdot\boldsymbol{\nabla} + \beta m)\psi. \tag{11.15}$$

Then,

$$\begin{aligned}\left(\mathrm{i}\frac{\partial}{\partial t}\right)^2\psi &= -\frac{\partial^2\psi}{\partial t^2} \\ &= (-\mathrm{i}\boldsymbol{\alpha}\cdot\boldsymbol{\nabla} + \beta m)(-\mathrm{i}\boldsymbol{\alpha}\cdot\boldsymbol{\nabla} + \beta m)\psi \\ &= -\tfrac{1}{2}\sum_{i,\,j=1}^{3}(\alpha_i\alpha_j + \alpha_j\alpha_i)\frac{\partial^2\psi}{\partial x^i\,\partial x^j} \\ &\quad - \mathrm{i}m\sum_{i=1}^{3}(\alpha_i\beta + \beta\alpha_i)\frac{\partial\psi}{\partial x^i} + \beta^2 m^2\psi \\ &= (-\nabla^2 + m^2)\psi.\end{aligned}$$

These relations impose conditions on the coefficients α_i and β and inspection shows that in order that the last equality be satisfied

$$\alpha_i\alpha_j + \alpha_j\alpha_i = \{\alpha_i, \alpha_j\} = 2\delta_{ij}I \tag{11.16a}$$

$$\alpha_i\beta + \beta\alpha_i = \{\alpha_i, \beta\} = 0 \tag{11.16b}$$

$$\alpha_i^2 = \beta_i^2 = I \tag{11.16c}$$

where I is the unit matrix. It is now apparent, from the anticommutation properties (11.16a, b), that the α_i and β must be matrices and not simply numbers. In order that the Hamiltonian be a hermitian operator the α_i and β must be hermitian matrices. It can be shown that the smallest dimension in which the α_i and β can be realized is $n = 4$. One conventional choice for these 4 × 4 matrices is the Dirac–Pauli representation

$$\alpha_i = \begin{bmatrix} 0 & \sigma_i \\ \sigma_i & 0 \end{bmatrix} \qquad \beta = \begin{bmatrix} I & 0 \\ 0 & -I \end{bmatrix} \tag{11.17}$$

where the σ_i are the 2 × 2 Pauli spin matrices

$$\sigma_1 = \begin{bmatrix} 0 & 1 \\ 1 & 0 \end{bmatrix} \qquad \sigma_2 = \begin{bmatrix} 0 & -\mathrm{i} \\ \mathrm{i} & 0 \end{bmatrix} \qquad \sigma_3 = \begin{bmatrix} 1 & 0 \\ 0 & -1 \end{bmatrix} \tag{11.18}$$

and I is the 2 × 2 unit matrix. The wavefunction $\psi(\boldsymbol{x}, t)$ in (11.14) will then have four components and is known as a Dirac spinor,

$$\psi(\boldsymbol{x}, t) = \begin{bmatrix} \psi_1 \\ \psi_2 \\ \psi_3 \\ \psi_4 \end{bmatrix}.$$

We investigate immediately whether the Dirac equation (11.14) gives rise to a continuity equation with a positive definite probability density. We introduce the hermitian conjugate wavefunction, a row vector,

$$\psi^\dagger = [\psi_1^* \quad \psi_2^* \quad \psi_3^* \quad \psi_4^*]$$

and rewrite the Dirac equation as

$$\mathrm{i}\frac{\partial\psi}{\partial t} = -\mathrm{i}\sum_{k=1}^{3} \alpha_k \frac{\partial}{\partial x^k}\psi + m\beta\psi. \tag{11.19}$$

Multiplying from the left by $\psi^\dagger$ gives

$$\mathrm{i}\psi^\dagger\frac{\partial\psi}{\partial t} = -\mathrm{i}\sum_{k=1}^{3} \psi^\dagger\alpha_k \frac{\partial\psi}{\partial x^k} + m\psi^\dagger\beta\psi. \tag{11.20}$$

The hermitian conjugate of the Dirac equation is

$$-\mathrm{i}\frac{\partial\psi^\dagger}{\partial t} = \mathrm{i}\sum_{k=1}^{3} \frac{\partial\psi^\dagger}{\partial x^k}\alpha_k + m\psi^\dagger\beta \tag{11.21}$$

since $\alpha_k^\dagger = \alpha_k$ and $\beta^\dagger = \beta$ (α_k, β hermitian). On multiplying (11.21) from the right by ψ we obtain

$$-\mathrm{i}\frac{\partial\psi^{\dagger}}{\partial t}\psi = \mathrm{i}\sum_{k=1}^{3}\frac{\partial\psi^{\dagger}}{\partial x^{k}}\alpha_{k}\psi + m\psi^{\dagger}\beta\psi. \tag{11.22}$$

Subtraction of (11.22) from (11.20) gives

$$\frac{\partial}{\partial t}\psi^{\dagger}\psi + \sum_{k=1}^{3}\frac{\partial}{\partial x^{k}}(\psi^{\dagger}\alpha_{k}\psi) = 0 \tag{11.23}$$

which we recognize as an equation of continuity $\partial\rho/\partial t + \nabla\cdot\boldsymbol{j} = 0$ if we make the association $\rho = \psi^{\dagger}\psi$ and $\boldsymbol{j} = \psi^{\dagger}\boldsymbol{\alpha}\psi$. The probability current density $\boldsymbol{j}$ has three components $j^{k} = \psi^{\dagger}\alpha_{k}\psi$ with $k = 1, 2, 3$ and the probability density

$$\rho = \psi^{\dagger}\psi = \sum_{i=1}^{4}|\psi_{i}|^{2} > 0$$

is now positive definite.

The Dirac equation can be cast into covariant form by introducing the Dirac γ matrices to replace the matrices α_i and β. They are defined as

$$\gamma^{0} = \beta \qquad \gamma^{k} = \beta\alpha^{k} \qquad (k = 1, 2, 3)$$

or equivalently

$$\gamma^{\mu} = (\beta, \beta\boldsymbol{\alpha}) \qquad (\mu = 0, 1, 2, 3). \tag{11.24}$$

It is a simple matter to show from the anticommutation properties of the α_k and β matrices (11.16) that the γ matrices satisfy the anticommutation relations

$$\gamma^{\mu}\gamma^{\nu} + \gamma^{\nu}\gamma^{\mu} = 2g^{\mu\nu}I. \tag{11.25}$$

In terms of these γ matrices and the covariant derivarive, ∂_{μ}, the Dirac equation takes on the covariant form

$$(\mathrm{i}\gamma^{\mu}\,\partial_{\mu} - m)\psi = 0 \tag{11.26}$$

and the equation of continuity becomes

$$\partial_{\mu}j^{\mu} = 0 \tag{11.27}$$

where $j^{\mu} = \bar{\psi}\gamma^{\mu}\psi$ is a four-vector current. Here, $\bar{\psi}$ is the row spinor defined by $\bar{\psi} = \psi^{\dagger}\gamma^{0}$. We identify the probability density ρ with the time component of j^μ;

$$\rho = \bar{\psi}\gamma^0\psi = \psi^\dagger(\gamma^0)^2\psi = \psi^\dagger\psi.$$

The space components are

$$j^k = \bar{\psi}\gamma^k\psi = \psi^\dagger\gamma^0\gamma^k\psi = \psi^\dagger\alpha_k\psi$$

in agreement with the result obtained earlier in this section.

11.4.4 The Dirac equation in the presence of an electromagnetic field: intrinsic spin of the electron

We can look for plane-wave solutions to the Dirac equation for a free particle in the form

$$\psi = u(\boldsymbol{p})\exp(-\mathrm{i}p\cdot\boldsymbol{x}) \tag{11.28}$$

where $u(\boldsymbol{p})$ is a four-component spinor independent of the space–time coordinates x. On substituting (11.28) into the Dirac equation we get the Dirac equation for a free particle spinor,

$$(\gamma^\mu p_\mu - m)u(\boldsymbol{p}) = 0 \tag{11.29}$$

in which we note that p_μ is a covariant four-vector with components $(E, -\boldsymbol{p})$.

In non-relativistic quantum mechanics, the wave equation for an electron in the presence of an external electromagnetic field, specified by the scalar and vector potentials ϕ and $\boldsymbol{A}$, is set up by making the substitution

$$\mathrm{i}\frac{\partial}{\partial t} \to \mathrm{i}\frac{\partial}{\partial t} + e\phi \qquad -\mathrm{i}\nabla \to -\mathrm{i}\nabla + e\boldsymbol{A} \tag{11.30}$$

in the free particle Schrödinger equation. In (11.30) $-e$ is the charge on the electron. In terms of the four-vector potential $A^\mu = (\phi, \boldsymbol{A})$, the 'minimal substitution', as (11.30) is often called, takes on the form

$$\partial_\mu \to \partial_\mu - \mathrm{i}eA_\mu. \tag{11.31}$$

Then the Dirac equation becomes

$$[\gamma^\mu(p_\mu + eA_\mu) - m]u(\boldsymbol{p}) = 0. \tag{11.32}$$

It is convenient to write equation (11.32) in terms of the matrices $\boldsymbol{\alpha}$ and β. We recall that $\gamma^\mu \equiv (\beta, \beta\boldsymbol{\alpha})$, then

$$(\beta E - \beta\boldsymbol{\alpha}\cdot\boldsymbol{p} + e\beta\phi - e\beta\boldsymbol{\alpha}\cdot\boldsymbol{A} - m)u(\boldsymbol{p}) = 0.$$

If we multiply from the left by β and use the fact that $\beta^2 = I$ we have

$$[\boldsymbol{\alpha}\cdot(\boldsymbol{p} + e\boldsymbol{A}) + \beta m - e\phi]u(\boldsymbol{p}) = Eu(\boldsymbol{p}). \tag{11.33}$$

In attempting to solve (11.33) it is usual to express the four-component spinor $u(\boldsymbol{p})$ in terms of two two-component spinors,

$$u \equiv \begin{pmatrix} u_A \\ u_B \end{pmatrix}.$$

Then, using the explicit expressions for the matrices $\boldsymbol{\alpha}$ and β, (11.33) becomes

$$\begin{pmatrix} m - e\phi & \boldsymbol{\sigma}\cdot(\boldsymbol{p} + e\boldsymbol{A}) \\ \boldsymbol{\sigma}\cdot(\boldsymbol{p} + e\boldsymbol{A}) & -m - e\phi \end{pmatrix} \begin{pmatrix} u_A \\ u_B \end{pmatrix} = E \begin{pmatrix} u_A \\ u_B \end{pmatrix}. \tag{11.34}$$

This corresponds to the two coupled equations

$$[\boldsymbol{\sigma}\cdot(\boldsymbol{p} + e\boldsymbol{A})]u_B = [E - m + e\phi]u_A \tag{11.35}$$

and

$$[\boldsymbol{\sigma}\cdot(\boldsymbol{p} + e\boldsymbol{A})]u_A = [E + m + e\phi]u_B. \tag{11.36}$$

Eliminating u_B from these equations gives

$$[\boldsymbol{\sigma}\cdot(\boldsymbol{p} + e\boldsymbol{A})(E + m + e\phi)^{-1}\boldsymbol{\sigma}\cdot(\boldsymbol{p} + e\boldsymbol{A})]u_A = [E - m + e\phi]u_A. \tag{11.37}$$

Now, in the non-relativistic limit, with kinetic energies and field interaction energies small compared with the rest energy m, we have

$$E + m + e\phi \to 2m$$
$$E - m \to E_{NR}$$

where E_{NR} is the non-relativistic energy, so (11.37) approximates to

$$\left[\frac{1}{2m}(\boldsymbol{\sigma}\cdot\boldsymbol{\pi})(\boldsymbol{\sigma}\cdot\boldsymbol{\pi}) - e\phi\right]u_A = E_{NR}u_A \tag{11.38}$$

where $\boldsymbol{\pi} \equiv \boldsymbol{p} + e\boldsymbol{A}$.

Now, if $\boldsymbol{a}$ and $\boldsymbol{b}$ are any two three-vectors it can be shown (see example 11.9) that

$$(\boldsymbol{\sigma}\cdot\boldsymbol{a})(\boldsymbol{\sigma}\cdot\boldsymbol{b}) = (\boldsymbol{a}\cdot\boldsymbol{b}) + \mathrm{i}\boldsymbol{\sigma}\cdot(\boldsymbol{a} \wedge \boldsymbol{b}).$$

Then, with $\boldsymbol{a} = \boldsymbol{b} = \boldsymbol{\pi}$ it follows that

$$\left\{\frac{1}{2m}[\boldsymbol{\pi}\cdot\boldsymbol{\pi} + \mathrm{i}\boldsymbol{\sigma}\cdot(\boldsymbol{\pi} \wedge \boldsymbol{\pi})] - e\phi\right\}u_{\mathrm{A}} = E_{\mathrm{NR}}u_{\mathrm{A}}. \tag{11.39}$$

In terms of $\boldsymbol{p}$ and $\boldsymbol{A}$ the vector product term is

$$\begin{aligned}(\boldsymbol{\pi} \wedge \boldsymbol{\pi})u_{\mathrm{A}} &= (\boldsymbol{p} + e\boldsymbol{A}) \wedge (\boldsymbol{p} + e\boldsymbol{A})u_{\mathrm{A}} \\ &= (\boldsymbol{p} \times \boldsymbol{p})u_{\mathrm{A}} + e(\boldsymbol{p} \wedge \boldsymbol{A} + \boldsymbol{A} \wedge \boldsymbol{p})u_{\mathrm{A}} + e^2(\boldsymbol{A} \wedge \boldsymbol{A})u_{\mathrm{A}}.\end{aligned}$$

The first and last terms are zero and, with $\boldsymbol{p} \equiv -\mathrm{i}\boldsymbol{\nabla}$, the middle term becomes

$$-e\mathrm{i}[\boldsymbol{\nabla} \wedge (\boldsymbol{A}u_{\mathrm{A}}) + \boldsymbol{A} \wedge (\boldsymbol{\nabla}u_{\mathrm{A}})] = -e\mathrm{i}(\boldsymbol{\nabla} \wedge \boldsymbol{A})u_{\mathrm{A}}$$

since $\boldsymbol{\nabla} \wedge (\boldsymbol{A}u_{\mathrm{A}}) = (\boldsymbol{\nabla} \wedge \boldsymbol{A})u_{\mathrm{A}} - \boldsymbol{A} \wedge (\boldsymbol{\nabla}u_{\mathrm{A}})$. Furthermore, $\boldsymbol{\nabla} \wedge \boldsymbol{A} = \boldsymbol{B}$, so that equation (11.39) becomes

$$\left[\frac{1}{2m}(\boldsymbol{p} + e\boldsymbol{A})^2 + \frac{e}{2m}\boldsymbol{\sigma}\cdot\boldsymbol{B} - e\phi\right]u_{\mathrm{A}} = E_{\mathrm{NR}}u_{\mathrm{A}}. \tag{11.40}$$

The expression in square brackets is, apart from the term $(e/2m)\boldsymbol{\sigma}\cdot\boldsymbol{B}$, the same as the classical Hamiltonian for a slowly moving electron in an electromagnetic field. This extra term may be interpreted as arising from the interaction of the *magnetic moment of the electron* $-e\boldsymbol{\sigma}/2m$ with the magnetic field $\boldsymbol{B}$.

We wish to show explicitly that this corresponds to an intrinsic spin $\frac{1}{2}\boldsymbol{\sigma}$ for the electron. To do this we work with potentials ϕ and $\boldsymbol{A}$, such that no angular momentum is transferred to the electron, i.e. we consider the situation in which $\boldsymbol{A} = 0$ and ϕ is spherically symmetric – the field is central. With $\boldsymbol{A} = 0$ the Hamiltonian in (11.33) becomes

$$H = \boldsymbol{\alpha}\cdot\boldsymbol{p} + \beta m - e\phi. \tag{11.41}$$

We might expect that with a central potential the orbital angular momentum, $\boldsymbol{L} = \boldsymbol{x} \wedge \boldsymbol{p}$, would be conserved. Consider the component

$L_1 = x_2 p_3 - x_3 p_2$; the time rate of change of L_1 is given by

$$
\begin{aligned}
\mathrm{i}\frac{\mathrm{d}L_1}{\mathrm{d}t} &= [L_1, H] \\
&= \boldsymbol{\alpha}\cdot\{(x_2 p_3 - x_3 p_2)\boldsymbol{p} - \boldsymbol{p}(x_2 p_3 - x_3 p_2)\} \\
&= \mathrm{i}(\alpha_2 p_3 - \alpha_3 p_2)
\end{aligned}
$$

where we have used the basic commutation relations $[x_i, p_j] = \mathrm{i}\delta_{ij}$. Similar results hold for the components L_2 and L_3. We have, therefore,

$$\mathrm{i}\frac{\mathrm{d}\boldsymbol{L}}{\mathrm{d}t} = \mathrm{i}(\boldsymbol{\alpha} \wedge \boldsymbol{p}) \tag{11.42}$$

and consequently the orbital angular momentum is not a conserved quantity. On physical grounds we might expect that there is some *total* angular momentum which is conserved in a central field and to this end we look for another operator whose commutation relation with the Hamiltonian gives the negative of the right-hand side of equation (11.42). Then the sum of the orbital angular momentum and this new quantity will be conserved. Consider the operator

$$\boldsymbol{\sigma}' = \begin{pmatrix} \boldsymbol{\sigma} & 0 \\ 0 & \boldsymbol{\sigma} \end{pmatrix} \tag{11.43}$$

and specifically the component σ'_1. It is a simple matter, using the definitions of $\boldsymbol{\alpha}$ and β and the commutation relations for the Pauli spin matrices, to show that

$$[\sigma'_1, \alpha_1] = [\sigma'_1, \beta] = 0$$

and

$$
\begin{aligned}
[\sigma'_1, \alpha_2] &= 2\mathrm{i}\alpha_3 \\
[\sigma'_1, \alpha_3] &= -2\mathrm{i}\alpha_2 .
\end{aligned}
$$

Then

$$\mathrm{i}\frac{\mathrm{d}\sigma'_1}{\mathrm{d}t} = [\sigma'_1, H] = -2\mathrm{i}(\alpha_2 p_3 - \alpha_3 p_2)$$

with similar results for the components σ'_2 and σ'_3. Then

$$\mathrm{i}\frac{\mathrm{d}\boldsymbol{\sigma}'}{\mathrm{d}t} = -2\mathrm{i}(\boldsymbol{\alpha} \wedge \boldsymbol{p}). \tag{11.44}$$

It follows that the operator

$$J = L + \tfrac{1}{2}\boldsymbol{\sigma}' \tag{11.45}$$

commutes with the Hamiltonian and may be interpreted as a total angular momentum. The quantity $s = \frac{1}{2}\boldsymbol{\sigma}'$ is interpreted as the intrinsic spin of the electron. We thus come to the important conclusion that according to equations (11.40) and (11.45) an electron has an intrinsic spin $\frac{1}{2}$, associated with which is an intrinsic magnetic moment

$$\boldsymbol{\mu} = -\frac{e\boldsymbol{\sigma}}{2m} = -g\frac{e}{2m}\,s. \tag{11.46}$$

The Dirac equation, therefore, predicts that the g factor of the electron is $g = 2$. Although experimentally $g - 2$ for the electron is not quite zero, the departure is small (and well understood) and the prediction $g = 2$ must be regarded as a great triumph of the Dirac equation.

11.4.5 *Free particle solutions of the Dirac equation*

Encouraged by the physical interpretation of the Dirac equation in the non-relativistic limit we turn to the problem of finding solutions in the relativistic case.

For a free particle the spinor equation (11.33) becomes

$$[\boldsymbol{\alpha}\cdot \boldsymbol{p} + \beta m]u(\boldsymbol{p}) = Eu(\boldsymbol{p}). \tag{11.47}$$

First, to enumerate the number of solutions we consider the particle to be at rest, then, recalling the explicit form of the matrix β, (11.47) becomes

$$\begin{pmatrix} mI & 0 \\ 0 & -mI \end{pmatrix} u = Eu \tag{11.48}$$

where as usual I is the 2×2 unit matrix and u is a four-component spinor. Inspection shows that there are four solutions to (11.48),

$$u^{(1)} = \begin{pmatrix} 1 \\ 0 \\ 0 \\ 0 \end{pmatrix} \quad \text{and} \quad u^{(2)} = \begin{pmatrix} 0 \\ 1 \\ 0 \\ 0 \end{pmatrix}$$

both with positive energy $E = m$, and

$$u^{(3)} = \begin{pmatrix} 0 \\ 0 \\ 1 \\ 0 \end{pmatrix} \quad \text{and} \quad u^{(4)} = \begin{pmatrix} 0 \\ 0 \\ 0 \\ 1 \end{pmatrix}$$

both with negative energy $E = -m$. This situation is reminiscent of that with the Klein–Gordon equation for which both $E > 0$ and $E < 0$ solutions arose. It remains to interpret these negative energy solutions. This we postpone for the time being but note with hindsight from the previous section that the two solutions for a given energy may somehow be connected with the two possible orientations of the spin vector of a spin $\frac{1}{2}$ particle.

For $\boldsymbol{p}$ non-zero (11.47) becomes

$$\begin{pmatrix} m & \boldsymbol{\sigma}\cdot\boldsymbol{p} \\ \boldsymbol{\sigma}\cdot\boldsymbol{p} & -m \end{pmatrix}\begin{pmatrix} u_{\mathrm{A}} \\ u_{\mathrm{B}} \end{pmatrix} = E\begin{pmatrix} u_{\mathrm{A}} \\ u_{\mathrm{B}} \end{pmatrix} \tag{11.49}$$

where, as in the last section, we have written the four-component spinor in terms of the two-component spinors $u_{\mathrm{A}}(\boldsymbol{p})$ and $u_{\mathrm{B}}(\boldsymbol{p})$ and have used the explicit form of the matrices $\boldsymbol{\alpha}$. The matrix equation (11.49) corresponds to the two coupled equations

$$\boldsymbol{\sigma}\cdot\boldsymbol{p}u_{\mathrm{B}} = (E - m)u_{\mathrm{A}} \tag{11.50a}$$

$$\boldsymbol{\sigma}\cdot\boldsymbol{p}u_{\mathrm{A}} = (E + m)u_{\mathrm{B}}. \tag{11.50b}$$

We want to find solutions $u(\boldsymbol{p})$ which reduce to the zero-momentum solutions obtained above as $\boldsymbol{p} \to 0$. We consider first the positive energy solutions and take $u_{\mathrm{A}}^{(s)} = \chi^{(s)}$ with

$$\chi^{(1)} = \begin{pmatrix} 1 \\ 0 \end{pmatrix} \quad \text{and} \quad \chi^{(2)} = \begin{pmatrix} 0 \\ 1 \end{pmatrix}.$$

On substituting into (11.50b) for u_{A} we obtain

$$u_{\mathrm{B}} = \frac{\boldsymbol{\sigma}\cdot\boldsymbol{p}\chi^{(s)}}{E + m}. \tag{11.51}$$

Then, the positive energy solutions are

$$u^{(1)}(\boldsymbol{p}) = N\begin{pmatrix} 1 \\ 0 \\ \dfrac{\boldsymbol{\sigma}\cdot\boldsymbol{p}}{E+m} \\ 0 \end{pmatrix} \qquad u^{(2)}(\boldsymbol{p}) = N\begin{pmatrix} 0 \\ 1 \\ 0 \\ \dfrac{\boldsymbol{\sigma}\cdot\boldsymbol{p}}{E+m} \end{pmatrix} \tag{11.52}$$

where N is a normalization constant. The negative energy solutions are obtained in a similar fashion. We take in this case $u_{\mathrm{B}}^{(s)} = \chi^{(s)}$ and write the energy as $-|E|$; then, from (11.50a),

$$u_{\mathrm{A}} = -\frac{\boldsymbol{\sigma}\cdot\boldsymbol{p}\chi^{(s)}}{|E|+m} \tag{11.53}$$

and the negative energy solutions are

$$u^{(3)}(\boldsymbol{p}) = N\begin{pmatrix} -\dfrac{\boldsymbol{\sigma}\cdot\boldsymbol{p}}{|E|+m} \\ 0 \\ 1 \\ 0 \end{pmatrix} \qquad u^{(4)}(\boldsymbol{p}) = N\begin{pmatrix} 0 \\ -\dfrac{\boldsymbol{\sigma}\cdot\boldsymbol{p}}{|E|+m} \\ 0 \\ 1 \end{pmatrix}. \tag{11.54}$$

The reader may readily verify that the spinors $u^{(1)}, \ldots, u^{(4)}$ are orthogonal, i.e. $u^{(r)\dagger}u^{(s)} = 0$ for $r \neq s$. The normalization constant can be determined by setting $u^{(s)\dagger}u^{(s)} = 1$ in which case $N = [(E+m)/2E]^{1/2}$. Frequently, instead of this normalization a covariant normalization is used in which by convention there are considered to be $2E$ particles per unit volume. Then

$$\int \rho \, \mathrm{d}V = \int \bar{\psi}\psi \, \mathrm{d}V = 2E$$

so that $u^{(s)\dagger}u^{(s)} = 2E$, in which case $N = (E+m)^{1/2}$.

11.4.6 Interpretation of the Dirac spinors

Let us first turn our attention to the states with the same energy and consider further the suggestion in the last section that the internal degree of freedom which might distinguish the states is the spin orientation. One well-defined direction in the problem at hand is the direction of motion of the particle, so we consider first the spin projection in this direction.

It is straightforward to show that the operator

$$\Lambda = \begin{pmatrix} \boldsymbol{\sigma}\cdot\hat{\boldsymbol{p}} & 0 \\ 0 & \boldsymbol{\sigma}\cdot\hat{\boldsymbol{p}} \end{pmatrix} \tag{11.55}$$

where $\hat{\boldsymbol{p}} = \boldsymbol{p}/|\boldsymbol{p}|$ is a unit vector in the direction of the momentum, commutes with the Hamiltonian and therefore has eigenvalues which are good quantum numbers and which may be used to distinguish the states. No other component can be found which commutes with the Hamiltonian. Furthermore, since $(\boldsymbol{\sigma}\cdot\boldsymbol{p})^2 = \boldsymbol{p}^2$ we have $\boldsymbol{\sigma}\cdot\boldsymbol{p} = \pm|\boldsymbol{p}|$, i.e. $\boldsymbol{\sigma}\cdot\hat{\boldsymbol{p}} = \pm 1$, and the helicity eigenvalues of the operator Λ are ± 1. For simplicity, consider the case in which the particle moves along the 3 axis. Then,

$$\Lambda = \begin{pmatrix} \sigma_3 & 0 \\ 0 & \sigma_3 \end{pmatrix} = \begin{pmatrix} 1 & 0 & 0 & 0 \\ 0 & -1 & 0 & 0 \\ 0 & 0 & 1 & 0 \\ 0 & 0 & 0 & -1 \end{pmatrix} \tag{11.56}$$

and it is a simple matter to show that

$$\Lambda u^{(1)} = +1u^{(1)} \qquad \Lambda u^{(2)} = -1u^{(2)}. \tag{11.57}$$

The positive energy spinors $u^{(1)}$ and $u^{(2)}$ thus describe states of helicity $+1$ and -1 respectively. Similarly,

$$\Lambda u^{(3)} = +1u^{(3)} \qquad \Lambda u^{(4)} = -1u^{(4)} \tag{11.58}$$

and the spinors $u^{(3)}$ and $u^{(4)}$ describe negative energy states with helicity $+1$ and -1 respectively. But what is the physical interpretation of these negative energy solutions?

When the Dirac equation is used to calculate, for instance, the energy levels of the hydrogen atom, the results agree well with experiments, but there remains the problem of the stability of the ground state. The existence of negative energy solutions might lead one to expect that radiative transitions could be made from the ground state to the negative energy states; indeed if the totality of negative energy states is included in a calculation of the transition rate the latter becomes infinite. The single-particle interpretation of the Dirac equation therefore needs some reappraisal.

In 1930 Dirac[12] formulated his 'hole' theory to overcome the difficulty. He invoked the Pauli exclusion principle and envisaged the negative energy states to be filled, two to each energy level, with electrons. In this picture the vacuum state is the state with all negative energy levels occupied and all positive energy levels unoccupied, as shown schematically in figure 11.9(a). If an energy $E \geqslant 2m$, where m is the rest energy of the electron, is available for instance in the form of electromagnetic radiation, an electron in the 'sea' of negative energy states may be elevated to a positive energy state leaving a 'hole' in the negative energy sea. This hole, being an *absence* of a negatively charged electron and an *absence* of a negative energy, was interpreted by Dirac as a positively charged 'electron' with a positive energy, i.e. as a positron, the antiparticle of the electron. The net result of the process is electron–positron pair production (figure 11.9(b)). The reverse process (figure 11.9(c)), in which a positive energy electron makes a transition to a vacancy or hole in the negative energy sea, results in the annihilation of the electron–positron pair with the emission of radiation. Dirac thus associated the negative energy solutions with the positron, the two positron solutions being distinguished by the helicity eigenvalues as shown above. Even though there are difficulties connected with this interpretation it was nevertheless a great triumph for the Dirac equation when Anderson[13] discovered the positron in 1932.

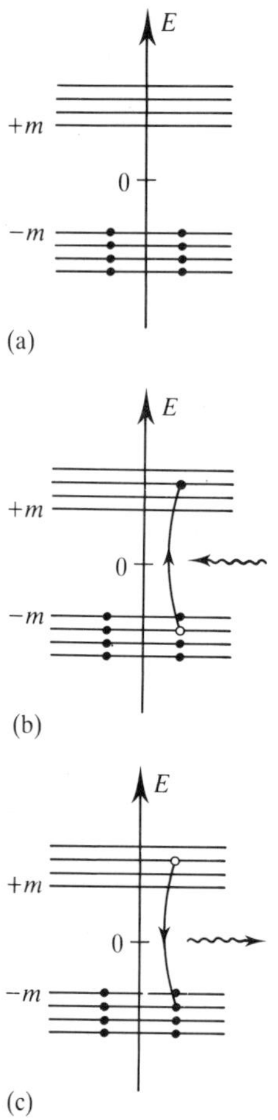

Figure 11.9
(a) The vacuum state in which all negative energy levels are filled with electrons; (b) e^+e^- pair production; (c) e^+e^- annihilation.

Following this success, Pauli and Weisskopf reconsidered the Klein–Gordon equation which we recall had been rejected as a possible relativistic wave equation on the grounds that there were negative energy solutions and the probability density was not positive definite. In relativistic notation the probability density and probability current density (section 11.4.1) become

$$j^\mu = \mathrm{i}(\phi^* \partial^\mu \phi - \phi \, \partial^\mu \phi^*). \tag{11.59}$$

The Pauli–Weisskopf proposal was that this should be regarded as a *charge* current density by incorporating into j^μ the electric charge: thus

$$j^\mu = -e\mathrm{i}(\phi^* \partial^\mu \phi - \phi \, \partial^\mu \phi^*) \tag{11.60}$$

and it becomes physically reasonable that this electron current could be negative. The Klein–Gordon equation does not of course possess the extra degrees of freedom embodied in the Dirac equation, nevertheless it is now regarded as a suitable relativistic equation for spin 0 bosons.

An alternative to the Dirac hole theory is the interpretation due to Stückelberg[14] and Feynman[15] which takes the view that the negative energy solutions describe a particle propagating backward in time or equivalently correspond to a *positive* energy *antiparticle* propagating forward in time. This prescription is commonly used in the evaluation of Feynman diagrams but since this will not concern us we do not develop the idea any further here. The interested reader is referred to the book by Halzen and Martin.[16]

11.5 Application of the Dirac theory to β decay

11.5.1 The Fermi theory

Having established a relativistic description of spin $\frac{1}{2}$ particles we are now in a position to investigate the form of the matrix element for β decay and to consider what restrictions might be imposed on it by the experimental results, discussed in section 11.3, that parity is violated and that neutrinos exist in nature only as 'left-handed' particles, i.e. having helicity -1.

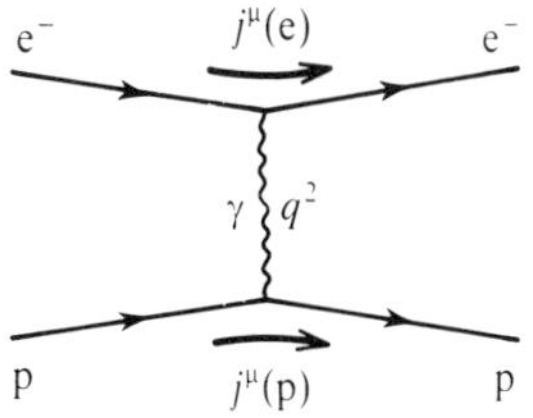

Figure 11.10 Feynman diagram for the electromagnetic interaction between an electron and a proton.

Fermi's original theory of β decay (section 5.2.3) used the well-understood electromagnetic interaction as an analogy. The electromagnetic interaction between an electron and a proton, for example, is described in lowest order by the Feynman diagram (figure 11.10). We can write down the matrix element $\mathscr{M}_{fi}$ for this process by considering the interaction between the electron current $j^{\mu}(\mathrm{e})$ with the electromagnetic field A^{μ} generated by the proton current $j^{\mu}(\mathrm{p})$:

$$\mathscr{M}_{fi} \approx j_{\mu}(\mathrm{e}) A^{\mu} \approx -\frac{1}{q^2} j_{\mu}(\mathrm{e}) j^{\mu}(\mathrm{p})$$

where the identification of the electromagnetic potential A^{μ} with its source $j^{\mu}(\mathrm{p})$ is made through the Maxwell equations

$$\square^2 A^{\mu} = j^{\mu}(\mathrm{p}). \tag{11.61}$$

The term $-1/q^2$, where q^2 is the square of the four-momentum transferred to the photon, is essentially the photon propagator. Thus the interaction is viewed as a current–current interaction and, in terms of the Dirac spinors, the matrix element has the form

$$\mathscr{M}_{fi} \approx e^2 \bar{u}_{\mathrm{p}} \gamma^{\mu} u_{\mathrm{p}} \left(-\frac{1}{q^2} \right) \bar{u}_{\mathrm{e}} \gamma_{\mu} u_{\mathrm{e}}. \tag{11.62}$$

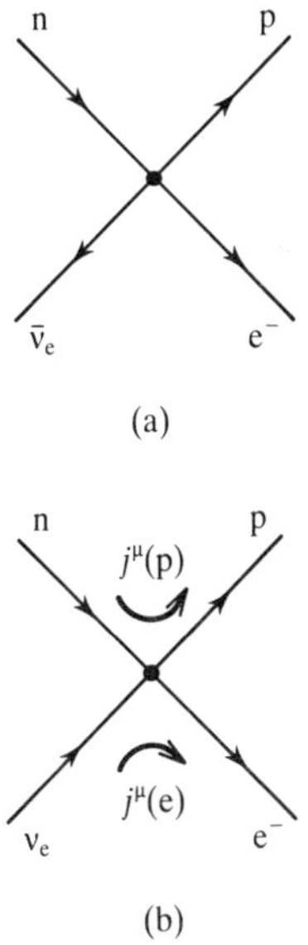

Figure 11.11 (a) Point-like β decay of the neutron; (b) the crossed reaction $\mathrm{n} + \nu_{\mathrm{e}} \rightarrow \mathrm{p} + \mathrm{e}^-$.

The β decay process $\mathrm{n} \rightarrow \mathrm{p e^- \bar{\nu}_e}$ was originally assumed to be a 'point' interaction as indicated in figure 11.11(a). The decay is conventionally analysed in terms of the 'crossed' process $\mathrm{n} + \nu_{\mathrm{e}} \rightarrow \mathrm{p} + \mathrm{e}^-$ in which the outgoing antineutrino becomes an incoming neutrino (figure 11.11(b)). Fermi assumed that the interaction could be expressed as the product of two *weak* currents $j^{\mu}(\mathrm{h})$ and $j^{\mu}(\mathrm{l})$, where $j^{\mu}(\mathrm{h})$ is the weak hadron current and $j^{\mu}(\mathrm{l})$ the lepton current, and wrote the matrix element as

$$\mathscr{M}_{fi} \approx G(\bar{u}_{\mathrm{p}} \gamma^{\mu} u_{\mathrm{n}})(\bar{u}_{\mathrm{e}} \gamma_{\mu} u_{\nu}). \tag{11.63}$$

Note that since the interaction is regarded as taking place at a point there is no propagator term. In this expression the four-component spinors are interpreted as follows:

$\bar{u}_p$ creates a proton (destroys an antiproton in general)

u_n destroys a neutron (creates an antineutron in general)

$\bar{u}_e$ creates an electron (destroys a positron in general)

u_ν destroys a neutrino (creates an antineutrino in general).

The weak coupling constant G is known as the Fermi constant and, in analogy with (11.62) and in the spirit of the discussion in chapter 7, may be related to the square of the 'weak charge'.

As in the case of the electromagnetic interaction the currents in the matrix element (11.63) are four-vector (or simply vector) currents, i.e. they transform like a four-vector under Lorentz transformations. While the matrix element successfully describes some of the features of β decay it does not give rise either to parity violation or to left-handed neutrinos.

11.5.2 Generalization of the Fermi theory

There is no *a priori* reason why the weak currents should be vector currents; any bilinear covariant of the form $\bar{\psi}O_i\psi$, where the operators O_i are products of γ matrices, is in principle a possible candidate for the weak interactions. In specifying the operators O_i it is convenient to introduce a further γ matrix, γ_5, defined by

$$\gamma^5 \equiv \gamma_5 = i\gamma^0\gamma^1\gamma^2\gamma^3. \tag{11.64}$$

In the Dirac–Pauli representation (11.17), γ_5 is given explicitly by

$$\gamma_5 = \begin{pmatrix} 0 & I \\ I & 0 \end{pmatrix} \tag{11.65}$$

and it is straightforward to verify that

$$\gamma_5^\dagger = \gamma_5, \qquad (\gamma_5)^2 = I \qquad \text{and} \qquad \gamma^5\gamma^\mu + \gamma^\mu\gamma^5 = 0.$$

The possible forms of O_i are distinguished by their transformation properties under proper Lorentz transformations and space inversion (the parity transformation) and are listed below. The number of components of each type of current is shown in parentheses. For brevity they are generally referred to simply as S, V, T, A and P.

$\bar{\psi}\psi$	scalar(1)	S
$\bar{\psi}\gamma^\mu\psi$	vector(4)	V
$i\bar{\psi}\gamma^\mu\gamma^\nu\psi \equiv \bar{\psi}\sigma^{\mu\nu}\psi$	tensor(6)	T
$i\bar{\psi}\gamma^5\gamma^\mu\psi$	axial vector(4)	A
$\bar{\psi}\gamma^5\psi$	pseudoscalar(1)	P

A Lorentz transformation may be regarded as a rotation in four-dimensional space so that $\bar{\psi}\psi$ for example transforms as a scalar (invariant) under Lorentz transformations *and* the parity transformation, whereas $\bar{\psi}\gamma^5\psi$ transforms as a scalar under Lorentz transformations but changes sign under the parity transformation and is therefore known as a pseudoscalar. On the other hand $\bar{\psi}\gamma^\mu\psi$ transforms as a vector under Lorentz transformations and changes sign under the parity transformation whereas $i\bar{\psi}\gamma^5\gamma^\mu\psi$ transforms as a vector under Lorentz transformations but is invariant under the parity transformation. It is therefore known as a pseudovector or axial vector.

Let us consider the parity transformation in more detail. Suppose $\psi(x_0, \boldsymbol{x})$ satisfies the Dirac equation (11.26). Under the parity transformation x_0 remains unchanged, $\boldsymbol{x} \to -\boldsymbol{x}$ and $\psi(x_0, \boldsymbol{x}) \to \psi(x_0, -\boldsymbol{x})$ which satisfies

$$\left(i\gamma^0 \frac{\partial}{\partial x^0} - i\gamma^k \frac{\partial}{\partial x^k} - m\right)\psi(x_0, -\boldsymbol{x}) = 0 \tag{11.66}$$

which is *not* the Dirac equation. However, on multiplying from the left by γ^0 and using the anticommutation relations for the γ matrices, equation (11.66) becomes

$$\left(i\gamma^\mu \frac{\partial}{\partial x^\mu} - m\right)\gamma^0\psi(x_0, -\boldsymbol{x}) = 0. \tag{11.67}$$

Thus the correct spatially inverted state which satisfies the Dirac equation is $\gamma^0\psi(x_0, -\boldsymbol{x})$. If we consider the spinors $u^{(s)}$ in the particle rest frame (section 11.4.5) it can immediately be verified that

$$\gamma^0 u^{(s)} = u^{(s)} \qquad (s = 1, 2)$$
$$\gamma^0 u^{(s)} = -u^{(s)} \qquad (s = 3, 4).$$

It follows that in the zero-momentum limit the positive and negative energy spinors are eigenstates of parity with opposite eigenvalues, i.e. the electron and positron have opposite intrinsic parities.

11.5.3 General form of the weak interaction Hamiltonian

The matrix element suggested by Fermi for the β decay $n \rightarrow pe^- \bar{\nu}_e$, being a contraction of two vector currents, is a Lorentz scalar and therefore cannot account for parity violation. At the time of the Fermi theory there was no reason to suspect that parity was violated in the weak interactions. A more general scalar, or parity-conserving, Hamiltonian can be written down by contracting nucleon and lepton currents with the same properties under the parity transformation. Thus in general

$$\mathcal{M}_{fi} \approx \sum_i C_i(\bar{u}_p O_i u_n)(\bar{u}_e O_i u_\nu) \tag{11.68}$$

where the sum is over the possible forms of the bilinear covariants $i = S, V, T, A, P$. In order to accommodate parity-violating effects one must add terms to the matrix element which are pseudoscalars, obtained by contracting two covariants which have the opposite behaviour under the parity transformation. The most general pseudoscalar is thus

$$\mathcal{M}_{fi} \approx \sum_i C_i'(\bar{u}_p O_i u_n)(\bar{u}_e O_i \gamma_5 u_\nu) \tag{11.69}$$

with different coefficients C_i' for the parity-violating terms. Combining (11.68) and (11.69) gives the most general β decay Hamiltonian:

$$\mathcal{M}_{fi} \propto \sum_i C_i(\bar{u}_p O_i u_n)\left[\bar{u}_e O_i\left(1 + \frac{C_i'}{C_i}\gamma_5\right)u_\nu\right]. \tag{11.70}$$

If, as the experimental evidence suggests, the β decay process is time-reversal invariant, the coefficients C_i and C_i' must be real. Furthermore, experiment shows that neutrinos and antineutrinos have a definite handedness – parity violation is *maximal* – and this implies that $C_i' = \pm C_i$; scalar and pseudoscalar terms appear in the Hamiltonian with equal magnitude. Thus

$$\mathcal{M}_{fi} = \frac{G}{\sqrt{2}}\sum_i C_i(\bar{u}_p O_i u_n)[u_e O_i(1 \pm \gamma_5)u_\nu] \tag{11.71}$$

is the most general form of the weak interaction Hamiltonian. The factor $\sqrt{2}$ is introduced so that G is defined as in the Fermi theory.

11.5.4 The two-component neutrino theory

We turn our attention to the terms $(1 \pm \gamma_5)u_\nu$ in (11.71) and our desire to show that these give rise to neutrinos of a definite handedness. If we persist with the Dirac–Pauli representation of the γ matrices, which we have used so far, it turns out that $(1+\gamma_5)u_\nu$ represents left-handed neutrinos (right-handed antineutrinos) while $(1-\gamma_5)u_\nu$ gives rise to right-handed neutrinos (left-handed antineutrinos). It is unfortunate that in the literature the present topic is most frequently discussed using a different representation of the γ matrices. Of course the physical content of the theory is independent of the particular choice of representation, the important requirement being the anticommutation relations of the matrices given in equations (11.25). An alternative to the Dirac–Pauli representation is one in which γ^5 is diagonal. With

$$\alpha_k = \begin{pmatrix} -\sigma_k & 0 \\ 0 & \sigma_k \end{pmatrix} \qquad \beta = \begin{pmatrix} 0 & I \\ I & 0 \end{pmatrix}$$

we have

$$\gamma^0 = \begin{pmatrix} 0 & I \\ I & 0 \end{pmatrix} \qquad \gamma^k = \begin{pmatrix} 0 & \sigma_k \\ -\sigma_k & 0 \end{pmatrix} \qquad \gamma^5 = \begin{pmatrix} -I & 0 \\ 0 & I \end{pmatrix}.$$

We use this representation in what follows.

If we assume that the mass of the neutrino is zero the Dirac equation may be written

$$H\psi = \boldsymbol{\alpha}\cdot\boldsymbol{p}\psi = E\psi. \tag{11.72}$$

Writing the four-component spinor as $\psi = \binom{\chi}{\phi}$ we have

$$\begin{pmatrix} -\boldsymbol{\sigma}\cdot\boldsymbol{p} & 0 \\ 0 & \boldsymbol{\sigma}\cdot\boldsymbol{p} \end{pmatrix}\begin{pmatrix} \chi \\ \phi \end{pmatrix} = E\begin{pmatrix} \chi \\ \phi \end{pmatrix} \tag{11.73}$$

corresponding to the two decoupled equations

$$-\boldsymbol{\sigma}\cdot\boldsymbol{p}\chi = E\chi \tag{11.74}$$

$$\boldsymbol{\sigma}\cdot\boldsymbol{p}\phi = E\phi. \tag{11.75}$$

Since, for a massless neutrino, $E^2 = p^2$, there are two solutions for each of these equations, $E > 0$ corresponding to neutrinos and $E < 0$ corresponding to antineutrinos.

For the positive energy solution to equation (11.74), with $E = |\boldsymbol{p}|$, we have

$$\frac{\boldsymbol{\sigma}\cdot\boldsymbol{p}}{|\boldsymbol{p}|}\chi = -\chi$$

which, since $(\boldsymbol{\sigma}\cdot\boldsymbol{p})/|\boldsymbol{p}|$ is the helicity operator, corresponds to a neutrino with helicity -1. For the negative energy solution, $E = -|\boldsymbol{p}|$, we have

$$\frac{\boldsymbol{\sigma}\cdot\boldsymbol{p}}{|\boldsymbol{p}|}\chi = +\chi \tag{11.76}$$

which corresponds to an antineutrino with helicity $+1$. Alternatively, the positive energy solution to (11.75) gives rise to right-handed neutrinos (helicity $+1$) and the negative energy solution to left-handed antineutrinos (helicity -1). In the representation of the γ matrices introduced in this section we note that

$$\tfrac{1}{2}(1-\gamma^5)u_\nu = \begin{pmatrix} I & 0 \\ 0 & 0 \end{pmatrix}\begin{pmatrix} \chi \\ \phi \end{pmatrix} = \begin{pmatrix} \chi \\ 0 \end{pmatrix}, \tag{11.77}$$

i.e. the factor $\frac{1}{2}(1-\gamma^5)$ projects out left-handed neutrino and right-handed antineutrino solutions.

We saw in section 11.3.2 that the neutrino has helicity -1 and thus the appropriate form of the β decay matrix element (11.71) must be

$$\mathcal{M}_{fi} = \frac{G}{\sqrt{2}}\sum_i C_i(\bar{u}_p O_i u_n)[\bar{u}_e O_i(1-\gamma_5)u_\nu]. \tag{11.78}$$

11.5.5 The V–A interaction

It remains to determine the form of O_i in the matrix element (11.78), and to this end we must be guided by a comparison of experimental results with theoretical predictions for the possible forms of O_i. In β decay the pseudoscalar interaction is unimportant; it introduces a factor v/c in the matrix element, where v is the nucleon velocity and typically this is about 10^{-3}. We therefore consider the four possible couplings S, V, T and A. Neither the S nor V couplings can produce a nuclear spin change so they can contribute, in principle, only to Fermi transitions for which $\Delta J = 0$, J being the nuclear spin. If *both* S and V are present there will be an interference term, the so-called Fierz interference, which will affect the shape of the energy spectrum. Compared with that derived in section 5.2.3 the Fierz interference term gives rise to an enhancement in the region of low electron energies. Both the tensor and axial-vector couplings can give rise to a change in nuclear spin and can therefore contribute to Gamow–Teller transitions ($\Delta J = 0, 1$). Again, if both couplings are present the statistical spectrum is modified. Experimental studies of the energy spectra of allowed transitions show that no interference terms are required so we conclude that Fermi transitions are S *or* V coupling and Gamow–Teller transitions are T *or* A.

Which type of coupling is involved can in principle be determined by measuring either the electron–neutrino angular correlation or the helicity of the electron. Using the appropriate matrix element one finds, after summing over the electron and neutrino spin states, that the decay probability depends on the angle θ between the electron and neutrino through a factor of the form

$$I(\theta) = 1 + a\frac{v}{c}\cos\theta$$

where v is the electron velocity and a is a parameter which has the values -1, $+1$, $+\frac{1}{3}$, $-\frac{1}{3}$ for S, V, T and A couplings respectively. In the Gamow–Teller transitions (T or A) the factor $\frac{1}{3}$ arises from the three possible orientations of the total lepton spin ($s = 1$) and this dilutes the correlation.

Since neutrinos have a minute interaction cross-section they are extremely difficult to detect so that experimentally angular correlations between the electron and the recoil nucleus were measured. Even this is notoriously difficult; indeed for some time it was erroneously thought that the interactions were S and T whereas in fact it is now known that they are V and A. With reference to figure 11.12 one can see that for

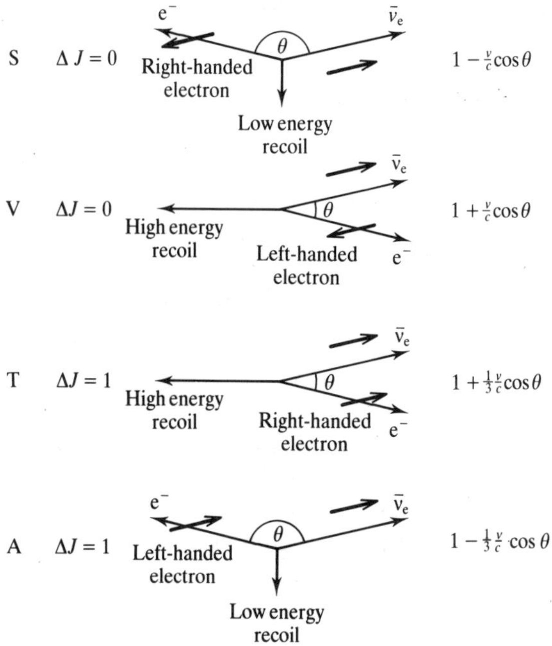

Figure 11.12 Electron–antineutrino angular correlations for the S, V, T and A interactions. The V and A interactions give rise to left-handed electrons while the S and T interactions yield right-handed electrons.

scalar and tensor interactions, assuming that antineutrinos are right handed, the electrons should be longitudinally polarized with, in the relativistic limit, helicity +1. The V and A interactions on the other hand predict an electron helicity −1. Thus the type of coupling in Fermi and Gamow–Teller transitions may be determined by measuring the longitudinal polarization of the electrons. Lack of space prevents us from giving a detailed description of the many techniques which have been used to do this; details may be found in the review article by Grodzins.[8] There is now overwhelming evidence that the electrons produced in nuclear β decay are longitudinally polarized with helicity $-v/c$, i.e. they are left handed; positrons have helicity $+v/c$ and are right handed. The β decay couplings are therefore V and A.

Then, with $O_i = \gamma^\mu$ for the vector coupling and $O_i = i\gamma^\mu\gamma^5$ for the axial vector coupling the matrix element (11.78) becomes

$$\begin{aligned}\mathcal{M}_{fi} &= \frac{G}{\sqrt{2}}\{C_V[\bar{u}_p\gamma^\mu u_n][\bar{u}_e\gamma^\mu(1-\gamma^5)u_\nu] \\ &\quad + C_A[\bar{u}_p i\gamma^\mu\gamma^5 u_n][\bar{u}_e i\gamma^\mu\gamma^5(1-\gamma^5)u_\nu]\} \\ &= \frac{G}{\sqrt{2}}[\bar{u}_p\gamma^\mu(C_V + C_A\gamma^5)u_n][\bar{u}_e\gamma^\mu(1-\gamma^5)u_\nu] \end{aligned} \tag{11.79}$$

where C_A and C_V are coupling constants, in units of G, for the axial vector and vector interactions.

Let us investigate further the nucleon current, i.e. the first term in square brackets in (11.79). In a pure Fermi transition a measurement of the ft value determines the product GC_V. When this is compared with the value of G determined from a purely leptonic interaction such as μ decay (see section 11.6) there is very good agreement, so that $C_V = 1$. The ratio of the absolute values of C_A and C_V determines the relative strengths of the Fermi and Gamow–Teller couplings and can be determined for instance by comparing the ft values of a pure Fermi transition such as $^{14}O \to {}^{14}N + e^+ + \nu_e$ and a mixed transition such as $n \to p + e^- + \bar{\nu}_e$. In fact

$$\frac{(ft)_{^{14}O}}{(ft)_n} = \frac{C_V^2 + 3C_A^2}{2C_V^2} = \frac{3100 \pm 20}{1080 \pm 16}. \tag{11.80}$$

The factor 3 arises in the numerator because of the three possible orientations of the total lepton spin in the Gamow–Teller transition (axial vector) and the factor 2 in the denominator arises because ^{14}O, $^{14}N^*$ and ^{14}C form an I spin triplet with $I_3 = 1$ for ^{14}O and $I_3 = 0$ for $^{14}N^*$. The I spin coupling rules give $\langle 1, 0|I_-|1, 1\rangle = \sqrt{2}$ where I_- is the I spin lowering operator.* Equation (11.80) gives

* Less formally, the decay $^{14}O \to {}^{14}N^*$ can arise from two equivalent protons outside the ^{12}C core.

$$\frac{C_A^2}{C_V^2} = 1.58 \pm 0.04 \qquad \left|\frac{C_A}{C_V}\right| = 1.26 \pm 0.02.$$

The sign of the ratio can in principle be determined from the longitudinal polarization of the proton in neutron decay; the factor $(1 \pm C_A/C_V)$ is related to the proton polarization in the same way that $1 \pm \gamma_5$ is related to the helicity of the neutrino. The velocity of recoil of the proton, however, is too small to allow such a measurement. Measurements of the angular correlation of the electrons emitted in the decay of *polarized* neutrons have detected a small anisotropy with respect to the neutron spin direction resulting from destructive interference between the Fermi and Gamow–Teller terms. This implies that the sign of the ratio is negative. With a value of $C_V \approx 1$ the axial vector coupling constant is then $C_A \approx -1.26$. If in (11.79) we put $C_A = -C_V = -1$, we have

$$\mathcal{M}_{fi} = \frac{G}{\sqrt{2}}[\bar{u}_p\gamma^\mu(1-\gamma^5)u_n][\bar{u}_e\gamma^\mu(1-\gamma^5)u_\nu] \qquad (11.81)$$

the so-called V–A interaction. It is interesting to note that, apart from the factors $1 - \gamma^5$, the matrix element is the same as that originally proposed by Fermi.

11.6 The universal Fermi interaction

The matrix element for the purely leptonic decay $\mu^- \to e^- + \bar{\nu}_e + \nu_\mu$, considered as a four-fermion point interaction as shown in figure 11.13, is

$$\mathcal{M}_{fi} = \frac{G}{\sqrt{2}}[\bar{u}_{\nu_\mu}\gamma^\rho(1-\gamma^5)u_\mu][\bar{u}_e\gamma_\rho(1-\gamma^5)u_{\nu_e}] \qquad (11.82)$$

and is a pure V–A interaction, i.e. the purely leptonic vector and axial vector currents have opposite sign but equal magnitudes. On calculating the phase space factor for the decay $\mu^- \to e^- + \bar{\nu}_e + \nu_\mu$ and using the matrix element (11.82) in Fermi's 'golden rule', the muon lifetime is found to be

$$\tau_\mu = \frac{192\pi^3}{G^2 m_\mu^5}. \qquad (11.83)$$

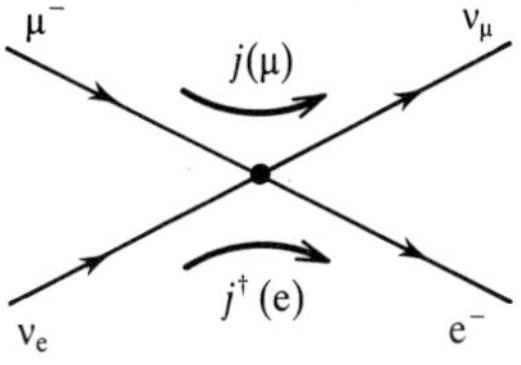

Figure 11.13
The purely leptonic decay $\mu^- \to e^-\bar{\nu}_e\nu_\mu$ viewed as a point interaction between the two leptonic currents.

The experimental values of the muon lifetime and mass when inserted into (11.83) give the weak coupling constant

$$G = (1.4358 \pm 0.0001) \times 10^{-62}\ \mathrm{J\ m^3}. \qquad (11.84)$$

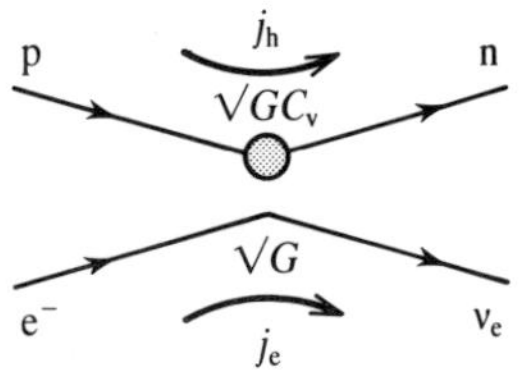

Figure 11.14
A pure Fermi nuclear β decay such as $^{14}O \to {}^{14}N + e^+ + \nu_e$.

Figure 11.14 represents a pure Fermi nuclear β decay such as $^{14}O \to {}^{14}N^* + e^+ + \nu_e$ and it is evident that the effective coupling constant which results from a determination of the *ft* value in such cases is GC_V. The directly observed value of GC_V has been obtained from the pure Fermi superallowed transitions of the mass $(4n + 2)$ nuclei ^{14}O, $^{26}Al^m$, ^{34}Cl, $^{38}K^m$, ^{42}Sc, ^{46}V, ^{50}Mn and ^{54}Co. All these decays are between states with $J^P = 0^+$ and have $I = 1$, $\Delta I = 0$. After the introduction of small charge-dependent corrections the $ft_{1/2}$ values are closely similar and have a mean of 3088 s. This gives a value

$$GC_V = (1.4116 \pm 0.0008) \times 10^{-62} \text{ J m}^3. \tag{11.85}$$

On inserting the value of G obtained from muon decay (equation (11.84)) into this expression we obtain a value 0.98 for C_V. Thus C_V is close but not quite equal to 1. We shall return to this point when we discuss the Cabibbo theory in section 11.10. The near equality of the Fermi constant obtained from an analysis of nuclear β decay, involving hadrons as well as leptons, and that derived from muon decay involving only leptons suggests a *universality* of the weak charge; the value of the weak charge is the same for all particles which possess it.* This is similar to the situation regarding the electromagnetic charge e; the interaction of a proton with an electromagnetic field is the same, apart from the sign, as that of an electron. The so-called universal Fermi interaction[17–20] assigns a single global coupling constant G for the coupling between any four fermion fields.

11.7 *The conserved vector current hypothesis*

Since the proton and neutron are strongly interacting composite objects and not structureless Dirac particles like the leptons one might expect that their weak couplings would be modified from the purely leptonic value G. We have seen above that indeed $C_A \approx -1.25$ but it is something of a surprise therefore that $C_V \approx 1$. The situation was clarified by Gerstein and Zel'dovitch[21] and independently by Feynman and Gell-Mann[22] in terms of the conserved vector current (CVC) hypothesis.

To gain some insight into this proposal we draw an analogy with electromagnetism, in which the currents are conserved vector currents. The interaction of a 'bare' proton with an electromagnetic field may be represented by the diagram figure 11.15(a). Since there is a finite probability

* Electron–muon universality is strictly true. In section 11.10 we shall see more precisely how universality extends to other particles.

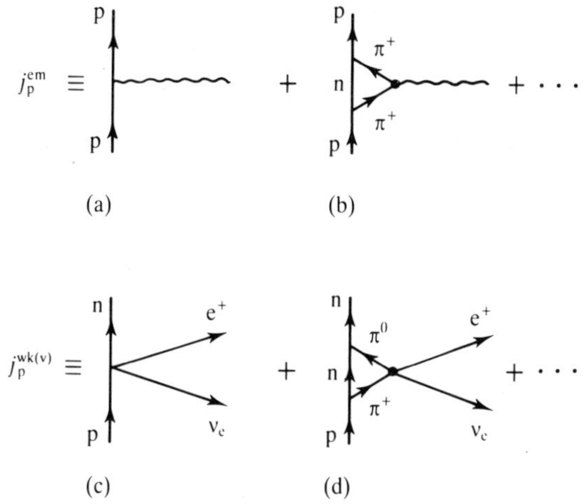

Figure 11.15
Coupling of a proton to the electromagnetic and weak interaction fields: (a) and (c) represent the 'bare' proton and (b) and (d) the modification due to virtual pion emission.

that the proton may emit a pion one might expect that the coupling of the proton to the electromagnetic field would be modified by diagrams such as figure 11.15(b). The electric charge, in fact, is not *renormalized* by the emission of virtual pions; the pion couples to the electromagnetic field with the same strength as the proton, with the result that the electromagnetic current is free of divergence, $\partial_\mu j^\mu(\text{em}) = 0$.

The CVC hypothesis asserts that the vector part of the hadronic weak current is *strictly* analogous to the electromagnetic current and is therefore also free of divergence: it is a conserved vector current. Physically, the situation is as shown in figures 11.15(c) and 11.15(d). One might expect the existence of the situation shown in figure 11.15(d) to alter the weak charge of the proton. As in the electromagnetic case the virtual pion couples to the weak field in such a way that the weak charge of the proton is not renormalized. The virtual pion itself can decay according to

$$\pi^+ \to \pi^0 + e^+ + \nu_e \tag{11.86}$$

for which $\Delta J = 0$ and $\Delta I = 0$, where J and I refer to the spins and isospins of the pions. It is therefore a superallowed Fermi transition in which the axial vector current plays no part. The decay (11.86) has been observed for real pions with the correct basic rate or $ft_{1/2}$ value; the net effect is that the overall decay probability is unaltered by the emission of virtual pions.

11.8 The current–current hypothesis of weak interactions

We have seen that neutron decay is described by the product of two currents, the nucleon current, which is approximately $j_N^\mu = \bar{u}_p \gamma^\mu (1 - \gamma^5) u_n$, and the leptonic current, $j_e^\mu = \bar{u}_e\gamma^\mu(1-\gamma^5)u_\nu$. Similarly, muon decay is described by the product of two leptonic currents $\bar{u}_\mu\gamma^\rho(1-\gamma^5)u_\nu$ and $\bar{u}_e\gamma^\rho(1-\gamma^5)u_\nu$. Each current is the sum of a vector and an axial vector current. This description was generalized by Feynman and Gell-Mann[22] to include *all** weak processes. They defined a weak current J^μ which is the sum of a leptonic current

$$J_e^\mu = \bar{u}_e\gamma^\mu(1-\gamma^5)u_{\nu_e} + \text{corresponding terms for other leptons (with equal amplitudes in keeping with universality)}$$

and a hadronic current

$$J_h^\mu = \bar{u}_p\gamma^\mu(1-\gamma^5)u_n + \text{corresponding terms for strange particles.}$$

The current–current hypothesis regards all weak processes as arising from the interaction of the current J^μ with itself:

$$\mathscr{M} \approx \frac{G}{\sqrt{2}} J^\mu J_\mu^\dagger. \tag{11.87}$$

The product (11.87) contains terms corresponding to μ decay, nuclear β decay, electron and muon capture, weak decays of strange particles either to leptons or hadrons and so on. Universality is a consequence of this self-interaction of the weak current but we will find in section 11.10 that important modifications have to be made to account for the different behaviour of the strange and non-strange hadrons.

11.9 The intermediate boson

We recall from section 11.5 that the matrix element for the electromagnetic interaction visualized in figure 11.10 is of the form

$$\mathscr{M} \approx j_\mu(\text{e}) \frac{1}{q^2} j^\mu(\text{p})$$

where q^2 is the photon propagator. In the weak processes discussed so

* We note that all the weak currents we have discussed so far are charge-changing weak currents n → p, e → ν etc. In their current–current hypothesis Feynman and Gell-Mann deliberately ignored neutral currents for which there was no experimental evidence at the time.

far we have always considered the interaction as point-like, i.e. the four fermion fields interact at the same space–time point. In accordance with this the matrix elements have not included a propagator term. When used to calculate cross-sections for high energy processes serious difficulties are encountered. Consider as an example elastic neutrino–electron scattering, $\nu_e + e^- \to \nu_e + e^-$. The appropriate diagram, assuming a point-like interaction, is shown in figure 11.16 and is described by the matrix element

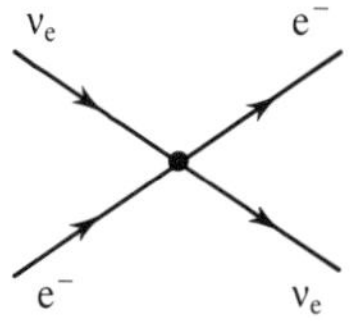

Figure 11.16
Point-like neutrino–electron scattering.

$$\mathscr{M} = \frac{G}{\sqrt{2}}[\bar{u}_e\gamma^\mu(1-\gamma^5)u_{\nu_e}][\bar{u}_{\nu_e}\gamma_\mu(1-\gamma^5)u_e]. \tag{11.88}$$

Using this matrix element and assuming that at very high energies the mass of the electron is negligible, the total cross-section is found to be

$$\sigma(\nu_e e \to \nu_e e) = \frac{G^2 s}{\pi} \tag{11.89}$$

where s is the square of the centre-of-mass energy.

It can be argued on purely dimensional grounds that the total cross-section for point-like ν_e–e scattering must vary as G^2s. A total cross-section is an invariant quantity and is necessarily proportional to G^2. In natural units with $\hbar = c = 1$ a cross-section has dimensions $[M]^{-2}$ (see appendix F). Example 11.10 shows that in natural units G has dimensions $[M]^{-2}$ and thus to restore the correct dimensions for the total cross-section we must multiply G^2 by a suitable invariant quantity with dimensions $[M]^2$. In the present problem of point-like scattering at high energies the only available quantity is the square of the centre-of-mass energy, hence $\sigma \approx G^2s$. Indeed the heart of the problem of the divergent cross-section (11.89) is the very fact that the weak coupling constant as defined in the Fermi interaction, unlike the electromagnetic coupling constant, is not a dimensionless quantity. Using arguments based on the partial wave formalism of chapter 9 it is possible to show that the cross-section for a point-like interaction violates unitarity at centre-of-mass energies of approximately 300 GeV. Since we are dealing here with particles which both possess spin the formulae of chapter 9 are not immediately applicable. Nevertheless, if we ignore spin effects equation (9.22) shows that for a given partial wave the maximum elastic cross-section allowed by unitarity is

$$\sigma_{\text{el}}^{\max} = \frac{4\pi}{k^2}(2l+1) = \frac{4\pi}{k^2}$$

for point-like or S wave scattering. This *decreases* as the centre-of-mass energy increases and is clearly in conflict with (11.89). When spins are

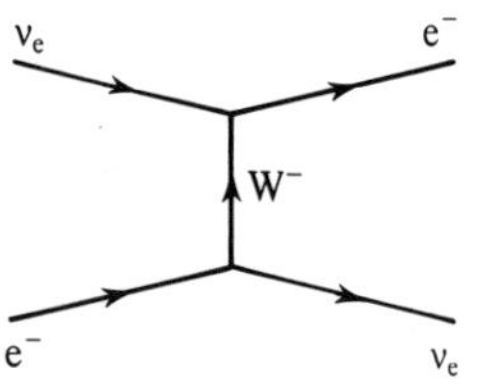

Figure 11.17
Elastic ν_e–e scattering via the exchange of a virtual intermediate boson W^-.

properly taken into account it is found that the Fermi cross-section violates unitarity when $\sqrt{s} \gtrsim G^{-1/2} \approx 300$ GeV.

The divergent behaviour of the point-like cross-section can be avoided if the analogy with the electromagnetic interaction is extended to include a virtual intermediate boson as the mediator of the weak interaction. The appropriate diagram for the scattering process $\nu_e + e^- \rightarrow \nu_e + e^-$ is that shown in figure 11.17 and the matrix element describing this process is

$$\mathscr{M} = \left[\frac{g}{\sqrt{2}}\bar{u}_e\gamma^\mu\tfrac{1}{2}(1-\gamma^5)u_{\nu_e}\right]\frac{1}{M_W^2 - q^2}\left[\frac{g}{\sqrt{2}}\bar{u}_{\nu_e}\gamma_\mu\tfrac{1}{2}(1-\gamma^5)u_e\right] \tag{11.90}$$

where $(M_W^2 - q^2)^{-1}$ is the boson propagator. M_W is the mass of the intermediate boson and q^2 is the square of the four-momentum carried by the intermediate boson. In (11.90) we have introduced a *dimensionless* weak coupling constant g and have included the factors $\sqrt{2}$ and $\frac{1}{2}$ in accordance with the conventional definition of g. Because the range of the weak interaction is extremely small the mass of the intermediate boson must be very large. For low energy weak processes such as muon decay and nuclear β decay the values of q^2 are small and for $q^2 \ll M_W^2$ the propagator term in (11.90) vanishes and the process is then essentially point-like. Comparison with (11.88) then gives

$$\frac{G}{\sqrt{2}} = \frac{g^2}{8M_W^2}. \tag{11.91}$$

In chapter 14 we shall see that the measured mass of the W boson is about 80 GeV and equation (11.91) therefore suggests that the apparent weakness of the weak interaction compared with the electromagnetic interaction is due more to the very large mass of the intermediate boson than to the smallness of the weak coupling constant g compared with the electromagnetic coupling constant e.

11.10 *Quark–lepton universality and the Cabibbo theory*

In this section we return to a discussion of the slight discrepancy between the values for the Fermi coupling constant G obtained from measurements of nuclear β decay processes on the one hand and the purely leptonic decay of the muon on the other.

As pointed out already, the weak currents involved in muon decay (figure 11.18(a)) and β decay (figure 11.18(b)) are charge-changing weak currents; in the intermediate boson theory the exchanged boson is charged. In the β decay process the hadrons involved have the same

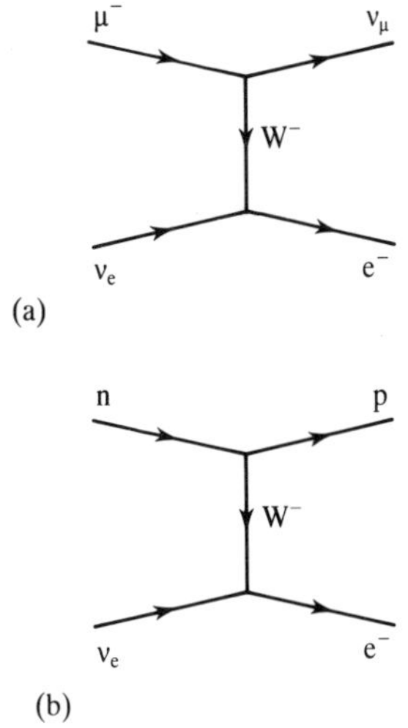

Figure 11.18
The decays
(a) $\mu^- \to e^-\bar{\nu}_e\nu_\mu$ and
(b) $n \to pe^-\bar{\nu}_e$ in the intermediate boson theory.

strangeness ($S = 0$) and the hadron current is additionally described as a strangeness-conserving, or $\Delta S = 0$, current.

On a fundamental level the β decay process is $d \to ue^-\bar{\nu}_e$ (figure 11.19(a)); one of the d quarks in the neutron (*ddu*) transforms into a u quark with the remaining u and d quarks acting as 'spectators'. In contrast, in the β decay of the Λ^0, which has quark content *uds*, the strange quark in the Λ^0 transforms into a u quark (figure 11.19(b)). Again, this involves charge-changing weak currents but in this case there is also a change of strangeness at the baryon vertex and the hadronic weak current is therefore called a strangeness-changing, or $\Delta S = 1$, weak current. The quark currents have the same V–A structure encountered earlier, namely

$$J_\mu^{q \to q'} \approx \bar{u}_{q'}\gamma^\mu(1 - \gamma^5)u_q \qquad (11.92)$$

and, if the notion of universality introduced in section 11.6 applies equally to the u, d and s quarks, the matrix elements for the neutron and Λ^0 β decay processes would be

$$\mathcal{M}_{d \to u} = \frac{g^2}{\sqrt{2}}\left[\bar{u}_u\gamma^\mu\tfrac{1}{2}(1 - \gamma^5)u_d\right]\left[\bar{u}_e\gamma^\mu\tfrac{1}{2}(1 - \gamma_5)u_{\nu_e}\right] \qquad (11.93)$$

and

$$\mathcal{M}_{s \to u} = \frac{g^2}{\sqrt{2}}\left[\bar{u}_u\gamma^\mu\tfrac{1}{2}(1 - \gamma^5)u_s\right]\left[\bar{u}_e\gamma^\mu\tfrac{1}{2}(1 - \gamma_5)u_{\nu_e}\right] \qquad (11.94)$$

respectively, with the *same* coupling constant g in each case. The decay rates for these processes, when the different phase space factors are taken into account, should then be equal.

Experimentally, the $\Delta S = 0$ hadronic current, which we have seen in section 11.5.5 to be very slightly weaker than the purely leptonic current, is some 20 times stronger than the $\Delta S = 1$ hadronic current and therefore universality appears to break down when extended to the quark states u, d and s.

In 1963 Cabibbo[23] suggested that universality could be resurrected if the weak interaction quark eigenstates are not the same as the mass or strong interaction eigenstates. He proposed that the weak interaction

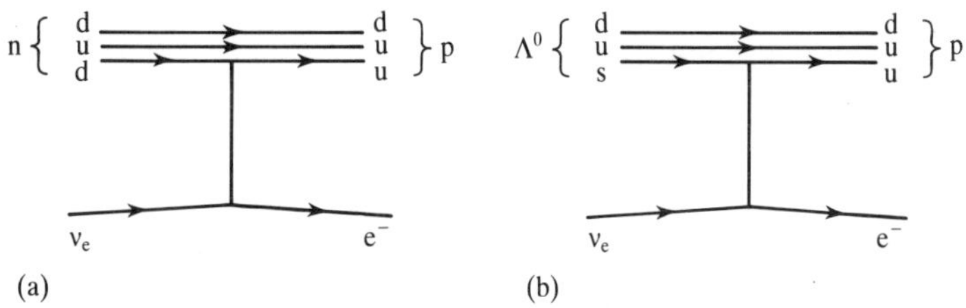

Figure 11.19
(a) Neutron β decay showing the quark transformation $d \to ue^-\bar{\nu}_e$ and (b) Λ^0 β decay, $s \to ue^-\bar{\nu}_e$.

eigenstates are linear superpositions of the strong interaction eigenstates and assigned the quarks to a 'weak isospin' doublet

$$\begin{pmatrix} u \\ d' \end{pmatrix} = \begin{pmatrix} u \\ d \cos \theta_C + s \sin \theta_C \end{pmatrix} \tag{11.95}$$

where θ_C is the Cabibbo angle and d' is the Cabibbo 'rotated' quark.* The Cabibbo structure of the charge-raising hadronic current is then

$$\begin{aligned} J_\mu^+(q) &\approx g(\bar{u}, \bar{d} \cos \theta_C + \bar{s} \sin \theta_C) \begin{pmatrix} 0 & 1 \\ 0 & 0 \end{pmatrix} \begin{pmatrix} u \\ d \cos \theta_C + s \sin \theta_C \end{pmatrix} \\ &= g(\bar{u}d \cos \theta_C + \bar{u}s \sin \theta_C). \end{aligned} \tag{11.96}$$

Note that the matrix

$$\begin{pmatrix} 0 & 1 \\ 0 & 0 \end{pmatrix} = \tfrac{1}{2}(\tau_1 + i\tau_2) = \tfrac{1}{2}\tau_+$$

is the (charge) raising operator for an isospin doublet, so that the charge-raising weak current may be written succinctly as

$$J^+(q) \approx g\bar{q}_L \tau_+ q_L \tag{11.97}$$

where

$$q_L = \begin{pmatrix} u \\ d' \end{pmatrix}$$

and the subscript L is included to indicate that, as in the case of the leptons, it is only the left-handed components of the quark currents which couple to the weak field.

In the Cabibbo theory, then, all particles – quarks as well as leptons – carry a weak charge g, but the quarks are mixed, with the consequence that

$$J_\mu^+(q) \approx g \cos \theta_C \text{ for } \Delta S = 0 \text{ currents}$$

and

$$J_\mu^+(q) \approx g \sin \theta_C \text{ for } \Delta S = 1 \text{ currents.}$$

* It is a matter of convention to express the quark mixing between the charge $-\frac{1}{3}$ quarks, leaving the charge $+\frac{2}{3}$ quark unmixed.

The transition rates for the three decays mentioned above then become

$$\Gamma(\mu^- \to e^-\bar{\nu}_e\nu_\mu) \propto g^4 \qquad \text{purely leptonic}$$

$$\Gamma(n \to pe^-\bar{\nu}_e) \propto g^4\cos^2\theta_C \qquad \Delta S = 0 \text{ semi-leptonic}$$

$$\Gamma(\Lambda^0 \to pe^-\bar{\nu}_e) \propto g^4\sin^2\theta_C \qquad \Delta S = 1 \text{ semi-leptonic.}$$

Thus, for instance, by comparing the rate for nuclear β decay with that for μ decay and taking into account the kinematic factors due to the different masses involved, a value for $\cos\theta_C$ can be determined. Similarly

$$\frac{\Gamma(\Lambda^0 \to pe^-\bar{\nu}_e)}{\Gamma(n \to pe^-\bar{\nu}_e)} \approx \frac{g^4\sin^2\theta_C}{g^4\cos^2\theta_C} = \tan^2\theta_C.$$

Data on these and several other decays are consistent with a Cabibbo angle $\theta_C \approx 13°$. Because of the small value of θ_C, those decays which have amplitudes proportional to the $\cos\theta_C$ are known as 'Cabibbo favoured' decays while those with amplitudes proportional to $\sin\theta_C$ are 'Cabibbo suppressed'.

In summary, the Cabibbo theory establishes quark–lepton universality, removes the slight discrepancy between the vector coupling constant determined from nuclear β decay compared with that from μ decay and explains the suppression of $\Delta S = 1$ hadronic currents relative to $\Delta S = 0$ currents.

11.11 *The absence of strangeness-changing neutral currents and the need for charm*

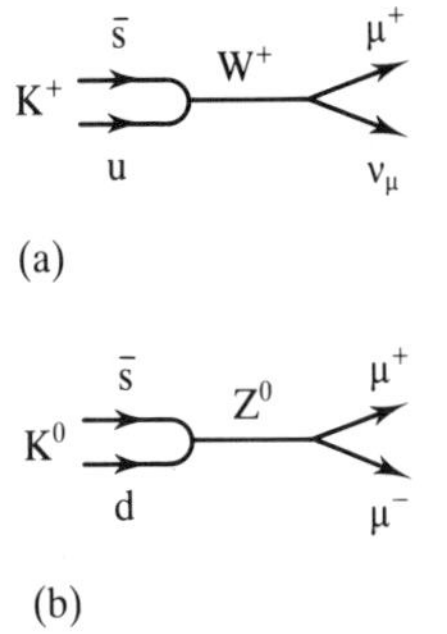

Figure 11.20
(a) Charged-current decay $K^+ \to \mu^+\nu_\mu$; (b) the highly suppressed neutral-current decay $K^0 \to \mu^+\mu^-$.

A major problem, the solution of which has far-reaching consequences, was the experimental observation that the decay $K_L^0 \to \mu^+\mu^-$* is suppressed by many orders of magnitude relative to the decay $K^+ \to \mu^+\nu_\mu$. The quark content of the K^+ is $u\bar{s}$ while that of the K^0 is $d\bar{s}$ and one can visualize the decays taking place via the first-order diagrams shown in figure 11.20. The measured branching fraction[24] for the charged-current process $K^+ \to \mu^+\nu_\mu$ is 63.51 ± 0.19 per cent while that for the neutral-current process $K_L^0 \to \mu^+\mu^-$ is only $(7.3 \pm 0.4) \times 10^{-7}$ per cent. We note that this neutral current is a *strangeness-changing* neutral current and will be of the form

$$J^0(q) \approx g\bar{q}\tau_3 q \tag{11.98}$$

* The neutral, long-lived kaon state, K_L^0, is defined in section 11.13.4..

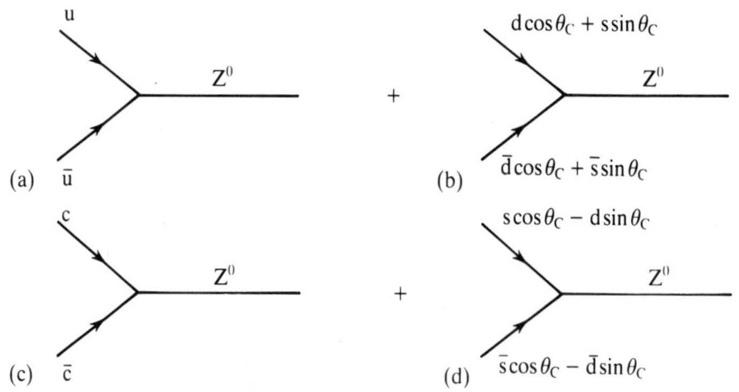

Figure 11.21
(a), (b) The coupling of the Z^0 to u, d and s quarks;
(c), (d) The coupling of the Z^0 to c, d and s quarks.

where τ_3 is the 2 × 2 matrix

$$\begin{pmatrix} 1 & 0 \\ 0 & -1 \end{pmatrix}.$$

Thus, according to the Cabibbo theory, the weak coupling of the quarks to the Z^0 boson shown schematically in figure 11.21 is of the form

$$\begin{aligned} J^0(q) &\approx u\bar{u} - d'\bar{d}' \\ &= \underbrace{u\bar{u} - d\bar{d}\cos^2\theta_C - s\bar{s}\sin^2\theta_C}_{\Delta S = 0} - \underbrace{(s\bar{d} + \bar{s}d)\sin\theta_C\cos\theta_C}_{\Delta S = 1}. \end{aligned} \tag{11.99}$$

For clarity we have omitted the factors $\gamma^\mu(1 - \gamma^5)$ in this expression. The last term in (11.99) is a strangeness-changing neutral current and might be expected to be responsible for the decay $K_L^0 \to \mu^+\mu^-$. We have indicated already, however, that this decay is highly suppressed with respect to the charged-current decay $K^+ \to \mu^+\nu_\mu$: the amplitude for the decay should be proportional to $\sin\theta_C\cos\theta_C$, but the calculated rate is many orders of magnitude greater than the actual rate. A way out of the dilemma was proposed in 1970 by Glashow, Iliopoulos and Maiani (GIM).[25] They introduced a new quark, the charmed quark c, with the same electric charge as the u quark, and suggested it belongs to a 'second generation' doublet

$$\begin{bmatrix} c \\ s' \end{bmatrix} = \begin{bmatrix} c \\ s\cos\theta_C - d\sin\theta_C \end{bmatrix} \tag{11.100}$$

in which the weak interaction eigenstate s' is orthogonal to d'. The relationship between the strong and weak quark eigenstates can be visualized as a rotation; the basis states are connected by a rotation

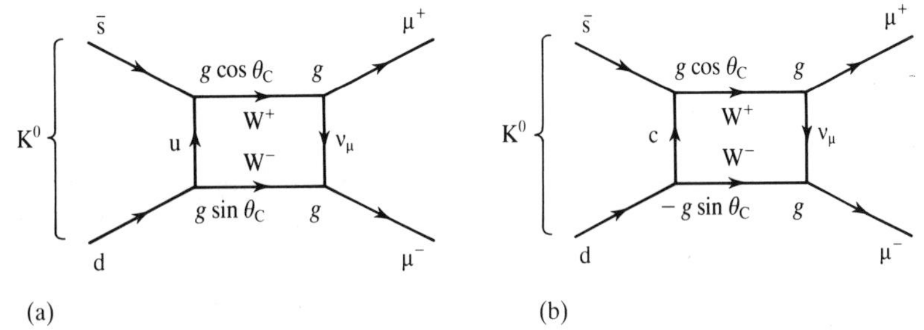

Figure 11.22
Box diagrams showing possible mechanisms for the decay $K_L^0 \to \mu^+\mu^-$: (a) a u-exchange graph; (b) a c-exchange graph.

matrix,

$$\begin{pmatrix} d' \\ s' \end{pmatrix} = \begin{pmatrix} \cos\theta_C & \sin\theta_C \\ -\sin\theta_C & \cos\theta_C \end{pmatrix} \begin{pmatrix} d \\ s \end{pmatrix}. \tag{11.101}$$

According to the so-called GIM mechanism then, the complete neutral current has, in addition to the couplings shown in figures 11.21(a) and 11.21(b), those shown in figures 11.21(c) and 11.21(d). Explicitly,

$$\begin{aligned} J^0(q) &\approx u\bar{u} - d'\bar{d}' + c\bar{c} - s'\bar{s}' \\ &= \underbrace{u\bar{u} + c\bar{c} - (d\bar{d} + s\bar{s})\cos^2\theta_C - (s\bar{s} + d\bar{d})\sin^2\theta_C}_{\Delta S = 0} \\ &\quad + \underbrace{(s\bar{d} + \bar{s}d - \bar{s}d - s\bar{d})\cos\theta_C \sin\theta_C}_{\Delta S = 1} \\ &= u\bar{u} - d\bar{d} - s\bar{s} + c\bar{c}. \end{aligned} \tag{11.102}$$

Thus, by introducing a fourth quark, the unwanted strangeness-changing terms $s\bar{d}$ and $\bar{s}d$ have been explicitly cancelled. The Z^0 couples directly only to $u\bar{u}$, $d\bar{d}$, $s\bar{s}$ and $c\bar{c}$ states. There are no flavour-changing neutral currents.

Although the first-order diagram, involving a single virtual Z^0, figure 11.20(b), makes no contribution to the decay $K_L^0 \to \mu^+\mu^-$, a possible second-order contribution involving two intermediate W bosons is shown in figure 11.22. Again, in the absence of a charmed quark, the decay would proceed via the process shown in figure 11.22(a), the calculated rate for which is much greater than the measured value. The GIM mechanism involving the exchange of a c quark (figure 11.22(b)) suppresses the rate. As can be seen from the weak couplings shown at each vertex in the figure, the amplitudes are

$$\mathscr{M}_u \propto g^4 \cos\theta_C \sin\theta_C \qquad \text{for the u-exchange graph}$$

and

$$\mathcal{M}_c \propto -g^4 \cos\theta_C \sin\theta_C \qquad \text{for the c-exchange graph.}$$

If the masses of the u and c quarks were equal the two diagrams would exactly cancel. In order to obtain agreement with the experimental decay rate, Glashow, Iliopoulos and Maiani predicted that the mass of the charmed quark should lie in the range 1–3 GeV. As we have seen in section 10.7.1 this prediction was strikingly confirmed in 1974, some four years after the GIM mechanism was introduced, by the discovery of the J/ψ meson, a $c\bar{c}$ bound state with a mass $m_{J/\psi} = 3097$ MeV, and the subsequent discovery of open charm states such as the D^0 and $D^\pm$ mesons.

11.12 A third generation of quarks

Even before charmed quarks had been discovered Kobayashi and Maskawa[26] extended the Cabibbo–GIM scheme to include a *third* generation of quarks – the top t and bottom b quarks. The six quarks are arranged into three weak isospin doublets,

$$\begin{pmatrix} u \\ d' \end{pmatrix} \begin{pmatrix} c \\ s' \end{pmatrix} \begin{pmatrix} t \\ b' \end{pmatrix}$$

and these weak interaction eigenstates are related to the strong interaction eigenstates by the Kobayashi–Maskawa (K–M) mixing matrix:

$$\begin{pmatrix} d' \\ s' \\ b' \end{pmatrix} = \begin{pmatrix} V_{ud} & V_{us} & V_{ub} \\ V_{cd} & V_{cs} & V_{cb} \\ V_{td} & V_{ts} & V_{tb} \end{pmatrix} \begin{pmatrix} d \\ s \\ b \end{pmatrix}. \qquad (11.103)$$

In this extension to three generations the 2×2 Cabibbo–GIM matrix in equation (11.101) is replaced by the 3×3 K–M 'rotation' matrix in which, for example, the element V_{ud} specifies the coupling of the u and d quarks: $d \to u + W^-$.

The K–M matrix is unitary and can be parametrized in various ways. The Particle Data Group[24] recommends the form

$$V = \begin{pmatrix} c_{12}c_{13} & s_{12}c_{13} & s_{13}\exp(-i\delta_{13}) \\ -s_{12}c_{23} - c_{12}s_{23}s_{13}\exp(i\delta_{13}) & c_{12}c_{23} - s_{12}s_{23}s_{13}\exp(i\delta_{13}) & s_{23}c_{13} \\ s_{12}s_{23} - c_{12}c_{23}s_{13}\exp(i\delta_{13}) & -c_{12}s_{23} - s_{12}c_{23}s_{13}\exp(i\delta_{13}) & c_{23}c_{13} \end{pmatrix}. \qquad (11.104)$$

In this expression $c_{ij} = \cos\theta_{ij}$ and $s_{ij} = \sin\theta_{ij}$ where $i, j = 1, 2, 3$ are generation labels. In the limit $\theta_{13} = \theta_{23} = 0$ the third generation decouples and if θ_{12} is identified with the Cabibbo angle θ_C the situation reduces to the original Cabibbo mixing of the first two generations. Kobayashi and Maskawa were motivated by a desire to explain *CP* violation within the Cabibbo–GIM scheme. To this end it was necessary to introduce a complex number into the Cabibbo rotation matrix, equation (11.101), but such a term can always be eliminated by a redefinition of the quark phases. They boldly introduced the third generation of quarks and a phase δ_{13} which lies in the range 0–2π with non-zero values giving rise to *CP* violation in the weak interactions. We return to this topic in section 14.3.10. The original appeal of the particular parametrization of the K–M matrix (11.104) is that it is in a form which can be readily generalized to an arbitrary number of generations. Recent results from LEP and SLC strongly suggest that the number of generations is in fact only three.

11.13 CP violation in kaon decay

11.13.1 Neutral kaons

The I spin doublet (K^0, K^+) and the antiparticle doublet (K^-, $\bar{K}^0$) should be regarded as strong interaction eigenstates; it is these states which are produced in strong interactions. For example, it is relatively easy to produce K^0s via the reaction $\pi^- p \to \Lambda^0 K^0$ but the production of $\bar{K}^0$ in $\pi^- p$ interactions requires a more exotic process such as $\pi^- p \to \bar{\Sigma}^+ \bar{K}^0 pn$. We note, for what follows, that since the threshold for the first reaction is lower than that for the second it is possible to produce a pure beam of K^0 mesons free from contamination from $\bar{K}^0$.

The kaons are unstable and, since they are the lightest strange particles, they cannot decay via the strangeness-conserving strong interactions; they can decay only via the weak interactions which do not conserve strangeness. In section 11.3.3 we saw that while the weak interactions violate parity and *C*-parity conservation separately they are invariant under the combined operation *CP*. It is therefore reasonable to assume that the states which participate in the weak interaction are *CP* eigenstates and not strangeness eigenstates. Although the K^0 and $\bar{K}^0$ are strangeness eigenstates they are not *CP* eigenstates, as can be seen as follows. Both the K^0 and $\bar{K}^0$ are eigenstates of parity with eigenvalue -1. Thus, we may write

$$P|K^0\rangle = -|K^0\rangle$$

and

$$P|\bar{K}^0\rangle = -|\bar{K}^0\rangle.$$

The charge conjugation operator simply changes particle to antiparticle so that

$$CP|K^0\rangle = -C|K^0\rangle = -|\bar{K}^0\rangle$$

and

$$CP|\bar{K}^0\rangle = -C|\bar{K}^0\rangle = -|K^0\rangle,$$

i.e. neither $|K^0\rangle$ nor $|\bar{K}^0\rangle$ are CP eigenstates. However, the linear combinations

$$|K_1^0\rangle = \frac{1}{\sqrt{2}}(|K^0\rangle - |\bar{K}^0\rangle) \tag{11.105}$$

and

$$|K_2^0\rangle = \frac{1}{\sqrt{2}}(|K^0\rangle + |\bar{K}^0\rangle) \tag{11.106}$$

are CP eigenstates with eigenvalues $+1$ and -1 respectively.

If we consider decays to pions both 2π and 3π decay modes are allowed kinematically, so, in order to determine the possible decay modes of the CP eigenstates $|K_1^0\rangle$ and $|K_2^0\rangle$, we must determine the CP eigenvalues of 2π and 3π systems. Consider first the two-pion systems $\pi^0\pi^0$ and $\pi^+\pi^-$. Suppose the relative orbital angular momentum between the two pions π_1 and π_2 is l.* Since the pions have negative intrinsic parity, $P(\pi_1\pi_2) = (-1)^l$. Since the π^0 and its antiparticle are indistinguishable ($B = L = S = Q = 0$) and the π^+ and π^- are particle and antiparticle, the charge conjugation operation is equivalent to the parity operation. Therefore, $C(\pi_1\pi_2) = (-1)^l$ and $CP(\pi_1\pi_2) = +1$.

Consider now the three-pion systems $\pi^0\pi^0\pi^0$ and $\pi^+\pi^-\pi^0$ (figure 11.23). We are free to couple the pions as we choose. Let π_1 and π_2 be either π^+ and π^- or $\pi^0\pi^0$. Kaons, like the pions, have spin $s = 0$ so conservation of angular momentum requires $l = l'$. The small Q values of the decays (≈ 80 MeV) suggest that $l = l' = 0$. Bose–Einstein statistics require that $l = l'$ is even for overall symmetry of the $3\pi^0$ system; values of $l = 2$ will be highly suppressed by angular momentum barrier effects. We assume therefore that in each case the three pions are in a relative S state. By the

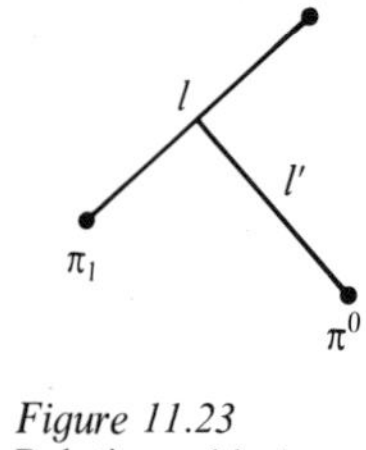

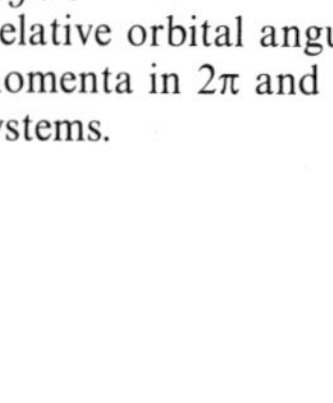

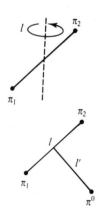

Figure 11.23
Relative orbital angular momenta in 2π and 3π systems.

* Bose–Einstein symmetry limits l to even values but we do not need to use this result.

previous argument $CP(\pi_1\pi_2) = +1$. The π^0 has $C = +1$ and $P = -1$ so when we combine the π^0 with the dipion system $\pi_1\pi_2$ we obtain $CP = -1$ for the overall 3π systems. Thus, in CP-conserving weak decays the state $|K_1^0\rangle$ must decay to two pions and $|K_2^0\rangle$ to three pions. The Q value for the 2π decay is much larger than that for the 3π decay so the phase space available, and hence the decay rate for $K_1 \to 2\pi$, is much larger than that for $K_2 \to 3\pi$. Equivalently, the K_2 lifetime is much greater than the K_1 lifetime.

To summarize, neutral kaons produced in strong interactions are the strangeness eigenstates $|K^0\rangle$ and $|\bar{K}^0\rangle$ with $S = +1$ and -1 respectively. The weak interaction eigenstates $|K_1^0\rangle$ with $CP = +1$ and $|K_2^0\rangle$ with $CP = -1$ are distinguished by their lifetimes and decay modes, the former decaying to 2π and the latter to 3π in CP-conserving weak decays.

11.13.2 Strangeness oscillations

A very interesting and important phenomenon, known as strangeness oscillations, occurs in the time evolution of the strong interaction eigenstates. Suppose, at time $t = 0$, we produce a beam of K^0 mesons, for example through the strong interaction process $\pi^- p \to \Lambda^0 K^0$.

From (11.105) and (11.106) we have

$$|K^0\rangle = \frac{1}{\sqrt{2}}(|K_1^0\rangle + |K_2^0\rangle)$$

and

$$|\bar{K}^0\rangle = \frac{1}{\sqrt{2}}(|K_2^0\rangle - |K_1^0\rangle).$$

At time t the wavefunction $\psi(t)$ is

$$|\psi(t)\rangle = |K^0(t)\rangle = \frac{1}{\sqrt{2}}[|K_1^0(t)\rangle + |K_2^0(t)\rangle].$$

Now, for an unstable particle with mass m and proper lifetime $\tau = 1/\Gamma$, the time dependence of the wavefunction, expressed in the particle rest system in which the total energy $E = m$, is

$$\psi(t) = \psi(0)\exp(-imt)\exp(-\Gamma t/2).$$

Note, this is consistent with the normal exponential decay law for unstable particles,

$$N(t) = |\psi(t)|^2 = |\psi(0)|^2\exp(-\Gamma t) = N(0)\exp(-\Gamma t).$$

Since they have different weak interactions the K_1^0 and K_2^0 will have different masses and decay widths which we denote m_1, Γ_1 and m_2, Γ_2 respectively. Thus,

$$|\psi(t)\rangle = \frac{1}{\sqrt{2}}[|K_1^0(0)\rangle \exp(-im_1 t)\exp(-\tfrac{1}{2}\Gamma_1 t) + |K_2^0(0)\rangle \exp(-im_2 t)\exp(-\tfrac{1}{2}\Gamma_2 t)].$$

At time t the K^0 intensity in the beam is just $|\langle K^0|\psi(t)\rangle|^2$, so

$$I(K^0) = \tfrac{1}{4}[\exp(-\Gamma_1 t) + \exp(-\Gamma_2 t) + \exp[-\tfrac{1}{2}(\Gamma_1 + \Gamma_2)t]\cos(\Delta m t)$$

where the mass difference $\Delta m = m_2 - m_1$. Similarly the $\bar{K}^0$ intensity at time t is

$$I(\bar{K}^0) = \tfrac{1}{4}[\exp(-\Gamma_1 t) + \exp(-\Gamma_2 t) - \exp[-\tfrac{1}{2}(\Gamma_1 + \Gamma_2)t]\cos(\Delta m t)].$$

Thus the K^0 and $\bar{K}^0$ intensities *oscillate* with frequency $\Delta m/2\pi$.

One can determine the number of $\bar{K}^0$ mesons in a beam, which initially consists of 100 per cent K^0, by virtue of the very different strong interactions of the $S = -1$ $\bar{K}^0$ mesons compared with those of the $S = +1$ K^0 mesons. Since there are no $S = +1$ baryons, K^0 mesons can interact essentially only via elastic or charge exchange scattering whereas the $S = -1$ $\bar{K}^0$ mesons can produce hyperons in reactions such as $\bar{K}^0 p \to \Lambda^0\pi^+$, $\Sigma^0\pi^+$ etc. Thus, by measuring the hyperon yield as a function of the distance from the production target, the mass difference $|\Delta m|$ can be deduced. The current value is

$$|\Delta m|\tau_1 = 0.477 \pm 0.002.$$

The sign of the mass difference has been determined in separate regeneration experiments and it is found that $m_2 > m_1$. The actual mass difference is minute:

$$\Delta m = (0.535 \pm 0.002) \times 10^{10}\,\hbar\,\mathrm{s}^{-1}$$
$$= (3.52 \pm 0.01) \times 10^{-6}\,\mathrm{eV}.$$

Figure 11.24 shows the variation in intensities $I(K^0)$ and $I(\bar{K}^0)$ as a function of time, in units of τ_1, for a value $\Delta m\tau_1 = 0.5$.

Physically, this strangeness oscillation arises because the K^0–$\bar{K}^0$ system is a coupled system; they are coupled through their common decays to virtual 2π and 3π intermediate states.

At the quark level the strangeness oscillation is visualized as arising from the Cabibbo-mixing of quark flavours. A detailed calculation

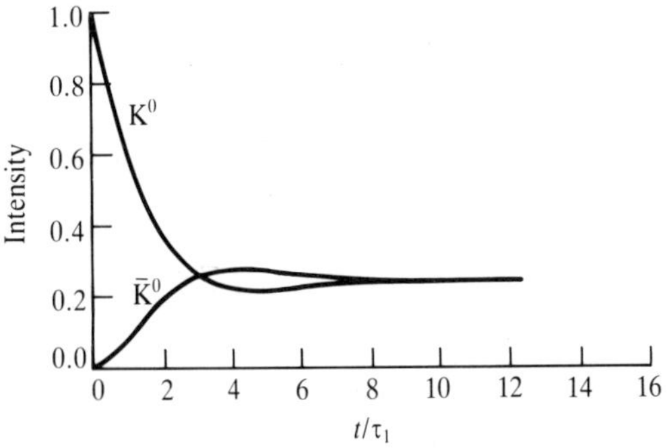

Figure 11.24
Strangeness oscillations. Variation in intensities of K^0 and $\bar{K}^0$ as a function of time in units of τ_1, for a value $\Delta m\tau_1 = 0.5$.

involving u, d, s and c quarks gives a mass difference of

$$\Delta m \approx \frac{G^2}{4\pi^2} f_K^2 m_K m_c^2 \cos^2\theta_C \sin^2\theta_C$$

where G is the Fermi constant, $f_k \approx 1.2m_\pi$ is the kaon decay constant, m_c is the mass of the charmed quark and θ_C is the Cabibbo angle. This expression agrees well with the measured mass difference for $m_c \approx 1.5$ GeV. In this way the mass of the charmed quark was predicted by Gaillard, Lee and Rosner[27] before charmonium states were discovered.

11.13.3 K^0 regeneration

In 1955 Pais and Piccioni[28] pointed out that the existence of the $|K_1^0\rangle$ and $|K_2^0\rangle$ states should give rise to the phenomenon known as *regeneration*.

Suppose we produce a pure beam of K^0 mesons and allow it to coast in vacuum. Initially the beam consists of an equal mixture of the states $|K_1^0\rangle$ and $|K_2^0\rangle$ and

$$|\psi(0)\rangle = |K^0(0)\rangle = \frac{1}{\sqrt{2}}[|K_1^0(0)\rangle + |K_2^0(0)\rangle].$$

For times $t \gg \tau_1$ the short-lived component $|K_1^0\rangle$ will have decayed and the wavefunction will bey

$$|\psi(t)\rangle \approx \frac{1}{\sqrt{2}}|K_2^0(0)\rangle \exp(-\Gamma_2 t),$$

i.e. the beam consists purely of the long-lived component $|K_2^0\rangle$, which we

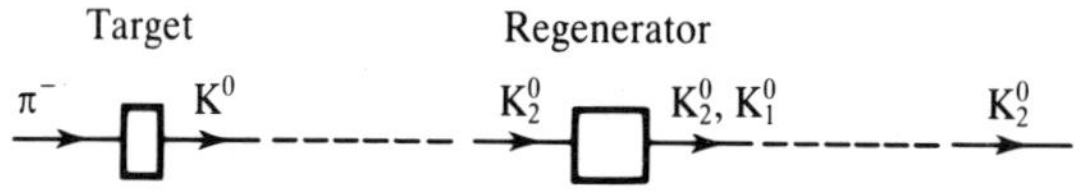

Figure 11.25
K^0 regeneration.

recall is given by

$$|K_2^0\rangle = \frac{1}{\sqrt{2}}(|K^0\rangle + |\bar{K}^0\rangle).$$

Suppose now we place a block of material in the beam as shown in figure 11.25. As indicated in the last section, K^0 and $\bar{K}^0$ have very different strong interactions; in particular the $S = -1$ $\bar{K}^0$ mesons will be more strongly absorbed in the block. Let f and $\bar{f}$ be the fraction of K^0 and $\bar{K}^0$ mesons remaining in the beam after passing through the block. Since the $\bar{K}^0$ mesons have a higher interaction cross-section we have $\bar{f} < f < 1$. The strangeness content of the beam which emerges from the block is therefore, neglecting the time dependence,

$$|\psi\rangle = \frac{1}{\sqrt{2}}(f|K^0\rangle + \bar{f}\,|\bar{K}^0\rangle).$$

In terms of the states $|K_1^0\rangle$ and $|K_2^0\rangle$ we have

$$\begin{aligned}|\psi\rangle &= \tfrac{1}{2}[f(|K_1^0\rangle + |K_2^0\rangle) + \bar{f}(|K_2^0\rangle - |K_1^0\rangle)]\\ &= \tfrac{1}{2}[(f-\bar{f})|K_1^0\rangle + (f+\bar{f})|K_2^0\rangle].\end{aligned}$$

Since $f \neq \bar{f}$, it follows that the short-lived state $|K_1^0\rangle$ has been regenerated. This regeneration phenomenon has been confirmed experimentally.

11.13.4 *CP violation and the K_L^0–K_S^0 system*

The K_2^0 state, which has $CP = -1$, cannot decay into two pions if CP is conserved in the weak interactions. The first experiment to show conclusively that the K_2^0 mesons do in fact decay into two pions, thereby violating CP conservation, was that of Christenson, Cronin, Fitch and Turlay.[29] This discovery led to a change in nomenclature for the neutral kaons. The short-lived state (predominantly $CP = +1$) was henceforth labelled K_S^0 and the long-lived state (predominantly $CP = -1$) was labelled K_L^0.

Figure 11.26 shows a plan view of the apparatus used in the experiment. It was performed at the Brookhaven alternating-gradient synchrotron (AGS), where a beam from an internal Be target was selected at an angle of 30° to the direction of the 30 GeV internal proton beam by a lead collimator. A 4 cm thick lead block, on the target side of the collimator, attenuated γ rays and a bending magnet after the collimator deflected

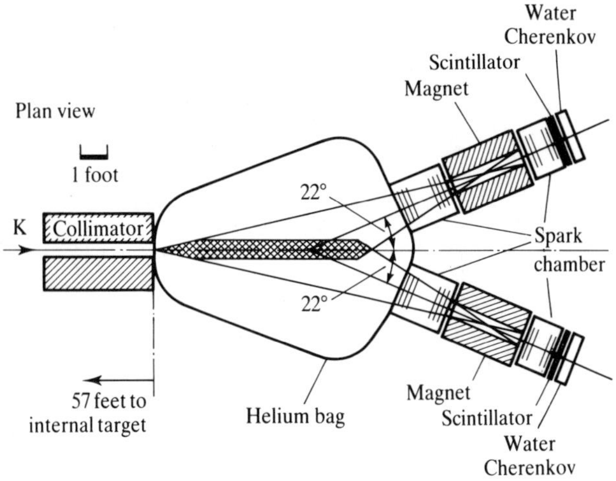

Figure 11.26
Schematic diagram of apparatus used in the discovery of *CP* violation in K^0 decays (Christenson J H *et al.* 1964 *Phys Rev Lett* **13** (138)).

charged particles from the beam. The detector was placed behind a further collimator some 17 m downstream of the target, at which point the beam consisted of the long-lived K^0 mesons (K_2^0), neutrons and some unattenuated γ rays. The detector was a double-armed spectrometer with each arm containing two spark chambers separated by a magnet which provided a momentum measurement. The spark chambers were triggered on a coincidence between the scintillators and water Cherenkov counters placed immediately behind the spectrometers. To minimize interactions, K_2^0 decays were observed in a volume, shown shaded in the figure, contained within a helium-filled bag.

The dominant decay modes of the K_2^0 meson are the three-pion decays $K_{\pi 3}$ and the three-body semi-leptonic decays K_{e3} and $K_{\mu 3}$. The identification of the two-pion decay mode $K_L^0 \to \pi^+\pi^-$ in this large background was performed as follows. For the two-pion decay mode the resultant vector momentum of the decay products should coincide with the direction of the tightly collimated K_2^0 beam and the effective mass of the two pions should be equal to the K^0 mass, within experimental errors. In general, neither of these conditions will be fulfilled for a three-body decay mode. The angular distribution in the very forward direction, for two oppositely charged particles, is shown for three different effective mass ranges in figure 11.27. The pronounced forward peak for the central mass range corresponds to the *CP*-violating decays $K_2^0 \to \pi^+\pi^-$. A three-body decay would not exhibit this strong correlation between K^0 mass and angle. Furthermore, the density of helium in the decay region was insufficient to provide a large enough regeneration of the short-lived K_S^0 to explain the number of events observed. Christenson, Cronin, Fitch and Turlay obtained

$$R = \frac{\Gamma K_L^0 \to \pi^+\pi^-)}{\Gamma(K_L^0 \to \text{all charged})} = (2.0 \pm 0.4) \times 10^{-3}$$

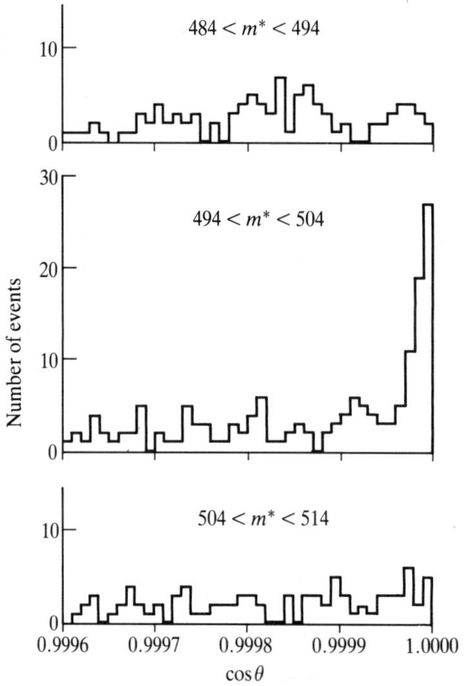

Figure 11.27 Angular distribution of two oppositely charged pions in three mass ranges for events with $\cos\theta > 0.9995$. The strong forward peak in the central mass interval is due to π^+ and π^- from the *CP*-violating decays $K_2^0 \to \pi^+\pi^-$.

and this result has been confirmed in a number of experiments with K_L^0 beams covering a wide range of momenta.

This important discovery means that we cannot identify $|K_S^0\rangle$ with $|K_1^0\rangle$ and $|K_L^0\rangle$ with $|K_2^0\rangle$. Instead, if *CP* is violated, but *CPT* conserved through a corresponding violation of *T*, we have

$$|K_S^0\rangle = \frac{|K_1^0\rangle + \epsilon|K_2^0\rangle}{\sqrt{(1+|\epsilon|^2)}}$$

and

$$|K_L^0\rangle = \frac{|K_2^0\rangle + \epsilon|K_1^0\rangle}{\sqrt{(1+|\epsilon|^2)}}$$

where ϵ is a small complex number which measures the degree of *CP* violation induced by kaon state mixing. *CP* violation in the 2π decay mode is commonly expressed in terms of the amplitude ratios

$$\eta_{+-} = \frac{\langle\pi^+\pi^-|T|K_L^0\rangle}{\langle\pi^+\pi^-|T|K_S^0\rangle} = |\eta_{+-}|\exp(i\phi_{+-})$$

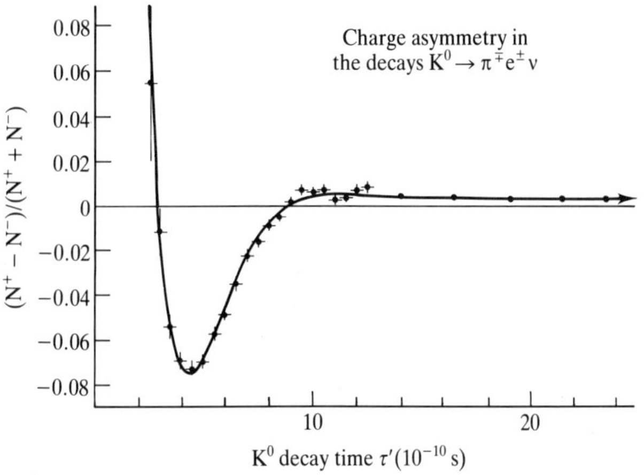

Figure 11.28
Time distribution of the charge asymmetry in the semi-leptonic decays $K^0 \to \pi^{\mp}e^{\pm}\nu$ (after Gjesdal S *et al.* 1974 *Phys Lett* **B52** (113)).

$$\eta_{00} = \frac{\langle \pi^0\pi^0|T|K_L^0\rangle}{\langle \pi^0\pi^0|T|K_S^0\rangle} = |\eta_{00}| \exp(i\phi_{00})$$

and all four quantities $|\eta_{+-}|$, $|\eta_{00}|$, ϕ_{+-} and ϕ_{00} have been measured.[30]

CP violation has also been observed in the semi-leptonic decays of neutral kaons (K_{l3} decays). In the decays

$$K^0 \to l^+\nu_l\pi^- \qquad (\Delta S = \Delta Q)$$

$$K^0 \to l^-\bar{\nu}_l\pi^+ \qquad (\Delta S = -\Delta Q)$$

where the lepton l is either e or μ, the final states transform into each other under *CP*. Therefore *CP* violation will give rise to a small charge asymmetry, defined as $\delta = (\Gamma^+ - \Gamma^-)/(\Gamma^+ + \Gamma^-)$, where Γ^+ and Γ^- are the rates for the decays $K^0 \to l^+\nu_l\pi^-$ and $K^0 \to l^-\bar{\nu}_l\pi^+$ respectively. Additionally, this asymmetry will vary with time and show interference effects between the K_L^0 and K_S^0 states. This is clearly demonstrated in figure 11.28 which shows the results of Gjesdal *et al.*[31] for the K_{e3} decays $K^0 \to e^-\bar{\nu}_e\pi^+$ and $K^0 \to e^+\nu_e\pi^-$.

The current values[24] of the *CP* violation parameters are

$$|\eta_{00}| = (2.253 \pm 0.024) \times 10^{-3} \quad |\eta_{+-}| = (2.268 \pm 0.023) \times 10^{-3}$$

$$\phi_{00} = (46.6 \pm 2.0)^0 \qquad \phi_{+-} = (46.6 \pm 1.2)^0$$

$$\delta = (0.327 \pm 0.012) \text{ per cent.}$$

The value quoted for δ is a weighted average of the asymmetry parameters for K_{e3} and $K_{\mu 3}$ decays.

11.13.5 Direct CP violation

Even in the absence of K_L^0–K_S^0 mixing ($\epsilon = 0$), a mechanism known as direct CP violation can result in non-zero values of η_{00} and η_{+-}.

Consider the decays of K_L^0 and K_S^0 into two pions. Bose symmetry restricts the two pions to symmetric I spin states; we designate these states $|0\rangle$ and $|2\rangle$ corresponding to $I = 0$ and $I = 2$ respectively. There are thus four amplitudes describing the 2π decays of K_S^0 and K_L^0:

$$\langle 0|H_w|K_S^0\rangle \qquad \langle 2|H_w|K_S^0\rangle$$

$$\langle 0|H_w|K_L^0\rangle \qquad \langle 2|H_w|K_L^0\rangle$$

where H_w is the weak-interaction Hamiltonian responsible for the decays. We can express these amplitudes in terms of the physical pion states $\pi^+\pi^-$ and $\pi^0\pi^0$ using Clebsch–Gordan coefficients and obtain

$$\langle \pi^+\pi^-| = \sqrt{\tfrac{1}{3}}\langle 2| + \sqrt{\tfrac{2}{3}}\langle 0|$$

$$\langle \pi^0\pi^0| = \sqrt{\tfrac{2}{3}}\langle 2| - \sqrt{\tfrac{1}{3}}\langle 0|$$

where by $\langle \pi^+\pi^-|$ we mean the properly symmetrized state

$$2^{-1/2}(\langle \pi_1^+\pi_2^-| + \langle \pi_1^-\pi_2^+|).$$

When the kaons decay the final state pions undergo phase shifts which depend on the I spin states of the two pions. Defining $\exp(i\delta_0)$ and $\exp(i\delta_2)$ as the π–π phase shifts at the kaon mass for the $I = 0$ and $I = 2$ states respectively we have

$$\langle \pi^+\pi^-| = \sqrt{\tfrac{1}{3}}\exp(i\delta_2)\langle 2| + \sqrt{\tfrac{2}{3}}\exp(i\delta_0)\langle 0|$$

$$\langle \pi^0\pi^0| = \sqrt{\tfrac{2}{3}}\exp(i\delta_2)\langle 2| - \sqrt{\tfrac{1}{3}}\exp(i\delta_0)\langle 0|.$$

We define the amplitudes

$$A_0 = \langle 0|H_w|K^0\rangle \qquad \text{and} \qquad A_2 = \langle 2|H_w|K^0\rangle$$

from which, assuming CPT invariance, we can determine amplitudes for the decays of $\bar{K}^0$. We recall that $CP|K^0\rangle = -|\bar{K}^0\rangle$, therefore $CPT|K^0\rangle = -\langle \bar{K}^0|$. Since any two-pion state has $CP = +1$ we have

$$CPT\langle 0| = |0\rangle$$

$$CPT\langle 2| = |2\rangle.$$

Therefore, if the weak Hamiltonian is CPT invariant

$$\langle 0|\mathrm{H_w}|\bar{K}^0\rangle \xrightarrow{CPT} -\langle K^0|\mathrm{H_w}|0\rangle = -A_0^*$$
$$\langle 2|\mathrm{H_w}|\bar{K}^0\rangle \xrightarrow{CPT} -\langle K^0|\mathrm{H_w}|2\rangle = -A_2^*$$

It is conventional to eliminate an overall phase by defining A_0 to be real. Using the expressions

$$|K_S^0\rangle = \frac{(1+\epsilon)|K^0\rangle - (1-\epsilon)|\bar{K}^0\rangle}{\sqrt{[2(1+|\epsilon|^2)]}}$$
$$|K_L^0\rangle = \frac{(1+\epsilon)|K^0\rangle + (1-\epsilon)|\bar{K}^0\rangle}{\sqrt{[2(1+|\epsilon|^2)]}}$$

we can express the observed transitions $K_L^0 \to \pi^+\pi^-$, $\pi^0\pi^0$ and $K_S^0 \to \pi^+\pi^-$, $\pi^0\pi^0$ in terms of A_0, A_2 and the CP-violating, CPT-conserving parameter ϵ, and hence obtain the ratios of η_{+-} and η_{00}. If we neglect second-order terms in the small parameters ϵ and A_2 we obtain (see example 11.15)

$$\eta_{+-} \approx \epsilon + \epsilon'$$

and

$$\eta_{00} \approx \epsilon - 2\epsilon'$$

where

$$\epsilon' = \frac{1}{\sqrt{2}}\frac{\operatorname{Im} A_2}{A_0}\exp[\mathrm{i}(\delta_2 - \delta_0)].$$

Observation of a non-zero value of ϵ' would imply the existence of CP violation without kaon state mixing, i.e. direct CP violation.

Such an observation would be important not only in its own right but also because it would help to distinguish between various models of CP violation. The most important of these is the superweak model proposed by Wolfenstein.[32] In this model CP violation is presumed to arise through a new $\Delta S = 2$ superweak interaction which transforms $K^0 \leftrightarrow \bar{K}^0$. The CP-violating $K_L^0 \to 2\pi$ decays are assumed to take place by a two-step process in which the K_L^0 couples to K_S^0 through the superweak interaction, which then decays to 2π through the normal weak interaction. Because of the very small mass difference between K_L^0 and K_S^0 a tiny perturbation can induce the transition $K_L^0 \to K_S^0$. The superweak coupling is required to be only of the order of 10^{-10} of the normal weak coupling to explain the observed (state mixing) CP violation. The superweak model has the advantage that it makes definite predictions for the parameters used in the description of CP violation. These are:

(a) $\epsilon' = 0$ and consequently $\left|\dfrac{\eta_{00}}{\eta_{+-}}\right| = 1$

(b) $\phi_{+-} = \phi_{00} = \tan^{-1}\left(\dfrac{2\Delta m \tau_s}{\hbar}\right)$

(c) $\mathrm{Re}\,\epsilon = |\eta_{+-}|\left[1 + \left(\dfrac{2\Delta m \tau_s}{\hbar}\right)^2\right]^{-1/2} \approx \dfrac{\delta}{2}.$

Using the most recent values,[24] $\Delta m = (0.5351 \pm 0.0024) \times 10^{10}\,\hbar\,\mathrm{s}^{-1}$, $\tau_S = (0.8922 \pm 0.0020) \times 10^{-10}$ s and $|\eta_{+-}| = (2.268 \pm 0.023) \times 10^{-3}$, the superweak model predicts

$$\phi_{+-} = \phi_{00} = (43.68 \pm 0.14)^0 \qquad \text{and}$$
$$\mathrm{Re}\,\epsilon = (1.648 \pm 0.015) \times 10^{-3}.$$

These predictions compare favourably with the experimental values

$$\left|\frac{\eta_{00}}{\eta_{+-}}\right| = 0.9935 \pm 0.0032 \qquad \phi_{+-} = (46.6 \pm 1.2)^0$$
$$\phi_{00} = (46.6 \pm 2)^0 \qquad \mathrm{Re}\,\epsilon = (1.635 \pm 0.006) \times 10^{-3}.$$

Evidence for direct CP violation was first observed in an experiment[33] at CERN where the double ratio

$$R = \left|\frac{\eta_{00}}{\eta_{+-}}\right|^2 = \frac{\Gamma(K_L^0 \to \pi^0\pi^0)/\Gamma(K_L^0 \to \pi^+\pi^-)}{\Gamma(K_S^0 \to \pi^0\pi^0)/\Gamma(K_S^0 \to \pi^+\pi^-)}$$

was measured to be $0.980 \pm 0.004 \pm 0.005$; the uncertainties are statistical and systematic respectively. The deviation of R from unity implies that $\epsilon' \neq 0$ and corresponds to a ratio $\epsilon'/\epsilon = (3.3 \pm 1.1) \times 10^{-3}$, a three-standard deviation departure from the prediction of the superweak model. However, measurements of this ratio at Fermilab are consistent with zero.

In chapter 14 we shall see that direct CP violation as well as that induced by kaon state mixing can be accommodated in the standard model of electroweak interactions by transitions involving heavy-quark intermediate states.

REFERENCES 11

1 **Perl M L** *et al.* 1975 *Phys Rev Lett* **35** (1489)

2 **Perl M L** *et al.* 1976 *Phys Lett* **63B** (366)

3 **Lee T D and Yang C N** 1956 *Phys Rev* **104** (254)

4 **Wu C S, Ambler E, Haywood R W, Hoppes D D and Hudson R P** 1957 *Phys Rev* **105** (1413)

5 **Gorter C J 1948** *Physica* **14** (504)

6 **Rose M E** 1949 *Phys Rev* **75** (213)

7 **Goldhaber M, Grodzins L and Sunyar A W 1958** *Phys Rev* **109** (1015)

8 **Grodzins L** 1959 *Prog Nucl Phys* **7** (163)

9 **Burgy M T, Krohn V E, Novey T B, Ringo G R and Telegdi V A** 1958 *Phys Rev* **110** (1214)

10 **Garwin R L, Lederman L M and Weinrich M** 1957 *Phys Rev* **105** (1415)

11 **Dirac P A M** 1928 *Proc Roy Soc* (*London*) **A117** (610) and **A118** (351)

12 **Dirac P A M** 1930 *Proc. Roy Soc* (*London*) **A126** (360)

13 **Anderson C D** 1933 *Phys Rev* **43** (491)

14 **Stueckelberg E C G** 1941 *Helv Phys Acta* **14** (588)

15 **Feynman R P** 1949 *Phys Rev* **76** (749, 769)

16 **Halzen F and Martin A D** 1984 *Quarks and Leptons: An Introductory Course in Modern Particle Physics* Wiley

17 **Klein O** 1948 *Nature* **161** (897)

18 **Puppi G** 1948 *Nuovo Cimento* **5** (587)

19 **Lee T D, Rosenbluth M and Yang C N** 1949 *Phys Rev* **75** (905)

20 **Timono J and Wheeler J A** 1949 *Rev Mod Phys* **21** (144)

21 **Gerstein S S and Zel'dovitch Ya B** 1956 *Soviet Phys JETP* **2** (579)

22 **Feynman R P and Gell-Mann M** 1958 *Phys Rev* **109** (193)

23 **Cabibbo N** 1963 *Phys Rev Lett* **10** (531)

24 **Particle Data Group** 1992 'Review of particle properties' *Phys Rev* **D45**

25 **Glashow S L, Iliopoulos J and Maiani L** 1970 *Phys Rev* **D2** (1585)

26 **Kobayashi M and Maskawa K** 1973 *Prog Theor Phys* **49** (652)

27 **Gaillard M K, Lee B W and Rosner J L** 1975 *Rev Mod Phys* **47** (277)

28 **Pais A and Piccioni O** 1955 *Phys Rev* **100** (1487)

29 **Christenson J H, Cronin J, Fitch V and Turlay R** 1964 *Phys Rev Lett* **13** (138)

30 **Christenson J H** *et al.* 1979 *Phys Rev Lett* **43** (1209, 1212)

31 **Gjesdal S** *et al.* 1974 *Phys Lett* **B52** (113)

32 **Wolfenstein L** 1964 *Phys Rev Lett* **13** (562)

33 **Burkhardt H** *et al.* 1988 *Phys Lett* **B206** (169)

EXAMPLES 11

11.1 The helicity of a particle with spin $\boldsymbol{s}$ is defined as $\lambda = \boldsymbol{s}\cdot\hat{\boldsymbol{p}}$ where $\hat{\boldsymbol{p}}$ is a unit vector in the direction of the particle momentum. By considering how the helicity expectation value behaves under the parity transformation show that $\langle\lambda\rangle$ must be zero in a parity-conserving interaction.

11.2 ^{152}Eu can decay via K electron capture to an excited state of samarium (energy E_0) according to the reaction $e^- + {}^{152}\text{Eu} \rightarrow {}^{152}\text{Sm}^* + \nu_e$. If the neutrino has an energy E_ν show that the recoil velocity of the ^{152}Sm* nucleus is $v/c = E_\nu/Mc^2$, where M is the mass of the samarium nucleus. Suppose the recoiling ^{152}Sm* nucleus emits a γ ray at an angle θ with respect to its direction of motion. Determine the energy of this γ ray and hence show that the condition for resonant absorption to the level E_0 is $E_\nu \cos\theta = E_0$.

11.3 In the parity-violating weak decay $\Lambda \rightarrow p\pi^-$, both S and P waves are present. Show that the decay angular distribution relative to the Λ spin direction is

$$W(\theta) = \tfrac{1}{4}(|S|^2 + |P|^2)\left(1 - \frac{2\,\text{Re}\,S^*P}{|S|^2 + |P|^2}\cos\theta\right)$$

where S and P denote the (complex) amplitudes for S and P wave decay respectively.

11.4 Obtain equation (11.2) in the text by multiplying the Klein–Gordon equation by $-i\phi^*$ and its complex conjugate by $-i\phi$ and subtracting. Write down a plane wave solution to the Klein–Gordon equation for a free particle with energy E and momentum $\boldsymbol{p}$ and show that for this solution $\rho = 2|N|^2E$ and $\boldsymbol{j} = 2|N|^2\boldsymbol{p}$, where N is a normalization constant.

11.5 Use the definitions of α_i and β given in equation (11.17) to verify that

$$\{\alpha_i, \alpha_j\} = 2\delta_{ij}I \qquad \{\alpha_i, \beta\} = 0$$

where I is the unit matrix.

11.6 Use the results of the last example and the definitions $\gamma^0 = \beta$, $\gamma^k = \beta\alpha_k$ $(k = 1, 2, 3)$, to verify the anticommutation relations

$$\gamma^\mu\gamma^\nu + \gamma^\nu\gamma^\mu = 2g^{\mu\nu}I \qquad (\mu, \nu = 0, 1, 2, 3).$$

Show that the γ matrices and their hermitian conjugates satisfy

$$(\gamma^0)^\dagger = \gamma^0 \qquad \text{and} \qquad (\gamma^k)^\dagger = -\gamma^k.$$

Given that $\gamma^5 = \mathrm{i}\gamma^0\gamma^1\gamma^2\gamma^3$, show that $(\gamma^5)^2 = I$, $(\gamma^5)^\dagger = \gamma^5$ and $\gamma^\mu\gamma^5 + \gamma^5\gamma^\mu = 0$.

11.7 From the definition of the γ matrices show that the Dirac equation $(\mathrm{i}(\partial/\partial t) + \mathrm{i}\boldsymbol{\alpha}\cdot\boldsymbol{\nabla} - \beta m)\psi = 0$ can be written in the covariant form

$$(\mathrm{i}\gamma^\mu\,\partial_\mu - m)\psi = 0.$$

11.8 This is an exercise to obtain the covariant form of the continuity equation.

(a) The Dirac equation may be written

$$\mathrm{i}\gamma^0\frac{\partial\psi}{\partial t} + \mathrm{i}\gamma^k\frac{\partial\psi}{\partial x^k} - m\psi = 0$$

where summation over the repeated index k is implied. Write down the hermitian conjugate of this equation, multiply from the right by γ^0 and show that the row spinor $\bar\psi = \psi^\dagger\gamma^0$ satisfies the adjoint equation

$$\mathrm{i}\,\partial_\mu\bar\psi\gamma^\mu + m\bar\psi = 0.$$

(b) Multiply the Dirac equation from the left by $\bar\psi$, the adjoint equation from the right by ψ and add to obtain

$$\partial_\mu j^\mu = 0$$

where $j^\mu = \bar\psi\gamma^\mu\psi$.

11.9 Show that for arbitrary vectors $\boldsymbol{a}$ and $\boldsymbol{b}$

$$(\boldsymbol{\sigma}\cdot\boldsymbol{a})(\boldsymbol{\sigma}\cdot\boldsymbol{b}) = \boldsymbol{a}\cdot\boldsymbol{b} + \mathrm{i}\boldsymbol{\sigma}\cdot(\boldsymbol{a}\times\boldsymbol{b})$$

where the components of $\boldsymbol{\sigma}$ are the Pauli spin matrices.

11.10 The measured value of the Fermi coupling constant is $G_\mathrm{F} = 1.4355 \times 10^{-62}\ \mathrm{J\,m^3}$. Show that in natural units this corresponds to

$$G_\mathrm{F} = 1.1664 \times 10^{-5}\ \mathrm{GeV}^{-2} \approx \frac{10^{-5}}{m_\mathrm{p}^2}$$

where m_p is the proton mass.

11.11 In units in which $c = 1$ the Dirac equation for a relativistic electron of mass m, momentum p and total energy E is

$$(\boldsymbol{\alpha}\cdot\boldsymbol{p} + \beta m)u = Eu$$

where u is a four-component spinor. Write down the two positive energy solutions (see section 11.4.5) for states with momentum p in the positive z direction and z component of spin $+\frac{1}{2}$ and $-\frac{1}{2}$. In β decay the probability of producing an electron in a state described by the spinor u is $v^\dagger v$ where $v = \frac{1}{2}(1 - \gamma^5)u$. Hence show that the longitudinal polarization of the electron, defined as

$$\frac{P(+\frac{1}{2}) - P(-\frac{1}{2})}{P(+\frac{1}{2}) + P(-\frac{1}{2})}$$

where $P(\pm\frac{1}{2})$ is the probability that the spin component is $\pm\frac{1}{2}$, is $-p/E$.

11.12 In a general weak leptonic current, $\bar{\psi}_e O_i(1 - \gamma^5)\psi_{\nu_e}$, the operator O_i can have one of the five possible forms

$O_S = I$	(scalar S)
$O_V = \gamma^\lambda$	(vector V)
$O_T = i/2(\gamma^\lambda\gamma^\sigma - \gamma^\sigma\gamma^\lambda)$	(tensor T)
$O_A = \gamma^5\gamma^\lambda$	(axial vector A)
$O_P = \gamma^5$	(pseudoscalar P).

The operator $1 - \gamma^5$ annihilates left-handed neutrinos (creates right-handed antineutrinos). Making use of the anticommutation relations for the γ matrices, show schematically that V and A currents produce predominantly left-handed electrons while S, T and P currents produce predominantly right-handed electrons.

Hint: Move the operator $1 - \gamma^5$ to the left until it, or $1 + \gamma^5$, is operating on the electron spinor.

11.13 In the weak decays $\pi^- \to l^-\bar{\nu}_l$, where $l = \mu$ or e, conservation of angular momentum forces the charged leptons to have the 'wrong' handedness. The V–A theory predicts that the decay rate $\Gamma(\pi^- \to l^-\bar{\nu}_l)$ is proportional to the two-body phase space factor multiplied by $1 - v/c$ where v is the speed of the lepton in the pion rest frame. Derive the phase space factor $p^2\, dp/dE$, where p is the lepton momentum and E is the total energy in the pion rest frame, and hence estimate the branching ratio $\Gamma(\pi \to e\nu)/\Gamma(\pi \to \mu\nu)$.

11.14 Estimate the Cabibbo angle θ_C by comparing the β decays of the neutron and Λ^0, given the following information.

	Lifetime τ/s	Branching fraction f	Energy release E/MeV
$n \to pe^-\bar{\nu}_e$	900	1	1.3
$\Lambda^0 \to pe^-\bar{\nu}_e$	2.63×10^{-10}	8.3×10^{-4}	177.3

You may assume that the phase space factors are approximately $E^5/30$ where E is the energy release in mega-electronvolts.

11.15 In section 11.13.5 the states K_L^0 and K_S^0 were given in terms of the CP-violating, CPT-conserving parameter ϵ as

$$|K_L^0\rangle = \frac{(1+\epsilon)|K^0\rangle + (1-\epsilon)|\bar{K}^0\rangle}{\sqrt{[2(1+|\epsilon|^2)]}}$$

$$|K_S^0\rangle = \frac{(1+\epsilon)|K^0\rangle - (1-\epsilon)|\bar{K}^0\rangle}{\sqrt{[2(1+|\epsilon|^2)]}}.$$

Compute the CP violation parameters η_{+-} and η_{00} in terms of the amplitudes A_0 and A_2 and the π–π phase shifts defined in the text, assuming the $I = 0$ amplitude A_0 is real. Hence, neglecting second-order terms in the small parameters ϵ and A_2, show that

$$\eta_{+-} \approx \epsilon + \epsilon' \qquad \text{and} \qquad \eta_{00} \approx \epsilon - 2\epsilon'$$

where

$$\epsilon' = \frac{1}{\sqrt{2}} \frac{\operatorname{Im} A_2}{A_0} \exp[i(\delta_2 - \delta_0)].$$

12 Hadron structure and the parton model

12.1 Introduction

The modern approach to the study of hadron structure has its origins in the pioneering work of Hofstadter and collaborators at Stanford who, in the 1950s, used beams of electrons to probe the electric charge distributions of nuclei. This work was described in section 3.3. Here, we reiterate the principles of the technique in order to establish a theoretical framework in which the results of more recent experiments may be explained.

Consider Coulomb scattering of an electron by a stationary point proton as shown in figure 12.1. The scattering process is viewed as the emission by the proton of a virtual photon which, when absorbed by the initial electron with momentum $\boldsymbol{p}_i$, produces the final state electron with momentum $\boldsymbol{p}_f$. The differential cross-section for this process is the well-known Rutherford formula given in equation (1.15) but modified for a relativistic particle by writing $\mu v_1^2 = p_i c$. In natural units (appendix F) the formula then becomes

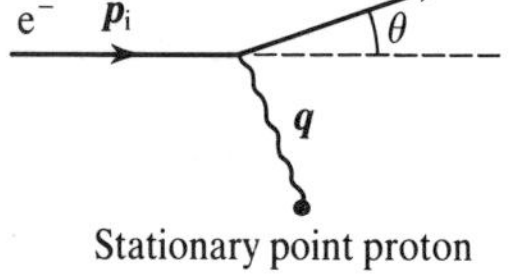

Figure 12.1
Coulomb scattering of an electron by a stationary point proton.

$$\frac{d\sigma}{d\Omega} = \frac{\alpha^2}{4p_i^2 \sin^4(\theta/2)}. \tag{12.1}$$

The change in momentum of the electron, or momentum transfer, is equal

to the momentum $\boldsymbol{q}$ of the virtual photon:

$$\boldsymbol{q} = \boldsymbol{p}_{\mathrm{i}} - \boldsymbol{p}_{\mathrm{f}} \qquad \text{or} \qquad q^2 = p_{\mathrm{i}}^2 + p_{\mathrm{f}}^2 - 2\boldsymbol{p}_{\mathrm{i}} \cdot \boldsymbol{p}_{\mathrm{f}}.$$

For a stationary proton $|\boldsymbol{p}_{\mathrm{i}}| = |\boldsymbol{p}_{\mathrm{f}}|$ and

$$q^2 = 2p_{\mathrm{i}}^2(1 - \cos\theta) = 4p_{\mathrm{i}}^2 \sin^2(\theta/2).$$

Furthermore, since

$$\mathrm{d}\Omega = 2\pi \mathrm{d}(\cos\theta) = \pi \mathrm{d}q^2/p_{\mathrm{i}}^2$$

the Rutherford scattering formula may be written as

$$\frac{\mathrm{d}\sigma}{\mathrm{d}q^2} = \frac{4\pi\alpha^2}{q^4}. \tag{12.2}$$

In reality, the charge of the proton is not localized at a point. In order to determine the charge distribution the measured differential cross-section for scattered electrons could in principle be compared with that expected for scattering from a point charge (the Rutherford cross-section) and expressed in the form

$$\left(\frac{\mathrm{d}\sigma}{\mathrm{d}\Omega}\right)_{\text{measured}} = \left(\frac{\mathrm{d}\sigma}{\mathrm{d}\Omega}\right)_{\text{Rutherford}} [F(\boldsymbol{q})] \tag{12.3}$$

where $F(\boldsymbol{q})$, the *form factor*,* is the Fourier transform of the electric charge density distribution:

$$F(\boldsymbol{q}) = \int \rho(\boldsymbol{r}) \exp(\mathrm{i}\boldsymbol{q} \cdot \boldsymbol{r})\, \mathrm{d}\tau. \tag{12.4}$$

However, even if the proton is considered as point-like the Rutherford calculation can readily be improved by treating the electron as a spin $\frac{1}{2}$ Dirac particle and allowing the proton to recoil. This situation is depicted in figure 12.2 and the relativistic treatment leads to the Mott[1] formula which may be expressed as

$$\left(\frac{\mathrm{d}\sigma}{\mathrm{d}\Omega}\right)_{\text{Mott}} = \left(\frac{\mathrm{d}\sigma}{\mathrm{d}\Omega}\right)_{\text{Rutherford}} \frac{\cos^2(\theta/2)}{1 + (2E/M)\sin^2(\theta/2)} \tag{12.5}$$

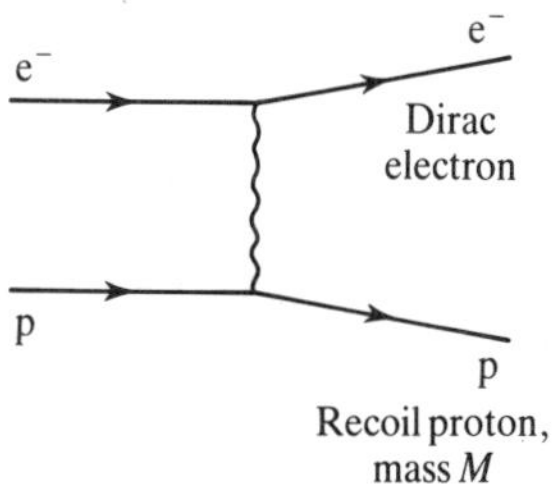

Figure 12.2
Feynman diagram for the Coulomb scattering of an electron by a proton.

* The form factor may be expressed in the form shown in equation (3.12) by integrating over the angle variable and dividing by the nuclear charge *Ze*. See also examples 12.3 and 12.4.

where E is the energy of the incident electron and M is the proton mass. Still further improvements can be made to the Mott formula if the proton is treated as a spin $\frac{1}{2}$ Dirac-type particle. The electron will be influenced not only by the electric charge of the proton but also by its magnetic moment which is known to be anomalous with a value of 2.79 nuclear magnetons. This gives rise to two form factors, electric and magnetic. A calculation based on these further considerations was performed by Rosenbluth,[2] and it is more appropriate to compare measured differential cross-sections with the Rosenbluth formula rather than the Rutherford or Mott formulae. In its essentials the Rosenbluth formula is

$$\frac{d\sigma}{d\Omega} = \left(\frac{d\sigma}{d\Omega}\right)_{\text{Mott}} [A(q^2) + B(q^2)\tan^2(\theta/2)] \qquad (12.6)$$

where the two form factors A and B are now functions of the square of the four-momentum transfer.

Figure 12.3 shows the differential cross-section for the elastic scattering of 188 MeV electrons from hydrogen measured by Hofstadter and McAllister.[3] The figure shows that at large scattering angles the measured differential cross-section is less than predicted by the Rosenbluth formula indicating that the proton has a diffuse structure.

With the advent of the two-mile linear accelerator at SLAC higher energy electron beams became available leading to much higher q^2 (shorter wavelength) probes which gave access to the so-called deep

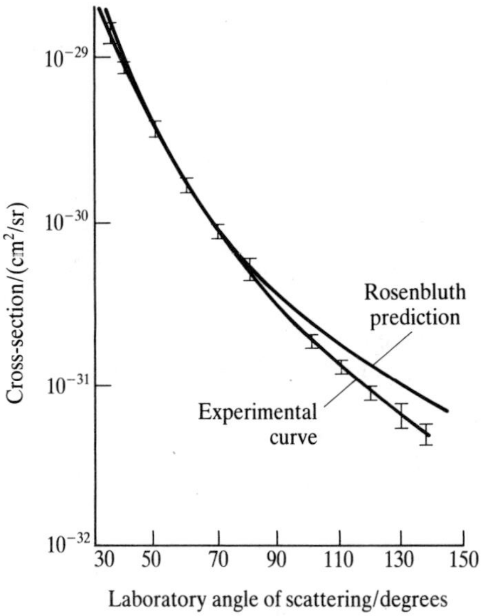

Figure 12.3 Differential cross-section for the elastic scattering of 188 MeV electrons from hydrogen (after Hofstadter R and McAllister R W 1955 *Phys Rev* **98** (217)).

inelastic scattering region. In this region the differential cross-sections for electron scattering are consistent with the picture that the scattering is due to point-like *partons*, constituent parts of the nucleon. In section 12.5 we will show that the properties of the partons are precisely those of the quarks discussed in chapter 10.

High energy muons and neutrinos have also been used to study hadron structure; like electrons they are believed to be structureless and free from complexity due to the strong interaction. Moreover, the coupling of electrons and muons to the electromagnetic field is well understood and cross-sections should therefore be exactly calculable. We illustrate this in principle in the following section.

12.2 *Elastic electron–muon scattering*

Elastic electron–muon scattering

$$e^- + \mu^- \to e^- + \mu^-$$

$$1 + 2 \to 3 + 4$$

is dominated by single photon exchange and is therefore described by the Feynman diagram shown in figure 12.4.

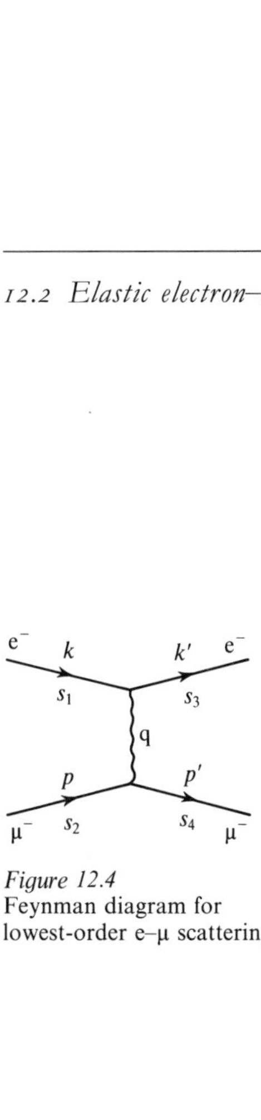

Figure 12.4
Feynman diagram for lowest-order e–μ scattering.

The invariant amplitude for this process is

$$\mathcal{M}_{fi} = [\bar{u}(k')\gamma^\mu u(k)]\frac{e^2}{q^2}[\bar{u}(p')\gamma_\mu u(p)] \tag{12.7}$$

where $\bar{u}(k')\gamma^\mu u(k)$, for example, is the (vector) electromagnetic current of the electron and $q = (k - k')$ is the exchanged four-momentum (see section 11.5.1). For unpolarized initial and final states an average over initial and sum over final spin states is performed to give the spin-averaged amplitude

$$\begin{aligned}\overline{|\mathcal{M}_{fi}|^2} &= \frac{1}{4}\sum_{s_1s_2s_3s_4}\left|\bar{u}(k', s_3)\gamma^\mu u(k, s_1)\frac{e^2}{q^2}\bar{u}(p', s_4)\gamma_\mu u(p, s_2)\right|^2 \\ &= \frac{e^4}{4q^4}\sum_{s_1s_2s_3s_4}[\bar{u}(k', s_3)\gamma^\mu u(k, s_1)][\bar{u}(p', s_4)\gamma_\mu u(p, s_2)] \\ &\quad \times [\bar{u}(k', s_3)\gamma^\nu u(k, s_1)]^*[\bar{u}(p', s_4)\gamma_\nu u(p, s_2)]^* \end{aligned} \tag{12.8}$$

where s_i is the spin component of particle i. Equation (12.8) may be written

$$|\mathscr{M}_{fi}|^2 = \frac{e^4}{4q^4} L_{(e)}^{\mu\nu} L_{\mu\nu}^{(\mu)} \tag{12.9}$$

where the electron tensor

$$L_{(e)}^{\mu\nu} = \sum_{s_1 s_3} [\bar{u}(k', s_3)\gamma^\mu u(k, s_1)][\bar{u}(k', s_3)\gamma^\nu u(k, s_1)]^* \tag{12.10}$$

with a similar expression for the muon tensor $L_{\mu\nu}^{(\mu)}$. In order to evaluate (12.10) we note that $[\bar{u}(k', s_3)\gamma^\nu u(k, s_1)]$ is just a complex number, a 1×1 matrix, so that taking its complex conjugate is equivalent to taking its hermitian conjugate. Thus

$$\begin{aligned}[\bar{u}(k', s_3)\gamma^\nu u(k, s_1)]^* &= [u^\dagger(k', s_3)\gamma^0\gamma^\nu u(k, s_1)]^* \\ &= [u^\dagger(k, s_1)\gamma^{\nu\dagger}\gamma^0 u(k', s_3)] \\ &= [u^\dagger(k, s_1)\gamma^0\gamma^\nu u(k', s_3)] \\ &= [\bar{u}(k, s_1)\gamma^\nu u(k', s_3)].\end{aligned}$$

In the penultimate step we have used the fact that $\gamma^{\nu\dagger}\gamma^0 = \gamma^0\gamma^\nu$ for,

with $\nu = 0$ $\quad \gamma^{0\dagger}\gamma^0 = \gamma^0\gamma^0$

and

with $\nu = i = 1, 2, 3$ $\quad \gamma^{i\dagger}\gamma^0 = -\gamma^i\gamma^0 = \gamma^0\gamma^i$.

Then,

$$L_{(e)}^{\mu\nu} = \sum_{s_1 s_3} \bar{u}(k', s_3)\gamma^\mu u(k, s_1)\bar{u}(k', s_1)\gamma^\nu u(k, s_3). \tag{12.11}$$

The evaluation of this expression is facilitated by writing the matrix indices explicitly; the usual summation over repeated indices is implied. Thus,

$$L_{(e)}^{\mu\nu} = \sum_{s_3} \bar{u}_\alpha(k', s_3)(\gamma^\mu)_{\alpha\beta} \sum_{s_1} u_\beta(k, s_1)\bar{u}_\gamma(k, s_1)(\gamma^\nu)_{\gamma\delta} u_\delta(k', s_3).$$

Now

$$\sum_{s_1} u_\beta(k, s_1)\bar{u}_\gamma(k, s_1) = (\not{k} + m)_{\beta\gamma}$$

by the completeness relation for Dirac spinors (see appendix K). Here, we have introduced the notation $\gamma^\mu a_\mu \equiv \not{a}$, where a is a four-vector. Then

$$L_{(e)}^{\mu\nu} = \sum_{s_3} \bar{u}_\alpha(k', s_3)(\gamma^\mu)_{\alpha\beta}(\not{k} + m)_{\beta\gamma}(\gamma^\nu)_{\gamma\delta} u_\delta(k', s_3).$$

Since the matrix elements are just numbers their order is unimportant so that

$$L^{\mu\nu}_{(e)} = \sum_{s_3} u_\delta(k', s_3)\bar{u}_\alpha(k', s_3)(\gamma^\mu)_{\alpha\beta}(\not{k} + m)_{\beta\gamma}(\gamma^\nu)_{\gamma\delta}$$

$$= (\not{k}' + m)_{\delta\alpha}(\gamma^\mu)_{\alpha\beta}(\not{k} + m)_{\beta\gamma}(\gamma^\nu)_{\gamma\delta}$$

$$= \mathrm{Tr}[(\not{k}' + m)\gamma^\mu(\not{k} + m)\gamma^\nu]. \tag{12.12}$$

Here, m is the electron mass.

Similarly, the muon tensor becomes

$$L^{(\mu)}_{\mu\nu} = \mathrm{Tr}[(\not{p}' + M)\gamma_\mu(\not{p} + M)\gamma_\nu] \tag{12.13}$$

where M is the muon mass.

The problem is thus reduced to the evaluation of traces and this is readily achieved by making use of the trace theorems proved in appendix L. We have

$$L^{\mu\nu}_{(e)} = \mathrm{Tr}[\not{k}'\gamma^\mu\not{k}\gamma^\nu] + m\,\mathrm{Tr}[\gamma^\mu\not{k}\gamma^\nu] + m\,\mathrm{Tr}[\not{k}'\gamma^\mu\gamma^\nu] + m^2\,\mathrm{Tr}[\gamma^\mu\gamma^\nu].$$

The terms $m\,\mathrm{Tr}[\gamma^\mu\not{k}\gamma^\nu]$ and $m\,\mathrm{Tr}[\not{k}'\gamma^\mu\gamma^\nu]$ are both zero because they contain an odd number of γ matrices. Then,

$$L^{\mu\nu}_{(e)} = \mathrm{Tr}[\not{k}'\gamma^\mu\not{k}\gamma^\nu] + 4m^2 g^{\mu\nu}$$

by theorem (iii) of appendix L. We can evaluate the first term by multiplying by two arbitrary four-vectors a and b and noting that

$$a_\mu b_\nu\,\mathrm{Tr}[\not{k}'\gamma^\mu\not{k}\gamma^\nu] = \mathrm{Tr}[\not{k}'\not{a}\not{k}\not{b}].$$

Using theorem (vii) of appendix L we have

$$\mathrm{Tr}[\not{k}'\not{a}\not{k}\not{b}] = 4[(k'\cdot a)(k\cdot b) + (k'\cdot b)(k\cdot a) - (k'\cdot k)(a\cdot b)]$$

$$= 4a_\mu b_\nu[k'^\mu k^\nu + k'^\nu k^\mu - (k'\cdot k)g^{\mu\nu}].$$

Thus,

$$\mathrm{Tr}[\not{k}'\gamma^\mu\not{k}\gamma^\nu] = 4[k'^\mu k^\nu + k'^\nu k^\mu - (k'\cdot k)g^{\mu\nu}]$$

and therefore,

$$L^{\mu\nu}_{(e)} = 4[k'^\mu k^\nu + k'^\nu k^\mu + (m^2 - k'\cdot k)g^{\mu\nu}]. \tag{12.14}$$

The corresponding expression for the muon is

$$L^{(\mu)}_{\mu\nu} = 4[p'_\mu p_\nu + p'_\nu p_\mu + (M^2 - p'\cdot p)g_{\mu\nu}]. \tag{12.15}$$

On forming the product of the electron and muon tensors we find that the spin-averaged invariant amplitude is finally

$$\overline{|\mathscr{M}_{fi}|^2} = \frac{8e^4}{q^4}[(k'\cdot p')(k\cdot p) + (k'\cdot p)(k\cdot p') - m^2(p'\cdot p) - M^2(k'\cdot k) + 2m^2M^2]. \quad (12.16)$$

To arrive at our stated goal of deriving equation (12.6) let us evaluate this expression in the 'laboratory' frame, i.e. the frame in which the muon is at rest. If we neglect terms involving the electron mass we have

$$\overline{|\mathscr{M}_{fi}|^2} = \frac{8e^4}{q^4}[(k'\cdot p')(k\cdot p) + (k'\cdot p)(k\cdot p') - M^2(k'\cdot k)]. \quad (12.17)$$

The kinematic variables in the laboratory frame are shown in figure 12.5. It is evident that the four-momentum transfer is $q = k - k' = p' - p$ and therefore $p' = k - k' + p$. On eliminating p' (see example 12.1) the invariant amplitude becomes

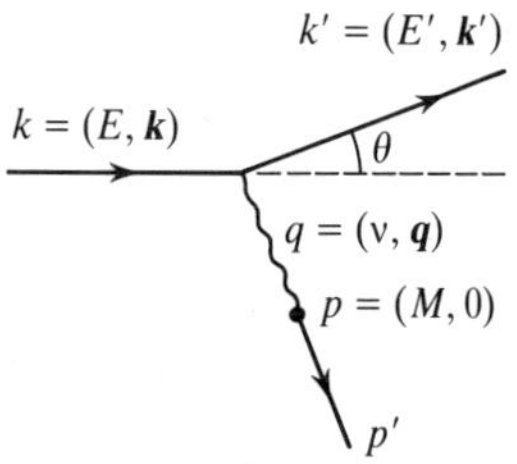

Figure 12.5
Definition of kinematic variables in e–μ scattering in the muon rest frame.

$$\overline{|\mathscr{M}_{fi}|^2} = \frac{8e^4}{q^4}[-\tfrac{1}{2}q^2(k\cdot p - k'\cdot p) + 2(k'\cdot p)(k\cdot p) + \tfrac{1}{2}M^2q^2]. \quad (12.18)$$

When expressed in terms of the directly measurable quantities E, E' and θ, equation (12.18) becomes (see example 12.2)

$$\overline{|\mathscr{M}_{fi}|^2} = \frac{8e^4}{q^4}2EE'M^2\left[\cos^2\left(\frac{\theta}{2}\right) - \frac{q^2}{2M^2}\sin^2\left(\frac{\theta}{2}\right)\right]. \quad (12.19)$$

When this matrix element and the Lorentz invariant phase space factor are used in Fermi's golden rule we obtain the differential cross-section for the scattering of an electron into solid angle $\mathrm{d}\Omega$ with energy in the range E' to $E' + \mathrm{d}E'$:

$$\frac{\mathrm{d}^2\sigma}{\mathrm{d}\Omega\,\mathrm{d}E'} = \frac{4\alpha^2E'^2}{q^4}\left[\cos^2\left(\frac{\theta}{2}\right) - \frac{q^2}{2M^2}\sin^2\left(\frac{\theta}{2}\right)\right]\delta\left(\nu + \frac{q^2}{2M}\right). \quad (12.20)$$

After integration over E' (see, for example, reference 4 for details) we obtain

$$\frac{\mathrm{d}\sigma}{\mathrm{d}\Omega} = \frac{\alpha^2}{4E^2\sin^4(\theta/2)}\frac{1}{1 + (2E/M)\sin^2(\theta/2)} \times\left[\cos^2\left(\frac{\theta}{2}\right) - \frac{q^2}{2M^2}\sin^2\left(\frac{\theta}{2}\right)\right]. \quad (12.21)$$

This may be rewritten in the form

$$\frac{d\sigma}{d\Omega} = \left(\frac{d\sigma}{d\Omega}\right)_{\text{Mott}} \left[1 - \frac{q^2}{2M^2} \tan^2\left(\frac{\theta}{2}\right)\right] \tag{12.22}$$

where

$$\left(\frac{d\sigma}{d\Omega}\right)_{\text{Mott}} = \frac{\alpha^2 \cos^2(\theta/2)}{4E^2 \sin^4(\theta/2)[1 + (2E/M)\sin^2(\theta/2)]}. \tag{12.23}$$

Equation (12.22) plays an important role in the study of the structure of the proton through e–p scattering. The $\sin^2(\theta/2)$ term in this equation arises from scattering from the magnetic moment of the muon.

12.3 Elastic electron–proton scattering

Elastic electron–proton scattering, like elastic electron–muon scattering, is dominated by single photon exchange as shown in figure 12.6. The main difference between these two processes is that, unlike the known photon–muon coupling, the photon–proton coupling is unknown. We can, nevertheless, use the electron–muon calculation of the previous section as a model.

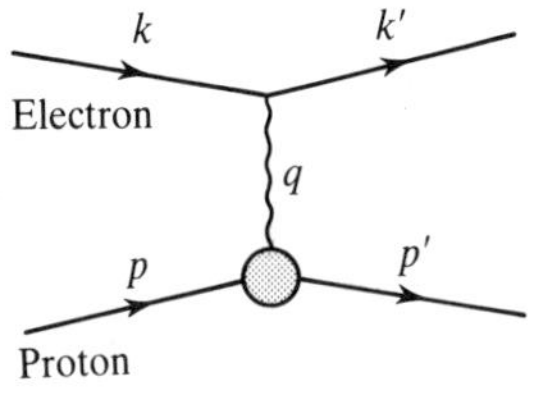

Figure 12.6
Feynman diagram for elastic e–p scattering.

The invariant amplitude takes the same form, namely

$$\mathcal{M}_{fi} = j_\mu \frac{1}{q^2} J^\mu.$$

As before, the electron current is given by

$$j_\mu = -e\bar{u}(k')\gamma_\mu u(k)$$

but the proton current J^μ must reflect the complex proton structure. The proton spinors $\bar{u}(p')$ and $u(p)$ satisfy the Dirac equation and the proton electromagnetic current will have the form

$$J^\mu = e\bar{u}(p')\Gamma^\mu u(p).$$

J^μ must be a Lorentz four-vector and the most general form which satisfies this condition is[5]

$$\Gamma^\mu = \left[F_1(q^2)\gamma^\mu + \frac{\kappa}{2m} F_2(q^2) i\sigma^{\mu\nu} q_\nu\right]$$

where $\sigma^{\mu\nu} = (i/2)[\gamma^\mu, \gamma^\nu]$ and $F_1(q^2)$, $F_2(q^2)$ are two independent form factors. The quantity κ (=1.79 nuclear magnetons) is the anomalous part of the magnetic moment of the proton and, of course, m is now the mass of the proton. In the limit $q^2 \to 0$, the virtual photon has a very long wavelength and is insensitive to the structure of the proton which therefore appears to be a particle with charge e and magnetic moment $(1 + \kappa)e/2m$. The form factors in this limit must therefore have the values $F_1(0) = 1$ and $F_2(0) = 1$.

In calculating the differential cross-section the electron tensor $L^{(e)}_{\mu\nu}$ is as before but the proton tensor

$$W^{\mu\nu} = \mathrm{Tr}[(\not{p}' + m)\Gamma^\mu(\not{p} + m)\Gamma^\nu]$$

replaces the muon tensor $L^{\mu\nu}_{(\mu)}$. With this modification the calculation proceeds as before with the result

$$\frac{\mathrm{d}\sigma}{\mathrm{d}\Omega} = \left(\frac{\mathrm{d}\sigma}{\mathrm{d}\Omega}\right)_{\mathrm{Mott}} \left\{\left[F_1^2(q^2) - \frac{\kappa^2 q^2}{4m^2} F_2^2(q^2)\right] - \frac{q^2}{2m}[F_1(q^2) + \kappa F_2(q^2)]^2 \tan^2\left(\frac{\theta}{2}\right)\right\}. \tag{12.24}$$

This is the Rosenbluth formula, with $(\mathrm{d}\sigma/\mathrm{d}\Omega)_{\mathrm{Mott}}$ given by equation (12.23). If the proton were structureless like the muon, κ would be zero and $F_1(q^2)$ would be unity for all values of q^2; the Rosenbluth formula would then revert to equation (12.22). As it stands, equation (12.24) contains an interference term between F_1 and F_2 and it is conventional to define the electric and magnetic form factors of the proton as

$$G_{\mathrm{E}} = F_1 + \frac{\kappa q^2}{4m^2} F_2$$

$$G_{\mathrm{M}} = F_1 + \kappa F_2.$$

In the limit $q^2 \to 0$, $G_{\mathrm{E}}(0) = 1$ and $G_{\mathrm{M}}(0) = 1 + \kappa = \mu_{\mathrm{p}}$, the magnetic moment of the proton. In terms of these form factors the interference term disappears and the expression for the differential cross-section becomes

$$\frac{\mathrm{d}\sigma}{\mathrm{d}\Omega} = \left(\frac{\mathrm{d}\sigma}{\mathrm{d}\Omega}\right)_{\mathrm{Mott}} \left[\frac{G_{\mathrm{E}}^2 - (q^2/4m^2)G_{\mathrm{M}}^2}{1 - q^2/4m^2} - \frac{q^2}{2m^2} G_{\mathrm{M}}^2 \tan^2\left(\frac{\theta}{2}\right)\right]. \tag{12.25}$$

The electric and magnetic form factors for the proton can thus be determined by comparing the differential cross-section for elastic electron–proton scattering, measured in the laboratory system, with that expected on the basis of the Mott formula. In practice, equation (12.25) is often rewritten with $Q^2 = -q^2$ so that

$$\frac{\mathrm{d}\sigma/\mathrm{d}\Omega}{(\mathrm{d}\sigma/\mathrm{d}\Omega)_{\mathrm{Mott}}} = A(Q^2) + B(Q^2)\tan^2\left(\frac{\theta}{2}\right)$$

where

$$A = \frac{G_{\mathrm{E}}^2 + (Q^2/4m^2)G_{\mathrm{M}}^2}{1 + Q^2/4m^2} \qquad B = \frac{Q^2 G_{\mathrm{M}}^2}{2m^2}.$$

The form factors G_{E} and G_{M} can then be determined by performing a series of experiments at different values of q^2 at each of which $\mathrm{d}\sigma/\mathrm{d}\Omega$ is measured as a function of θ. For a given fixed q^2, figure 12.7 shows a typical dependence of $(\mathrm{d}\sigma/\mathrm{d}\Omega)/(\mathrm{d}\sigma/\mathrm{d}\Omega)_{\mathrm{Mott}}$ on $\tan^2(\theta/2)$. The experimental observation of a linear dependence on $\tan^2(\theta/2)$ validates the assumption of single photon exchange as the dominant mechanism in elastic electron–proton scattering. The magnetic form factor at a particular value of q^2 is determined directly from the slope of the graph and, using this value of $G_{\mathrm{M}}(q^2)$, $G_{\mathrm{E}}(q^2)$ is determined from the intercept.

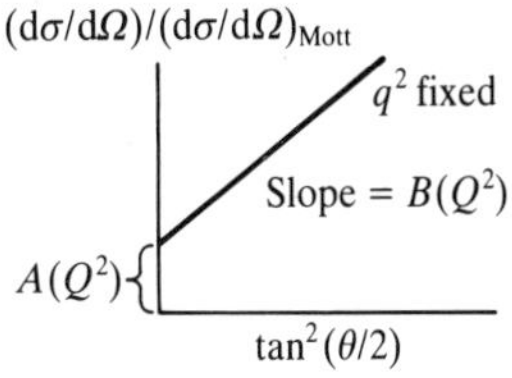

Figure 12.7
Graph showing the linear relationship between $(\mathrm{d}\sigma/\mathrm{d}\Omega)/(\mathrm{d}\sigma/\mathrm{d}\Omega)_{\mathrm{Mott}}$ and $\tan^2(\theta/2)$ at a fixed value of q^2.

Because free neutron targets are not available, deuterium or heavier nuclei have to be used to measure the neutron form factor. Because of its low binding energy and relatively simple structure, deuterium is a natural choice. Nonetheless, in analysing electron–deuteron scattering, complications do arise from the nuclear physics of the deuteron.

Typical results[6] for the form factors of the proton and neutron are shown in figure 12.8. It is found that they satisfy a simple *scaling*

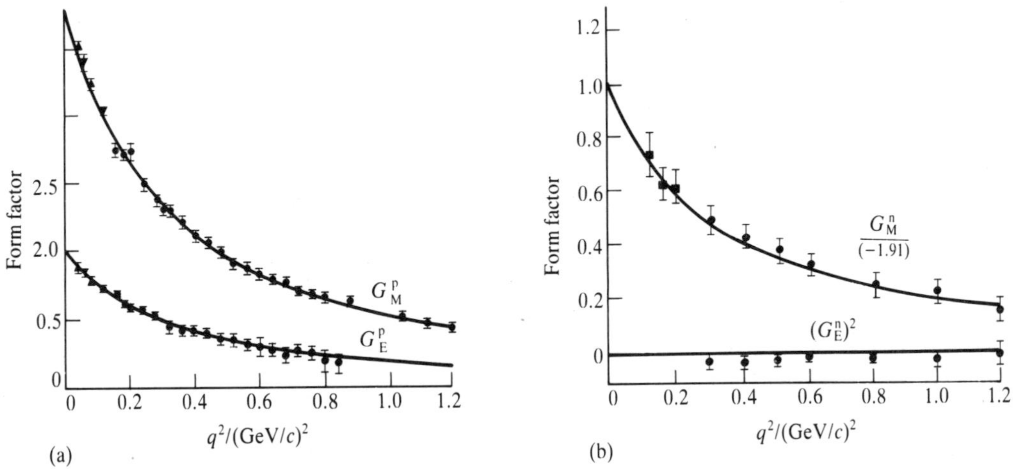

Figure 12.8 Electric and magnetic form factors as a function of q^2 for (a) the proton and (b) the neutron. (After Hughes E B *et al.* 1965 *Phys Rev* **139B** (458).)

law

$$G_E^p(q^2) = \frac{G_M^p(q^2)}{\mu_p} = \frac{G_M^n(q^2)}{\mu_n} \qquad G_E^n(q^2) = 0 \qquad (12.26)$$

and are well described by the *dipole formula*

$$G(q^2) = \left(1 - \frac{q^2}{m^2}\right)^{-2}$$

with $m^2 = 0.71\ \text{GeV}^2$. It is straightforward to show that these form factors correspond to a charge (and magnetic moment) distribution of the form $\rho \approx \exp(-mr)$ with a root-mean-square radius of 0.8 fm (see examples 12.3 and 12.4).

12.4 Inelastic electron–proton scattering

At large values of q^2 the elastic cross-section is very small and inelastic scattering becomes much more probable. We shall consider the process $\text{ep} \to \text{e}X$, where X is any system of hadrons. For relatively small values of q^2 the proton may merely be excited into a resonant state which then decays into a nucleon and a pion for example. At higher values of q^2 the energy transferred to the proton may be so great that it breaks up into many hadrons and loses its identity completely.

We assume that, as in the case of elastic scattering, single photon exchange is the dominant mechanism. The Feynman diagram describing the process is shown in figure 12.9. Experimentally, the hadronic system

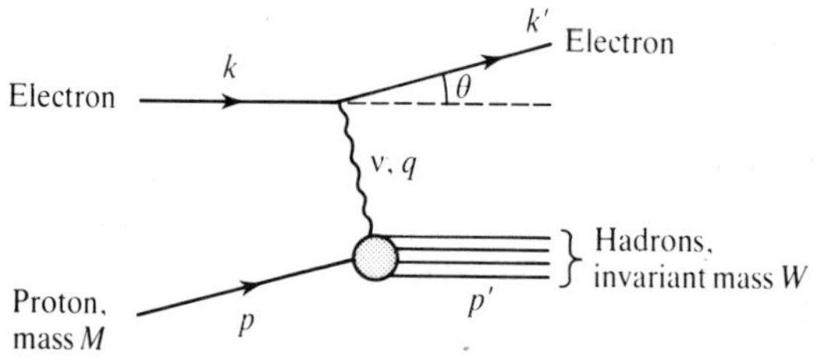

Figure 12.9
Feynman diagram for inelastic e–p scattering.

is disregarded and measurements are made on the scattered electron only. Specifically, the event rate and electron energy for electrons scattered through some angle θ with respect to the incident beam direction are measured. The cross-section measured in this way is called the 'inclusive' cross-section.

In the case of elastic scattering the energy transfer ν and the four-momentum transfer q^2 are related by the expression $\nu = -q^2/2M$ and are thus not independent variables. In contrast, in inelastic scattering ν and q^2 are *independent* scalar variables. For, from conservation of energy and momentum at the hadron vertex in figure 12.9, we have

$$p' = p + q$$

and therefore

$$p'^2 = p^2 + 2p \cdot q + q^2.$$

Now p'^2 is just the invariant mass squared, W^2 say, of the hadronic system. Further, $p \cdot q = M\nu$ and, defining $-q^2 = Q^2$, we have

$$Q^2 = 2M\nu + M^2 - W^2.$$

Since the invariant mass of the hadron system can vary, Q^2 (and hence q^2) and ν are independent variables in inelastic electron–proton scattering.

In analogy with equation (12.24) or equation (12.25) the differential cross-section for the inelastic scattering of an electron with energy in the range E' to $E' + \mathrm{d}E'$ into the solid angle $\mathrm{d}\Omega$ is

$$\frac{\mathrm{d}^2\sigma}{\mathrm{d}\Omega\,\mathrm{d}E'} = \frac{4\alpha^2 E'^2}{Q^4}\left[W_2(Q^2, \nu)\cos^2\left(\frac{\theta}{2}\right) + 2W_1(Q^2, \nu)\sin^2\left(\frac{\theta}{2}\right)\right]. \tag{12.27}$$

In inelastic scattering the functions $W_1(Q^2, \nu)$ and $W_2(Q^2, \nu)$, which replace the form factors $G_E(q^2)$ and $G_M(q^2)$, are functions of the two independent variables Q^2 and ν. They are commonly called *structure functions.*

It is convenient at this stage to introduce the variable $x = Q^2/2M\nu$ which plays an important role in what follows. In order to gain some familiarity with these variables we show the kinematic relationships between them in figure 12.10.

The condition for elastic scattering is $W = M$, in which case $Q^2 = 2M\nu$ as required. This is a straight line at 45° to the axes as shown in figure 12.10 and corresponds to $x = 1$. The region above this line is kinematically forbidden. Inelastic scattering corresponds to $W^2 > M^2$ and therefore $Q^2 < 2M\nu$, i.e. to the region below the elastic scattering line. The lines drawn parallel to the line $x = 1$ correspond to the production of a hadron system with a fixed invariant mass W and may, for instance, represent the electroproduction of a nucleon resonance. The line corresponding to the production of a resonance with mass W' intercepts the horizontal axis at $2M\nu = W'^2 - M^2$. From the definition of x we have $Q^2 = x2M\nu$ and therefore lines of constant x pass through the origin and have slope x.

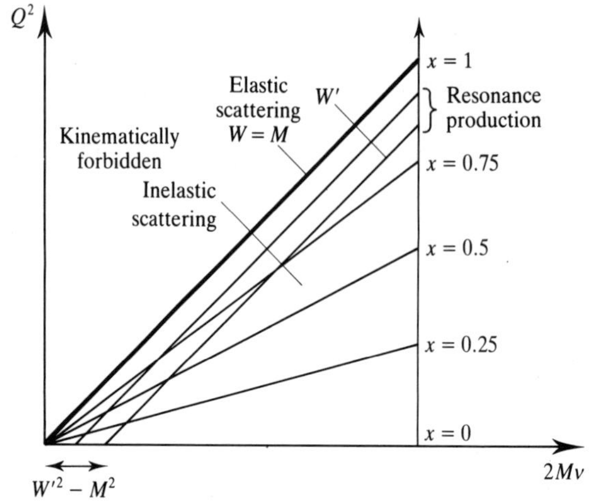

Figure 12.10 Diagram showing the relationship between the kinematic variables Q^2 and ν. M is the mass of the proton and W is the mass of the hadronic system produced in the process $\mathrm{ep} \to \mathrm{e}X$ (see figure 12.9).

Finally, the region in which both Q^2 and ν are large is known as the *deep inelastic* scattering region. Scattering experiments in this region are of the utmost importance for it is here that the internal structure of the proton is revealed; the proton consists of point-like partons.

In order to understand better the arguments on which this latter statement is based we draw on examples from nuclear physics and develop the ideas put forward in section 3.3. Specifically, we consider the scattering of electrons by ^{4}He nuclei and present the data taken at 400 MeV incident electron energy by Hofstadter.[7] Figure 12.11(a) shows the cross-section in arbitrary units for electrons scattered through 45° in the laboratory system plotted as a function of $x = Q^2/2M_\alpha \nu$, where M_α is the mass of the helium nucleus. At $x \approx 1$ one sees a pronounced peak due to coherent elastic scattering from the helium nucleus. At smaller values of x, i.e. larger values of energy transfer to the nucleus, there is a broad peak due to inelastic scattering. Shown for reference is the elastic scattering peak from free protons which occurs at $x \approx 0.25$. This suggests that the inelastic peak, which is distributed about $x \approx 0.25$, is due to the incoherent elastic scattering from the individual constituents, i.e. the nucleons, in the helium nucleus. The effective mass of each nucleon in ^{4}He will be roughly $m = M_\alpha/4$ so that if elastic scattering is taking place from individual nucleons it should occur at $x = Q^2/2m\nu$. Hence this quasi-elastic scattering peak should appear at $x = m/M_\alpha \approx 1/N$ where N is the number of constituent nucleons (four in the present case). The quasi-elastic scattering peak is smeared out because the nucleons are not free but are bound inside the nuclear volume and have a Fermi momentum $\Delta p \approx R^{-1}$ where R is the nuclear radius. Figure 12.11(b) shows the cross-section for elastic and inelastic electron–helium scattering again at 400 MeV but at an

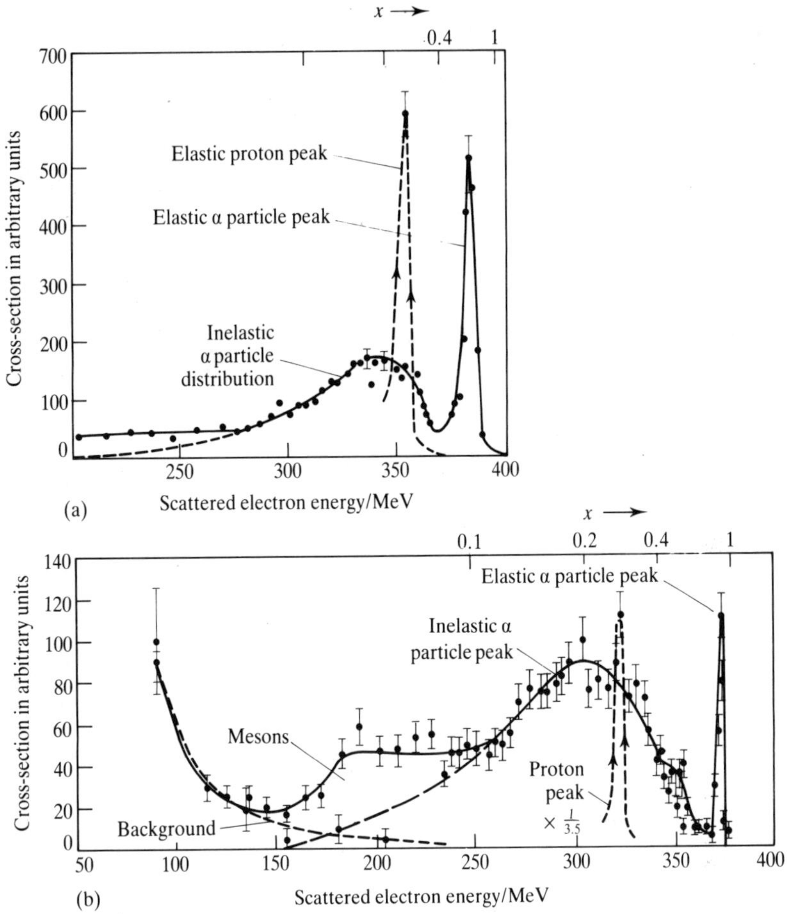

Figure 12.11 Cross-sections for the elastic and inelastic scattering of 400 MeV electrons by ^{4}He nuclei as a function of x. The scattering angle of the electrons in the laboratory system is 45° in part (a) and 60° in part (b). (After Hofstadter R 1956 *Rev Mod Phys* **28** (214).)

increased scattering angle of 60°. This corresponds to a higher value of Q^2. The first point to notice is that the elastic e–α cross-section is much reduced at this higher value of Q^2; the cross-section is suppressed by the form factor. On the other hand, the quasi-elastic scattering from the individual nucleons is essentially independent of Q^2; the cross-section is said to *scale*. This behaviour is typical for scattering from a point-like or structureless particle.

To gain some insight into this scaling behaviour consider a dipole form factor $F(Q^2) = 1/(1 + Q^2/\Lambda_{\text{nuc}}^2)^2$. In this expression Λ_{nuc} sets a scale and the behaviour of the cross-section (through the form factor) depends on the relative values of Q^2 and the scale Λ_{nuc}^2. For $Q^2 \ll \Lambda_{\text{nuc}}^2$, $F(Q^2) \rightarrow 1$. In this situation the electromagnetic probe has a very long wavelength

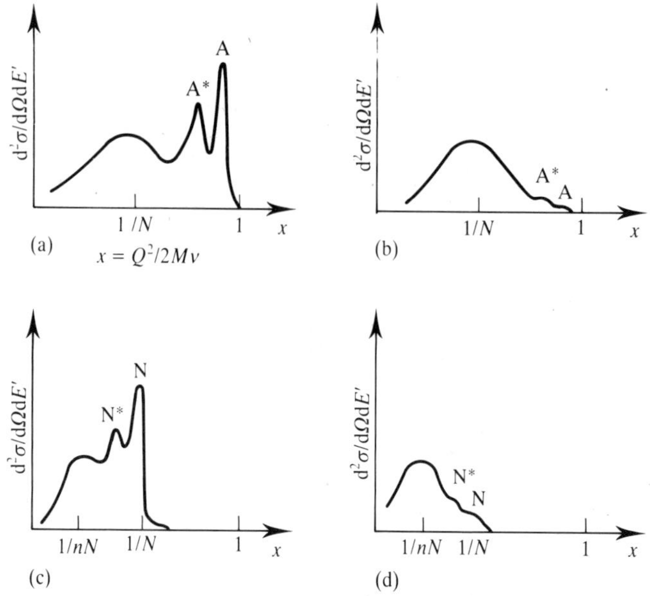

Figure 12.12 Schematic diagram showing the development of the scattering cross-section for electrons on a hypothetical nucleus A, as a function of x, as Q^2 increases. (a) The pronounced peaks are due to elastic scattering, eA → eA, at $x \approx 1$ and formation of excited nuclear states A*. The broad peak, due to quasi-elastic scattering from individual nucleons, is centred around $x = 1/N$, where N is the number of nucleons in the nucleus, and is smeared due to Fermi motion. (b) At higher values of Q^2 the elastic peaks become much reduced due to the nuclear form factor but the quasi-elastic scattering peak is virtually unaffected; it scales. (c) At still higher values of Q^2 the nucleon constituents are revealed. The pronounced peaks are due to elastic e–N scattering and formation of excited nucleon states N*. The quasi-elastic scattering peak is centred around $x = 1/nN$ where n is the number of nucleon constituents. Fermi motion of the nucleon constituents smears out this peak. (d) As Q^2 increases further the only remaining feature is the quasi-elastic scattering from the nucleon constituents; this cross-section scales.

compared with the scale and is therefore insensitive to the detailed internal structure of the target; scattering takes place as if from a point. As Q^2 increases the elastic cross-section decreases. There is a different scale, Λ_{nucleon}, for the nucleons but provided $Q^2 \ll \Lambda^2_{\text{nucleon}}$ no internal structure of the nucleons will be revealed and quasi-elastic scattering will take place from the nucleons as though they were point-like; the quasi-elastic e–nucleon scattering is scale invariant – the cross-section scales. The quasi-elastic peak will occur at $x \approx 1/N$ where N is the number of nucleon constituents and it will be spread out due to the Fermi motion of the nucleons inside the nucleus. One can imagine continuing this process to investigate the substructure of the nucleons themselves. Suppose for the sake of argument there is another, perhaps ultimate, scale Λ_0. As Q^2 increases beyond $\Lambda^2_{\text{nucleon}}$ the elastic e–α peak will tend to disappear, the quasi-elastic scattering peak will become reduced due to the form factor of the nucleon and quasi-elastic scattering from the nucleon constituents will set in. If there are n nucleon constituents the quasi-elastic scattering

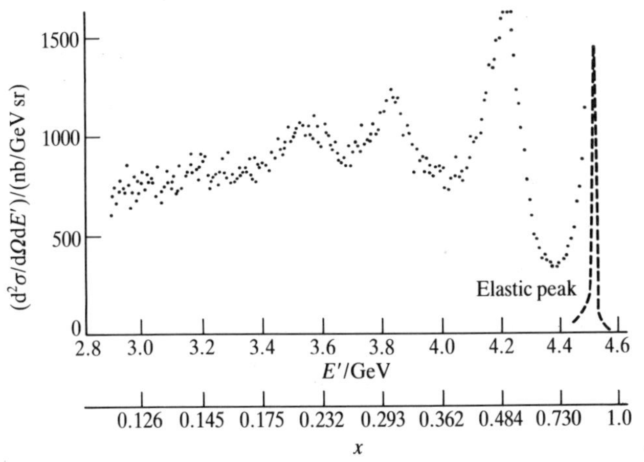

Figure 12.13 Differential cross-section for e–p scattering at 10° as a function of E', the energy of the scattered electron in the laboratory system, and x. The elastic peak at $x = 1$ has been reduced by a factor of 15. The incident beam energy was 4.879 GeV. (After Bartel W *et al.* 1968 *Phys Lett* **28B** (148).)

from these will appear at $x \approx 1/nN$ and again will be smeared out due to Fermi motion. The cross-section for this quasi-elastic scattering from the nucleon constituents will remain constant as Q^2 is increased further and if indeed there is no other scale, $\Lambda < \Lambda_0$, the constancy of the cross-section would indicate a lack of any further substructure. This phenomenon of scaling and rescaling as Q^2, and hence the resolution, increases to reveal deeper and deeper levels of matter is summarized in figure 12.12. Note the gradual shift of the quasi-elastic scattering peak to lower and lower values of x as more and more constituents are revealed.

Consider now the scattering of electrons from hydrogen. In figure 12.13 we show results from the electron synchrotron at DESY obtained by Bartel *et al.*[8] These data are at much higher values of Q^2 than the electron–helium data but the similarity between figure 12.11 and figure 12.13 is unmistakable. A large peak due to elastic e–p scattering is clearly visible at $x = 1$, as are peaks at lower x values corresponding to the excitation of nucleon resonances through the processes

$$e + p \to \begin{cases} e + \Delta(1232) \\ e + N(1450) \\ e + \Delta(1688). \end{cases}$$

Beyond the resonances, at higher energy transfers to the nucleon (lower values of x) there is a broad continuum which, in analogy with the case of electron–helium scattering, is interpreted as quasi-elastic scattering from the nucleon constituents. The absence of a peak in this region is due to the Fermi motion of the constituents. At higher values of Q^2 the elastic and resonance peaks decrease due to the fall-off in the form factors but the quasi-elastic scattering is virtually unaffected – the cross-section scales indicating scattering from point-like constituents.

12.5 Bjorken scaling and the parton model

In this section we develop further our investigation into the structure of the proton and to this end we begin by collecting together the relevant pieces of formalism presented earlier in this chapter.

The differential cross-sections for the processes discussed so far may all be expressed in the form

$$\frac{d^2\sigma}{d\Omega\, dE'} = \frac{4\alpha^2 E'^2}{Q^4} S$$

where S in general represents the structure, if any, of the target particle. For example, the differential cross-section for elastic e–μ scattering, in which both the electron and muon are structureless, is given by equation (12.20) and

$$S_{e\mu\to e\mu} = \left[\cos^2\left(\frac{\theta}{2}\right) + \frac{Q^2}{2M^2}\sin^2\left(\frac{\theta}{2}\right)\right]\delta\left(\nu - \frac{Q^2}{2M}\right). \qquad (12.28)$$

In this expression M is the mass of the muon. The presence of the δ function merely stresses the fact that in elastic scattering the energy transfer ν and the four-momentum transfer Q^2 are not independent; they are related by the equation $\nu = Q^2/2M$.

In contrast, in inelastic scattering Q^2 and ν are independent variables, and the differential cross-section for the inelastic process ep → eX, see equation (12.27), has

$$S_{ep\to eX} = W_2(Q^2, \nu)\cos^2\left(\frac{\theta}{2}\right) + 2W_1(Q^2, \nu)\sin^2\left(\frac{\theta}{2}\right). \qquad (12.29)$$

The complex structure of the proton is reflected in the presence of the two structure functions W_1 and W_2 which, for values of Q^2 less than about 1 $(\mathrm{GeV}/c)^2$, are functions of both Q^2 and ν.

In the last section we presented evidence which pointed to the existence of point-like constituents (partons) in the proton. A natural guess would be that these partons are in fact the spin $\frac{1}{2}$ quarks. If, at high values of Q^2, the virtual photon does indeed elastically scatter from an essentially free spin $\frac{1}{2}$ quark, expression (12.29), which describes the proton structure, should reduce to (12.28) which describes elastic scattering from a structureless spin $\frac{1}{2}$ Dirac particle – the muon. Comparison of (12.29) and (12.28) shows that if inelastic e–p scattering is an *incoherent* superposition of elastic scattering from quarks the proton structure functions should reduce to the point form

$$2W_1 = \frac{Q^2}{2m^2}\,\delta\left(\nu - \frac{Q^2}{2m}\right) \tag{12.30}$$

$$W_2 = \delta\left(\nu - \frac{Q^2}{2m}\right) \tag{12.31}$$

where m is the quark mass. If we make use of the property $\delta(ax) = a^{-1}\delta(x)$, (12.30) and (12.31) may be rewritten as

$$2mW_1(Q^2, \nu) = \frac{Q^2}{2m\nu}\,\delta\left(1 - \frac{Q^2}{2m\nu}\right) \tag{12.32}$$

$$\nu W_2(Q^2, \nu) = \delta\left(1 - \frac{Q^2}{2m\nu}\right). \tag{12.33}$$

These point 'structure functions' have the remarkable property that the independent variables Q^2 and ν appear only in the dimensionless ratio $x = Q^2/2m\nu$; the structure functions are no longer functions of Q^2 and ν separately. This phenomenon is known, somewhat paradoxically, as Bjorken scaling. Its occurrence would signal the fact that, as Q^2 increases into the deep inelastic region and the wavelength of the virtual photon becomes shorter and shorter, elastic scattering from the proton, which may be regarded as due to the *coherent* action of all the quarks inside the proton, is replaced by an *incoherent* superposition of elastic scattering from individual point-like quarks.

To stress that there is *no* scale of mass or length in this deep inelastic region let us consider again elastic e–p scattering. From equation (12.25) we have

$$S_{\mathrm{ep}\to\mathrm{ep}} = \left[\frac{G_E^2 + \tau G_M^2}{1+\tau}\cos^2\left(\frac{\theta}{2}\right) + 2\tau G_M^2 \sin^2\left(\frac{\theta}{2}\right)\right]\delta\left(\nu - \frac{Q^2}{2M}\right) \tag{12.34}$$

where $\tau = Q^2/4M^2$ and M is now the proton mass. Let us simplify this expression by assuming that the proton does not possess an anomalous magnetic moment. Then, $G_E = G_M = G(Q^2)$, say, and (12.34) becomes

$$S_{\mathrm{ep}\to\mathrm{ep}} = G^2(Q^2)\left[\cos^2\left(\frac{\theta}{2}\right) + \frac{Q^2}{2M^2}\sin^2\left(\frac{\theta}{2}\right)\right]\delta\left(\nu - \frac{Q^2}{2M}\right). \tag{12.35}$$

On comparing this expression with (12.29) we can write the elastic structure functions of the proton as

$$W_1(Q^2, \nu) = G^2(Q^2)\frac{Q^2}{4M^2}\delta\left(\nu - \frac{Q^2}{2M}\right)$$
$$W_2(Q^2, \nu) = G^2(Q^2)\delta\left(\nu - \frac{Q^2}{2M}\right). \tag{12.36}$$

Because of the presence of the form factor $G(Q^2)$ these expressions cannot be rewritten as functions of the dimensionless variable x. We saw in section 12.3 that the form factors are well described by the dipole formula

$$G(Q^2) = \left(1 + \frac{Q^2}{m^2}\right)^{-2}$$

in which the *mass scale* is determined experimentally to be $m^2 = 0.71\ \text{GeV}^2$. In deep inelastic scattering there is no such mass scale.

In summary, the Bjorken scaling hypothesis may be stated as follows: in the limit $Q^2 \to \infty$, $\nu \to \infty$, with $x = Q^2/2M\nu$ fixed, the structure functions scale as

$$MW_1(Q^2, \nu) \to F_1(x) \tag{12.37}$$

$$\nu W_2(Q^2, \nu) \to F_2(x). \tag{12.38}$$

Experimental support for this scaling hypothesis is given in figures 12.14 and 12.15. In figure 12.14 we show the results in inelastic e–p scattering obtained at SLAC by Miller *et al.*[9] The two structure functions are plotted against $\omega = 1/x$ for different values of $Q^2 > 1\ (\text{GeV}/c)^2$. To ensure that the continuum region is being probed, the data are restricted to hadron masses $M_X > 2.6$ GeV, i.e. well away from the resonance region. Within experimental errors, both $2MW_1$ and νW_2 scale: they are functions of x only. Figure 12.15 shows data from Friedman and Kendall[10] for $M_X >$ 2 GeV; νW_2 is plotted as a function of Q^2 for the fixed value of $x = 0.25$ and it is seen to be independent of Q^2.

A physical interpretation of Bjorken scaling, and in particular the scaling variable x, was first given by Feynman.[11] Feynman postulated that each parton in the proton carries only a fraction of the energy and momentum of the proton. The scattering process in the deep-inelastic region is visualized as in figure 12.16. The virtual photon, with four-momentum q, is absorbed by a particular parton. Let x be the fraction of the four-momentum of the proton carried by this parton. There are different types of parton (quarks) in the proton so a parton of type i has four-momentum $p_i = xp$ where p is the four-momentum of the proton, and a mass $m_i \approx xM$, M being the proton mass (see example 12.5).

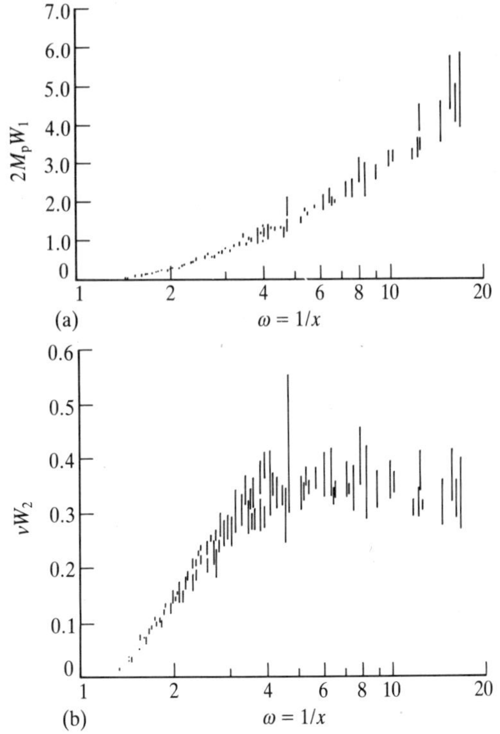

Figure 12.14 Evidence for the scaling of the proton structure functions: (a) $2M_p W_1$ and (b) νW_2 are shown as functions of $\omega = 1/x$ for values of $Q^2 > 1\,(\text{GeV}/c)^2$. Masses of the hadronic system were required to be greater than 2.6 GeV. (After Miller G *et al.* 1972 *Phys Rev* **D5** (528).)

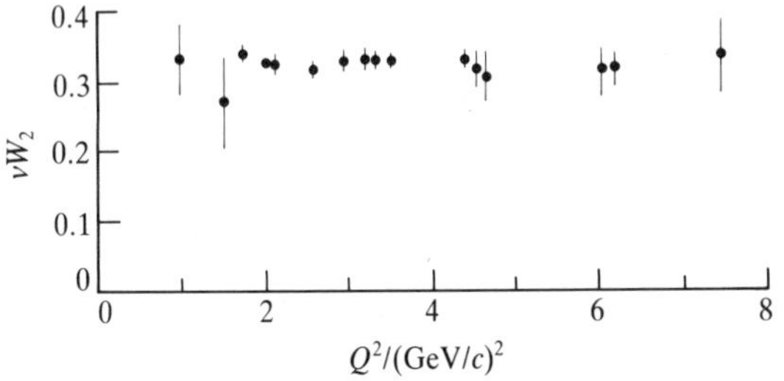

Figure 12.15 The proton structure function νW_2 plotted as a function of Q^2 for the fixed value of $x = 0.25$ and hadron masses greater than 2 GeV. The structure function is independent of Q^2. (After Friedman J I and Kendall H W 1972 *Ann Rev Nucl Sci* **22** (203).)

Assuming, as we are, that the partons are spin $\frac{1}{2}$ quarks, we can write down the differential cross-section for this process by using that for e–μ scattering as a model. The only change in the formula will be the replacement of α by αe_i, where e_i is the fractional charge of quark of type i. Thus, the differential cross-section for elastic scattering of an electron

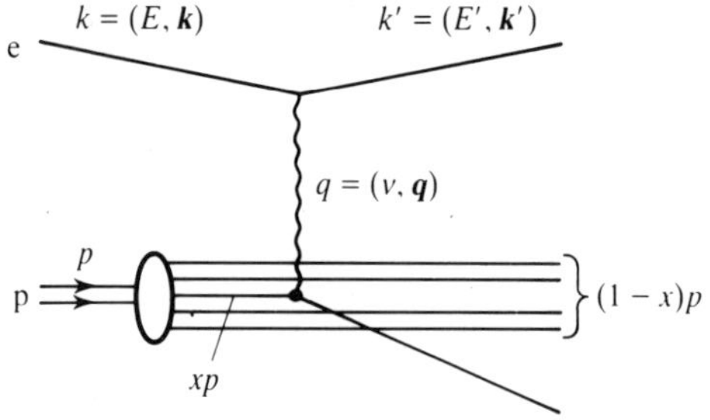

Figure 12.16
Deep inelastic e–p scattering in the parton model.

by a quark of type i becomes

$$\frac{d^2\sigma^i}{d\Omega\, dE'} = \frac{4\alpha^2 E'^2}{Q^4}\left[e_i^2 \cos^2\left(\frac{\theta}{2}\right) + e_i^2 \frac{Q^2}{2m_i^2} \sin^2\left(\frac{\theta}{2}\right)\right]\delta\left(\nu - \frac{Q^2}{2m_i}\right). \tag{12.39}$$

On comparing this with (12.27), the differential cross-section for inelastic e–p scattering, we find, putting $m_i = xM$, that the contribution of parton i to the proton structure functions W_1 and W_2 is

$$W_1^i = e_i^2 \frac{Q^2}{4M^2x^2}\,\delta\left(\nu - \frac{Q^2}{2Mx}\right) \tag{12.40}$$

$$W_2^i = e_i^2\,\delta\left(\nu - \frac{Q^2}{2Mx}\right). \tag{12.41}$$

Each parton can, of course, carry a different fraction x of the proton momentum; let $f_i(x)$ be the probability that a parton of type i has momentum fraction x. In the electron–quark scattering process the non-participating partons merely act as 'spectators' so we assume that the contributions of individual quarks to the inelastic e–p differential cross-section add incoherently. We may therefore write

$$W_1(Q^2, \nu) = \sum_i \int e_i^2 \frac{Q^2}{4M^2x^2} f_i(x)\,\delta\left(\nu - \frac{Q^2}{2Mx}\right) dx.$$

We integrate this expression using property (iv) of the Dirac δ function given in appendix I and obtain

$$MW_1(Q^2, \nu) = \sum_i \frac{e_i^2}{2} f_i(x) \equiv F_1(x) \tag{12.42}$$

with $x = Q^2/2M\nu$. Furthermore,

$$W_2(Q^2, \nu) = \sum_i \int e_i^2 f_i(x)\,\delta\left(\nu - \frac{Q^2}{2Mx}\right) dx$$

and on performing the integration we get

$$\nu W_2(Q^2, \nu) = \sum_i e_i^2 x f_i(x) \equiv F_2(x). \tag{12.43}$$

It follows that

$$2xF_1(x) = F_2(x). \tag{12.44}$$

This last relation, which is valid only for spin $\frac{1}{2}$ partons, is known as the Callan–Gross[12] relation.

Some insight into the Callan–Gross relation can be obtained from a consideration of the cross-sections for virtual photon–proton interactions. Real photons have $q^2 = 0$ and can exist only in the transverse helicity states $\lambda = \pm 1$, whereas virtual photons have $q^2 < 0$ and can exist in addition in the longitudinal or scalar state with helicity $\lambda = 0$; virtual photons behave like spin 1 particles with non-zero mass. The cross-sections for the production of a hadronic system with mass M_X by transverse and scalar photons are[13]

$$\sigma_T = \frac{4\pi\alpha^2}{K} W_1 \tag{12.45}$$

and

$$\sigma_S = \frac{4\pi\alpha^2}{K}\left[\left(1 + \frac{\nu^2}{Q^2}\right) W_2 - W_1\right]. \tag{12.46}$$

In these expressions K is a flux factor given by $K = (M_X^2 - M^2)/2M$ where M is the proton mass. Since any cross-section must be positive or zero we have

$$W_1 \geqslant 0$$

and

$$\left(1 + \frac{\nu^2}{Q^2}\right) W_2 - W_1 \geqslant 0.$$

In the scaling limit $Q^2 \to \infty$, $\nu \to \infty$ while $x = Q^2/2M\nu$ remains finite, $MW_1(Q^2, \nu) \to F_1(x)$ and $\nu W_2(Q^2, \nu) \to F_2(x)$ so that

$$\sigma_T \to \frac{4\pi\alpha^2}{KM} F_1(x) \tag{12.47}$$

and

$$\sigma_S \to \frac{4\pi\alpha^2}{KM}\frac{1}{2x}[F_2(x) - 2xF_1(x)]. \tag{12.48}$$

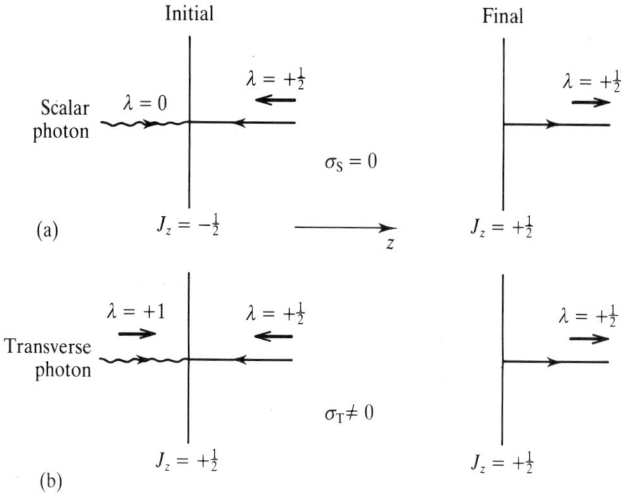

Figure 12.17
Absorption of (a) scalar and (b) transverse photons by helicity conserving partons viewed in the Breit frame of reference.

Let us consider the constraints, if any, imposed on these cross-sections by angular momentum conservation. We work in the Breit frame in which the photon and parton are collinear (see Figure 12.17). On absorption of the photon, the three-momentum of the parton is reversed; momentum is transferred in this frame but not energy. Take the z axis as the direction of the incident photon. In the limit in which its mass may be neglected the parton will have definite helicity, i.e. its component of spin along the direction of motion will be conserved. Figure 12.17(a) shows the absorption of a scalar photon ($\lambda = 0$) by a spin $\frac{1}{2}$ parton with helicity $\lambda = +\frac{1}{2}$. In the initial state the z component of angular momentum is $-\frac{1}{2}$ while in the final state it is $+\frac{1}{2}$. Since angular momentum is not conserved the cross-section for absorption of a scalar photon by a spin $\frac{1}{2}$ parton should be zero. With reference to (12.48) we see that $\sigma_S \to 0$ if $2xF_1 = F_2$, i.e. if the Callan–Gross relation is satisfied. Figure 12.17(b) shows that angular momentum is conserved in the absorption of transverse photons by spin $\frac{1}{2}$ partons; $\sigma_T \neq 0$. Thus, if partons have spin $\frac{1}{2}$, $\sigma_S/\sigma_T \to 0$ and the Callan–Gross relation should be satisfied. On the other hand, partons with spin 0 cannot absorb transverse photons in an angular-momentum-conserving process so that if the partons were spin 0 particles one would expect $\sigma_T/\sigma_S \to 0$. Support for the validity of the Callan–Gross relation and hence for the hypothesis that the partons which interact with the photon, i.e. those which carry electric charge,* have spin $\frac{1}{2}$, is given in figure 12.18.

It is intriguing that the four-momentum fraction x is identical to the dimensionless kinematic variable $x = Q^2/2M\nu$ introduced for the virtual

* Here, we are anticipating the existence of gluons. These have spin 1, but, since they are neutral, do not interact with the photon.

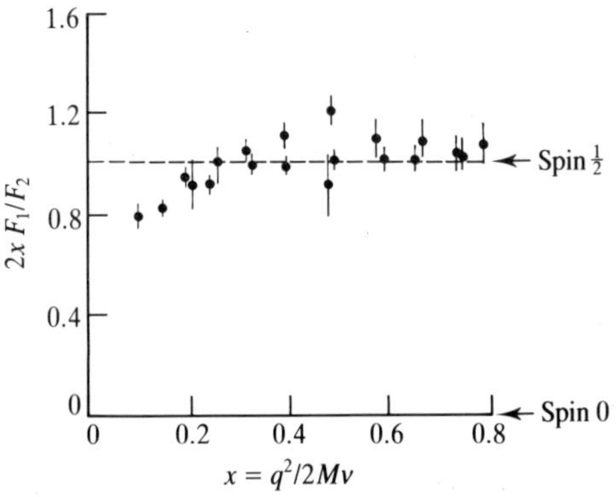

Figure 12.18 Experimental test of the Callan–Gross relation. The data are from a series of e–N scattering experiments performed at the Stanford Linear Accelerator Centre. F_1 and F_2 are extracted from fits to the differential cross-sections in the range $1.5 < q^2 < 16\ \text{GeV}^2$. For values of $x > 0.2$ the ratio $2xF_1/F_2$ is consistent with unity, the value expected for spin $\frac{1}{2}$ partons.

photon in section 12.4. This means that *in order that the photon be absorbed by a parton with four-momentum x it must have just the right values of Q^2 and ν to give this value of x.* In essence, it is the elastic scattering constraint, $\nu = Q^2/2m_i = Q^2/2Mx$, i.e. $x = Q^2/2M\nu$, which results in the observed scaling behaviour in the deep-inelastic scattering region.

12.6 Quark structure of the nucleon

12.6.1 Electron–nucleon scattering

The phenomenon of Bjorken scaling embodied in the relations

$$MW_1(Q^2, \nu) \rightarrow F_1(x) = \sum_i \frac{e_i^2}{2} f_i(x) \tag{12.49}$$

$$\nu W_2(Q^2, \nu) \rightarrow F_2(x) = \sum_i e_i^2 x f_i(x) \tag{12.50}$$

and the experimental evidence in favour of the Callan–Gross relation indicates that the nucleon contains point-like fermion constituents (partons). We associate these partons with the quarks which we saw in chapter 10 were so successful in describing the static properties of the hadrons. The quantum numbers of the proton, for instance, are correctly predicted if one assumes that the proton consists of two u quarks and a d quark. These are known as 'valence' quarks. It should be noted, however, that the same quantum numbers would result if, in addition to the valence quarks, there exists any number of quark–antiquark pairs $(f, \bar{f})$ so that for any quark flavour f the contribution to the overall quantum numbers of the proton from these pairs is exactly zero. Deep-inelastic scattering experiments point to the existence of these quark–antiquark pairs in addition to the valence quarks; they are known as 'sea' quarks.

Using (12.50) and the quantum numbers of the quarks shown in table 10.2 we may write the structure function F_2^{ep} for electron–proton scattering as

$$F_2^{\text{ep}} = x\{\tfrac{4}{9}[u^p(x) + \bar{u}^p(x)] + \tfrac{1}{9}[d^p(x) + \bar{d}^p(x)] + \tfrac{1}{9}[s^p(x) + \bar{s}^p(x)]\}.$$

In this expression $u^p(x)$, for example, is the probability density distribution of u quarks in the proton, $\bar{u}^p(x)$ that for u antiquarks in the proton, etc. We are assuming here that there is negligible contribution from c, b, . . . quarks in the proton. Similarly, the structure function for e–n scattering may be written

$$F_2^{\text{en}} = x\{\tfrac{4}{9}[u^n(x) + \bar{u}^n(x)] + \tfrac{1}{9}[d^n(x) + \bar{d}^n(x)] + \tfrac{1}{9}[s^n(x) + \bar{s}^n(x)]\}.$$

Now, since the proton and neutron and the u and d quarks form I spin doublets it is expected that

$$\begin{aligned} u^p(x) &= d^n(x) \equiv u(x) \\ d^p(x) &= u^n(x) \equiv d(x) \\ s^p(x) &= s^n(x) \equiv s(x) \end{aligned} \qquad (12.51)$$

with similar constraints for the antiquark distribution functions. The e–p and e–n structure functions then become

$$F_2^{\text{ep}} = x\{\tfrac{4}{9}[u(x) + \bar{u}(x)] + \tfrac{1}{9}[d(x) + \bar{d}(x)] + \tfrac{1}{9}[s(x) + \bar{s}(x)]\} \qquad (12.52)$$

$$F_2^{\text{en}} = x\{\tfrac{4}{9}[d(x) + \bar{d}(x)] + \tfrac{1}{9}[u(x) + \bar{u}(x)] + \tfrac{1}{9}[s(x) + \bar{s}(x)]\}. \qquad (12.53)$$

We can obtain bounds on the ratio of these structure functions by expressing the quark distribution functions in terms of valence and sea quarks. Thus, in general, we write for any quark flavour q,

$$q(x) = q_{\text{v}}(x) + q_{\text{s}}(x)$$

where the subscripts v and s refer to valence and sea quarks respectively. If the valence quarks in the proton are u_{v}, u_{v} and d_{v} then we have immediately

$$q_{\text{v}}(x) = 0 \qquad \text{for} \qquad q \equiv s,\ \bar{s},\ \bar{u} \text{ and } \bar{d}.$$

The strange quarks and the antiquarks in the proton must belong to the sea. Then,

$$u(x) = u_v(x) + u_s(x)$$

$$d(x) = d_v(x) + d_s(x).$$

If we make the further simplifying assumption that the three light quarks occur in the sea with the same frequency and momentum distributions we have $u_s(x) = d_s(x) = s_s(x) = \bar{u}_s(x) = \bar{d}_s(x) = \bar{s}_s(x) = s(x)$, say. With this parametrization, then, the proton and neutron structure functions become

$$F_2^{ep} = \frac{x}{9}[4u_v(x) + d_v(x)] + \tfrac{4}{3}xs(x)$$

and

$$F_2^{en} = \frac{x}{9}[u_v(x) + 4d_v(x)] + \tfrac{4}{3}xs(x).$$

Consider now two extreme cases. If sea quarks are dominant we expect $F_2^{en}(x)/F_2^{ep}(x) \to 1$ and if u_v quarks are dominant the ratio should approach $\frac{1}{4}$. In figure 12.19 we show the ratio as a function of x measured in the deep inelastic region by Bodek *et al.*[14] at SLAC. At very small values of x the ratio appears to be approaching unity while at large x values it is consistent with $\frac{1}{4}$ suggesting, indeed, that sea quarks are dominant at small x and valence quarks at large x.

The quark probability functions satisfy simple *sum rules*. The proton, for example, has two u valence quarks and one d valence quark so

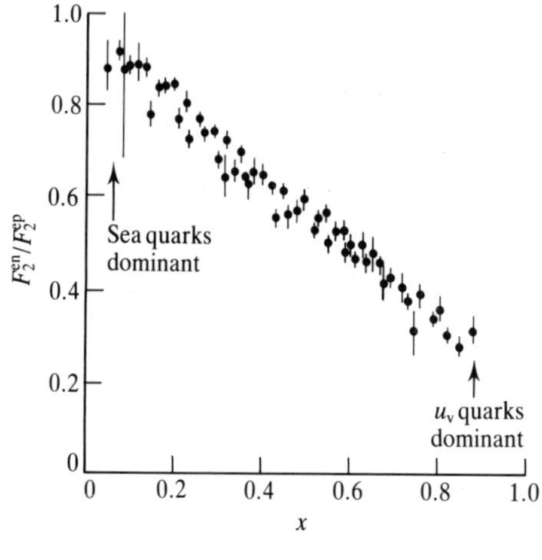

Figure 12.19
The ratio F_2^{en}/F_2^{ep} as a function of x (after Bodek K *et al.* 1974 *Phys Lett* **51B** (417).)

that

$$\int_0^1 [u(x) - \bar{u}(x)]\, dx = 2$$

$$\int_0^1 [d(x) - \bar{d}(x)]\, dx = 1.$$

Additionally, since the proton has zero strangeness,

$$\int_0^1 [s(x) - \bar{s}(x)]\, dx = 0.$$

The experimental test of these sum rules requires data on neutrino and antineutrino scattering which, as we shall see in the next section, probe the quark and antiquark distributions separately.

12.6.2 Deep inelastic neutrino–nucleon scattering

As a starting point for the study of ν–N scattering we take ν–e scattering as a model. The Feynman diagram for the charged-current contribution to the elastic scattering process $\nu_e + e^- \to \nu_e + e^-$ is shown in figure 12.20. In this case the reaction proceeds via the exchange of a W boson. The procedure for calculating the differential cross-section for this process is similar to that used in section 12.1 for electron–muon scattering. The currents involved here are charge-changing weak currents with the V–A structure $\gamma^\mu(1 - \gamma^5)$ rather than the pure vector electromagnetic currents γ^μ in e–μ scattering. The matrix element, provided $q^2 \ll M_W^2$ so that the propagator for the W boson approaches unity, is

Figure 12.20
Feynman diagram for the charged-current contribution to the elastic scattering process $\nu_e + e^- \to \nu_e + e^-$.

$$\mathscr{M}_{fi} = \frac{G}{\sqrt{2}} [\bar{u}(k')\gamma^\mu(1 - \gamma^5)u(p)][\bar{u}(p')\gamma_\mu(1 - \gamma_5)u(k)]$$

where G is the Fermi coupling constant. On squaring the matrix element, summing over the final spin states and averaging over the two spin states of the initial electron (the neutrino has only one helicity state) and inserting the flux and phase space factors, we get

$$\frac{d\sigma}{d\Omega}(\nu_e e^-) = \frac{G^2 s}{4\pi^2}. \tag{12.54}$$

Here, s is the square of the total energy in the centre-of-mass system. The angular distribution (12.54) is isotropic and integration over the angles

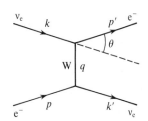

gives for the total $\nu_e e^-$ cross-section

$$\sigma(\nu_e e^-) = \frac{G^2 s}{\pi} \approx \frac{2G^2 mE}{\pi} \tag{12.55}$$

where m is the electron mass and E is the neutrino energy in the laboratory system. The total cross-section grows linearly with the laboratory energy of the neutrino. The differential and total cross-sections for antineutrino–positron scattering are given by the same formulae. The differential cross-sections for the elastic scattering processes $\bar{\nu}_e e^- \to \bar{\nu}_e e^-$ and $\nu_e e^+ \to \nu_e e^+$, on the other hand, are given by

$$\frac{d\sigma}{d\Omega}(\bar{\nu}_e e^-) = \frac{d\sigma}{d\Omega}(\bar{\nu}_e e^+) = \frac{G^2 s}{16\pi^2}(1 - \cos\theta)^2 \tag{12.56}$$

where θ is the scattering angle in the centre-of-mass system and is defined in figure 12.21. When integrated over the angles we have

$$\sigma(\bar{\nu}_e e^-) = \sigma(\nu_e e^+) = \frac{G^2 s}{3\pi}. \tag{12.57}$$

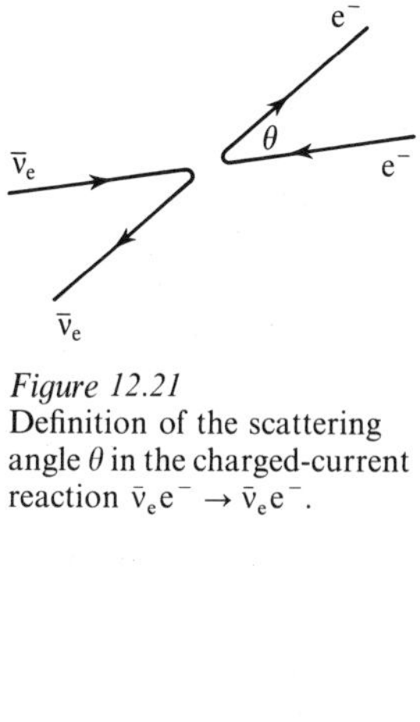

Figure 12.21
Definition of the scattering angle θ in the charged-current reaction $\bar{\nu}_e e^- \to \bar{\nu}_e e^-$.

On comparing with (12.55) we see that

$$\frac{\sigma(\bar{\nu}_e e^-)}{\sigma(\nu_e e^-)} = \frac{\sigma(\nu_e e^+)}{\sigma(\bar{\nu}_e e^+)} = \tfrac{1}{3}. \tag{12.58}$$

These differences between particle–particle and antiparticle–antiparticle scattering on the one hand, and particle–antiparticle scattering on the other, have their origin in the helicity structure of the interactions as shown in figure 12.22. For point-like (S wave) scattering, the only angular

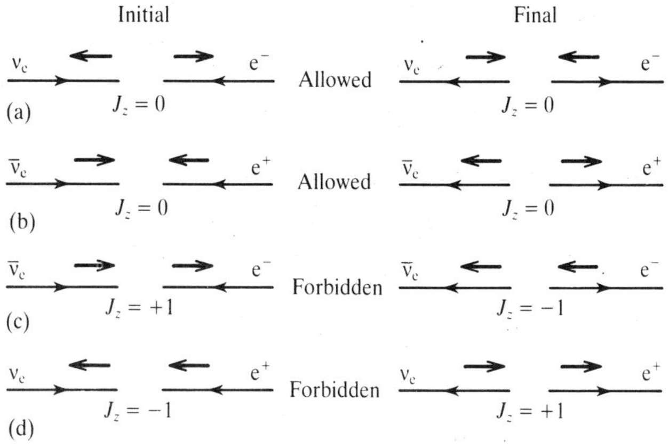

Figure 12.22
Helicity structure of the reactions (a) $\nu_e e^- \to \nu_e e^-$, (b) $\bar{\nu}_e e^+ \to \bar{\nu}_e e^+$, (c) $\bar{\nu}_e e^- \to \bar{\nu}_e e^-$ and (d) $\nu_e e^+ \to \nu_e e^+$.

momenta involved are the spins of the interacting particles. At high energies we can neglect the masses of the electron and positron; they are then left handed and right handed respectively. With the quantization axis taken as the direction of the incident $\nu_e(\bar{\nu}_e)$, backward scattering $(\theta = 0)$ is forbidden by angular momentum conservation in particle–antiparticle scattering, figures 12.22(c) and 12.22(d), and hence the term $(1 - \cos\theta)^2$ in the differential cross-section. The factor $\frac{1}{3}$ in the ratios of the total cross-sections arises from the fact that the particle–antiparticle reactions have $J = 1$ and only one of the three helicity states is allowed; the cross-section is therefore reduced in comparison with the particle–particle and antiparticle–antiparticle cross-sections.

To probe the nucleon structure via the weak neutrino–nucleon interaction beams of muon-type neutrinos, for example from the decay $\pi^+ \to \mu^+\nu_\mu$, are scattered from hydrogen or heavier nuclei. We shall concentrate here on charged-current interactions, mediated by $W^\pm$ exchange, such as $\nu_\mu N \to \mu^- X$ where X is any possible hadronic final state. At the quark level, conservation of charge and lepton number constrains the possible interactions to

$$\nu_\mu d \to \mu^- u$$

$$\nu_\mu \bar{u} \to \mu^- \bar{d}$$

$$\bar{\nu}_\mu u \to \mu^+ d$$

$$\bar{\nu}_\mu \bar{d} \to \mu^+ \bar{u}.$$

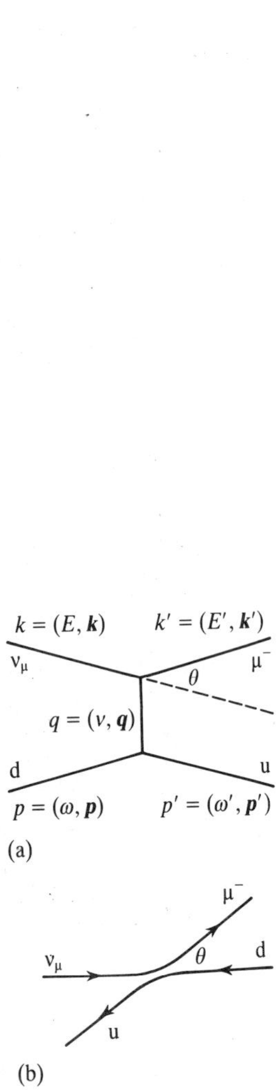

Figure 12.23
(a) Feynman diagram for the process $\nu_\mu d \to \mu^- u$; (b) the centre-of-mass scattering angle is defined as the angle between the outgoing μ^- and the incoming ν_μ.

The electromagnetic currents of the quarks are, apart from the fractional charges, the same as the lepton currents. We therefore assume that the quark weak currents are the same as the leptonic weak currents so that the cross-sections for neutrino–quark scattering can be taken over directly from the ν–e case above.

We now introduce the Lorentz scalar variable y, commonly used in the formulation of deep-inelastic scattering. In terms of the four-momenta indicated in figure 12.23(a) $y = p\cdot q/p\cdot k$. It is a simple matter to show that $y = \nu/E_{\text{lab}}$ where ν is the energy transfer and E_{lab} is the neutrino energy measured in the laboratory system. The variable y is thus the fractional energy transfer and lies in the range $0 \leqslant y \leqslant 1$. In terms of the scattering angle θ in the centre-of-mass system, defined in figure 12.23(b), $y = \frac{1}{2}(1 - \cos\theta)$ and $d\Omega = 4\pi\, dy$ (see example 12.6). Note that in this case backward scattering corresponds to $\theta = \pi$. In analogy with the ν–e differential cross-sections we have for ν–q scattering

$$\frac{d\sigma}{d\Omega}(\nu_\mu d \to \mu^- u) = \frac{d\sigma}{d\Omega}(\bar{\nu}_\mu \bar{d} \to \mu^+ \bar{u}) = \frac{G^2 \hat{s}}{4\pi^2}$$

and

$$\frac{d\sigma}{d\Omega}(\nu_\mu \bar{u} \to \mu^- \bar{d}) = \frac{d\sigma}{d\Omega}(\bar{\nu}_\mu u \to \mu^+ d) = \frac{G^2 \hat{s}}{16\pi^2}(1 + \cos\theta)^2.$$

In terms of y these become

$$\frac{d\sigma}{dy}(\nu_\mu d \to \mu^- u) = \frac{d\sigma}{dy}(\bar{\nu}_\mu \bar{d} \to \mu^+ \bar{u}) = \frac{G^2 \hat{s}}{\pi} \tag{12.59}$$

and

$$\frac{d\sigma}{dy}(\nu_\mu \bar{u} \to \mu^- \bar{d}) = \frac{d\sigma}{dy}(\bar{\nu}_\mu u \to \mu^+ d) = \frac{G^2 \hat{s}}{\pi}(1 - y)^2. \tag{12.60}$$

In these expressions, $\hat{s}$ is the square of the centre-of-mass energy in the neutrino–quark system. If x is the fraction of the four-momentum carried by quark q_i in the nucleon, $\hat{s} = xs$, where s refers to the neutrino–nucleon centre-of-mass system. As in the case of electron–nucleon scattering the differential cross-section for the inclusive process $\nu_\mu N \to \mu X$ can be regarded as an incoherent sum, over all quarks, of the differential cross-sections for the neutrino–quark processes $\nu_\mu q_i \to \mu q_f$ weighted by the quark distribution functions. Thus,

$$\frac{d^2\sigma}{dx\, dy}(\nu_\mu N \to \mu^- X) = \sum_i f(x_i) \left[\frac{d\sigma}{dy}(\nu_\mu q_i \to \mu q_f)\right]_{\hat{s} = xs} \tag{12.61}$$

where $f(x_i)$ is the quark distribution function for quark of type i.

For simplicity, consider scattering from an isoscalar target, i.e. nuclei containing equal numbers of neutrons and protons. As pointed out above, the neutrinos ν_μ interact only with d and ū quarks and therefore measure the distribution functions

$$d^p(x) + d^n(x) = d(x) + u(x) \equiv Q(x) \tag{12.62}$$

$$\bar{u}^p(x) + \bar{u}^n(x) = \bar{u}(x) + \bar{d}(x) \equiv \bar{Q}(x) \tag{12.63}$$

where the notation* is that used in (12.51). On substituting the constituent cross-sections (12.59) and (12.60) and the distribution functions (12.62) and (12.63) into (12.61) we get the inclusive cross-section

$$\frac{d^2\sigma}{dx\, dy}(\nu_\mu N \to \mu^- X) = \frac{G^2 xs}{2\pi}[Q(x) + (1 - y)^2 \bar{Q}(x)]. \tag{12.64}$$

* The commonly used notation $Q(x)$ and $\bar{Q}(x)$ for the quark and antiquark distribution functions should not be confused with $Q^2 = -q^2$, the four-momentum transfer squared.

In contrast, beams of antineutrinos interact with $\bar{d}$ and u quarks and the $\bar{\nu}_\mu N$ inclusive cross-section is given by

$$\frac{d^2\sigma}{dx\,dy}(\bar{\nu}_\mu N \to \mu^+ X) = \frac{G^2 xs}{2\pi}[\bar{Q}(x) + (1-y)^2 Q(x)]. \tag{12.65}$$

As in the case of e–N scattering these differential cross-sections can be written in terms of the nucleon structure functions. In terms of Q^2 and ν the result is

$$\frac{d^2\sigma^{\nu,\bar{\nu}}}{dQ^2\,d\nu} = \frac{G^2}{2\pi}\frac{E'}{E}\left[W_2^{\nu,\bar{\nu}}(Q^2,\nu)\cos^2\left(\frac{\theta}{2}\right) + 2W_1^{\nu,\bar{\nu}}(Q^2,\nu)\sin^2\left(\frac{\theta}{2}\right) \mp \frac{(E+E')}{M}W_3^{\nu,\bar{\nu}}(Q^2,\nu)\right] \tag{12.66}$$

where M is the nucleon mass. The main difference compared with the electromagnetic case is the appearance of a third structure function $W_3(Q^2, \nu)$, which arises from interference between vector and axial-vector currents; the latter are absent in the electromagnetic case. The negative sign in (12.66) applies for ν–N scattering and the positive for $\bar{\nu}$–N scattering.

In analogy with the electromagnetic case the weak interaction structure functions can be related to the cross-sections for absorption of a W boson which, because of its mass, can exist in three polarization states corresponding to right-handed, left-handed and 'scalar' bosons respectively. The relationships are of the form

$$W_1 \approx \sigma_R + \sigma_L$$

$$W_2 \approx \sigma_R + \sigma_L + 2\sigma_S$$

$$W_3 \approx \sigma_R - \sigma_L.$$

In the parity-conserving electromagnetic interaction $\sigma_R = \sigma_L$ and hence the absence of W_3 in e–N scattering. In the electromagnetic case the cross-section for transverse photons σ_T is given by $\frac{1}{2}(\sigma_R + \sigma_L)$.

The parton model predicts that the structure functions scale,

$$MW_1(Q^2,\nu) \to F_1(x) \qquad \text{and} \qquad \nu W_{2,3}(Q^2,\nu) \to F_{2,3}(x).$$

On substituting into (12.66) and changing the variables to x and y we have

$$\frac{d^2\sigma^{\nu,\bar{\nu}}}{dx\,dy} = \frac{G^2 s}{2\pi}\left[(1-y)F_2^{\nu,\bar{\nu}}(x) + y^2 x F_1^{\nu,\bar{\nu}}(x) \pm y\left(1-\frac{y}{2}\right)xF_3^{\nu,\bar{\nu}}(x)\right]. \tag{12.67}$$

In principle there are 12 weak structure functions for the nucleons, three each for ν–p, ν–n, ν̄–p and ν̄–n scattering, but if we apply charge symmetry we have

$$F_i^{\nu n} = F_i^{\bar{\nu} p} \quad \text{and} \quad F_i^{\bar{\nu} n} = F_i^{\nu p} \quad (i = 1, 2, 3), \tag{12.68}$$

i.e. six independent structure functions. If we further restrict outselves to nuclei with roughly equal numbers of neutrons and protons we can form 'neutron–proton-averaged' structure functions

$$F_i^{\nu N} = \tfrac{1}{2}(F_i^{\nu n} + F_i^{\nu p}) = \tfrac{1}{2}(F_i^{\bar{\nu} p} + F_i^{\bar{\nu} n}) = F_i^{\bar{\nu} N} \equiv F_i$$

and reduce the number to three. Equation (12.67) then becomes

$$\frac{d^2\sigma^{\nu N, \bar{\nu} N}}{dx\, dy} = \frac{G^2 s}{2\pi}\left[(1 - y)F_2(x) + y^2 x F_1(x) \pm y\left(1 - \frac{y}{2}\right)xF_3(x)\right]. \tag{12.69}$$

To facilitate comparison with (12.64) and (12.65) we rewrite (12.69) in powers of $1 - y$;

$$\frac{d^2\sigma^{\nu N, \bar{\nu} N}}{dx\, dy} = \frac{G^2 s}{2\pi}\left[\left(xF_1 \pm \frac{xF_3}{2}\right) + (F_2 - 2xF_1)(1 - y) + \left(xF_1 \mp \frac{xF_3}{2}\right)(1 - y)^2\right]. \tag{12.70}$$

We are now in a position to determine some further properties of the partons.

Fractional quark charge

From our study of e–N scattering we have seen that the partons have spin $\frac{1}{2}$ and the Callan–Gross relation, $2xF_1 = F_2$, is satisfied. The second term in (12.70) is therefore zero and

$$\frac{d^2\sigma^{\nu N, \bar{\nu} N}}{dx\, dy} = \frac{G^2 s}{4\pi}[(F_2 \pm xF_3) + (F_2 \mp xF_3)(1 - y)^2]. \tag{12.71}$$

If we compare, for example, this expression for ν–N scattering with (12.64), we find

$$F_2^{\nu N}(x) = 2x[Q(x) + \bar{Q}(x)] \tag{12.72a}$$

$$xF_3^{\nu N}(x) = 2x[Q(x) - \bar{Q}(x)]. \tag{12.72b}$$

By comparing $F_2^{\nu N}$ with F_2^{eN} it is possible to check the fractional charge values assigned to the quarks. On combining (12.52) and (12.53) we find, for an isoscalar target,

$$F_2^{eN} = x\{\tfrac{5}{18}[u(x) + \bar{u}(x) + d(x) + \bar{d}(x)] + \tfrac{1}{9}[s(x) + \bar{s}(x)]\}. \tag{12.73}$$

From (12.62), (12.63) and (12.72a) we obtain

$$F_2^{\nu N} = x[d(x) + u(x) + \bar{u}(x) + \bar{d}(x)]. \tag{12.74}$$

Thus,

$$\frac{F_2^{eN}}{F_2^{\nu N}} \geqslant \frac{5}{18}$$

where the equality holds if we neglect the s and $\bar{s}$ quark contributions. The numerical value of the ratio is just the mean square charge of the u and d quarks.

The fractional charge hypothesis is well supported by experiment. In figure 12.24 we show a comparison of $F_2^{\nu N}$ measured in the heavy-liquid bubble chamber Gargamelle at CERN and F_2^{eN} measured at SLAC in the same q^2 region.

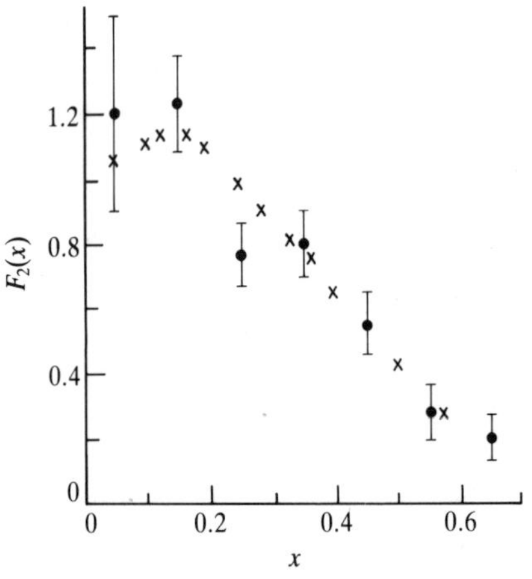

Figure 12.24 Comparison of $F_2^{\nu N}$ (•), measured in the heavy-liquid bubble chamber Gargamelle at CERN, and F_2^{eN} (×), measured at SLAC, in the region $Q^2 > 1$. The electron results have been multiplied by 18/5; see text for details. (From Perkins D H 1986 *Introduction to High Energy Physics* Addison-Wesley.)

Number of valence quarks

From (12.72b) it can be seen that $F_3^{\nu N}$ measures the difference between quark and antiquark concentrations in the nucleon. Since the sea contains equal numbers of quarks and antiquarks the integral of $F_3^{\nu N}(x)$ must equal the number of valence quarks, i.e.

$$\int_0^1 F_3^{\nu N}(x)\,dx = 3.$$

This sum rule, known as the Gross–Llewellyn Smith sum rule has been verified by de Groot *et al.*[15] and Benvenuti *et al.*[16] who obtained values of 3.2 ± 0.5 and 2.8 ± 0.6 respectively.

Quark and antiquark distribution functions

Measurements of the differential cross-sections for ν–N and ν̄–N deep-inelastic scattering permit the quark and antiquark distribution functions to be separated. Specifically, if we add and substruct $d^2\sigma^{\nu N}/dx\,dy$ and $d^2\sigma^{\bar{\nu}N}/dx\,dy$, and assume that the Callan–Gross relation holds, then

$$\frac{d^2\sigma^{\nu N}}{dx\,dy} + \frac{d^2\sigma^{\bar{\nu}N}}{dx\,dy} = \frac{G^2 s}{2\pi}\{F_2[1 + (1 - y)^2]\} \tag{12.75}$$

$$\frac{d^2\sigma^{\nu N}}{dx\,dy} - \frac{d^2\sigma^{\bar{\nu}N}}{dx\,dy} = \frac{G^2 s}{2\pi}\{xF_3[1 - (1 - y)^2]\}. \tag{12.76}$$

From these relations $F_2(x)$ and $F_3(x)$ can be determined and hence, through (12.72), the quark and antiquark distribution functions may be obtained. Figure 12.25 shows typical quark and antiquark momentum distributions in the nucleon obtained from measurements at CERN and Fermilab. The antiquarks, which must come from the quark–antiquark sea, are concentrated at low values of x and at very low values of x the sea is dominant. The valence quark distribution, shown by the dashed line, peaks around $x \approx 0.2$ and is dominant at higher values of x. These findings are in accord with those from e–N scattering.

The need for gluons

If the nucleon is made entirely from quarks and antiquarks then the integrals of the structure functions, or equivalently the sum of the fractional momenta of all the constituents, should be unity; the total momentum of the constituents should equal the momentum of the nucleon. Thus we expect

$$\frac{18}{5}\int_0^1 F_2^{eN}(x)\,dx = \int_0^1 F_2^{\nu N}(x)\,dx$$

$$= \int_0^1 x[u(x) + \bar{u}(x) + d(x) + \bar{d}(x)]\,dx \approx 1.$$

The data shown in figure 12.25 give a value of about 0.5 for these integrals

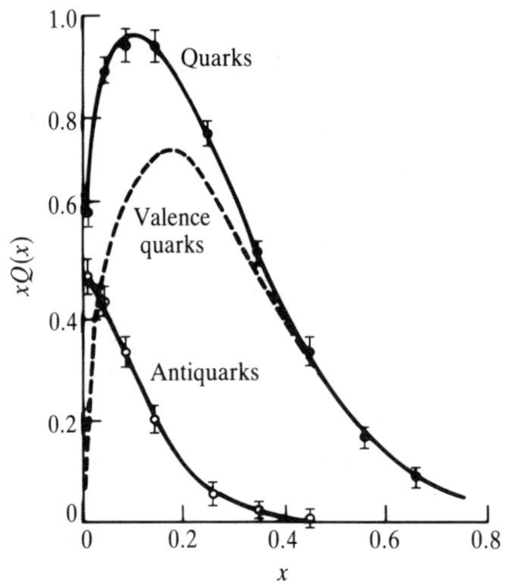

Figure 12.25 Momentum distributions of quarks and antiquarks in the nucleon. As explained in the text, the sum of the differential cross-sections for νN and $\bar{\nu}$N measures the structure function F_2 and the difference F_3. From these the quark and antiquark distribution functions can be obtained through equations (12.72). The difference between the quark and antiquark distributions gives the valence quark distribution shown by the broken line. This peaks around $x \approx 0.2$ and is dominant at large x. The antiquarks from the sea are concentrated towards small x and for very small values of x the sea is dominant. (From Perkins D H 1986 *Introduction to High Energy Physics* Addison-Wesley.)

implying that the quarks carry only about one-half of the momentum of the proton. The momentum fraction carried by the strange quarks in the nucleon can be safely ignored in these considerations. We are therefore forced to the conclusion that roughly half the momentum of the proton must be carried by constituents other than the quarks which are 'invisible' to both the electromagnetic and weak probes. These constituents, which possess neither electric nor weak charge, are called gluons; they carry colour or strong charge and are responsible for binding the quarks together inside the nucleon.

12.6.3 Summary

Deep inelastic scattering experiments have produced firm dynamical evidence for the existence of quarks and gluons. Whether probed by virtual photons or W bosons the same internal structure of the nucleon is revealed. The phenomenon of scaling indicates that the constituents are point-like or structureless; at high values of Q^2 and ν the structure functions are functions only of the single variable $x = Q^2/2M\nu$. $F(Q^2, \nu) \rightarrow F(x)$ as Q^2 and ν approach infinity while x remains finite. The variable x turns out to be the fraction of the momentum carried by the partons. The Callan–Gross relation, $2xF_1 = F_2$, is well supported by experiment indicating that the partons have spin $\frac{1}{2}$. The ratio of the structure functions from e–N scattering, F_2^{eN}, and ν–N scattering, $F_2^{\nu N}$, supports the hypothesis that the (charged) partons have fractional charges which we identify as the quarks. Only about 50 per cent of the momentum of the nucleon is carried by the quarks, the remainder being carried by gluons. The quark–antiquark sea is confined to low values of x while the valence quarks are dominant at high x values.

The nucleon then is a fairly complex particle. The proton, for example, may be visualized as containing three valence quarks u_v, u_v and d_v which carry a large fraction of the momentum of the proton. As they move in their mutual field they may emit gluons in a bremsstrahlung-like process. These in turn give rise to a predominantly low-momentum sea of quark–antiquark pairs.

12.7 The Drell–Yan process

The Drell–Yan process is the name associated with the inclusive production of di-leptons in hadron–hadron collisions, $h + h \to l^+ + l^- + X$. It is important in several respects. First, it provides a further test of the parton model and, secondly, it allows the structure functions of hadrons other than nucleons to be determined. In addition, it provides a mechanism for the production of $W^\pm$ and Z^0 bosons in hadron–hadron collisions. Our main concern here is with the parton model predictions and the structure functions of hadrons.

The process can be visualized as in figure 12.26. We restrict ourselves to centre-of-mass energies which are sufficiently large that masses and transverse momenta of the quarks and leptons are negligible. The incoming hadrons h_1 and h_2, with four-momenta p_1 and p_2, consist of quarks and antiquarks with distribution functions $q_i(x)$ and $\bar{q}_i(x)$ respectively; the index i represents the different quark flavours. The constituent process, responsible for the production of lepton pairs l^+l^- with mass M, is shown as $q_i\bar{q}_i \to \gamma^* \to l^+l^-$. A quark and an antiquark of the same flavour fuse to produce a virtual photon γ^* which then materializes into

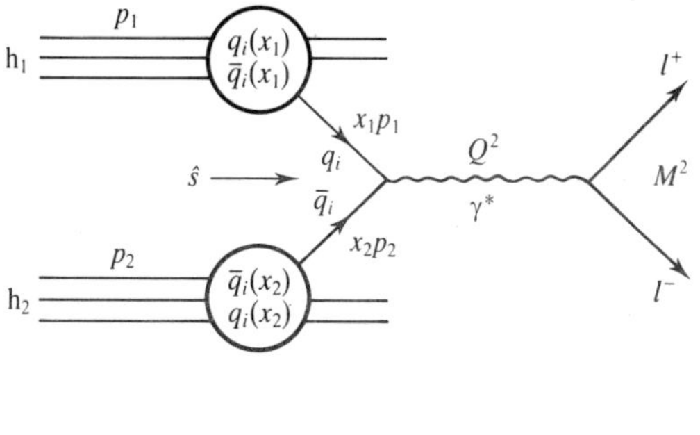

Figure 12.26
The Drell–Yan process in the parton model.

the lepton pair. If quark q_i has a momentum fraction x_1 and antiquark $\bar{q}_i$ a momentum fraction x_2, the centre-of-mass energy $\hat{s}$ for the constituent process is

$$\hat{s} = (x_1 p_1 + x_2 p_2)^2 \approx x_1 x_2 s = Q^2 = M^2. \qquad (12.77)$$

The cross-section for this point-like constituent process is

$$\hat{\sigma}(q_i\bar{q}_i \to l^+l^-) = \frac{4\pi\alpha^2}{3\hat{s}} e_{q_i}^2 \qquad (12.78)$$

where e_{q_i} is the charge of quark q_i in units of e. To obtain the cross-section for the process $h_1h_2 \to l^+l^-X$ we follow the procedure used in deep-inelastic scattering, i.e. we form the incoherent sum of the constituent cross-sections for all quarks. Thus,

$$d^2\sigma(h_1h_2 \to l^+l^-X) = \tfrac{1}{3}\frac{4\pi\alpha^2}{3M^2}\sum_i e_{q_i}^2[q_i(x_1)\bar{q}_i(x_2) + \bar{q}_i(x_1)q_i(x_2)]dx_1\,dx_2. \qquad (12.79)$$

Here, $q_i(x_1)$ is the probability that a quark of flavour i carries the momentum fraction x_1 in hadron h_1 and $\bar{q}_i(x_2)$ the probability that an antiquark of the same flavour carries momentum fraction x_2 in hadron h_2. The second term in the square brackets allows for the probability that the antiquark comes from h_1 and the quark from h_2. The extra factor $\frac{1}{3}$ is a colour factor. This takes account of the fact that the virtual photon is a colour singlet so that there must be appropriate matching of the colours of the annihilating quarks; for three colours the probability that a red quark annihilates with an antired antiquark, for example, is $\frac{1}{3}$.

In order to compare the basic equation for the differential cross-section (12.79) with experiment, we recast it in terms of measurable variables. For example, the differential cross-section for the production of a lepton pair of mass M may be written

$$\frac{d\sigma}{dM^2} = \int dx_1\,dx_2 \frac{d^2\sigma}{dx_1\,dx_2}\delta(M^2 - x_1x_2s). \qquad (12.80)$$

The δ function ensures that the kinematic constraint $M^2 = x_1x_2s$ is satisfied. On substitution of $d^2\sigma/dx_1dx_2$ from (12.79) we obtain

$$\frac{d\sigma}{dM^2} = \frac{4\pi\alpha^2}{9M^4}\int dx_1\,dx_2\,x_1x_2\,\delta(x_1x_2 - \tau)$$
$$\times \sum_i e_{q_i}^2[q_i(x_1)\bar{q}_i(x_2) + \bar{q}_i(x_1)q_i(x_2)] \qquad (12.81)$$

where the dimensionless variable $\tau = M^2/s$. Upon integration we obtain a function $F(\tau)$ so that, although the cross-section depends on M^2 and s, it does so only through the ratio $\tau = M^2/s$, i.e. the quantity

$$M^4 \frac{\mathrm{d}\sigma}{\mathrm{d}M^2} = \tfrac{4}{9}\pi\alpha^2 F\left(\frac{M^2}{s}\right) \tag{12.82}$$

should exhibit scaling.

A frequently used variable in the study of the Drell–Yan process is the Feynman scaling variable $x_F = x_1 - x_2$. A measurement of the four-momenta of the leptons determines M^2 and x_F and hence fixes the x values of the annihilating quark and antiquark. In terms of M and x_F the differential cross-section is

$$\frac{\mathrm{d}^2\sigma}{\mathrm{d}M\,\mathrm{d}x_F} = \frac{8\pi\alpha^2}{9M^3}\frac{\tau}{(x_F^2 + 4\tau)^{1/2}} \sum_i e_{q_i}^2 [q_i(x_1)\bar{q}_i(x_2) + \bar{q}_i(x_1)q_i(x_2)]. \tag{12.83}$$

The scaling behaviour of this cross-section and hence the validity of the parton model is displayed in figure 12.27 which shows data on inclusive di-muon production in pp collisions at values of $\sqrt{s}$ in the range 24–62 GeV.

In proton–proton collisions the quark and antiquark distribution functions appearing in (12.83) are just those determined from deep inelastic lepton–proton scattering which may therefore be used to predict

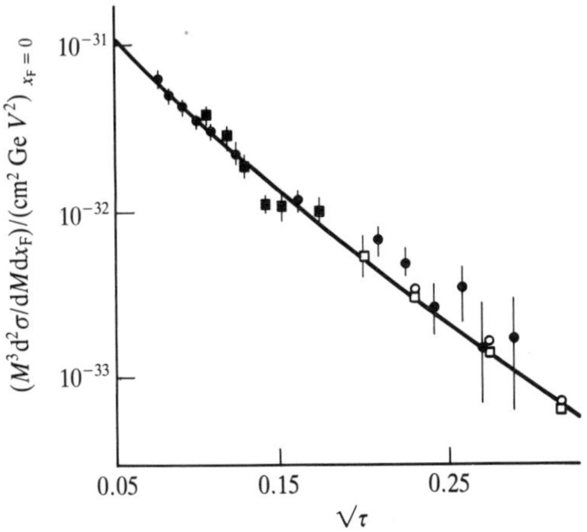

Figure 12.27 Experimental test of scaling in di-muon production in pp collisions. The differential cross-section $M^3(\mathrm{d}^2\sigma/\mathrm{d}M\,\mathrm{d}x_F)$ at $x_F = 0$, measured over a range of $\sqrt{s}$ from 24 to 62 GeV, depends only on the scaling variable $\tau = M^2/s$ where M is the di-muon mass: ○, 23.8 GeV; □, 27.4 GeV; ■, 44 GeV; ●, 62 GeV. (After Kenyon I R 1982 *Rep Prog Phys* **45** (1213).)

Table 12.1
The x dependence of the valence and sea quark distributions, $xq(x)$, in the nucleon and the pion

	Nucleon	Pion
Valence quarks	$x^{1/2}(1-x)^3$	$x^{1/2}(1-x)$
Sea quarks	$(1-x)^7$	$(1-x)^5$

the cross-section for $pp \to \mu^+\mu^- X$. On the other hand the Drell–Yan process enables the pion structure functions to be determined by measuring the cross-sections for the processes $\pi^\pm p \to \mu^+\mu^- X$. It is found that the valence quarks in the mesons are 'harder' than those in the nucleon; the valence quarks in a meson carry about one and a half times the momentum fraction carried by the valence quarks in a nucleon. This is consistent with the view that a meson consists of a $q\bar{q}$ pair of valence quarks while the nucleon has three valence quarks. Table 12.1 compares the quark distribution functions $xq(x)$ of the valence and sea quarks in nucleons and pions.

12.8 Quark jets in e^+e^- annihilation

The production of hadrons in electron–positron annihilation at high energies is closely related to the Drell–Yan process. Consider first the reaction $e^+e^- \to \mu^+\mu^-$, which is described in lowest order by the Feynman diagram in figure 12.28(a). The differential cross-section for this process is

$$\frac{d\sigma}{d(\cos\theta)} = \frac{\pi\alpha^2}{2s}(1+\cos^2\theta) \tag{12.84}$$

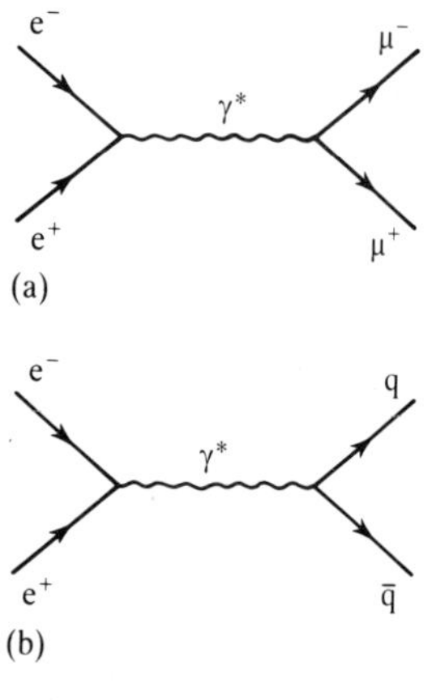

Figure 12.28
Lowest order Feynman diagrams for the processes (a) $e^+e^- \to \mu^+\mu^-$ and (b) $e^+e^- \to q\bar{q}$.

where $\sqrt{s}$ is the energy in the centre-of-mass system and θ is the angle between the μ^- and the incident e^-. On integrating (12.84) we get for the total cross-section

$$\sigma(e^+e^- \to \mu^+\mu^-) = \frac{4\pi\alpha^2}{3s}. \tag{12.85}$$

A possible mechanism for hadron production in the process $e^+e^- \to$ hadrons is simply obtained from figure 12.28(a) by replacing the muons by quarks as in figure 12.28(b). The electron and positron annihilate to produce a virtual photon which then materializes into a $q\bar{q}$ pair. The cross-section for this process is

$$\sigma(e^+e^- \to q_i\bar{q}_i) = \frac{4\pi\alpha^2}{3s}e^2_{q_i} \tag{12.86}$$

where e_{q_i} is the charge of the quark with flavour i in units of the charge on the electron. Of course, the quarks do not appear as free particles in the laboratory – they must 'fragment' into colourless hadrons. In this fragmentation process the momenta of the hadrons transverse to the line of flight of the parent quark are restricted to values of the order of a few hundred MeV/c so that at high centre-of-mass energies the hadrons appear 'back to back' in narrow cones or jets as in figure 12.29. A typical two-jet event is shown in figure 12.30. The axis of a jet may be determined, for instance, by finding the angle θ, with respect to the incident beam direction, along which the sum of the longitudinal momenta of the hadrons in the jet is maximized. The evidence that the hadrons really originate from a spin $\frac{1}{2}$ quark is that the angular distribution of the jet axes is given by (12.84); spin 0 partons would give rise to a $\sin^2\theta$ distribution in disagreement with experimental results.

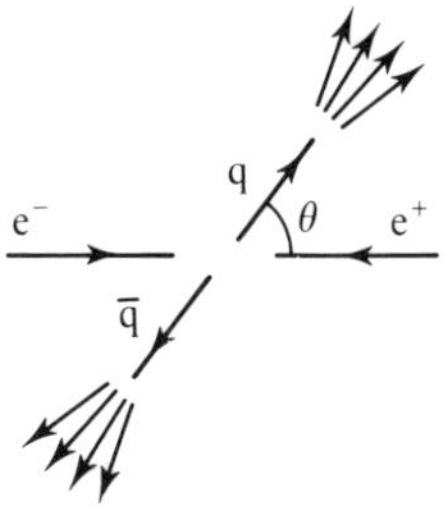

Figure 12.29
Schematic diagram of the production of two 'back-to-back' hadron jets in e^+e^- annihilation.

Although the hadrons retain a 'memory' of the quark from which they originate, we assume that the fragmentation process does not affect the cross-section for the process $e^+e^- \to q\bar{q} \to$ hadrons and we are led to the simple and remarkable prediction that at high energies

$$R = \frac{\sigma(e^+e^- \to \text{hadrons})}{\sigma(e^+e^- \to \mu^+\mu^-)} = 3\sum_i e_{q_i}^2. \qquad (12.87)$$

The factor 3 arises because of the three possible colour combinations of the $q\bar{q}$ pair.

The ratio R is shown as a function of centre-of-mass energy in

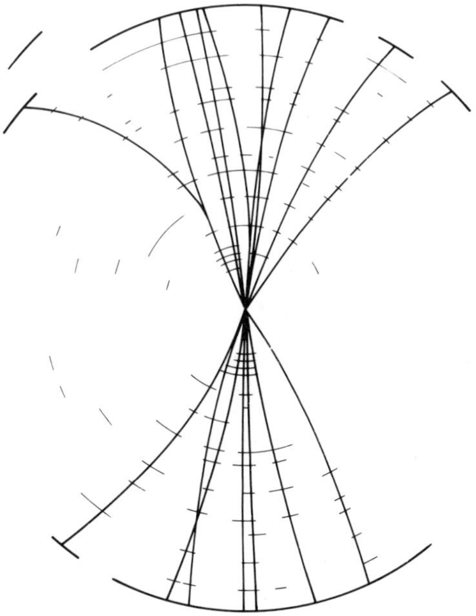

Figure 12.30
Sketch of a typical two-jet event viewed along the beam line in e^+e^- annihilation.

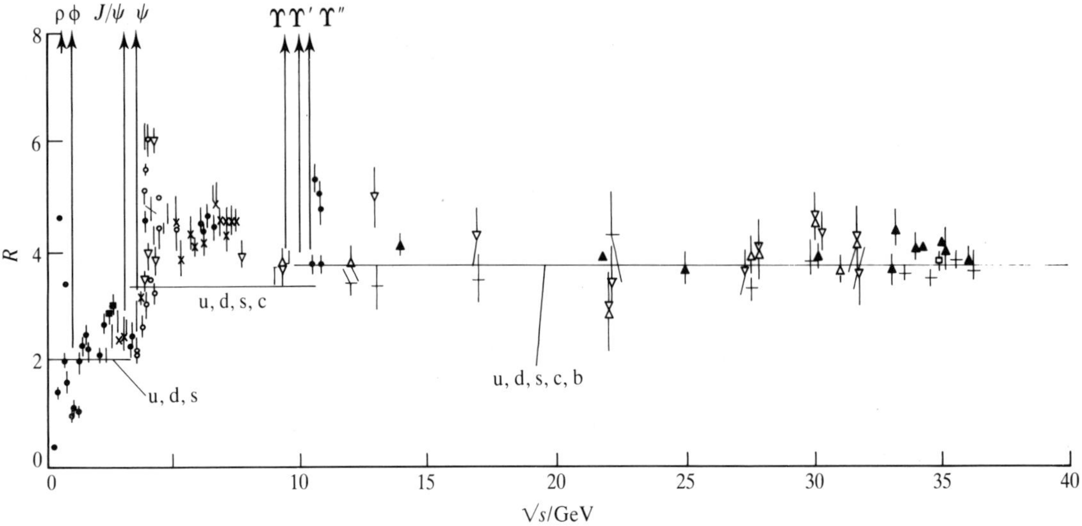

Figure 12.31 Plot of the ratio R, defined in equation (12.88) as a function of the total centre-of-mass energy. The sharp peaks correspond to the production of narrow vector meson resonances.

figure 12.31. For the light quarks u, d and s with charges $+\frac{2}{3}$, $-\frac{1}{3}$ and $-\frac{1}{3}$ respectively, R is predicted to be 2. The charmed quark threshold is around $s = 9\ \mathrm{GeV}^2$ and below this value there is reasonable agreement between the experimental results and the prediction. Above the upsilon states ($b\bar{b}$), i.e. above the b quark threshold, R is expected to be

$$R = 3[(\tfrac{2}{3})^2 + (-\tfrac{1}{3})^2 + (-\tfrac{1}{3})^2 + (\tfrac{2}{3})^2 + (-\tfrac{1}{3})^2] = 3\tfrac{2}{3} \qquad (12.88)$$

in good agreement with the data. This may be regarded as further confirmation of the validity of the quark parton model and equally importantly firm evidence for the existence of colour.

REFERENCES 12

1 **Mott N F** 1929 *Proc Roy Soc* **A124** (425)

2 **Rosenbluth M N** 1950 *Phys Rev* **79** (615)

3 **Hofstadter R and McAllister R W** 1955 *Phys Rev* **98** (217)

4 **Halzen F and Martin A D** 1984 *Quarks and Leptons: An Introductory Course in Modern Particle Physics* Wiley pp. 88–91

5 **Gasiorowicz S** 1966 *Elementary Particle Physics* Wiley p. 435

6 **Hughes E B** *et al.* 1965 *Phys Rev* **139B** (458)

7 **Hofstadter R** 1956 'Electron scattering and nuclear structure' *Rev Mod Phys* **28** (214)

8 **Bartel W** *et al.* 1968 *Phys Lett* **28B** (148)

9 **Miller G** *et al.* 1972 *Phys Rev* **D5** (528)

10 **Friedman J I and Kendall H W** 1972 *Ann Rev Nucl Sci* **22** (203)

11 **Feynman R P** 1969 *Phys Rev Lett* **23** (1415)

12 **Callan C G and Gross D** 1969 *Phys Rev Lett* **22** (156)

13 **Aitchison I J R and Hey A J G** 1982 *Gauge Theories in Particle Physics* Adam Hilger pp. 96–9

14 **Bodek K** *et al.* 1974 *Phys Rev* **51B** (417)

15 **de Groot J G H** *et al.* 1979 *Z Phys* **C1** (143)

16 **Benvenuti A** *et al.* 1979 *Phys Rev Lett* **42** (1317)

EXAMPLES 12

12.1 Show that equation (12.18) follows from equation (12.17) if terms of order m^2, where m is the electron mass, are neglected.

12.2 With reference to figure 12.5 evaluate equation (12.18) in the laboratory frame to show that, neglecting the electron mass,

$$\overline{|\mathcal{M}|^2} = \frac{8e^4}{q^2} 2EE'M^2\left[\cos^2\left(\frac{\theta}{2}\right) - \frac{q^2}{2M^2}\sin^2\left(\frac{\theta}{2}\right)\right].$$

12.3 If the charge density distribution of the proton, $\rho(\boldsymbol{r}) = \rho_0 \exp(-mr)$, is normalized to unity show, using equation (12.4), that the form factor is given by

$$F(q) = \frac{m^4}{(m^2 + q^2)^2}.$$

If $m^2 = 0.71\ \text{GeV}^2$ determine the root-mean-square radius of the charge distribution.

12.4 For small values of $|\boldsymbol{q}|$ the proton form factor may be expressed as

$$F(q) = \int\left[1 + \mathrm{i}\boldsymbol{q}\cdot\boldsymbol{r} - \frac{(\boldsymbol{q}\cdot\boldsymbol{r})^2}{2!} + \cdots\right]\rho(\boldsymbol{r})\,\mathrm{d}\tau.$$

Assuming $\rho(\boldsymbol{r})$ is spherically symmetric and normalized so that $\int \rho(\boldsymbol{r})\,\mathrm{d}\tau = 1$, show that the mean square radius of the charge distribution is

$$\langle r^2\rangle = -6\frac{\partial F(q)}{\partial q^2}.$$

Hence calculate the root-mean-square radius for the proton using the result of example 12.3 and evaluating the derivative at $q^2 = 0$. Take $m^2 = 0.71\ \mathrm{GeV}^2$.

12.5 The frame of reference used in the parton model is one in which the proton has such a large momentum that all masses may be neglected – the so-called infinite momentum frame. In this frame suppose the proton has four-momentum $p = (E, P) = (p, 0, 0, P)$. The proton is visualized as a stream of partons each with zero momentum *transverse* to the direction of motion of the proton and each carrying some variable fraction x of the four-momentum, energy and mass of the proton. With reference to figure 12.16 show that x is precisely the Bjorken scaling variable

$$x = -\frac{q^2}{2M\nu} = \frac{Q^2}{2M\nu}$$

where M is the proton mass. Hence show that $\nu = Q^2/2m$ where m is the struck parton mass.

12.6 The Lorentz scalar y was defined in the text as $y = (p \cdot q)/(p \cdot k)$ (see figure 12.23). Show that

$$y = \nu/E_{\mathrm{lab}} = \tfrac{1}{2}(1 - \cos\theta)$$

where ν is the energy transfer, E_{lab} is the neutrino energy in the laboratory system and θ is the scattering angle in the centre-of-mass system. Hence, show that the element of solid angle is $\mathrm{d}\Omega = 4\pi\, \mathrm{d}y$.

13 *The standard model*

Introduction · Mathematical preliminaries · Lagrangians and single-particle wave equations · Symmetries and conservation laws · Local gauge invariance and quantum electrodynamics · Unification of the weak and electromagnetic interactions · Quantum chromodynamics and the standard model · The standard model Lagrangian · Renormalization and running coupling constants

13.1 Introduction

In chapter 7 we described, in general terms, the properties of the fundamental interactions – strong, electromagnetic and weak. At low energies these interactions appear to be totally unrelated. For example, they have quite different coupling constants which give rise to typical cross-sections which differ by about 12 orders of magnitude. Nevertheless, in chapter 7 we briefly discussed the possibility that at some extremely high energy, the coupling constants may converge to a single value (see figure 7.21) and that interactions between elementary particles would be explained in terms of a *single unified field.* In the late 1960s a major breakthrough along the road to unification was made by Glashow, Weinberg and Salam (reference 8 of chapter 7) when they unified the weak and electromagnetic interactions. This discovery reinforced the belief in the existence of a single unified theory of the fundamental interactions. The most significant theoretical step in this direction is the realization that *all* the fundamental interactions are invariant under *local gauge transformations* and the hope is that gauge theories will provide a basis for a comprehensive unification of the fundamental interactions.

Our task in this chapter is to formulate these gauge theories. In chapter 14 we will compare the predictions of the standard model with experiment. The basic requirement in the formulation of a gauge theory is to obtain a Lagrangian describing the interactions between the particles in the theory which is invariant under the relevant symmetry transformations. By relevant we mean those that give rise to the conservation laws appropriate to the particular interaction, such as conservation of electric charge, colour, weak isospin and weak hypercharge. (We shall introduce the last two concepts later in this chapter.) It is important to realize that these conserved physical quantities are conserved *locally*, i.e. at each point in space, and not just globally. For example, any mechanism which purports to annihilate electric charge at one point in space and simultaneously create an equal amount of charge at another point in space – *global* charge conservation – would be in conflict with special relativity. Electric charge is conserved locally. This property of local conservation is at the heart of the local gauge symmetries exhibited by the fundamental interactions.

We shall formulate the theories in the framework of the Lagrangian formalism. For those readers unfamiliar with the subject we give a brief mathematical introduction.

13.2 Mathematical preliminaries

13.2.1 The calculus of variations

In any but the simplest problems in mechanics it is convenient to have a general prescription for expressing the equations of motion of a system in arbitrary coordinates. A method of doing this, due to Lagrange, is based on what is known as a variational principle. We illustrate the technique by considering a very simple problem, namely what is the shortest distance between two points in a plane? Let the two points in question (figure 13.1) have coordinates (x_0, y_0) and (x_1, y_1). The equation of any curve which lies in the plane and connects the two points may be written

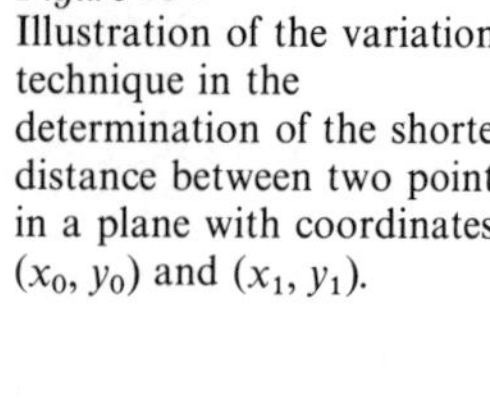

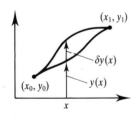

Figure 13.1
Illustration of the variational technique in the determination of the shortest distance between two points in a plane with coordinates (x_0, y_0) and (x_1, y_1).

$$y = y(x).$$

The function $y(x)$ must satisfy the boundary conditions

$$y(x_0) = y_0 \qquad y(x_1) = y_1.$$

Two neighbouring points on the curve have a distance dl between them given by

$$dl = (dx^2 + dy^2)^{1/2} = (1 + y'^2)^{1/2}\,dx$$

where $y' = dy/dx$, so that the total length of the curve is given by

$$l = \int_{x_0}^{x_1} (1 + y'^2)^{1/2}\,dx.$$

The problem is therefore to find a function $y(x)$ which satisfies the boundary conditions and minimizes this integral. Before solving this specific problem let us generalize and consider how to find the minimum* value of the integral

$$I = \int_{x_0}^{x_1} f(y, y')\,\mathrm{d}x$$

where $f(y, y')$ is a known function of y and its first derivative. When the integral has a minimum value it must be unchanged to first order when small changes are made in the function $y(x)$. Consider a small variation $\delta y(x)$ in the function $y(x)$, made in a such a way that

$$\delta y(x_0) = \delta y(x_1) = 0,$$

i.e. the values of y at the endpoints are unchanged (see figure 13.1). The variation in the function f, to first order, is given by

$$\delta f = \frac{\partial f}{\partial y}\delta y + \frac{\partial f}{\partial y'}\delta y'$$

where

$$\delta y' = \frac{\mathrm{d}}{\mathrm{d}x}\delta y.$$

The variation δI in the integral is therefore

$$\delta I = \int_{x_0}^{x_1} \left(\frac{\partial f}{\partial y}\delta y + \frac{\partial f}{\partial y'}\frac{\mathrm{d}}{\mathrm{d}x}\delta y\right)\mathrm{d}x.$$

The second term in the integrand may be integrated by parts:

$$\int_{x_0}^{x_1} \frac{\partial f}{\partial y'}\frac{\mathrm{d}}{\mathrm{d}x}\delta y\,\mathrm{d}x = \left[\frac{\partial f}{\partial y'}\delta y\right]_{x_0}^{x_1} - \int_{x_0}^{x_1} \frac{\mathrm{d}}{\mathrm{d}x}\left(\frac{\partial f}{\partial y'}\right)\delta y\,\mathrm{d}x.$$

Since $\delta y = 0$ at the endpoints, we have

$$\delta I = \int_{x_0}^{x_1} \left[\frac{\partial f}{\partial y} - \frac{\mathrm{d}}{\mathrm{d}x}\left(\frac{\partial f}{\partial y'}\right)\right]\delta y(x)\,\mathrm{d}x.$$

In order that I has a minimum value, the variation δI must be zero

* Strictly speaking the technique finds the *stationary* values of the integral.

for an arbitrarily small variation $\delta y(x)$. This can only be so if

$$\frac{\partial f}{\partial y} - \frac{\mathrm{d}}{\mathrm{d}x}\left(\frac{\partial f}{\partial y'}\right) = 0. \tag{13.1}$$

Equation (13.1) is known as the Euler–Lagrange equation. In general, it is a second-order differential equation for the function $y(x)$. Its solution will therefore contain two integration constants which may be determined from the boundary conditions, $y(x_0) = y_0$ and $y(x_1) = y_1$.

We now return to our original problem which amounted to finding the minimum of the integral

$$I = \int_{x_0}^{x_1} (1 + y'^2)^{1/2}\,\mathrm{d}x.$$

Taking $f(y, y') = (1 + y'^2)^{1/2}$ we have

$$\frac{\partial f}{\partial y} = 0 \qquad \text{and} \qquad \frac{\partial f}{\partial y'} = y'(1 + y'^2)^{-1/2}$$

and the Euler–Lagrange equation becomes

$$\frac{\mathrm{d}}{\mathrm{d}x}[y'(1 + y'^2)^{-1/2}] = 0.$$

On integrating once we have $y' = m$, where m is a constant. A second integration yields

$$y = mx + c$$

which of course represents a straight line with slope m and intercept c, both of which are readily determined from the boundary conditions.

In the static problem we have just considered x was used as the independent variable. We want to consider dynamical problems and will thus be concerned rather with functions of the time t. Suppose we have a function f of n variables $q_1(t), q_2(t), \ldots, q_n(t)$, and their derivatives $\dot{q}_1, \dot{q}_2, \ldots, \dot{q}_n$. Then, in order that the integral

$$I = \int_{t_0}^{t_1} f(q_1, q_2, \ldots, q_n, \dot{q}_1, \dot{q}_2, \ldots, \dot{q}_n)\,\mathrm{d}t$$

be stationary, it must be unchanged to first order under a variation of any of the functions $q_i(t)$ $(i = 1, 2, \ldots, n)$, subject to the conditions

$\delta q_i(t_0) = \delta q_i(t_1) = 0$. This leads to n Euler–Lagrange equations

$$\frac{\partial f}{\partial q_i} - \frac{\mathrm{d}}{\mathrm{d}t}\left(\frac{\partial f}{\partial \dot{q}_i}\right) = 0 \qquad i = 1, 2, \ldots, n$$

which have to be satisfied. These second-order differential equations can be solved to give the n functions $q_i(t)$ and the $2n$ integration constants can be determined from the boundary conditions.

13.2.2 Hamilton's principle and the Euler–Lagrange equations

Let us consider the three-dimensional motion of a particle of mass m in a central potential. In Cartesian coordinates the kinetic energy is

$$T = \tfrac{1}{2}m(\dot{x}^2 + \dot{y}^2 + \dot{z}^2)$$

and the potential energy $V(x, y, z)$ depends only on the magnitude of $r = (x^2 + y^2 + z^2)^{1/2}$. We introduce the Lagrangian

$$L = T - V = \tfrac{1}{2}m(\dot{x}^2 + \dot{y}^2 + \dot{z}^2) - V(x, y, z). \tag{13.2}$$

It has derivatives

$$\frac{\partial L}{\partial x} = -\frac{\partial V}{\partial x} = F_x \qquad \frac{\partial L}{\partial \dot{x}} = m\dot{x} = p_x$$

with similar expressions for the y and z components. The equation of motion, $F_x = \dot{p}_x$, can thus be written

$$\frac{\partial L}{\partial x} - \frac{\mathrm{d}}{\mathrm{d}t}\left(\frac{\partial L}{\partial \dot{x}}\right) = 0$$

which has the form of an Euler–Lagrange equation for the integral

$$I = \int_{t_0}^{t_1} L\,\mathrm{d}t. \tag{13.3}$$

This integral is called the *action* and Hamilton's principle of least action states that a system will evolve in such a way as to minimize the action.

The above formalism is readily extended to the case where the Lagrangian can be expressed in terms of generalized coordinates $q_i(t)$ and their time derivatives $\dot{q}_i(t)$. Then, the Euler–Lagrange equations become

$$\frac{\partial L}{\partial q_i} - \frac{\mathrm{d}}{\mathrm{d}t}\left(\frac{\partial L}{\partial \dot{q}_i}\right) = 0 \qquad (i = 1, 2, 3). \tag{13.4}$$

They ensure that the action is stationary with respect to arbitrary variations δq_1, δq_2 and δq_3 subject to the condition that the variations are zero at the limits of integration t_0 and t_1.

Lagrange's equations are applicable not only to classical and quantum particle dynamics but also to classical and relativistic quantum field theory. In the latter case we deal with fields, φ, which are functions of the continuously varying space–time coordinates x_μ, and formulate Lagrange's equations in terms of a Lagrangian *density* $\mathscr{L}$ such that the Lagrangian L is given by

$$L = \int \mathscr{L}\, \mathrm{d}^3x.$$

The Lagrangian density $\mathscr{L}$ is commonly referred to simply as the Lagrangian. In the theories which concern us here it is a function only of the fields φ_i and their first derivatives with respect to space and time: $\mathscr{L} = \mathscr{L}(\phi, \partial\phi/\partial x_\mu)$. In the Euler–Lagrange equation (13.4) of classical, non-relativistic mechanics, the second term contains derivatives with respect to time only. In a relativistic theory the space and time coordinates must be given equal status and in this case the Euler–Lagrange equations generalize to

$$\frac{\partial \mathscr{L}}{\partial \varphi_i} - \frac{\partial}{\partial x_\mu}\left[\frac{\partial \mathscr{L}}{\partial(\partial\varphi_i/\partial x_\mu)}\right] = 0 \qquad (i = 1, 2, 3, \ldots) \tag{13.5}$$

with $\mu = 0, 1, 2, 3$. In what follows we find it convenient to reintroduce the shorthand notation (see equations (11.10) and (11.11))

$$\partial^\mu \equiv \frac{\partial}{\partial x_\mu} \equiv \left(\frac{\partial}{\partial t}, -\nabla\right) \qquad \partial_\mu \equiv \frac{\partial}{\partial x^\mu} \equiv \left(\frac{\partial}{\partial t}, \nabla\right).$$

Then, equation (13.5) becomes

$$\frac{\partial \mathscr{L}}{\partial \varphi_i} - \partial^\mu\left[\frac{\partial \mathscr{L}}{\partial(\partial^\mu \varphi_i)}\right] = 0 \qquad (i = 1, 2, 3, \ldots) \tag{13.6a}$$

or, equivalently,

$$\frac{\partial \mathscr{L}}{\partial \varphi_i} - \partial_\mu\left[\frac{\partial \mathscr{L}}{\partial(\partial_\mu \varphi_i)}\right] = 0 \qquad (i = 1, 2, 3, \ldots) \tag{13.6b}$$

We now go on to consider the Lagrangians and wave equations for a variety of fields with different characteristics.

13.3 Lagrangians and single-particle wave equations

13.3.1 The Lagrangian for a scalar (spin 0) field

Consider the Lagrangian

$$\mathscr{L} = \tfrac{1}{2}(\partial_\lambda \varphi)(\partial^\lambda \varphi) - \tfrac{1}{2}m^2\varphi^2 \tag{13.7}$$

where φ is a real, one-component field. Provided that φ is a scalar (or pseudoscalar) the Lagrangian is invariant since, in either case, φ^2 is an ordinary scalar and $\partial_\lambda \varphi \partial^\lambda \varphi$ is the square of a four-vector and therefore also a scalar. In terms of the metric tensor introduced in section 11.4.2 the Lagrangian may be written

$$\mathscr{L} = \tfrac{1}{2}g^{\mu\nu}\partial_\mu \varphi \partial_\nu \varphi - \tfrac{1}{2}m^2\varphi^2. \tag{13.8}$$

The derivatives of (13.8) are

$$\frac{\partial \mathscr{L}}{\partial(\partial_\mu \varphi)} = g^{\mu\nu}\partial_\nu \varphi = \partial^\mu \varphi$$

and

$$\frac{\partial \mathscr{L}}{\partial \varphi} = -m^2\varphi.$$

Hence, by (13.6b), we have

$$\partial_\mu \partial^\mu \varphi + m^2\varphi = (\Box^2 + m^2)\varphi = 0 \tag{13.9}$$

which we recognize as the Klein–Gordon equation (11.1), which thus describes the motion of a particle of spin 0 and mass m. Of course, in writing down the Lagrangian (13.7) we have used the benefit of hindsight: this form of the Lagrangian was specifically chosen to ensure that its use in the Euler–Lagrange equation resulted in the correct equation of motion.

13.3.2 The Lagrangian for a spinor (spin ½) field

We assert that the Lagrangian for a spinor field ψ is

$$\mathscr{L} = \mathrm{i}\bar{\psi}\gamma^\mu \partial_\mu \psi - m\bar{\psi}\psi \tag{13.10}$$

where $\bar{\psi} = \psi^\dagger\gamma^0$ is the adjoint spinor, introduced in section 11.4.3. We regard each of the four components of ψ and $\bar{\psi}$ as independent variables.

The derivatives of (13.10) are

$$\frac{\partial \mathscr{L}}{\partial(\partial_\mu \psi)} = \mathrm{i}\bar{\psi}\gamma^\mu$$

and

$$\frac{\partial \mathscr{L}}{\partial \psi} = -m\bar{\psi}$$

which, when substituted into the Euler–Lagrange equation, give the Dirac adjoint equation

$$\mathrm{i}\partial_\mu \bar{\psi}\gamma^\mu + m\bar{\psi} = 0$$

(see example 11.8). In order to obtain an equation of motion for ψ we rearrange the first term in the Lagrangian, which becomes

$$\mathscr{L} = -\mathrm{i}(\partial_\mu \bar{\psi})\gamma^\mu \psi - m\psi\bar{\psi}.$$

This manipulation does not change the action $I = \int L\,\mathrm{d}t = \int \mathscr{L}\,\mathrm{d}^4x$. Then,

$$\frac{\partial \mathscr{L}}{\partial(\partial_\mu \bar{\psi})} = -\mathrm{i}\gamma^\mu\psi \qquad \text{and} \qquad \frac{\partial \mathscr{L}}{\partial \bar{\psi}} = -m\psi.$$

On substituting into (13.6b) we get the Dirac equation for ψ, the equation of motion for a spin $\frac{1}{2}$ particle with mass m,

$$(\mathrm{i}\gamma^\mu\partial_\mu - m)\psi = 0. \tag{13.11}$$

13.3.3 The Lagrangian for a massless vector (spin 1) field

As an example of a vector field we consider the Langrangian for the electromagnetic field,

$$\mathscr{L} = -\tfrac{1}{4}F_{\mu\nu}F^{\mu\nu} - j^\mu A_\mu. \tag{13.12}$$

Here, j^μ is the four-vector current, the source of the field, and A_μ is the four-vector electromagnetic potential (see section 8.12). The electromagnetic field-strength tensor, $F_{\mu\nu}$, is a four-dimensional curl and is defined as

$$F_{\mu\nu} = \partial_\mu A_\nu - \partial_\nu A_\mu. \tag{13.13}$$

On substituting this Lagrangian into the Euler–Lagrange equation for each compoent of A_ν,

$$\frac{\partial \mathscr{L}}{\partial A_\nu} - \partial_\mu \frac{\partial \mathscr{L}}{\partial(\partial_\mu A_\nu)} = 0 \tag{13.14}$$

one expects to obtain the Maxwell equations.

Explicitly, the Lagrangian is

$$\mathscr{L} = -\tfrac{1}{4}(\partial_\mu A_\nu - \partial_\nu A_\mu)(\partial^\mu A^\nu - \partial^\nu A^\mu) - j^\mu A_\mu$$

with μ, $\nu = 0, 1, 2, 3$. Consider the first term in the Lagrangian which we write as

$$-\tfrac{1}{4}(\partial_\alpha A_\beta - \partial_\beta A_\alpha)(\partial^\alpha A^\beta - \partial^\beta A^\alpha).$$

In order to carry out the differentiation we lower the indices of $F^{\alpha\beta}$. Thus,

$$\mathscr{L} = -\tfrac{1}{4}g^{\alpha\lambda}g^{\beta\sigma}(\partial_\alpha A_\beta - \partial_\beta A_\alpha)(\partial_\lambda A_\sigma - \partial_\sigma A_\lambda)$$

and

$$\frac{\partial \mathscr{L}}{\partial(\partial_\mu A_\nu)} = -\tfrac{1}{4}g^{\alpha\lambda}g^{\beta\sigma}(\delta^\alpha_\mu \delta^\beta_\nu F_{\lambda\sigma} - \delta^\beta_\mu \delta^\alpha_\nu F_{\lambda\sigma} + \delta^\lambda_\mu \delta^\sigma_\nu F_{\alpha\beta} - \delta^\sigma_\mu \delta^\lambda_\nu F_{\alpha\beta}).$$

Since $g^{\mu\nu}$ is symmetric and $F_{\mu\nu}$ is antisymmetric all four terms in this expression are equal and the derivative becomes

$$\frac{\partial \mathscr{L}}{\partial(\partial_\mu A_\nu)} = -g^{\mu\lambda}g^{\nu\sigma}F_{\lambda\sigma} = -F^{\mu\nu}.$$

Furthermore,

$$\frac{\partial \mathscr{L}}{\partial A_\nu} = -j^\nu.$$

On substituting the derivatives into (13.14) we obtain

$$\partial_\mu F^{\mu\nu} = j^\nu \tag{13.15}$$

the Maxwell equations in covariant form.

13.4 Symmetries and conservation laws

Symmetry transformations and conservation laws have been considered in some detail, from an elementary standpoint, in chapter 8. A major advantage of the Lagrangian formulation is that through studying the invariance properties of the Lagrangian one is led naturally to the identification of conserved quantities. As we saw in chapter 8, there are many types of symmetry transformations: continuous or discrete, geometrical or internal and, as we implied in the introduction to the present chapter, global or local. The symmetries observed in nature may be used to constrain the form of the Lagrangian and, indeed, the Lagrangians discussed in the last section all satisfy the fundamental requirements of Lorentz covariance, i.e. they are all Lorentz scalars. The link between a continuous symmetry transformation under which the Lagrangian is invariant and the corresponding conservation law is provided by Noether's theorem.

In chapter 8 we saw that the conservation of momentum resulted from invariance under translations in space. In a relativistic theory space and time appear on an equal footing: we might therefore expect that the invariance of the Lagrangian under space–time translations will lead to four-momentum conservation. Let us consider translations of the space–time variables of the form

$$x_\mu \rightarrow x'_\mu = x_\mu + \delta x_\mu \tag{13.16}$$

where the arbitrary infinitesimal displacement δx_μ is independent of the coordinate x_μ. If the Lagrangian is invariant *in form* under this transformation it will change by an amount

$$\delta \mathscr{L} = \mathscr{L}(x') - \mathscr{L}(x) = \delta x^\mu \frac{\mathrm{d}\mathscr{L}}{\mathrm{d}x^\mu}. \tag{13.17}$$

We assume as before that the Lagrangian has no *explicit* dependence on the space–time coordinates but is a function only of the fields φ and their derivatives $\partial_\mu \varphi$. Then, as an alternative to (13.17) we can determine the change in $\mathscr{L}$ from

$$\delta \mathscr{L} = \frac{\partial \mathscr{L}}{\partial \varphi} \delta\varphi + \frac{\partial \mathscr{L}}{\partial(\partial_\mu \varphi)} \delta(\partial_\mu \varphi) \tag{13.18}$$

where

$$\delta\varphi = \varphi(x') - \varphi(x) = \delta x^\mu \partial_\mu \varphi(x) \tag{13.19}$$

and

$$\delta(\partial_\mu \varphi) = \partial_\mu \varphi(x') - \partial_\mu \varphi(x) = \delta x^\nu \partial_\nu \partial_\mu \varphi(x). \tag{13.20}$$

From the Euler–Lagrange equation,

$$\frac{\partial \mathscr{L}}{\partial \varphi} = \partial_\nu \frac{\partial \mathscr{L}}{\partial(\partial_\nu \varphi)}$$

so that (13.18) becomes

$$\delta\mathscr{L} = \left[\partial_\nu \frac{\partial\mathscr{L}}{\partial(\partial_\nu\varphi)}\right]\delta x^\mu \partial_\mu\varphi + \frac{\partial\mathscr{L}}{\partial(\partial_\nu\varphi)}\delta x^\mu \partial_\mu \partial_\nu \varphi$$

$$= \partial_\nu \frac{\partial\mathscr{L}}{\partial(\partial_\nu\varphi)}\delta x^\mu \partial_\mu\varphi. \tag{13.21}$$

On equating (13.17) and (13.21) we get

$$\delta x_\mu \partial_\nu \left[\frac{\partial\mathscr{L}}{\partial(\partial_\nu\varphi)}\partial^\mu\varphi - g^{\mu\nu}\mathscr{L}\right] = 0. \tag{13.22}$$

For this equation to be satisfied for arbitrary infinitesimal displacements, δx_μ, we have

$$\partial_\mu T^{\mu\nu} = 0, \tag{13.23}$$

where $T^{\mu\nu}$, the energy–momentum tensor, is given by

$$T^{\mu\nu} \equiv \frac{\partial\mathscr{L}}{\partial(\partial_\nu\varphi)}\partial^\mu\varphi - g^{\mu\nu}\mathscr{L}. \tag{13.24}$$

Equation (13.23) has the form of a continuity equation so that $T^{\mu\nu}$ can be thought of as a conserved 'current'. The component T^{00} is the Hamiltonian density

$$\mathscr{H} = \frac{\partial\mathscr{L}}{\partial(\partial_0\varphi)}\partial^0\varphi - \mathscr{L}$$

and the total energy is

$$H \equiv \int T^{00}\, d^3x. \tag{13.25}$$

The components T^{0i}, with $i = 1, 2, 3$, correspond to momentum densities so that momenta are given by

$$p^i = \int T^{0i}\, d^3x. \tag{13.26}$$

Combining (13.25) and (13.26) gives the energy–momentum four-vector

$$p^\mu = \int T^{0\mu}\, d^3x$$

which, through (13.23), satisfies

$$\frac{\mathrm{d}}{\mathrm{d}x^0}\,p^\mu = 0. \tag{13.27}$$

Thus, invariance of the Lagrangian, or equivalently the action, under space–time translations, leads to four-momentum conservation.

Equations (13.23) and (13.24) together form the essence of Noether's theorem, which may be stated in general as follows: if an action is invariant under a continuous group of transformations of the fields the corresponding Lagrangian determines a conserved tensor and an associated time-independent observable.

As an example of an internal symmetry consider the invariance of the Lagrangian for a free electron

$$\mathscr{L} = \bar{\psi}(\mathrm{i}\gamma^\mu \partial_\mu - m)\psi \tag{13.28}$$

under a global gauge (or phase) transformation

$$\psi \to \psi' = \mathrm{e}^{\mathrm{i}\Lambda}\psi \tag{13.29}$$

where Λ is an arbitrary real constant, independent of the coordinate x. In other words, the parameter Λ has the same value at every space–time point. For this reason the transformation is known as global.

Since a finite phase change can be built up from a series of infinitesimal phase changes it is sufficient to consider the variation of $\mathscr{L}$ under an infinitesimal transformation

$$\psi \to \psi' = (1 + \mathrm{i}\Lambda)\psi. \tag{13.30}$$

This gives rise to the infinitesimal variations

$$\delta\psi = \psi' - \psi = \mathrm{i}\Lambda\psi \tag{13.31}$$

$$\delta(\partial_\mu\psi) = \partial_\mu\psi' - \partial_\mu\psi = \mathrm{i}\Lambda(\partial_\mu\psi). \tag{13.32}$$

For variations with respect to ψ and $\bar{\psi}$ the variation in the Lagrangian is

$$\begin{aligned}
0 &= \delta\mathscr{L} \\
&= \frac{\partial\mathscr{L}}{\partial\psi}\,\delta\psi + \frac{\partial\mathscr{L}}{\partial(\partial_\mu\psi)}\,\delta(\partial_\mu\psi) + \delta\bar{\psi}\,\frac{\partial\mathscr{L}}{\partial\bar{\psi}} + \delta(\partial_\mu\bar{\psi})\,\frac{\partial}{\partial(\partial_\mu\bar{\psi})} \\
&= \frac{\partial\mathscr{L}}{\partial\psi}\,(\mathrm{i}\Lambda\psi) + \frac{\partial\mathscr{L}}{\partial(\partial_\mu\psi)}\,(\mathrm{i}\Lambda\partial_\mu\psi) - \mathrm{i}\Lambda\bar{\psi}\,\frac{\partial\mathscr{L}}{\partial\bar{\psi}} - \mathrm{i}\Lambda(\partial_\mu\bar{\psi})\,\frac{\partial}{\partial(\partial_\mu\bar{\psi})}.
\end{aligned}$$

Since

$$\partial_\mu\left(\frac{\partial\mathscr{L}}{\partial(\partial_\mu\psi)}\psi\right) = \partial_\mu\left[\frac{\partial\mathscr{L}}{\partial(\partial_\mu\psi)}\right]\psi + \frac{\partial\mathscr{L}}{\partial(\partial_\mu\psi)}\partial_\mu\psi$$

we have

$$0 = \delta\mathscr{L} = \mathrm{i}\Lambda\left[\frac{\partial\mathscr{L}}{\partial\psi} - \partial_\mu\left(\frac{\partial\mathscr{L}}{\partial(\partial_\mu\psi)}\right)\right]\psi + \mathrm{i}\Lambda\partial_\mu\left(\frac{\partial\mathscr{L}}{\partial(\partial_\mu\psi)}\psi\right)$$
$$- \mathrm{i}\Lambda\bar{\psi}\left[\frac{\partial\mathscr{L}}{\partial\bar{\psi}} - \partial_\mu\left(\frac{\partial\mathscr{L}}{\partial(\partial_\mu\bar{\psi})}\right)\right] - \mathrm{i}\Lambda\partial_\mu\left(\bar{\psi}\frac{\partial\mathscr{L}}{\partial(\partial_\mu\bar{\psi})}\right).$$

The terms in square brackets are zero by virtue of the Euler–Lagrange equations so that

$$0 = \delta\mathscr{L} = \mathrm{i}\Lambda\partial_\mu\left[\frac{\partial\mathscr{L}}{\partial(\partial_\mu\psi)}\psi - \bar{\psi}\frac{\partial\mathscr{L}}{\partial(\partial_\mu\bar{\psi})}\right]. \tag{13.33}$$

Insertion of the Lagrangian (13.28) into (13.33) yields

$$2\Lambda\partial_\mu(\bar{\psi}\gamma^\mu\psi) = 0. \tag{13.34}$$

Equation (13.34) must be satisfied for arbitrary Λ. Global gauge invariance of the Lagrangian for a free electron thus leads to the continuity equation

$$\partial_\mu j^\mu = 0 \tag{13.35}$$

where the conserved four-current density is given by

$$j^\mu = \bar{\psi}\gamma^\mu\psi. \tag{13.36}$$

This is precisely the form given in equation (11.27).

The group of phase transformations $U(\alpha) \equiv \mathrm{e}^{\mathrm{i}\Lambda}$, where the single real parameter Λ can take on a continuous range of values, is the unitary group $U(1)$. It is an Abelian group, i.e. the group multiplication is commutative

$$[U(\Lambda_1), U(\Lambda_2)] = 0.$$

Invariance of the Lagrangian under this group of transformations leads to the conserved current (13.36). Had we included the electric charge q in the phase transformation, i.e. $\psi \to \psi' = \mathrm{e}^{\mathrm{i}\Lambda q}\psi$, which then may be regarded as a rotation in 'charge space', we would have arrived at the conserved electromagnetic current density

$$j^\mu = q\bar{\psi}\gamma^\mu\psi. \tag{13.37}$$

The electric charge is given by

$$q = \int j^0 \, d^3x \tag{13.38}$$

where the integration is over all space. Hence, from the continuity equation,

$$\frac{dq}{dt} = -\int_V \partial_\alpha j^\alpha \, d^3x \qquad (\alpha = 1, 2, 3). \tag{13.39}$$

The volume integral of the divergence of the current can be written as a surface integral by using the divergence theorem so that, if S is the surface bounding the volume V,

$$\frac{dq}{dt} = -\int_S \boldsymbol{j} \cdot d\boldsymbol{s}. \tag{13.40}$$

If we assume that the fields, and hence the current density $\boldsymbol{j}$, approach zero sufficiently quickly at infinity, the surface integral vanishes. Consequently, $dq/dt = 0$, and q is constant. Global gauge invariance of the Lagrangian thus leads to the conservation of electric charge.

13.5 *Local gauge invariance and quantum electrodynamics*

Let us now attempt to find a Lagrangian which is invariant under a local gauge transformation, i.e. one in which the parameter Λ is allowed to vary from point to point in space–time, $\Lambda = \Lambda(x)$. Under such a transformation the fields transform as

$$\begin{aligned} \psi \to \psi' &= \exp[iq\Lambda(x)]\psi(x) \\ \bar{\psi} \to \bar{\psi}' &= \exp[-iq\Lambda(x)]\bar{\psi}(x). \end{aligned} \tag{13.41}$$

The Lagrangian for a free Dirac particle of mass m,

$$\mathcal{L} = i\bar{\psi}\gamma^\mu\partial_\mu\psi - m\bar{\psi}\psi$$

is not invariant under this local gauge transformation, for, although the mass term becomes

$$m\bar{\psi}'\psi' = m\bar{\psi}\exp[-\mathrm{i}q\Lambda(x)]\exp[\mathrm{i}q\Lambda(x)]\psi = m\bar{\psi}\psi$$

and is thus invariant, the field derivative transforms as

$$\begin{aligned}\partial_\mu\psi \to \partial_\mu\psi' &= \partial_\mu\{\exp[\mathrm{i}q\Lambda(x)]\psi(x)\}\\ &= \exp[\mathrm{i}q\Lambda(x)]\partial_\mu\psi(x) + \mathrm{i}q\exp[\mathrm{i}q\Lambda(x)]\psi(x)\partial_\mu\Lambda(x)\end{aligned} \tag{13.42}$$

and the last term involving $\partial_\mu\Lambda(x)$ destroys the invariance of $\mathscr{L}$. In order to preserve the invariance of the Lagrangian one needs to introduce derivatives $\mathscr{D}_\mu\psi$, which undergo the same phase transformation as the fields themselves, i.e.

$$\mathscr{D}_\mu\psi \to \exp[\mathrm{i}q\Lambda(x)]\mathscr{D}_\mu\psi.$$

The gauge-covariant derivative

$$\mathscr{D}_\mu \equiv \partial_\mu + \mathrm{i}qA_\mu(x) \tag{13.43}$$

will achieve this provided that the vector field A_μ transforms as

$$A_\mu(x) \to A_\mu(x) - \partial_\mu\Lambda(x) \tag{13.44}$$

for then the last term in (13.42) will be exactly cancelled. We recognize (13.43) as the 'minimal' substitution introduced in section 11.4.4 and (13.44) is precisely the gauge freedom that exists in the choice of the classical electromagnetic four-potential (section 8.12.1).

The Lagrangian

$$\mathscr{L} = \mathrm{i}\bar{\psi}\gamma^\mu\mathscr{D}_\mu\psi - m\bar{\psi}\psi \tag{13.45}$$

is now locally gauge invariant. Explicitly,

$$\begin{aligned}\mathscr{L} &= \mathrm{i}\bar{\psi}\gamma^\mu\partial_\mu\psi - m\bar{\psi}\psi - qA_\mu\bar{\psi}\gamma^\mu\psi\\ &= \mathscr{L}_{\mathrm{free}} - j^\mu A_\mu\end{aligned}$$

where the conserved electromagnetic current,

$$j^\mu = q\bar{\psi}\gamma^\mu\psi$$

has precisely the form required by global gauge invariance, and the additional term, $-j^\mu A_\mu$, is familiar as the *interaction* between the Dirac particle and the classical electromagnetic field. The requirement of *local* gauge invariance has thus forced us to introduce a gauge field A_μ, which we associate with the physical photon field. To arrive at the complete Lagrangian for quantum electrodynamics (QED) we must add the kinetic energy term, $-\frac{1}{4}F_{\mu\nu}F^{\mu\nu}$, which describes the propagation of free photons (see examples 13.8 and 13.9). Then, the complete QED Lagrangian is

$$\mathscr{L} = \bar{\psi}(i\gamma^\mu \partial_\mu - m)\psi - j^\mu A_\mu - \tfrac{1}{4}F_{\mu\nu}F^{\mu\nu}. \tag{13.46}$$

It is interesting to note that if the photon were not massless, one would be obliged to add to the Lagrangian a photon mass term of the form

$$\mathscr{L}_\gamma = \tfrac{1}{2}m_\gamma^2 A_\mu A^\mu.$$

As a consequence, the local gauge invariance of the Lagrangian would be destroyed, because

$$A_\mu A^\mu \to (A_\mu - \partial_\mu \Lambda)(A^\mu - \partial^\mu \Lambda) \neq A_\mu A^\mu.$$

In summary, we have seen that global gauge invariance of the Lagrangian leads to the conservation of electric charge. More importantly, the requirement of local gauge invariance necessitates the introduction of a vector (spin 1) field A_μ: the gauge boson of this field is the photon. To preserve local gauge invariance the photon must have zero mass, consistent with the fact that the range of the electromagnetic interaction is infinite. Moreover, the form of the *interaction* of radiation with matter is specified. In the case of an electron, described by the Dirac equation, the interaction term has the form $-j^\mu A_\mu$ where j^μ is the conserved current of the free-electron Lagrangian.

13.6 Unification of the weak and electromagnetic interactions

13.6.1 Weak neutral currents and the Z^0 boson

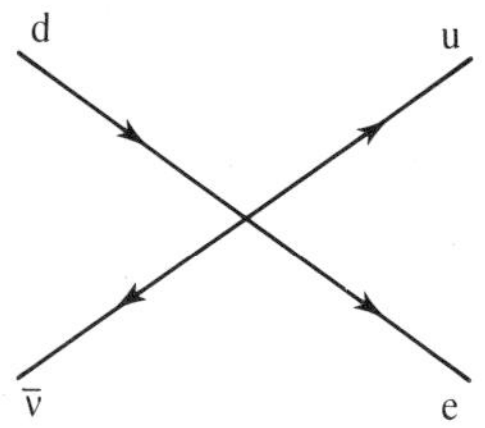

Figure 13.2
Quark level β decay process.

We recall from section 11.5 that the original Fermi theory of β decay assumed point-like coupling between the four fermions as shown in figure 11.11(a). In reality, the neutron and proton have a rich substructure of quarks and gluons so that the β decay diagram is oversimplified. However, at the quark level, the process $n \to p + e^- + \bar{\nu}_e$ can be considered as $d \to u + e^- + \bar{\nu}_e$, i.e. a d quark changes via the weak coupling to a u quark, an electron and an antineutrino and, assuming quarks to be structureless, the four-fermion point-like interaction is still valid (figure 13.2).

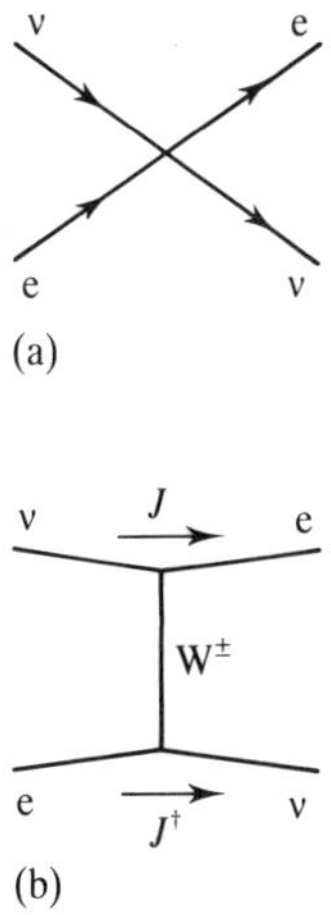

Figure 13.3
(a) Point-like elastic ν_e–e scattering; (b) elastic ν_e–e scattering via $W^\pm$ exchange.

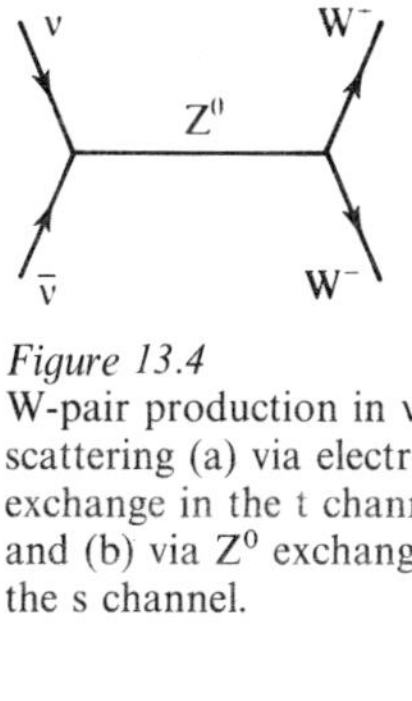

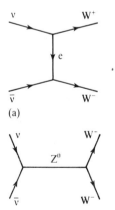

Figure 13.4
W-pair production in ν–ν̄ scattering (a) via electron exchange in the t channel and (b) via Z^0 exchange in the s channel.

As pointed out in section 11.9, a serious difficulty arises when the Fermi theory is applied to lepton scattering processes at high energies. For example, the cross-section for elastic ν_e e scattering, depicted as a point-like interaction in figure 13.3(a) is proportional to G^2s, where s is the square of the centre-of-mass energy. This cross-section violates unitarity at a centre-of-mass energy of about 300 GeV. The divergent high energy behaviour of the point-like cross-section can be avoided by introducing a gauge boson, the W^+ or W^-, as the mediator of the weak interaction, as shown in figure 13.3(b). The amplitude for this process (see equation (11.90)) is of the form

$$M \approx \frac{g}{\sqrt{2}}(J^\mu)^\dagger \frac{1}{M_W^2 - q^2}\frac{g}{\sqrt{2}}(J_\mu),$$

i.e. is a product of a charge-lowering weak current $J^{\mu\dagger}$, a charge-raising weak current J_μ, both of which have a V–A structure, and the boson propagator. Such processes, in which the weak currents are charge-changing currents, are known as *charged current* weak interactions: they are mediated by the exchange of charged bosons, $W^\pm$. All the weak interactions which we have met so far are of this type.

The introduction of the W boson circumvents the problem of a divergent cross-section in ν_e–e scattering but, at first sight, appears to introduce other problems elsewhere. For instance, the cross-section for W-pair production in neutrino–antineutrino scattering via the mechanism shown in figure 13.4(a) diverges at high energy. This 'bad' high energy behaviour of figure 13.4(a) can, however, be cancelled by introducing a neutral gauge boson, Z^0, as shown in figure 13.4(b). In itself this may not be regarded as sufficient justification for the introduction of a Z^0 boson, but the hypothesis is strengthened by the fact that the same neutral boson (figures 13.5(b) and 13.5(c)) cancels the divergent behaviour of figure 13.5(a), which shows W-pair production via a virtual photon in e^+e^- annihilation, an *electromagnetic* process. Each diagram in figure 13.5 has divergent high energy behaviour but, taken together, cancellation occurs and leaves the cross-section for the process $e^+e^- \rightarrow W^+W^-$ finite at high energies. In order that this cancellation takes place the coupling of the gauge bosons, γ, $W^\pm$ and Z^0, to the leptons must be of comparable strength: roughly speaking, the weak coupling constant g must be equal to the electromagnetic coupling e. This *electroweak* unification implies that the W and Z^0 bosons must have masses of the order of 100 GeV – precise predictions will be given in section 14.3.8. In analogy with QED one might expect an electroweak theory to be locally gauge invariant and contain gauge bosons which are massless, like the photon: the requirement of large masses for the $W^\pm$ and Z^0 would thus appear to be a stumbling block. We shall see later that the requirement of local gauge invariance does indeed introduce, in addition to the photon, a triplet of zero-mass bosons. Fortunately, there exists a mechanism, the Higgs[1] mechanism,

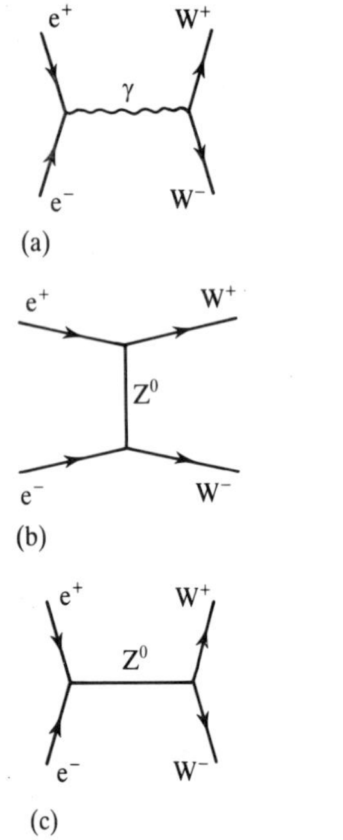

Figure 13.5
W-pair production in e^+–e^- scattering via (a) photon exchange in the s channel, (b) Z^0 exchange in the t channel and (c) Z^0 exchange in the s channel.

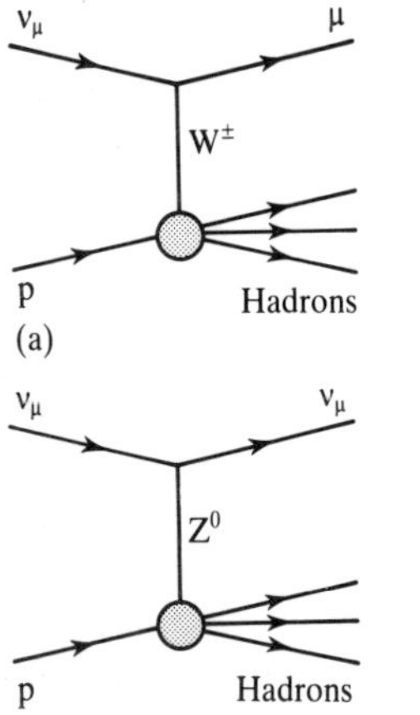

Figure 13.6
(a) A charged-current neutrino interaction mediated by $W^\pm$ exchange; (b) a neutral-current neutrino interaction mediated by Z^0 exchange.

which endows this triplet with mass at the expense of introducing a scalar particle, the Higgs boson H^0, into the theory.

One important consequence of this unification of the weak and electromagnetic interactions is that weak *neutral* current neutrino interactions ought to exist. A typical charged current neutrino interaction such as $\nu_\mu + p \to \mu + \text{hadrons}$ is shown in figure 13.6(a). As pointed out earlier these charge current interactions are mediated by the exchange of the charged gauge bosons, $W^\pm$, and the charge of the lepton changes. The existence of the neutral boson Z^0 implies the existence of interactions in which the lepton retains its identity: the weak currents are neutral and the interactions proceed via the exchange of a Z^0 boson as in figure 13.6(b). Such neutral current interactions were discovered in 1973 at CERN and Fermilab (see section 14.3.2).

13.6.2 Structure of the weak neutral current

In section 12.6.2 we saw that the *charged* weak currents of quarks have the same V–A structure as the lepton currents. For example, the charge-raising leptonic current is

$$J_{\mathrm{e}}^{\mu} = \bar{u}(\nu)\gamma^{\mu}\tfrac{1}{2}(1-\gamma^5)u(\mathrm{e})$$

and the corresponding charge-raising quark current is

$$J_{\mathrm{q}}^{\mu} = \bar{u}(\nu)\gamma^{\mu}\tfrac{1}{2}(1-\gamma^5)u(\mathrm{q}).$$

These expressions, through the factor $\frac{1}{2}(1-\gamma^5)$, embody the fact that the coupling is to left-handed particles (or right-handed antiparticles). Indeed, the ν–q and $\bar{\nu}$–q cross-sections are essentially the same as those for ν_e–e^- and $\bar{\nu}_e$–e scattering respectively. The particle–particle (and antiparticle–antiparticle) differential cross-sections are isotropic while the particle–antiparticle cross-sections are anisotropic: thcy contain a factor $(1-y)^2$. To highlight the handedness of the particles involved we rewrite the charged-current differential cross-sections (equations (12.59) and (12.60)) as

$$\frac{d\sigma}{dy}(\nu_L q_L \to \mu_L q'_L) = \frac{d\sigma}{dy}(\bar{\nu}_R \bar{q}_R \to \mu_R \bar{q}'_R) = \frac{G^2 s}{\pi} \qquad (13.47)$$

$$\frac{d\sigma}{dy}(\nu_L \bar{q}_R \to \mu_L \bar{q}'_R) = \frac{d\sigma}{dy}(\bar{\nu}_R q_L \to \mu_R q'_L) = \frac{G^2 s}{\pi}(1-y)^2 \qquad (13.48)$$

where s is the square of the centre-of-mass energy in the neutrino–quark system. These pure V–A constituent processes led to the differential cross-sections for the inclusive charged-current processes $\nu N \to \mu^- X$,

$\bar{\nu}N \to \mu^+ X$ for isoscalar targets

$$\frac{d^2\sigma}{dx\,dy} = \frac{G^2 xs}{2\pi}[Q(x) + (1-y)^2\bar{Q}(x)] \qquad (\nu \to \mu^-)$$

$$\frac{d^2\sigma}{dx\,dy} = \frac{G^2 xs}{2\pi}[\bar{Q}(x) + (1-y)^2 Q(x)] \qquad (\bar{\nu} \to \mu^+).$$

$Q(x)$ and $\bar{Q}(x)$ are the quark and antiquark distribution functions. Integration over the momentum fraction x leads to the neutrino and antineutrino charged-current differential cross-sections

$$\frac{d\sigma^{CC}(\nu)}{dy} = \frac{G^2 s}{2\pi}[Q + (1-y)^2\bar{Q}] \qquad (\nu \to \mu^-) \tag{13.49}$$

$$\frac{d\sigma^{CC}(\bar{\nu})}{dy} = \frac{G^2 s}{2\pi}[\bar{Q} + (1-y)^2 Q] \qquad (\bar{\nu} \to \mu^+) \tag{13.50}$$

where

$$Q \equiv \int xQ(x)\,dx = \int x[u(x) + d(x)]\,dx \tag{13.51}$$

$$\bar{Q} \equiv \int x\bar{Q}(x)\,dx = \int x[\bar{u}(x) + \bar{d}(x)]\,dx \tag{13.52}$$

and we have neglected contributions from s, c, . . . quarks in the nucleon. There is no *a priori* reason why the helicity structure of the weak *neutral* current should be the same as that of the weak charged current. Indeed, the (neutral) electromagnetic current couples to both right-handed and left-handed fermions and, given the possibility of a unified electroweak force, one might expect the weak neutral current similarly to couple to both right-handed and left-handed fermions. Simple helicity arguments (see section 12.6.2) show that 180° scattering of a left-handed neutrino and a right-handed quark is forbidden: the differential cross-section $d\sigma/dy(\nu_L q_R \to \nu_L q_R)$ would then be proportional to $(1-y)^2$. On the other hand, 180° $\nu_L \bar{q}_L$ scattering would not be forbidden and $d\sigma/dy(\nu_L \bar{q}_L \to \nu_L \bar{q}_L)$ would be isotropic. Thus, allowing for neutral current couplings to both left-handed and right-handed fermions with relative strengths g_L and g_R, a parton model calculation similar to that for the charged current processes yields for the differential cross-sections for the inclusive neutral current processes $\nu N \to \nu X$ and $\bar{\nu}N \to \bar{\nu}X$,

$$\frac{d^2\sigma(\nu N \to \nu X)}{dx\,dy} = \frac{G^2 xs}{2\pi}\{g_L^2[Q(x) + (1-y)^2\bar{Q}(x)] + g_R^2[\bar{Q}(x) + (1-y)^2 Q(x)]\} \tag{13.53}$$

and

$$\frac{d^2\sigma(\bar{\nu}N \to \bar{\nu}X)}{dx\,dy} = \frac{G^2xs}{2\pi}\{g_L^2[\bar{Q}(x) + (1-y)^2Q(x)] + g_R^2[Q(x) + (1-y)^2\bar{Q}(x)]\}. \quad (13.54)$$

The coupling constants g_L and g_R may be determined by experiment. If we assume that there are only u, d and $\bar{u}$, $\bar{d}$ quarks in the nucleon then

$$g_L^2 \equiv (g_L^u)^2 + (g_L^d)^2 \quad \text{and} \quad g_R^2 \equiv (g_R^u)^2 + (g_R^d)^2 \quad (13.55)$$

and, with Q and $\bar{Q}$ defined as in (13.51) and (13.52), the neutral current differential cross-sections, per nucleon, for isoscalar targets become

$$\frac{d\sigma(\nu N \to \nu X)}{dy} = \frac{G^2s}{2\pi}\{g_L^2[Q + (1-y)^2\bar{Q}] + g_R^2[\bar{Q} + (1-y)^2Q]\} \quad (13.56)$$

and

$$\frac{d\sigma(\bar{\nu}N \to \bar{\nu}X)}{dy} = \frac{G^2s}{2\pi}\{g_L^2[\bar{Q} + (1-y)^2Q] + g_R^2[Q + (1-y)^2\bar{Q}]\}. \quad (13.57)$$

Using equations (13.49) and (13.50) these neutral-current (NC) cross-sections can be related to the charged-current (CC) cross-sections as follows:

$$\frac{d\sigma^{NC}(\nu)}{dy} = g_L^2\frac{d\sigma^{CC}(\nu)}{dy} + g_R^2\frac{d\sigma^{CC}(\bar{\nu})}{dy} \quad (13.58)$$

$$\frac{d\sigma^{NC}(\bar{\nu})}{dy} = g_L^2\frac{d\sigma^{CC}(\bar{\nu})}{dy} + g_R^2\frac{d\sigma^{CC}(\nu)}{dy}. \quad (13.59)$$

These fundamental relationships between neutral-current and charged-current differential cross-sections were first derived by Llewellyn Smith[2] and form the basis for a determination of g_L and g_R. Figure 13.7 shows the differential cross-sections for neutrino- and antineutrino-induced charged-current and neutral-current reactions determined by the CHARM collaboration.[3] A maximum likelihood fit to the relations (13.58) and (13.59) gives

$$g_L^2 = 0.287 \pm 0.008$$

$$g_R^2 = 0.042 \pm 0.010$$

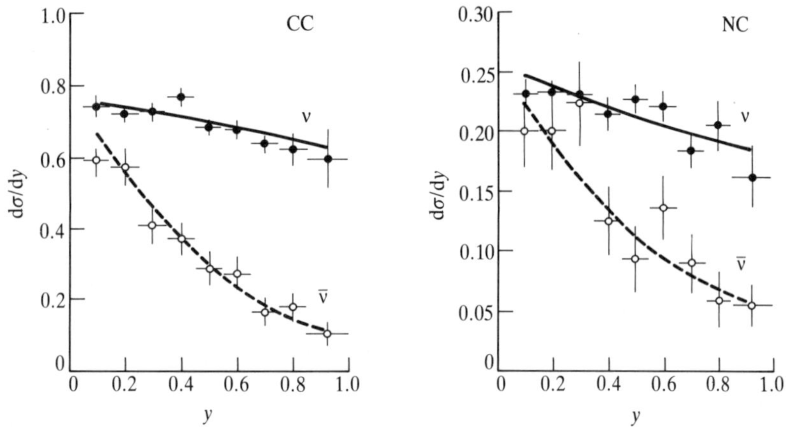

Figure 13.7
Differential cross-sections $d\sigma/dy$ for neutrino- and antineutrino-induced charged-current (CC) and neutral-current (NC) reactions. (Allaby J V *et al.* 1987 *Z Phys* **C36** (611))

showing that the weak neutral current does indeed couple not only to left-handed quarks but also to right-handed quarks ($g_R^2 \neq 0$), and therefore, unlike the charged weak current, it is not pure V–A.

A general neutral current is customarily written as

$$J_\mu^{NC}(f) = \bar{u}_f \gamma_\mu \tfrac{1}{2}(c_V^f - c_A^f \gamma^5) u_f \tag{13.60}$$

where u_f is a fermion spinor and c_V^f, c_A^f are respectively the vector and axial vector coupling constants for fermion f. The constants c_V^f and c_A^f are related to g_L and g_R through the definitions

$$g_L = \tfrac{1}{2}(c_V^f + c_A^f) \qquad g_R = \tfrac{1}{2}(c_V^f - c_A^f). \tag{13.61}$$

The neutrino is left handed so that $c_V^\nu = c_A^\nu = \frac{1}{2}$ and

$$J_\mu^{NC}(\nu) = \tfrac{1}{2}[\bar{u}_\nu \gamma_\mu \tfrac{1}{2}(1 - \gamma^5) u_\nu]. \tag{13.62}$$

On the other hand, we have seen above that for quarks $g_R \neq 0$ so that $c_V^q \neq c_A^q$ and consequently the neutral current

$$J_\mu^{NC}(q) = \bar{u}_q \gamma_\mu \tfrac{1}{2}(c_V^q - c_A^q \gamma^5) u_q \tag{13.63}$$

is not pure V–A. We shall see in section 13.6.4 that in the standard model of electroweak interactions these coupling constants are all given in terms of a single parameter, the Weinberg angle θ_W.

13.6.3 Weak isospin and weak hypercharge

The charge-raising weak current has the form

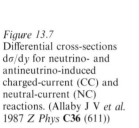

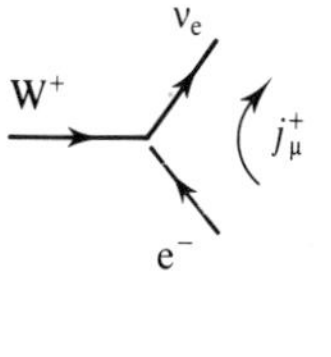

$$j_\mu^+ = \bar{u}(\nu_e)\gamma_\mu\left(\frac{1-\gamma^5}{2}\right)u(e).$$

Table 13.1
Chiral spinors

Particle states	Antiparticle states
$u_L = \frac{1}{2}(1 - \gamma^5)u$	$v_L = \frac{1}{2}(1 + \gamma^5)v$
$u_R = \frac{1}{2}(1 + \gamma^5)u$	$v_R = \frac{1}{2}(1 - \gamma^5)v$
$\bar{u}_L = \bar{u}\frac{1}{2}(1 + \gamma^5)$	$\bar{v}_L = \bar{v}\frac{1}{2}(1 - \gamma^5)$
$\bar{u}_R = \bar{u}\frac{1}{2}(1 - \gamma^5)$	$\bar{v}_R = \bar{v}\frac{1}{2}(1 + \gamma^5)$

* The subscripts L and R correspond to helicity states −1 and +1 respectively.

We recall that the factor $\frac{1}{2}(1 - \gamma^5)$ projects out left-handed particle states and right-handed antiparticle states:

$$\left(\frac{1 - \gamma^5}{2}\right)u = u_L$$

$$\left(\frac{1 - \gamma^5}{2}\right)v = v_R$$

where u is a particle spinor and v an antiparticle spinor. The spinors u_L and v_R are known as chiral spinors. Calculations similar to those in section 11.5.4 result in the chiral spinors summarized in table 13.1.

Using the properties of the γ matrices, it is an easy matter to show that

$$\gamma_\mu\left(\frac{1 - \gamma^5}{2}\right) = \left(\frac{1 + \gamma^5}{2}\right)\gamma_\mu\left(\frac{1 - \gamma^5}{2}\right).$$

Hence, the charge-raising weak current can be written

$$j_\mu^+ = \bar{\nu}\left(\frac{1 + \gamma^5}{2}\right)\gamma_\mu\left(\frac{1 - \gamma^5}{2}\right)e = \bar{\nu}_L\gamma_\mu e_L$$

where, for convenience, we have used the particle name to denote the corresponding spinor. Written in this way, j_μ^+ can be regarded as a pure *vector* current which couples only to left-handed chiral states. It is reminiscent of the pure vector electromagnetic current

$$j_\mu^{em} = -\bar{e}\gamma_\mu e$$

except that the coupling in this case is to right-handed as well as left-handed states:

$$j_\mu^{em} = -\bar{e}_R\gamma_\mu e_R - \bar{e}_L\gamma_\mu e_L. \tag{13.64}$$

In this respect it is similar to the weak *neutral* current discussed in the last section.

In addition to the charge-raising weak current, there is the charge-lowering current

$$j_\mu^- = \bar{e}\left(\frac{1+\gamma^5}{2}\right)\gamma_\mu\left(\frac{1-\gamma^5}{2}\right)\nu = \bar{e}_L\gamma_\mu\nu_L.$$

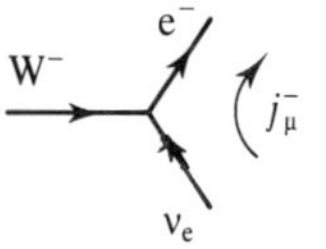

These two charged currents can be written in a compact form by introducing a left-handed doublet

$$\chi_L = \begin{pmatrix}\nu_e \\ e^-\end{pmatrix}_L$$

and the 2 × 2 matrices

$$\tau^+ \equiv \begin{pmatrix}0 & 1\\ 0 & 0\end{pmatrix} \qquad \tau^- \equiv \begin{pmatrix}0 & 0\\ 1 & 0\end{pmatrix}$$

so that

$$j_\mu^\pm = \bar{\chi}_L\gamma_\mu\tau^\pm\chi_L. \tag{13.65}$$

These matrices are just the raising and lowering operators introduced in our discussion of (strong) isospin in section 8.7, i.e. $\tau^\pm = \frac{1}{2}(\tau_1 \pm i\tau_2)$ where τ_1 and τ_2 are the Pauli matrices. Because of the mathematical similarity, χ_L is called a 'weak isospin' doublet but it must be stressed that apart from this mathematical similarity there is no other connection with strong isospin. Imagine, for the moment, a world in which the only weak interactions were these charged current interactions mediated by $W^\pm$ exchange. The weak interactions would then exhibit only a *partial* symmetry. If we demand that the weak interactions be invariant under weak isospin rotations were are forced to introduce a *third* charge-preserving weak isospin current

$$j_\mu^3 = \bar{\chi}_L\gamma_\mu\tfrac{1}{2}\tau_3\chi_L = \tfrac{1}{2}\bar{\nu}_L\gamma_\mu\nu_L - \tfrac{1}{2}\bar{e}_L\gamma_\mu e_L \tag{13.66}$$

where

$$\tau_3 = \begin{pmatrix}1 & 0\\ 0 & -1\end{pmatrix}.$$

Unfortunately, we cannot associate this immediately with the weak neutral current because it couples only to left-handed states and we have seen that experimentally the weak neutral current has right-handed as well as left-handed components. Nevertheless, the idea of a triplet of weak isospin currents is appealing as they could form the basis for a gauge theory of weak interactions. Can we somehow include the electromagnetic current, j_μ^{em}, which couples to left- and right-handed particles, and at the same time preserve the $SU(2)_L$ symmetry?

To see how this is done we rewrite the electromagnetic current more precisely as

$$j_\mu^{\text{em}} = e\bar{\psi}\gamma_\mu Q\psi$$

where now e is the coupling constant, Q is the charge operator and ψ is the particle spinor: the eigenvalue of Q is -1 for the electron. The operator Q is the generator of a $U(1)_{\text{em}}$ symmetry group of the electromagnetic interactions. In 1961, Glashow[4] suggested the introduction of a 'weak hypercharge' current, j_μ^Y, given by

$$j_\mu^Y = \bar{\psi}\gamma_\mu Y\psi \tag{13.67}$$

in which the weak hypercharge Y is related to the third component of weak isospin through the analogue of the Gell-Mann–Nishijima relation

$$Q = I_3 + \tfrac{1}{2}Y. \tag{13.68}$$

Thus,

$$j_\mu^{\text{em}} = j_\mu^3 + \tfrac{1}{2}j_\mu^Y \tag{13.69}$$

so that the electromagnetic current is a linear combination of the third component of the weak isospin current and the weak hypercharge current. The weak isospin current couples only to doublets of left-handed particles while the weak hypercharge couples to both left-handed doublets and right-handed singlets. A link has thus been forged between the electromagnetic current and the weak currents through the introduction of the weak hypercharge. The hypercharge is the generator of a group $U(1)_Y$ so that this unification of the weak and electromagnetic interactions has revealed a larger underlying symmetry group, $SU(2)_L \otimes U(1)_Y$, where $SU(2)_L$ refers to weak isospin, involving only left-handed particles, while $U(1)_Y$ refers to weak hypercharge in which particles of both chirality or handedness are involved. It is remarkable that these ideas were put forward well before the discovery of weak neutral currents.

Before continuing with the unification of the weak and electromagnetic interactions let us determine the new quantum numbers, weak isospin and weak hypercharge, of the participating particles. We do this for the first generation of particles consisting of the neutrino, the electron and the u and d quarks. We assign the neutrino and the left-handed electron to a weak isospin doublet, the neutrino having $I_3 = +\frac{1}{2}$ and the electron $I_3 = -\frac{1}{2}$, and the right-handed electron to a singlet. As noted earlier, the underlying symmetry group is in fact a product of groups so that the group generators commute. In other words, members of a given weak isospin multiplet will have a common hypercharge. From (13.69)

Table 13.2
Weak isospin and weak hypercharge assignments for fermions

	I	I_3	Q	Y
ν_e, ν_μ, ν_τ	$\frac{1}{2}$	$+\frac{1}{2}$	0	-1
e_L^-, μ_L^-, τ_L^-	$\frac{1}{2}$	$-\frac{1}{2}$	-1	-1
e_R^-, μ_R^-, τ_R^-	0	0	-1	-2
u_L, c_L, t_L	$\frac{1}{2}$	$+\frac{1}{2}$	$+\frac{2}{3}$	$+\frac{1}{3}$
d'_L, s'_L, b'_L	$\frac{1}{2}$	$-\frac{1}{2}$	$-\frac{1}{3}$	$+\frac{1}{3}$
u_R, c_R, t_R	0	0	$+\frac{2}{3}$	$+\frac{4}{3}$
d'_R, s'_R, b'_R	0	0	$-\frac{1}{3}$	$-\frac{2}{3}$

we have

$$j_\mu^Y = 2j_\mu^{\text{em}} - 2j_\mu^3$$

so that, for the electron multiplets,

$$\begin{aligned} j_\mu^Y &= -2(\bar{e}_R\gamma_\mu e_R + \bar{e}_L\gamma_\mu e_L) - (\bar{\nu}_L\gamma_\mu\nu_L - \bar{e}_L\gamma_\mu e_L) \\ &= -2(\bar{e}_R\gamma_\mu e_R) - (\bar{\nu}_L\gamma_\mu\nu_L + \bar{e}_L\gamma_\mu e_L) \\ &= -2(\bar{e}_R\gamma_\mu e_R) - 1(\bar{\chi}_L\gamma_\mu\chi_L). \end{aligned}$$

The isospin singlet state e_R has $Y = -2$ and the doublet $(\nu_e, e)_L$ has $Y = -1$. In a similar fashion the left-handed quark states (u_L, d'_L), where d' is the Cabibbo-rotated state, are assigned to a doublet with $I_3 = +\frac{1}{2}$ for u_L and $I_3 = -\frac{1}{2}$ for d'_L and the right-handed quarks u_R and d'_R are weak isospin singlets. In this case we have

$$\begin{aligned} j_\mu^Y &= \tfrac{4}{3}(\bar{u}_R\gamma_\mu u_R + \bar{u}_L\gamma_\mu u_L) - \tfrac{2}{3}(\bar{d}'_R\gamma_\mu d'_R + \bar{d}'_L\gamma_\mu d'_L) - (\bar{u}_L\gamma_\mu u_L - \bar{d}'_L\gamma_\mu d'_L) \\ &= \tfrac{4}{3}(\bar{u}_R\gamma_\mu u_R) - \tfrac{2}{3}(\bar{d}'_R\gamma_\mu d'_R) + \tfrac{1}{3}(\bar{u}_L\gamma_\mu u_L + \bar{d}'_L\gamma_\mu d'_L) \end{aligned}$$

so that the left-handed doublet has $Y = \frac{1}{3}$ while the singlet states u_R and d'_R have $Y = \frac{4}{3}$ and $-\frac{2}{3}$ respectively. The extension to the second and third generation is straightforward and the results are summarized in table 13.2.

13.6.4 The Glashow–Weinberg–Salam model

In the Glashow–Weinberg–Salam (GWS) model of electroweak interactions the three weak isospin currents couple with a strength g to a weak isotriplet of vector gauge bosons, **W**, and the weak hypercharge current couples with strength conventionally written $g'/2$ to an isosinglet vector gauge boson B. The interaction, of the form

$$-\mathrm{i}\left(g\boldsymbol{j}_\mu\cdot\boldsymbol{W}^\mu + \frac{g'}{2}j_\mu^Y B^\mu\right) \tag{13.70}$$

completely describes the whole of electrodynamics and the weak interactions. The quantities $\boldsymbol{j}_\mu$ and $\boldsymbol{W}^\mu$ are vectors in weak isospin space. Writing out the scalar product explicitly, we have

$$\boldsymbol{j}_\mu \cdot \boldsymbol{W}^\mu = j_\mu^1 W^{\mu 1} + j_\mu^2 W^{\mu 2} + j_\mu^3 W^{\mu 3}$$

and, in terms of the charged currents,

$$j_\mu^\pm = j_\mu^1 \pm \mathrm{i} j_\mu^2$$

we obtain

$$\boldsymbol{j}_\mu \cdot \boldsymbol{W}^\mu = \frac{1}{\sqrt{2}} j_\mu^+ W^{\mu +} + \frac{1}{\sqrt{2}} j_\mu^- W^{\mu -} + j_\mu^3 W^{\mu 3} \tag{13.71}$$

where

$$W^{\mu\pm} = \frac{1}{\sqrt{2}}(W^{\mu 1} \mp \mathrm{i} W^{\mu 2}).$$

In (13.70) and (13.71) the fields $W^{\mu\pm}$ describe massive charged bosons, $W^\pm$, while $W^{\mu 3}$ and B^μ are neutral fields. In the GWS model the $SU(2)_L \otimes U(1)_Y$ symmetry is 'broken' and these neutral fields mix in such a way as to produce one linear combination which is massless (the photon) and an orthogonal combination which is massive (the Z^0 boson). Thus

$$A_\mu = B_\mu \cos\theta_W + W_\mu^3 \sin\theta_W \tag{13.72}$$

$$Z_\mu = -B_\mu \sin\theta_W + W_\mu^3 \cos\theta_W \tag{13.73}$$

where θ_W is the weak mixing angle. It is commonly called the Weinberg angle although it was first introduced by Glashow.[4] Expressions (13.72) and (13.73) are readily inverted to give

$$W_\mu^3 = A_\mu \sin\theta_W + Z_\mu \cos\theta_W \tag{13.74}$$

$$B_\mu = A_\mu \cos\theta_W - Z_\mu \sin\theta_W. \tag{13.75}$$

Then, from (13.70), the electroweak neutral-current interaction becomes

$$-\mathrm{i}\left(g j_\mu^3 W^{\mu 3} + \frac{g'}{2} j_\mu^Y B^\mu\right) = -\mathrm{i}\left(g \sin\theta_W j_\mu^3 + g' \cos\theta_W \frac{j_\mu^Y}{2}\right) A^\mu$$
$$- \mathrm{i}\left(g \cos\theta_W j_\mu^3 - g' \sin\theta_W \frac{j_\mu^Y}{2}\right) Z^\mu. \tag{13.76}$$

We identify the first term on the right-hand side with the electromagnetic interaction $-iej_\mu^{\text{em}}\mathbf{A}^\mu$, and, using equation (13.69), we find that the electroweak theory is consistent with ordinary QED provided

$$g \sin\theta_\text{W} = g' \cos\theta_\text{W} = e. \tag{13.77}$$

Thus, the weak mixing angle depends directly on the $\text{SU}(2)_\text{L}$ and $\text{U}(1)_Y$ coupling constants:

$$\tan\theta_\text{W} = \frac{g'}{g}. \tag{13.78}$$

The GWS theory does not predict the value of θ_W; it must be determined from experiment and, of course, for the theory to be valid, all electroweak phenomena must be describable in terms of a unique value of θ_W.

The second term in (13.76) is the weak neutral-current interaction. Again, using the expression

$$j_\mu^Y = 2j_\mu^{\text{em}} - 2j_\mu^3$$

and equation (13.77), this term may be rewritten

$$-\mathrm{i}\frac{g}{\cos\theta_\text{W}}(j_\mu^3 - \sin^2\theta_\text{W}\, j_\mu^{\text{em}})\mathbf{Z}^\mu \equiv -\mathrm{i}\frac{g}{\cos\theta_\text{W}} J_\mu^{\text{NC}}\mathbf{Z}^\mu. \tag{13.79}$$

Then,

$$J_\mu^{\text{NC}} = j_\mu^3 - \sin^2\theta_\text{W}\, j_\mu^{\text{em}}. \tag{13.80}$$

This equation shows the intimate connection between the weak and electromagnetic interactions. It demonstrates that, to the extent to which j_μ^3 is completely specified, through SU(2) symmetry, by the weak isospin currents j_μ^+ and j_μ^-, the charge-preserving or weak neutral current is completely specified by the charge-changing weak interactions and the electromagnetic interaction. Experimentally, the weak neutral current and the electromagnetic current couple both to left- and right-handed particles while the weak isospin currents j_μ^+ and j_μ^- couple only to left-handed particles. In the linear combination $J_\mu^{\text{NC}} + \sin^2\theta_\text{W}\, j_\mu^{\text{em}}$, the right-handed components exactly cancel to leave a pure left-handed component, j_μ^3, of $\text{SU}(2)_\text{L}$.

The weak neutral current was given explicitly in equation (13.60):

$$J_\mu^{\text{NC}}(\text{f}) = \bar{u}_\text{f}\gamma_\mu\tfrac{1}{2}(c_\text{V}^\text{f} - c_\text{A}^\text{f}\gamma^5)u_\text{f}.$$

This expression reflects the fact that the weak neutral current is not pure V–A, i.e. it couples to both left- and right-handed particles. According

Table 13.3
Standard model predictions for the vector and axial vector couplings of the fermions to the Z^0

Fermion f	I_3^f	Q^f	c_A^f	c_V^f
ν_e, ν_μ, ν_τ	$+\frac{1}{2}$	0	$\frac{1}{2}$	$\frac{1}{2}$
e_L^-, μ_L^-, τ_L^-	$-\frac{1}{2}$	-1	$-\frac{1}{2}$	$-\frac{1}{2} + 2\sin^2\theta_W$
u_L, c_L, t_L	$+\frac{1}{2}$	$+\frac{2}{3}$	$\frac{1}{2}$	$\frac{1}{2} - \frac{4}{3}\sin^2\theta_W$
d'_L, s'_L, b'_L	$-\frac{1}{2}$	$-\frac{1}{3}$	$-\frac{1}{2}$	$-\frac{1}{2} + \frac{2}{3}\sin^2\theta_W$
e_R^-, μ_R^-, τ_R^-	0	-1	0	$2\sin^2\theta_W$
u_R, c_R, t_R	0	$+\frac{2}{3}$	0	$-\frac{4}{3}\sin^2\theta_W$
d'_R, s'_R, b'_R	0	$-\frac{1}{3}$	0	$\frac{2}{3}\sin^2\theta_W$

to (13.79) the weak neutral-current interaction is

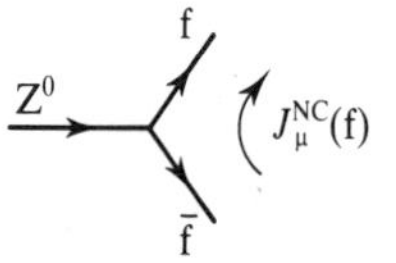

$$-i\frac{g}{\cos\theta_W}(j_\mu^3 - \sin^2\theta_W j_\mu^{em})Z^\mu$$

$$= -i\frac{g}{\cos\theta_W}\bar{u}_f\gamma_\mu[\tfrac{1}{2}(1-\gamma^5)I_3 - Q\sin^2\theta_W]u_f Z^\mu. \tag{13.81}$$

The factor $\frac{1}{2}(1-\gamma^5)$ simply expresses the fact that the weak isospin doublets are left handed. The vector and axial vector couplings, c_V^f and c_A^f, are given by the coefficients of the terms $\bar{u}_f\gamma_\mu u_f$ and $\bar{u}_f\gamma_\mu\gamma^5 u_f$ respectively. Examination of (13.81) shows that the GWS model predictions for c_V^f and c_A^f are

$$\begin{aligned} c_V^f &= I_3^f - 2Q^f\sin^2\theta_W \\ c_A^f &= I_3^f \end{aligned} \tag{13.82}$$

where I_3^f and Q^f are respectively the third component of weak isospin and the charge of fermion f. The standard model predictions are given explicitly in table 13.3.

In section 11.9 we found a relation between the Fermi coupling constant G and the $SU(2)_L$ coupling g by comparing the two forms of the amplitude for charged-current interactions: we obtained

$$\frac{G}{\sqrt{2}} = \frac{g^2}{8m_W^2}. \tag{13.83}$$

A similar comparison can be made for the amplitudes for neutral current processes but one must be aware of the normalization convention commonly used for neutral currents. As we know, neutral currents are not pure V–A, i.e. $c_V \neq c_A$, and a general neutral current is written

$$J_\mu^{NC}(f) = \bar{u}_f \gamma_\mu \tfrac{1}{2}(c_V^f - c_A^f \gamma^5) u_f.$$

However, for neutrinos, $c_V = c_A = \frac{1}{2}$, and

$$J_\mu^{NC}(\nu) = \tfrac{1}{2}[\bar{u}_\nu \gamma_\mu \tfrac{1}{2}(1 - \gamma^5) u_\nu].$$

The invariant amplitude for an arbitrary neutral current process is therefore written

$$\mathcal{M}^{NC} = \frac{4G}{\sqrt{2}} 2(J^{NC})^\mu (J^{NC})_\mu.$$

This is to be compared with

$$\mathcal{M}^{NC} = \frac{g}{\cos\theta_W}(J^{NC})^\mu \frac{1}{m_Z^2} \frac{g}{\cos\theta_W}(J^{NC})_\mu$$

and hence

$$\frac{G}{\sqrt{2}} = \frac{g^2}{8m_Z^2 \cos^2\theta_W}. \tag{13.84}$$

Together, (13.83) and (13.84) show that the boson masses and the weak mixing angle are related by

$$m_W = m_Z \cos\theta_W. \tag{13.85}$$

Finally, on eliminating θ_W from the expressions $g \sin\theta_W = g' \cos\theta_W = e$ we obtain the universal relation

$$\frac{gg'}{\sqrt{(g^2 + g'^2)}} = e. \tag{13.86}$$

13.6.5 Yang–Mills fields and SU(2) symmetry

As a preliminary to a consideration of the gauge invariance of the electroweak interactions let us explore the consequences of imposing local gauge invariance on the Lagrangian for two non-interacting spin $\frac{1}{2}$ fields ψ_1 and ψ_2. The free-field Lagrangian is simply the sum of two Dirac Lagrangians, namely

$$\mathcal{L} = i\bar{\psi}_1 \gamma^\mu \partial_\mu \psi_1 - m_1 \bar{\psi}_1 \psi_1 + i\bar{\psi}_2 \gamma^\mu \partial_\mu \psi_2 - m\bar{\psi}_2 \psi_2. \tag{13.87}$$

Equation (13.87) can be written more compactly by assuming that ψ_1 and ψ_2 transform as a doublet under an internal SU(2) symmetry group such as isospin. Then, with $m_1 = m_2$ (13.87) becomes

$$\mathscr{L} = \mathrm{i}\bar{\psi}\gamma^{\mu}\partial_{\mu}\psi - m\bar{\psi}\psi \tag{13.88}$$

where

$$\psi \equiv \begin{pmatrix}\psi_1\\ \psi_2\end{pmatrix}.$$

This looks like the ordinary Dirac Lagrangian, but here $\bar{\psi}$ is a row vector and ψ a column vector in isospin space.

We require the Lagrangian (13.88) to be invariant under an infinitesimal local gauge transformation

$$\psi(x) \to [1 - \mathrm{i}g\boldsymbol{\Lambda}(x)\cdot\boldsymbol{I}]\psi(x) \tag{13.89}$$

where $\boldsymbol{\Lambda}(x)$ is an arbitrary infinitesimal vector in isospin space and $\boldsymbol{I} = (I_1, I_2, I_3)$ is the isospin operator. The components I_i are the generators of SU(2) transformations. We recall that the I_i do not commute:

$$[I_i, I_j] = \mathrm{i}\epsilon_{ijk}I_k$$

(cf. equation (8.39)). For this reason the gauge group is said to be non-Abelian. In analogy with QED (cf. equation (13.43)) the Lagrangian in the present case can be made gauge invariant by introducing a covariant derivative,

$$\mathscr{D}_{\mu} \equiv \partial_{\mu} + \mathrm{i}g\boldsymbol{I}\cdot\boldsymbol{W}_{\mu}$$

where the $W_{i\mu}$ $(i = 1, 2, 3)$ are an isospin triplet of Yang–Mills gauge fields, which, in order to maintain gauge invariance, must transform as

$$\boldsymbol{W}_{\mu}(x) \to \boldsymbol{W}_{\mu}(x) + \partial_{\mu}\boldsymbol{\Lambda}(x) + g\boldsymbol{\Lambda}(x) \wedge \boldsymbol{W}_{\mu}(x). \tag{13.90}$$

This transformation on the gauge fields is more complicated than the corresponding one, equation (13.44), in QED. The essential difference is the third term which arises because the generators I_i do not commute.

To complete the Lagrangian, one might proceed as in QED by introducing a kinetic energy term

$$\mathscr{L}_{\mathrm{W}} = -\tfrac{1}{4}\boldsymbol{W}_{\mu\nu}\cdot\boldsymbol{W}^{\mu\nu}$$

which might be expected to describe the propagation of the free gauge bosons. However, in the present case, the form of $\boldsymbol{W}_{\mu\nu}$ required to maintain gauge invariance of $\mathscr{L}_W$ is

$$\boldsymbol{W}_{\mu\nu} = \partial_\mu \boldsymbol{W}_\nu - \partial_\nu \boldsymbol{W}_\mu - g\boldsymbol{W}_\mu \wedge \boldsymbol{W}_\nu \tag{13.91}$$

so that, in addition to the normal kinetic energy term, we have a term in $\boldsymbol{W}_\mu \wedge \boldsymbol{W}_\nu$ which introduces the *self-coupling* of three and four gauge bosons into the theory. With this choice of $\boldsymbol{W}_{\mu\nu}$, the complete Lagrangian

$$\mathscr{L} = \bar{\psi}(\mathrm{i}\gamma^\mu \mathscr{D}_\mu - m)\psi - \tfrac{1}{4}\boldsymbol{W}_{\mu\nu}\cdot\boldsymbol{W}^{\mu\nu} \tag{13.92}$$

is locally gauge invariant. As in the QED case, the addition of a mass term, $m^2\boldsymbol{W}^\mu\cdot\boldsymbol{W}_\mu$, to (13.92) would spoil the gauge invariance. Consequently, the Yang–Mills theory requires the existence of massless gauge bosons.

Yang and Mills[5] were originally motivated by a desire to incorporate (strong) isospin invariance in the strong interactions. They envisaged the isospin doublet of equal mass spin $\frac{1}{2}$ particles to be the proton and neutron: the small mass difference would presumably be attributed to the breaking of the isospin symmetry by the electromagnetic interaction. A stumbling block to the validity of the theory is the requirement of the existence of a massless isotriplet of spin 1 particles: such particles do not exist. This example of a non-Abelian gauge theory does, however, provide a useful model which, when extended to a higher symmetry than SU(2), namely $\mathrm{SU(3)_{colour}} \times \mathrm{SU(2)_L} \times \mathrm{U(1)}_Y$, together with the Higgs mechanism as a means of providing masses to the gauge bosons, leads to the standard model of elementary particle physics.

13.6.6 Gauge invariance of electroweak interactions

In the GWS model left-handed leptons and quarks are assigned to weak isospin doublets, i.e. they transform as doublets under $\mathrm{SU(2)_L}$. Massive leptons and quarks can exist in right-handed states and these are assigned to weak isospin singlets. They are unaffected by $\mathrm{SU(2)_L}$ transformations. We assume zero mass for the neutrinos which are therefore uniquely assigned to left-handed doublets. In order to incorporate the electric charge and bring about the unification of the weak and electromagnetic interactions a new gauge symmetry, $\mathrm{U(1)}_Y$, was introduced. The charge, weak isospin and weak hypercharge are related through the analogue of the Gell-Mann–Nishijima relation $Q = I_3 + \frac{1}{2}Y$. Left-handed particles transform in a non-trivial way under both $\mathrm{SU(2)_L}$ and $\mathrm{U(1)}_Y$ while right-handed particles transform non-trivially under $\mathrm{U(1)}_Y$ but are unaffected by $\mathrm{SU(2)_L}$ transformations.

We require local gauge invariance under both $\mathrm{SU(2)_L}$ and, independently, $\mathrm{U(1)}_Y$, and, as in QED, this will introduce *interactions* into the free-field

Lagrangian. The case of $\mathrm{SU}(2)_{\mathrm{L}}$ is formally equivalent to the Yang–Mills theory of the last section. In the present case the interaction, with a strength g, is between a triplet of weak isospin currents and a triplet of massless gauge fields $\boldsymbol{W}^{\mu}$. Invariance under $\mathrm{U}(1)_{Y}$ introduces an interaction, with strength $g'/2$, between a weak hypercharge current and a fourth massless gauge field B^{μ}.

We write the free-field Lagrangian for a left-handed fermion doublet and a right-handed singlet as*

$$\mathscr{L} = \mathrm{i}\bar{\psi}_{\mathrm{L}}\gamma^{\mu}\partial_{\mu}\psi_{\mathrm{L}} + \mathrm{i}\bar{\psi}_{\mathrm{R}}\gamma^{\mu}\partial_{\mu}\psi_{\mathrm{R}}. \tag{13.93}$$

Under local infinitesimal gauge transformations the fermion fields transform as indicated below:

$$\begin{array}{ll} \mathrm{SU}(2)_{\mathrm{L}} & \mathrm{U}(1)_{Y} \\ \psi_{\mathrm{L}}(x) \to [1 - \mathrm{i}g\boldsymbol{\Lambda}(x)\cdot\boldsymbol{I}]\psi_{\mathrm{L}}(x) & \psi_{\mathrm{L}}(x) \to [1 - \mathrm{i}(g'/2)\lambda(x)Y]\psi_{\mathrm{L}}(x) \\ \psi_{\mathrm{R}} \to \psi_{\mathrm{R}} & \psi_{\mathrm{R}}(x) \to [1 - \mathrm{i}(g'/2)\lambda(x)Y]\psi_{\mathrm{R}}(x). \end{array} \tag{13.94}$$

In (13.94) $\boldsymbol{\Lambda}(x)$ is an arbitrary infinitesimal vector in weak isospin space and $\lambda(x)$ is an arbitrary infinitesimal scalar in weak hypercharge space. The Lagrangian can be made invariant by introducing the covariant derivative

$$\mathscr{D}_{\mu} = \partial_{\mu} + \mathrm{i}g\boldsymbol{I}\cdot\boldsymbol{W}_{\mu} + \mathrm{i}(g'/2)YB_{\mu} \tag{13.95}$$

provided that under $\mathrm{SU}(2)_{\mathrm{L}}$ and $\mathrm{U}(1)_{Y}$ the gauge fields transform as

$$\begin{array}{ll} \mathrm{SU}(2)_{\mathrm{L}} & \mathrm{U}(1)_{Y} \\ \boldsymbol{W}_{\mu} \to \boldsymbol{W}_{\mu} + \partial_{\mu}\boldsymbol{\Lambda}(x) + g\boldsymbol{\Lambda}(x) \wedge \boldsymbol{W}_{\mu} & \boldsymbol{W}_{\mu} \to \boldsymbol{W}_{\mu} \\ B_{\mu} \to B_{\mu} & B_{\mu} \to B_{\mu} + \partial_{\mu}\lambda(x). \end{array} \tag{13.96}$$

Finally, we introduce the 'kinetic energy' terms for the gauge fields, $-\frac{1}{4}\boldsymbol{W}_{\mu\nu}\cdot\boldsymbol{W}^{\mu\nu}$ and $-\frac{1}{4}B_{\mu\nu}B^{\mu\nu}$, and arrive at the gauge invariant electroweak Lagrangian

$$\begin{aligned} \mathscr{L} = {} & \bar{\psi}_{\mathrm{L}}\gamma^{\mu}[\mathrm{i}\partial_{\mu} - g\boldsymbol{I}\cdot\boldsymbol{W}_{\mu} - (g'/2)YB_{\mu}]\psi_{\mathrm{L}} \\ & + \bar{\psi}_{\mathrm{R}}\gamma^{\mu}[\mathrm{i}\partial_{\mu} - (g'/2)YB_{\mu}]\psi_{\mathrm{R}} - \tfrac{1}{4}\boldsymbol{W}_{\mu\nu}\cdot\boldsymbol{W}^{\mu\nu} - \tfrac{1}{4}B_{\mu\nu}B^{\mu\nu}. \end{aligned} \tag{13.97}$$

* We neglect the fermion mass because the mass term $m\bar{\psi}\psi$ is not invariant under $\mathrm{SU}(2)_{\mathrm{L}}$.

Here,

$$B_{\mu\nu} \equiv \partial_\mu B_\nu - \partial_\nu B_\mu$$

but, as in the Yang–Mills theory,

$$\boldsymbol{W}_{\mu\nu} = \partial_\mu \boldsymbol{W}_\nu - \partial_\nu \boldsymbol{W}_\mu - g\boldsymbol{W}_\mu \wedge \boldsymbol{W}_\nu.$$

Thus, in addition to the kinetic energy term,

$$(\partial_\mu \boldsymbol{W}_\nu - \partial_\nu \boldsymbol{W}_\mu)\cdot(\partial^\mu \boldsymbol{W}^\nu - \partial^\nu \boldsymbol{W}^\mu),$$

self-coupling of the $\boldsymbol{W}_\mu$ fields also appears in the theory. Note that mass terms such as $\frac{1}{2}m^2 B_\mu B^\mu$ are not gauge invariant and therefore cannot be added to the Lagrangian. The theory as it stands is therefore deficient in this respect. We turn to this difficulty next.

13.6.7 Spontaneous symmetry breaking and the Higgs vacuum

The actual mass spectrum of gauge bosons is quite different from that required by local gauge invariance of the electroweak interaction under $SU(2)_L$ and $U(1)_Y$ transformations. The symmetry demands massless gauge bosons while in practice the $W^\pm$ and Z^0 are massive, 81 and 91 GeV respectively, and the photon has zero mass. The symmetry is said to be 'spontaneously broken' by the Higgs[1] mechanism, which postulates the existence of an all-pervading matter field – the Higgs field. This field is scalar under spatial rotations, and therefore has spin 0 quanta, but is a doublet in weak isospin space. The Higgs field couples in a symmetric manner to leptons, quarks and the massive gauge bosons $W^\pm$ and Z^0, but crucially, *the ground state of the system – the vacuum – is assumed to be asymmetric.* This asymmetry arises from a Hamiltonian that is *symmetric* in weak isospin space but which has a minimum when one component of the doublet has a *non-zero* value in the vacuum. There is then a 'preferred direction' in weak isospin space and the weak isospin symmetry is 'hidden'.

This apparently abstract idea in fact occurs in many physical phenomena, the best known of which is probably ferromagnetism. This analogy helps us to understand how it may be energetically more favourable for the ground state to be one in which a particular field, in this case the magnetization $M(\boldsymbol{x})$, has a non-zero value. Consider a ferromagnetic crystal. The Hamiltonian describing the spin–spin interaction is invariant under spatial rotations, and yet below the Curie temperature T_C (the ferromagnetic transition temperature) the ground state is not. In the ground state the spins are aligned in the direction of magnetization, which is thus a preferred direction in space, although *any* direction of spin alignment is equally possible. An observer inside the crystal would be unaware of the rotational symmetry: although hidden it is, nevertheless, still there. This situation, in which the ground state does not manifest the symmetry of the Hamiltonian, is commonly described as 'spontaneously broken symmetry', although a more accurate term would be 'hidden symmetry'. It would be difficult, but possible, for our observer inside the crystal to make appropriate measurements which would reveal the underlying rotational symmetry.

Below the Curie temperature the ground state of the ferromagnet has a non-zero value of the total spin. At the Curie temperature a phase transition occurs, ordering of the spins takes place and the rotational symmetry becomes hidden: spontaneous magnetization occurs at $T = T_C$. The ground state configuration is determined by minimizing the energy density of the ferromagnet. The appropriate energy density is the Gibbs free energy density, G, which may be expanded in terms of the spontaneous magnetization $M(\boldsymbol{x})$,

$$G = \alpha M^2(\boldsymbol{x}) + \beta M^4(\boldsymbol{x}) + \text{terms in } \nabla M(\boldsymbol{x}). \tag{13.98}$$

In the magnetically disordered phase, above the Curie temperature, the minimum occurs at $M = 0$, but at temperatures less than T_C, in the ordered phase, spontaneous magnetization takes place and the Gibbs free energy density has a minimum at some value $M = M_s \neq 0$. This behaviour can be modelled by taking $\beta > 0$ and allowing α to be temperature dependent with $\alpha < 0$ for $T < T_C$ and $\alpha > 0$ for $T > T_C$, as shown in figure 13.8. Below the transition temperature a state of stable equilibrium exists with a non-zero value of M.

Figure 13.8
The variation of the Gibbs free energy G with magnetization: curve (a), $T > T_C$; curve (b), $T < T_C$.

In particle physics the analogous entity, with a non-zero vacuum expectation value, is the Higgs field. The Higgs field is unlike all the other fields encountered in particle physics: the electromagnetic, weak and strong fields and those that describe the fermions have fluctuations about a vanishing expectation value in the vacuum. Due to the asymmetry in the 'Higgs vacuum', phenomena arising from the coupling of the Higgs field to fermions and gauge bosons no longer manifest the underlying hidden gauge symmetry. At energies much greater than 100 GeV all masses become negligible and the symmetry becomes manifest. At low energies, however, the symmetry is hidden and it is difficult to observe the gauge invariance of the electroweak interaction. Here, we are in the position of our observer inside the ferromagnet attempting to discover the underlying rotational symmetry. At low energies the symmetry is broken in such a way that the coupling of the Higgs field to the gauge fields, $\boldsymbol{W}_\mu$ and B_μ, yields $W^\pm$ and Z^0 masses in the region of 100 GeV while the photon remains massless. It is remarkable that in recent years 'low energy' observations have been made on weak and electromagnetic phenomena which have revealed the underlying gauge symmetry of the electroweak interaction.

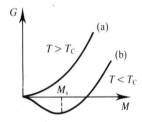

Whether or not the Higgs mechanism is indeed the correct symmetry-breaking mechanism remains to be seen. In its simplest form the theory requires the existence of an electrically neutral, scalar Higgs boson which to date has escaped discovery. Searches for the Higgs boson are made more difficult by the fact that the theory sheds no light on its expected mass. In the next sections we give a more quantitative account of spontaneous symmetry breaking in preparation for a discussion of the application of the Higgs mechanism to the GWS model of electroweak interactions.

13.6.8 Spontaneous breaking of a discrete symmetry

We recall that the Lagrangian for a scalar field

$$\mathscr{L} = \tfrac{1}{2}(\partial_\mu\varphi)(\partial^\mu\varphi) - \tfrac{1}{2}m\varphi^2$$

leads to the equation of motion

$$\partial_\mu\partial^\mu\varphi + m^2\varphi = 0$$

describing a particle of spin 0 and mass m. Consider now the Lagrangian

$$\mathscr{L} = \tfrac{1}{2}(\partial_\mu\varphi)(\partial^\mu\varphi) - \tfrac{1}{2}\mu^2\varphi^2 - \tfrac{1}{4}\lambda\varphi^4 \qquad (13.99)$$

in which μ and λ are constants with $\mu^2 < 0$ and $\lambda > 0$. This Lagrangian has reflection symmetry: it is invariant under the operation $\varphi \to -\varphi$. With the condition $\mu^2 < 0$ we cannot immediately interpret the φ^2 term as a mass term because the mass would be imaginary. In order to interpret this Lagrangian correctly one has to understand that the calculation of amplitudes using the Feynman rules is a perturbation technique in which the fields are treated as fluctuations around the state of minimum energy – the ground state or the 'vacuum'. In the Lagrangians we have studied so far the ground state has always been the trivial one, $\varphi = 0$. In the present case, however, $\varphi = 0$ is not the ground state. To find the true ground state we regard the Lagrangian as a kinetic energy term $T = \tfrac{1}{2}(\partial_\mu\varphi)(\partial^\mu\varphi)$ minus a potential energy term V with

$$V(\varphi) = \tfrac{1}{2}\mu^2\varphi^2 + \tfrac{1}{4}\lambda\varphi^4.$$

The extrema of V satisfy

$$\frac{\partial V}{\partial\varphi} = \varphi(\mu^2 + \lambda\varphi^2) = 0$$

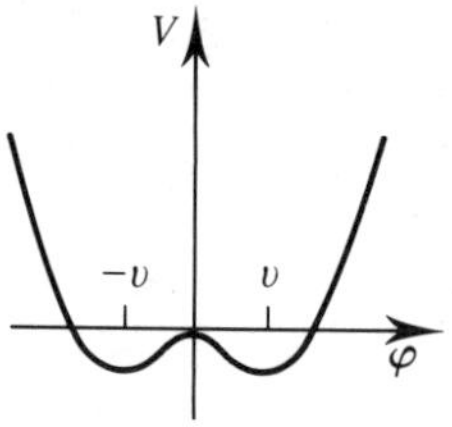

Figure 13.9
The potential $V(\varphi) = \frac{1}{2}\mu^2\varphi^2 + \frac{1}{4}\lambda\varphi^4$ with $\mu^2 < 0$ and $\lambda > 0$.

so that either $\varphi = 0$ or $\varphi = \pm v$ with $v = \sqrt{(-\mu^2/\lambda)}$. Figure 13.9 shows a sketch of $V(\varphi)$ for $\mu^2 < 0$ and $\lambda > 0$. As can be seen, the extremum $\varphi = 0$ is not a minimum:* there are two minima at $\varphi = \pm v$. The Feynman calculus must be formulated in terms of quantum fluctuations around either of these ground states. Without loss of generality we choose $\varphi = +v$ and introduce a new field, $\chi(x)$, in terms of which the original field is given by

$$\varphi(x) = v + \chi(x)$$

so that $\chi(x)$ represents fluctuations around the ground state $\varphi = +v$. In terms of this new field the Lagrangian becomes

$$\mathscr{L} = \tfrac{1}{2}(\partial_\mu\chi)(\partial^\mu\chi) - \lambda v^2\chi^2 - \lambda v\chi^3 - \tfrac{1}{4}\lambda\chi^4 + \tfrac{1}{4}\lambda v^4. \tag{13.100}$$

The last term in the Lagrangian, being a constant, has no significance. But, on comparing (13.99) and (13.100), we see that the particular operation we have performed, a simple translation of the axes, has led to an intriguing result. The second term now has the correct sign to be interpreted as a mass term with the mass of the χ field quantum given by

$$m_\chi = \sqrt{(2\lambda v^2)} = \sqrt{(-2\mu^2)}.$$

The third and fourth terms represent respectively cubic and quartic self-interactions of the χ field as shown in figure 13.10. We stress that the Lagrangians (13.99) and (13.100) describe the same physical system. In (13.99) the mass is 'hidden' but, through a simple translation of axes, has been revealed in (13.100). The original Lagrangian has reflection symmetry – it is even in φ – whereas the new Lagrangian (13.100) is not even in χ: the symmetry has been spontaneously† broken. The vacuum around which the perturbation calculation is performed does not possess the reflection symmetry of the Lagrangian: the overall symmetry of the system is hidden by our selection of a particular ground state, $\varphi = +v$ rather than $\varphi = -v$. If one knew how to perform the calculations correctly the two equivalent Lagrangians would give the same result. However, the Feynman calculus involves a perturbation expansion. Lagrangian (13.99) leads to a divergent series because the expansion is about the unstable point $\varphi = 0$, and the correct physics cannot be extracted, whereas Lagrangian (13.100) leads to a convergent series which does describe the physics correctly.

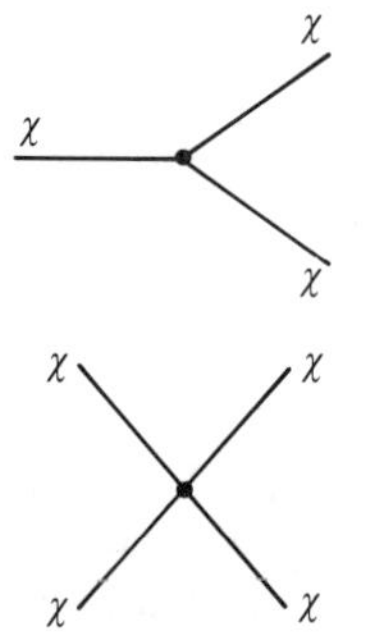

Figure 13.10
Cubic and quartic self-interactions of the χ field.

The spontaneously broken symmetry discussed above is an example of

---

* Had we chosen $\mu^2 > 0$, $V(\varphi)$ would have had one minimum at $\varphi = 0$. The Lagrangian would then have a standard mass term $m_\varphi = \mu$.

† The symmetry breaking is spontaneous because no *external* influence is responsible.

a *discrete* symmetry because there are only two ground states. In the next section we consider what happens when a *continuous* symmetry is spontaneously broken.

13.6.9 Spontaneous breaking of a continuous symmetry: the Goldstone theorem

Consider a complex scalar field, $\varphi = 2^{-1/2}(\varphi_1 + i\varphi_2)$, described by the Lagrangian

$$\mathscr{L} = (\partial_\mu \varphi)^*(\partial^\mu \varphi) - \mu^2 \varphi^* \varphi - \lambda(\varphi^* \varphi)^2. \qquad (13.101)$$

It is clear on inspection that this Lagrangian possesses U(1) global gauge symmetry, i.e. it is invariant under the transformation $\varphi \to \varphi' = e^{i\alpha}\varphi$ where α is a constant. Written in terms of φ_1 and φ_2 (13.101) becomes

$$\mathscr{L} = \tfrac{1}{2}(\partial_\mu \varphi_1)^2 + \tfrac{1}{2}(\partial_\mu \varphi_2)^2 - \tfrac{1}{2}\mu^2(\varphi_1^2 + \varphi_2^2) - \tfrac{1}{4}\lambda(\varphi_1^2 + \varphi_2^2)^2. \qquad (13.102)$$

As in the previous section we identify the potential energy as

$$V(\varphi_1, \varphi_2) = \tfrac{1}{2}\mu^2(\varphi_1^2 + \varphi_2^2) + \tfrac{1}{4}\lambda(\varphi_1^2 + \varphi_2^2)^2.$$

$V(\varphi_1, \varphi_2)$ is sketched in figure 13.11 on the assumption that $\mu^2 < 0$ and

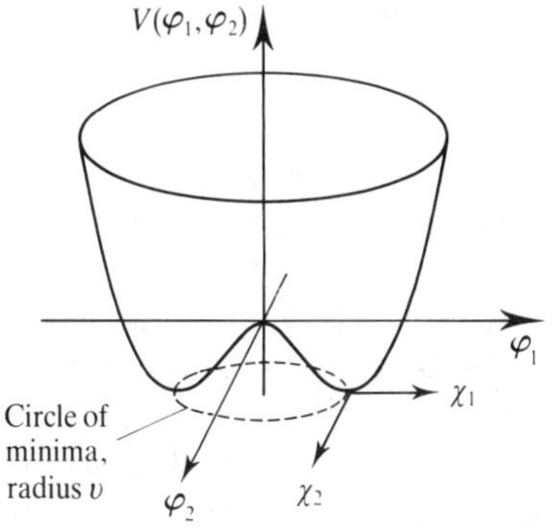

Figure 13.11
The potential $V(\varphi_1, \varphi_2)$ for a complex scalar field with $\mu^2 < 0$ and $\lambda > 0$.

$\lambda > 0$. In this case $V(\varphi_1, \varphi_2)$ has minima on the circle, $\varphi_1^2 + \varphi_2^2 = v^2$, where $v = \sqrt{(-\mu^2/\lambda)}$. As before, we select a particular ground state which, without loss of generality, we choose to be $\varphi_1 = v$ and $\varphi_2 = 0$ and introduce new fields $\chi_1(x)$ and $\chi_2(x)$ such that

$$\varphi_1(x) = v + \chi_1(x)$$

$$\varphi_2(x) = \chi_2(x).$$

Then,

$$\varphi(x) = 2^{-1/2}[v + \chi_1(x) + i\chi_2(x)] \tag{13.103}$$

so that $\chi_1(x)$ and $\chi_2(x)$ represent fluctuations about the ground state $\varphi_1 = v$ and $\varphi_2 = 0$. In terms of the fields χ_1 and χ_2 the Lagrangian (13.102) becomes

$$\begin{aligned}\mathscr{L} = [\tfrac{1}{2}(\partial_\mu \chi_1)(\partial^\mu \chi_1) - \lambda v^2 \chi_1^2] + [\tfrac{1}{2}(\partial_\mu \chi_2)(\partial^\mu \chi_2)] \\ - [\lambda v(\chi_1^3 + \chi_1 \chi_2^2) + (\lambda/4)(\chi_1^4 + \chi_2^4 + 2\chi_1^2\chi_2^2)] + (\lambda/4)v^4.\end{aligned} \tag{13.104}$$

As before, the last term is constant and has no significance. The first term is a standard Klein–Gordon Lagrangian for a scalar field. It describes 'radial' oscillations χ_1, which have a mass

$$m_{\chi_1} = \sqrt{(2\lambda v^2)} = \sqrt{(-2\mu^2)}$$

which, since $\mu^2 < 0$, is acceptable. The third term represents various cubic and quartic field interactions shown in figure 13.12. There is a new and

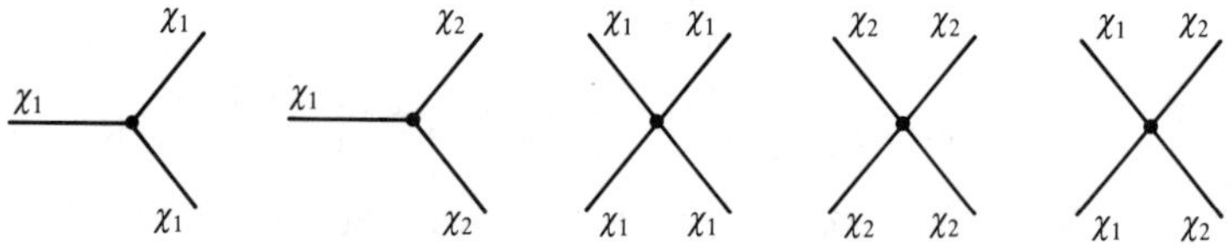

Figure 13.12
Cubic and quartic interactions of χ_1 and χ_2 fields.

important feature, however, which did not appear in the spontaneous breaking of a *discrete* symmetry. This is embodied in the second term of (13.104) which represents a scalar field with a *massless* field quantum. Equivalently, the second term describes oscillations, χ_2, around the equilibrium circle, with zero mass. Oscillations around the potential minimum are 'resistanceless' and such excitations are known as Goldstone bosons.

This model is a simple example of the Goldstone theorem[6,7] which states that the spontaneous breaking of a continuous global symmetry inevitably generates one or more massless scalar bosons. In the case of a ferromagnet, for example, these excitations are spin waves which tend to rotate the spins away from their aligned ground-state position. If the system is governed by short-range interactions, little energy is required to produce a gradual change with long wavelength and the excitations behave like massless Goldstone bosons.

13.6.10 *The Higgs mechanism*

The final step required to achieve our goal of generating masses for the $W^\pm$ and Z^0 bosons, while retaining a massless photon, is to extend our analysis to the spontaneous breaking of a *local* gauge symmetry, namely $SU(2)_L \times U(1)_Y$. The mechanism responsible for this spontaneous symmetry breaking is the Higgs mechanism.

We are familiar with the notion that space is filled with electromagnetic fields, the sources of which are electrically charged particles. In the Higgs mechanism the assumption is made that everywhere in space, fluctuations in the vacuum can occur which correspond to the emission or absorption of a Higgs boson, a spin 0, electrically neutral particle which carries weak isospin and weak hypercharge. Additionally, the Higgs boson is assumed to be a singlet in colour space. As a result of their interactions with the Higgs field, the $W^{\pm}$ and Z^0 bosons and the fermions (leptons and quarks) acquire mass, but gluons and the photon, which cannot interact with the Higgs field, remain massless. If the mechanism is correct, a specific choice of one of the vacuum states results in the spontaneous breaking of the local $SU(2) \times U(1)$ gauge symmetry and gives rise to the spectrum of particles we observe in the laboratory. Unfortunately, as we shall see, the theory does not predict the mass of the Higgs boson.

In its simplest form, the Higgs mechanism is essentially the Goldstone model of the last section with the addition of an electromagnetic interaction. This is introduced via the gauge principle of section 13.5, where we saw that the *interaction* between the matter field ψ and the gauge field A_μ was determined by demanding invariance of the Lagrangian under a local U(1) gauge transformation (see equation (13.41)),

$$\varphi(x) \to \varphi'(x) = \exp[iq\Lambda(x)]\,\varphi(x). \qquad (13.105)$$

We recall that when this transformation is performed on the Lagrangian, a term $\partial_\mu \Lambda(x)$ arises which can be cancelled by the introduction of a vector field $A_\mu(x)$ such that when φ changes according to (13.105), A_μ transforms as

$$A_\mu \to A'_\mu = A_\mu - \partial_\mu \Lambda. \qquad (13.106)$$

Simultaneously, ∂_μ is replaced in the Lagrangian by the U(1) covariant derivative

$$\mathscr{D}_\mu = \partial_\mu + iqA_\mu. \qquad (13.107)$$

With the introduction of the Goldstone potential $V(\varphi)$, the Lagrangian becomes

$$\mathscr{L} = (\partial_\mu - iqA_\mu)\varphi^*(\partial^\mu + iqA^\mu)\varphi - \mu^2\varphi^*\varphi - \lambda(\varphi^*\varphi)^2 - \tfrac{1}{4}F_{\mu\nu}F^{\mu\nu} \qquad (13.108)$$

with, as usual,

$$F_{\mu\nu} = \partial_\mu A_\nu - \partial_\nu A_\mu.$$

If, as in the last section, we take φ to be a complex scalar field and, as before, choose the particular ground state

$$\varphi_1 = v + \chi_1(x)$$

$$\varphi_2 = \chi_2(x)$$

the Lagrangian becomes

$$\mathscr{L} = [\tfrac{1}{2}(\partial_\mu \chi_1)(\partial^\mu \chi_1) - \lambda v^2 \chi_1^2] + [\tfrac{1}{2}(\partial_\mu \chi_2)(\partial^\mu \chi_2)] + \tfrac{1}{2}q^2 v^2 A_\mu A^\mu$$
$$- qvA_\mu \partial^\mu \chi_2 - \tfrac{1}{4}F_{\mu\nu}F^{\mu\nu} + \text{interaction terms.} \qquad (13.109)$$

If we try to interpret this Lagrangian in the usual way we run into difficulty. True, as before, the mass spectrum consists of a scalar field with a mass $m_{\chi_1} = \sqrt{(2\lambda v^2)}$ and a massless Goldstone boson χ_2. An intriguing additional feature, which encourages us in our attempt to generate masses for the W and Z bosons, is that the gauge field A_μ has acquired mass, $m_A = qv$. The presence of a cross term in the fields, $A_\mu \partial^\mu \chi_2$, which apparently allows the gauge field to transform into a χ_2 as it propagates, casts doubt on our interpretation of the mass spectrum. More importantly, in making our particular choice for the vacuum we have introduced an extra degree of freedom. We started with a Lagrangian in which there were four fields, or degrees of freedom, the two real scalar fields φ_1 and φ_2 and the massless vector field A_μ, with its two degrees of freedom corresponding to the two possible helicity states of the photon. By endowing the field with mass we inadvertently introduce an extra, $\lambda = 0$, helicity state. This is unphysical. A mere choice of ground state cannot introduce an extra degree of freedom into the system.

A way out of the dilemma is to note that the local gauge transformation (13.105) multiplies $\varphi(x)$ by a space–time dependent phase factor $q\Lambda(x)$. If, instead of (13.103) we parametrize φ in terms of its 'modulus' and 'phase'

$$\varphi(x) = \frac{1}{\sqrt{2}}[v + H(x)] \exp\left[\frac{i\theta(x)}{v}\right] \qquad (13.110)$$

with the fields $H(x)$ and $\theta(x)$ real, we should be able to find a suitable gauge $\Lambda(x)$ in (13.105) which enables us to eliminate the field $\boldsymbol{\theta}(x)$. According to (13.105), we have

$$\varphi'(x) = \exp[iq\Lambda(x)]\,\varphi(x)$$

so that, using (13.110),

$$[v + H'(x)] \exp[i\theta'(x)/v] = \exp[iq\Lambda(x)][v + H(x)] \exp[i\theta(x)/v] \qquad (13.111)$$

from which it follows that

$$
\begin{aligned}
H'(x) &= H(x) \\
\theta'(x) &= \theta(x) + qv\Lambda(x).
\end{aligned}
\tag{13.112}
$$

Thus, if we choose

$$\Lambda(x) = -\frac{1}{qv}\,\theta(x) \tag{13.113}$$

we have $\theta'(x) = 0$. How is this interpreted physically? The Goldstone modes that we introduced in the last section are actually oscillations in the parameter which distinguishes different vacuum states. In the present case this is the phase $q\Lambda(x)$. Equivalently, the Goldstone modes correspond to the quanta of the θ field. Through our choice of gauge, equation (13.113), we have $\theta' = 0$ so that the massless Goldstone boson will not appear in the particle spectrum. We have 'gauged away' the unwanted degree of freedom.

With the parametrization (13.110) of the complex scalar field $\varphi(x)$ we therefore expect the θ field not to appear explicitly in the Lagrangian. In the above 'unitary gauge' A_μ becomes

$$A'_\mu(x) = A_\mu(x) + \frac{1}{qv}\,\partial_\mu\theta(x) \tag{13.114}$$

and

$$\varphi'(x) = \frac{1}{\sqrt{2}}\,[v + H(x)]. \tag{13.115}$$

On substituting these expressions into (13.108) the Lagrangian becomes

$$
\begin{aligned}
\mathscr{L} = {} & [\tfrac{1}{2}(\partial_\mu H)^2 - \lambda v^2 H^2] + \tfrac{1}{2}q^2v^2A_\mu A^\mu + \tfrac{1}{2}q^2A_\mu A^\mu H^2 \\
& + q^2vA_\mu A^\mu H - \lambda v H^3 - \frac{\lambda}{4}H^4 - \tfrac{1}{4}F_{\mu\nu}F^{\mu\nu} + \frac{\lambda v^4}{4}
\end{aligned}
\tag{13.116}
$$

which is indeed independent of $\theta(x)$ as expected: the Goldstone boson has disappeared! The Lagrangian now correctly describes the desired mass spectrum: it represents two interacting massive particles, a Higgs scalar boson H with mass $m_H = \sqrt{(2\lambda v^2)}$, and a vector gauge boson A_μ, with mass $m_A = qv$. The other terms in the Lagrangian describe interactions between the fields and self-interactions. As usual, the final constant term has no significance. One can think of the massless Goldstone boson as being 'swallowed' by the gauge field to provide the extra longitudinal polarization required as the gauge boson acquires mass. The foregoing is known as the (Abelian) Higgs mechanism.

13.6.11 The Higgs mechanism and the Glashow–Weinberg–Salam model

In order to apply the Higgs mechanism to the GWS model we have to extend our study of the Abelian Higgs mechanism in the previous section to the appropriate symmetry, i.e. we have to study the spontaneous breaking of a local SU(2) × U(1) gauge symmetry.

We begin with SU(2) and, as before, take a Lagrangian

$$\mathscr{L} = (\partial_\mu \varphi)^\dagger (\partial^\mu \varphi) - \mu^2 \varphi^\dagger \varphi - \lambda(\varphi^\dagger \varphi)^2 \tag{13.117}$$

where φ is an SU(2) doublet of complex scalar fields:

$$\varphi = \begin{pmatrix} \varphi_a \\ \varphi_b \end{pmatrix} = \frac{1}{\sqrt{2}} \begin{pmatrix} \varphi_1 + i\varphi_2 \\ \varphi_3 + i\varphi_4 \end{pmatrix}. \tag{13.118}$$

The Lagrangian is manifestly invariant under global SU(2) transformations

$$\varphi \to \varphi' = \exp\left(\frac{i\Lambda_j \tau_j}{2}\right)\varphi \qquad (j = 1, 2, 3) \tag{13.119}$$

where the Λ_j are constant parameters independent of x and the τ_j are the usual Pauli matrices. To arrive at a locally gauge invariant Lagrangian we follow the steps of the last section (see also section 13.6.6) and introduce a gauge parameter $\boldsymbol{\Lambda}(x)$, which varies from point to point in space–time, and replace ∂_μ by the covariant derivative, analogous to (13.107),

$$\mathscr{D}_\mu = \partial_\mu + ig\frac{\tau_j}{2} W^j_\mu. \tag{13.120}$$

The W^j_μ are a triplet of gauge fields which, under an infinitesimal gauge transformation

$$\varphi(x) \to \varphi'(x) = [1 + \boldsymbol{\Lambda}(x)\cdot\boldsymbol{\tau}/2]\varphi(x) \tag{13.121}$$

transform as

$$\boldsymbol{W}_\mu \to \boldsymbol{W}_\mu - \frac{1}{g}\partial_\mu \boldsymbol{\Lambda} - \boldsymbol{\Lambda} \wedge \boldsymbol{W}_\mu. \tag{13.122}$$

We note that the potential

$$V(\varphi) = \mu^2 \varphi^\dagger \varphi - \lambda(\varphi^\dagger \varphi)^2 \tag{13.123}$$

in (13.117) is invariant under the local gauge transformation (13.121) and thus the gauge invariant Lagrangian is

$$\mathscr{L} = \left(\partial_\mu \varphi + \mathrm{i}g\frac{\tau}{2}\cdot \boldsymbol{W}_\mu \varphi\right)^\dagger \left(\partial^\mu \varphi + \mathrm{i}g\frac{\tau}{2}\cdot \boldsymbol{W}_\mu \varphi\right) - V(\varphi) - \tfrac{1}{4}\boldsymbol{W}_{\mu\nu}\cdot \boldsymbol{W}^{\mu\nu}. \tag{13.124}$$

The last term is the kinetic energy term of the gauge fields (see section 13.6.6).

As usual, we are interested in the case $\mu^2 < 0$ and $\lambda > 0$. Proceeding as before, $V(\varphi)$ has a minimum at

$$\varphi^\dagger \varphi = -\frac{\mu^2}{2\lambda} = \frac{v^2}{2}. \tag{13.125}$$

Now, φ is a column vector and $\varphi^\dagger$ a row vector so that

$$\varphi^\dagger \varphi = (\varphi_a^* \varphi_b^*)\begin{pmatrix}\varphi_a \\ \varphi_b\end{pmatrix} = \varphi_a^* \varphi_a + \varphi_b^* \varphi_b$$

or, in terms of the real field components,

$$\varphi^\dagger \varphi = \tfrac{1}{2}(\varphi_1^2 + \varphi_2^2 + \varphi_3^2 + \varphi_4^2) = v^2/2. \tag{13.126}$$

Clearly, the manifold of points satisfying (13.126) is continuous. We make the specific choice

$$\varphi_1 = \varphi_2 = \varphi_4 = 0 \qquad \varphi_3^2 = v^2 \tag{13.127}$$

and thereby spontaneously break the SU(2) symmetry which was manifest in (13.126). By singling out a specific direction in SU(2) space, the symmetry has become hidden.

We now expand $\varphi(x)$ about our chosen vacuum,

$$\varphi_0 = \frac{1}{\sqrt{2}}\begin{pmatrix}0 \\ v\end{pmatrix}. \tag{13.128}$$

As in the case of the U(1) symmetry in the last section we choose a gauge so that

$$\varphi(x) = \frac{1}{\sqrt{2}}\begin{pmatrix}0 \\ v + H(x)\end{pmatrix}. \tag{13.129}$$

In doing so we have gauged away three of the scalar fields and are left only with the Higgs field $H(x)$. The argument is similar to that used in the last section. We seek to parametrize arbitrary states $\varphi(x)$, which describe fluctuations around the vacuum state. By demanding local SU(2) invariance we are free to choose the direction of the isospin axes independently at each space–time point x so that we can align any arbitrary $\varphi(x)$ along the 'down' direction by performing the appropriate SU(2) rotation. Different $\varphi(x)$ will have different phases with respect to the 'down' direction, i.e. the phase $\boldsymbol{\theta}(x)$ is space–time dependent. An arbitrary φ may thus be parametrized in terms of its 'modulus' and 'phase'

$$\varphi(x) = \frac{1}{\sqrt{2}}\begin{pmatrix} 0 \\ v + H(x) \end{pmatrix} \exp\left[\frac{\mathrm{i}\boldsymbol{\theta}(x)\cdot\boldsymbol{\tau}}{2v}\right] \tag{13.130}$$

and, by suitably choosing the gauge parameter, $\boldsymbol{\Lambda}(x)$, we will be able to gauge away the $\boldsymbol{\theta}$ field. Indeed, under a local SU(2) transformation

$$\varphi(x) \to \varphi'(x) = \exp\left[\frac{\mathrm{i}\boldsymbol{\Lambda}(x)\cdot\boldsymbol{\tau}}{2}\right]\varphi(x)$$

so that, using (13.130),

$$\begin{pmatrix} 0 \\ v + H(x) \end{pmatrix} \exp\left[\frac{\mathrm{i}\boldsymbol{\theta}'(x)\cdot\boldsymbol{\tau}}{2v}\right] = \begin{pmatrix} 0 \\ v + H(x) \end{pmatrix} \exp\left\{\frac{\mathrm{i}[v\boldsymbol{\Lambda}(x) + \boldsymbol{\theta}(x)]\cdot\boldsymbol{\tau}}{2v}\right\}$$

and

$$\boldsymbol{\theta}'(x) \to \boldsymbol{\theta}(x) + v\boldsymbol{\Lambda}(x).$$

Thus, if we choose

$$\boldsymbol{\Lambda}(x) = -\boldsymbol{\theta}(x)/v$$

we get

$$\boldsymbol{\theta}'(x) = 0$$

and, dropping the prime, the field φ is just

$$\varphi(x) = \frac{1}{\sqrt{2}}\begin{pmatrix} 0 \\ v + H(x) \end{pmatrix}$$

which is indeed independent of $\boldsymbol{\theta}(x)$.

On inserting (13.129) into the Lagrangian (13.124) we find, after a little algebra, that

$$\mathscr{L} = [\tfrac{1}{2}(\partial_\mu H)^2 - \lambda v^2 H^2] + \frac{g^2 v^2}{8}[(W_\mu^1)^2 + (W_\mu^2)^2 + (W_\mu^3)^2]$$

$$+ \text{ higher order terms} + \text{kinetic energy terms for the } W \text{ fields.} \qquad (13.131)$$

This Lagrangian describes a massive Higgs scalar field with

$$m_{\text{H}} = \sqrt{(2\lambda v^2)} = \sqrt{(-2\mu^2)}$$

and three massive gauge fields with mass

$$m_{\text{W}} = \tfrac{1}{2} g v.$$

In acquiring this mass the gauge fields have 'swallowed' the three unwanted Goldstone bosons and the scalar degrees of freedom have provided the necessary longitudinal polarizations of the massive vector bosons.

The final step in our stated aim of assigning masses to the W and Z bosons in such a way that the photon remains massless is to extend the above arguments to the full SU(2) × U(1) symmetry of the electroweak interactions. In section 13.6.6 we arrived at the gauge invariant electroweak Lagrangian

$$\mathscr{L} = \bar{\psi}_{\text{L}}\gamma^\mu\left[\mathrm{i}\partial_\mu - g\boldsymbol{I}\cdot\boldsymbol{W}_\mu - \frac{g'}{2}YB_\mu\right]\psi_{\text{L}} + \bar{\psi}_{\text{R}}\gamma^\mu\left[\mathrm{i}\partial_\mu - \frac{g'}{2}YB_\mu\right]\psi_{\text{R}}$$

$$+ \text{ kinetic energy terms for the } W \text{ and } B \text{ fields.} \qquad (13.132)$$

We note once more that the fermion mass term has been omitted since such a mass term is not invariant under SU(2)_{L}. For the same reason, mass terms for the gauge fields such as $\frac{1}{2}m_{\text{B}}^2 B_\mu B^\mu$ cannot be added to the Lagrangian so that the three Ws and the B are massless. The Higgs mechanism is invoked by introducing, as before, four real scalar fields φ_i. To the Lagrangian (13.132) we add an SU(2) × U(1) invariant Lagrangian for these scalar fields,

$$\mathscr{L} = \mathscr{D}_\mu\varphi^\dagger\mathscr{D}^\mu\varphi - \mu^2\varphi^\dagger\varphi - \lambda(\varphi^\dagger\varphi)^2 \qquad (13.133)$$

where the covariant derivative is

$$\mathscr{D}_\mu = [\mathrm{i}\partial_\mu - g\boldsymbol{I}\cdot\boldsymbol{W}_\mu - (g'/2)YB_\mu]$$

and, as usual, we are interested in the case $\mu^2 < 0$ and $\lambda > 0$. To guarantee gauge invariance of the Lagrangian, the four scalar fields φ_i must belong to SU(2) × U(1) multiplets. We follow Weinberg and arrange the φ_i into a weak isospin doublet with weak hypercharge $Y = 1$:

$$\varphi = \begin{pmatrix} \varphi^+ \\ \varphi^0 \end{pmatrix} = \frac{1}{\sqrt{2}} \begin{pmatrix} \varphi_1 + i\varphi_2 \\ \varphi_3 + i\varphi_4 \end{pmatrix} \tag{13.134}$$

where φ^+ and φ^0 have electric charge $+1$ and 0 respectively. Again, we choose the vacuum by selecting a specific direction in SU(2) space

$$\varphi_0 = \frac{1}{\sqrt{2}} \begin{pmatrix} 0 \\ v \end{pmatrix}$$

and, as before, we study the spectrum by expanding around the vacuum, i.e. we choose for arbitrary $\varphi(x)$

$$\varphi(x) = \frac{1}{\sqrt{2}} \begin{pmatrix} 0 \\ v + H(x) \end{pmatrix}. \tag{13.135}$$

By the same argument used previously we arrive at the desired result by substituting (13.135) into the Lagrangian (13.133) and, retaining terms only up to second order, obtain

$$\begin{aligned} \mathscr{L} = [\tfrac{1}{2}(\partial_\mu H)^2 - \lambda v^2 H^2] + \frac{g^2 v^2}{8}(W^1_\mu W^{1\mu} + W^2_\mu W^{2\mu}) \\ + \frac{v^2}{8}(gW^3_\mu - g'B_\mu)(gW^{3\mu} - g'B^\mu) + \text{higher order terms} \\ + \text{kinetic energy terms for the } W \text{ and } B \text{ fields.} \end{aligned} \tag{13.136}$$

Inspection of (13.136) shows that the W^1_μ and W^2_μ mass terms are conventional but the fields W^3_μ and B_μ are mixed. We have already met this situation in section 13.6.4 where we introduced the linear combinations

$$\begin{aligned} A_\mu &= B_\mu \cos\theta_W + W^3_\mu \sin\theta_W \\ Z_\mu &= -B_\mu \sin\theta_W + W^3_\mu \cos\theta_W \end{aligned} \tag{13.137}$$

with the Weinberg angle given by $\tan\theta_W = g'/g$. With these new fields the free Lagrangian, i.e. with interaction terms ignored, is

$$\begin{aligned}\mathscr{L} = {} & \tfrac{1}{2}(\partial_\mu H)^2 - \lambda v^2 H^2 \\ & - \tfrac{1}{4}(\partial_\mu W^1_\nu - \partial_\nu W^1_\mu)(\partial^\mu W^{1\nu} - \partial^\nu W^{1\mu}) + (g^2 v^2/8)(W^1_\mu W^{1\mu}) \\ & - \tfrac{1}{4}(\partial_\mu W^2_\nu - \partial_\nu W^2_\mu)(\partial^\mu W^{2\nu} - \partial^\nu W^{2\mu}) + (g^2 v^2/8)(W^2_\mu W^{2\mu}) \\ & - \tfrac{1}{4}(\partial_\mu Z_\nu - \partial_\nu Z_\mu)(\partial^\mu Z^\nu - \partial^\nu Z^\mu) + (v^2/8)(g^2 + g'^2) Z_\mu Z^\mu \\ & - \tfrac{1}{4}(\partial_\mu A_\nu - \partial_\nu A_\mu)(\partial^\mu A^\nu - \partial^\nu A^\mu). \end{aligned} \tag{13.138}$$

Thus, the spontaneous breaking of the local SU(2) × U(1) symmetry has given rise to precisely the mass spectrum for which we were searching, namely

a Higgs boson, $m_{\rm H} = \sqrt{(2\lambda v^2)} = \sqrt{(-2\mu^2)}$
two W bosons, $m_{\rm W} = \frac{1}{2} g v$
a Z boson, $m_{\rm Z} = \frac{1}{2}(g^2 + g'^2)^{1/2} v = m_{\rm W}/\cos\theta_{\rm W}$
and a photon, $m_\gamma = 0$.

Before we leave this section let us try to achieve some further physical insight into what has happened. We started with a Lagrangian (13.133) which contained three massless Ws and a massless B, i.e. eight degrees of freedom. In addition, there were four scalar fields φ_i, which gives a total of 12 degrees of freedom. The four scalar fields φ_i were arranged to form an SU(2) doublet

$$\varphi = \begin{pmatrix} \phi^+ \\ \phi^0 \end{pmatrix}$$

with weak hypercharge $Y = 1$. We chose to break the local gauge symmetry in such a way that only the neutral member of the doublet acquired a non-zero vacuum expectation value:

$$\varphi_0 = \frac{1}{\sqrt{2}} \begin{pmatrix} 0 \\ v \end{pmatrix}.$$

By expanding around this vacuum we arrived at a final Lagrangian which contained three massive gauge bosons $W^\pm$ and Z^0, i.e. nine degrees of freedom, a massless photon which contributes two extra degrees of freedom and finally a Higgs scalar, giving 12 degrees of freedom in all, as required. In choosing a 'unitary gauge' the three unwanted Goldstone bosons were 'swallowed' by the gauge fields to provide the extra longitudinal polarization that their mass requires. But why is it that the photon remained massless? To answer this question we need to look more closely at our choice of the vacuum. We recall that the electric charge, the third component of weak isospin and the weak hypercharge are related by the expression

$$Q = I_3 + \frac{Y}{2}. \tag{13.139}$$

Thus with $Y = 1$ for the doublet, the $I_3 = +\frac{1}{2}$ component has charge $+1$ (in units of e) and the $I_3 = -\frac{1}{2}$ component is electrically neutral. Now the picture that we have developed, namely that fluctuations around the vacuum correspond to the emission or absorption of a Higgs boson, means that any quantum numbers carried by the Higgs boson can be spontaneously created or annihilated. Conservation of charge forces us to choose a non-zero vacuum expectation value for the neutral component only: a non-zero vacuum expectation value for φ^+ would imply non-conservation of electric charge. Now, the choice of φ^0 with $I_3 = -\frac{1}{2}$ and $Y = 1$ breaks both the SU(2) and $\mathrm{U}(1)_Y$ gauge symmetries, but if we can find some symmetry of the vacuum which is a subgroup of the overall $\mathrm{SU}(2) \times \mathrm{U}(1)_Y$ symmetry, then the gauge boson associated with that symmetry will remain massless. Such a symmetry does exist, for, if we operate on the vacuum with the electric charge operator Q, we have

$$Q\varphi_0 = \left(I_3 + \frac{Y}{2}\right)\varphi_0 = 0 \tag{13.140}$$

so that the vacuum is invariant under a transformation

$$\varphi_0 \to \varphi_0' = \exp[\mathrm{i}\alpha(x)Q]\varphi_0 = \varphi_0$$

for any value of $\alpha(x)$. This is also a U(1) transformation, whose generator is a linear combination (13.139) of the generators of the overall $\mathrm{SU}(2) \times \mathrm{U}(1)_Y$ transformations, and it is, of course, just the U(1) transformation of electromagnetism, $\mathrm{U}(1)_{\mathrm{em}}$. It is a subgroup of $\mathrm{SU}(2) \times \mathrm{U}(1)_Y$. Of the four generators, $\boldsymbol{I}$ and $\boldsymbol{Y}$ of $\mathrm{SU}(2) \times \mathrm{U}(1)$, only the combination Q (equation (13.139)), the generator of $\mathrm{U}(1)_{\mathrm{em}}$, satisfies (13.140) and consequently, the photon remains massless. The other three generators break the symmetry and the associated bosons become massive. The fact that the photon is massless should not be regarded as a prediction of the model: the existence of a massless gauge boson is a necessary consequence of electric charge conservation which in turn necessitates the choice of a neutral vacuum state.

Finally, can we give numerical values for the masses of the other bosons in the model? We saw above that the mass of the W boson was predicted to be $m_{\mathrm{W}} = \frac{1}{2}vg$. In section 11.9 we obtained the relation

$$\frac{g^2}{8m_{\mathrm{W}}^2} = \frac{G}{\sqrt{2}}$$

so that using $m_W = \frac{1}{2}vg$ we have $v = (\sqrt{2}G)^{-1/2}$. Remarkably the vacuum expectation value of φ^0 depends only on the Fermi coupling constant G. Using the value $G = 1.17 \times 10^{-5}$ GeV^{-2} we find $v \approx 246$ GeV. In section 13.6.4 we obtained the relationship $g \sin\theta_W = e$ so that we have

$$m_W = \left(\frac{\pi\alpha}{\sqrt{2}G}\right)^{1/2} \frac{1}{\sin\theta_W} \tag{13.141}$$

where $\alpha = e^2/4\pi$ is the fine-structure constant. The Weinberg angle, θ_W, must be measured experimentally. The best estimate for θ_W is

$$\sin^2\theta_W \approx 0.23$$

which gives

$$m_W \approx 80 \text{ GeV}/c^2 \qquad \text{and} \qquad m_Z = m_W/\cos\theta_W \approx 90 \text{ GeV}/c^2.$$

Although the GSW model predicts the masses of the W and Z bosons, the mass of the Higgs boson depends on the unknown parameter λ which appears in the potential $V(\varphi)$, so that m_H is not predicted by the model.

13.6.12 *Fermion masses*

We now take up the problem of fermion masses. Recall that in the original electroweak Lagrangian (13.97), mass terms for both the gauge bosons and the fermions would destroy the gauge invariance and therefore could not simply be added to the Lagrangian. Specifically, the electron mass term $-m\bar{e}e$ may be written

$$-m\bar{e}e = -m\bar{e}[\tfrac{1}{2}(1-\gamma^5) + \tfrac{1}{2}(1+\gamma^5)]e.$$

Recalling the projection properties of the operators $1 \pm \gamma^5$, see table 13.1, we have

$$-m\bar{e}e = -m(\bar{e}_R e_L + \bar{e}_L e_R). \tag{13.142}$$

Since e_R is a weak isospin singlet while e_L is a member of a weak isospin doublet this mass term clearly breaks gauge invariance.

For definiteness we will work with the lighest generation of leptons and quarks: the formalism extends without change to the other generations. We begin with the leptons and recall that their weak isospin and hypercharge quantum numbers are

	I	I_3	Y
ν_e	$\frac{1}{2}$	$+\frac{1}{2}$	-1
e_L	$\frac{1}{2}$	$-\frac{1}{2}$	-1
e_R	0	0	-2

The Higgs boson, with $I = \frac{1}{2}$, $I_3 = -\frac{1}{2}$ and $Y = 1$, has just the correct quantum numbers to couple to $\bar{e}_L e_R$ as shown in figure 13.13. To generate a mass term for the electron we add to the Lagrangian the gauge invariant term

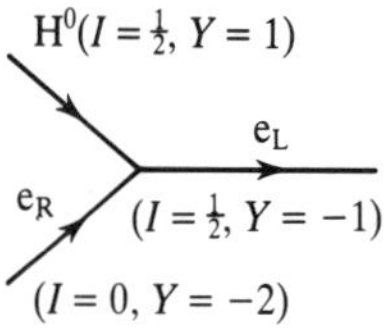

Figure 13.13
Coupling of the Higgs boson to the electron in the standard model.

$$\mathscr{L} = -g_e[\bar{L}\varphi e_R + \bar{e}_R\bar{\varphi}L] \tag{13.143}$$

where

$$L = \begin{pmatrix} \nu_e \\ e \end{pmatrix}_L \quad \text{and} \quad \varphi = \begin{pmatrix} \varphi^+ \\ \varphi^0 \end{pmatrix}.$$

Considering the first term in the square brackets we have

$$(\bar{\nu}_e \bar{e}_L)\begin{pmatrix} \varphi^+ \\ \varphi^0 \end{pmatrix} = (\bar{\nu}_e \varphi^+ + \bar{e}_L \varphi^0)$$

which is an SU(2) invariant. Multiplication by the singlet e_R does not spoil this invariance. The second term in (13.143) is just the Hermitian conjugate of the first and therefore is also gauge invariant. The coupling g_e is arbitrary.

Following the now familiar procedure we spontaneously break the symmetry and substitute

$$\varphi = \frac{1}{\sqrt{2}}\begin{pmatrix} 0 \\ v + H \end{pmatrix}$$

into the Lagrangian and obtain

$$\mathscr{L} = \frac{-g_e v}{\sqrt{2}}(\bar{e}_R e_L + \bar{e}_L e_R) - \frac{g_e}{\sqrt{2}}(\bar{e}_R e_L + \bar{e}_L e_R)H. \tag{13.144}$$

On comparing this with (13.142) we see that the first term has precisely the form of an electron mass term with

$$m_e = \frac{g_e v}{\sqrt{2}}. \tag{13.145}$$

Since g_e is arbitrary the theory does not predict the mass of the electron but it is an attractive feature that, through the Higgs mechanism, the model can at least accommodate massive fermions. In terms of m_e the Lagrangian becomes

$$\mathscr{L} = -m_e \bar{e}e - (m_e/v)\bar{e}eH. \tag{13.146}$$

In addition to the mass term the Lagrangian contains a term which describes the coupling of the Higgs boson to the electron. The strength of the coupling is m_e/v, or, in terms of the W mass, $\frac{1}{2}g(m_e/m_W)$. The Higgs boson couples to (charged) leptons with a strength proportional to the lepton mass. Notice that there is no coupling of the Higgs boson to neutrinos in the above formalism. This is because, with an assumed neutrino mass of zero, the theory has been constructed with a left-handed neutrino only. The absence of a right-handed neutrino prevents us from adding to the Lagrangian a term analogous to (13.143) which would lead to both a mass term and an interaction term for the neutrino.

Turning to the problem of quark masses we first observe that, in contrast to the lepton doublets, the $I_3 = +\frac{1}{2}$ member of a quark doublet is massive so that a corresponding right-handed singlet state, u_R for example, exists. Thus, in order to generate masses for the quarks, one introduces the conjugate Higgs doublet

$$\tilde{\varphi} = \mathrm{i}\tau_2\varphi^* = \frac{1}{\sqrt{2}}\begin{pmatrix} \bar{\varphi}^0 \\ -\varphi^- \end{pmatrix}. \tag{13.147}$$

This construction ensures that the conjugate doublet, $\tilde{\varphi}$, transforms in the same way as φ under SU(2) transformations. Notice that since φ has hypercharge $Y = +1$, $\tilde{\varphi}$ has $Y = -1$ so that the relation $Q = I_3 + Y/2$ is still satisfied for each charge state. After spontaneous symmetry breaking the conjugate Higgs doublet becomes

$$\tilde{\varphi} = \frac{1}{\sqrt{2}}\begin{pmatrix} v + H \\ 0 \end{pmatrix}. \tag{13.148}$$

Then for u and d quarks we add to the Lagrangian the terms

$$\mathscr{L} = -g_d \bar{L}_q \varphi d_R - g_u \bar{L}_q \tilde{\varphi} u_R + \text{Hermitian conjugate} \tag{13.149}$$

where $L_q = \binom{u}{d}_L$ and g_d, g_u are arbitrary. Because $\tilde{\varphi}$ transforms identically to φ this addition to the Lagrangian is gauge invariant. After substitution of φ and $\tilde{\varphi}$ we obtain

$$\mathscr{L} = -m_d \bar{d}d - m_u \bar{u}u - \frac{m_d}{v}\bar{d}dH - \frac{m_u}{v}\bar{u}uH. \tag{13.150}$$

The arbitrary couplings $g_{\mathrm{d}}, g_{\mathrm{u}}$ have been expressed in terms of the quark masses by the same steps used in the case of leptons. In addition to quark mass terms, the Lagrangian describes the coupling of u and d quarks to the Higgs boson, again with a strength proportional to the quark mass. Strictly speaking, one should take into account quark mixing and use the electroweak eigenstates in the above formalism but the above arguments show how, in principle, the Higgs mechanism can generate masses for the quarks.

13.7 *Quantum chromodynamics and the standard model*

To complete our description of the gauge theories of the fundamental processes we turn to the strong interactions of coloured quarks, mediated by the exchange of coloured vector gluons. The theory, quantum chromodynamics (QCD), is analogous to QED but with the $U(1)_{em}$ group replaced by $SU(3)_c$, the group of phase transformations on the quark colour fields. The main difference between QED and QCD stems from the fact that the former is Abelian while the latter is not: the generators of $SU(3)_c$ do not commute and this leads to self-interactions between the gluons. Since they do not carry electric charge there are no self-interactions between photons.

The Lagrangian for free quarks may be written

$$\mathscr{L} = \sum_q \bar{\psi}_q^j \mathrm{i}\gamma^\mu \partial_\mu \psi_q^k - \sum_q m_q \bar{\psi}_q^j \psi_q^j. \tag{13.151}$$

The indices j and k refer to colour ($j, k = 1, 2, 3$) and the ψ_q^j are the four-component Dirac spinors associated with each quark flavour q and colour j. To simplify the notation let us, for the time being, consider a single quark flavour and omit the colour indices. We demand invariance of the Lagrangian under local gauge transformations

$$\psi_q(x) \rightarrow \psi_q'(x) = \exp[\mathrm{i}g_s \Lambda_a(x) T_a] \psi_q(x). \tag{13.152}$$

In this expression g_s is the strong coupling constant and a summation over the index a is implied. The generators T_a are a set of independent traceless 3×3 matrices which are conventionally chosen as the matrices $\lambda_a/2$ introduced in section 10.1.1. They satisfy the commutation relations

$$[T_a, T_b] = \mathrm{i} f_{abc} T_c \tag{13.153}$$

where the real constants f_{abc} are the structure constants of the group and are given in table 10.1. The quantities $\Lambda_a(x)$ are the group parameters.

Proceeding as in the case of QED we consider the infinitesimal transformation

$$\psi_q(x) \to \psi'_q(x) = [1 + ig_s\Lambda_a(x)T_a]\psi_q(x). \tag{13.154}$$

To maintain gauge invariance of the Lagrangian we are obliged to introduce eight gauge fields, G^a_μ, which transform as

$$G^a_\mu(x) \to G^a_\mu(x) - \partial_\mu\Lambda_a(x) - g_s f_{abc}\Lambda_b(x)G^c_\mu. \tag{13.155}$$

We simultaneously replace ∂_μ in the Lagrangian by the covariant derivative

$$\mathscr{D}_\mu = \partial_\mu + ig_s T_a G^a_\mu. \tag{13.156}$$

The Lagrangian then becomes

$$\mathscr{L} = \bar{\psi}_q i\gamma^\mu \partial_\mu \psi_q - g_s(\bar{\psi}_q\gamma^\mu T_a\psi_q)G^a_\mu - m_q\bar{\psi}_q\psi_q. \tag{13.157}$$

Finally, we add to the Lagrangian a gauge invariant kinetic energy term for each of the gluon fields, namely $-\frac{1}{4}G^a_{\mu\nu}G^{\mu\nu}_a$, with

$$G^a_{\mu\nu} = \partial_\mu G^a_\nu - \partial_\nu G^a_\mu - g_s f_{abc} G^b_\mu G^c_\nu. \tag{13.158}$$

The extra term in the transformation law for the gluon fields, equation (13.155), compared with that for the A_μ field in QED (equation (13.44)), arises from the non-Abelian nature of the $SU(3)_c$ group. For the same reason, there is an extra 'kinetic energy' term in (13.158), a gluon self-interaction term, which has no analogue in QED.

On reinstating the colour indices, j and k, and quark flavours, the final QCD Lagrangian becomes

$$\mathscr{L} = i\sum_q \bar{\psi}^j_q\gamma^\mu(\mathscr{D}_\mu)_{jk}\psi^k_q - \sum_q m_q\bar{\psi}^j_q\psi^j_q - \tfrac{1}{4}G^a_{\mu\nu}G^{\mu\nu}_a \tag{13.159}$$

with

$$(\mathscr{D}_\mu)_{jk} = \delta_{jk}\partial_\mu - ig_s(T_a)_{jk}G^a_\mu \qquad (a = 1, 2, \ldots, 8).$$

This describes interacting coloured quarks ψ^j_q and vector gluons G^a_μ. It was arrived at by requiring the free-field Lagrangian to be invariant under local $SU(3)_c$ transformations on the quark colour fields. The arbitrary variations, $\Lambda_a(x)$, in the phases of the three quark colour fields are compensated, at all space–time points, by eight vector gluon fields, G^a_μ with $a = 1, \ldots, 8$. As for the photon, local gauge invariance requires the gluons to have zero mass, but a very important new feature emerges in the case of QCD which was not present in QED, namely the gluon self-interactions. In addition to the free propagation terms for quarks and

Figure 13.14
Diagrams representing the propagation of a free quark and gluon and their interactions.

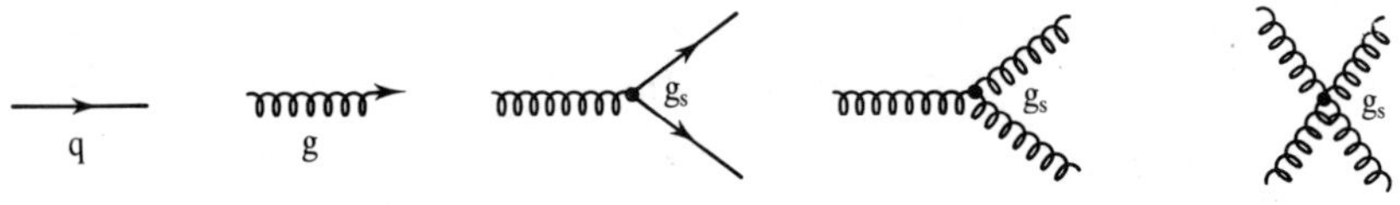

gluons the QCD Lagrangian describes quark–gluon and gluon–gluon interactions as shown in figure 13.14. The interactions have a characteristic coupling strength g_s.

13.8 The standard model Lagrangian

It is remarkable that although three families are known experimentally

$$\begin{pmatrix} \nu_e \\ e \\ u \\ d \end{pmatrix} \quad \begin{pmatrix} \nu_\mu \\ \mu \\ c \\ s \end{pmatrix} \quad \begin{pmatrix} \nu_\tau \\ \tau \\ t \\ b \end{pmatrix}$$

nature seems to have decreed that the standard model applies equally to all three families: the same set of gauge bosons, γ, Z^0, $W^\pm$ and g, interact with each family with the same coupling strengths.

It is perhaps helpful at this point to summarize what we have learned in this chapter and collect all the terms we have previously discussed into the fermion–gauge boson Lagrangian of the standard model:

$$\mathscr{L} = -\tfrac{1}{4}\boldsymbol{W}_{\mu\nu}\cdot\boldsymbol{W}^{\mu\nu} - \tfrac{1}{4}B_{\mu\nu}B^{\mu\nu} - \tfrac{1}{4}G^a_{\mu\nu}G^{\mu\nu}_a$$

{$W^\pm$, Z^0, γ and gluon kinetic energies and self-interactions

$$+ \bar{L}\gamma^\mu(\mathrm{i}\partial_\mu - \tfrac{1}{2}g\boldsymbol{\tau}\cdot\boldsymbol{W}_\mu - \tfrac{1}{2}g'YB_\mu)L$$
$$+ \bar{R}\gamma^\mu(\mathrm{i}\partial_\mu - \tfrac{1}{2}g'YB_\mu)R$$

{fermion kinetic energies and their interactions with $W^\pm$, Z^0 and γ

$$+ |(\mathrm{i}\partial_\mu - \tfrac{1}{2}g\boldsymbol{\tau}\cdot\boldsymbol{W}_\mu - \tfrac{1}{2}g'YB_\mu)\varphi|^2 - V(\varphi)$$

{masses and couplings of the $W^\pm$, Z^0, γ and Higgs boson

$$- (g_1\bar{L}\varphi R + g_2\bar{L}\tilde{\varphi}R + \text{Hermitian conjugate})$$

{fermion masses and couplings to the Higgs boson

$$+ \tfrac{1}{2}g_s(\bar{\psi}^j_q\gamma^\mu\lambda^a_{jk}\psi^k_q)G^a_\mu.$$

{quark–gluon couplings

In this Lagrangian, L represents a left-handed fermion doublet, R a right-handed singlet and $\varphi(\tilde{\varphi})$ the Higgs doublet and its conjugate. ψ^j_q represents a quark colour field.

Finally, we collect together some relations between the parameters of the $SU(3)_c \times SU(2)_L \times U(1)_Y$ standard model:

$$\frac{G}{\sqrt{2}} = \frac{g^2}{8m_W^2} \qquad g = e(\sin\theta_W)^{-1} \qquad g' = e(\cos\theta_W)^{-1}$$

$$\alpha = \frac{e^2}{4\pi} \approx \frac{1}{137} \qquad \alpha_1 = \frac{g'^2}{4\pi} \approx \frac{1}{100} \qquad \alpha_2 = \frac{g^2}{4\pi} \approx \frac{1}{30}$$

$$\alpha_3 = \frac{g_s^2}{4\pi} \approx 0.4 \rightarrow 0.1.$$

In the last four equations we have rationalized the couplings associated with the electromagnetic, weak hypercharge, weak isospin and strong interactions respectively. As we shall see in the next section, these 'constants' depend on a characteristic momentum Q (or, equivalently, a distance $1/Q$) of the interaction. The values quoted for α, α_1 and α_2 are for Q of the order of a few giga-electronvolts while for α_3 we give the variation over the range 1–100 GeV.

13.9 *Renormalization and running coupling constants*

In section 7.5 we explained why the charge on the electron, or equivalently the fine-structure 'constant' α, should really be regarded as a function of distance. In QED, vacuum polarization results in charge screening, the effect of which decreases as Q increases. The measured charge on the electron, or the fine-structure constant, is therefore a function of Q^2; $\alpha(Q^2)$ increases with increasing Q^2. We speak of $\alpha(Q^2)$ as a 'running coupling constant'.

Vacuum polarization also affects the strong and weak coupling constants but in a crucially different way. As we have stressed many times before, the non-Abelian nature of the strong and weak forces gives rise to self-interactions of the gauge bosons. Unlike the photon, which is electrically neutral, the W and Z bosons themselves carry weak charge and the gluons carry a strong or colour charge. In contrast to the QED case, this property gives rise to anti-screening effects with a consequent *decrease* in the coupling constants with increasing Q^2.

The calculation of the Q^2 dependence of the coupling constants is a very important but highly technical subject beyond the scope of this book. In what follows, we aim to show why difficulties arise in the calculation and indicate, in a semi-quantitative way, how these difficulties are overcome.

To gain some insight into the problem, consider electron–electron scattering. The amplitude for the lowest order Feynman diagram

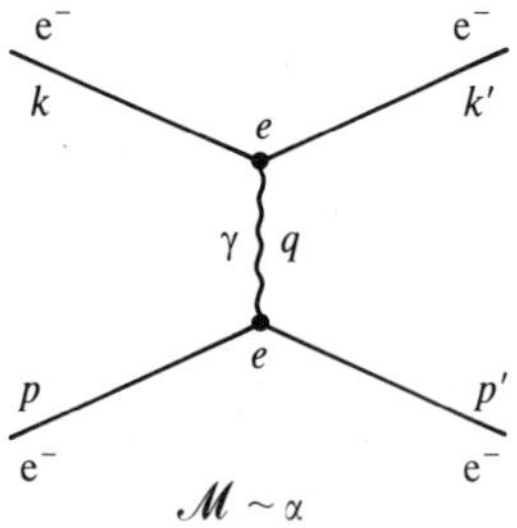

Figure 13.15
Lowest order Feynman diagram for the process $e^- + e^- \rightarrow e^- + e^-$.

contributing to this process, figure 13.15, is of the form

$$\mathcal{M} \approx J(k, k') \frac{1}{q^2} J(p, p') \tag{13.160}$$

where $J(k, k') = e\bar{u}(k')\gamma^{\mu}u(k)$ is the electron current at the top vertex and $1/q^2$ is the photon propagator. $J(p, p')$ is the electron current at the bottom vertex. The amplitude is proportional to e^2, i.e. $O(\alpha)$, and when evaluated gives the Rutherford cross-section

$$\frac{d\sigma}{d\Omega} \propto \frac{\alpha^2}{q^4}. \tag{13.161}$$

The one-photon exchange diagram is, however, not the only contribution to the scattering process. To this must be added the processes shown in figure 13.16, the amplitudes for which are proportional to α^2, α^3, α^4 and

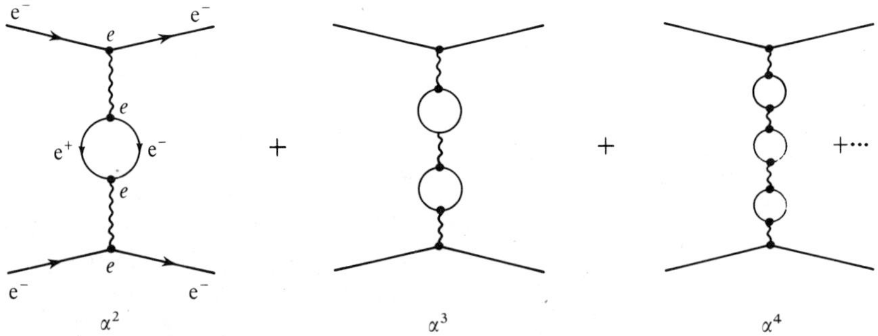

Figure 13.16
Higher order contributions to the process $e^- + e^- \rightarrow e^- + e^-$.

so on. Since the fine-structure constant is small compared with unity one might expect each successive diagram to give a rapidly diminishing contribution to the overall scattering amplitude. The series should converge and a perturbation calculation should give physically meaningful results. Unfortunately, even the $O(\alpha^2)$ correction term, the first diagram in figure 13.16, gives an infinite contribution.

In figure 13.16 the electron emits a virtual photon at the top vertex and is scattered. The virtual photon then produces an electron and a positron which, after a fleeting existence, annihilate to produce another virtual photon. The electron then absorbs this photon at the bottom vertex and is scattered. The problem arises from the electron–positron 'loop'. Although four-momentum is conserved at each vertex, the magnitude of the four-momentum circulating around the loop can take on any value from zero to infinity. Contributions from all possible loop four-momenta p, say, add. Since p is not an observable, an integration has to be performed over the loop momentum and this integral diverges: the $O(\alpha^2)$ correction is infinite. The higher order diagrams of figure 13.16 are plagued with the same problem so it would appear that a perturbation calculation of the cross-section is doomed to failure. However, one of the great achievements in theoretical particle physics has been the development of so-called *renormalization* techniques which eliminate these infinites in a consistent way at each order of α and lead to finite physical results. Of the greatest importance in this context is the proof by 't Hooft, some years after the formulation of the standard model, that for a theory to be renormalizable it has to be of the Yang–Mills type, i.e. it must be locally gauge invariant.

13.9.1 The running coupling constant of quantum electrodynamics

In this section we discuss how renormalization techniques are applied to QED processes and arrive at an expression for $\alpha(Q^2)$, the running coupling constant of QED. For definiteness we will analyse the electron–electron scattering process shown in figure 13.17.

The matrix element for this Feynman diagram is essentially

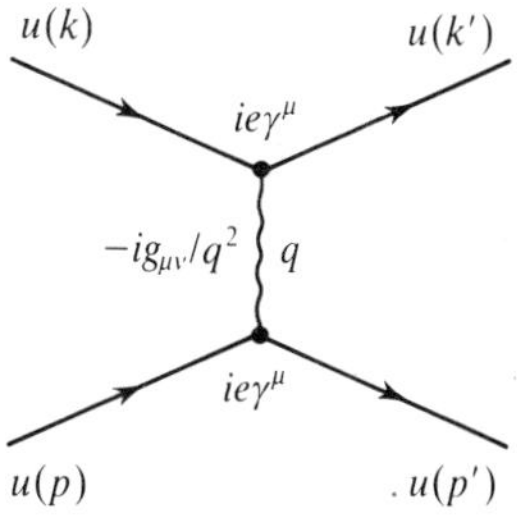

Figure 13.17
Feynman diagram for electron–electron scattering showing the kinematic variables used in the calculation of the amplitude.

$$\mathcal{M} \approx [e\bar{u}(k')\gamma^\mu u(k)]\left[\frac{g_{\mu\nu}}{q^2}\right][e\bar{u}(p')\gamma^\nu u(p)] \qquad (13.162)$$

i.e.

$$\mathcal{M} \approx \text{(electron current)} \times \text{(photon propagator)}$$
$$\times \text{(electron current)}.$$

Here, we are being cavalier in our omission of various factors of $\pm i$ (see figure 13.17), but the essentials are contained in (13.162). As indicated above, an exact evaluation of the matrix element requires the addition of correction terms, to all orders in α, arising from loop diagrams. The one-level loop diagram, with vertex factors and photon propagators given explicitly, is shown in figure 13.18. The matrix element for this

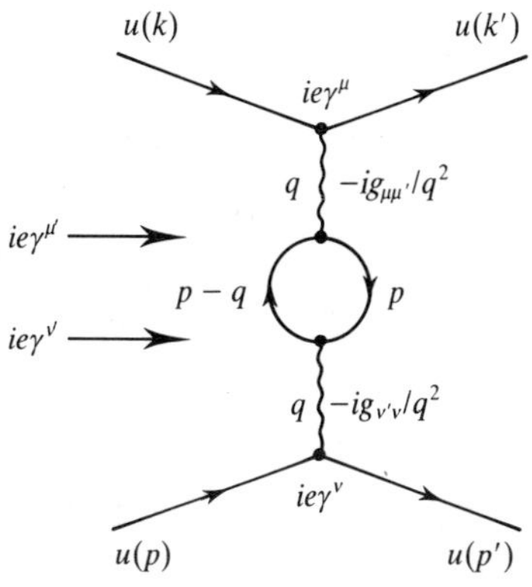

Figure 13.18
The one-level loop diagram contribution to electron–electron scattering.

process is

$$\mathcal{M} \approx [e\bar{u}(k')\gamma^{\mu}u(k)] \times \left[\frac{g_{\mu\mu'}}{q^2}\right]$$

$$\times (2\pi)^{-4} \int d^4p \, \frac{[e\bar{u}(p)\gamma^{\mu'}u(p-q)]}{p^2-m^2} \frac{[e\bar{u}(p-q)\gamma^{\nu'}u(p)]}{(p-q)^2-m^2}$$

$$\times \left[\frac{g_{\nu'\nu}}{q^2}\right] \times [e\bar{u}(p')\gamma^{\nu}u(p)]. \qquad (13.163)$$

Although this is a complicated expression, it is readily understood when broken down into its elements. The first line is simply the product of the electron current at the top vertex and the propagator for a photon with four-momentum q. As explained above, one has to integrate over p, the four-momentum circulating around the loop. The loop contribution is the second line in (13.163). The integrand perhaps needs some explanation. First we recall that in a Feynman diagram, an antiparticle with four-momentum p^{μ} which is incoming (outgoing) at a vertex, is physically equivalent to an outgoing (incoming) particle with four-momentum $-p^{\mu}$, figure 13.19. Hence, at the vertex with vertex-factor $ie\gamma^{\mu'}$ for instance,

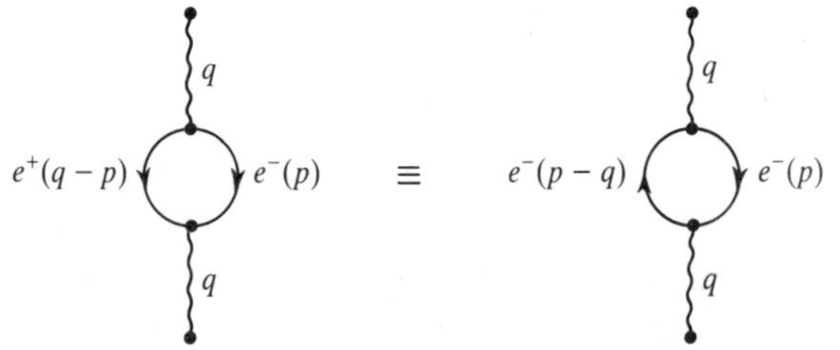

Figure 13.19
Correspondence between an outgoing positron and an incoming electron.

the outgoing positron with four-momentum $q - p$ becomes an incoming electron with four-momentum $p - q$. There are two similar terms in the integral because the electrons couple to photons at two vertices. The terms in the denominators are electron propagators: m is the electron mass. Finally, the third line in (13.163) is the product of the photon propagator and the electron current at the bottom vertex. Note that the matrix element is of the order α^2, the loop correction itself being of order α. The matrix element for this $O(\alpha^2)$ contribution is of the form

$$\mathcal{M} \approx (\text{electron current}) \times (\text{modified propagator}) \times (\text{electron current}).$$

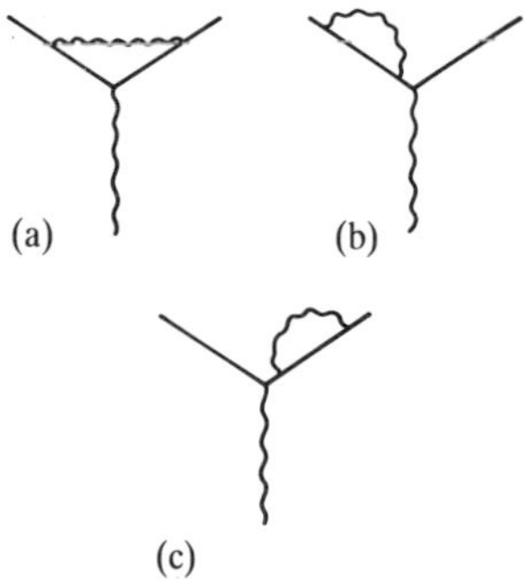

Figure 13.20
Feynman diagrams showing (a) a vertex correction and (b), (c) self-energy corrections.

The discerning reader might object that there are other $O(\alpha)$ corrections, such as those shown in figure 13.20, which ought to be taken into account. Figure 13.20(a) gives rise to a correction to the vertex factor whereas 13.20(b) and 13.20(c) are electron self-energy terms. Miraculously, a full calculation shows that the modifications induced by figures 13.20(b) and 13.20(c) exactly cancel the contribution of 13.20(a), regardless of whether one is dealing with an electron or a muon current for instance. The corrections can be parametrized in terms of a redefinition, or renormalization, of the electric charge and were it not for the cancellation one would be faced with different charge renormalization for the electron and muon. Since the charge on the electron and muon are identical, this would be a potential disaster. As a result of the cancellation, only loop diagrams which modify the photon propagator need to be taken into account in the evaluation of the matrix element. With this parenthetical remark in mind we return to the evaluation of the loop contribution.

The net effect of including the $O(\alpha^2)$ loop diagram in the calculation of the matrix element is a modification of the photon propagator. After a lengthy calculation it is found that in going from an $O(\alpha)$ to an $O(\alpha^2)$ calculation the propagator is modified according to

$$\frac{g_{\mu\nu}}{q^2} \to \frac{g_{\mu\nu}}{q^2}[1 - I(q^2)] \tag{13.164}$$

where

$$I(q^2) = \frac{\alpha}{3\pi}\int_{m^2}^{\infty}\frac{\mathrm{d}p^2}{p^2} - \frac{2\alpha}{\pi}\int_0^1 \mathrm{d}x\, x(1-x)\ln\left(1 - \frac{q^2 x(1-x)}{m^2}\right). \tag{13.165}$$

Explicit derivations of (13.164) and (13.165) are given in several advanced texts, see for instance reference 8. As expected, $I(q^2)$ is infinite but the infinity arises from the first integral which is only logarithmically divergent and which is independent of q^2. We can evaluate this integral by using the technique of replacing the upper limit by a finite cut-off parameter, Λ say, and then, if necessary, allowing Λ to approach infinity. We will evaluate $I(q^2)$ for the two extreme cases of large and small $-q^2$. First, for large $-q^2 \gg m^2$, we have

$$\ln\left(1 - \frac{q^2 x(1-x)}{m^2}\right) \approx \ln\left(\frac{-q^2}{m^2}\right)$$

so that

$$\begin{aligned} I(q^2) &= \frac{\alpha}{3\pi}\int_{m^2}^{\Lambda^2}\frac{\mathrm{d}p^2}{p^2} - \frac{2\alpha}{\pi}\int_0^1 \mathrm{d}x\, x(1-x)\ln\left(\frac{-q^2}{m^2}\right) \\ &= \frac{\alpha}{3\pi}\ln\left(\frac{\Lambda^2}{m^2}\right) - \frac{\alpha}{3\pi}\ln\left(\frac{-q^2}{m^2}\right) = \frac{\alpha}{3\pi}\ln\left(\frac{\Lambda^2}{-q^2}\right). \end{aligned} \tag{13.166}$$

Thus, for large $-q^2$, the photon propagator including corrections of order

α is changed only by the multiplicative factor $[1 - (\alpha/3\pi)\ln(\Lambda^2/m^2)]$, and the matrix element (13.163) becomes, in this limit,

$$\mathcal{M} \approx [e\bar{u}(k')\gamma^\mu u(k)] \frac{g_{\mu\nu}}{q^2}\left[1 - \frac{\alpha}{3\pi}\ln\left(\frac{\Lambda^2}{-q^2}\right)\right][e\bar{u}(p')\gamma^\nu(p)]. \qquad (13.167)$$

Let us write this symbolically as follows:

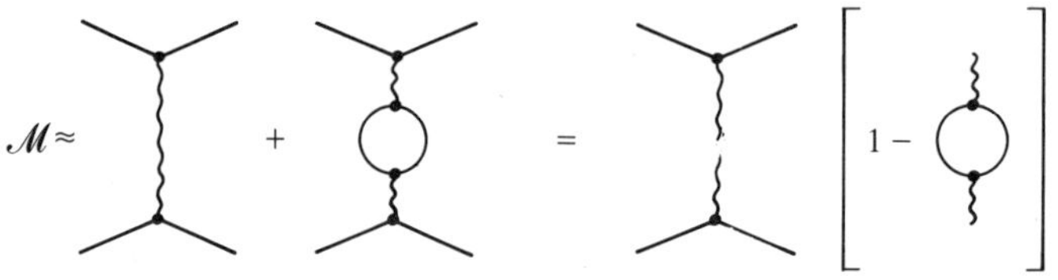

where the loop correction is $(\alpha/3\pi)\ln(\Lambda^2/-q^2)$. Now, if we wish to evaluate the matrix element exactly, we would have to include loop corrections to all orders in α, i.e.

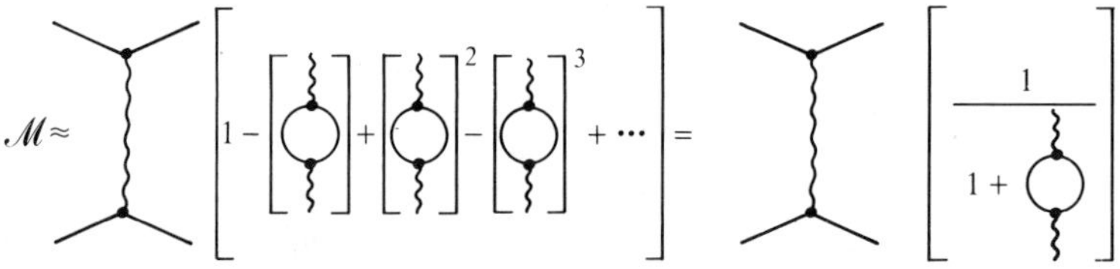

Thus, to all orders in α, the matrix element is

$$\mathcal{M} \approx \left[\frac{\alpha}{1 + (\alpha/3\pi)\ln(\Lambda^2/-q^2)}\right][\bar{u}(k')\gamma^\mu u(k)][\bar{u}(p')\gamma_\mu u(p)]. \qquad (13.168)$$

How do we interpret α in this expression? In all the steps leading to (13.168) we have used α as the coupling strength at the 'bare' e–γ vertex, i.e. the vertex stripped of all loop contributions. Call it the bare or unrenormalized 'charge' α_0. It is certainly not what is normally called the fine-structure constant, α, with the experimental value of about 1/137. The latter is actually the renormalized charge, α_R, i.e. the charge with all loop corrections included. This is what is measured experimentally. As is the convention, let us call this renormalized charge α_R simply α, we hope without risk of confusion. Then, in terms of the unrenormalized charge,

$$\alpha = \frac{\alpha_0}{1 + (\alpha_0/3\pi)\ln(\Lambda^2/Q^2)} \qquad (13.169)$$

where $Q^2 = -q^2$. But, of course, the measured value of α depends, albeit weakly, on the value of Q^2 at which the experimental measurement is performed. Let us say that we obtain a value $\alpha = 1/137$ at some value μ^2 of Q^2. Then,

$$\alpha(\mu^2) = \frac{\alpha_0}{1 + (\alpha_0/3\pi)\ln(\Lambda^2/\mu^2)}. \tag{13.170}$$

At any other value of Q^2 we have

$$\alpha(Q^2) = \frac{\alpha_0}{1 + (\alpha_0/3\pi)\ln(\Lambda^2/Q^2)}. \tag{13.171}$$

To cast this in the form that we require, note that

$$\ln\left(\frac{\Lambda^2}{Q^2}\right) = \ln\left(\frac{\Lambda^2}{Q^2}\frac{\mu^2}{\mu^2}\right) = \ln\left(\frac{\Lambda^2}{\mu^2}\right) + \ln\left(\frac{\mu^2}{Q^2}\right).$$

Then, (13.171) becomes

$$\alpha(Q^2) = \frac{\alpha_0}{1 + (\alpha_0/3\pi)[\ln(\Lambda^2/\mu^2) + \ln(\mu^2/Q^2)]}. \tag{13.172}$$

From (13.170)

$$1 + \frac{\alpha_0}{3\pi}\ln\left(\frac{\Lambda^2}{\mu^2}\right) = \frac{\alpha_0}{\alpha(\mu^2)}$$

so (13.172) becomes

$$\alpha(Q^2) = \frac{\alpha_0}{\alpha_0/\alpha(\mu^2) + (\alpha_0/3\pi)\ln(\mu^2/Q^2)}. \tag{13.173}$$

Finally, the factors of α_0 cancel and we obtain

$$\alpha(Q^2) = \frac{\alpha(\mu^2)}{1 - [\alpha(\mu^2)/3\pi]\ln(Q^2/\mu^2)}. \tag{13.174}$$

$\alpha(Q^2)$ is called the running coupling constant of QED. Remarkably, there is no dependence on the cut-off Λ which can therefore be allowed to approach infinity without any adverse effects. Nor does it depend on α_0: indeed, $\alpha(Q^2)$ depends only on finite, measurable quantities. Equation (13.174) embodies the charge screening of quantum electrodynamics which was discussed qualitatively in section 7.5. In essence (13.174) shows how the effective charge depends on Q^2 or, equivalently, on the distance between two charged particles. As Q^2 increases (smaller and smaller impact parameter) more and more charge is seen and $\alpha(Q^2)$ increases. At small Q^2, $\alpha(Q^2) \to \alpha(\mu^2) = 1/137$. This is precisely the behaviour of α shown in figures 7.16 and 7.17(b). Note that in the process of avoiding infinities by renormalizing the charge, we have introduced a parameter μ with dimensions of mass. μ is called the renormalization mass; different choices of μ correspond to different renormalization schemes but the final physical results are independent of the choice of μ. Essentially, the dependence of the matrix element on μ is cancelled by the μ dependence of $\alpha(\mu^2)$.

We must remark on further effects which modify $\alpha(Q^2)$ as given by equation (13.174). So far we have spoken only of electron–positron loops. As Q^2 increases there will also be contributions from $\mu^+\mu^-$, $\tau^+\tau^-$ and $q\bar{q}$ loop diagrams. In general, the correction term, i.e. the second term in the denominator of (13.174), should be multiplied by

$$n_l + 3(4/9)n_+ + 3(1/9)n_-$$

where n_l is the number of charged leptons, n_+ the number of quarks with charge $+2/3e$ and n_- the number of quarks with charge $-1/3e$, which participate at the particular value of Q^2.

Finally, in this section, we consider vacuum polarization effects at small values of $(-q^2)$ which are relevant in atomic physics. With this in mind, let us consider the interaction between an electron and a static point nucleus with charge Ze. The first- and second-order Feynman diagrams, shown in figure 13.21, are the same as those in figures 13.17 and 13.18

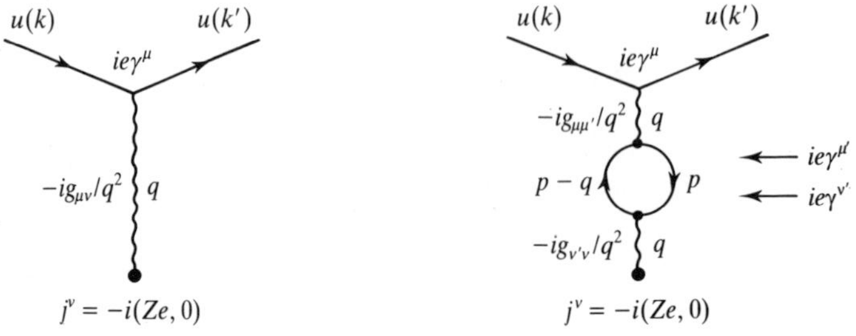

Figure 13.21
First- and second-order Feynman diagrams for the scattering of an electron by a static charge *Ze*.

with the replacement of the electron current $j^\nu(q)$ by a static charge distribution. In general, a four-vector current j^ν has the form $j^\nu = (\rho, \boldsymbol{j})$, but for a static point charge distribution located at the origin, $\boldsymbol{j} = 0$ and $\rho(\boldsymbol{x}) = Ze\delta(\boldsymbol{x})$. In order to write down the matrix element to $O(\alpha^2)$, we need to evaluate $I(q^2)$ given by equation (13.165) in the small $-q^2$ region. In the limit $-q^2 \to 0$, the integral simply reduces to

$$I(q^2) = \frac{\alpha}{3\pi}\int_{m^2}^{\Lambda^2} \frac{dp^2}{p^2} = \frac{\alpha}{3\pi}\ln\left(\frac{\Lambda^2}{m^2}\right) \qquad (13.175)$$

where we have used the same cut-off procedure as before. Then, to $O(\alpha^2)$, the matrix element for Coulomb scattering of an electron by a charge Ze becomes

$$\mathcal{M} \approx [e\bar{u}(k')\gamma^{\mu}u(k)]\left\{\frac{g_{\mu\nu}}{q^2}\left[1-\frac{\alpha}{3\pi}\ln\left(\frac{\Lambda^2}{m^2}\right)\right]\right\}[j^{\nu}(q)]$$

$$= Ze^2\left[1-\frac{\alpha}{3\pi}\ln\left(\frac{\Lambda^2}{m^2}\right)\right]\frac{\bar{u}(k')\gamma_0 u(k)}{q^2}$$

$$= Ze_{\mathrm{R}}^2\,\frac{\bar{u}(k')\gamma_0 u(k)}{q^2}. \tag{13.176}$$

As before, e is interpreted as the bare charge, and

$$e_{\mathrm{R}} \equiv e\left[1-\frac{\alpha}{3\pi}\ln\left(\frac{\Lambda^2}{m^2}\right)\right]^{1/2} \tag{13.177}$$

is the measured or renormalized charge, $e_{\mathrm{R}}^2 = 4\pi/137$. Looked at another way (13.176) expresses the fact that

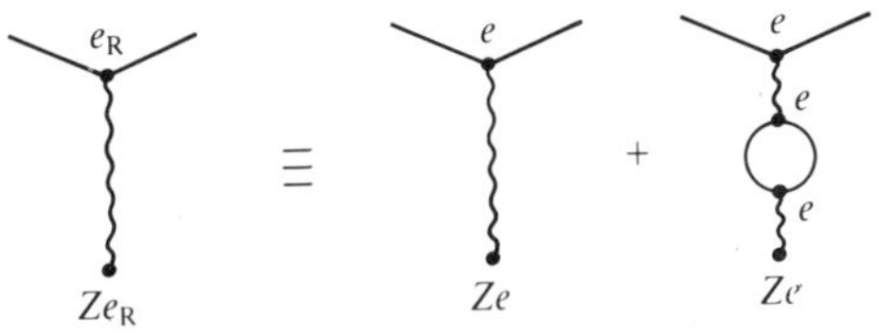

The divergence in the cross-section, calculated in terms of the bare charge e, is avoided if we rewrite the matrix element in terms of the observed or renormalized charge e_{R}.

13.9.2 *The running coupling constant of quantum chromodynamics*

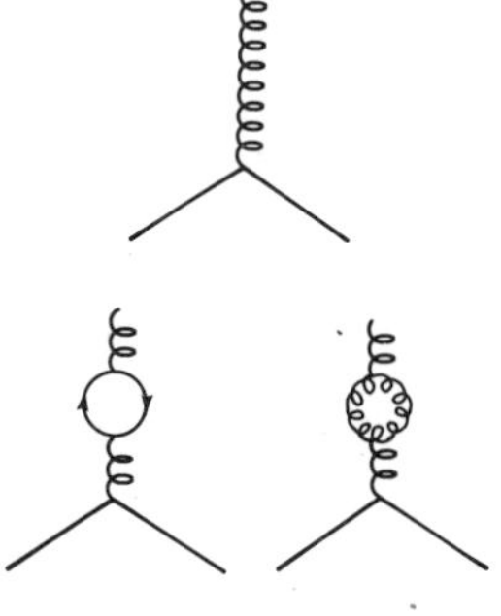

Figure 13.22
The basic quark–gluon interaction with quark- and gluon-loop corrections.

As we have already seen, the non-Abelian nature of QCD gives rise to self-interactions of the gluons. Were it not for this feature the Q^2 dependence of the QCD running coupling constant, $\alpha_3(Q^2)$, could essentially be taken over directly from the QED case. The basic quark–gluon interaction, together with first-order loop corrections, is shown in figure 13.22. Since the quark–gluon interaction is flavour independent, the quark loop gives the same contribution for every flavour of quark. Indeed, apart from a colour factor the contribution is the same as the electron loop contributions in QED: we replace $\alpha(\mu^2)/3\pi$ by a factor* $\alpha_3(\mu^2)/6\pi$ for each flavour. The crucial difference between QCD and QED arises from the diagram which contains a gluon loop. Although this diagram simply gives rise to another numerical factor its contribution is greater than that of the second diagram but is of the *opposite* sign.† The origin of this sign difference can be understood in terms of the anti-screening effect in QCD, discussed qualitatively in section 7.5. There, we saw that an incoming red quark, say, may spontaneously emit a bi-coloured gluon, such as $g_{R\bar{B}}$, and in the scattering process the red quark becomes a blue quark, as shown in figure 13.23. Thus, a probe would not see a localized red colour-charge, as this becomes diluted, or carried away from the incoming quark, by the gluon. The probability of emission of a gluon increases with increasing $-q^2$. In other words, as $-q^2$ increases, less and less colour charge is concentrated on the original quark so that, for very large $-q^2$, *it behaves like a free particle.*

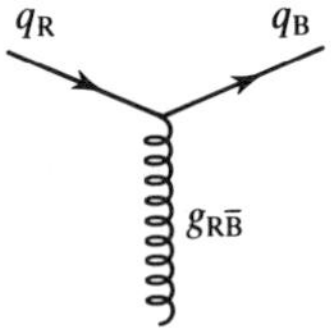

Figure 13.23
Colour flow in the basic quark–gluon interaction.

When the contributions from the quark loop and the gluon loop are combined the net result is that the QCD running coupling constant is obtained from the QED result, by the following replacement in equation (13.174):

$$\frac{\alpha(\mu^2)}{3\pi} \to \frac{\alpha_3(\mu^2)}{4\pi}\left(\tfrac{2}{3}n_f - 11\right) \tag{13.178}$$

where n_f is the number of quark flavours. Thus, the QCD running coupling constant is

$$\alpha_3(Q^2) = \frac{\alpha_3(\mu^2)}{1 + [\alpha_3(\mu^2)/12\pi](33 - 2n_f)\ln(Q^2/\mu^2)}. \tag{13.179}$$

With six quark flavours the correction term in α_3 is of the opposite sign from that in α: when Q^2 increases the denominator in (13.179) increases and $\alpha_3(Q^2)$ decreases. As $Q^2 \to \infty$, $\alpha_3(Q^2) \to 0$, a property known as asymptotic freedom. On the other hand, for sufficiently small Q^2, $\alpha_3(Q^2)$ becomes very large. In fact, the denominator in (13.179) becomes zero at

* The factor $\frac{1}{2}$ appears through an unfortunate difference in the definitions of α and α_3. In QED the strength of the coupling between two quarks of charge e_1 and e_2 is $e_1 e_2 \alpha$ while in QCD the (strong) coupling between two quarks via single-gluon exchange is $\frac{1}{2}c_1 c_2 \alpha_3$, where c_1 and c_2 are the colour coefficients associated with the two vertices.

† There are, in fact, two first-order gluon loop corrections which need to be considered. The first involves 'transverse' gluons and gives a contribution with the same sign as the QED correction. The other, which dominates, involves 'Coulomb' type gluons giving a contribution of opposite sign. (See reference 9 for further details.)

a particular value of $Q^2 = \Lambda^2$, say. This occurs when

$$\Lambda^2_{\mathrm{QCD}} = \mu^2 \exp\left[-\frac{12\pi}{(33 - 2n_{\mathrm{f}})\alpha_3(\mu^2)}\right]. \tag{13.180}$$

Using this result $\alpha_3(Q^2)$ becomes

$$\alpha_3(Q^2) = \frac{12\pi}{(33 - 2n_{\mathrm{f}})\ln(Q^2/\Lambda^2_{\mathrm{QCD}})}. \tag{13.181}$$

In rewriting α_3 in this way we have removed the parameter μ^2, which was a remnant of the renormalization process, and replaced it with the free parameter Λ_{QCD} (with dimensions of mass) which has to be determined by experiment. Experimentally, $\Lambda_{\mathrm{QCD}} \approx 200$ MeV, so, for values of $Q^2 \approx 100\ \mathrm{GeV}^2$ and five flavours of participating quarks, $\alpha_{\mathrm{s}} \cong 0.2$. It is therefore legitimate to use α_3 as a perturbation parameter in QCD calculations.

QCD is quite a remarkable theory: for values of Q^2 much greater than Λ^2_{QCD}, we have just seen that the quark–gluon effective coupling is small, so that the strong interactions between quarks can be treated perturbatively: in this Q^2 region quarks and gluons behave as though they are free particles. This is precisely the behaviour observed in deep-inelastic scattering processes in the quark–parton model. It is very satisfying that asymptotic freedom emerges naturally from QCD. In contrast, for $Q^2 \approx \Lambda^2_{\mathrm{QCD}}$, the quark–gluon coupling becomes large and perturbation calculations become meaningless. This large coupling is probably responsible for the confinement of quarks and gluons at large distances, where they form bound states of hadrons (pions, protons, etc.) with masses of the order of a few times Λ_{QCD}. The parameter Λ_{QCD} may thus be regarded as a natural strong interaction mass scale which separates a world of hadrons from a world of freely interacting quarks and gluons.

REFERENCES 13

1 **Higgs P W** 1964 *Phys Lett* **12** (232) and **13** (508)

2 **Llewellyn Smith C H** 1983 *Nucl Phys* **B228** (205)

3 CHARM Collaboration, **Allaby J V** *et al.* 1987 *Z Phys* **C36** (611)

4 **Glashow S L** 1961 *Nucl Phys* **22** (579)

5 **Yang C N and Mills R L** 1954 *Phys Rev* **96** (191)

6 **Goldstone J** 1961 *Nuovo Cimento* **19** (154)

7 **Goldstone J, Salam A and Weinberg S** 1962 *Phys Rev* **127** (965)

8 **Bjorken J D and Drell S D** 1964 *Relativistic Quantum Mechanics* McGraw-Hill

9 **Halzen F and Martin A D** 1984 *Quarks and Leptons: An Introductory Course in Modern Particle Physics* Wiley

EXAMPLES 13

13.1 Show that if a function $f(y, y')$ does not depend explicitly on x, the Euler equation

$$\frac{\partial f}{\partial y} - \frac{\mathrm{d}}{\mathrm{d}x}\frac{\partial f}{\partial y'} = 0$$

may be written

$$\frac{\mathrm{d}}{\mathrm{d}x}\left(f - y'\frac{\partial f}{\partial y'}\right) = 0.$$

13.2 This is a famous problem first proposed, in 1696, by John Bernoulli. A particle starts from rest at the origin and slides without friction in a vertical plane. Determine the path taken by the particle in sliding to a point P, displaced both vertically and horizontally from the origin, so that the time taken is the minimum possible. (Imagine a bead sliding without friction on a wire.)

13.3 Under a Lorentz transformation a contravariant four-vector transforms as

$$x^{\mu'} = \frac{\partial x^{\mu'}}{\partial x^{\mu}} = \Lambda^{\mu'}_{\mu} x^{\mu} \qquad (\mu', \mu = 0, \ldots, 3)$$

while a covariant four-vector transforms as

$$x_{\mu'} = \frac{\partial x^{\mu}}{\partial x^{\mu'}} x_{\mu} = \Lambda^{\mu}_{\mu'} x_{\mu}.$$

Show that $\Lambda^{\mu}_{\mu'}$ is the inverse of the matrix $\Lambda^{\mu'}_{\mu}$. If ϕ is a scalar function of the space–time coordinates show that $\partial_{\mu}\phi = \partial\phi/\partial x^{\mu}$ transforms as a covariant four-vector.

13.4 The electromagnetic field strength tensor is defined as

$$F^{\mu\nu} = \partial^{\mu} A^{\nu} - \partial^{\nu} A^{\mu}.$$

Recalling that $\partial^{\mu} = \partial/\partial x_{\mu} \equiv (\partial/\partial t, -\nabla)$ and $A^{\mu} \equiv (\phi, \boldsymbol{A})$ obtain $F^{\mu\nu}$ explicitly given that the $\boldsymbol{E}$ and $\boldsymbol{B}$ fields are given by $\boldsymbol{E} = -\nabla\phi - \partial\boldsymbol{A}/\partial t$ and $\boldsymbol{B} = \nabla \wedge \boldsymbol{A}$.

13.5 Show that the electromagnetic field strength tensor satisfies the identity

$$\partial_\alpha F_{\beta\gamma} + \partial_\beta F_{\gamma\alpha} + \partial_\gamma F_{\alpha\beta} = 0.$$

Hence show that if one of the indices (α, β or γ) is zero, and the other two are any two of 1, 2, 3, then

$$\nabla \wedge \boldsymbol{E} + \frac{\partial \boldsymbol{B}}{\partial t} = 0.$$

Furthermore, if $\alpha = 1$, $\beta = 2$ and $\gamma = 3$, show that $\nabla \cdot \boldsymbol{B} = 0$.

13.6 By evaluating $\partial_\mu F^{\mu\nu} = j^\nu$, where $j^\nu \equiv (\rho, \boldsymbol{j})$, show that

$$\nabla \cdot \boldsymbol{E} = \rho \qquad \text{and} \qquad \nabla \wedge \boldsymbol{B} = \boldsymbol{j} + \frac{\partial \boldsymbol{E}}{\partial t}.$$

13.7 Starting from the relation $j^\nu = \partial_\mu F^{\mu\nu}$ and using the fact that $F^{\mu\nu}$ is antisymmetric, derive the continuity equation $\partial_\nu j^\nu = 0$.

13.8 Evaluate $F_{\mu\nu} = \partial_\mu A_\nu - \partial_\nu A_\mu$ and, using the result of example 13.4 for $F^{\mu\nu}$, show that the Lagrangian density $\mathscr{L} = -\frac{1}{4}F_{\mu\nu}F^{\mu\nu} = \frac{1}{2}(\boldsymbol{E}^2 - \boldsymbol{B}^2)$.

13.9 In a particular frame of reference the Lagrangian for the electromagnetic field at a particular time is

$$L = \int \mathscr{L}\,\mathrm{d}\tau = -\int \tfrac{1}{4}F_{\mu\nu}F^{\mu\nu}\,\mathrm{d}\tau = \tfrac{1}{2}\int (\boldsymbol{E}^2 - \boldsymbol{B}^2)\,\mathrm{d}\tau$$

where $\mathrm{d}\tau$ is a volume element. The generalized momenta conjugate to $A_\mu(x)$ are defined as $\pi^\mu(x) = \dfrac{\partial \mathscr{L}}{\partial(\partial_0 A_\mu)}$. Show that $\pi^0(x) = 0$ and $\pi^i(x) = E^i$, $i = 1, 2, 3$. Hence, assuming that $\nabla \cdot \boldsymbol{E} = 0$, show that the Hamiltonian $H = \int \pi^\mu \partial_0 A_\mu\,\mathrm{d}\tau - L$ is the integral over all space of the energy density $\frac{1}{2}(\boldsymbol{E}^2 + \boldsymbol{B}^2)$.

13.10 Determine the field equation for a massive vector field A^μ if the Lagrangian is

$$\mathscr{L} = -\tfrac{1}{4}F_{\mu\nu}F^{\mu\nu} + \tfrac{1}{2}m^2 A^\nu A_\nu$$

where $F_{\mu\nu} = \partial_\mu A_\nu - \partial_\nu A_\mu$.

13.11 The Lagrangian for a spinor field may be written

$$\mathscr{L} = \frac{\mathrm{i}}{2}[\bar{\psi}\gamma^\mu(\partial_\mu\psi) - (\partial_\mu\bar{\psi})\gamma^\mu\psi] - m\bar{\psi}\psi.$$

Show that for this Lagrangian the Euler–Lagrange equations yield the Dirac equation and its adjoint.

13.12 Determine the weak isospin and weak hypercharge currents for the second generation of leptons and quarks ν_μ, μ^-, c and s′. (Leave your answers in terms of s′.)

13.13 In the standard model (neglecting fermion masses) the partial width of the decay of the Z^0 to a fermion–antifermion pair is

$$\Gamma(Z^0 \to f\bar{f}) = 2[(c_V^f)^2 + (c_A^f)^2]\frac{G^2 M_Z^3}{\sqrt{(2)}12\pi}$$

where c_V^f and c_A^f are the fermion couplings to the Z^0 given in table 13.3. Assuming three generations of fermions calculate the total width of the Z^0 if $G = 1.17 \times 10^{-5}\ \text{GeV}^{-2}$, $M_Z = 91.2$ GeV and $\sin^2\theta_W = 0.23$. (Remember to include a colour factor for quarks.)

14 *Experimental tests of the standard model*

Introduction · Experimental tests of quantum electrodynamics · Experimental tests of electroweak theory · Experimental tests of quantum chromodynamics	

14.1 Introduction

The fundamental constituents of matter are believed to be point-like fermions – leptons and quarks – in the following families of increasing mass

$$\begin{bmatrix} \nu_e \\ e \\ u \\ d \end{bmatrix} \begin{bmatrix} \nu_\mu \\ \mu \\ c \\ s \end{bmatrix} \begin{bmatrix} (\nu_\tau) \\ \tau \\ (t) \\ b \end{bmatrix}.$$

The top quark and the τ neutrino have not yet been observed. In the standard model the neutrinos are massless and exist only in left-handed helicity states. The massive charged leptons and quarks can be either left handed or right handed.

The interactions between these fundamental particles are to be described by renormalizable gauge theories. The requirement that the free-particle Lagrangian be invariant under $SU(3)_{colour} \times SU(2)_L \times U(1)_Y$ gauge transformations introduces 12 gauge bosons (eight gluons, the $W^{\pm}$ and Z and the photon) and determines the form of their interactions with the fermions. Spontaneous symmetry breaking through the Higgs mechanism endows the $W^{\pm}$ and Z with mass but leaves the photon massless.

In the present chapter we summarize evidence which supports these gauge theories and determines their unknown parameters. It will be convenient to deal separately with quantum electrodynamics (U(1)), electroweak theory (SU(2)) and quantum chromodynamics (SU(3)).

14.2 *Experimental tests of quantum electrodynamics*

Quantum electrodynamics (QED) has been verified to a higher degree of accuracy than any other gauge theory, in both the low energy (sections 14.2.1 and 14.2.2) and the high energy domains (section 14.2.3).

14.2.1 *Atomic hydrogen energy levels*

The basic electromagnetic coupling constant, or *fine-structure* constant, α (appendix A), may be obtained from the displacement of 10969.1 MHz between the $2^2P_{3/2}$ and $2^2P_{1/2}$ levels of the hydrogen atom (see, for example, reference 1). Each level of the hydrogen spectrum is in fact a doublet (*hyperfine splitting*) because of the interaction between the magnetic moments of the proton and electron. Transitions between the two substates of the $1^2S_{1/2}$ ground state (see figure 14.1) give rise to the famous 21 cm (1420.4 MHz) hydrogen line.[2] A calculation assuming the electron to be a Dirac particle with a magnetic moment of 1 Bohr magneton gives a value significantly different from the measured frequency, but when radiative corrections[3] are taken into account agreement is improved:

$$\Delta\nu(\text{experiment}) = 1420.4057517864 \pm 0.0000000017 \text{ MHz}$$
$$\Delta\nu(\text{theory}) = 1420.404 \pm 0.006 \text{ MHz}.$$

The error in the theoretical value is not due to a lack of understanding of QED processes but rather to a lack of knowledge of the internal spin structure of the proton.

According to the Dirac theory hydrogen-atom states with the same

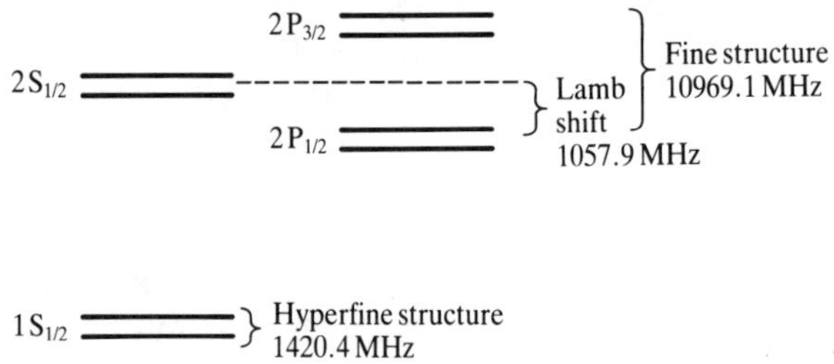

Figure 14.1
Detailed structure of the low-lying levels of atomic hydrogen.

values of principal and total angular momentum quantum numbers n and j but differing in orbital angular momentum l should have the same energy. This degeneracy is removed when vacuum polarization and other second-order effects are taken into account. The shift in energy, mainly to the S state, leads to the observed *Lamb shift*. Current experimental[4,5] and theoretical[6] results are in good agreement.

$$\Delta\nu(\text{experiment}) = 1057.878 \pm 0.014 \text{ MHz}$$
$$\Delta\nu(\text{theory}) = 1057.898 \pm 0.026 \text{ MHz}.$$

14.2.2 *Magnetic moment of the electron and the muon*

Comparison of the experimental and theoretical values for these quantities provides the best available test of the validity of QED.

In the Dirac theory, the electron and muon, with $s = \frac{1}{2}$ and $\mu = \mu_B$ should have a g factor (section 3.5) of 2. We know, however, that these particles are not bare charges but are surrounded by a fluctuating cloud of virtual photons, e^+e^- pairs etc. and the consequent corrections must be made in calculating the leptonic magnetic moments. These are therefore expressed in the form

$$\mu = \mu_B(1 + a) \tag{14.1}$$

where the anomaly a is given by

$$a = \frac{g - 2}{2}. \tag{14.2}$$

Experimental determination of the moments is based on the fact that the anomaly leads to a difference between the cyclotron frequency of orbital motion in a magnetic field, namely

$$\omega_c = \frac{eB}{m\gamma} \tag{14.3}$$

and the frequency of spin procession[7] in the same field, given by

$$\omega_s = \frac{eB}{m\gamma}(1 + a\gamma) \tag{14.4}$$

where γ is the Lorentz factor. Extremely precise measurements[8–11] of $g - 2$ have been made in this way for both the electron and the muon and the results compared with theory are as follows:

	a_e	a_μ
Experiment	$(1\,159\,652\,188.4 \pm 4.3) \times 10^{-12}$	$(11\,659\,230 \pm 84) \times 10^{-10}$
Theory	$(1\,159\,652\,133 \pm 29) \times 10^{-12}$	$(11\,659\,194.7 \pm 14.3) \times 10^{-10}$.

The error[12,13] in the theoretical value for a_e is governed by uncertainty in the value of α while that in the theoretical[14] value of a_μ is dependent on hadronic effects.[15]

14.2.3 Lepton structure and quantum electrodynamics at high energies

The most stringent test of the point-like nature of the electron comes from a study of Bhabha scattering using e^+e^- colliding beam machines. The measured cross-section is related to the calculated point-like cross-section by the equation

$$\sigma(e^+e^- \to e^+e^-) = F^2(x)\sigma_{\text{point}}(e^+e^- \to e^+e^-) \tag{14.5}$$

where $F(x)$ is a form factor with x representing the square of the centre-of-mass energy or the square of the four-momentum transfer. Results from PETRA[16] indicate that the electron is point-like down to a distance of about 2×10^{-19}cm.

The annihilation process $e^+e^- \to \mu^+\mu^-$ was used, also at PETRA,[17] to confirm the point-like nature of the muon down to distances of about 4×10^{-19} cm.

14.3 Experimental tests of electroweak theory

14.3.1 Introduction

The standard model of electroweak interactions demands the existence of $W^\pm$ and Z^0 bosons, of neutral current reactions and of the Higgs mechanism and its associated boson. The couplings effective in the model are determined once the fine-structure constant α (section 14.2.1), the Fermi constant G (section 11.5.1) and the weak mixing angle θ_W (section 13.6.4) are measured. In terms of these quantities the model predicts (section 13.6.11)

$$M_W^2 \sin^2 \theta_W = \frac{\pi\alpha}{\sqrt{2}G} \tag{14.6}$$

$$\sin^2 \theta_W = 1 - \frac{M_W^2}{M_Z^2}. \tag{14.7}$$

These equations should be modified by radiative corrections[18] dependent on the renormalization scheme adopted but these will not be considered here.

Since the experimental values of α and G are very accurate, we see that once M_Z is specified, M_W and $\sin^2 \theta_W$ are fixed. But M_Z itself is now well known (section 14.3.8) and may be taken as a fundamental quantity so that precision tests of the electroweak theory really depend on determinations of $\sin^2 \theta_W$, which must be the same for all leptons and quarks. Detailed experimental verification then comes from two distinct sources, first the study of purely *leptonic interactions* (sections 14.3.3 and 14.3.4) and secondly the study of *lepton–quark processes* (sections 14.3.5 and 14.3.6). The purely leptonic sector provides clean and direct tests but cross-sections, e.g. for neutrino–electron scattering, are low. In the lepton–quark sector the quark–parton model must of course be invoked and a further complication arises from flavour mixing of the quarks in their coupling to the weak currents. The elements of the Cabibbo–Kobayashi–Maskawa matrix (section 13.6.3) have to be determined experimentally.

14.3.2 The discovery of weak neutral currents

A major landmark in particle physics was reached in 1973 when the first neutral current event was seen[19] in the Gargamelle bubble chamber, exposed to a beam of muon antineutrinos at CERN (fgiure 14.2). That only three

$$\bar{\nu}_\mu + e^- \rightarrow \bar{\nu}_\mu + e^- \tag{14.8}$$

scatterings were seen in 1.4×10^6 beam pulses with approximately 10^9 antineutrinos per pulse testifies to the smallness of the cross-section ($\sigma/E_\nu \approx 10^{-42}\ \text{cm}^2\ \text{GeV}^{-1}$). The recoiling electron in (14.8) is recognized by the energy loss that it suffers through bremsstrahlung (and subsequent pair production) as it travels through the freon (CF_2Br) filling of the bubble chamber.

Subsequently the more common neutral-current processes

$$\bar{\nu}_\mu + N \rightarrow \bar{\nu}_\mu + \text{hadrons}$$

$$\nu_\mu + N \rightarrow \nu_\mu + \text{hadrons} \tag{14.9}$$

were seen in the same experiment.[20,21]

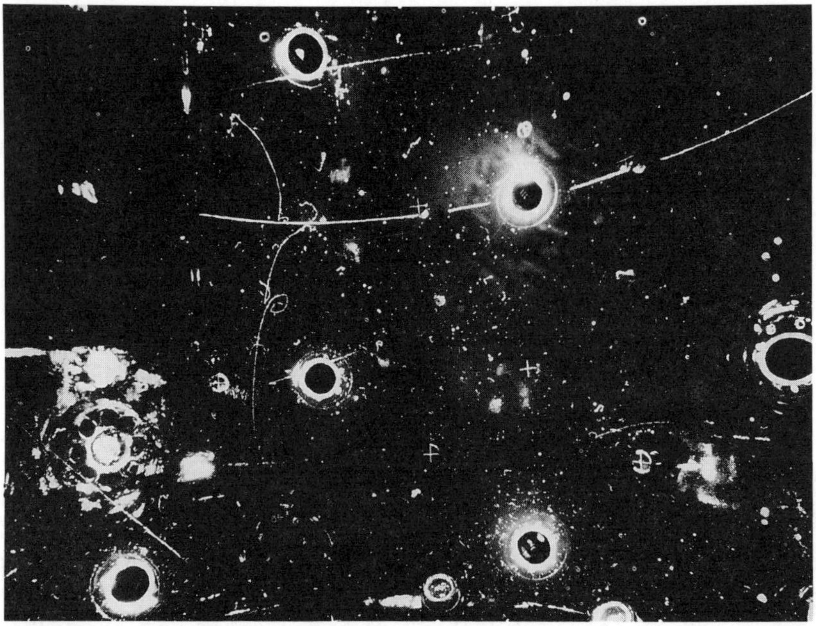

Figure 14.2 Example of a neutral-current interaction, $\bar{\nu}_\mu + e^- \rightarrow \bar{\nu}_\mu + e^-$, observed in the Gargamelle bubble chamber at CERN. Towards the end of its path the scattered electron loses energy through bremsstrahlung. The subsequent electron–positron pairs are clearly visible. (Courtesy of CERN.).

14.3.3 Elastic neutrino–electron scattering

The Feynman diagrams for the scattering of neutrinos by electrons, i.e. the processes $(\nu_\mu e^-)$, $(\bar{\nu}_\mu e^-)$, $(\nu_e e^-)$, $(\bar{\nu}_e e^-)$, are shown in figure 14.3. The ν_μ reactions can proceed only by neutral currents, with Z^0 exchange, but the ν_e processes also involve charged currents with W^- in the intermediate state. The formalism developed in chapter 13 can be used directly to write down the matrix element for each type of process as a product of currents for the two particles involved. Furthermore the helicity structure of the neutral current reactions and hence the dependence on the inelasticity $y = E_e/E_\nu$ is the same as that for the neutrino–quark scattering given in equations (13.56) and (13.57). This permits differential and total cross-sections to be evaluated in terms of the familiar vector and axial vector couplings c_V and c_A, remembering that the charged currents are pure V–A.

For the ν_μ reactions, under the assumption that the electron mass may be neglected in comparison with the neutrino energy, we obtain

$$\sigma(\nu_\mu e^-) = \frac{G^2 s}{3\pi}(c_V^2 + c_V c_A + c_A^2) \qquad (14.10)$$

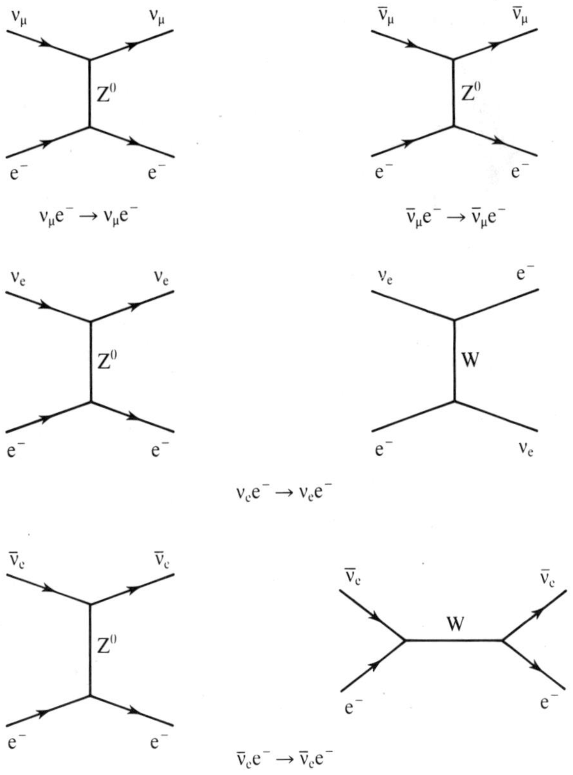

Figure 14.3
Feynman diagrams for ν–e scattering.

$$\sigma(\bar{\nu}_\mu e^-) = \frac{G^2 s}{3\pi}(c_V^2 + c_V c_A + c_A^2) \tag{14.11}$$

where G is the Fermi constant and s is the square of the centre-of-mass energy. We recall (section 13.6.4) that c_V and c_A are given in terms of the weak isospin I_3 and θ_W by

$$c_V = I_3 - 2Q \sin^2 \theta_W \qquad c_A = I_3 \tag{14.12}$$

where Q is the electron charge in units of e, so that a measurement of the cross-sections determines $\sin^2 \theta_W$. Although the discovery of neutral currents was made with the bubble chamber, present day experiments[22,23] use large electronic calorimeters and preferentially measure the cross-section ratio $R = \sigma(\nu_\mu e)/\sigma(\bar{\nu}_\mu e)$ since this eliminates the need to know the *absolute* neutrino flux and the electron detection efficiency. The world average result[24] for ν_μ–e and $\bar{\nu}_\mu$–e scattering is

$$\sin^2 \theta_W = 0.231 \pm 0.010.$$

Experiments with $\bar{\nu}_e$ and ν_e have also been made[25,26] but insufficient events have so far been seen to constrain further the value of $\sin^2 \theta_W$

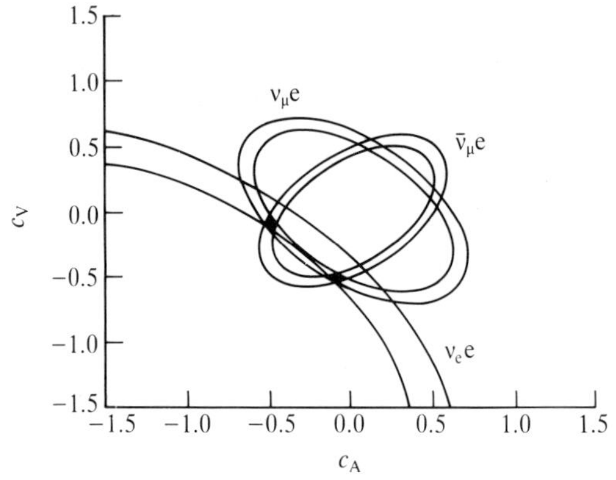

Figure 14.4 Plot of the vector and axial vector couplings, c_V and c_A, of charged leptons to the neutral current. The elliptical contours are the regions allowed by the measured ν_μ–e and $\bar{\nu}_\mu$–e cross-sections. Only two solutions (shaded) are consistent with recent results on ν_e–e scattering. The standard model favours the solution $c_V \approx 0$ and $c_A \approx -0.5$.

obtained from the muon neutrino experiments. The results of the scattering experiments are commonly presented (figure 14.4) as an ellipse of possible values of c_V and c_A in the c_V–c_A plane. There are two possible solutions, given by the intersection regions in the diagram, and of these the standard model favours the c_A dominant one ($c_A = -\frac{1}{2}$, $c_V = 0$).

14.3.4 Electroweak interference in electron–positron annihilation

In the annihilation process $e^+e^- \to \bar{f}f$ where f represents the fermion e, μ, τ or q, there are contributions to the scattering amplitude from both photon and Z^0 exchange as shown in figure 14.5. Interference between the corresponding partial amplitudes leads to an asymmetry in the differential cross-section for the process.

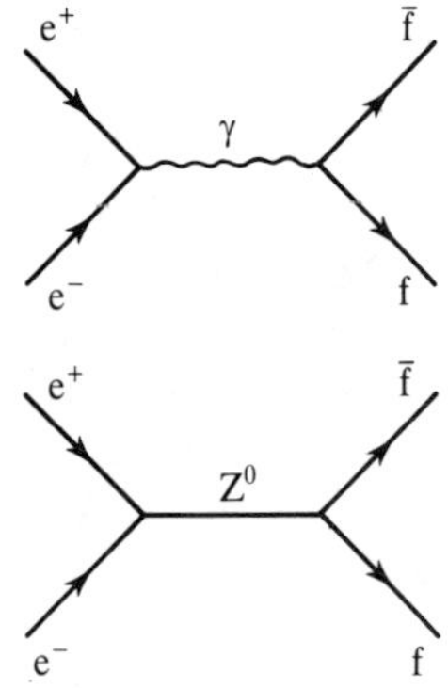

Figure 14.5
Feynman graphs for the process $e^+e^- \to \bar{f}f$ by photon and Z^0 exchange.

At centre-of-mass energies $\sqrt{s} \ll M_Z$ the standard model predicts that the forward–backward asymmetry in the reaction $e^+e^- \to \mu^+\mu^-$ is

$$A = \frac{F-B}{F+B} = -\frac{3s}{4\sqrt{2}\pi\alpha} c_A^e c_A^\mu. \tag{14.13}$$

The angular distribution for this reaction, obtained at the PETRA collider at $s = 1880\ \text{GeV}^2$, is shown in figure 14.6 in comparison with the symmetric prediction of QED for point-like fermions and photon exchange only. The s dependence of the asymmetry also agrees well with the predictions of the electroweak theory.

If we assume the theoretical value of the axial vector coupling constant ($c_A^e = c_A^\mu = -\frac{1}{2}$) the measured asymmetry can be used to deduce $\sin^2\theta_W$,

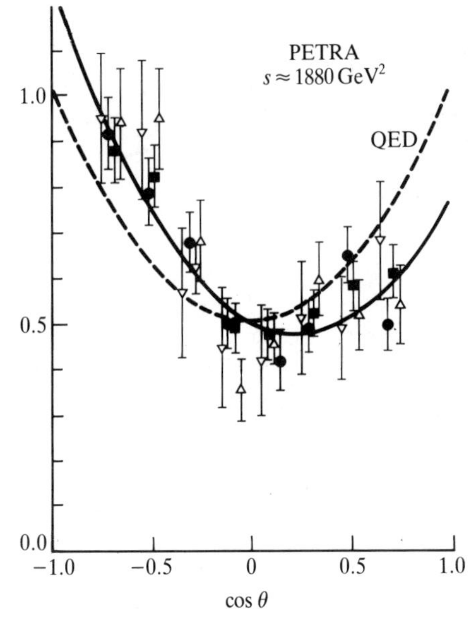

Figure 14.6 The angular distribution in the reaction $e^+e^- \to \mu^+\mu^-$ at $s = 1880$ GeV^2: ▽, CELLO; ●, JADE; ■, MARK J; △, TASSO. The best fit to the angular distribution, shown by the solid curve, gives an asymmetry $A = -0.18 \pm 0.2$. The symmetric QED prediction is shown by the broken curve.

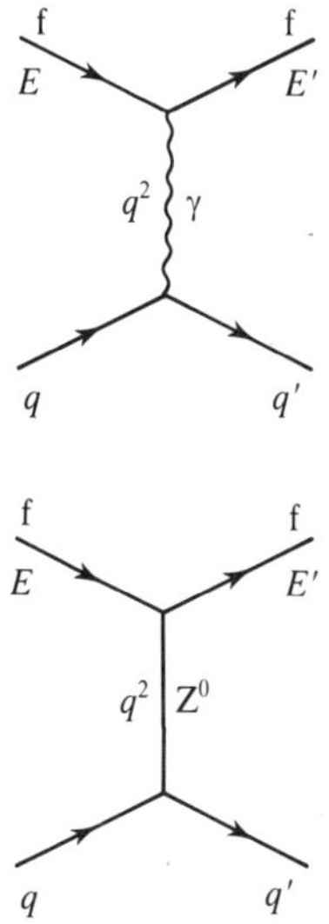

Figure 14.7
Feynman diagrams for lepton–quark scattering via γ and Z^0 exchange.

with the result[27]

$$\sin^2 \theta_W = 0.210 \pm 0.019 \pm 0.013$$

in which the errors are statistical and systematic respectively. Alternatively, if the value of $\sin^2 \theta_W$ from ν–e scattering is assumed, together with M_Z, then the coupling constants can be determined; they are found to be consistent with the hypothesis of lepton universality and with the predicted electroweak values (table 13.3).

14.3.5 Asymmetries in the scattering of polarized charged leptons from quarks

Electroweak interference effects may also be seen in the scattering of spin-polarized fermions from the quarks in nuclei; figure 14.7 gives the two contributing Feynman diagrams. The amplitude for the photon-exchange diagram is proportional to e^2/q^2 where q^2 is the four-momentum transfer squared while that for Z^0 exchange (neutral current) is proportional to the Fermi constant G. The resulting asymmetry is therefore

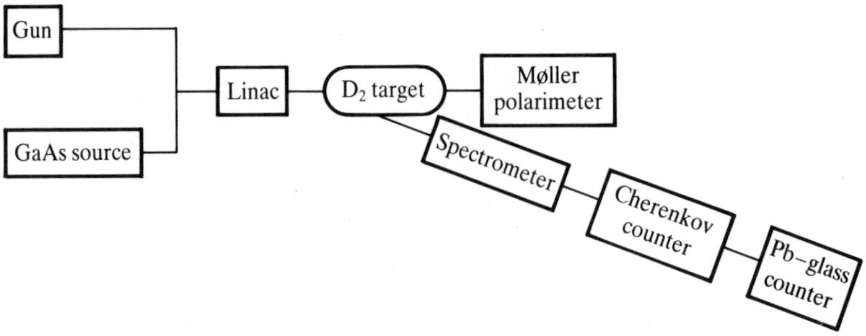

Figure 14.8 Schematic diagram of the experimental set-up at SLAC. Electrons from the GaAs source or the gun were accelerated by the linac. Particles scattered from the deuterium target were analysed in the spectrometer and detected by the Cherenkov and Pb-glass counters. The Møller polarimeter monitored the polarization of the electron beam.

roughly expected to be

$$A \approx \frac{|\mathscr{M}^{\mathrm{EM}}\mathscr{M}^{\mathrm{NC}}|}{|\mathscr{M}^{\mathrm{EM}}|^2} \approx \frac{Gq^2}{e^2} = \frac{10^{-5}}{m_{\mathrm{N}}^2}\frac{137}{4\pi}q^2 \approx \frac{10^{-4}q^2}{m_{\mathrm{N}}^2}$$

where m_{N} is the mass of the nucleon.

Asymmetry measurements were carried out in an experiment at SLAC[28, 29] in which longitudinally polarized electrons were scattered from a deuterium target (figure 14.8). The thermionic cathode in the usual electron gun was replaced by a gallium arsenide crystal and polarized electrons were produced by optical pumping with circularly polarized photons between the valence and conduction bands in the GaAs. A dye laser, operated at 710 nm and pulsed to match the linac, was used as the light source. Linearly polarized laser light was converted to circularly polarized light by a Pockels cell – a crystal with birefringence proportional to the applied electric field. The plane of polarization of the light incident on the Pockels cell could be altered by rotating a calcite prism. A reversal of the polarity of the high-voltage pulse driving the Pockels cell results in a reversal of the helicity of the photons which in turn reverses the polarization of the electrons. This reversal was done randomly on a pulse by pulse basis. The sign and magnitude of the polarization of the electron beam at the target were measured by observing the asymmetry produced in Møller scattering – the scattering of polarized electrons by polarized electrons.

The parity-violating asymmetry

$$A = \frac{\mathrm{d}\sigma_{\mathrm{R}} - \mathrm{d}\sigma_{\mathrm{L}}}{\mathrm{d}\sigma_{\mathrm{R}} + \mathrm{d}\sigma_{\mathrm{L}}}$$

was measured at incident electron energies between 16.2 and 22.2 GeV. Here $\mathrm{d}\sigma_{\mathrm{R}}$ and $\mathrm{d}\sigma_{\mathrm{L}}$ are the cross-sections $\mathrm{d}\sigma/\mathrm{d}y$ for the inelastic scattering of right- and left-handed electrons in the process $e_{R,L}q \to e_{R,L}q'$; the quantity $y = (E - E')/E$ is the inelasticity or fractional energy loss of the electron in the laboratory frame. Evaluation of the y dependence of the asymmetry[30] gives

$$A(y) = \frac{-9Gq^2}{20\sqrt{2}\pi\alpha}\left[a_1 + a_2\frac{1-(1-y)^2}{1+(1-y)^2}\right] \tag{14.14}$$

where $a_1 = 1 - (20/9)\sin^2\theta_W$ and $a_2 = 1 - 4\sin^2\theta_W$. In the experiment the asymmetry was found to be consistent with (14.14) with a value

$$\sin^2\theta_W = 0.22 \pm 0.02.$$

In an experiment at CERN,[31] beams of muons polarized by π, K decay were scattered from a carbon target at values of $q^2 \approx 100\ \text{GeV}^2$. The asymmetry measured in this case was between cross-sections of left-handed μ^+ and right-handed μ^- incident on carbon nuclei. The asymmetry

$$B = \frac{d\sigma_L^+ - d\sigma_R^-}{d\sigma_L^+ + d\sigma_R^-}$$

is shown as a function of

$$q^2\left[\frac{1-(1-y)^2}{1+(1-y)^2}\right]$$

in figure 14.9. The linear dependence on q^2 is verified and a value

$$\sin^2\theta_W = 0.23 \pm 0.08$$

is obtained.

14.3.6 Deep inelastic neutrino–quark scattering

Because of the larger mass of the target particle the cross-sections for neutrino–nucleon reactions are roughly three orders of magnitude greater than the corresponding cross-sections for neutrino–electron reactions. Estimates of $\sin^2\theta_W$ from νN processes therefore have the greater statistical accuracy.

The cross-sections for both neutral and charged current neutrino–nucleon (and antineutrino–nucleon) scattering were given in equations (13.49), (13.50), (13.56) and (13.57). If we consider only isoscalar targets and assume that contributions to the scattering processes come only from u and d valence quarks, the ratios of neutral to charged-current total

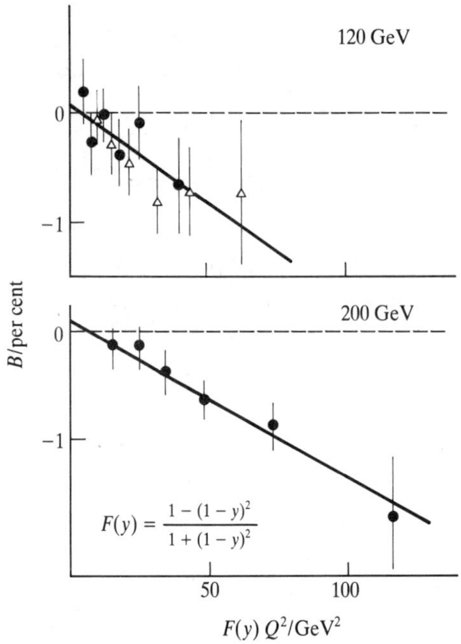

Figure 14.9
The asymmetry B, defined in the text, between cross-sections for the scattering of left-handed μ^+ and right-handed μ^- from carbon nuclei.

cross-sections are found to be (see example 14.1)

$$R = \frac{\sigma^{NC}(\nu)}{\sigma^{CC}(\nu)} = \frac{1}{2} - \sin^2\theta_W + \frac{20}{27}\sin^4\theta_W \tag{14.15}$$

$$\bar{R} = \frac{\sigma^{NC}(\bar{\nu})}{\sigma^{CC}(\bar{\nu})} = \frac{1}{2} - \sin^2\theta_W + \frac{20}{9}\sin^4\theta_W. \tag{14.16}$$

These ratios have been determined in several experiments. For an accurate determination of $\sin^2\theta_W$ small corrections have to be made for the effect of sea quarks, including contributions from c quarks above the charm threshold, and QCD scale-breaking effects. The most precise results[32,33] combine to give

$$\sin^2\theta_W = 0.230 \pm 0.004$$

a value whose accuracy is matched only by determinations from the mass of the W and Z bosons (section 14.3.8).

14.3.7 Electroweak interference in atomic transitions

One normally thinks of the binding of electrons in an atom as being due to the Coulomb force. The basic Hamiltonian of an atom H_0 commutes with the parity operator and has a spectrum of eigenstates of definite parity, either even or odd. In terms of Feynman diagrams the purely electromagnetic interaction between the electrons and the nucleus is described by photon exchange; the photons couple to the quarks in the nucleus through vector electromagnetic currents. However, because of the existence of weak neutral currents a Feynman diagram with Z^0 exchange must also contribute to the electron binding. This introduces both vector and axial vector couplings between the electrons and the quarks and the resulting Hamiltonian H_1 contains both scalar (parity-conserving) and pseudoscalar (parity-violating) terms:

$$H_1 = H_0 + H_s + H_p.$$

As a consequence of the term H_p a given energy eigenstate, formerly of definite parity, now contains a small admixture of states of opposite parity. The amplitude for a radiative transition between states then contains a small parity-violating component (e.g. E1 in a predominantly M1 transition) and interference between the two components gives rise to a small but observable asymmetry in the radiation intensity.

In the standard model (Table 13.3) the vector coupling of the electron c_V^e is small compared with the axial-vector coupling c_A^e so that the parity-violating interference term is governed by the product $c_A^e c_V^q$ where c_V^q is the vector coupling of the quarks. At the very low q^2 of atomic processes the exchanged boson sees the coherent effect of all the quarks in the nucleus and for a nucleus of mass number A $(= Z + N)$ the weak charge in the interference term is $\frac{1}{2}[-N + (1 - 4\sin^2\theta_W)Z]$ (see example 14.2). Detailed further investigation[34–36] shows that the effect is further enhanced by a factor Z^2, so the effects have been sought in heavy atoms.

Experiments on the absorption of right and left circularly polarized photons have been reported for the $6S_{1/2} \rightarrow 7S_{1/2}$ transition in Cs[37–39] and for the $6P_{1/2} \rightarrow 7P_{1/2}$ transition in Tl.[40–42] In an alternative approach the rotation of the plane of polarization of linearly polarized light passing through a vapour in which M1 transitions may be excited is observed.[43–46] The positive results obtained support the standard model and give a value of the Weinberg angle:

$$\sin^2\theta_W = 0.209 \pm 0.018$$

consistent with the more precise results.

14.3.8 Discovery of the W and Z bosons

The standard model formulae given in section 14.3.1 permit the mass of the W and Z bosons to be predicted from known values of the fine-structure constant α, the Fermi constant G and the mixing angle θ_W.

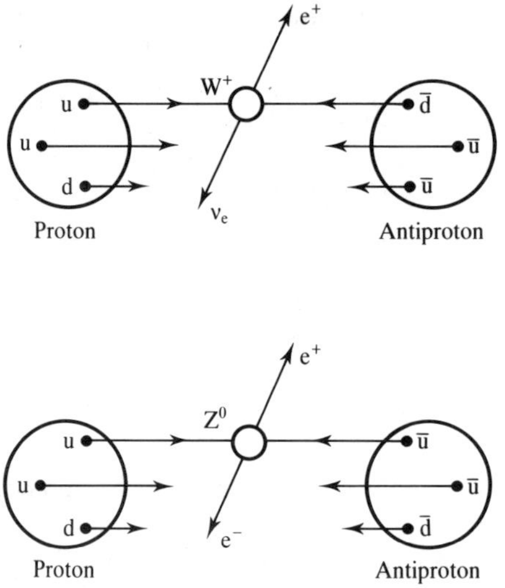

Figure 14.10
Schematic diagrams showing the production of W^+ and Z^0 bosons in proton–antiproton collisions.

Taking radiative corrections into account the predicted masses are

$$M_W = 80.2 \pm 1.1 \text{ GeV}/c^2 \qquad M_Z = 91.6 \pm 0.9 \text{ GeV}/c^2.$$

The CERN $\bar{p}p$ collider, which has been briefly described in section 2.5.4, was proposed[47] and built to produce these particles. The centre-of-mass energy in the collider was 540 GeV but because of the quark structure of the nucleon (section 12.6.2) the effective energy is that available in a $q\bar{q}$ collision (figure 14.10) and that was about 90 GeV, just adequate for the new particles. The successful outcome of the collider experiment led to the award of the 1984 Nobel Prize for Physics to Carlo Rubbia and Simon van der Meer.

A detailed description of the detector used by the UA1 collaboration at CERN, in which the W and Z were first observed, is given by Timmer;[48] a schematic diagram is shown in figure 14.11. The central detector is a 6 m long drift chamber (section 2.3.3); it is surrounded by electromagnetic and hadronic calorimeters (section 2.3.6) which are in turn surrounded by muon drift chambers. A magnetic field of strength 0.7 T transverse to the beam direction is provided by a dipole magnet.

When the W and Z are produced they decay via the weak interaction into pairs of fermions (leptons or quarks). The number of quark decay channels is larger than the number of lepton channels but decays into quarks are difficult to observe clearly because of background from QCD processes. The experimental searches for the W and Z therefore concentrated on the lepton channels

$$W \rightarrow e\nu_e,\ \mu\nu_\mu,\ \tau\nu_\tau$$
$$Z^0 \rightarrow e^+e^-,\ \mu^+\mu^-.$$

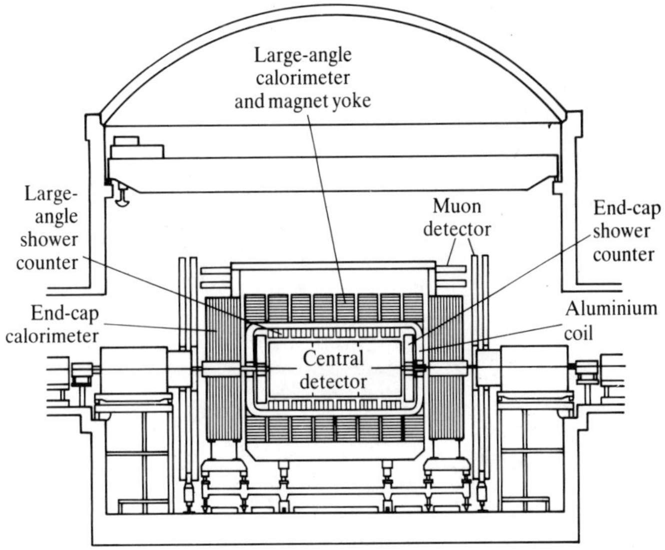

Figure 14.11
Side view of the UA1 apparatus showing the central detector, electromagnetic calorimeters, hadron calorimeters and muon detectors.

The experimental signature for all these processes is an electron or muon with a high transverse momentum relative to the beam direction.

In the leptonic decays of the W a neutrino is always produced. Since neutrinos interact only via the weak interaction the probability of observing a neutrino in the detector calorimetry is negligible: the presence of a neutrino has to be inferred from an observation of missing energy in the collision. In any single collision it is invariably impossible to make an accurate determination of the missing energy because of losses of particles down the beam pipe. However, any final-state particles which disappear down the beam pipe, or indeed approach the beam direction, have a very small *transverse* momentum, i.e. the momentum component in a plane perpendicular to the beam direction. It is therefore possible to make a reliable measurement of the missing energy in this plane: this missing energy is assigned to a neutrino.

In figure 14.12 we show, for events containing an electron candidate, the transverse momentum p_T^e, plotted against the missing transverse momentum p_T^ν. Because the W is produced essentially at rest, the momentum is shared equally between its decay products and W decay is therefore seen as a concentration of events about the line $p_T^e = p_T^\nu$. The clustering of points along the horizontal axis arises mainly from events in which hadrons are misidentified as electrons. To obtain a clean sample of $W \to e\nu_e$ events, relatively free from background, a cut of $p_T^\nu > 15$ GeV/c was made on the data. The p_T^e distribution for those events satisfying the cut are shown in figure 14.13.

Since the momentum of the neutrinos of these W events is not known, the W mass cannot simply be calculated on an event-by-event basis.

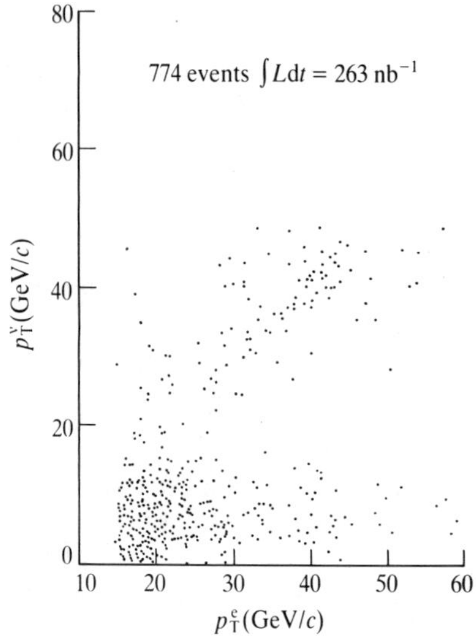

Figure 14.12
Plot of p_T^ν versus p_T^e for UA1 events containing at least one electron candidate. (Ganvey J 1987 *Rep Prog Phys* **50** (1311))

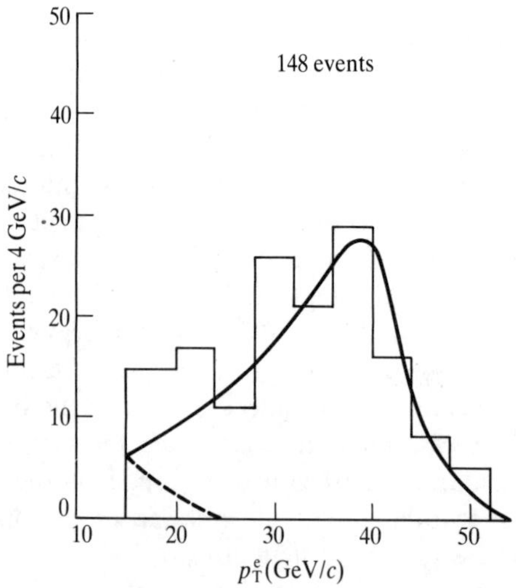

Figure 14.13
The p_T^e distribution for events in figure 14.12 in which $p_T^\nu > 15$ GeV/c. (Ganvey J 1987 *Rep Prog Phys* **50** (1311))

Instead, a quantity M_T, known as the transverse mass and given by

$$M_T^2 = 2p_T^e p_T^\nu[1 - \cos(\Delta\phi)]$$

is calculated for each event. The quantity $\Delta\phi$ is the difference in azimuth between p_T^e and p_T^ν. The actual mass of the W is then obtained from a detailed Monte Carlo simulation of the experimental results. The mass and width of the W are left as free parameters in the Monte Carlo program and the best fit to the data, shown as the solid line in figure

14.13, gives

$$M_W = 83.5 \pm {}^{1.1}_{1.0}(\text{stat}) \pm 2.7(\text{syst})\ \text{GeV}/c^2$$
$$\Gamma_W < 6.5\ \text{GeV}/c^2$$

at the 90 per cent confidence level. When LEP is upgraded in 1995 it is expected that the W mass will be measured with a precision of the order of 50 MeV.

An important test of the production mechanism of the W is provided by a study of the decay angular distribution. In figure 14.14 we show the production and subsequent decay of a W^+. The helicities, shown by the short arrows, are those appropriate for a V–A structure of the weak charged current. The decay angle θ^* is defined as the direction between the positron and the incoming antiproton. Conservation of angular momentum means that the W^+ (with spin $s = 1$) is polarized on production with $s_z = +1$. The probability that the W^+ decays to a positron, with helicity $\lambda = +1$, at an angle θ^* and a neutrino with helicity $\lambda = -1$ (at an angle $\pi + \theta^*$) with $s_z = +1$ is $|d^{(1)}_{11}|^2 = \frac{1}{4}(1 + \cos\theta^*)^2$, see appendix H. The angular distribution for the decay of a W^- is the same provided that in this case the angle θ^* is defined as the angle between the electron and the incoming proton. The UA1 results are shown in figure 14.15 and the agreement with the prediction is very good.

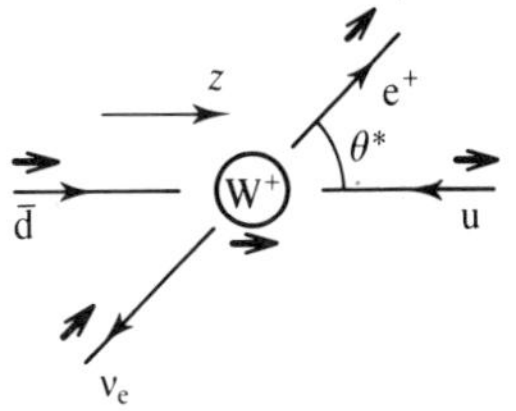

Figure 14.14
Production and decay of a W^+.

With its capability of detecting and identifying muons, the UA1 collaboration has measured the cross-sections σ^e_W, σ^μ_W and σ^τ_W for the production of a W followed by decay into the three different lepton channels. Their results[49] are

$$\sigma^\mu_W/\sigma^e_W = 1.07 \pm 0.17(\text{stat}) \pm 0.13(\text{syst})$$
$$\sigma^\tau_W/\sigma^e_W = 1.02 \pm 0.02(\text{stat}) \pm 0.1(\text{syst}).$$

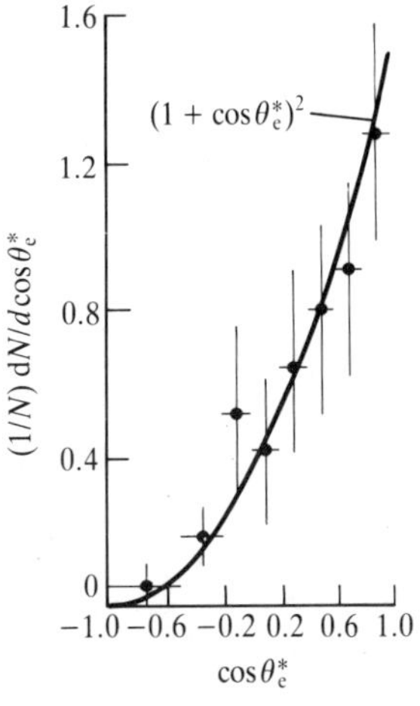

Figure 14.15
The angular distribution of the electron (positron) in the W^- (W^+) rest system relative to the incident quark (antiquark) measured by the UA1 collaboration. (Ganvey J 1987 *Rep Prog Phys* **50** (1311))

These ratios are consistent with e–μ–τ universality.

The Z^0 boson can decay into any fermion–antifermion pair, $f\bar{f}$, provided $m_f \leqslant M_Z/2$. The cross-section for Z^0 production is about one-tenth that of W production so that, although the Z^0 mass can be measured directly by reconstructing the invariant mass of the fermion–antifermion pair, the number of observed events in the pioneering experiment was low but the background was negligible. Figure 14.16 shows an example of a Z^0 decaying into an electron–positron pair. In figure 14.16(a) all tracks and calorimeter hits are shown whereas in 14.16(b) only those tracks with transverse momentum greater than 2 GeV/c and calorimeter cells with transverse energy greater than 2 GeV are shown. The rectangular symbols represent the energy depositions in the electromagnetic calorimeter. The mass and width of the Z^0, determined by fitting a Breit–Wigner resonance function to the invariant mass distribution of electron–positron pairs from

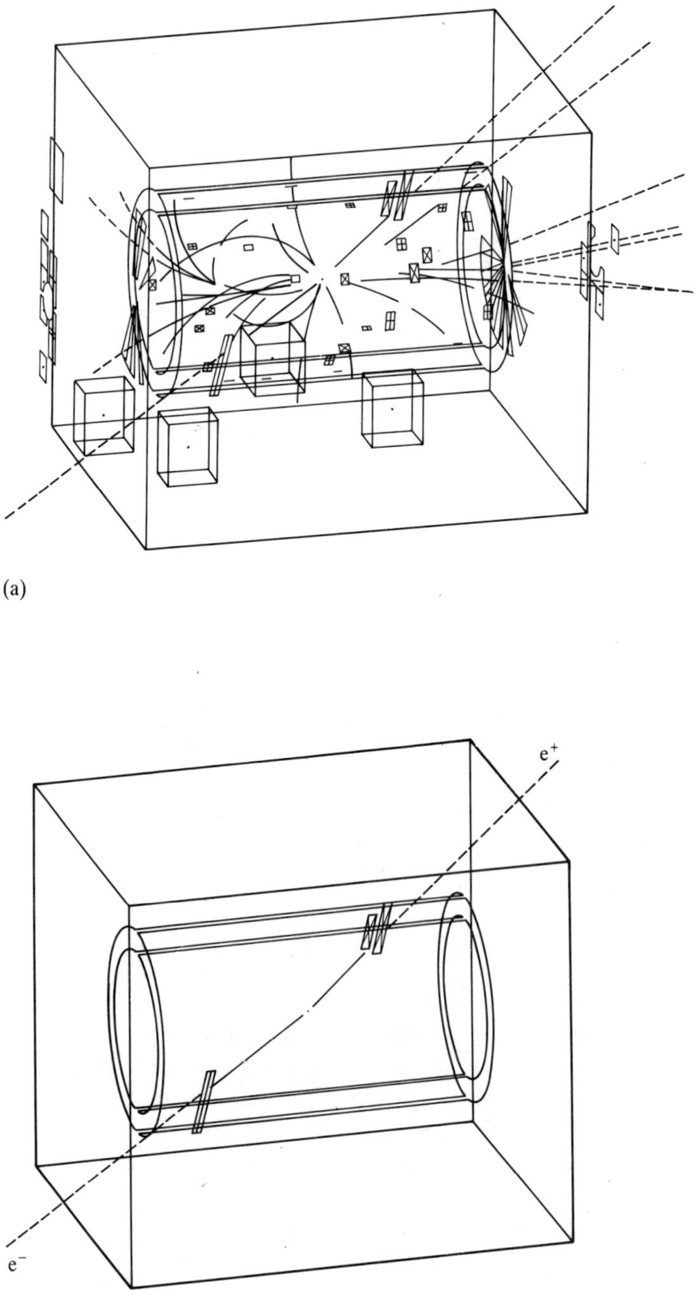

(a)

(b)

Figure 14.16 Computer display of an event (event 7433.1001) from the UA1 experiment showing the decay $Z^0 \rightarrow e^+e^-$. In (a) all tracks and energy depositions are shown. In (b) threshold cuts of 2 GeV/c in p_T and 2 GeV in E_T have been applied.

Table 14.1
Experimental values for the masses of the W and Z bosons

Detector	M_W/GeV	M_Z/GeV
UA2	$80.79 \pm 0.37 \pm 0.81$	$91.49 \pm 0.37 \pm 0.92$
CDF	$80.00 \pm 3.3 \pm 2.4$	$90.9 \pm 0.3 \pm 0.2$

the decays $Z^0 \to e^+e^-$ in the UA1 experiment, were[50,51]

$$M_Z = 93.0 \pm 1.4(\text{stat}) \pm 3.0(\text{syst})\ \text{GeV}/c^2$$
$$\Gamma_Z < 8.3\ \text{GeV}/c^2$$

at the 90 per cent confidence level. A fit to the di-muon mass distribution gave a value

$$M_Z = 88 \pm {}^{5.5}_{4.6}\ \text{GeV}/c^2.$$

The masses of the W and Z are in excellent agreement with the predictions of the standard model.

Since the discovery of the W and Z bosons, the CERN $\bar{p}p$ collider has been upgraded and the Fermilab Tevatron has come into operation. Masses of the W and Z have been reported by the UA2 collaboration[52] at CERN and the CDF (Collider Detector Facility) collaboration[53,54] at Fermilab, and these are given in table 14.1.

In 1989 the electron–positron colliders, SLC at Stanford and LEP at CERN, both with tunable centre-of-mass energies up to 100 GeV, came into operation. The MARK II collaboration[55] at SLC obtained $M_Z = 91.14 \pm 0.12$ GeV. Results from the four LEP detectors, ALEPH, DELPHI, L3 and OPAL, have recently been combined[56] to give

$$M_{Z^0} = 91.187 \pm 0.007\ \text{GeV}.$$

14.3.9 The Z^0 width and the number of light neutrino species

Measurements of the partial and total widths of the Z^0 are very important not only because they provide detailed tests of the standard model but also because they determine the number of fermion families.

The most accurate measurements of the mass and width of the Z^0 are those performed at LEP where the resonant line shape of the Z^0 can be determined accurately by scanning the beam energies across the Z^0 peak. Figure 14.17 shows the quality both of the LEP data and of the Breit–Wigner fit to the observations which follows the formula

$$\sigma_{q\bar{q}} = \frac{12\pi}{M_Z^2}\frac{s\Gamma_{e^+e^-}\Gamma_{q\bar{q}}}{(s - M_Z^2)^2 + s^2\Gamma_Z^2/M_Z^2}(1 - \delta_{\text{rad}}). \tag{14.17}$$

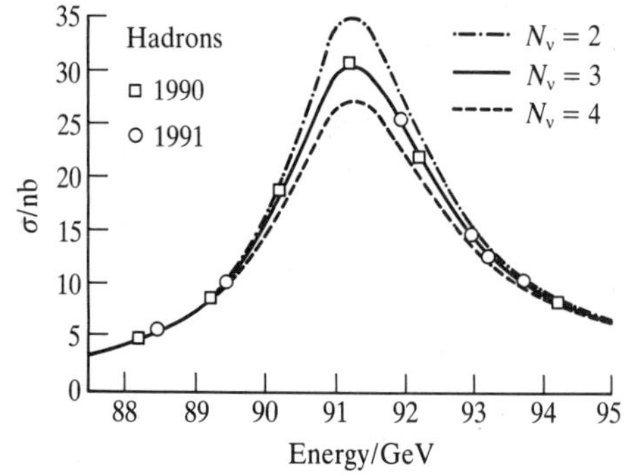

Figure 14.17
The cross-section $\sigma(e^+e^- \to Z^0 \to \text{hadrons})$ as a function of the centre-of-mass energy $\sqrt{s}$ measured by the ALEPH collaboration at LEP.

In this expression $\sigma_{q\bar{q}}$ is the cross-section for the production of the Z^0 at a centre-of-mass energy $\sqrt{s}$ followed by decay into hadrons and Γ_Z is the total decay width which is the sum of the entrance channel width, $\Gamma_{e^+e^-}$, and all other partial widths for accessible fermion–antifermion pairs, including neutrinos, and hadrons. The quantity δ_{rad} is a QED radiative correction. It is convenient to express the total width in the form

$$\Gamma_Z = \Gamma_{(\text{charged leptons})} + \Gamma_{(\text{hadrons})} + N_\nu \Gamma_\nu$$

where N_ν is the number of neutrino species, i.e. the number of neutrinos with mass $m_\nu < M_Z/2$. In terms of the known families of fermions $N_\nu = 3$.

If it is assumed that all fermion masses may be neglected in comparison with M_Z then it is possible to calculate the partial widths for both leptonic (l) and hadronic (q) decays and therefore the corresponding branching ratios. It is found that

$$\Gamma(Z^0 \to l\bar{l}) = 2[(c_V^l)^2 + (c_A^l)^2] \frac{GM_Z^3}{\sqrt{(2)}12\pi}$$

$$\Gamma(Z^0 \to q\bar{q}) = 6[(c_V^q)^2 + (c_A^q)^2] \frac{GM_Z^3}{\sqrt{(2)}12\pi}$$

where the extra factor 3 in the hadronic width arises from the quark colours and c_V, c_A are the coupling constants of the standard model given in table 13.3. The quantity $GM_Z^3/\sqrt{(2)}12\pi$ can be seen to be the neutrino width Γ_ν; it is also sometimes written Γ_Z^0 and has the value 0.166 GeV for a Z^0 mass of 91.2 GeV.

By substituting appropriate values of c_V and c_A and using $\sin^2\theta_W = 0.23$ we obtain a total width for three fermion families of 2.7 GeV. The results of the four LEP experiments, ALEPH, DELPHI, L3 and OPAL, have recently been combined[56] to give $\Gamma_Z = 2.488 \pm 0.007$ GeV which corresponds to $N_\nu = 2.99 \pm 0.03$. The peak cross-section at the Z^0 resonance is also sensitive to the number of neutrino types, as shown in figure 14.17. There is a clear preference for $N_\nu = 3$. Branching ratios calculated from

Table 14.2
Partial widths of the Z^0 measured at LEP

X	Γ_X/MeV	Standard model	BR($Z^0 \to X$)%	Standard model
e^+e^-	83.20 ± 0.55	83	3.35 ± 0.02	3.36
$\mu^+\mu^-$	83.35 ± 0.86	83	3.35 ± 0.03	3.36
$\tau^+\tau^-$	82.76 ± 1.02	83	3.33 ± 0.04	3.36
Hadrons	1740 ± 12	1759	69.9 ± 0.3	69.9
Invisible	498 ± 8	495	20.0 ± 0.3	20.0

The predictions of the standard model are for $M_Z = 91$ GeV, $M_t = 160$ GeV, $M_H = 100$ GeV and $\sin^2\theta_W = 0.23$. This gives a total width for the Z^0 of $\Gamma_Z = 2.50$ GeV.

the standard model formulae for the partial widths are also in excellent agreement with observation (table 14.2).

14.3.10 Quark mixing and CP *violation in the standard model*

The *origin* of CP violation remains one of the mysteries of particle physics but phenomenologically it can at least be accommodated within the standard model.

The CPT theorem (section 8.10) requires that if CP is violated there must be a compensating violation of T to preserve overall CPT invariance. What implications does this have for the weak interaction Hamiltonian? The matrix element for a transition from an initial state $|\psi\rangle$ to a final state $|\psi'\rangle$ via a Hamiltonian H is $\langle\psi'|H|\psi\rangle$. Under time reversal the matrix element becomes $\langle T\psi|THT^{-1}|T\psi'\rangle$ and if the transition $|\psi\rangle \to |\psi'\rangle$ is invariant under time reversal we must have

$$\langle\psi'|H|\psi\rangle = \langle T\psi|THT^{-1}|T\psi'\rangle.$$

In section 8.9 we saw that the time reversal operator was given by $T = UK$ where the matrix U is unitary and K is an operator which performs complex conjugation. Thus, violation of time-reversal invariance requires the Hamiltonian to be complex for then the complex conjugation operation ensures that $H \neq THT^{-1}$. In terms of the standard model this translates into the requirement that the elements of the Kobayashi–Maskawa (KM) matrix (section 11.12) are not all real.

In the standard model with three generations the quark sector has ten parameters, namely the six quark masses and four quark mixing parameters. Just as in the Cabibbo theory discussed in section 11.10, quark mixing arises because the mass eigenstates

$$U = \begin{pmatrix} u \\ c \\ t \end{pmatrix} \quad \text{and} \quad D = \begin{pmatrix} d \\ s \\ b \end{pmatrix}$$

are not identical to the eigenstates U' and D' which participate in the charged-current weak interactions. The quark charged current has the form

$$J \approx g\bar{U}'_{L}\gamma^{\mu}D'_{L}W_{\mu}$$

where the subscript L reminds us that only the left-handed weak isodoublets couple to the W. The 'gauge' eigenstates U' and D' arise from a mixing or 'rotation' of the mass eigenstates. This mixing is achieved formally by means of 3×3 unitary matrices and, as a result, the charged current between *mass* eigenstates becomes

$$J \approx g(U_{L}V_{U}^{\dagger})\gamma^{\mu}(V_{D}D_{L})W_{\mu} = g\bar{U}_{L}\gamma^{\mu}VD_{L}W_{\mu} \tag{14.18}$$

where the 3×3 unitary matrix $V = V_{U}^{\dagger}V_{D}$ is the KM matrix. It is a matter of convention that, as indicated in (14.18), mixing of the quark mass eigenstates is formulated in terms of the charge $-\frac{1}{3}$ quarks. In terms of the KM matrix we have

$$D'_{i} = \sum_{j} V_{ij}D_{j}$$

where the D_{j} are the quark mass eigenstates and D'_{i} the gauge eigenstates.

Let us, for the time being, assume generally that there are N quark doublets so that i and j run from 1 to N and V is an $N \times N$ unitary matrix. If we assume universality of quark couplings the unitarity of the mixing matrix guarantees the experimental requirement that the quark *neutral* currents are flavour conserving. Amongst the charge $-\frac{1}{3}$ quarks, the terms that appear in the quark neutral currents are $\bar{D}'_{i}D'_{i}$, see equation (11.102).

Now,

$$\sum_{i} \bar{D}'_{i}D'_{i} = \sum_{ijk} D_{j}V_{ji}^{\dagger}V_{ik}D_{k} = \sum_{i} \bar{D}_{j}D_{j}$$

provided $V_{ji}^{\dagger}V_{ik} = \delta_{jk}$. The quark neutral currents are therefore diagonal in flavour (flavour-conserving) provided the mixing matrix is unitary.

A general $N \times N$ matrix has $2N^{2}$ real parameters. The unitarity constraint reduces the number of parameters to N^{2}. Additionally, one has the freedom to vary the phase of each quark state independently but, since V is left invariant under a *common* phase change of all the quark states, only $2N - 1$ degrees of freedom (for $2N$ quark states) can be removed in this way. The matrix V therefore has

$$N^{2} - (2N - 1) = (N - 1)^{2}$$

physically independent parameters.

In the light of the discussion at the beginning of this section we ask whether this matrix can be real. A general real unitary matrix is simply an orthogonal matrix and is therefore specified by $\frac{1}{2}N(N-1)$ independent real parameters. The $N \times N$ unitary matrix therefore has $(N-1)^2$ independent parameters of which $\frac{1}{2}N(N-1)$ are real and

$$(N-1)^2 - \tfrac{1}{2}N(N-1) = \tfrac{1}{2}(N-1)(N-2)$$

are independent phase angles.

For two generations of quarks $N = 2$, so that the 2×2 (Cabibbo) matrix has only one real parameter, the Cabibbo angle, and no independent phase angle. *CP* violation could not therefore be accommodated in the standard model if only two generations of quarks existed. For $N = 3$ the KM mixing matrix has four independent parameters, of which three are real, the mixing angles θ_{12}, θ_{23} and θ_{13} between the three generations, and one independent phase angle δ_{13}, see equation (11.104). *CP* violation can therefore be accommodated in the standard model *provided there is mixing between all three generations and the phase angle is non-zero.* It is remarkable that Kobayashi and Maskawa took the bold step of introducing a third generation of quarks, as a means of providing a possible origin of *CP* violation, even before the second generation had been completed by the discovery of charmed quarks.

To facilitate comparison with experiment it is convenient to introduce a parametrization of the KM matrix due to Maiani. In the notation of section 11.12

$$V = \begin{pmatrix} c_{12} & s_{12} & s_{13}\exp(\mathrm{i}\delta_{13}) \\ -s_{12} & c_{12} & s_{23} \\ s_{12}s_{23} - s_{13}\exp(-\mathrm{i}\delta_{13}) & -s_{23} & 1 \end{pmatrix}$$

which is a considerable simplification compared with equation (11.104). Finally, following Wolfenstein,[57] we parametrize the mixing angles in terms of the real parameters λ, A and ρ:

$$\begin{aligned} s_{12} &= \lambda \approx 0.22 \\ s_{23} &= A\lambda^2 \\ s_{13} &= A\lambda^2\rho. \end{aligned}$$

Then, on dropping the subscript on δ, the KM matrix takes on the particularly simple form

$$V = \begin{pmatrix} 1-\frac{1}{2}\lambda^2 & \lambda & A\lambda^3\rho\exp(\mathrm{i}\delta) \\ -\lambda & 1-\frac{1}{2}\lambda^2 & A\lambda^2 \\ A\lambda^3[1-\rho\exp(-\mathrm{i}\delta)] & -A\lambda^2 & 1 \end{pmatrix} + 0(\lambda^4). \tag{14.19}$$

The KM matrix elements have been determined experimentally from studies of the appropriate flavour-changing weak charged current interactions. The experimental values of the *moduli* of the matrix elements are

$$|V| = \begin{array}{c} \\ \end{array}\begin{pmatrix} 0.9754 \pm 0.004 & 0.2206 \pm 0.0018 & 0.0045 \pm 0.0010 \\ 0.2203 \pm 0.0019 & 0.9743 \pm 0.0005 & 0.045 \pm 0.005 \\ 0.0101 \pm 0.0086 & 0.0449 \pm 0.0062 & 0.9990 \pm 0.0002 \end{pmatrix} \begin{matrix} (\mathrm{u}) \\ (\mathrm{c}) \\ (\mathrm{t}) \end{matrix} \quad \text{columns: (d), (s), (b)} \tag{14.20}$$

The most accurately *measured* matrix element is V_{ud} which is obtained directly from the Cabibbo angle (section 11.10) as $\cos\theta_C$. The coupling between up and strange quarks, V_{us}, is given by $\sin\theta_C$ or directly by the strength of hyperon β decays or the K_{e3} decay, $K \to \pi e\nu$. The charmed quark couplings, V_{cd} and V_{cs}, come from measurements of single charm production in the processes $\nu_\mu d \to \mu^- c$ and $\bar{\nu}_\mu \bar{s} \to \mu^+ \bar{c}$.

The most difficult matrix elements to measure are V_{cb} and V_{ub} which are small according to (14.19), but must be non-zero if the standard model is to allow *CP* violation. They have been obtained from observations of B^0 meson decays resulting from Υ production in e^+e^- collisions by the ARGUS collaboration[58–60] at DESY and by the CLEO collaboration[61] at the Cornell electron–positron storage ring CESR, and are seen to be finite. From the identity $|V_{cb}| = A\lambda^2$ and using $V_{us} = \lambda = 0.22$ we obtain the Wolfenstein parameter $A = 0.93 \pm 0.10$; from the ratio of V_{ub} to V_{cb} we find the parameter ρ to be within the range 0.3–0.8.

The bottom row of matrix elements in (14.20) refers to the top quark and have been obtained by using the unitarity property of the matrix; it is interesting to note that the most accurately known element of the matrix is V_{tb}.

14.3.11 Flavour oscillations and the standard model

The phenomenon of strangeness oscillations in the K^0–$\bar{K}^0$ system (section 11.13.2) is an example of a more general phenomenon, flavour oscillations, which can in principle occur in other neutral pseudoscalar meson systems such as D^0–$\bar{D}^0$ and B^0–$\bar{B}^0$. Here, we generalize the formalism given in section 11.13.2.

For an unstable particle of mass M and lifetime $\tau = 1/\Gamma$, the wavefunction in the particle rest frame has time dependence $\exp[-i(M - i\Gamma/2)t]$, and the Schrödinger equation, with $\hbar = 1$, is

$$i\frac{\partial\psi}{\partial t} = H\psi = \left(M - i\frac{\Gamma}{2}\right)\psi.$$

Here M and Γ are just positive numbers.

A *coupled* system of unstable particles (e.g. B^0 and $\bar{B}^0$) is represented by a two-component wavefunction

$$\psi = \begin{bmatrix} B^0(t) \\ \bar{B}^0(t) \end{bmatrix}$$

where $B^0(t)$ and $\bar{B}^0(t)$ are the amplitudes for finding B^0 and $\bar{B}^0$ respectively, at time t, when the initial state is B^0 say. In this case the Hamiltonian is a matrix, the 'mass' matrix, and the Schrödinger equation becomes

$$\mathrm{i}\frac{\partial}{\partial t}\begin{bmatrix} B^0 \\ \bar{B}^0 \end{bmatrix} = H\begin{bmatrix} B^0 \\ \bar{B}^0 \end{bmatrix} = \begin{bmatrix} M - \mathrm{i}\Gamma/2 & M_{12} - \mathrm{i}\Gamma_{12}/2 \\ M_{12}^* - \mathrm{i}\Gamma_{12}^*/2 & M - \mathrm{i}\Gamma/2 \end{bmatrix}\begin{bmatrix} B^0 \\ \bar{B}^0 \end{bmatrix}. \tag{14.21}$$

In the present case we define $\bar{B}^0$ as the CP conjugate of B^0, i.e. $CP|B^0\rangle = |\bar{B}^0\rangle$. Note that H is not hermitian; probability is not conserved because the B^0–$\bar{B}^0$ system decays. The CPT theorem requires that $H_{11} = H_{22}$. The quark rest masses and the strong binding force contribute to M. Decays $B^0 \to f$ and $\bar{B}^0 \to \bar{f}$, where f and $\bar{f}$ are distinct final states, contribute to Γ while decays to a common final state $f = \bar{f}$ contribute to Γ_{12}. CP is violated if the off-diagonal elements are different, $H_{12} \neq H_{21}$. In other words Im M_{12} and Im Γ_{12} contribute to CP violation. For, if Im M_{12} = Im $\Gamma_{12} = 0$, the off-diagonal elements are equal and the eigenvectors are then the CP eigenstates

$$|B_1\rangle = \frac{|B^0\rangle + |\bar{B}^0\rangle}{\sqrt{2}} \quad \text{and} \quad |B_2\rangle = \frac{|B^0\rangle - |\bar{B}^0\rangle}{\sqrt{2}}$$

with eigenvalues $CP = +1$ and -1 respectively. The eigenvalues of the mass matrix, corresponding to these eigenstates, are

$$M_1 = M + M_{12} \qquad \Gamma_1 = \Gamma + \Gamma_{12}$$

and

$$M_2 = M - M_{12} \qquad \Gamma_2 = \Gamma - \Gamma_{12}$$

so that the mass and width differences are

$$\Delta m = M_1 - M_2 = 2M_{12}$$
$$\Delta\Gamma = \Gamma_1 - \Gamma_2 = 2\Gamma_{12}. \tag{14.22}$$

Even without CP violation, flavour oscillations still occur because $|B_1\rangle$ and $|B_2\rangle$ evolve differently in time (see section 11.13.2).

In the more general case, with Im $M_{12} \neq 0$ and Im $\Gamma_{12} \neq 0$, the eigenvalues and eigenvectors are obtained by diagonalizing the mass matrix (see example 14.4). We obtain the eigenvalues

$$M_1 = M + \mathrm{Re}\, F \qquad M_2 = M - \mathrm{Re}\, F$$
$$\Gamma_1 = \Gamma - 2\,\mathrm{Im}\, F \qquad \Gamma_2 = \Gamma + 2\,\mathrm{Im}\, F$$

where

$$F = \sqrt{\left[\left(M_{12} - \frac{\mathrm{i}\Gamma_{12}}{2}\right)\left(M_{12}^{*} - \frac{\mathrm{i}\Gamma_{12}^{*}}{2}\right)\right]}. \tag{14.23}$$

In this case the mass and width differences are

$$\Delta m = M_1 - M_2 = 2\,\mathrm{Re}\, F \quad \text{and} \quad \Delta\Gamma = \Gamma_1 - \Gamma_2 = -4\,\mathrm{Im}\, F. \tag{14.24}$$

The normalized eigenvectors are

$$|B_1\rangle = \frac{(1+\epsilon)|B^0\rangle + (1-\epsilon)|\bar{B}^0\rangle}{\sqrt{[2(1+|\epsilon|^2)]}}$$
$$|B_2\rangle = \frac{(1+\epsilon)|B^0\rangle - (1-\epsilon)|\bar{B}^0\rangle}{\sqrt{[2(1+|\epsilon|^2)]}} \tag{14.25}$$

with

$$\eta \equiv \frac{1-\epsilon}{1+\epsilon} = \sqrt{\left(\frac{M_{12}^{*} - \mathrm{i}\Gamma_{12}^{*}/2}{M_{12} - \mathrm{i}\Gamma_{12}/2}\right)}. \tag{14.26}$$

The eigenvectors $|B_1\rangle$ and $|B_2\rangle$ evolve differently in time and as a result $\Delta B = 2$ oscillations take place in the B^0–$\bar{B}^0$ system. For example, suppose we start with a pure B^0 state at time $t = 0$. It is a simple matter to show (see example 14.5) that the 'non-flip' and 'flip' amplitudes $A(B^0 \to B^0)$ and $A(B^0 \to \bar{B}^0)$ are respectively

$$\langle B^0|\psi(t)\rangle = \tfrac{1}{2}[\exp(-\mathrm{i}M_1 t)\exp(-\tfrac{1}{2}\Gamma_1 t) + \exp(-\mathrm{i}M_2 t)\exp(-\tfrac{1}{2}\Gamma_2 t)]$$

and

$$\langle \bar{B}^0|\psi(t)\rangle = \eta\tfrac{1}{2}[\exp(-\mathrm{i}M_1 t)\exp(-\tfrac{1}{2}\Gamma_1 t) - \exp(-\mathrm{i}M_2 t)\exp(-\tfrac{1}{2}\Gamma_2 t)].$$

The measured B lifetime ($\approx 10^{-12}$ s) is roughly two orders of magnitude less than that of K_S^0 so that an experimental measurement of the detailed time variation of B^0–$\bar{B}^0$ mixing is an extremely difficult task. What has been measured is the ratio of the probabilities, integrated over time, of B^0

becoming $\bar{B}^0$ and B^0 remaining B^0. That is,

$$r = \frac{P(B^0 \to \bar{B}^0)}{P(B^0 \to B^0)}$$

$$= \frac{\int_0^\infty |A(B^0 \to \bar{B}^0)|^2 \,dt}{\int_0^\infty |A(B^0 \to B^0)|^2 \,dt}$$

$$= \left|\frac{1-\epsilon}{1+\epsilon}\right|^2 \frac{\int_0^\infty [\exp(-\Gamma_1 t) + \exp(-\Gamma_2 t) - 2\exp(-\Gamma t)\cos(\Delta m t)]\,dt}{\int_0^\infty [\exp(-\Gamma_1 t) + \exp(-\Gamma_2 t) + 2\exp(-\Gamma t)\cos(\Delta m t)]\,dt} \tag{14.27}$$

where $\Gamma = \frac{1}{2}(\Gamma_1 + \Gamma_2)$ is the average width of the B_1 and B_2 states and $\Delta m = M_1 - M_2$ is their mass difference. On performing the integration we finally obtain

$$r = \left|\frac{1-\epsilon}{1+\epsilon}\right|^2 \frac{x^2 + y^2}{2 + x^2 - y^2}$$

where the mixing parameters are given by

$$x = \frac{\Delta m}{\Gamma} \qquad y = \frac{\Delta \Gamma}{2\Gamma}.$$

Note that these parameters lie in the ranges

$$0 \leqslant x^2 \leqslant \infty \qquad \text{and} \qquad 0 \leqslant y^2 = \left(\frac{\Gamma_1 - \Gamma_2}{\Gamma_1 + \Gamma_2}\right)^2 \leqslant 1.$$

Then, neglecting CP violation, r is restricted to the range $0 \leqslant r \leqslant 1$.

An alternative parameter, $\chi = r/(1 + r)$, is sometimes used to describe particle mixing. From the definition of r, equation (14.27), it follows that χ is the time-averaged flip probability and lies in the range $0 \leqslant \chi \leqslant \frac{1}{2}$. If we neglect CP violation, i.e. put $\epsilon = 0$, we have

$$r = \frac{(\Delta m)^2 + \frac{1}{4}(\Delta\Gamma)^2}{(\Delta m)^2 + 2\Gamma^2 - \frac{1}{4}(\Delta\Gamma)^2} \qquad \chi = \frac{1}{2}\frac{(\Delta m)^2 + \frac{1}{4}(\Delta\Gamma)^2}{(\Delta m)^2 + \Gamma^2}. \tag{14.28}$$

Note that $\chi \to 0$ if $\Gamma \gg \Delta m$; the probability of a flip vanishes if the initial state decays before sufficient time has elapsed to enable a significant phase difference to be built up between the states B_1 and B_2. If, on the other hand, $\Delta m \gg \Gamma$ so that there are many oscillations during the lifetime of the initial state, $\chi \to \frac{1}{2}$.

It is instructive to estimate the mixing parameters x and y for the

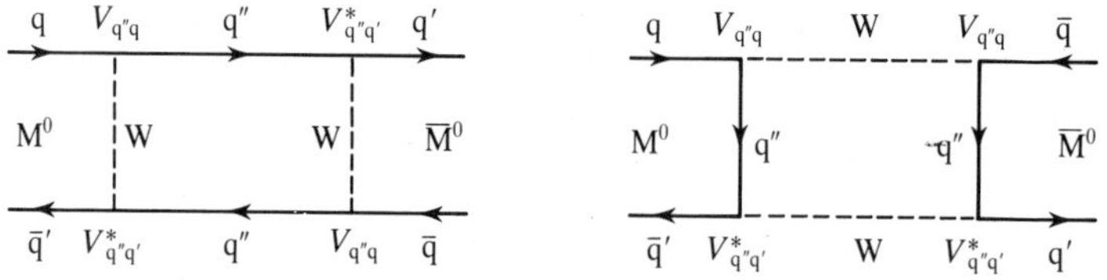

Figure 14.18
Box diagram contributions to flavour oscillations in neutral meson–antimeson systems.

K^0–$\bar{K}^0$, D^0–$\bar{D}^0$ and B^0–$\bar{B}^0$ systems. Such double changes of flavour are described in the standard model by box diagrams like those shown in figure 14.18; the vertex factors $V_{q''q}$ etc. are the appropriate elements of the KM matrix. In order to determine the mixing parameters we need to calculate M_{12} and Γ_{12}. As a general rule all possible quark exchanges contribute to M_{12} but only actual final states contribute to Γ_{12}. To facilitate an order-of-magnitude estimate of the mixing parameters we use an approximate form of the KM matrix, see equation (14.19):

$$V = \begin{array}{c} \\ \\ \end{array}\begin{matrix} (d) & (s) & (b) & \\ \end{matrix}$$

$$V = \begin{pmatrix} 1 & \lambda & \lambda^3 \\ -\lambda & 1 & \lambda^2 \\ \lambda^3 & -\lambda^2 & 1 \end{pmatrix} \begin{matrix} (u) \\ (c) \\ (t) \end{matrix} \qquad (14.29)$$

(columns labelled (d), (s), (b))

Figure 14.19(a) shows one of the diagrams for K^0–$\bar{K}^0$ mixing. One might naively expect the top quark, with its very large mass, to give the dominant contribution to M_{12} and hence to Δm. However, this contribution is proportional to $m_t^2(V_{td}V^*_{ts})^2 \approx m_t^2\lambda^{10}$ and is therefore extremely small. Furthermore, the mass of the u quark is negligible compared with that of the charmed quark and consequently the dominant contribution to Δm_K is $m_c^2(V_{cd}V^*_{cs})^2 \approx m_c^2\lambda^2$. This is in accord with the original estimate of Gaillard, Lee and Rosner (see reference 27 in chapter 11). Since only actual final states can contribute to the decay width Γ_K and since $m_c > m_s$, Γ_K is proportional to $(V_{us})^2 = \lambda^2$. We therefore expect $x_K \approx m_c^2$. Since K^0 and $\bar{K}^0$ decay essentially equally by the common $\pi\pi$ mode, $\Delta\Gamma_K \approx 2\Gamma_K$ and $y_K \approx -1$. Mixing in the K^0–$\bar{K}^0$ system is therefore expected to be maximal. This is in agreement with the measured values of the mass difference and lifetimes of K^0_S and K^0_L (see section 11.13.2 and table 7.2).

The standard model predictions for D^0–$\bar{D}^0$ mixing are quite different. The box diagram for the D^0 meson ($c\bar{u}$) is shown in figure 14.19(b). In this case d, s and b quarks can appear in the intermediate states and the dominant contributions to Δm_D are $m_s^2(V_{cs}V^*_{us})^2 \approx m_s^2\lambda^2$ and $m_b^2(V_{cb}V^*_{ub})^2 \approx (m_b\lambda^5)^2$, which are both extremely small. The dominant decay mode ($c \to s$) is described by V_{cs} which is of the order of unity so Γ_D is not at all suppressed. Hence one expects $x_D = \Delta m_D/\Gamma \approx 0$. Furthermore, decay modes which are common to D^0 and $\bar{D}^0$, and which therefore contribute

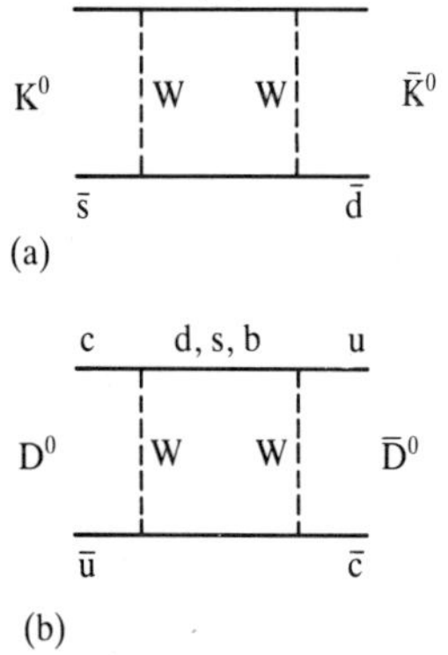

Figure 14.19
(a) K^0–$\bar{K}^0$ mixing;
(b) D^0–$\bar{D}^0$ mixing.

to $\Delta\Gamma$, are highly suppressed. For example

$$\frac{\Gamma(D^0 \to \pi^+\pi^-)}{\Gamma_{tot}} = 0.0013 \pm 0.0004$$

and

$$\frac{\Gamma(D^0 \to K^+K^-)}{\Gamma_{tot}} = 0.0045 \pm 0.0008$$

so that $y_D = \Delta\Gamma_D/2\Gamma_D \approx 0$. The standard model therefore predicts that mixing in the D^0–$\bar{D}^0$ system should be very small. To date, mixing has not been observed experimentally and typical limits for the D^0–$\bar{D}^0$ system are[62,63] $x_D^2 + y_D^2 < 0.01$.

For B^0 mesons we consider the two states $B_d^0 \equiv (\bar{b}d)$ and $B_s^0 \equiv (\bar{b}s)$. Mixing in the B_d^0–$\bar{B}_d^0$ system is described by the box diagram shown in figure 14.20(a). In this case, as with the K^0–$\bar{K}^0$ system, the u, c and t quarks can be exchanged. The dominant contribution to M_{12} is proportional to $m_t^2(V_{tb}V_{td}^*)^2 = (\lambda^3 m_t)^2$. The top quark cannot contribute to Γ_{12} and thus

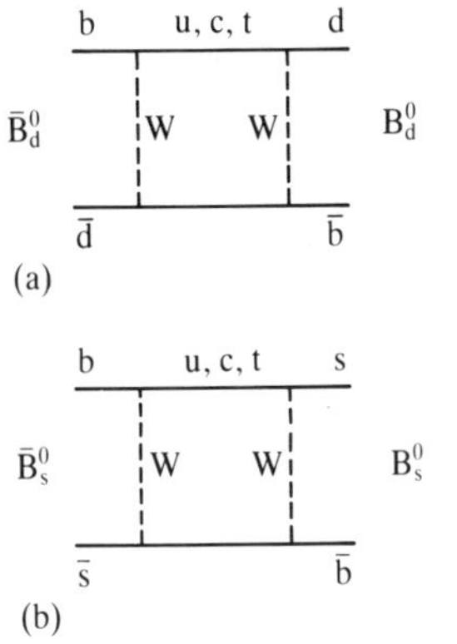

Figure 14.20
(a) B_d^0–$\bar{B}_d^0$ mixing; (b) B_s^0–$\bar{B}_s^0$ mixing.

$$\Gamma_{12} \propto m_b^2(V_{ub}V_{ud}^* + V_{cd})^2 = m_b^2(V_{tb}V_{td}^*)^2$$

where the equality follows from the unitarity of the KM matrix. Thus $\Gamma_{12} \approx (\lambda^3 m_b)^2$. Note that M_{12} and Γ_{12} have almost the same phase so that, from equation (14.23),

$$F \approx |M_{12}| - \frac{i}{2}|\Gamma_{12}|$$

and therefore

$$\Delta m_B \approx 2|M_{12}|$$

and

$$\Delta\Gamma_B \approx 2|\Gamma_{12}|.$$

Furthermore, $|\Gamma_{12}| \ll |M_{12}|$, and therefore $\Delta\Gamma_B \ll \Delta m_B$. The mixing parameter y_d is expected to be small and mixing arises essentially through $x_d = \Delta m/\Gamma$. The dominant contribution to the decay width Γ_{B_d} arises from transitions b → c which have a strength proportional to $(V_{cb})^2 = \lambda^4$. Then $x_d \approx (\lambda m_t)^2$.

The box diagram describing B_s^0–$\bar{B}_s^0$ mixing is shown in figure 14.20(b). Again, the top quark dominates M_{12} and in this case $M_{12} \propto m_t^2(V_{tb}V_{ts}^*)^2 = (\lambda^2 m_t)^2$. As for the B_d^0 states, $\Gamma(b \to c) \propto (V_{cb})^2 = \lambda^4$ and therefore

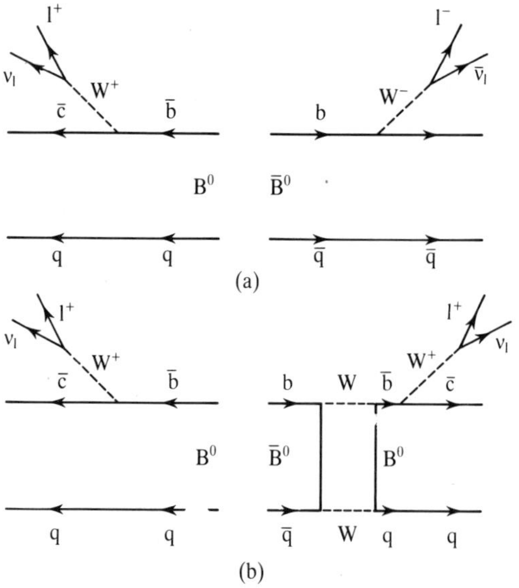

Figure 14.21
(a) 'Normal' decay of a $B^0\bar{B}^0$ pair producing unlike-sign leptons. (b) Decay of a $B^0\bar{B}^0$ pair in which a $\Delta B = 2$ oscillation occurs to produce like-sign leptons.

$x_s = \Delta m_{B_s}/\Gamma_{B_s} \approx m_t^2$. Moreover

$$\Gamma_{12} \propto m_b^2(V_{ub}V_{us}^* + V_{cb}V_{cs}^*)^2 \approx (\lambda^2 m_b)^2.$$

Thus

$$x_s \approx \frac{x_d}{\lambda^2} \quad \text{and} \quad y_s \approx \frac{y_d}{\lambda^2}$$

which implies that mixing should be greater in the B_s^0–$\bar{B}_s^0$ system than in the B_d^0–$\bar{B}_d^0$ system.

The first experimental evidence for B^0–$\bar{B}^0$ mixing was obtained by the UA1 collaboration[64] at the CERN proton–antiproton collider. With the convention that the B^0 meson contains a $\bar{b}$ quark, a 'normal' semi-leptonic decay of a B^0 meson yields a positively charged lepton while the decay of a $\bar{B}^0$ yields a negatively charged lepton. Thus normal decays of a $B^0\bar{B}^0$ pair yield unlike-sign di-leptons as shown in figure 14.21(a). If, on the other hand, a $\Delta B = 2$ oscillation takes place the final state contains like-sign di-leptons as shown in figure 14.21(b). From their observation of like-sign di-muon events, from admixtures of B_d^0 and B_s^0, the UA1 collaboration obtained a value $\chi = 0.12 \pm 0.05$ where χ is the time-averaged flip probability.

The ARGUS collaboration[60] have recently improved their earlier measurement of x_d obtained from an investigation of like-sign di-muon events from the B_d^0–$\bar{B}_d^0$ decay of the $\Upsilon(4S)$; the $\Upsilon(4S)$ is below the threshold for decay to $B_s^0\bar{B}_s^0$ pairs. They obtained the value $r = 0.21 \pm 0.06$, which corresponds to $x_d = 0.73 \pm 0.08$ in perfect agreement with their earlier measurement of 0.73 ± 0.18. This result has important consequences for the mass of the top quark. In the standard model the B_d^0 mixing parameter is given by

$$x_d = \frac{\Delta m}{\Gamma} = 2M_{12}\tau_B$$

A significant set of problems to

$$= \frac{G^2}{6\pi^2}\tau_B B_B f_B^2 |V_{td} V_{tb}^*| \eta_t F(m_t) m_t^2 .$$

The factor $\eta_t \approx 0.8$–0.85 is a QCD correction to the box diagram and $F(m_t)$ is a kinematic factor which slowly decreases with increasing m_t. For example, F decreases from 0.82 to 0.7 as the top quark mass increases from 60 to 100 GeV/c^2. The product $B_B f_B^2$ is a major source of uncertainty in the expression for x_d. B_B is expected to be of order unity and the coupling constant f_B of the same order as f_π and f_K. Altarelli and Franzini[65] obtain

$$x_d = 0.31 \frac{\tau_B |V_{td}|^2}{3.3 \times 10^{-16}\ \mathrm{s}} \frac{B_B f_B^2}{(140\ \mathrm{MeV})^2} \left(\frac{m_t}{60\ \mathrm{GeV}}\right)^2 \qquad (14.30)$$

where the expectation $\tau_B |V_{td}|^2 \approx 3.3 \times 10^{-16}$ s is obtained from the value of the CP violating parameter ϵ in K_L decays. This prediction is compatible with the measured value of x_d if $m_t \approx 100$ GeV.

It is useful and informative to represent our knowledge of the less well-known KM matrix elements in the form of the so-called unitarity triangle. The unitarity of the KM matrix requires that

$$V_{ub} V_{ud}^* + V_{cb} V_{cd}^* + V_{tb} V_{td}^* = 0.$$

To a good approximation $V_{ud} \approx V_{tb} \approx 1$ and $V_{cd} \approx -s_{12}$, so that

$$V_{ub} + V_{td}^* \approx s_{12} V_{cb}.$$

The matrix elements V_{ub} and V_{td} are the only two which have appreciable imaginary parts so this relationship is conveniently displayed in the form of a triangle in the complex plane as shown in figure 14.22. The sine of the Cabibbo angle, s_{12}, is well known, and, as we have seen in section 14.3.10, V_{cb} and V_{ub} have recently been measured. We use the values $|V_{cb}| = 0.045 \pm 0.005$, $|V_{ub}| = 0.005 \pm 0.001$ and the recently measured value $r_d = 0.21 \pm 0.06$ from B_d^0–$\bar{B}_d^0$ mixing, to obtain limits on $|V_{td}|$, which, as we have seen above, is directly related to x_d and hence r_d. The value $B_B^{1/2} f_B = 140$ MeV is used in (14.30) and the top mass is assumed to be in the range 78 GeV $< m_t <$ 190 GeV, where the lower limit arises from direct searches for the top quark and the upper limit is taken from an analysis of electroweak radiative corrections to the ratio M_W/M_Z.[66] From

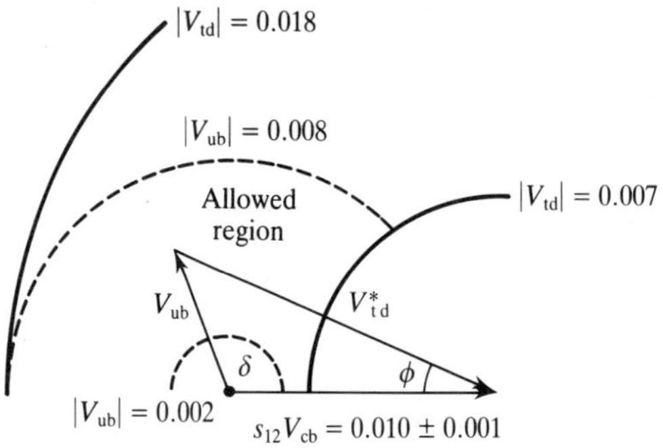

Figure 14.22
The unitarity triangle showing the relationship $V_{ub} + V^*_{td} \approx s_{12}V_{cb}$ between the *KM* matrix elements.

the measured value of x_d one obtains $0.007 \leqslant |V_{td}| \leqslant 0.04$. The upper limit is less restrictive than that inferred from the unitarity of the KM matrix which gives $|V_{td}| < 0.018$, and we have used the latter in figure 14.22. The limits shown for $|V_{ub}|$ correspond to three standard deviations from the central value. We shall see in section 14.3.12 that the angles δ and ϕ in the unitarity triangle can be determined from a study of *CP* violation in B decays.

14.3.12 CP *violation revisited*

In chapter 11 we discussed strangeness oscillations and *CP* violation in $\Delta S = 2$ and $\Delta S = 1$ transitions in some detail. In this section we return to these topics and discuss them in the light of the general formalism developed in section 14.3.11. There, we stated that the condition for *CP* invariance was $\text{Im}\, M_{12} = \text{Im}\, \Gamma_{12} = 0$, whereas in fact the condition for *CP* invariance is actually that M_{12} and Γ_{12} are in phase. For, let $M_{12} = |M_{12}|\, e^{i\phi}$ and $\Gamma_{12} = |\Gamma_{12}|\, e^{i\phi}$, then, from equation (14.26),

$$\frac{1-\epsilon}{1+\epsilon} = e^{-i\phi}.$$

In this situation, $\text{Re}\, \epsilon = 0$, i.e. ϵ is pure imaginary and can be eliminated from equations (14.25) by a phase redefinition. In practice there are thus two ways in which *CP* violation can arise: either $\text{Im}\, M_{12}$ and $\text{Im}\, \Gamma_{12}$ are small, in which case $|\epsilon|$ is small, or M_{12} and Γ_{12} have nearly the same phase. The first situation pertains in the kaon system and the second in the B^0 meson system.

For kaons the *CP* violating factor is $|\epsilon| = (2.25 \pm 0.17) \times 10^{-3}$, which implies that $\text{Im}\, M_{12} \ll \text{Re}\, M_{12}$ and $\text{Im}\, \Gamma_{12} \ll \text{Re}\, \Gamma_{12}$, since $\epsilon = 0$ if both M_{12} and Γ_{12} are real. Then, from (14.23) and (14.24), $F \approx M_{12} - i\Gamma_{12}/2$, $\Delta m_K \approx 2\text{Re}\, M_{12}$ and $\Delta\Gamma_K \approx 2\text{Re}\, \Gamma_{12}$. Note that this contrasts with the B^0 situation where it was found that M_{12} and Γ_{12} have nearly the same phase and $\Delta m_B \approx 2|M_{12}|$, $\Delta\Gamma_B \approx 2|\Gamma_{12}|$.

Starting from the general expression for ϵ, equation (14.26), we can perform an expansion in the small imaginary parts Im M_{12} and Im Γ_{12} and obtain

$$\frac{1-\epsilon}{1+\epsilon} \approx 1 - 2\epsilon \approx 1 - \frac{\mathrm{i}\,\mathrm{Im}\,M_{12} + \frac{1}{2}\mathrm{Im}\,\Gamma_{12}}{\mathrm{Re}\,M_{12} - \frac{\mathrm{i}}{2}\mathrm{Re}\,\Gamma_{12}},$$

i.e.

$$\epsilon \approx \frac{\mathrm{i}\,\mathrm{Im}\,M_{12} + \frac{1}{2}\mathrm{Im}\,\Gamma_{12}}{\Delta m - \frac{\mathrm{i}}{2}\Delta\Gamma}. \tag{14.31}$$

The main contribution to Γ_{12} is from the common $\pi\pi$ decay mode of K^0 and $\bar{K}^0$. We recall that in chapter 11 we chose the dominant $I = 0$ amplitudes to be real, apart from the final state $\pi\pi$ interaction which was represented by the $\pi\pi$ phase shift, δ_0, at the kaon mass. With this choice, Im $\Gamma_{12} \ll$ Im M_{12} and (14.31) becomes

$$\epsilon = \frac{\mathrm{i}\,\mathrm{Im}\,M_{12}}{(1+\mathrm{i})\Delta m} = \frac{\exp(\mathrm{i}\pi/4)\,\mathrm{Im}\,M_{12}}{\sqrt{2}\,\Delta m} \tag{14.32}$$

where we have used the experimental result $\Delta m \approx -\Delta\Gamma/2$ for kaons. Note that in our present treatment we have chosen $|\bar{K}^0\rangle = CP|K^0\rangle$ which contrasts with the phase convention chosen in chapter 11 where $-|\bar{K}^0\rangle = CP|K^0\rangle$. We recall that the measured value of ϵ corresponds to the definitions

$$\eta_{+-} = \frac{A(K_L^0 \to \pi^+\pi^-)}{A(K_S^0 \to \pi^+\pi^-)} \approx \epsilon + \epsilon'$$

$$\eta_{00} = \frac{A(K_L^0 \to \pi^0\pi^0)}{A(K_S^0 \to \pi^0\pi^0)} \approx \epsilon - 2\epsilon'.$$

In chapter 13 we saw that ϵ' was given by

$$\begin{aligned}\epsilon' &= \frac{\mathrm{i}}{\sqrt{2}}\,\mathrm{Im}\left(\frac{A_2}{A_0}\right)\exp[\mathrm{i}(\delta_2 - \delta_0)] \\ &= \frac{1}{\sqrt{2}}\,\mathrm{Im}\left(\frac{A_2}{A_0}\right)\exp\left[\mathrm{i}\left(\frac{\pi}{2} + \delta_2 - \delta_0\right)\right]\end{aligned}$$

where A_2 is the $I = 2$ amplitude with phase shift δ_2 and A_0 the $I = 0$ amplitude with phase shift δ_0. The experimental values of the phase shifts give for the phase of ϵ'

$$\frac{\pi}{2} + \delta_2 - \delta_0 = (48 \pm 8)^\circ \approx \pi/4$$

then

$$\epsilon' = \frac{\exp(i\pi/4)}{\sqrt{2}} \operatorname{Im}\left(\frac{A_2}{A_0}\right). \tag{14.33}$$

In the present context, instead of setting Im $A_0 = 0$, it is more appropriate to define $\xi = \operatorname{Im} A_0/\operatorname{Re} A_0$. This leads to slight modifications[67] to (14.32) and (14.33) which become

$$\epsilon \approx \frac{\exp(i\pi/4)}{\sqrt{2}}\left(\frac{\operatorname{Im} M_{12}}{\Delta m} + \xi\right)$$

$$\epsilon' \approx \frac{\exp(i\pi/4)}{\sqrt{2}}\left(\frac{\operatorname{Im} A_2}{\operatorname{Re} A_0} - \xi\frac{\operatorname{Re} A_2}{\operatorname{Re} A_0}\right).$$

To a very good approximation the empirical $\Delta I = \frac{1}{2}$ rule (dominance of A_0) applies in $K^0, \bar{K}^0 \to \pi\pi$ decays. In fact, experimentally, $\omega = \operatorname{Re} A_2/\operatorname{Re} A_0 \approx 0.045$, then

$$\epsilon' \approx \frac{\exp(i\pi/4)}{\sqrt{2}} \frac{\operatorname{Im} A_2 - \omega \operatorname{Im} A_0}{\operatorname{Re} A_0}$$

and ϵ' is thus determined by the imaginary parts of the $\Delta S = 1$ $K \to \pi\pi$ amplitudes. At tree level in the standard model these imaginary parts are predicted to be essentially zero since K decays can be described in terms of diagrams involving only light quarks for which, as we have seen, the KM matrix elements are predominantly real. At the one-loop level, however, the so-called 'penguin diagrams' (figure 14.23), which contribute only to the $\Delta I = \frac{1}{2}$ amplitudes A_0 (s → d), introduce a phase relative to the $\Delta I = \frac{3}{2}$ amplitudes A_2, and therefore generate an imaginary part to A_0. Thus, with Im $A_2 = 0$,

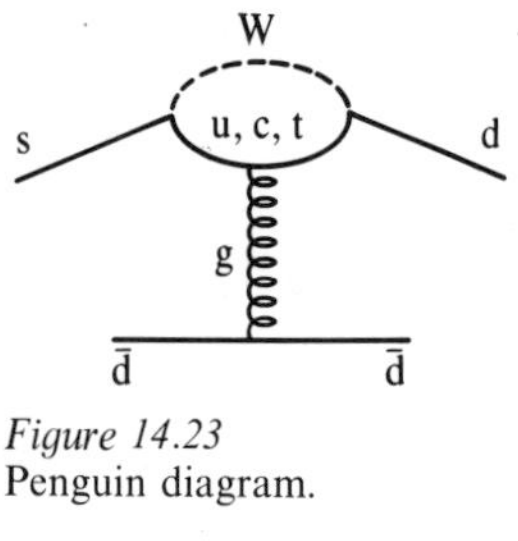

Figure 14.23
Penguin diagram.

$$\epsilon' \approx -\frac{\exp(i\pi/4)}{\sqrt{2}} \omega\xi.$$

The contribution of the penguin diagram has been calculated by Altarelli and Franzini to be of the form $\xi \approx -1.2 \operatorname{Im}(V_{ts}V_{td}^*)$. In the standard model calculation of ϵ, terms containing m_t dominate provided $m_t \gtrsim m_c/\lambda^2 \approx$ 30 GeV, and it is found that

$$\epsilon \propto \operatorname{Im}(V_{ts}V_{td}^*)[m_t^2 \operatorname{Re}(V_{ts}V_{td}^*) + \cdots].$$

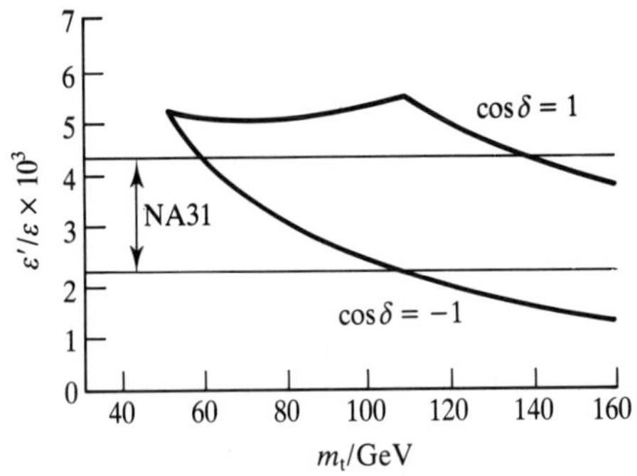

Figure 14.24
The standard model prediction for ϵ'/ϵ compared with the NA31 measurement (Burkhardt H *et al.* 1988 *Phys. Lett.* **B206** (169)).

Thus,

$$\frac{\epsilon'}{\epsilon} \propto \frac{1}{[m_t^2 \operatorname{Re}(V_{ts} V_{td}^*) + \cdots]}.$$

Figure 14.24 shows the standard model prediction for ϵ'/ϵ compared with the recent NA31 measurement of the ratio by Burkhardt *et al.* (reference 33 in chapter 11) who found

$$\frac{\epsilon'}{\epsilon} = (3.3 \pm 1.1) \times 10^{-3}.$$

The dependence on δ arises from Re V_{td}^* which is proportional to $1 - \rho \cos \delta$, where ρ is the Wolfenstein parameter introduced in section 14.3.10. As can be seen, the predicted sign and magnitude of the ratio ϵ'/ϵ are in good agreement with the measurement and provide strong support for the minimal standard model in which all *CP*-violating effects originate in the single phase δ in the KM matrix. In contrast, various gauge-theoretical extensions of the Wolfenstein superweak theory invoke a heavy Higgs boson or a new gauge boson to induce $\Delta S = 2$ transitions. In these theories there is no direct $\Delta S = 1$ *CP* violation and ϵ' is predicted to be zero.

Turning now to *CP* violation in B decays we have already noted that normal semi-leptonic decay of a B^0 leads to a positively charged lepton and $\bar{B}^0$ to a negatively charged lepton so that normal decays of $B^0\bar{B}^0$ pairs lead to unlike-sign di-leptons in the final state. If a $\Delta B = 2$ oscillation takes place the final state will contain like-sign di-leptons. For an initial B^0 meson we obtained,

$$r = \frac{P(B^0 \to \bar{B}^0 \to l^-)}{P(B^0 \to B^0 \to l^+)} = \left|\frac{1-\epsilon}{1+\epsilon}\right|^2 \frac{x^2 + y^2}{2 + x^2 - y^2}.$$

A similar calculation for an initial $\bar{B}^0$ meson gives

$$\bar{r} = \frac{P(\bar{B}^0 \to B^0 \to l^+)}{P(\bar{B}^0 \to \bar{B}^0 \to l^-)} = \left|\frac{1+\epsilon}{1-\epsilon}\right|^2 \frac{x^2+y^2}{2+x^2-y^2}.$$

If $\Delta B = 2$ CP violation occurs there should therefore be an asymmetry in the number of like-sign l^+l^+ and l^-l^- arising from $B^0\bar{B}^0$ pair production followed by semi-leptonic decay. Pais and Treiman[68] have shown that the expected asymmetry is

$$A(B) = \frac{N(l^+l^+) - N(l^-l^-)}{N(l^+l^+) + N(l^-l^-)} = \frac{r - \bar{r}}{r + \bar{r}} \simeq -4 \operatorname{Re} \epsilon.$$

We have seen previously that for B^0 mesons $|\Gamma_{12}| \ll |M_{12}|$ and, therefore, from equaton (14.26) we have

$$\operatorname{Re} \epsilon \approx \frac{1}{4} \operatorname{Im}\left(\frac{\Gamma_{12}}{M_{12}}\right).$$

Calculations of Γ_{12} and M_{12} based on the box diagrams for B^0–$\bar{B}^0$ mixing lead to the estimates

$$|A(B_d)| \leqslant 10^{-3} \qquad \text{and} \qquad |A(B_s)| \leqslant 5 \times 10^{-4}.$$

Unfortunately, some 10^9 $B^0\bar{B}^0$ pairs would be required to make statistically significant measurements of such small asymmetries.

CP violation can also be looked for in $\Delta B = 1$ transitions, the observation of which, in analogy with the determination of ϵ' in $\Delta S = 1$ K^0 transitions, would establish direct CP violation in B^0 decays. There are many decay modes of the B meson which can be used to search for CP-violating asymmetries defined as

$$A_f = \frac{\Gamma(B^0 \to f) - \Gamma(\bar{B}^0 \to \bar{f})}{\Gamma(B^0 \to f) + \Gamma(\bar{B}^0 \to \bar{f})}.$$

In some channels the asymmetry is expected to be large but unfortunately it is in just these channels that the branching ratios are very small and again it is estimated that some 10^9 $B^0\bar{B}^0$ events would be required to make useful measurements of the asymmetry.

However, there is a very important class of decays in which f is a CP eigenstate, common to both B^0 and $\bar{B}^0$ and for which the decay process is dominated by a single amplitude. Then $|\rho_f| \approx 1$, where

$$\rho_f = \frac{A(\bar{B}^0 \to f)}{A(B^0 \to f)}.$$

An important example is the channel $f \equiv J/\psi K^0_S$. An observation $\mathrm{Im}\,\rho_f \neq 0$ would constitute evidence for $\Delta B = 1$ *CP* violation. The initial B^0 and $\bar{B}^0$ decay with a time evolution

$$\Gamma(B^0 \to f) \propto \exp(-\Gamma t)\left[1 + \sin(\Delta m t)\,\mathrm{Im}\left(\frac{1-\epsilon}{1+\epsilon}\rho_f\right)\right]$$

$$\Gamma(\bar{B}^0 \to f) \propto \exp(-\Gamma t)\left[1 - \sin(\Delta m t)\,\mathrm{Im}\left(\frac{1-\epsilon}{1+\epsilon}\rho_f\right)\right]$$

which, after integration over time, gives an asymmetry

$$A_f = \frac{\Gamma(B^0 \to f) - \Gamma(\bar{B}^0 \to f)}{\Gamma(B^0 \to f) + \Gamma(\bar{B}^0 \to f)} \approx \frac{-x}{1+x^2}\,\mathrm{Im}\left(\frac{1-\epsilon}{1+\epsilon}\rho_f\right). \qquad (14.34)$$

We note that $A_f \to 0$ if there is no mixing ($x = 0$) or if the mixing is maximal ($x \to \infty$), but for the B^0_d meson, with a measured mixing parameter $x_d = 0.73$, the situation is ideal. Inspection of equation (14.34) shows that the asymmetry arises from both $\Delta B = 2$ ($\epsilon \neq 0$) and $\Delta B = 1$ ($\mathrm{Im}\,\rho_f \neq 0$) *CP* violation. Moreover, to a very good approximation both factors are pure phase. For we have

$$\frac{1-\epsilon}{1+\epsilon} \approx \sqrt{\left(\frac{M^*_{12}}{M_{12}}\right)} \approx \frac{V^*_{tb}V_{td}}{V_{tb}V^*_{td}} \approx \frac{V_{td}}{V^*_{td}} = \exp(2i\varphi)$$

since V_{tb} is real. The angle φ is the phase of V_{td} as shown in the unitarity triangle in figure 14.22. In addition, the decay $B^0_d \to J/\psi K^0_S$ is mediated by the transition $b \to c\bar{c}s$ and

$$\rho_f = \frac{V_{cb}V^*_{cs}}{V^*_{cb}V_{cs}} \approx 1$$

and therefore the asymmetry

$$A_{J/\psi K^0_S} \propto \mathrm{Im}\,\exp(2i\varphi) = \sin 2\varphi.$$

The angle δ can be determined from a measurement of $A_{\pi\pi}$ from decays $\bar{B}^0_d \to \pi\pi$ which is mediated by the transition $b \to u\bar{u}d$ and in this case

$$\rho_f = \frac{V_{ub}V^*_{ud}}{V^*_{ub}V_{ud}} \approx \frac{V_{ub}}{V^*_{ub}} = \exp(2i\delta).$$

In this case the asymmetry is

$$A_{\pi\pi} \propto \mathrm{Im}[\exp(2i\varphi)\exp(2i\delta)] = \sin[2(\varphi + \delta)].$$

Thus, the angles φ and δ in the unitarity triangle can be determined directly from measurements of these asymmetries. Unfortunately the branching ratios are expected to be so small that again some 10^9 $B^0\bar{B}^0$ pairs will be needed to make a useful measurement.

14.3.13 Search for the top quark

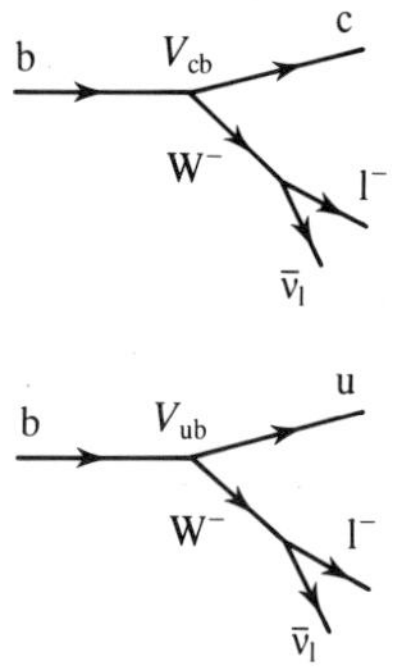

Figure 14.25
The semi-leptonic decays $b \to cl^-\bar{\nu}_l$ and $b \to ul^-\bar{\nu}_l$ in the standard model.

To date, all searches for the top quark have been unsuccessful, but there is compelling, if indirect, evidence that the top quark exists. This assertion is based on the observation that the b quark decays as though it belongs to a weak isospin doublet, exactly as required by the standard model. The b quark has weak isospin $I_3 = -\frac{1}{2}$, therefore the other member of the doublet, by definition the top quark with $I_3 = +\frac{1}{2}$, must exist. Presumably the failure to observe direct t quark production is due to the lack of sufficient energy in the presently available accelerators.

In the standard model, the b quark decays to c quarks and u quarks with rates which are proportional to the KM matrix elements $|V_{cb}|^2$ and $|V_{ub}|^2$: possible decay modes are shown in figure 14.25. Implicit in this picture is that the b quark belongs to a doublet. If we assume that the t quark does not exist and that the b quark is in fact a singlet, it would not couple directly to the W. It could, however, decay by mixing with the lighter quarks s and d, which, since they belong to doublets, can interact with the W in the usual way. In such a picture the decays $b \to cl^-\bar{\nu}_l$ and $b \to ul^-\bar{\nu}_l$ would occur by the mechanism shown in figure 14.26.

Alternatively, the b quark could decay, again via mixing with light quarks, through the neutral current processes of figure 14.27, leading to unlike-sign leptons in the final state. Evaluation of these diagrams leads to the expectation that the ratio of the neutral-current to the charged-current decay rate is

$$r = \frac{\Gamma(b \to l^+l^-X)}{\Gamma(b \to l^-\bar{\nu}_l X)} > 0.12$$

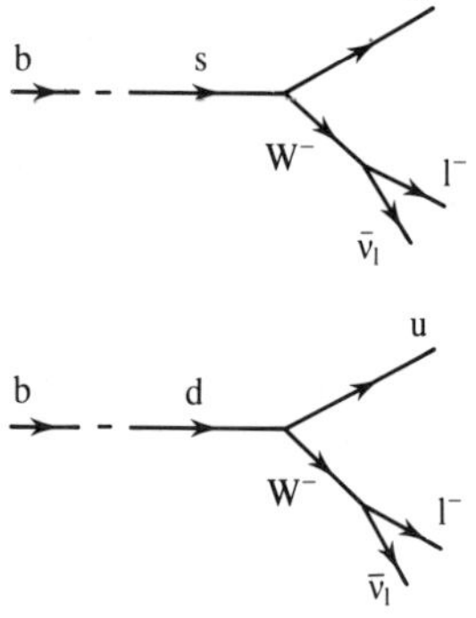

Figure 14.26
Possible mechanisms for non-standard decays of the b quark.

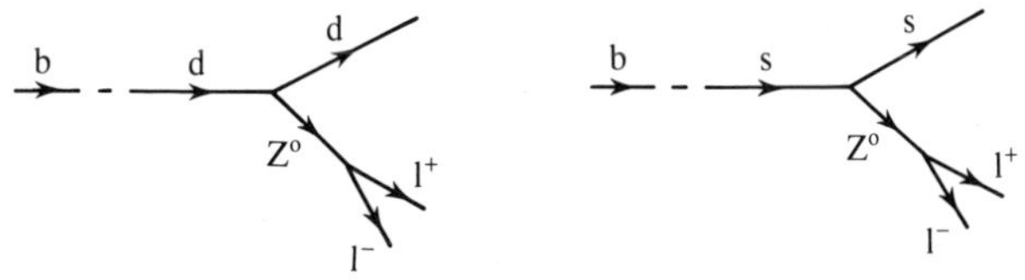

Figure 14.27
Non-standard decays of the b quark via the neutral current.

independently of the number of quarks with which the b can mix. Searches for such di-lepton decays have been made, for instance at CESR, in the process $e^+e^- \to \Upsilon(4S) \to B\bar{B}$. Di-lepton events were observed but can be attributed to the semi-leptonic decays of both the B and $\bar{B}$ mesons in accordance with the standard model. Recent results from CESR[69] give $r < 0.02$ and rule out the possibility that the b quark is an SU(2) singlet.

A more direct indication that the third quark generation is a doublet comes from a determination of I_3^b, the third component of weak isospin of the b quark. A measurement of I_3^b can be extracted from an analysis of the asymmetry in the differential cross-section for $\bar{b}b$ production in e^+e^- annihilation. Even at energies well below the Z^0, interference takes place and gives rise to a forward–backward asymmetry just as in the process $e^+e^- \to \mu^+\mu^-$ discussed in section 14.3.4. There, we saw that the asymmetry in the process $e^+e^- \to \bar{f}f$ was given approximately by equation (14.13)

$$A = -\frac{3s}{4\sqrt{2}\pi\alpha} c_A^e c_A^f.$$

In the standard model $c_A^f = I_3^f$, so a measurement of the forward–backward asymmetry determines I_3^b directly. A measurement of the asymmetry $A_{\bar{b}b}$ at a centre-of-mass energy of 55.2 GeV, performed at TRISTAN, the e^+e^- collider at Tsukuba, Japan, obtained a value

$$A_{\bar{b}b} = -0.72 \pm 0.23 \pm 0.13$$

consistent with the predictions of the standard model with $I_3^b = -\frac{1}{2}$. This result,[70] along with others at lower energies from PEP and PETRA and a more recent measurement at LEP,[71] confirm that the b quark belongs to a doublet and therefore the other member, the top quark, must exist.

At $\bar{p}p$ colliders the t quark can be produced through the weak interaction in which W^+ or W^- production is followed by the decay $W^+ \to t\bar{b}$ or $W^- \to \bar{t}b$. Of course these decays can occur only if $m_t < m_W - m_b$. The subsequent semi-leptonic decay of the t quark, $t \to b\mu^+\nu_\mu$ (or $t \to be^+\nu_e$) produces a muon (electron) which, because of the very large mass of the t quark, has a large transverse momentum and is therefore well isolated from the remaining b quark fragments. The experimental signature resulting from this chain of events is thus two quark jets together with an isolated high p_T muon or electron and some missing transverse energy associated with the neutrino. At the CERN $\bar{p}p$ collider at $\sqrt{s} = 630$ GeV, this is the dominant process for production of a top quark. There are, however, large backgrounds from other well-established sources such as $b\bar{b}$, $c\bar{c}$, W and Z production, the Drell–Yan process (section 14.4.6) and J/ψ and Υ production, and the UA1 collaboration, for example, have recently found that the inclusive muon p_T spectrum from the process $\bar{p}p \to \mu + X$ is well described by these known sources.

The UA1 collaboration has also searched for the top quark in other channels and in particular in di-muon final states. These could, in principle, arise from semi-leptonic decays of both the t and b quarks:

$$\bar{p}p \to W^+X$$
$$\quad\;\; \hookrightarrow t\bar{b}$$
$$\qquad\qquad t \to \bar{c}\mu^+\nu$$
$$\qquad\qquad \bar{b} \to b\mu^+\nu$$

As before, the muon arising from t decay should in general have the largest transverse momentum and be isolated while the muon from the $\bar{b}$ quark should not in general be isolated. Note that di-muons produced by this mechanism have the same charge and so provide a good signature for top. Again, the data are consistent with known sources of background. From their full data sample in all channels used, the UA1 collaboration[72] quote a lower limit for the top quark mass at the 95 per cent confidence level of $m_t > 61$ GeV/c^2. The UA2 collaboration has performed a similar search for top quark production using the decay mode $t \to be\nu_e$, because of their particular sensitivity to electrons rather than muons. They quote $m_t > 69$ GeV/c^2 at the 95 per cent confidence level.

In contrast at the Fermilab Tevatron with $\sqrt{s} = 1.8$ TeV, the dominant source of top quarks in $\bar{p}p$ collisions is expected to be $t\bar{t}$ pair production. In the standard model, the top quark can decay via the charged current process $t \to bW$. If both the W bosons in a $t\bar{t}$ event decay hadronically the final state consists only of jets and it is extremely difficult to isolate a t signal in this way because of the much higher rate expected for multijet events from QCD processes. If one W decays leptonically the final state will contain a lepton, a neutrino and four quarks, whereas if both Ws decay leptonically the final state contains two energetic leptons, two neutrinos and two b quark jets. The CDF collaboration[73] has searched for the top quark in both electron plus jets and $e^\pm\mu^\mp$ final states and quote top mass limits, at the 95 per cent confidence level, of

$$40 < m_t < 77 \text{ GeV}/c^2 \qquad (e + \text{jets})$$

$$28 < m_t < 72 \text{ GeV}/c^2 \qquad (e^\pm\mu^\mp).$$

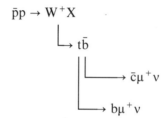

The most recent and best estimate of the top quark mass is that obtained from a global electroweak analysis of the Z^0 data from the four LEP experiments.[56] Within the framework of the standard model an observable or set of observables, X, can be expressed as a function of the known coupling constants, α, G and α_s, the mass of the Z^0 boson and the unknown mass of the top quark and the Higgs boson:

$$X = f(\alpha, G, \alpha_s, M_Z, m_t, m_H)$$

or, equivalently,

$$M_Z = F(X, \alpha, G, \alpha_s, m_t, m_H).$$

The dependence of X on m_t and m_H arises through loop corrections to the Z^0 propagator. The observables used were the total width of the Z^0, the ratio of partial widths $\Gamma_{\text{hadron}}/\Gamma_{\text{lepton}}$, the peak hadronic cross-section and the forward–backward charge asymmetries A^f_{FB} for fermions $f \equiv e, \tau$, b and c. In one such analysis the strong coupling constant was fixed at $\alpha_s(M_Z) = 0.12 \pm 0.006$ and the Higgs boson mass varied from 60 GeV to 1 TeV. The best estimate of the top quark mass was

$$m_t = (160^{+17}_{-19}{}^{+17}_{-20})\ \text{GeV}$$

where the second error quoted arises from the variation in m_H.

14.3.14 Search for the Higgs boson

The Higgs boson is an essential ingredient of the standard model. Because of the large and well-understood HZZ coupling LEP is ideal for searches covering the continuous range $0 < m_H < \approx 60$ GeV. Prior to LEP operation searches for a low mass Higgs boson ($m_H < 2m_b$) yielded null results at the 99 per cent confidence level.

The principal production mode in e^+e^- collisions, first suggested by Bjorken, is expected to be $e^+e^- \to Z^0 \to H^0Z^{0*} \to H^0f\bar{f}$ as shown in figure 14.28. The Higgs boson couples preferentially to high mass fermions and is expected to decay to hadrons ($H^0 \to q\bar{q}$) with a branching ratio of about 94 per cent and to $\tau^+\tau^-$ with a branching ratio of about 6 per cent. The branching ratios for the decays $Z^0 \to$ hadrons, $\nu\bar{\nu}$, l^+l^- are known to be of the order of 70 per cent, 20 per cent and 10 per cent respectively (table 14.2) so that the most abundant channel, $H^0Z^{0*} \to q\bar{q}q\bar{q}$, has an expected branching ratio of about 66 per cent. Unfortunately this channel suffers from a large QCD background and has therefore not been used in Higgs boson searches at LEP. The next most abundant channel $H^0Z^{0*} \to q\bar{q}\nu\bar{\nu}$ has a branching ratio of about 19 per cent and a very clear signature consisting of two acollinear and acoplanar quark jets with a

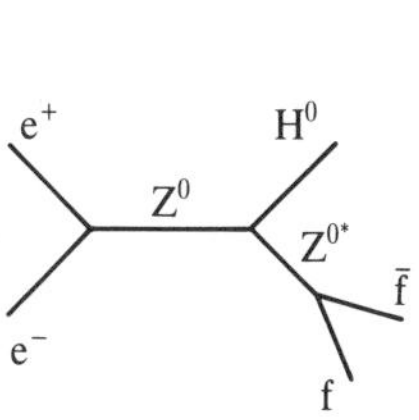

Figure 14.28
The dominant mechanism for Higgs boson production at LEP energies.

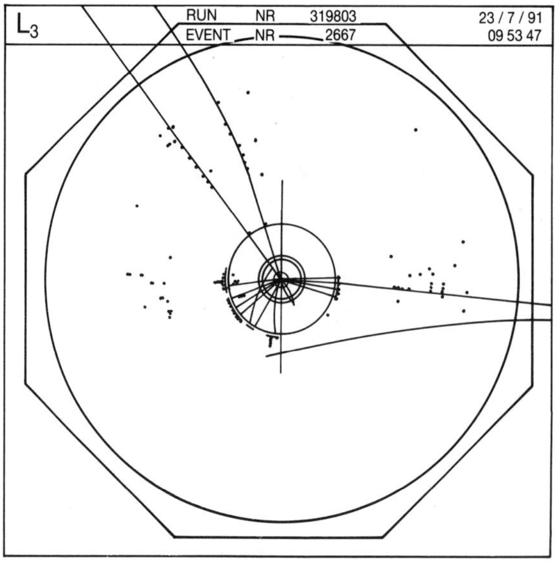

Figure 14.29 A Higgs boson candidate event in the channel $e^+e^- \to H^0\mu^+\mu^-$, $H^0 \to q\bar{q}$, observed by the L3 collaboration at LEP. The two tracks in the upper left of the computer display of the event were identified as muons as was the long track on the right of the display. (Gross E and Yepes P 1993 *Int J Mod Phys* **A8** (407))

large missing energy. The charged lepton channel, $H^0Z^{0*} \to q\bar{q}l^+l^-$, has a branching ratio (excluding τ leptons which have a low detection efficiency in the presence of hadrons) of the order of 6 per cent. An important source of background in this channel arises from $e^+e^- \to b\bar{b}$ events in which both the b quarks decay semi-leptonically. The main selection requirements aimed at removing this background are that two energetic tracks be identified as electrons or muons and that the two leptons be well isolated from the hadronic activity in the event.

A particularly interesting Higgs boson candidate in the muon channel has been reported by the L3 collaboration and is shown in figure 14.29. The H^0 mass, reconstructed as the recoil mass of the di-muon system, is 70.4 ± 0.7 GeV. A third muon, associated with the quark jet on the right in figure 14.29, was positively identified. This could indicate that the hadronic activity in the event is associated with a pair of heavy quarks with one of them decaying semi-leptonically; the dominant decay mode of a 70 GeV Higgs boson is $H^0 \to b\bar{b}$. The small opening angle of the muon pair which recoils against the two quark jets which are almost collinear is typical of this type of Higgs boson candidate.[74]

To date the four LEP experiments have analysed some 4 million hadronic Z decays and in this data sample one $q\bar{q}\nu\bar{\nu}$ and seven $q\bar{q}l^+l^-$ candidates have been observed. These are, however, consistent with known sources of background and collectively the experiments exclude a Higgs boson with a mass less than 63.5 GeV at the 95 per cent confidence level.

14.4 Experimental tests of quantum chromodynamics

14.4.1 Renormalization schemes, renormalization scales and the quantum chromodynamics parameter Λ[75]

The calculation of an observable in perturbative QCD takes the form of an expansion in the strong coupling constant α_s and requires the choice of a particular renormalization scheme and a renormalization scale μ (section 13.9). It is therefore important, when comparing values of α_s from different experiments, that the same renormalization scheme* has been used in the QCD calculations.

The renormalization group formalism[77,78] leads to the concept of running coupling (section 13.9), i.e. the QCD coupling constant is a function of energy Q. It is defined by the relation

$$t = \int_{\alpha_s(\mu)}^{\alpha_s(Q)} \frac{d\alpha_s}{\beta(\alpha_s)} \tag{14.35}$$

where $t = \ln(Q^2/\mu^2)$ and the initial value $\alpha_s(\mu)$ is specified at the chosen mass scale $Q = \mu$. The β function can be computed using perturbation theory and depends on the number of active quark flavours as well as on α_s. For n quark flavours[79]

$$\beta(\alpha_s) = -b_n\alpha_s^2(1 + b'_n\alpha_s + \cdots) \tag{14.36}$$

where $b_n = (33 - 2n)/12\pi$ and $b'_n = \frac{1}{2}(153 - 19n)/(33 - 2n)$. For $n = 5$, for example, we have

$$\beta(\alpha_s) = -0.61\alpha_s^2\left[1 + 1.26\left(\frac{\alpha_s}{\pi}\right) + \cdots\right]. \tag{14.37}$$

If we neglect b'_n and higher order terms we find from (14.35)

$$\ln\left(\frac{Q^2}{\mu^2}\right) = -\int_{\alpha_s(\mu)}^{\alpha_s(Q)} \frac{d\alpha_s}{b_n\alpha_s^2} = \frac{1}{b_n}\left[\frac{1}{\alpha_s(Q)} - \frac{1}{\alpha_s(\mu)}\right]$$

or

$$\alpha_s(Q) = \frac{\alpha_s(\mu)}{1 + b_n\alpha_s(\mu)\ln(Q^2/\mu^2)} \tag{14.38}$$

so that, in agreement with equation (13.179), $\alpha_s(Q)$ depends on the choice

* Of the various possibilities the 'minimal subtraction scheme' (MS) and the 'modified minimal subtraction scheme' ($\overline{\text{MS}}$)[61] are the ones most frequently used.

of renormalization scale μ. We note that the approach to asymptotic freedom ($\alpha_s(Q) = 0$ as $Q^2 \to \infty$) is slow because of the logarithmic term. We note also that the equation tells us how $\alpha_s(Q)$ varies with scale but not its absolute value, which has to be determined by experiment.

One might choose as the fundamental parameter of QCD the value of α_s at a mass large enough to justify the perturbative calculations – the mass of the Z^0 for example. Historically an alternative approach has been to replace the mass scale μ by another parameter Λ which is defined by the equation

$$\ln\left(\frac{Q^2}{\Lambda^2}\right) = -\int_{\alpha_s(Q)}^{\infty} \frac{d\alpha_s}{\beta(\alpha_s)} \tag{14.39}$$

which gives, again in leading order,

$$\alpha_s(Q) = \frac{1}{b_n \ln(Q^2/\Lambda^2)}. \tag{14.40}$$

The quantity Λ is then taken as the fundamental parameter of QCD, to be determined from equation (14.40) or, in practice, from a more elaborate equation including higher order terms, using the experimental value of α_s. A consistent value of Λ from analyses of different processes is clearly a requirement of QCD validity.

14.4.2 The cross-section for $e^+e^- \to$ hadrons

One of the most reliable predictions of perturbative QCD is R, the ratio of the total hadronic cross-section to the muon pair production cross-section in e^+e^- annihilation. Although the hadronization of quarks produced by the annihilation cannot be described by perturbative methods, we may avoid this difficulty by choosing an energy large enough to locate the primary process in a small space–time volume. Hadronization then follows by the process shown in figure 14.30 after a time interval too great to affect the probability of $q\bar{q}$ production.

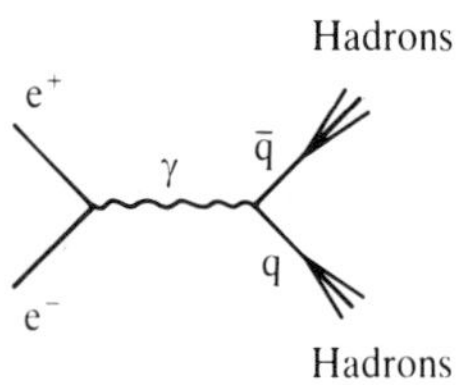

Figure 14.30
The sequence of events in the annihilation process $e^+e^- \to$ hadrons.

The total cross-section for the production of a fermion–antifermion pair in e^+e^- annihilation is given in section 12.8 as

$$\sigma = \frac{4\pi\alpha^2}{3s} \tag{14.41}$$

for centre-of-mass energies $\sqrt{s} \ll M_Z^0$ and for unit charge on the fermions. In leading-order perturbation theory the total hadronic cross-section at a particular energy is obtained by summing over all active quark flavours

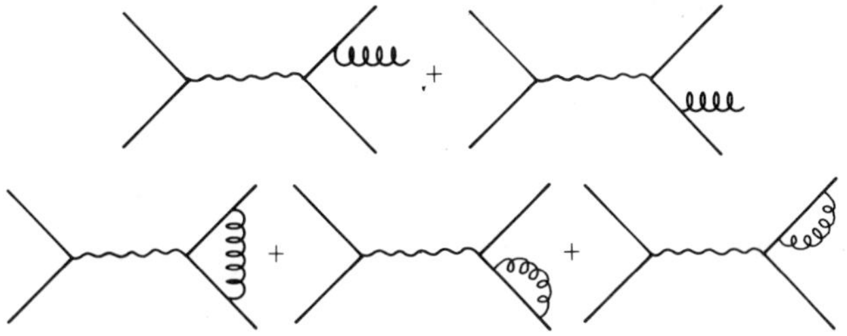

Figure 14.31.
The $O(\alpha_s)$ corrections to the total hadronic cross-section in e^+e^- annihilation. The upper diagrams contain 'real' gluons while the lower contain virtual gluons.

at that energy and

$$R = \frac{\sum_q \sigma(e^+e^- \to q\bar{q})}{\sigma(e^+e^- \to \mu^+\mu^-)} = 3\sum_q Q_q^2 \tag{14.42}$$

where Q_q is the quark charge. The factor 3 arises because each flavour can occur in each of three colours.

For u, d, s, c and b quarks $R = \frac{11}{3}$, but the measured value at $\sqrt{s} = 34$ GeV is 3.9 and, even allowing for a small contribution from the Z^0 ($\Delta R_{Z^0} \approx 0.05$), this result is approximately 5 per cent higher than the lowest order prediction. The difference can be attributed to higher order QCD corrections and a comparison between theory and experiment leads to one of the most accurate determinations of the strong coupling constant.

The $O(\alpha_s)$ corrections to the total hadronic cross-section involve real and virtual gluons as shown in figure 14.31. Calculations to higher order, $O(\alpha_s^2)$, have been performed[79] using the $\overline{\text{MS}}$ scheme and a choice of scale $\mu = \sqrt{s}$, with the result

$$R = 3\sum_q Q_q^2\left\{1 + \frac{\alpha_s(\sqrt{s})}{\pi} + 1.41\left[\frac{\alpha_s(\sqrt{s})}{\pi}\right]^2 + \cdots\right\}. \tag{14.43}$$

Note that this expression is obtained assuming s channel photon exchange only – effects of the Z^0 have been neglected. Figure 14.32 shows a fit[80] to measurements of R over a wide energy range. Using the second-order QCD prediction and electroweak effects a value

$$\alpha_s(34\ \text{GeV}) = 0.158 \pm 0.020 \tag{14.44}$$

was obtained, corresponding to

$$\Lambda_{\overline{\text{MS}}}^{(5)} = 440^{+320}_{-220}\ \text{MeV}. \tag{14.45}$$

If in the hadronization of a quark the hadronic fragments have limited transverse momentum relative to the line of flight of the quark, the leading-order process $e^+e^- \to q\bar{q}$ (figure 14.30) will at high energy lead to

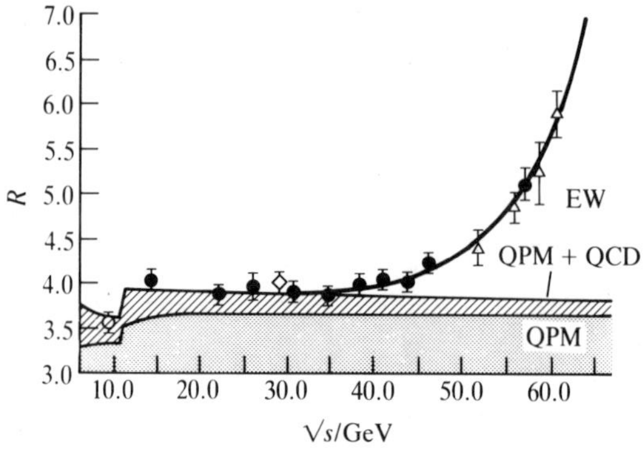

Figure 14.32 Experimental measurements of $R = \sigma(e^+e^- \rightarrow \text{hadrons})/\sigma(e^+e^- \rightarrow \mu^+\mu^-)$ from CESR (□), PETRA (●), PEP (◇) and TRISTAN (△), over the centre-of-mass energy range 9 GeV $< \sqrt{s} <$ 60 GeV. The curve is the result of a QCD fit including electroweak effects. The individual contributions of the 'naive' quark–parton model (shaded) and QCD corrections (cross-hatched) are also shown.

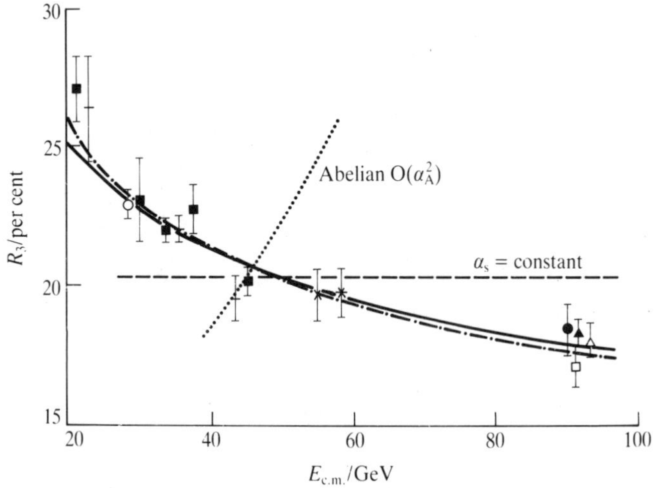

Figure 14.33 The three-jet fraction R_3 (at $y = 0.08$) in the centre-of-mass energy range 20 GeV $\lesssim \sqrt{s} \lesssim$ 90 GeV. The QCD fits (——, $\mu^2 = E^2_{\text{c.m.}}$ and $\Lambda_{\overline{\text{MS}}} = 255$ MeV; ----, $\mu^2 = 0.0017E^2_{\text{c.m.}}$ and $\Lambda_{\overline{\text{MS}}} = 111$ MeV) are clearly preferred over an Abelian $O(\alpha^2_{\text{A}})$ prediction and the prediction for constant α_s. ■, JADE; +, TASSO; ○, Mk-II; ×, AMY; ∗, VENUS; ▲, OPAL; □, DELPHI; ●, L3; △, ALEPH.

the production of *two* back-to-back jets. The next-to-leading order process, $e^+e^- \rightarrow q\bar{q}g$ (figure 14.31), is suppressed in cross-section with respect to leading order by a factor α_s but it can lead to *three* jets as well as two. The faction R_3 of the total hadronic cross-section that appears in three-jet events has been determined over a wide energy range by a number of collaborations and is shown as a function of centre-of-mass energy in figure 14.33. The energy dependence of the three-jet fraction resides exclusively in the coupling $\alpha_s(\sqrt{s})$ and the 'running' of the strong coupling constant is clearly demonstrated in figure 14.33. A detailed analysis of the jet event rates at $\sqrt{s} = M_{Z^0}$ by the OPAL collaboration[81] yields

$$\alpha_s(M_{Z^0}) = 0.118 \pm 0.008.$$

14.4.3 Scaling violations in deep inelastic scattering

In principle, deep inelastic lepton–hadron scattering provides a powerful test of perturbative QCD and yields precise measurements of α_s. Since the process is completely inclusive there are no problems arising from the experimental definition of jets and the problem of relating theoretical cross-sections at the parton level with hadronic cross-sections measured experimentally does not exist. Furthermore, analyses of the data determine the momentum distributions of the quarks and gluons inside the hadrons and this information is invaluable in predicting the cross-sections in hadron collisions at higher energies and therefore extremely useful in the design of experiments at present and future accelerators.

In chapter 12 we discussed the phenomenon of Bjorken scaling in deep inelastic scattering. The cross-section for the process shown in figure 14.34 was expressed in terms of structure functions F_1, F_2, F_3 which are a convenient parametrization of the structure of the target particle. These quantities are functions of the variables x and Q^2 where $Q^2 = -q^2$ is the four-momentum transfer squared and x is the dimensionless quantity $Q^2/2p\cdot q$, where p is the four-momentum of the initial-state hadron. Bjorken scaling asserts that at high Q^2 the structure functions obey the law

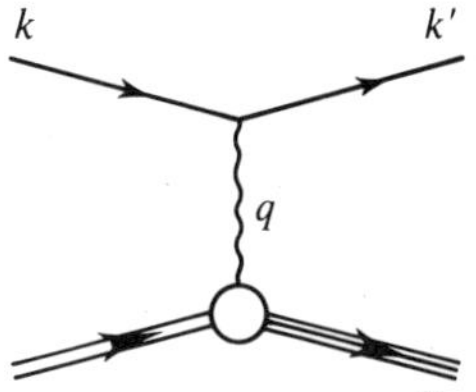

Figure 14.34
Feynman diagram for deep inelastic lepton–hadron scattering.

$$F_i(x, Q^2) \rightarrow F_i(x),$$

i.e. they depend on the dimensionless variable x. The scaling law arises because at high Q^2 the constituents of the proton appear to be structureless, otherwise the structure functions would depend upon some scale, Q_0 say, characteristic of the size of the constituents.

On close examination of deep inelastic scattering data it is found that there are systematic deviations of the structure functions from exact Bjorken scaling. Figure 14.35, for example, shows the structure function F_2^{em} measured in high energy muon–proton scattering by the BCDMS collaboration.[82] The measurements cover a wide range of x values from 0.07 to 0.75 and Q^2 values up to several hundred giga-electronvolts squared. At low values of x the structure function increases with increasing Q^2 while at high values of x it decreases as Q^2 increases. As a result of a QCD fit to the data (solid lines in figure 14.35) the BCDMS collaboration quote a value for the scale parameter in next to leading order of

$$\Lambda_{\overline{MS}}^{(4)} = 205 \pm 22 \pm 60 \text{ MeV}$$

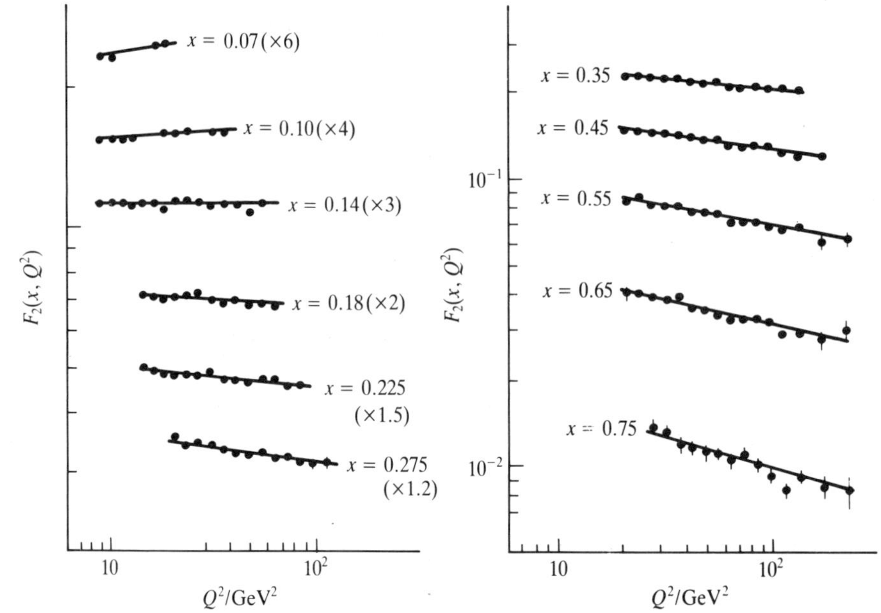

Figure 14.35 The electromagnetic structure function $F_2^{em}(x, Q^2)$ plotted as a function of Q^2 for different values of x ranging from $x = 0.07$ to $x = 0.75$. The data were obtained in μ–p scattering by the BCDMS collaboration. The solid lines are the result of a next-to-leading order QCD fit. (After Benvenuti A C *et al.* 1989 *Phys Lett* **223B** (490).)

corresponding to a strong coupling constant of

$$\alpha_s(Q^2 = 100\ \text{GeV}^2) = 0.156 \pm 0.004 \pm 0.011.$$

The errors on these quantities are statistical and systematic respectively.

We saw in chapter 12 that scaling occurs when the virtual probe, with energy ν and four-momentum Q^2, elastically scatters from a quark with momentum fraction $x = Q^2/2m\nu$ as shown in figure 14.36. In this 'naive' parton model the quarks are considered as free, non-interacting, structureless particles. In the 'QCD-improved' parton model other diagrams, involving gluons, contribute to the scattering process. For example, a quark with momentum fraction $y > x$ can radiate a gluon with momentum fraction $y - x$ leaving a quark, with momentum fraction x, to absorb the virtual photon as shown in figure 14.37(a). As a result, at least for values of $x \geqslant 0.3$, the quark distribution function, or equivalently the structure function, shrinks towards smaller x as Q^2 increases. Additionally, the target proton contains gluons with distribution function $G(x, Q^2)$, say, and these may produce quark–antiquark pairs and hence 'feed' the quark distribution, $q^f(x, Q^2)$, where f is the quark flavour (figure 14.37(b)). The effect is that, particularly at very small values of x, the structure function increases as Q^2 increases.

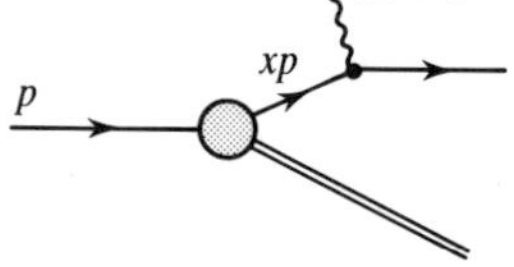

Figure 14.36
Deep inelastic scattering at the quark level in the 'naive' parton model.

The evolution of the quark and gluon distribution functions with Q^2

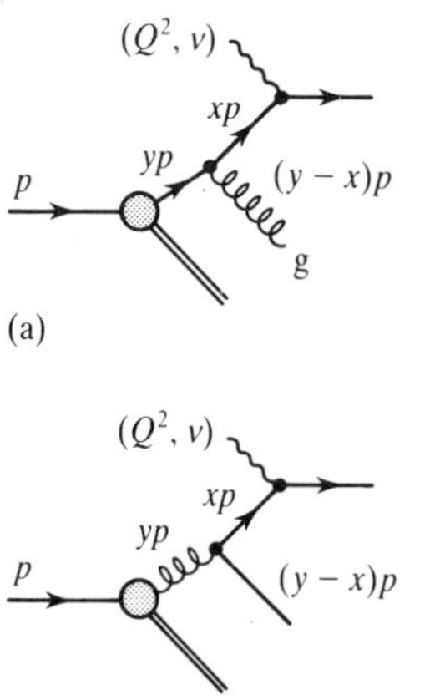

Figure 14.37
(a) Deep inelastic scattering in the 'QCD-improved' parton model. A parent quark, with momentum fraction $y > x$, radiates a gluon with momentum fraction $y - p$. The daughter quark, with momentum fraction x, is scattered by the virtual photon. (b) Diagram illustrating how the gluon constituents of the proton contribute to deep inelastic scattering.

is described by the Altarelli–Parisi[83] equations which may be written

$$\frac{\mathrm{d}q^f(x, Q^2)}{\mathrm{d}\ln Q^2} = \frac{\alpha_s(Q)}{2\pi}\int_x^1 \frac{\mathrm{d}y}{y}\left[q^f(y, Q^2)P_{qq}\left(\frac{x}{y}\right) + G(y, Q^2)P_{qg}\left(\frac{x}{y}\right)\right] \tag{14.46}$$

$$\frac{\mathrm{d}G(x, Q^2)}{\mathrm{d}\ln Q^2} = \frac{\alpha_s(Q)}{2\pi}\int_x^1 \frac{\mathrm{d}y}{y}\left[\sum_f q^f(y, Q^2)P_{gq}\left(\frac{x}{y}\right) + G(y, Q^2)P_{gg}\left(\frac{x}{y}\right)\right] \tag{14.47}$$

The 'splitting function', $P_{gq}(x/y)$ for example, is the probability that a quark will emit a gluon with a fraction x/y of the original momentum. The splitting functions can be written as a perturbative expansion in the running coupling constant and have been calculated in reference 83. If the quark and gluon distribution functions are known over the complete range of x at a particular value of Q^2 they can be determined at other Q^2 values through the Altarelli–Parisi equations. The Q^2 evolution of some typical quark and gluon distributions is shown in figure 14.38.

Figure 14.39 shows the logarithmic Q^2 derivative of the structure function F_2, as a function of x, calculated from the data in figure 14.35 for $Q^2 > 20\ \mathrm{GeV}^2$. In this region the derivatives are negative as expected for a structure function which decreases with increasing Q^2. Also shown in the figure are the predictions of next-to-leading order QCD for a range of values of $\Lambda_{\overline{\mathrm{MS}}}$.

In conclusion, QCD explains scaling violation in deep inelastic scattering;

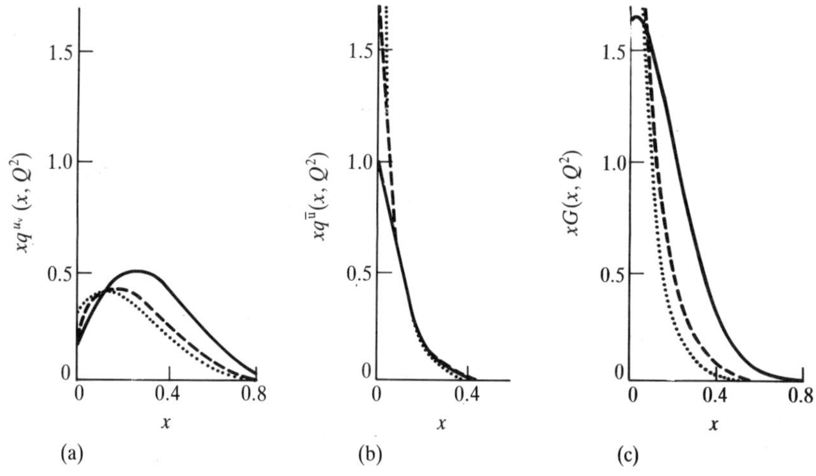

Figure 14.38 Q^2 evolution of parton distributions (——, $Q^2 = 4\ \mathrm{GeV}^2$; – – –, $Q^2 = 400\ \mathrm{GeV}^2$; . . . , $Q^2 = 40\,000\ \mathrm{GeV}^2$): (a) valence quarks u_v; (b) sea quarks $\bar{u}$; (c) gluons.

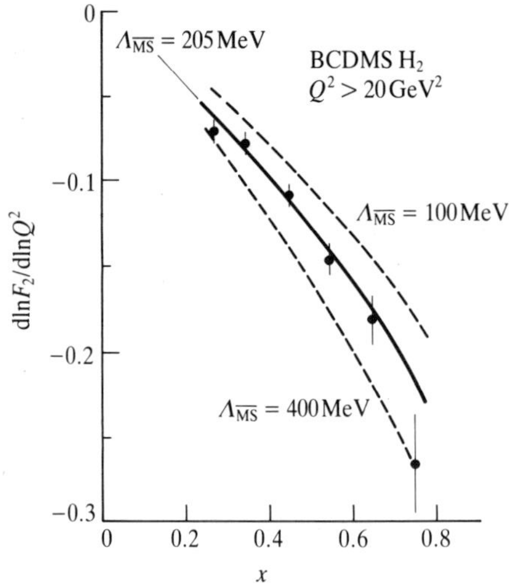

Figure 14.39 Logarithmic Q^2 derivative of the structure function $F_2^{em}(x, Q^2)$ as a function of x, calculated from the data in figure 14.35 for Q^2 values greater than 20 GeV^2. The curves are next-to-leading order QCD predictions for $\Lambda_{\overline{MS}}$ = 100 MeV, 205 MeV and 400 MeV. (After Benvenuti A C *et al.* 1989 *Phys Lett* **223B** (490).)

the agreement between the data and theoretical predictions is impressive and lends great support to the validity of perturbative QCD.

14.4.4 *Quarkonium decays*

In chapter 10 we described the discovery and properties of the ψ family ($c\bar{c}$) and the Υ family ($b\bar{b}$), collectively known as quarkonia. The measurement of the decay rates of quarkonium, and in particular the Υ, should in principle lead to a rather precise value of α_s and $\Lambda_{\overline{MS}}$. As we saw in chapter 10, in a non-relativistic theory the decay rates are proportional to the absolute square of the quark wavefunction at the origin, see equation (10.51). Although a comparison of the leptonic widths of the vector mesons leads to the expectation $|\psi(0)|^2 \approx m_V^2$, where m_V is the mass of the vector meson, the wavefunction is in fact unknown. This problem can be avoided by considering *ratios* of decay rates since these are independent of the wavefunction. The most convenient ratios to use in the determination of α_s are $\Gamma_{\mu\mu}/\Gamma_{ggg}$ and $\Gamma_{\gamma gg}/\Gamma_{ggg}$. The diagrams contributing to these ratios are shown in figure 14.40.

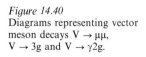

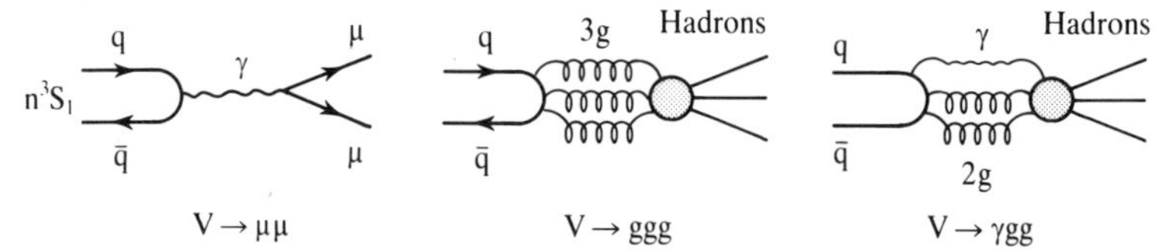

Figure 14.40
Diagrams representing vector meson decays V → μμ, V → 3g and V → γ2g.

Note that one-gluon exchange is forbidden by colour conservation. A colour singlet state may in principle couple to two gluons but, in the present case of vector mesons with $J^{PC} = 1^{--}$, two-gluon coupling is forbidden because such a state is even under charge conjugation.[84] This is reminiscent of positronium: the orthopositronium state with $J^{PC} = 1^{--}$, is forbidden to decay to two photons because the latter have $C = +1$. A totally symmetric three-gluon state is odd under C-parity so the simplest gluonic intermediate state which can couple to a $^3S_1$ vector meson contains three gluons (or two gluons and a photon). Similarly, orthopositronium decays into at least three photons.

Next-to-leading order calculations of the ratios $\Gamma_{\mu\mu}/\Gamma_{ggg}$ and $\Gamma_{\gamma gg}/\Gamma_{ggg}$ have been performed in the $\overline{\rm MS}$ scheme by several authors.[85–88] The rates for the upsilon are

$$\frac{\Gamma_{\mu\mu}}{\Gamma_{ggg}} = \frac{9\pi}{10(\pi^2-9)}\frac{\alpha_2}{\alpha_s^3(\mu)}\left\{1 - \frac{\alpha_s(\mu)}{\pi}\left[3\pi b_4 \ln\left(\frac{\mu^2}{m_Q^2}\right) + 0.43\right] + \cdots\right\} \tag{14.48}$$

$$\frac{\Gamma_{\gamma gg}}{\Gamma_{ggg}} = \frac{4}{5}\frac{\alpha}{\alpha_s(\mu)}\left\{1 - \frac{\alpha_s(\mu)}{\pi}\left[\pi b_4 \ln\left(\frac{\mu^2}{m_Q^2}\right) + 2.6\right] + \cdots\right\} \tag{14.49}$$

where

$$b_4 = \frac{33-2n}{12\pi} \qquad (n = \text{number of quark flavours} = 4)$$

and μ is an arbitrary scale of the order of the heavy quark mass, $m_Q \approx m_\Upsilon/2$.

The values of $\Gamma_{\mu\mu}/\Gamma_{ggg}$ for the Υ(1S), Υ(2S) and Υ(3S) obtained from measurements by the CUSB and CLEO collaborations,[89] together with the resulting values of $\alpha_s(m_b)$ and $\Lambda_{\overline{\rm MS}}^{(4)}$ for $\mu = m_b \approx 4.9$ GeV, are shown in table 14.3. The world average value of $\Gamma_{\gamma gg}/\Gamma_{ggg}$, measured by the CUSB, CLEO, ARGOS and Crystal Ball collaborations, is 0.0278 ± 0.0015. Inserting this number into (14.49) gives

$$\alpha_s(m_b) = 0.181 \pm 0.009.$$

Table 14.3
Values of the strong coupling constant α_s and $\Lambda_{\overline{\rm MS}}$ determined from the ratio $\Gamma_{\mu\mu}/\Gamma_{ggg}$ obtained for the Υ(1S), Υ(2S) and Υ(3S) states by the CUSB and CLEO collaborations

	$\Gamma_{\mu\mu}/\Gamma_{ggg}$	$\alpha_s(m_b)$	$\Lambda_{\overline{\rm MS}}^{(4)}$/MeV
Υ(1S)	0.032 ± 0.001	0.1743 ± 0.0024	159 ± 9
Υ(2S)	0.031 ± 0.008	0.175 ± 0.015	162 ± 54
Υ(3S)	0.032 ± 0.003	0.1742 ± 0.0021	155 ± 18

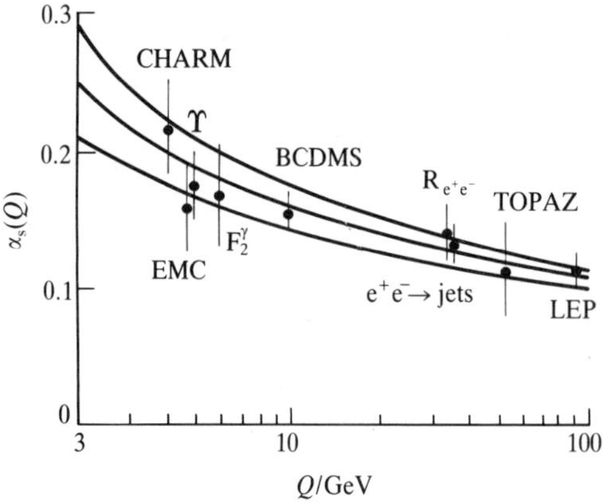

Figure 14.41 Variation of the strong coupling constant $\alpha_s(Q)$ with Q. The curves are QCD predictions for $\Lambda_{\overline{MS}}^{(5)} = 80$ MeV (lower curve), $\Lambda_{\overline{MS}}^{(5)} = 140$ MeV (middle curve) and $\Lambda_{\overline{MS}}^{(5)} = 200$ MeV (upper curve).

Consistent values of α_s have been obtained from charmonium decays but uncertainties are greater than with bottomonium. An overall fit of the available data has been performed by Kwong *et al.*[90] who found

$$\alpha_s(m_c) = 0.278 \pm 0.014 \qquad \text{and} \qquad \alpha_s(m_b) = 0.185 \pm 0.006.$$

14.4.5 *Variation of α_s with energy*

The determination of α_s from a variety of quite different sources has been described in the preceding sections. A selection of experimental values of $\alpha_s(Q)$ is shown as a function of Q in figure 14.41 together with QCD predictions for values of $\Lambda_{\overline{MS}}^{(5)}$ of 80 MeV (lower curve), 140 MeV (middle) and 200 MeV (upper curve). The consistency of the results provides the best quantitative test of QCD. The running of the coupling constant with increasing Q is perhaps not firmly established by the data over the presently available energy range. This is due in the main to the slow logarithmic decrease of $\alpha_s(Q)$. However, the measured values of α_s (≈ 0.12) at large values of Q constitute a powerful test of the running of α_s because such a relatively weak force could not provide the tight binding observed in hadrons.

In the following sections we briefly summarize other phenomena which test quantum chromodynamics.

14.4.6 *Drell–Yan processes and W/Z production*

High energy hadron–hadron scattering is fertile ground for testing the validity of QCD. In the parton model a hadron is visualized as a 'swarm'

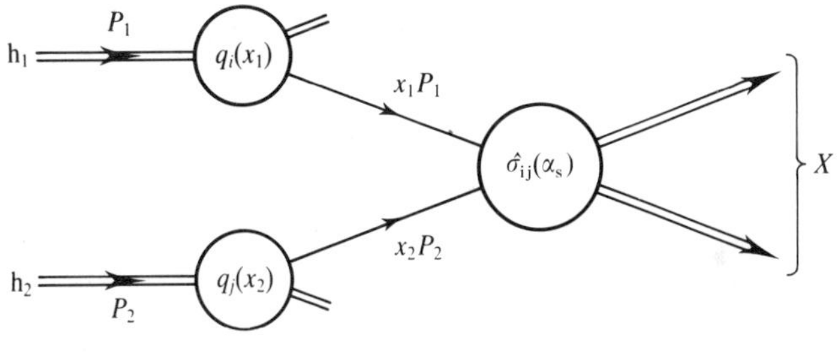

Figure 14.42
Schematic diagram of a hard scattering process between two hadrons.

of constituents – valence quarks, sea quarks and gluons – moving with characteristic momentum distributions. A hadron effectively provides a broad-band beam of quarks and gluons and when two hadrons interact at high energy the basic process contributing to the hadron–hadron cross-section takes place between *constituents* of the parent hadrons: the hadron–hadron cross-section arises from an incoherent sum of these individual partonic subprocesses. This parton approach is implemented in QCD through the factorization theorem,[91] the central assertion of which is that the parton distributions are *universal*: the Q^2 dependent distribution functions for quarks and gluons, measured for a given hadron in one process and evolved in Q^2, as appropriate, through the Altarelli–Parisi equations, are valid in other processes involving the same hadron.

The cross-section for a hard scattering process between two hadrons with four-momenta P_1 and P_2 is a convolution of the parton distribution functions with the parton cross-section. Thus, for the inclusive process $h_1 + h_2 \to X +$ anything, shown schematically in figure 14.42, the cross-section is

$$\sigma(P_1P_2) = \sum_{ij} \int dx_1\, dx_2 q_i(x_1, \mu) q_j(x_2, \mu) \hat{\sigma}_{ij}[p_1, p_2, \alpha_s(Q)]. \quad (14.50)$$

The momenta of the interacting partons are $p_1 = x_1P_1$ and $p_2 = x_2P_2$, and $q_i(x_1, \mu)$ is the distribution function for parton of type i in hadron 1 at the factorization scale μ. The cross-section for the scattering of partons of type i and j is denoted by $\hat{\sigma}_{ij}$. At high energies the running coupling constant, $\alpha_s(Q)$, is small and $\hat{\sigma}_{ij}$ can be calculated as a perturbation series in α_s. For simplicity the factorization scale μ, which appears in the parton distribution functions, is frequently identified with the renormalization scale which enters in $\alpha_s(Q)$. The value of Q can be chosen with some freedom around the natural scale of the particular process under consideration, for example the mass of a weak boson, W/Z, in the process $h_1 + h_2 \to$ W/Z + anything. A change in the choice of scale is compensated by a corresponding change in $\hat{\sigma}$. Naturally, the compensation is complete only if the exact expression is used for $\hat{\sigma}$. However, if the expression for $\hat{\sigma}$ is truncated at a given order in α_s, a change of scale produces a variation in the cross-section which involves terms of higher order in α_s.

In section 12.7 we briefly discussed the inclusive production of lepton pairs in hadron–hadron collisions, via virtual photon exchange, the Drell–Yan process (see figure 12.26). This is among the simplest of hard hadron–hadron processes in that the final state can be totally inclusive and the interactions of the observed lepton pair are not complicated by strong interactions. In chapter 12 we illustrated how hadron structure functions can be extracted from studies of such processes. Here, we wish to change emphasis and show that Drell–Yan processes (including W/Z production) provide important tests of the validity of QCD.

We recall that the lowest order cross-section for quark–antiquark annihilation to a lepton pair via a virtual intermediate photon (figure 12.26) is

$$\hat{\sigma}(q\bar{q} \to l^+l^-) = \frac{4\pi\alpha^2}{3\hat{s}} \frac{1}{N_c} e_{q_i}^2. \tag{14.51}$$

In this expression $\hat{s}$ is the square of the parton centre-of-mass energy, which is related to the corresponding hadronic quantity s by $\hat{s} = x_1 x_2 s$, and e_{q_i} is the quark charge. The cross-section is inversely proportional to N_c, the number of colour replicas for quarks, because a particular quark can annihilate only with an antiquark of the appropriate anticolour to produce a colourless lepton pair. The differential cross-section for the production of a lepton pair of mass M is then

$$\frac{d\hat{\sigma}}{dM^2} = \frac{4\pi\alpha^2}{3M^2} \frac{1}{N_c} e_{q_i}^2 \delta(\hat{s} - M^2). \tag{14.52}$$

Then, according to equation (14.50) the parton model cross-section for the process $h_1 + h_2 \to l^+ + l^- +$ anything, calculated to leading order, is

$$\frac{d\sigma}{dM^2} = \frac{4\pi\alpha^2}{3N_c M^2} \int_0^1 dx_1\, dx_2 \delta(x_1 x_2 s - M^2)$$
$$\times \left\{ \sum_i e_{q_i}^2 [q_i(x_1, Q)\bar{q}_i(x_2, Q) + \bar{q}_i(x_1, Q) q_i(x_2, Q)] \right\}. \tag{14.53}$$

Precise measurements of muon pair production cross-sections in fixed target experiments and at the ISR have been instrumental in establishing the validity of the parton model approach to Drell–Yan processes. Certain characteristic properties have emerged. Experiments on nuclei with mass number A have established a linear A dependence of the cross-section, reflecting the correctness of the assumption that the partons contribute incoherently. The angular distribution of the lepton pair in the centre-of-mass system is predominantly $1 + \cos^2 \theta$. Differential cross-sections exhibit approximate scaling – QCD effects lead only to logarithmic

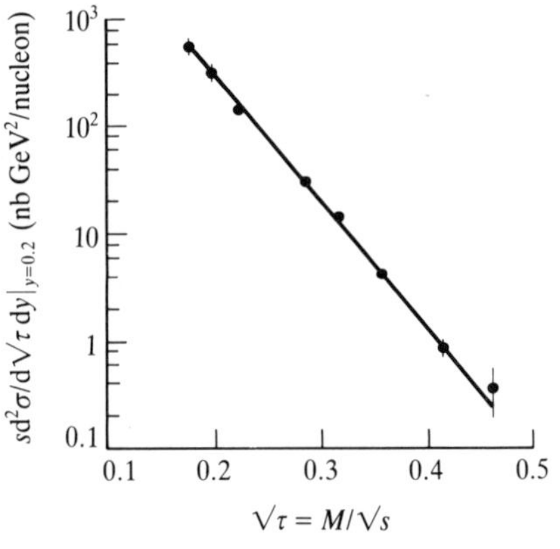

Figure 14.43 Differential cross-section for inclusive di-muon production in the Drell–Yan process $pN \to \mu^+\mu^- X$, obtained by the E605 collaboration at Fermilab. The curve is the result of a next-to-leading order QCD calculation. (After Brown C N *et al.* 1989 *Phys Rev Lett* **63** (2637).)

variations. Cross-sections for $\pi^\pm N$, K^-N and $\bar{p}N$ interactions are significantly greater than those for K^+N and pN showing the dominance of valence–valence over valence–sea scattering.

To the bare quark–antiquark annihilation diagram (figure 12.26), which leads to the leading order differential cross-section (equation (14.53)), must be added terms arising from the gluonic content of the hadrons, terms in which the quark (or antiquark) has been radiated from a parent quark, and terms in which a virtual gluon is exchanged. These corrections arise in next-to-leading order in perturbative QCD and depend on both the mass of the lepton pair and the centre-of-mass energy $\sqrt{s}$. Figure 14.43 shows the differential cross-section for inclusive di-muon production in proton–nucleon collisions $pN \to \mu^+\mu^- X$ via the Drell–Yan process, obtained by the E605 collaboration[91] at Fermilab. The agreement with the QCD prediction (solid line) is impressive.

The cross-sections for W and Z production in hadronic interactions are calculated in the same way as the Drell–Yan cross-section. The quark subprocesses in this case are $q\bar{q}' \to W$ and $q\bar{q} \to Z$ with cross-sections

$$\hat{\sigma}(q\bar{q}' \to W) = 2\pi|V_{qq'}|^2 \frac{G}{\sqrt{2}} M_W^2 \delta(\hat{s} - M_W^2)$$

$$\hat{\sigma}(q\bar{q} \to Z) = 8\pi \frac{G}{\sqrt{2}} [(c_V^q)^2 + (c_A^q)^2] M_Z^2 \delta(\hat{s} - M_Z^2)$$

where $V_{qq'}$ is the appropriate Kobayashi–Maskawa matrix element and c_V and c_A are the vector and axial-vector couplings to quarks. The $O(\alpha_s)$ QCD correction to the cross-sections for W and Z production is the same as the Drell–Yan correction, calculated at $Q^2 = M_{W/Z}^2$, and amounts to

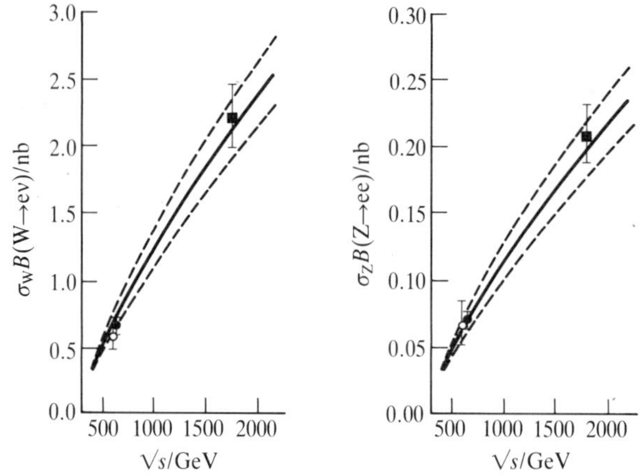

Figure 14.44
Experimental measurements of W and Z production by UA1 (○), UA2 (●) and CDF (■) compared with theoretical predictions.

about a 30 per cent increase in the cross-section for bare quark–antiquark annihilation. Figure 14.44 shows the cross-sections for W and Z production, multiplied by the leptonic branching fractions $B(W \to e\nu)$ and $B(Z \to ee)$, measured by the UA1 and UA2 collaborations at the CERN Sp$\bar{p}$S ($\sqrt{s} = 630$ GeV) and by the CDF collaboration at the Fermilab Tevatron ($\sqrt{s} = 1.8$ TeV). The errors on the measured cross-sections are a combination of statistical and systematic errors. Also shown are theoretical predictions which have errors of about ± 10 per cent due mainly to the only partially known $O(\alpha_S^2)$ QCD corrections, uncertainties in the parton distributions and higher order electroweak corrections. It is important to note that this comparison constitutes an important test of the validity of the parton approach. Since the cross-sections are quadratic in the parton distribution functions one is testing the parton model in a complex dynamical configuration. Furthermore, it provides a non-trivial check on the evolution of the parton densities since in the calculation they are evaluated at much higher Q^2 values than pertain in deep inelastic scattering data.

Of even greater dynamical significance is the transverse momentum distribution of the W and Z. In the naive parton model the interacting partons have zero transverse momentum whereas experimentally the average p_T for W and Z production is large ($\langle p_T \rangle \approx 8$ GeV at $\sqrt{s} = 630$ GeV) compared with all possible hadronic scales. This must arise solely from QCD radiation. Figure 14.45 shows the p_T distribution for the W measured in the UA1 experiment.[92] A QCD calculation[93–95] using the Duke–Owens[96] parametrization of parton densities and a value of $\Lambda_{\overline{MS}}$ of 0.2 GeV reproduces the observed p_T distribution very well.

14.4.7 Hard processes in pp and $\bar{p}p$ collisions

In the last decade or so the study of quark–quark and quark–gluon interactions in hadron collisions has provided overwhelming support for

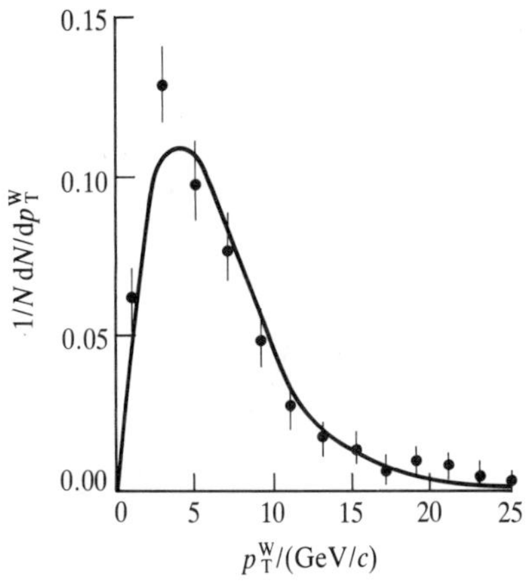

Figure 14.45
The transverse momentum distribution of $W^{\pm}$ bosons produced in the UA1 experiment, compared with a QCD calculation. (Albajou C *et al.* 1989 *Z Phys* **C44** (15))

the validity of QCD. During this time the scale Q of energy has increased over a wide range from $\sqrt{s} = 63$ GeV at the ISR to $\sqrt{s} = 630$ GeV at the CERN $\bar{p}p$ collider and to $\sqrt{s} = 1.8$ TeV at the Fermilab Tevatron (chapter 2). Over this energy range the main experimental observations relevant to QCD relate to jet production, high transverse momentum photons and heavy flavour production.

In hadron–hadron collisions most of the cross-section arises from soft processes which at present cannot be reliably calculated but, at sufficiently high energies and in selected kinematic regions, it is possible to isolate events arising from the hard scattering of the hadron constituents. Examples of quark–quark and quark–gluon scattering are shown in figure 14.46. Cross-sections for these parton–parton subprocesses can be reliably calculated in perturbative QCD.

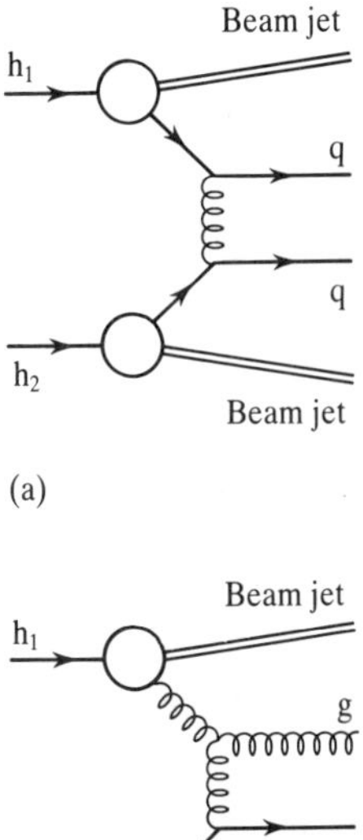

(a)

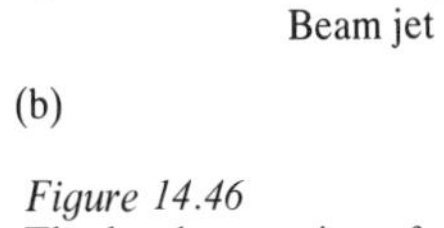

(b)

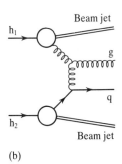

Figure 14.46
The hard scattering of two hadrons, h_1 and h_2, via (a) quark–quark scattering and (b) quark–gluon scattering.

In collider experiments the kinematic variables of the final state particles are measured in the centre-of-mass system of the colliding hadrons. In this reference frame the parton–parton centre-of-mass system will normally be moving (along the z axis, say). It is therefore convenient to use kinematic variables which transform in a simple manner under a Lorentz transformation along the z axis. To this end we introduce the rapidity y, the trasverse momentum p_T and the azimuthal angle ϕ. In terms of these variables the energy–momentum four-vector of a particle can be written

$$(E, p_x, p_y, p_z) = (\sqrt{(p_T^2 + m^2)} \cosh y, p_T \sin \varphi, p_T \cos \varphi, \sqrt{(p_T^2 + m^2)} \sinh y)$$

where m is the particle mass. It follows that the rapidity is defined as

$$y = \tfrac{1}{2} \ln\left(\frac{E + p_z}{E - p_z}\right).$$

Under a Lorentz boost along the z axis to a frame moving with velocity

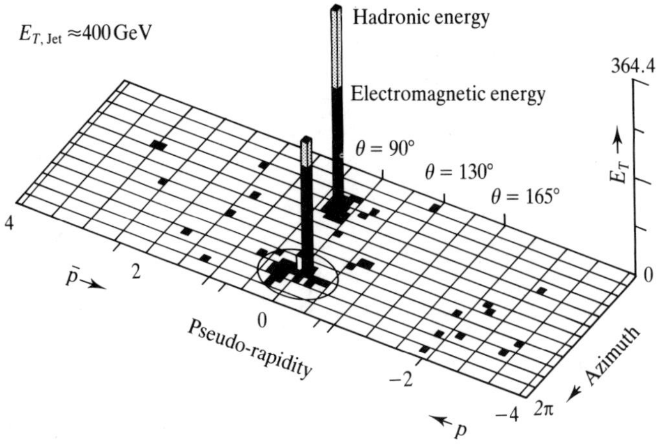

Figure 14.47
Example of a two-jet event obtained by the CDF collaboration.

β it can be readily shown that (example 14.6)

$$y \to y' = y + \tfrac{1}{2}\ln\left(\frac{1-\beta}{1+\beta}\right)$$

so that a rapidity distribution, dN/dy, is invariant. In practice it is more convenient to use the pseudo-rapidity η,

$$\eta = -\ln[\tan(\theta/2)]$$

where θ is the polar angle with respect to the beam direction (the z axis). In the limit $m \to 0$, the two coincide.

The CDF detector at FNAL and the UA1 and UA2 detectors at CERN all employ electromagnetic and hadron calorimeters which are segmented into cells, or towers. The natural variables for tower segmentation in these detectors are φ, the azimuthal angle around the beam, and the pseudo-rapidity. The angular coverage of the towers is such that a typical jet extends over more than one tower. The CDF collaboration defines a jet as a cluster of transverse energy E_T in a cone of radius

$$\Delta R = \sqrt{[(\Delta\eta)^2 + (\Delta\varphi)^2]}.$$

The transverse energy is defined in terms of the energy in the towers in the cone and the angle of the cluster centroid.

$$E = \sum_{i=1}^{N} E_i \qquad P = \sum_{i=1}^{N} P_i$$

$$\sin\theta = P_T/P \qquad \text{and} \qquad E_T = E\sin\theta.$$

The sums run over the towers in the cone which have $E_T > 100$ MeV. An example of a CDF jet event is shown in figure 14.47. The circle round the energy deposition indicates the boundary of the cone.

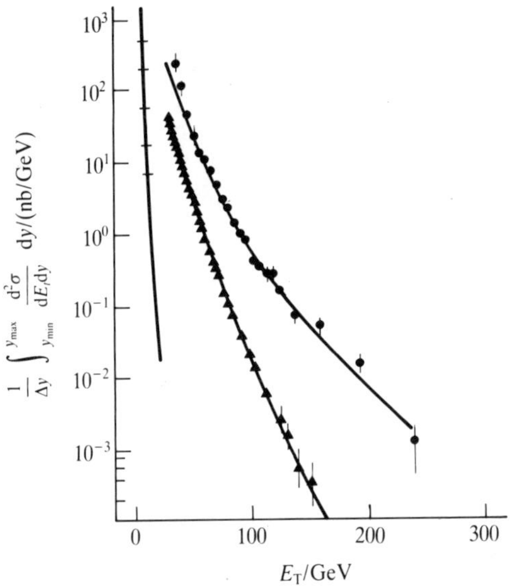

Figure 14.48 Inclusive jet production at large transverse energy E_T measured at the ISR (+, $\sqrt{s} = 63$ GeV), the CERN p̄p collider (▲, $\sqrt{s} = 630$ GeV) and the Fermilab Tevatron (●, $\sqrt{s} = 1800$ GeV). The curves are QCD predictions based on the parton densities due to Duke and Owens. (Atarelli G 1989 *Ann Rev Nucl Part Sci* **39** (367))

Experimental observations are compared with calculations which start with the cross-sections for the basic constituent processes (figure 14.46) evaluated in perturbative QCD using the coupling constant α_s and parton densities, derived from deep inelastic scattering experiments and evolved according to the Altarelli–Parisi equations (section 14.4.3). Figure 14.48 shows data on inclusive jet production taken over a wide range of transverse energy compared with QCD predictions based on the Duke and Owens[96] parametrization of the parton densities; the agreement over the full range of $\sqrt{s}$ is excellent. The angular distribution of di-jet events has been measured at CERN[97,98] (figure 14.49) and has the characteristic cosec^4 $(\theta/2)$ dependence expected from the exchange of a massless vector gluon (cf. Rutherford scattering), consistent with a short-range QCD potential $V(r) \approx 1/r$.

The inclusive production of high p_T direct photons is closely related to high p_T jet production and has the advantage that the energy resolution of electromagnetic calorimeters is generally superior to that of hadron calorimeters. Furthermore, since photons do not fragment, there is no need for a parton → hadron algorithm such as is required to reconstruct a jet. Direct photons are produced in leading order subprocesses by the mechanisms shown in figure 14.50. The production of high p_T photons has been measured in fixed-target experiments, at the ISR and by UA1 and UA2 at the CERN p̄p collider and CDF at the Tevatron. Over the full energy range explored, the data show good agreement with next-to-leading order QCD predictions. Figure 14.51 shows the inclusive

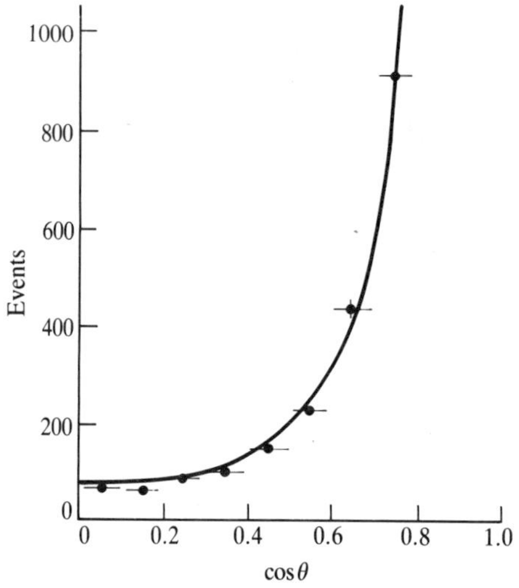

Figure 14.49 The angular distribution of di-jet events, measured by the UA1 collaboration, showing the characteristic Rutherford singularity $(1 - \cos\theta)^{-2}$ expected from the exchange of a massless vector gluon. (After Arnison G *et al.* 1985 *Phys Lett* **158B** (494).).

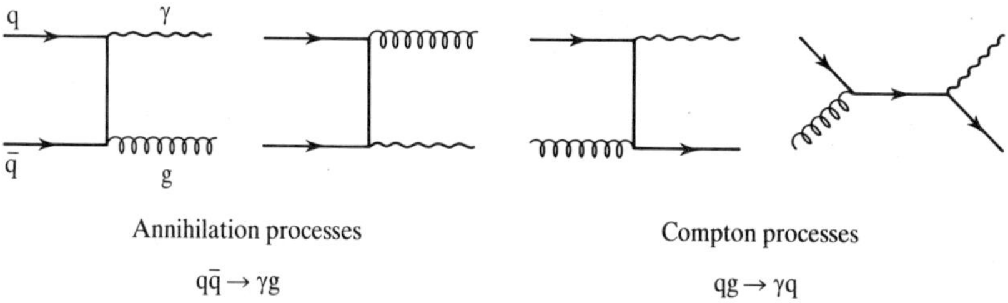

Figure 14.50
Leading order subprocesses giving rise to direct photon production.

cross-section for direct photon production measured by UA1 and UA2[99,100] compared with the QCD prediction of Aurenche *et al.*[101] At relatively low $\sqrt{s}$ and medium p_T^γ the Compton process $qg \to \gamma q$ is dominant and provides an important probe of the gluon structure function of the proton.

The study of heavy flavour production is important not only because it provides non-trivial tests of QCD but also because an understanding of heavy quark production is necessary in top quark and new physics searches: heavy quark production may give rise to a large background to a new physics signal. In the QCD-improved parton model the cross-section for the inclusive production of a heavy quark Q in hadron–hadron collisions is obtained as usual by convoluting the cross-section at the parton level with the parton structure functions. The leading order (α_s^2) processes for heavy flavour production in hadron–hadron collisions are gluon–gluon fusion, $g + g \to Q + \bar{Q}$, and quark–antiquark annihilation, $q + \bar{q} \to Q + \bar{Q}$, for which Feynman diagrams are shown in figure 14.52,

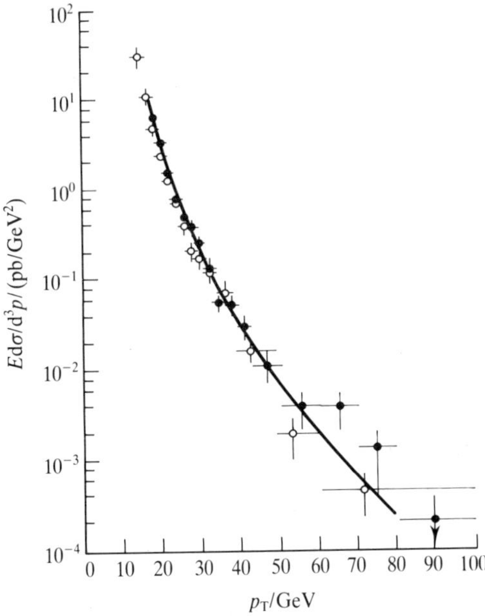

Figure 14.51 Inclusive cross-section for direct photon production in the reaction $\bar{p}p \to \gamma X$, measured by the UA1 (●) and UA2 (○) collaborations at $\sqrt{s} = 630$ GeV, compared with a QCD prediction. (Aurenche P *et al.* 1988 *Nuclear Physics* **B297** (661))

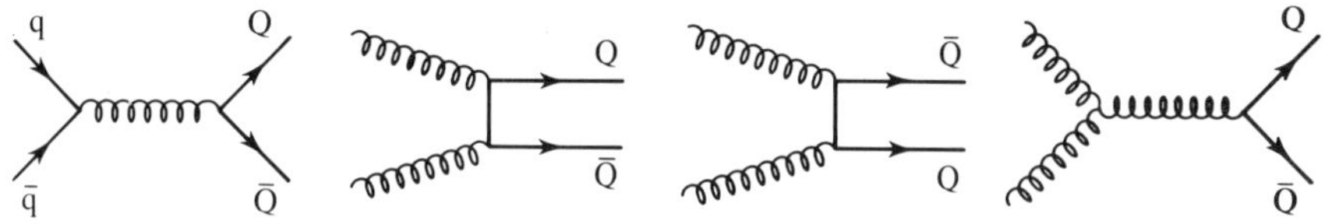

Figure 14.52
Leading order ($O(\alpha_s^2)$) parton subprocesses for the production of heavy quark pairs ($Q\bar{Q}$).

but contributions of order α_s^3 are also important. A complete calculation of all the parton-level cross-sections to order α_s^3 has been given by Nason, Dawson and Ellis.[102] There are uncertainties, however, in the QCD predictions in respect of uncertainties in the parton distribution functions, the Λ parameter, the mass renormalization scale μ and the heavy quark mass m_Q.*

At fixed target energies the yield of b quarks is extremely low but the first explicit observation of a bottom event was made in the WA75 experiment using a 350 GeV/c π^- beam from the CERN SPS. This

* There are different kinds of quark masses – the *current mass* which appears in the Lagrangian, the *constituent mass* derived from analyses of quarkonium states and the *effective mass* which is the current mass extrapolated to the appropriate range of Q^2 under study. Typically, QCD calculations on bottom production consider a mass range $4.5\ \text{GeV}/c^2 < m_b < 5\ \text{GeV}/c^2$.

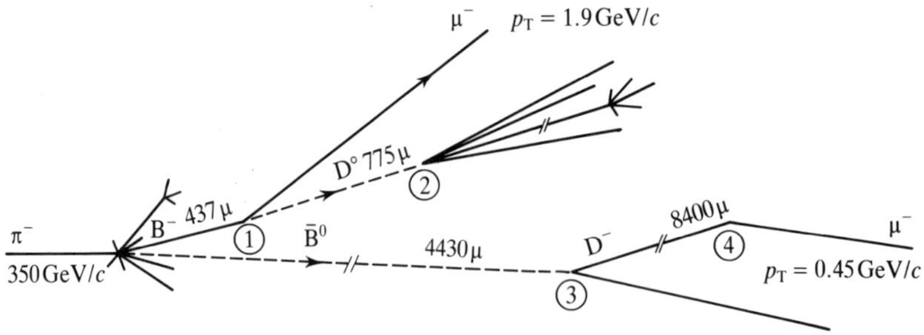

Figure 14.53
Sketch of the bottom event recorded in the emulsion target in the WA75 experiment.

historic event was recorded in the photographic emulsion target used in the experiment and is sketched in figure 14.53.

The higher cross-sections for bottom production at the CERN and Fermilab $\bar{p}p$ colliders permit the study of b production in channels with clear signatures and consequently low backgrounds. High p_T muons have been used by the UA1 collaboration as a tag for heavy flavour jets. However, since high p_T muons arise not only from semi-muonic B decays and the decays $B \to J/\psi \to \mu^+\mu^-$ but also from several other sources, it is imperative to understand the contributions from these other sources in detail if a reliable estimate of the cross-section for b production is to be made. The unwanted sources of high p_T muons include (i) the Drell–Yan mechanism, which gives rise to pairs of isolated muons, (ii) W decays, $W \to \mu\nu$, leading to isolated muons and large missing transverse energy, (iii) decays of J/ψ and Υ states giving pairs of isolated muons, (iv) semi-muonic charm decays, $c \to s\mu\nu$, and (v) background muons from the in-flight decays of π and K mesons.

Figure 14.54 shows the p_T^μ distribution[103] for events containing a muon-associated jet with $E_T > 10$ GeV after applying cuts on the muon–neutrino transverse mass $m_T^{\mu\nu}$ to remove $W \to \mu\nu$ decays. The curve is an absolute prediction from a QCD-based Monte Carlo program and a calculation of the background from in-flight π and K decays. Roughly two-thirds of the muons arise from charm and bottom semi-muonic decays and one-third from π and K decays. Contributions from the Drell–Yan mechanism, W, Z, J/ψ and Υ decays are small. There is reasonable agreement between the measurements and the prediction in the transverse momentum range 10 GeV $< p_T^\mu <$ 50 GeV.

The fraction of muons arising from $b \to \mu$ decays can be measured by exploiting the decay kinematics: the maximum transverse momentum of a muon in the semi-muonic decay of a heavy quark is proportional to the Q value of the decay, which is much greater for b decay than for c decay. To this end the UA1 collaboration used the distribution of muon momenta p_T^{rel}, perpendicular to the axes of their associated jets. The variable p_T^{rel} is defined in figure 14.55 and the measured distribution, together with the predicted shapes for $b \to \mu$, $c \to \mu$ and for the in-flight π and K decays, is shown in figure 14.56. As expected, the spectrum for

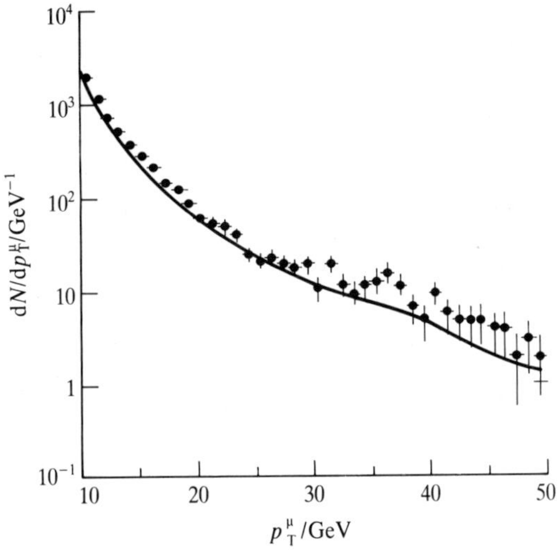

Figure 14.54 Inclusive muon transverse momentum distribution measured by the UA1 collaboration. The curve is an absolute prediction from a QCD-based Monte Carlo program for $b\bar{b} + c\bar{c}$, $J/\psi + \Upsilon$, D–Y, W, Z, $\pi/K \to \mu\nu$. (Ellis N 1990 *Phys Rep* **195** (23))

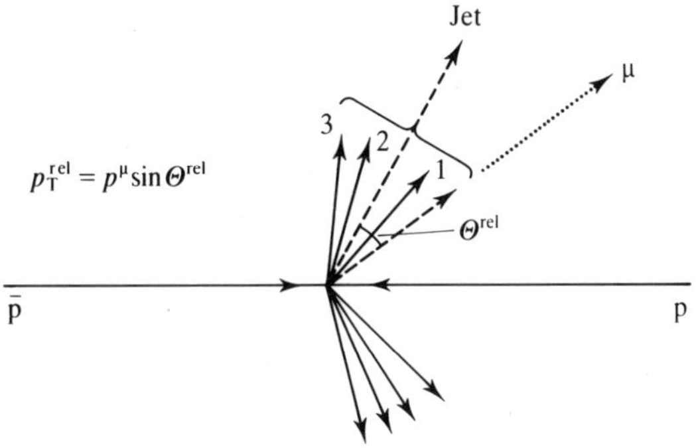

Figure 14.55
Definition of the variable p_T^{rel} used by the UA1 collaboration. (Ellis N 1990 *Phys Rep* **195** (23))

b quark decays extends to higher p_T^{rel} values because of the higher b quark mass. The solid curve in figure 14.56 is the result of fitting the data with a sum of the three distributions. The fraction of muons from b quark decays was determined to be 33 ± 4 per cent. In the UA1 analysis the b quark cross-section is presented integrated above thresholds p_T^{min}. Using a Monte Carlo program the cross-section for $p_T^b > p_T^{min}$ was obtained from the measured cross-section $\sigma_{meas}(p_T^\mu > x)$ using the formula

$$\sigma(p_T^b > p_T^{min}) = \sigma_{meas}(p_T^\mu > x) \cdot \frac{\sigma_{mc}(p_T^b > p_T^{min})}{\sigma_{mc}(p_T^\mu > x)}.$$

The results are shown in figure 14.57. In addition to the measurements from muon-jet events (triangles) a cross-section derived from the measurement of $B \to J/\psi + X$ is shown as a circle. Also shown are the QCD

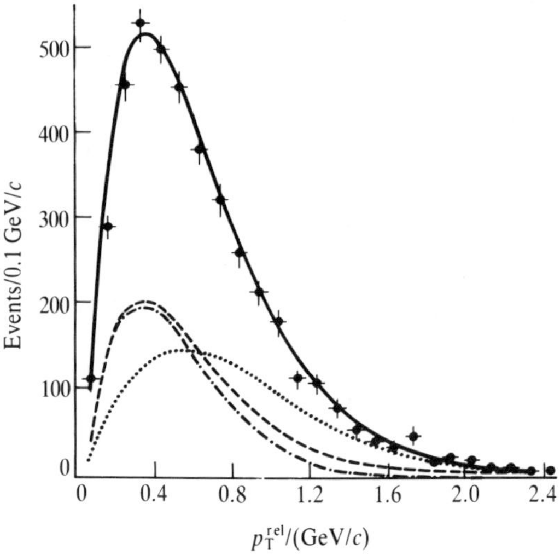

Figure 14.56 Distribution of p_T^{rel} measured by the UA1 collaboration. The curves show Monte Carlo predictions for the different processes and the result of a fit to the data: ———, all processes, ······, $b\bar{b}$; —·—·—, $c\bar{c}$; -----, decay background; $p_T^{\mu} > 10$ GeV/c ($|\eta| < 1.5$); $E_T^{jet} > 10$ GeV. (Ellis N 1990 *Phys. Rep.* **195** (23))

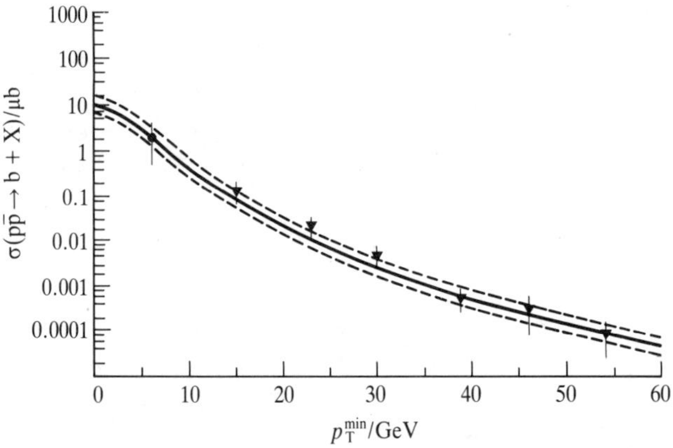

Figure 14.57 Cross-section for b quark production in $p\bar{p}$ collisions in the rapidity range $|y| < 1.5$ as a function of the b quark threshold p_T^{min}. (Ellis N 1990 *Phys Rep* **195** (23))

predictions of Nason, Dawson and Ellis using the parton distributions of reference 104.

Although the results discussed in this section provide important tests of QCD, B physics is still in its infancy and progress will depend on the operation of new colliders (LHC, SSC, see chapter 2). A comprehensive review of heavy quark production has been given by Ellis and Kernan.[105]

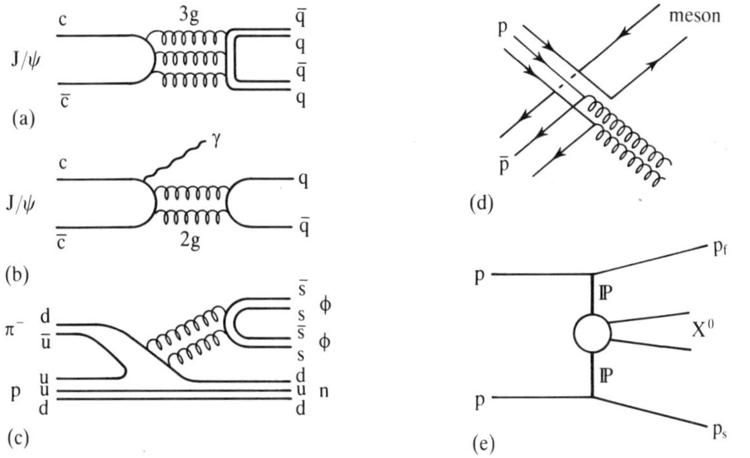

Figure 14.58
Possible mechanisms for the production of glueball states.

14.4.8 Glueballs and other unconventional states

An important consequence of the non-Abelian nature of QCD is the possibility of the existence of particles consisting solely of gluon constituents. Such states are called glueballs or gluonium. Other objects composed of valence quarks, antiquarks and gluons are also expected to exist and are called hybrids. A further possibility is the existence of $q\bar{q}q\bar{q}$ states. To date the positive identification of such states has eluded experimentalists largely because of the complexity of the $q\bar{q}$ meson spectrum in the mass range 1–2 GeV where $q\bar{q}$, gg, $q\bar{q}g$, $q\bar{q}q\bar{q}$ states and radial excitations may overlap in mass and mix. If a state were discovered with quantum numbers which are forbidden for conventional $q\bar{q}$ states, such as $J^{PC} = 1^{-+}$ for example, such a state could be a glueball candidate. Alternatively, if an extra state having the same quantum numbers as an already-filled nonet were discovered, this too could be a glueball candidate.

The search for gluonic states has been performed in experiments which exploit production mechanisms believed to have a high gluon content. Examples are shown in figure 14.58. The hadronic and radiative decays of the J/ψ (figures 14.58(a) and 14.58(b) respectively) can take place via channels rich in gluons and could give rise to glueball states. Certain OZI-forbidden hadronic reactions, which proceed via an intermediate state containing gluons, may produce glueballs in the final state. An example is the reaction $\pi^- p \to \varphi\varphi n$ shown in figure 14.58(c). A further possibility is the production of glueballs in $\bar{p}p$ annihilation via the mechanism shown in 14.58(d). Finally, the central production of states via pomeron–pomeron* scattering (figure 14.58(d)) is considered to be a fruitful area in which to search for glueballs, since the pomeron is thought to be a multi-gluon state.

* A pomeron is a particle with the quantum numbers of the vacuum.

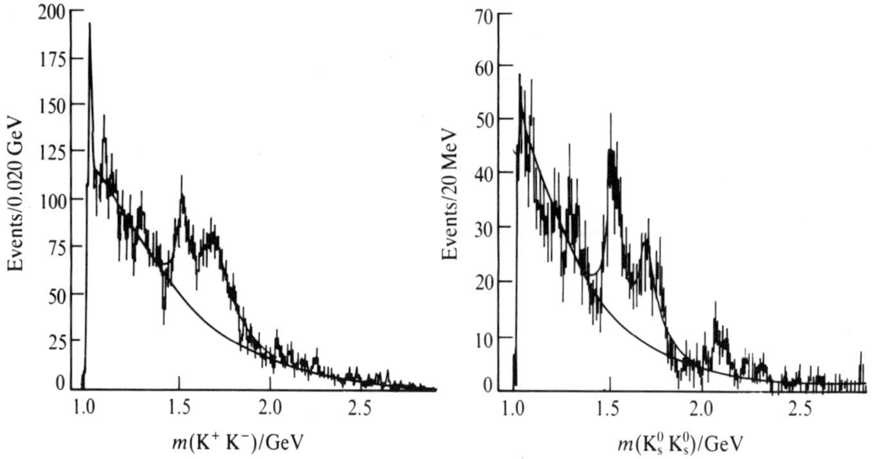

Figure 14.59 Observation of the $f_2'(1525)$ and the $\theta/f_2(1720)$ in the K^+K^- and $K^0_S K^0_S$ mass distributions obtained by the WA76 collaboration in the central production process $pp \to p_f(X^0)p_s$. (After Armstrong T A *et al.* 1989 *Phys Lett* **B227** (186).)

One of the best glueball candidates to date is the $\theta/f_2(1720)$ which has been observed in the radiative decay of the J/ψ to the final states $\eta\eta$,[106] $K\bar{K}$ and $\pi\pi$.[107,108] From an analysis of the K^+K^- and $\eta\eta$ decay modes, the favoured quantum numbers are $J^{PC} = 2^{++}$. A structure in the $\theta/f_2(1720)$ region is also observed in the $K\bar{K}$ system recoiling against the φ and ω mesons in hadronic J/ψ decays.[109] On the other hand there is no clear evidence for $\theta/f_2(1720)$ production in reactions in which, were it a conventional $q\bar{q}$ meson, it should be produced.[110–113] The $\theta/f_2(1720)$ has $I = 0$ and the $I = 0$ sector of the $J^{PC} = 2^{++}$ meson nonet is already filled with the $f_2'(1525)$ and the $f_2(1270)$. This, together with the fact that it is produced apparently only in gluon-rich environments, makes the $\theta/f_2(1720)$ a prime glueball candidate, or possibly a hybrid state.[114,115]

The first clear observation of the production of the $\theta/f_2(1720)$ in hadronic collisions has been reported by the WA76 collaboration,[116] which was designed specifically to search for non-$q\bar{q}$ states in the central region. They observe a strong enhancement in the centrally produced K^+K^- and $K^0_S K^0_S$ systems in pp interactions at incident momenta of 85 and 300 GeV/c, using the Omega spectrometer at the CERN SPS. The $f_2'(1525)$ and the $\theta/f_2(1720)$ are clearly visible in both the K^+K^- and $K^0_2 K^0_2$ mass distributions shown in figure 14.59. By analysing the decay angular distributions of the $f_2'(1525)$ and the $\theta/f_2(1720)$ both resonances were found to have J^{PC} consistent with 2^{++}.

Since the $J^{PC} = 2^{++}$ ground-state nonet is complete and well established, the $\theta/f_2(1720)$ can only be a conventional $q\bar{q}$ meson if it belongs to an excited nonet. The lowest-lying such multiplet is the 2P radially excited nonet for which candidate states already exist, namely the $f_2(1810)$[117,118] and the $f_2(1410)$.[119,120] Godfrey and Isgur[121] have developed a relativistic quarkonium model, including QCD, in which all $q\bar{q}$

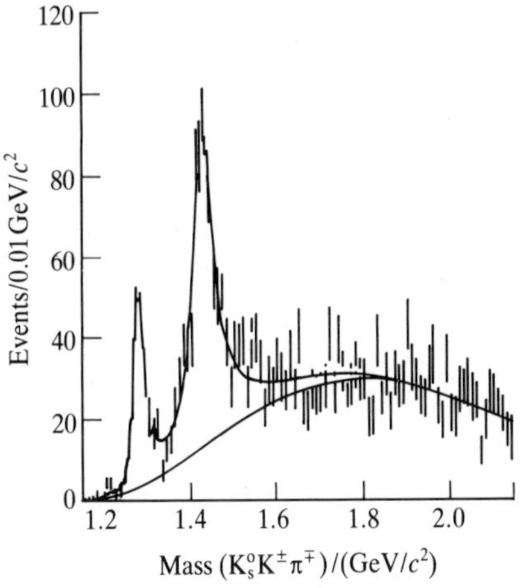

Figure 14.60 Observation of the $f_2(1285)$ and $E/f_1(1420)$ in the $K^0_S K^{\pm}\pi^{\mp}$ mass distribution obtained by the WA76 collaboration in the central production process $pp \rightarrow p_f(X^0)p_s$. (After Armstrong T A *et al.* 1989 *Phys Lett* **B221** (216).)

mesons from pions to upsilons are described in a unified framework. Their model successfully predicts not only the masses of most known meson states but also their decay modes. According to this model the next excited nonet is expected to contain isoscalar ($I = 0$) states with masses greater than 2.0 GeV/c^2.

Despite its dominant $K\bar{K}$ decay mode the $\theta/f_2(1720)$ is not observed in K^-p reactions,[111] nor is it observed in $\gamma\gamma$ collisions where, on the other hand, the $f_2(1270)$ and $f'_2(1525)$ are produced.[112,113] Thus, the fact that the $\theta/f_2(1720)$ is an extra $J^{PC} = 2^{++}$ state which has been observed only in reactions which are believed to be gluon rich, reinforces the possibility that the $\theta/f_2(1720)$ is a gluonic state.

The WA76 collaboration has also made a comparative study of the central production of the $f_1(1285)$ and $E/f_1(1420)$ states in the reaction $pp \rightarrow p_f(X^0)p_s$ (see figure 14.58(e)) in an attempt to clarify the uncertainty surrounding the nature of the $E/f_1(1420)$.

In the $K^0_S K^{\pm}\pi^{\mp}$ channel, clear $f_1(1285)$ and $E/f_1(1420)$ signals are seen (figure 14.60). An analysis of the Dalitz plot of the $K^0_S K^{\pm}\pi^{\mp}$ system has been performed[122] and in the $f_1(1285)$ region the best solution was obtained for a superposition of a $1^{++}(\delta/a_0(980)\pi)$ state plus phase space background, roughly in the proportions 70 per cent and 30 per cent. In the $E/f_1(1420)$ region the fit required only the presence of a $1^{++}(K^*\bar{K})$ state plus phase space background. Thus both states are consistent with having $J^{PC} = 1^{++}$. In other channels such as $\eta\pi\pi$, $\pi^+\pi^-\pi^+\pi^-$ and $\rho^0\gamma$, strong $f_1(1285)$ signals are seen but there is no evidence for $E/f_1(1420)$ production. In the $\eta\pi^+\pi^-$ channel a strong $\delta/a_0(980)$ signal is seen in the $\eta\pi^{\pm}$ mass spectrum after removing $\eta'(975)$ events with a mass cut $m_{\eta\pi^+\pi^-} < 1.1$ GeV. A Dalitz plot analysis of the $\eta\pi^+\pi^-$ system again

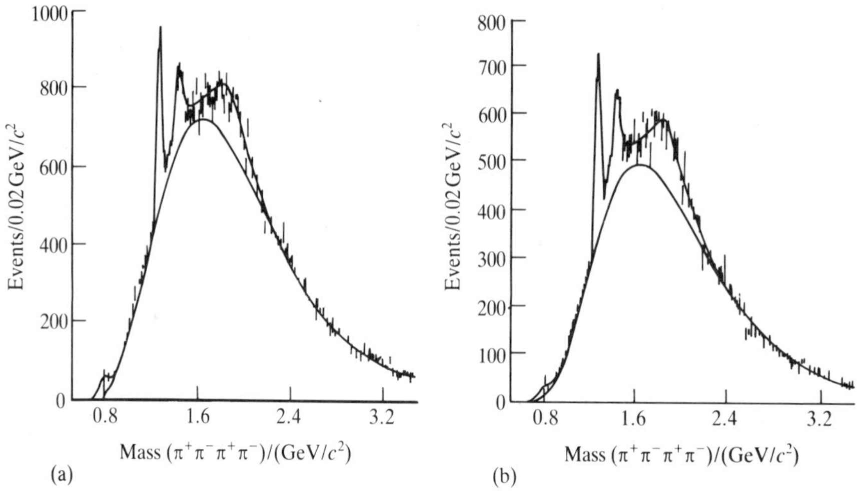

Figure 14.61 Observation by the WA76 collaboration of a possible exotic state at 1.45 GeV/c^2 decaying to $\pi^+\pi^-\pi^+\pi^-$. (a) The total $\pi^+\pi^-\pi^+\pi^-$ effective mass spectrum and (b) the $\pi^+\pi^-\pi^+\pi^-$ mass spectrum for events in which no γ rays were detected in the electromagnetic calorimeter. The curves are fits to the data described in the text. (After Armstrong T A *et al.* 1989 *Phys Lett* **B228** (536).)

requires only the presence of a $1^{++}(\delta/a_0(980)\pi)$ state plus phase space background, confirming the J^{PC} assignment of 1^{++} for the $f_1(1285)$. In this experiment then, the $E/f_1(1420)$ is produced centrally, i.e. via a supposedly rich gluon exchange mechanism, and decays only to $K^*\bar{K}$.

In principle, the $E/f_1(1420)$ can be assigned to the ground state 1^{++} nonet as the $s\bar{s}$ isoscalar member, the other members being the $a_1(1260)$ isotriplet, the $K_1(1270)$ isodoublet and the isosinglet, $f_1(1285)$. However, it is not seen in experiments with incident K^- beams in which $s\bar{s}$ states should preferentially be produced. In contrast, in the reaction[111, 123]

$$K^-p \to K_S^0K^\pm\pi^\mp\Lambda$$

a state is observed with a mass of 1527 ± 5 MeV/c^2 and a width of 106 ± 14 MeV/c^2 – the $f_1(1530)$. A partial-wave analysis shows that this state has $J^{PC} = 1^{++}$ and that it decays to $K^*\bar{K}$. It has been suggested that the $f_1(1530)$ is a better candidate than the $E/f_1(1420)$ for the $s\bar{s}$ member of the 1^{++} nonet. If this is the case then the $E/f_1(1420)$ requires explanation. If the $E/f_1(1420)$ is a conventional $q\bar{q}$ state it would have to be a member of an excited nonet. According to the Godfrey–Isgur model the lowest mass excited 1^{++} state should have a mass of 1820 MeV/c^2. It appears, therefore, that the $E/f_1(1420)$ cannot be explained as a conventional $q\bar{q}$ state. As a 1^{++} state its mass is too low to be a glueball: it has been suggested that it could be a hybrid,[124] a four-quark[125] or a $K^*\bar{K}$ molecule-like state.[126]

In the $\pi^+\pi^-\pi^+\pi^-$ channel the WA76 collaboration has found evidence for a possible new state. Figure 14.61(a) shows the effective mass spectrum

Table 14.4
Resonance parameters determined from the fit to the $\pi^+\pi^-\pi^+\pi^-$ mass spectrum

State	Mass/MeV	Width/MeV
$f_1(1285)$	1281 ± 1	31 ± 5
X(1450)	1449 ± 4	78 ± 18
X(1900)	1901 ± 13	312 ± 61

of the four pions in which there is clear evidence for $f_1(1285)$ production. There is also clear evidence for a structure around 1.45 GeV. A fit was performed on this distribution using three relativistic Breit–Wigner resonances in the 1.28, 1.45 and 1.9 GeV regions together with two histograms generated from real data to simulate the $\eta'(975)$ and $f_1(1285)$ reflections from the $\eta\pi^+\pi^-$ channel. The resulting resonance parameters are given in table 14.4. Figure 14.61(b) shows the 4π mass spectrum for events in which no γ rays were detected in the electromagnetic calorimeter. The $\eta'(975)$ and $f_1(1285)$ reflections are reduced but the peaks at 1.28, 1.45 and 1.9 GeV are enhanced showing that they are not themselves reflectons from a channel involving a π^0. The structure at 1.45 GeV was found[127] to decay to $\rho^0\pi^+\pi^-$ and that at 1.9 GeV equally to $a_2\pi$ and $f_2\pi\pi$. An analysis of the state at 1.45 GeV shows that it is not a 4π decay mode of the $E/f_1(1420)$ nor the $\iota/\eta(1440)$. A spin-parity analysis[127] of the state at 1.45 GeV shows that it is consistent with having $J^{PC} = 2^{++}$ or 1^{-+}, both of which could suggest an exotic nature, the former because the ground state 2^{++} nonet is full and the latter because $J^{PC} = 1^{-+}$ are exotic quantum numbers not allowed for a $q\bar{q}$ state.

REFERENCES 14

1 **Mandl F** 1992 *Quantum Mechanics* Wiley

2 **Vessot R** *et al.* 1966 *IEEE Trans Instrum Meas* **15** (165)

3 **Lautrup B E, Peterman A and de Rafael E** 1972 *Phys Rep* **3** (193)

4 **Lundeen S R and Pipkin F M** 1975 *Phys Rev Lett* **34** (1368)

5 **Andrews D A and Newton G** 1976 *Phys Rev Lett* **37** (1254)

6 **Kinoshita T** 1979 in Homma S *et al.* (eds) *Proceedings of the 19th International Conference on High Energy Physics, Tokyo, 1978* Physical Society of Japan p. 571

7 **Bargmann V, Michel L and Telegdi V L** 1959 *Phys Rev Lett* **2** (435)

8 **Van Dyck R S, Schwinberg P B and Dehmelt H G** 1977 *Phys Rev Lett* **38** (310)

9 **Van Dyck R S, Schwinberg P B and Dehmelt H G** 1987 *Phys Rev Lett* **59** (26)

10 **Dehmelt H G** 1988 *Phys Scripta* **T22** (102)

11 **Bailey J** *et al.* 1979 *Nucl Phys* **B150** (1)

12 **Kinoshita T and Lindquist W B** 1983 *Phys Rev* **D27** (886)

13 **Cvitanovic P and Kinoshita T** 1974 *Phys Rev* **D10** (4007)

14 **Hughes V W** 1988 *Phys Scripta* **T22** (111)

15 **Tsai Y S** 1989 *Phys Rev* **D40** (760)

16 **Braunschweig W** *et al.* 1988 *Z Phys* **C37** (171)

17 **Bartel W** *et al.* 1986 *Z Phys* **C30** (371)

18 **Sirlin A** 1980 *Phys Rev* **D22** (971)

19 **Hasert F J** *et al.* 1973 *Phys Lett* **46B** (121)

20 **Hasert F J** *et al.* 1973 *Phys Lett* **46B** (138)

21 **Hasert F J** *et al.* 1974 *Nucl Phys* **B73** (1)

22 **Bergsma F** *et al.* 1982 *Phys Lett* **117B** (272)

23 **Bergsma F** *et al.* 1984 *Phys Lett* **147B** (481)

24 **Particle Data Group** 1992 'Review of particle properties' *Phys Rev* **D45**

25 **Reines F, Gurr H S and Sobel H W** 1976 *Phys Rev Lett* **37** (315)

26 **Allen R C** *et al.* 1985 *Phys Rev Lett* **55** (2401)

27 **Naroska B** 1986 in Aubert B and Montanet L (eds) *Proceedings of the International Conference on Physics in Collision V, Autun, 1985* Editions Frontières p. 287

28 **Prescott C Y** *et al.* 1978 *Phys Lett* **77B** (347)

29 **Prescott C Y** *et al.* 1979 *Phys Lett* **84B** (524)

30 **Cahn R N and Gilman F J** 1978 *Phys Rev* **D17** (1313)

31 **Argento A** *et al.* 1983 *Phys Lett* **120B** (245)

32 **CDHS collaboration, Abramowicz H** *et al.* 1986 *Phys Rev Lett* **57** (298)

33 **CHARM collaboration, Allaby J V** *et al.* 1986 *Phys Lett* **B177** (446)

34 **Bouchiat M A and Bouchiat C** 1974 *Phys Lett* **B48** (111)

35 **Bouchiat M A and Bouchiat C** 1974 *J Phys (Paris)* **35** (899)

36 **Bouchiat M A and Bouchiat C** 1975 *J Phys (Paris)* **36** (493)

37 **Bouchiat M A** *et al.* 1982 *Phys Lett* **117B** (358)

38 **Bouchiat M A** *et al.* 1983 *Phys Lett* **121B** (456)

39 **Bouchiat M A** *et al.* 1984 *Phys Lett* **134B** (463)

40 **Bucksbaum P H** *et al.* 1981 *Phys Rev Lett* **46** (640)

41 **Bucksbaum P H** *et al.* 1981 *Phys Rev* **D24** (1134)

42 **Drell P S and Commins E D** 1984 *Phys Lett* **53** (968)

43 **Piketty C A** 1984 in Kleinknecht K and Paschos E A (eds) *Proceedings of the 11th International Conference on Neutrino Physics and Astrophysics, Nordkirchen* World Scientific p. 308

44 **Barkov L M and Zolotorev M S** 1979 *Phys Lett* **85B** (308)

45 **Hollister J H** *et al.* 1981 *Phys Rev Lett* **46** (643)

46 **Emmons T P** *et al.* 1983 *Phys Rev Lett* **51** (2089)

47 **Rubbia C, McIntyre P and Cline D** 1977 in Faissner H, Reithler H and Zerwas P (eds) *Proceedings of the International Neutrino Conference, Aachen, 1976* Vieweg p. 683

48 **Timmer J** 1983 in Tran Thanh Van J (ed) *Proceedings of the Moriond Workshop on Antiproton–Proton Physics and the W Discovery* Editions Frontières p. 593

49 **Garvey J** 1987 *Rep Prog Phys* **50** (1311)

50 **Arnison G** *et al.* 1985 *Nuovo Cimento Lett* **44** (1)

51 **Arnison G** *et al.* 1986 *Phys Lett* **166B** (484)

52 **UA2 collaboration, Alitti J** *et al.* 1990 *Phys Lett* **241B** (150)

53 **CDF collaboration, Abe F** *et al.* 1989 *Phys Rev Lett* **63** (720)

54 **CDF collaboration, Abe F** *et al.* 1989 *Phys Rev Lett* **62** (1005)

55 **Mark II collaboration, Abrams G S** *et al.* 1989 *Phys Rev Lett* **63** (2173)

56 **Watkins P M** 1993 *Proceedings of the International Conference on Neutral Currents Twenty Years Later*, Paris, World Scientific

57 **Wolfenstein L** 1983 *Phys Rev Lett* **51** (1945)

58 **Albrecht H** *et al.* 1987 *Phys Lett* **197B** (452)

59 **Albrecht H** *et al.* 1989 *Phys Lett* **219B** (121)

60 **Argus Collaboration, Danilov M V** 1989 *Proccedings of the International Symposium on Lepton and Photon Interactions at High Energies* Stanford p. 139

61 **CLEO collaboration, Kreinick D L** 1989 *Proceedings of the International Symposium on Lepton and Photon Interactions at High Energies* Stanford p. 129

62 **Anjos J C** *et al.* 1988 *Phys Rev Lett* **60** (1239)

63 **Anjos J C** *et al.* 1987 *Phys Lett* **199B** (447)

64 **Albajar C** *et al.* 1987 *Phys Lett* **B186** (247)

65 **Altarelli G and Franzini P** 1988 *Z Phys* **C37** (271)

66 **Costa G** *et al.* 1988 *Nucl Phys* **B297** (244)

67 **Donoghue J F, Holstein B R and Valencia G** 1987 *Int J Mod Phys* **2** (319)

68 **Pais A and Treiman S B** 1975 *Phys Rev* **D12** (2744)

69 **Bean A** *et al.* 1987 *Phys Rev* **D35** (3533)

70 **Maki A** 1989 *Proceedings of the International Symposium on Lepton and Photon Interactions at High Energies* Stanford p. 203

71 **Wormser G** 1993 *Proceedings of the International Conference on Neutral Currents Twenty Years Later*, Paris, World Scientific

72 **UA1 collaboration, Eggert K** 1989 *Proceedings of the International Symposium on Lepton and Photon Interactions at High Energies* Stanford p. 305

73 **CDF collaboration, Abe F** *et al.* 1990 *Phys Rev Lett* **64** (147, 142)

74 **Gross E and Yepes P** 1993 *Int J Mod Phys A* **8** (407)

75 **Duke D W and Roberts R G** 1985 *Phys Rep* **120** (275)

76 **Bardeen W A** *et al.* 1978 *Phys Rev* **D18** (3998)

77 **Gell-Mann M** 1954 *Phys Rev* **95** (1300)

78 **Callan G C** 1970 *Phys Rev* **D2** (1541)

79 **Altarelli G** 1989 *Ann Rev Nucl Part Sci* **39** (357)

80 **D'Agostini G, de Boer W and Grindhammer G** 1989 *Phys Lett* **B229** (160)

81 **OPAL collaboration, Akrawy M Z** *et al.* 1991 *Z Phys C – Particles and Fields* **49** (375)

82 **Benvenuti A C** *et al.* 1989 *Phys Lett* **223B** (490)

83 **Altarelli G and Parisi G** 1977 *Nucl Phys* **B126** (298)

84 **Navikov V A** *et al.* 1978 *Phys Rep* **41C** (1)

85 **Mackenzie B P and Lepage G P** 1981 *Phys Rev Lett* **47** (1244)

86 **Barbieri R, Gatto R, Kögerler R and Kunszt Z** 1975 *Phys Lett* **57B** (455)

87 **Celmaster W** 1979 *Phys Rev* **D19** (1517)

88 **Barbieri R, Catto M, Gatto R and Remiddi E** 1980 *Phys Lett* **95B** (93)

89 **Franzini P** 1989 in Greco M (ed) *Proc Les Rencontres de Physique de la Vallee d'Aoste* Editions Frontières

90 **Kwong M, Mackenzie P, Rosenfeld R and Rosner J L** 1988 *Phys Rev* **D37** (3210)

91 **E605 collaboration, Brown C N** *et al.* 1989 *Phys Rev Lett* **63** (2637)

92 **UA1 collaboration, Albajar C** *et al.* 1989 *Z Phys* **C44** (15)

93 **Altarelli G, Ellis R K, Greci M and Martinelli G** 1984 *Nucl Phys* **B246** (12)

94 **Altarelli G, Ellis R K and Martinelli G** 1985 *Z Phys* **C27** (617)

95 **Altarelli G, Ellis R K and Martinelli G** 1985 *Phys Lett* **151B** (457)

96 **Duke D W and Owens J F** 1984 *Phys Rev* **D30** (49)

97 **UA1 collaboration, Arnison G** *et al.* 1985 *Phys Lett* **158B** (494); **Arnison G** *et al.* 1986 *Phys Lett* **177B** (244)

98 **UA2 collaboration, Bagnaia P** *et al.* 1984 *Phys Lett* **144B** (283)

99 **UA1 collaboration, Albajar C** *et al.* 1988 *Phys Lett* **209B** (385)

100 **UA2 collaboration, Appel J A** *et al.* 1986 *Phys Lett* **176B** (239)

101 **Aurenche P** *et al.* 1984 *Phys Lett* **140B** (87); **Aurenche P** *et al.* 1988 *Nucl Phys* **B297** (661)

102 **Nason P, Dawson S and Ellis R K** 1988 *Nucl Phys* **B305** (607)

103 **UA1 collaboration, Albajar C** *et al.* 1991 *Phys Lett* **B256** (121) and **B262** (497)

104 **Diemoz M, Ferroni F, Longo E and Martinelli G** 1988 *Z Phys* **C39** (21)

105 **Ellis N and Kernan A** 1990 *Phys Rep* **195** (23)

106 **Edwards C** *et al.* 1982 *Phys Rev Lett* **48** (458)

107 **Baltrusaitis R M** *et al.* 1987 *Phys Rev* **D35** (2077)

108 **Augustin J E** *et al.* 1988 *Phys Rev Lett* **60** (2238)

109 **Falvard A** *et al.* 1988 *Phys Rev* **D38** (2706)

110 **Longacre R S** *et al.* 1986 *Phys Lett* **B177** (223)

111 **Aston D** *et al.* 1988 *Nucl Phys* **B301** (525)

112 **Althoff M** *et al.* 1985 *Z Phys* **C29** (189)

113 **Aihara H** *et al.* 1986 *Phys Rev Lett* **57** (404)

114 **Chanowitz M S and Sharpe S R** 1983 *Nucl Phys* **B222** (211)

115 **Barnes T and Close F E** 1983 *Nucl Phys* **B224** (241)

116 **Armstrong T A** *et al.* 1989 *Phys Lett* **B227** (186)

117 **Costa G** *et al.* 1980 *Nucl Phys* **B175** (402)

118 **Cason N M** *et al.* 1982 *Phys Rev Lett* **48** (1316)

119 **Beusch W** *et al.* 1967 *Phys Lett* **25B** (357)

120 **Daum C** *et al.* 1984 *Z Phys* **C23** (339)

121 **Godfrey S and Isgur N 1985** *Phys Rev* **D32** (189)

122 **Armstrong T A** *et al.* 1989 *Phys Lett* **B221** (216)

123 **Gavillet Ph** *et al.* 1982 *Z Phys* **C16** (119)

124 **Ishida S** *et al.* 1989 *Prog Theor Phys* **82** (119)

125 **Caldwell D O** 1987 *Mod Phys Lett* **A2** (771)

126 **Longacre R S** 1990 *Phys Rev.* **D42** (874)

127 **Armstrong T A** *et al.* 1989 *Phys Lett* **B228** (536)

EXAMPLES 14

14.1 The charged and neutral current differential cross-sections for neutrino and antineutrino scattering may be written

$$\frac{d\sigma^{CC}(\nu)}{dy} = \frac{G^2 sQ}{2\pi} \qquad \frac{d\sigma^{CC}(\bar{\nu})}{dy} = \frac{G^2 s}{2\pi}(1-y)^2 Q$$

$$\frac{d\sigma^{NC}(\nu)}{dy} = \frac{G^2 s}{2\pi}[g_L^2 + g_R^2(1-y)^2]Q$$

$$\frac{d\sigma^{NC}(\bar{\nu})}{dy} = \frac{G^2 s}{2\pi}[g_L^2(1-y)^2 + g_R^2]Q$$

where Q is the integral of the quark density distributions of the target nucleus. Assume an isoscalar target with contributions to the scattering from u and d valence quarks only. Using the definitions $g_L = \frac{1}{2}(c_V + c_A)$, $g_R = \frac{1}{2}(c_V - c_A)$ and the vector and axial vector couplings to the Z^0 given in table 13.3 show that the total cross-section ratios are

$$\frac{\sigma^{NC}(\nu)}{\sigma^{CC}(\nu)} = \frac{1}{2} - \sin^2\theta_W + \frac{20}{27}\sin^4\theta_W$$

$$\frac{\sigma^{NC}(\bar{\nu})}{\sigma^{CC}(\bar{\nu})} = \frac{1}{2} - \sin^2\theta_W + \frac{20}{9}\sin^4\theta_W.$$

14.2 The parity-violating interference term in atomic transitions is governed by the product $c_A^e c_V^q$ where c_A^e is the axial vector coupling of the electron, c_V^q the vector coupling of quark q, to the Z^0 boson. Assuming coherent contributions from u and d quarks determine the 'weak charge', $\sum_q c_V^q$, for a nucleus of mass number A $(= Z + N)$ and comment on your result.

14.3 The number of light neutrino species can in principle be determined from the total width of the W. If all fermion masses are neglected the standard model prediction of the partial width for the decay $W \to e\bar{\nu}_e$ is

$$\Gamma(W \to e\bar{\nu}_e) = \frac{G}{\sqrt{2}}\frac{M_W^3}{6\pi} = \Gamma_W^0.$$

The partial widths for hadronic decay modes, assuming three quark colours, is

$$\Gamma(W \to q'\bar{q}) = 3|V_{qq'}|^2\Gamma_W^0$$

where $V_{qq'}$ are the elements of the Kobayashi–Maskawa mixing matrix. If the mass of the W is 80 GeV and the total width is 2.8 GeV estimate the number of light neutrino species. Take $G = 1.2 \times 10^{-5}\ \text{GeV}^{-2}$ and assume universality.

14.4 Determine the eigenvalues and normalized eigenvectors of the mass matrix

$$\begin{pmatrix} M - \dfrac{i\Gamma}{2} & M_{12} - \dfrac{i\Gamma_{12}}{2} \\ M_{12}^* - \dfrac{i\Gamma_{12}^*}{2} & M - \dfrac{i\Gamma}{2} \end{pmatrix}.$$

14.5 A beam of B^0 mesons is prepared at time $t = 0$ and is described by the wavefunction

$$|\psi(0)\rangle = |B^0(0)\rangle = \frac{\sqrt{(1 + |\epsilon|^2)}}{\sqrt{2}(1 + \epsilon)}[|B_1(0)\rangle + |B_2(0)\rangle]$$

where B_1 and B_2 are the normalized eigenvectors of example 14.4. Obtain an expression for the wavefunction at time t in terms of the states $|B^0\rangle$ and $|\bar{B}^0\rangle$ and hence determine the 'non-flip' and 'flip' amplitudes $A(B^0 \to B^0)$ and $A(B^0 \to \bar{B}^0)$.

The ratio of the probabilities, integrated over time, of B^0 becoming $\bar{B}^0$ and B^0 remaining B^0 is

$$r = \frac{\int_0^\infty |A(B^0 \to \bar{B}^0)|^2 \, dt}{\int_0^\infty |A(B^0 \to B^0)|^2 \, dt}.$$

Show that, neglecting CP violation ($\varepsilon = 0$),

$$r = \frac{(\Delta m)^2 + \frac{1}{4}(\Delta\Gamma)^2}{(\Delta m)^2 + 2\Gamma^2 - \frac{1}{4}(\Delta\Gamma)^2}$$

where $\Delta m = M_1 - M_2$ and $\Gamma = \frac{1}{2}(\Gamma_1 + \Gamma_2)$.

14.6 The four-momentum of a particle of mass m may be written

$$(E, p_x, p_y, p_z) = (\sqrt{(p_T^2 + m^2)} \cosh y, p_T \sin\phi, p_T \cos\phi, \sqrt{(p_T^2 + m^2)} \sinh y)$$

where the transverse momentum is given by $p_T^2 = p_x^2 + p_y^2$, ϕ is the azimuthal angle with respect to the z axis and y is the rapidity. Show that

$$y = \tfrac{1}{2} \ln\left(\frac{E + p_z}{E - p_z}\right).$$

Show that under a Lorentz boost along the z axis to a frame moving with velocity β

$$y \to y' = y + \tfrac{1}{2} \ln\left(\frac{1 - \beta}{1 + \beta}\right).$$

15 Beyond the standard model: a brief survey

Grand unification · The SU(5) model · Neutrino masses and oscillations · Grand unification and the Big Bang · Towards a theory of everything?

15.1 Grand unification

In chapter 14 we described an impressive array of experimental tests of the $SU(3)_C \times SU(2)_L \times U(1)_Y$ standard model of the fundamental interactions. To date there is no known discrepancy between the standard model and experiment. Confirmation of the symmetry-breaking mechanism awaits the discovery of the Higgs boson.

The great achievement of the Glashow–Weinberg–Salam model was the 'unification' of the weak and electromagnetic interactions. Strictly speaking, their theory is not a unification in the sense of both couplings arising from a common source. Indeed, the $SU(2) \times U(1)$ gauge group is a product of two disconnected groups of gauge transformations and the coupling strengths g and g' are not related by the theory: their ratio

$$\frac{g'}{g} = \tan\theta_W \tag{15.1}$$

where θ_W is the Weinberg angle, has to be measured experimentally. Only if an appropriate unifying group G can be found such that

$$G \supset SU(2) \times U(1) \tag{15.2}$$

(that is to say SU(2) and U(1) are subgroups of the larger group G) will it be possible to predict the relationship between g and g'. Some of the transformations of the new group G will link the previously disconnected groups SU(2) and U(1) thereby relating the coupling strengths g and g'. In fact they will be related by a Clebsch–Gordan coefficient of G.

The standard model is completed by the inclusion of the SU(3) colour group of gauge transformations which describes the strong interactions. Again, this group is disconnected from the electroweak SU(2) × U(1) groups but it is natural to attempt to unify the strong, weak and electromagnetic interactions by searching for a 'grand unifying' group, G, such that

$$G \supset SU(3) \times SU(2) \times U(1). \tag{15.3}$$

The basic idea of grand unification is that the symmetry is not broken above some mass scale $\mu = M_X$ where the gauge couplings g_i are related to a single gauge coupling g_G, which evolves with increasing Q^2 in accordance with the β function of G. Below M_X the symmetry is spontaneously broken, presumably by a Higgs mechanism, and the couplings g_i evolve separately in accordance with the β functions of their respective groups until eventually they coincide with their measured values at the mass scale $\mu = M_W$. One possible scenario for this evolution of the coupling constants to the grand unification scale M_X is shown in figure 15.1. The gauge couplings g_i (section 13.8) are related to the

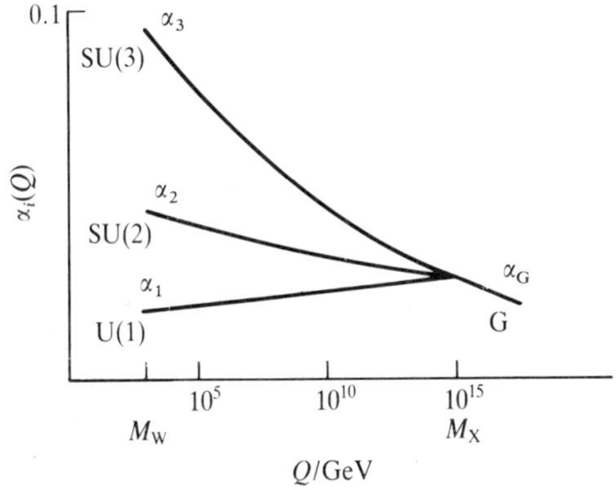

Figure 15.1
Evolution of the gauge couplings $\alpha_i = g_i^2/4\pi$ with Q in a grand unification scheme. Above the grand unification scale, $\mu = M_X \approx 10^{15}$ GeV, all couplings coincide.

couplings of the standard model as follows:

$$\begin{aligned} g_3(Q) &= g_s(Q) \qquad && SU(3) \\ g_2(Q) &= g(Q) && SU(2) \\ g_1(Q) &= Cg'(Q) && U(1) \end{aligned} \tag{15.4}$$

where C is a Clebsch–Gordan coefficient of G and the 'fine-structure constants' are given by $\alpha_i = g_i^2/4\pi$. In order that SU(3) × SU(2) × U(1) be embedded in G it is necessary that G possesses at least four commuting generators corresponding to I_3 and Y of weak isospin and I_3^c and Y^c of the SU(3) colour group. Thus G must have rank 4 at least. The simplest group satisfying this requirement is SU(5), originally proposed by Georgi and Glashow.[1] In SU(5), C has the value $\sqrt{(\frac{5}{3})}$.

We can determine an approximate value for the grand unification scale by evolving the couplings from their known values at the W mass through their respective evolution equations to a common intersection $Q = M_X$. For example, the running of the strong coupling was given in equation (13.181) which we rewrite as

$$\alpha_3(Q) = \frac{\alpha_3(\mu)}{1 + 2b_3\alpha_3(\mu)\ln(Q/\mu)}. \tag{15.5}$$

This expression is valid for correction terms at the one-loop level (see section 13.9.2). Simple rearrangement of (15.5) leads to the result

$$\alpha_3^{-1}(\mu) = \alpha_3^{-1}(Q) + 2b_3 \ln(\mu/Q). \tag{15.6}$$

Equation (15.6) holds generally for SU(3), SU(2) and U(1), thus,

$$\alpha_i^{-1}(\mu) = \alpha_i^{-1}(Q) + 2b_i \ln(\mu/Q). \tag{15.7}$$

The characteristic values of the b coefficients are

$$b_i = \frac{1}{12\pi}(11n_b - 4n_g) \tag{15.8}$$

where n_b is the number of vector bosons and n_g the number of fermion generations which contribute to the one-loop vacuum polarization diagrams. The values of n_b are 0, 2 and 3 for U(1), SU(2) and SU(3) respectively, and the number of fermion generations is 3. In (15.8) we have neglected numerically unimportant Higgs scalar contributions to b_1 and b_2. Further details can be found in the review by Langacker.[2]

The different approaches of $\alpha_i(Q)$ to the unification scale M_X, depicted in figure 15.1, are governed by the values of b_i given in equation (15.8). The experimental values of the couplings at $Q = M_W$ are

$$\alpha_1^{-1}(M_W) \approx \frac{3}{5}\frac{1 - \sin^2\theta_W}{\alpha(M_W)} \approx 59$$

$$\alpha_2^{-1}(M_W) \approx \frac{\sin^2\theta_W}{\alpha(M_W)} \approx 29$$

$$\alpha_3^{-1}(M_W) \approx 8$$

where we have used the values $\sin^2\theta_W = 0.23$ and $\alpha^{-1}(M_W) = 128$. When evolved from the above values at $Q = M_W$ to the unification scale $\mu = M_X$ the couplings converge approximately to the common value $\alpha_G(M_X) = 0.024$ at $M_X \approx 10^{15}$ GeV: the number of fermion generations does not affect this result (see example 15.1).

One immediate consequence of grand unification is that the weak mixing angle θ_W becomes a prediction of the theory rather than a parameter that has to be determined experimentally. For, in terms of g_1 and g_2, equation (15.1) becomes

$$\frac{g_1(Q)}{Cg_2(Q)} = \tan\theta_W \tag{15.9}$$

and since, for $Q = M_X$, $g_1(M_X) = g_2(M_X)$, θ_W is determined by C. In SU(5), $C = \sqrt{(\frac{5}{3})}$, thus the SU(5) prediction for the weak mixing angle at the unification scale is

$$\sin^2\theta_W = \tfrac{3}{8}. \tag{15.10}$$

When evolved to $Q = M_W$ (see example 15.1) the predicted value of $\sin^2\theta_W$ is 0.205, somewhat lower than the measured value[3] of

$$\sin^2\theta_W = 0.2325 \pm 0.0008. \tag{15.11}$$

Although this result makes it unlikely that SU(5) is the correct grand unifying group, it contains so many important and dramatic features that we will use it as an illustrative model.

15.2 The SU(5) model

Many attempts have been made to formulate ‘grand unified theories’ or GUTs. In this section we discuss some of the far-reaching predictions of the simplest model – SU(5).

15.2.1 The SU(5) multiplets

In previous chapters we have learnt that there are three distinct generations of fermions: (ν_e, e; u, d), (ν_μ, μ; c, s) and (ν_τ, τ; t, b). Each generation consists of 15 states. In the first generation, for example, there is the electron e^- with two helicity states and the massless neutrino ν with one helicity only. The u and d quarks come in three colours each with two helicity states. By convention, the left-handed helicity states are grouped together. Thus, in the first generation the states under consideration are

$$(\nu_e, e^-, e^+, u_R, u_G, u_B, \bar{u}_R, \bar{u}_G, \bar{u}_B, d_R, d_G, d_B, \bar{d}_R, \bar{d}_G, \bar{d}_B)_L$$

where the subscript L denotes left-handed helicity states. Note that under a CP transformation $e_L^+ \equiv e_R^-$, $\bar{u}_L \equiv u_R$, etc. These 15 states can be accommodated in the $\bar{\mathbf{5}}$ and $\mathbf{10}$ representations of SU(5) which decompose into ($SU(3)_C$, $SU(2)_L$) multiplets as follows:

$$\begin{aligned}
\bar{\mathbf{5}} &= (\bar{\mathbf{3}}, \mathbf{1}) + (\mathbf{1}, \mathbf{2}) = (\bar{d}_R, \bar{d}_G, \bar{d}_B)_L + (\nu_e, e^-)_L \\
\mathbf{10} &= (\mathbf{3}, \mathbf{2}) + (\bar{\mathbf{3}}, \mathbf{1}) + (\mathbf{1}, \mathbf{1}) \\
&= (u_R, u_G, u_B, d_R, d_G, d_B)_L + (\bar{u}_R, \bar{u}_G, \bar{u}_B)_L + e_L^+ .
\end{aligned}$$

The quintet can be represented as a vector

$$Q = \begin{bmatrix} \bar{d}_R \\ \bar{d}_G \\ \bar{d}_B \\ e^- \\ \nu_e \end{bmatrix}_L . \tag{15.12}$$

The decuplet arises from the antisymmetric part of the product of two fundamental 5-representations (conjugates to the $\bar{5}$-representation)

$$\mathbf{5} \times \mathbf{5} = \mathbf{15} + \mathbf{10}$$

and can be represented as an antisymmetric tensor

$$D = \frac{1}{\sqrt{2}} \begin{bmatrix} 0 & \bar{u}_B & -\bar{u}_G & -u_R & -d_R \\ -\bar{u}_B & 0 & \bar{u}_R & -u_G & -d_G \\ \bar{u}_G & -\bar{u}_R & 0 & -u_B & -d_B \\ u_R & u_G & u_B & 0 & -e^+ \\ d_R & d_G & d_B & e^+ & 0 \end{bmatrix}_L . \tag{15.13}$$

The heavier fermion generations belong to multiplets which are replicas of these.

The gauge bosons belong to the 24-dimensional representation of $\mathbf{5} \times \bar{\mathbf{5}} = \mathbf{1} + \mathbf{24}$. The (SU(3), $SU(2)_L$) decomposition of the $\mathbf{24}$ is

$$\mathbf{24} = \underbrace{(\mathbf{8}, \mathbf{1})}_{\text{gluons}} + \underbrace{(\mathbf{1}, \mathbf{3}) + (\mathbf{1}, \mathbf{1})}_{W^\pm, Z, \gamma} + \underbrace{(\mathbf{3}, \mathbf{2}) + (\bar{\mathbf{3}}, \mathbf{2})}_{X, Y \text{ bosons}} \tag{15.14}$$

In addition to the familiar gluons and W, Z and γ bosons there are now superheavy bosons X and Y which form a weak doublet (and antidoublet) and come in three colours giving a total of 12 in all. The X and Y bosons have electric charges $Q = +\frac{4}{3}$ and $+\frac{1}{3}$ respectively: the antiparticles have the opposite sign of charge.

Thus in SU(5) it is necessary to accommodate each generation of fermions in two multiplets, a $\bar{\mathbf{5}}$ and a **10**. In these multiplets quarks and leptons and quarks and antiquarks appear on the same footing and therefore transitions between them can be induced by the appropriate gauge bosons. The colour octet of gluons induces transitions between coloured quarks, the W bosons couple to weak isospin doublets and the Z^0 and γ to fermion–antifermion pairs, transformations which are all beautifully described by the standard model. The new ingredients in SU(5) are the massive gauge bosons X and Y whose existence leads inevitably to dramatic new and far-reaching consequences. These gauge bosons will induce transitions in which baryon number (B) and/or lepton number (L) are no longer conserved. As a result, proton decay would no longer be forbidden: processes such as $p \to \pi^0 e^+$ ($\Delta B \neq 0$, $\Delta L \neq 0$) would be allowed. Neutrinoless double β decay of nuclei should occur and, provided neutrinos have non-zero mass, $\Delta L \neq 0$ transitions will give rise to neutrino oscillations in which transformations between different neutrino species occur. Furthermore, GUTs predict the existence of magnetic monopoles with masses comparable with M_X.

15.2.2 *Charge quantization*

There are no theoretical constraints in the standard model which demand the quantization of electric charge. Indeed, the electric charge operator is a linear combination of the weak isospin and the weak hypercharge and the latter, being a generator of the Abelian U(1) group, can take on a continuous range of values and can be assigned independently for each representation. The only theoretical constraint is that the charge *difference* between members of a specific doublet is one unit. The charges of the leptons and quarks need not be related by simple factors like 1 or 3. One of the appealing features of the SU(5) model, and others, is that charge quantization occurs naturally, basically because the GUT symmetry fixes the values of I_3 and Y for each member of a multiplet. Since all the fermions of a particular generation appear in the same multiplets of SU(5) their charges are uniquely determined relative to the electron charge.

In general, in any representation of a simple non-Abelian group the generators are traceless. This means that the sum of the eigenvalues of any diagonal generator is zero when taken over all members in a representation. In particular, the electric charge operator is a linear combination of the diagonal generators I_3 and Y, and therefore the sum of the charges of the fermions in any representation must be zero. The fractional charges of the quarks then arise naturally because *the electron is colourless and the quarks come in three colours.* For example, the members of the $\bar{\mathbf{5}}$ are $(\bar{d}_R, \bar{d}_G, \bar{d}_B, e^-, \nu_e)_L$ and therefore the charge of the $\bar{d}$ quark must be $Q_{\bar{d}} = +\frac{1}{3}$ to balance the charge of the electron. The charge of the d quark is then $-\frac{1}{3}$ and because the u_L and d_L quarks form a weak isospin doublet the charge of the u quark is $+\frac{2}{3}$. This charge quantization then guarantees the exact equality between the charges of the electron and proton.

15.2.3 *Magnetic monopoles*

More than 60 years ago Dirac[4] predicted the existence of magnetic monopoles with magnetic charge e_m given by

$$e_m = n\frac{\hbar c}{2e}$$

where n is an integer. In 1974 't Hooft[5] and Polyakov[6] showed that magnetic monopoles occur naturally in GUTs, thus the discovery of such an object would be a triumph for grand unification schemes. The mass of a magnetic monopole is expected to be in excess of the X boson mass ($\approx 2 \times 10^{14}$ GeV) so that there is no possibility of monopole production in accelerator experiments. However, it is possible that magnetic monopoles could be a remnant of the 'big bang' in which it is envisaged that grand unification held until the temperature dropped below the grand unification mass M_X. Experimental searches for magnetic monopoles are therefore important both for cosmology and particle physics.

The techniques most widely used are based either on ionization or superconducting induction devices. Ionization experiments rely on the fact that a magnetic charge will produce much more ionization than an electric charge with the same velocity. In induction devices the passage of a monopole through the coil will produce a sudden change in the magnetic flux linking the coil and hence a sudden change in the current flowing in the coil. In 1982 Cabrera[7] observed such a flux increase in an experiment at Stanford University but most experiments obtain negative results and isolated candidate events need confirmation.

15.2.4 *Proton decay*

The most spectacular prediction of the SU(5) grand unification scheme is that protons, which we have hitherto regarded as stable, should decay via the exchange of virtual superheavy gauge bosons X and Y. Some possible mechanisms for the decays are shown in figure 15.2.

In SU(5) the dominant decay mode of the proton is expected to be

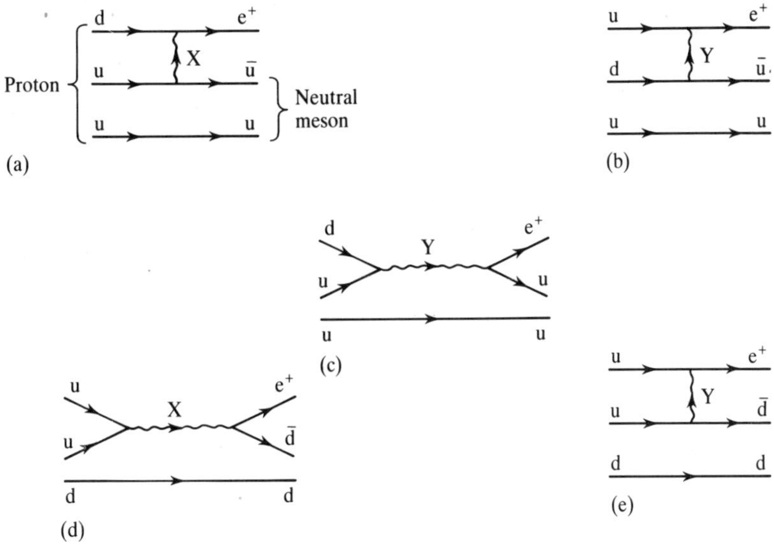

Figure 15.2
Possible mechanisms for proton decay. The quark–antiquark pairs in the final state can combine to produce mesons such as π^0, ρ^0, ω^0, etc.

$p \to e^+\pi^0$. The matrix element for this decay will contain a factor $(q^2 + m_X^2)^{-1}$ for the boson propagator and since the momentum transfer is only of the order of $1\ \text{GeV}^2$, $m_X^2 \gg q^2$ and the decay rate will be proportional to m_X^{-4}. The proton lifetime thus depends crucially on the value of the gauge boson mass. Refined estimates[8] of m_X yield a value of about 2×10^{14} GeV and a proton lifetime

$$\tau_p \approx 2 \times 10^{29 \pm 1.7}\ \text{years}. \tag{15.15}$$

The error includes uncertainties arising from the measured value of $\Lambda_{\overline{MS}}$ and other model-dependent factors. Calculations of branching ratios are very model dependent but typical values for exclusive decay modes are given in table 15.1.

The main experimental difficulty in the detection of proton decay arises from the enormous predicted lifetime and the consequent need to shield the detectors from background cosmic radiation. The huge lifetime necessitates the use of massive detectors which are basically of two types. Purified water Cherenkov detectors viewed by thousands of photomultiplier tubes have been designed to detect the Cherenkov radiation arising from electromagnetic showers generated by the decays $p \to e^+\pi^0$. This is the technique used by the IMB (Irvine–Michigan–Brookhaven) and Kamiokande experiments. The experimental difficulties become apparent when one realizes that a 1000 tonne detector contains some 6×10^{32} nucleons so that for a lifetime of 10^{32} years only six nucleons on average will decay in one year. The other type of detector uses sampling calorimeters consisting of iron plates separated by arrays of track detectors such as streamer chambers, proportional wire chambers or drift chambers.

Table 15.1
Typical branching fractions B for exclusive decay modes of the proton

Decay mode	$e^+\pi^0$	$e^+\rho^0$ and $e^+\omega$	$\bar{\nu}_e\pi^+$	μ^+K^0	$\bar{\nu}_\mu K^+$
Branching fraction, %	40	30	16	3	3

To minimize the cosmic ray background the detectors are located either in deep underground mines, in mountain tunnels such as the Mont Blanc and Fréjus tunnels or in purpose-built underground laboratories such as Baksan in the Caucasus.

The present experimental limit[3] for the favoured decay is

$$\tau/B(p \to e^+\pi^0) > 9 \times 10^{32} \text{ years} \tag{15.16}$$

which rules out SU(5) as the grand unification group even allowing for the generous errors quoted in (15.15). Longer proton lifetimes can be accommodated in GUTs based on larger groups than SU(5) but for lifetimes greater than 10^{33} years the background from reactions such as $\bar{\nu}_e p \to e^+\pi^0 n$, induced by cosmic ray antineutrinos, will overwhelm the signal so that positive evidence for proton decay may be difficult to obtain: a positive signal is crucial for the health of grand unification schemes.

15.3 Neutrino masses and oscillations

In the standard model neutrinos are assumed to be massless and exist in only one helicity state but there is no fundamental reason why this should be so. In some grand unification schemes neutrino masses appear naturally: a positive observation of a non-zero neutrino mass would help discriminate between the various schemes.

The question of neutrino mass has important implications for cosmology. Various astronomical observations indicate that about 90 per cent of the total gravitational mass of the universe consists of invisible or 'dark matter': a component of this dark matter could be massive neutrinos.

Massive neutrinos could also provide a solution to the so-called solar neutrino problem – the discrepancy between the solar neutrino flux expected from calculations based on the standard solar model (SSM) and the experimentally observed flux of solar neutrinos. The source of energy in the Sun is a series of nuclear reactions which convert hydrogen into helium and produce solar neutrinos with a predicted flux of about $10^{11}\ \text{cm}^{-2}\ \text{s}^{-1}$ at the Earth. The main chain of reactions is initiated by the processes

$$p + p \to {}^2\text{H} + e^+ + \nu_e \qquad (E_\nu^{\max} = 0.42 \text{ MeV}) \tag{15.17}$$

and, with considerably less probability,

$$p + e^- + p \rightarrow {}^2H + \nu_e \qquad (E_\nu = 1.44\ \text{MeV}). \tag{15.18}$$

The resulting deuterons are converted to ^{3}He via the reaction

$$p + {}^2H \rightarrow {}^3He + \gamma \tag{15.19}$$

which is followed by

$${}^3He + {}^3He \rightarrow {}^4He + 2p. \tag{15.20}$$

As an alternative to (15.20) the ^{3}He can interact with ^{4}He in the Sun to produce energetic neutrinos ($E_\nu^{max} \approx 14$ MeV) via the chain

$$\begin{aligned} &{}^3He + {}^4He \rightarrow {}^7Be + \gamma: \qquad {}^7Be + p \rightarrow {}^8B + \gamma: \\ &{}^8B \rightarrow {}^8Be^* + e^+ + \nu_e: \qquad {}^8Be^* \rightarrow 2{}^4He. \end{aligned} \tag{15.21}$$

Only about one in a thousand ^{7}Be nuclei undergo this particular process: the rest are converted to ^{7}Li by electron capture,

$${}^7Be + e^- \rightarrow {}^7Li\ (\text{or}\ {}^7Li^*) + \nu_e \qquad (E_\nu = 0.862\ \text{or}\ 0.383\ \text{MeV}) \tag{15.22}$$

followed by

$${}^7Li + p \rightarrow 2{}^4He.$$

In summary, there are three main sources of solar neutrinos:

(a) The so-called p–p neutrinos (equation (15.17)) are the most copious and have a continuous energy spectrum with an endpoint energy of 420 keV.
(b) Reaction (15.22) produces monoenergetic neutrinos with energies of 862 keV (90 per cent) and 383 keV (10 per cent) and an integrated flux about 0.08 times that of the p–p neutrinos.
(c) The ^{8}B decay produces the most energetic neutrinos with an endpoint energy of approximately 14 MeV but the integrated flux is only about 10^{-4} times the p–p neutrino flux and the intensity is less well predicted than for the p–p neutrinos.

There are also contributions to the solar neutrino flux from the p–e–p reaction (15.18) and from ^{13}N, ^{15}O and, to a lesser extent, ^{17}F decays, produced in the carbon–nitrogen–oxygen (CNO) cycle in the Sun. These contributions are much weaker than that from the p–p reaction and much less energetic than that from ^{8}B.

The pioneering chlorine-37 experiment of Davis *et al.*[9,10] has a threshold energy of 0.81 MeV and is therefore sensitive mainly to ^{7}Be and ^{8}B neutrinos. The rate of detection of solar neutrinos through the reaction

$$\nu_e + {}^{37}\text{Cl} \rightarrow {}^{37}\text{Ar} + e^- \tag{15.23}$$

in the period 1970–85 was approximately one-quarter of that predicted by the SSM. More recent data, accumulated in the same detector in 1987–8, gave a value of about one-half of the SSM prediction. This result is supported by measurements made during the same period in the Kamiokande-II experiment,[11] which is sensitive mainly to ^{8}B solar neutrinos. If neutrinos have mass it is possible that oscillations may take place between neutrino species. The ^{37}Cl detector cannot detect muon-type neutrinos and the Kamiokande-II nucleon decay detector is relatively insensitive to low energy ν_μ so that $\nu_e \rightarrow \nu_\mu$ oscillations could account for the deficiencies in detected flux.

The necessary conditions for such neutrino oscillations to occur *in vacuo* are that at least one of the neutrino species should have non-zero mass and that the neutrino masses be not all degenerate. In addition, there must be a non-conservation of the separate lepton numbers so that the different neutrino types, as defined by the weak charged current, are mixtures of the mass eigenstates. The weak interaction eigenstates ν_e, ν_μ and ν_τ are related to the mass eigenstates ν_1, ν_2 and ν_3 by a unitary mixing matrix similar to the KM matrix describing quark mixing:

$$|\nu_\alpha\rangle = \sum_i U_{\alpha i}|\nu_i\rangle \qquad \alpha = e, \mu, \tau; \; i = 1, 2, 3.$$

In the restricted case of mixing between only two neutrino species the mixing matrix reduces to a 2×2 matrix with only one free parameter, the mixing angle between the neutrino species. For example, the mixing between ν_e and ν_μ is given by

$$\begin{pmatrix} \nu_e \\ \nu_\mu \end{pmatrix} = \begin{pmatrix} \cos\theta & \sin\theta \\ -\sin\theta & \cos\theta \end{pmatrix} \begin{pmatrix} \nu_1 \\ \nu_2 \end{pmatrix}. \tag{15.24}$$

This approach to the problem reveals the important features of neutrino oscillations, has the virtue of simplicity and is often the approach adopted by experimentalists.

If we assume neutrinos are stable and propagation takes place through free space, the mass eigenstates $|\nu_1\rangle$ and $|\nu_2\rangle$ develop in space–time like

$$|\nu_l(x, t)\rangle = |\nu_l(0, 0)\rangle \exp[i(p_l x - E_l t)] \qquad l = 1, 2. \tag{15.25}$$

If these states are to be spatially coherent we must have $p_1 = p_2 = p$, say.

Then, for $m_l \ll p$, the energies are, to a good approximation,

$$E_l = (p^2 + m_l^2)^{1/2} \approx p + \frac{m_l^2}{2p} \tag{15.26}$$

and, with $c = 1$ and therefore $x = t$,

$$|v_l(t)\rangle = |v_l(0)\rangle \exp\left(-i\frac{m_l^2 t}{2p}\right). \tag{15.27}$$

Because of the different masses, $|v_1(t)\rangle$ and $|v_2(t)\rangle$ acquire different phase factors as a function of time. If initially at $x = 0$, $t = 0$, we have a pure v_e state, as is the case in the interior of the Sun, then it is a simple matter to show that at time t the state is a mixture of ν_e and ν_μ such that

$$P(\nu_e \to \nu_e) = 1 - \sin^2(2\theta)\sin^2\left(\frac{\Delta m^2 t}{4p}\right) \tag{15.28}$$

and

$$P(\nu_e \to \nu_\mu) = \sin^2(2\theta)\sin^2\left(\frac{\Delta m^2 t}{4p}\right) \tag{15.29}$$

where $\Delta m^2 = m_2^2 - m_1^2$ is the difference in mass squared of the mass eigenstates. Equations (15.28) and (15.29) give, respectively, the probability at time t of finding ν_e or ν_μ in an initially pure ν_e state, and show that the intensities of the weak eigenstates oscillate with an amplitude that depends on the mixing angle and a periodicity that depends on the mass difference Δm^2. The characteristic oscillation length in vacuum is

$$\begin{aligned} L_\nu &= 4\pi p/(m_2^2 - m_1^2) \\ &= 2.48[p(\text{MeV}/c)/\Delta m^2((\text{eV}/c^2)^2)] \text{ metres.} \end{aligned}$$

Experimental tests of the neutrino oscillation hypothesis are essentially of two types. In the first class of experiments, 'disappearance' experiments, the flux of neutrinos of one species ν_l is measured at two distances x_1 and x_2 from the point of production. The ratio of the fluxes at the two positions is

$$R = \frac{P_{ll}(x_1/E)}{P_{ll}(x_2/E)}$$

where $P_{ll} \equiv P(\nu_l \to \nu_l)$. In 'appearance' experiments, neutrinos of a specific species, ν_l, travel a distance x to a detector designed to be sensitive to neutrinos of a different species, ν_k. The flux of appearing neutrinos ν_k, relative to the initial ν_l flux is given by $P_{lk}(x/E)$. Several such experiments have been performed at nuclear reactors and particle accelerators and to date no positive evidence for neutrino oscillations has been found. Experimental results are presented as allowed regions on a plot of Δm^2 versus $\sin^2(2\theta)$; for example, experiments at reactors give a limit $\Delta m^2 < 10^{-1}$ $(\mathrm{eV}/c^2)^2$ provided $\sin^2(2\theta) > 0.1$.

It must be stressed that the above formalism holds for propagation in vacuum. When propagation through matter is considered account must be taken of the phase factors which arise from coherent forward scattering of neutrinos. In the standard model, in which the neutral current interaction is diagonal and symmetric with respect to neutrino species, neutral-current scattering gives rise to an overall phase shift which has no importance in the present context. Charged-current scattering, however, is not the same for all neutrino species and singles out electron-type neutrinos. As a result, resonant amplification of neutrino oscillations can take place and result in an increased probability that an electron-type neutrino, produced for example in the core of the Sun, arrives at the Earth as a muon-type neutrino. This possibility was first pointed out by Mikheyev and Smirnov[12,13] and is referred to as the Mikheyev–Smirnov–Wolfenstein (MSW) effect.[10,14] The effect is energy dependent and it is possible, for example, to obtain suppression of high energy neutrinos from ^{8}B decay and virtually no suppression of low energy p–p and p–e–p neutrinos. Other scenarios exist in which both low and high energy neutrinos are suppressed.

The GALLEX collaboration has recently measured the rate of ^{71}Ge production from ^{71}Ga by solar neutrinos via the inverse β decay process $^{71}\mathrm{Ga}(\nu_e, e^-)^{71}\mathrm{Ge}$ which has a threshold neutrino energy of 0.236 GeV. The target consists of 30.3 tons of gallium in the form of 8.13 molar aqueous gallium chloride solution (101 tons), shielded by about 3300 metres water equivalent of standard rock in the Gran Sasso Underground Laboratory in Italy. After the first year of operation they reported the first observation of solar p–p neutrinos and obtained an average production rate of ^{71}Ge atoms from solar neutrinos of $(81 \pm 17 \pm 9)$ SNU where the quoted errors are statistical and systematic respectively.* When combined with more recent results[15] the average production rate is $87 \pm 14 \pm 7$ SNU. This experiment is sensitive to solar neutrinos of all energies, particularly p–p and p–e–p neutrinos, and the result is consistent with the observation of the full p–p neutrino flux expected from the SSM together with a reduced flux of ^{8}B and ^{7}Be neutrinos as observed in the chlorine-37 and Kamiokande experiments. The results from all three experiments can be described in terms of the MSW effect with a consistent set of values of the mass and mixing angle parameters, summarized in figure 15.3. The

* 1 SNU = 10^{-36} captures per second per target atom.

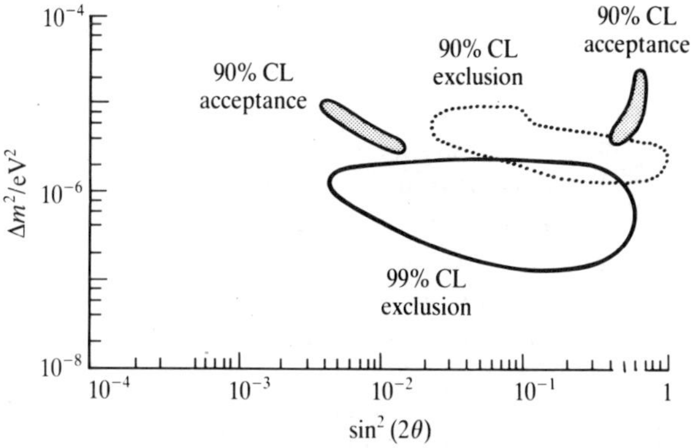

Figure 15.3 Limits on neutrino oscillation parameters. The difference in mass squared of the mass eigenstates is plotted against $\sin^2(2\theta)$, where θ is the mixing angle. In the shaded regions the MSW effect successfully reconciles the chlorine-37 Kamiokande and GALLEX experiments with standard solar models (at the 90 per cent confidence level (CL)). The area inside the dotted line is excluded at the 90 per cent confidence level by the Kamiokande collaboration as a result of a study of day–night effects (Hirata K *et al.* 1991 *Phys Rev Lett* **66** (9)). The area inside the full line is excluded at the 99 per cent confidence level by the GALLEX result.

90 per cent confidence level acceptance regions are shown shaded; at the 99 per cent confidence level the range $2 \times 10^{-7} < \Delta m^2 < 2 \times 10^{-6}(\text{eV}/c^2)^2$ and $6 \times 10^{-3} < \sin^2(2\theta) < 0.6$ is excluded.

At present (1993) the solar neutrino problem is not finally resolved. As we have seen, the GALLEX work, and similar results from a Soviet–American collaboration (SAGE), fall short of the predictions[16] of the SSM (132 ± 7 SNU) and suggest that a mechanism such as the MSW effect must operate. This requires neutrino properties not envisaged by the electroweak theory and not evident in other contexts. The possibility that the SSM does not fully describe conditions in the core of the Sun seems to be ruled out by the observations of Elsworth *et al.*[17] on acoustic waves in the body of the Sun; the frequencies found for the low-order modes which penetrate to the central regions accord well with SSM prediction. The whole question may be clarified when a large heavy-water detector at the Sudbury Neutrino Observatory (SNO) in Canada comes into operation since this will detect not only the flux of electron-type neutrinos but also the total flux of all flavours of neutrino with energy above 2.2 MeV that reach the Earth.

Neutrino oscillation experiments do not measure neutrino masses: they are sensitive to differences of mass squared. Limits on neutrino masses have been obtained in experiments which are sensitive to the kinematics of appropriate decay processes. For example, the detailed shape and endpoint energy of the electron energy spectrum in nuclear β decay is sensitive to the mass of the electron antineutrino, $\bar{\nu}_e$. Greatest sensitivity is achieved if the endpoint energy E_0 is small. The most suitable decay, and one which has been investigated by several groups,[18–23] is tritium decay,

$$^3\mathrm{H} \to {}^3\mathrm{He} + \mathrm{e}^- + \bar{\nu}_\mathrm{e}$$

which has an endpoint energy of 18.6 keV and a half-life of 12.3 years. The current best results[3] are consistent with $m_{\bar{\nu}_e} = 0$ with an upper limit of the order of 7 eV at the 90 per cent confidence level.

A comparable upper limit on the neutrino mass $m_{\bar{\nu}_e}$ was obtained from the observation, in February 1987, of the characteristics of the burst of neutrinos associated with the spectacular collapse of the blue giant star, Sanduleak-69 202, with $M \approx 20 \pm 5\, M_\odot$, which led to the brightest supernova, known as SN 1987a, since Tycho's supernova of 1604. It was a slice of good fortune that scattered around the world were the detectors dedicated to the observation of proton decay. In particular the IMB[24] and Kamiokande[25] experiments observed coincident bursts of neutrinos, lasting for about 10 s, which were well above the normal backgrounds in the detectors, and unambiguously associated with SN 1987a. The neutrino energy distributions were consistent with a thermal spectrum of temperature $T \approx 4$–5 MeV and the pulse length (≈ 10 s) was as expected in conventional models of stellar collapse in which the central core of the star reaches sufficiently high densities that the neutrinos are trapped and diffuse to the surface on this timescale. It is interesting to note that while the neutrinos are emitted essentially directly from the core, electromagnetic radiation has to diffuse out through the supernova atmosphere with the result that the first optical observation of the supernova was some hours after the observation of the neutrino pulse. Massless neutrinos travel with the speed of light so that a burst of such neutrinos would travel through space without dispersion. Massive neutrinos on the other hand would result in a pulse lengthening. The difference δt in time of flight for two neutrinos emitted from the supernova with different energies but the same mass is given by

$$\delta t \approx L\delta v \approx L\delta\gamma/\gamma^3 \approx L(m/E)^3 \delta E/m$$

where L is the distance to the supernova, approximately 17×10^4 light years. The absence of any indication of neutrino pulse lengthening resulted in the conservative upper limit*

$$m_{\bar{\nu}_e} < 25 \text{ eV}.$$

The limits on muon-type and tau-type neutrino masses are obtained in a similar fashion to the limits on the mass of electron-type neutrinos

* Since the cross-section $\sigma(\bar{\nu}_e p \to e^+ n)$ is larger than other neutrino cross-sections at low energies it is believed that most of the events observed were induced by electron-type antineutrinos.

from tritium decay. The limit on m_{ν_μ} has been obtained from a study[26] of the muon spectrum in the decay $\pi \to \mu + \nu_\mu$ and that on m_{ν_τ} from a study[27] of the pion spectrum in the decay $\tau \to 5\pi + \nu_\tau$. In summary the current limits on neutrino masses are[3]

$$m_{\nu_e} < 7.3 \text{ eV} \qquad m_{\nu_\mu} < 270 \text{ keV} \qquad m_{\nu_\tau} < 35 \text{ MeV}.$$

Finally, searches for neutrinoless double β decay, although extremely difficult, are important experiments which may help ascertain the exact nature of neutrinos. Double β decay is energetically allowed in only a few nuclei such as, for example,

$$^{76}_{32}\text{Ge} \to {}^{76}_{34}\text{Se} + 2\text{e}^-.$$

Such processes violate total lepton number conservation and are forbidden if neutrinos are Dirac particles. They can proceed if the neutrino and its antiparticle are identical (Majorana neutrinos) and have non-zero mass. Simplistically, one can imagine these decays proceeding via the emission and reabsorption of a neutrino,

$$\text{n} \to \text{p} + \text{e}^- + \bar{\nu}_e$$

$$\text{n} + \nu_e \to \text{p} + \text{e}^-$$

with the net result

$$\text{n} + \text{n} \to \text{p} + \text{p} + \text{e}^- + \text{e}^-.$$

These reactions have been written as though neutrinos are Dirac particles and the weak interaction has the familiar V–A structure. Evidently the reaction can proceed only if the neutrino and its antiparticle are identical, lepton number conservation is violated and the weak interactions have a right-handed component.

The observation of neutrinoless β decay, with the full decay energy carried by the electrons, would establish that the electron neutrino is a Majorana particle. To date, neutrinoless double β decay has not been observed. Recent experiments have placed lower limits on the half-lives of such decays, for example $t_{1/2} > 1.1 \times 10^{24}$ years for ^{76}Ge. A recent review of the field has been given by Caldwell.[28] Limits on neutrino mass from double β decay searches are dependent on how the nuclear matrix element is calculated and recent estimates give upper limits to a Majorana neutrino mass in the range 0.5–5 eV (for $t_{1/2} = 10^{24}$ years).

15.4 Grand unification and the big bang

The long-standing cosmological problem of the asymmetry which exists in the universe between matter and antimatter can be understood in terms of the hot big bang model of the origin of the universe and its evolution and the grand unification of the interactions of particle physics. The big bang hypothesis, firmly based on Hubble's discovery of the expansion of the universe, the discovery in 1965 by Penzias and Wilson of the 3 K cosmic background radiation and the abundances of light nuclei, is now the standard model of the origin of the universe.

If the universe were created in a state with the quantum numbers of the vacuum the number of fermions would equal the number of antifermions and naively one might expect this symmetry between matter and antimatter to persist as the universe expands and cools. Our very existence and the stability of the world around us is ample evidence of a local asymmetry between matter and antimatter. No plausible mechanism which might lead to a large-scale separation of matter and antimatter has yet been formulated. Although antiprotons have been observed in cosmic ray studies their flux relative to the proton flux is so small that their presence can be attributed to interactions of primary cosmic rays of the matter variety: there is no need to postulate the existence of a source of antimatter. If some distant galaxy indeed consisted of antimatter there would be intense gamma radiation arising from collisons with intergalactic matter. No such radiation has been observed. It is therefore generally believed that the matter–antimatter asymmetry is not just local but universal.

The average density of matter in the universe is estimated to be

$$\rho_{\mathrm{m}} \approx 10^{-31}\ \mathrm{g\,cm^{-3}}. \tag{15.30}$$

This corresponds to a baryon number density

$$n_{\mathrm{B}} \approx 10^{-7}\ \mathrm{cm^{-3}} \tag{15.31}$$

which is considerably less than the density of photons ($\approx 400\ \mathrm{cm^{-3}}$) in the 3 K background radiation. Thus, at the present time the number density ratio of baryons to photons is

$$\frac{n_{\mathrm{B}}}{n_{\gamma}} \approx 10^{-9\pm 1}. \tag{15.32}$$

In a universe which expands isotropically and adiabatically this ratio should be independent of the time.

In the early universe ($t \lesssim 10^{-6}$ s) when the temperature was greater than the nucleon mass (1 GeV $\equiv 10^{13}$ K) radiation and matter would be in thermal equilibrium through the processes of baryon–antibaryon pair creation and annihilation and the number densities of baryons and photons would be comparable. When the universe expanded and cooled below the threshold for pair creation the annihilation process would continue and cause the baryon number density to fall dramatically, with the result that, at the present time, from an initially matter–antimatter symmetric universe, the ratio of baryons to photons would be

$$\frac{n_B}{n_\gamma} \approx 10^{-20}$$

many orders of magnitude less than the observed ratio (equation (15.32)). It therefore appears that there must have been a matter–antimatter asymmetry at temperatures approximately greater than or equal to 1 GeV.

The presently observed ratio (15.32) implies a primordial quark–antiquark asymmetry

$$\frac{n_B}{n_\gamma} \approx \frac{n_q - n_{\bar{q}}}{n_q + n_{\bar{q}}} \approx 10^{-9}.$$

In a pioneering paper in 1967 Sakharov[29] enunciated the general requirements for the generation of a baryon asymmetry. Clearly, there must be interactions which violate baryon number conservation in order to change an initial state with the quantum numbers of the vacuum ($B = 0$) into one in which $B \neq 0$. Additionally, these B-violating interactions must also violate charge conjugation invariance because if they were C conserving the C transformation, which interchanges quark and antiquark, would leave $n_q = n_{\bar{q}}$. The interactions must also violate CP because a parity transformation leaves n_q and $n_{\bar{q}}$ unchanged so that a combined CP operation, if exact, would leave $n_q = n_{\bar{q}}$. The final requirement is that there be a departure from thermal equilibrium at some early stage in the evolution of the universe. The reason for this is that in an equilibrium state we lose sense of the direction of time (the interactions are time-reversal invariant) and therefore, through the CPT theorem, the interactions are CP invariant and leave $n_q = n_{\bar{q}}$.

GUTs satisfy these requirements although the SU(5) model, outlined in section 15.2, cannot produce an asymmetry large enough to generate the ratio (15.32). Larger groups with more free parameters and hence less predictive power are required. Nevertheless, let us speculatively extrapolate back in time towards the initial singularity to an epoch at $t \lesssim 10^{-36}$ s when $kT \approx 10^{16}$ GeV, i.e. beyond the grand unification mass M_X, when matter consisted mainly of quarks and leptons in thermal equilibrium with the superheavy bosons, the vector bosons X or the Higgs boson H_X. In this equilibrium period the abundances of X and $\bar{X}$, q and $\bar{q}$, etc. are equal. The dominant decays in simple models such as SU(5) are

$$\left.\begin{matrix} H_X \\ X \end{matrix}\right\} \rightarrow \bar{q} + \bar{l} \text{ and } q + q.$$

Provided that C and CP are violated and provided also that the processes are slow enough relative to the expansion rate of the universe at that time to allow non-equilibrium effects to build up, the universe, as it cools through the transition temperature, can acquire an excess of baryons over antibaryons. The CPT theorem guarantees that the decay rates of the heavy bosons and their antiparticles are identical:

$$\Gamma_{tot}(\mathrm{X}) = \Gamma(\mathrm{X} \to \bar{\mathrm{q}}\bar{\mathrm{l}}) + \Gamma(\mathrm{X} \to \mathrm{qq}) = \Gamma_{tot}(\bar{\mathrm{X}}) = \Gamma(\bar{\mathrm{X}} \to \mathrm{ql}) + \Gamma(\bar{\mathrm{X}} \to \bar{\mathrm{q}}\bar{\mathrm{q}}).$$

When the universe expanded and cooled below the grand unification mass, i.e. when the reverse reactions maintaining the abundances of X and $\bar{\mathrm{X}}$ were not sustainable, a baryon-antibaryon asymmetry could occur, leading to a 'freeze-out' of baryon number. This would happen if, through C and CP violation, the partial decay rates of X and $\bar{\mathrm{X}}$ are not equal, i.e. if, for example,

$$\mathrm{B} \equiv \frac{\Gamma(\mathrm{X} \to \mathrm{qq})}{\Gamma_{tot}(\mathrm{X})} \neq \bar{\mathrm{B}} \equiv \frac{\Gamma(\bar{\mathrm{X}} \to \bar{\mathrm{q}}\bar{\mathrm{q}})}{\Gamma_{tot}(\bar{\mathrm{X}})}.$$

Detailed calculations show that several grand unification schemes lead to an asymmetry of the order of 10^{-9} and hence to the present ratio of $n_{\mathrm{B}}/n_{\gamma}$. After this phase transition the superheavy bosons no longer participated in the evolution of the universe. A similar fate was to befall the W and Z bosons when the universe expanded and cooled through the 'Weinberg–Salam' transition at $kT \approx 100$ GeV.

The next important event in the evolution of the universe was the 'freeze-out' of electron neutrinos, an event of crucial importance since it determines the neutron–proton ratio which in turn determines the abundance of light elements, particularly ^{4}He, in the universe. At time $t \approx 10^{-2}$ s after the big bang, the matter in the universe consisted of neutrons, protons, electrons, positrons, electron-type neutrinos and antineutrinos. At this epoch the density of matter in the universe was sufficiently high that even the neutrinos were trapped within the characteristic size of the universe. In such a cosmic fluid the light particles would predominate: there would be about one proton or neutron for every 10^9 photons, electrons or neutrinos. The fluid would be driven to thermal equilibrium by the weak interactions

$$\begin{aligned} &\nu_e + \mathrm{n} \rightleftarrows \mathrm{e}^- + \mathrm{p} \\ &\bar{\nu}_e + \mathrm{p} \rightleftarrows \mathrm{e}^+ + \mathrm{n} \end{aligned} \qquad (15.33)$$

which would occur so rapidly that there would be roughly equal numbers of neutrons and protons. At equilibrium the neutron–proton ratio is given by the Boltzmann law

$$\frac{n}{p} = \exp\left(-\frac{\Delta mc^2}{kT}\right)$$

where Δm is the neutron–proton mass difference and $T \approx 10^{11}$ K at this epoch. As the universe expanded and cooled further the n/p ratio steadily dropped until, at $t \approx 1$ s, the rate of the reactions (15.33) became small compared with the expansion rate at this time and the equilibrium could not be maintained: the neutrinos decoupled from the nucleons, electron–positron annihilation began to dominate and the neutron–proton ratio was frozen at about 15 per cent. Some 13 s later the temperature of the universe had dropped sufficiently that e^+e^- pairs could no longer be created and light nuclei, deuterium and helium began to form. When the photon energy dropped further still, so that photodisintegration of the newly formed nuclei could no longer occur, the abundances of ^{4}He became frozen at ^{4}He/p $\approx$ 25 per cent. At this stage, $t \approx 35$ minutes, the temperature was still too high for neutral atoms to be formed: this only happened some 10^5 years later. With electrons locked in neutral atoms the universe became transparent to the electromagnetic radiation which continued to cool with the expansion of the universe to the present temperature (2.7 K) of the background radiation.

Detailed calculations, although fraught with difficulty, yield a value for the primordial ^{4}He abundance of 24 ± 2 per cent in good agreement with the observed abundance. This primordial ^{4}He abundance depends sensitively on the rate of cooling of the universe just prior to the epoch of nucleosynthesis and this in turn depends on the number of fundamental fermion species produced earlier, with each additional neutrino species contributing about 1 per cent to the helium mass fraction. The observed helium abundance constrains the number of light neutrino species to be less than four. This observation was strikingly confirmed by recent measurements of the width of the Z^0 at LEP which limit the number of light neutrino species to three.

The important events in the evolution of the universe since the big bang are summarized in figure 15.4.

15.5 Towards a theory of everything?

Although it seems inevitable that the strong, electromagnetic and weak interactions are unified at some extremely high energy, there are some features of GUTs which are unsatisfactory. Perhaps the most unsatisfactory feature is that gravity is not included in the unification schemes. The main difficulty in developing a theory which unifies gravity with the

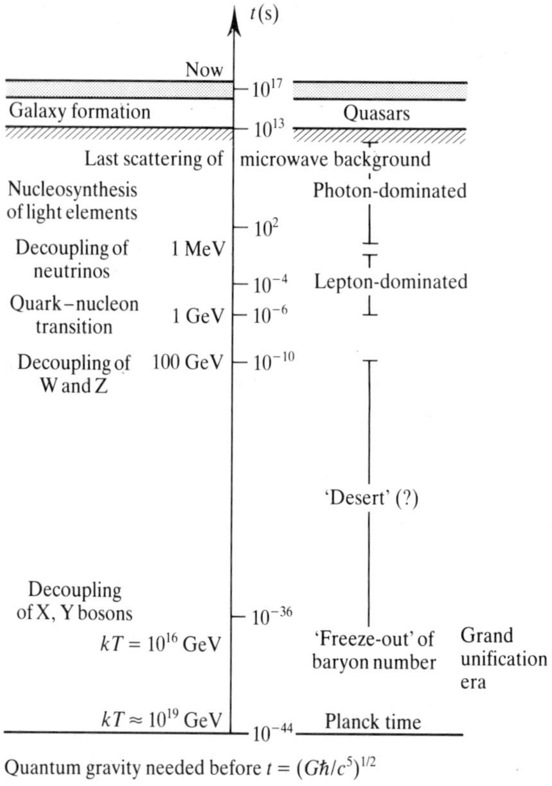

Figure 15.4
The main stages in the evolution of the universe from the Planck time ($\approx 10^{-44}$ s) to the present.

other forces is that general relativity, although a gauge theory, does not incorporate quantum effects, while the standard model of elementary particle physics depends on quantum mechanics in an essential way.

Another problem, which at first sight is unrelated to attempts to find a 'theory of everything' (TOE), is the so-called hierarchy problem which concerns the enormous difference between the unification scales of the electromagnetic and weak interactions ($M_W \approx 10^2$ GeV) and the grand unification scale ($M_X \approx 10^{15}$ GeV). Presumably, a Higgs mechanism analogous to that associated with electroweak symmetry breaking is also responsible for the GUT symmetry breaking. It is expected that these Higgs bosons, H_W and H_X, have masses of the order of M_W and M_X respectively. It is conceivable that the parameters of the scalar potential could be 'fine-tuned' to give this hierarchy but not in a 'natural' way. One of the problems encountered in this approach concerns the mass of the light Higgs boson. There will be contributions to the Higgs mass from radiative corrections involving gauge boson, scalar boson and fermion loops. To obtain a well-defined Higgs boson mass, $M_H \approx M_W$, requires fine tuning of the parameters of the theory so that cancellations at a precision of $(M_W/M_X)^2 \approx 10^{-26}$ take place in each order of perturbation theory. This 'naturalness' problem can be solved by introducing a

Table 15.2
Spectrum of SUSY particles

Particle	Spin	Sparticle	Spin
Quark q	$\frac{1}{2}$	Squark $\tilde{q}$	0
Lepton l	$\frac{1}{2}$	Slepton $\tilde{l}$	0
Neutrino ν	$\frac{1}{2}$	Sneutrino $\tilde{\nu}$	0
Photon γ	1	Photino $\tilde{\gamma}$	$\frac{1}{2}$
Gluon g	1	Gluino $\tilde{g}$	$\frac{1}{2}$
W boson	1	Wino $\tilde{W}$	$\frac{1}{2}$
Z boson	1	Zino $\tilde{Z}$	$\frac{1}{2}$
Higgs boson H	0	Shiggs $\tilde{H}$	$\frac{1}{2}$

symmetry between bosons and fermions known as supersymmetry or SUSY. Each point-like particle is postulated to have a SUSY partner, known as a 'sparticle', with a spin which differs from that of the particle by half a unit. If the fermion–boson pairs have identical couplings their contributions to the radiative corrections have opposite sign and exactly cancel. Divergences in the mass renormalization problem are controlled, or, to put it another way, the naturalness (fine-tuning) problem is solved, provided that the masses of the fermion–boson pairs satisfy the condition $|m_B^2 - m_F^2| \lesssim 1\ \text{TeV}^2$.

If the above ideas are correct there should be a doubling of the spectrum of known particles. These, together with their supersymmetric partners, are shown in table 15.2. With the exception of spin, the supersymmetric particles have the same quantum numbers as their normal partners. For example, like the gluon, the gluino is a colour octet, flavour singlet with $C = -1$. The selectron, like the electron, carries a conserved electron number. In supersymmetric theories particles are assigned a new *multiplicative* quantum number known as R-parity. All ordinary particles have an R-parity of $+1$ while the supersymmetric partners have $R = -1$. Formally, the R-parity of any particle (sparticle) with spin j, baryon number B and lepton number L is defined as

$$R = (-1)^{2j+3B+L}. \qquad (15.34)$$

R-parity is not necessarily conserved but is *imposed* as a discrete symmetry with the consequence that SUSY particles are always produced in pairs. Furthermore, the lightest supersymmetric particle must be stable because, through R-conservation, it cannot decay into ordinary particles. It is generally assumed that the photino ($\tilde{\gamma}$) is the lightest SUSY particle. If, on the other hand, the scalar neutrino (or sneutrino) were the lightest SUSY particle the photino would decay, $\tilde{\gamma} \to \nu\tilde{\nu}$.

Several experimental searches for supersymmetric particles have been made in the last decade or so but to date there is no evidence for such particles. The charged scalar leptons, for example, interact electromagnetically and should be produced in pairs in e^+e^- annihilations.

Recent searches for sleptons produced in the reactions

$$\begin{array}{l} e^+e^- \to Z^0 \to \tilde{l}^+\tilde{l}^- \\ \qquad\qquad\qquad \lfloor \to l^-\tilde{\gamma} \\ \qquad\qquad\quad \lfloor \to l^+\tilde{\gamma} \end{array} \tag{15.35}$$

have been performed at LEP. (Note that the photino is a neutral Majorana fermion so that $\tilde{\bar{\gamma}} \equiv \tilde{\gamma}$.) If photinos are light the sleptons will decay very rapidly, with approximately 100 per cent branching ratio, into an ordinary lepton and a photino. Since they interact extremely weakly the photinos will escape detection and give a very characteristic signature for the processes (15.35): the sleptons could have masses of about 1 TeV so the final state will contain an unlike-sign lepton pair with a large momentum imbalance. Searches of this kind have placed lower limits on the masses of sleptons of the order of 40 GeV. Current lower limits on the masses of other SUSY particles are $m_{\tilde{\gamma}} > 5$ GeV, $m_{\tilde{q}} > 100$ GeV and $m_{\tilde{g}} > 100$ GeV. If supersymmetry is indeed a symmetry of nature, and provides a solution to the naturalness problem, SUSY particles should have masses less than 1 TeV. This hypothesis could be tested definitively at the proposed high-luminosity supercolliders, LHC and SSC, in which beams of protons will collide with total centre-of-mass energies of 16 and 40 TeV respectively.

Supersymmetry impinges on the question of the stability of the proton: supersymmetric models predict the predominance of $K^0\mu^+$, $K^+\bar{\nu}_\mu$ and $K^+\bar{\nu}_\tau$ final states in contrast to the predictions of SU(5) (see table 15.1), which favours the decay $p \to \pi^0 e^+$ and in which second generation fermions are suppressed. A possible identification of decay modes involving kaons would signal the presence of supersymmetry and explain a longer proton lifetime than that predicted by SU(5).

A compelling and attractive feature of supersymmetry is that locally supersymmetric theories relate the generators of supersymmetry to the generators of space–time transformations so that there is an inevitable connection with general relativity which may lead to the ultimate unification of gravity with the strong and electroweak forces.

In order to appreciate this connection let us recall (chapter 8) that the momentum operators are the generators of translations in space. Correspondingly, the four-momentum operators p^μ generate space–time translations. The generators of rotations in space are the angular momentum operators. Lorentz transformations may be regarded as rotations in space–time and the rotation group is in fact a subgroup of the Lorentz group of transformations. The laws of physics are invariant under this group of space–time transformations, collectively known as the Poincaré group. In addition to these space–time symmetries we have met various internal symmetries: the generators T_a of a non-Abelian internal symmetry form a Lie algebra

$$[T_a, T_b] = \mathrm{i} f_{abc} T_c$$

where the f_{abc} are the structure constants of the group. The generators T_a commute with the Hamiltonian and therefore with the generators, p^μ and $M^{\mu\nu}$ of the Poincaré group:

$$[T_a, H] = [T_a, p^\mu] = [T_a, M^{\mu\nu}] = 0.$$

A supersymmetric transformation, connecting fermion fields ψ and boson fields φ, and changing the total angular momentum by half a unit, is effected by a spin $\frac{1}{2}$ Majorana generator Q_α:

$$Q_\alpha \psi = \varphi$$

where $\alpha = 1, 2, 3, 4$ is a spinor index. With the introduction of supersymmetry the algebra is modified and now includes anticommutators as well as commutators:

$$[Q_\alpha, p^\mu] = 0 \tag{15.36}$$

$$[Q_\alpha, M^{\mu\nu}] = \tfrac{1}{2}(\sigma^{\mu\nu} Q)_\alpha \tag{15.37}$$

$$\{Q_\alpha, \bar{Q}_\beta\} = -2(\gamma_\mu)_{\alpha\beta} p^\mu \tag{15.38}$$

where γ^μ are the Dirac matrices, $\sigma^{\mu\nu} = (\mathrm{i}/2)[\gamma^\mu, \gamma^\nu]$ and $\bar{Q}_\beta = Q_\beta^{\mathrm{T}} \gamma^0$, where the superscript T signifies the transpose. Equation (15.37) expresses the fact that Q_α transforms as a spinor, while equation (15.36) shows that the spinor charges are conserved. The anticommutation relation (15.38) shows that *two successive supersymmetry transformations generate a translation in space–time*, and herein lies the hope of achieving the ultimate unification of all the known forces in nature.

In special relativity the line element

$$(\delta s)^2 = \sum_{\mu,\nu=0}^{3} g_{\mu\nu} \delta x^\mu \delta x^\nu \tag{15.39}$$

is invariant, i.e. is the same in all inertial frames of reference. In (15.39) $g_{\mu\nu}$ is the Minkowski metric whose only non-vanishing components are

$$g_{00} = 1 \qquad g_{11} = g_{22} = g_{33} = -1.$$

The central postulate of general relativity is that the gravitational field, arising from the presence of matter, can be described by replacing the Minkowski 'flat space' metric by a more general metric which depends on the space–time coordinates

$$(\delta s)^2 = \sum_{\mu,\nu=0}^{3} g_{\mu\nu}(x)\delta x^\mu \delta x^\nu. \qquad (15.40)$$

The curvature of the metric is determined by solving the Einstein field equations, a set of ten non-linear, second-order, hyperbolic partial differential equations, for the ten components $(g_{\mu\nu}(x) = g_{\nu\mu}(x))$ of the metric tensor. The gravitational force can be viewed as arising from deviations, or fluctuations, of the curved space from the flat Minkowski space

$$g_{\mu\nu}(x) = g_{\mu\nu} + h_{\mu\nu}(x) \qquad (15.41)$$

where the $h_{\mu\nu}(x)$ measure the size of the fluctuations. For sufficiently small fluctuations the Einstein equations become a set of ten *linear* equations in $h_{\mu\nu}(x)$.

From the particle physics viewpoint, forces are conveyed via the exchange of field quanta. Particles with half-integer spin (fermions) cannot give rise to static forces between interacting particles, so that the field quanta must be bosons. Furthermore, detailed arguments show that static forces can arise only if the boson spin is less than or equal to 2. The exchange of a spin 1 boson (the photon for example) gives rise to a repulsive force between identical particles so that the quantum of the gravitational field, the *graviton*, must have spin 0 or spin 2. Only a spin 2 graviton has enough degrees of freedom to correspond to the ten fields $h_{\mu\nu}(x)$.

If supersymmetry is made locally gauge invariant new fields are introduced whose quanta are spin $\frac{3}{2}$ *gravitinos*, the supersymmetric partners of the graviton, and *gauginos*, the spin $\frac{1}{2}$ partners of the vector gauge bosons. A local supersymmetry is called supergravity. There are in fact eight supergravity theories corresponding to the supersymmetry generators Q_α^N $(N = 1, 2, \ldots, 8)$, where N gives the number of gravitinos in the theory. Note that, because gravitinos are fermions, they will not themselves give rise to static forces so that the predictions of general relativity are protected in supergravity theories. Unfortunately, these attempts to unify the fundamental forces of nature seem doomed to failure because they are plagued with the usual infinities arising from radiative corrections: it appears that the theories are not renormalizable.

The notion that space–time is a continuum of space–time 'points' would seem to be singularly inappropriate in a quantum theory that purports to unify gravitation with the other fundamental forces: localization of a particle at a 'point' would require an infinite amount of energy. It has been conjectured that the difficulties which arise in attempts to create renormalizable theories of supergravity are unavoidable when this basic inconsistency is ignored. Quantum gravity, with its natural scale given by the Planck length $L_P = (G\hbar/c^3)^{1/2} \approx 10^{-35}$ m, where G is the gravitational constant, raises the possibility that the notion of a space–time continuum may not be valid at distances less than L_P and that a different model of space–time may be needed. In *supersymmetric string theories* the structureless 'point-like' particles of conventional quantum field theories are replaced by one-dimensional string-like objects. These theories produce finite results but for internal consistency require the space–time in which these distributed objects move to be ten-dimensional! The six extra spatial dimensions are visualized as being compactified, or 'rolled up' into closed loops on a scale of 10^{-35} m or less. These ideas are currently causing considerable excitement but much work remains to be done before the physicists' dream of a theory of everything becomes a reality.

REFERENCES 15

1 **Georgi H and Glashow S L** 1974 *Phys Rev Lett* **32** (438)

2 **Langacker P** 1981 *Phys Rep* **72c** (185)

3 **Particle Data Group** 1992 'Review of particle properties' *Phys Rev* **D45**

4 **Dirac P A M** 1931 *Proc Roy Soc* **A133** (60)

5 **'t Hooft G** 1974 *Nucl Phys* **B79** (276)

6 **Polyakov A M** 1974 *JETP Lett* **20** (194)

7 **Cabrera B** 1982 *Phys Rev Lett* **48** (1378)

8 **Frampton P H** 1987 *Gauge Field Theories* Benjamin p. 526

9 **Davis R, Harmer D S and Hoffman K C** 1968 *Phys Rev Lett* **20** (1205)

10 **Davis R, Mann A K and Wolfenstein L** 1989 *Ann Rev Nucl Part Sci* **39** (467)

11 **Hirata K** *et al.* 1989 *Phys Rev Lett* **63** (16)

12 **Mikheyev S P and Smirnov A Yu** 1986 *Nuovo Cimento* **9c** (17)

13 **Mikheyev S P and Smirnov A Yu** 1987 *Soviet Phys Usp* **30** (759)

14 **Wolfenstein L** 1978 *Phys Rev* **D17** (2369)

15 **von Feilitzsch F** 1993 *Proceedings of the International Conference on Neutral Currents Twenty Years Later*, Paris, World Scientific

16 **Bahcall J N and Ulrich R K** 1988 *Rev Mod Phys* **60** (279)

17 **Elsworth Y, Howe R, Isaak G R, McLeod C P and New R** 1990 *Nature* **347** (536)

18 **Bergkvist K E** *et al.* 1972 *Nucl Phys* **B39** (317, 371)

19 **Lubimov V A** *et al.* 1980 *Phys Lett* **94B** (266)

20 **Boris S** *et al.* 1987 *Phys Rev Lett* **58** (2019)

21 **Fritschi M** *et al.* 1986 *Phys Lett* **B173** (485)

22 **Wilkerson J F** *et al.* 1987 *Phys Rev Lett* **58** (2023)

23 **Kawakami H** *et al.* 1987 *Phys Lett* **B187** (198)

24 **Bionta R M** *et al.* 1987 *Phys Rev Lett* **58** (1494)

25 **Hirata K** *et al.* 1987 *Phys Rev Lett* **58** (1490)

26 **Abela R** *et al.* 1984 *Phys Lett* **B146** (431)

27 **Albrecht H** *et al.* 1988 *Phys Lett* **B202** (149)

28 **Caldwell D O** 1989 *Int J Mod Phys* **A4** (1851)

29 **Sakharov A D** 1967 *JETP Lett* **5** (24)

EXAMPLES 15

15.1 The gauge couplings $\alpha_i(\mu)$ evolve with Q according to the equation

$$\alpha_i^{-1}(\mu) = \alpha_i^{-1}(Q) + 2b_i \ln\left(\frac{\mu}{Q}\right) \qquad (i = 1, 2, 3).$$

The coefficients b_i were defined in equation (15.8) in the text but more precise values include small Higgs scalar contributions, δ_H, so that in fact

$$b_i = \frac{1}{12\pi}(11n_b - 4n_g - \delta_H).$$

The values of n_b, n_g and δ_H are

i	n_b	n_g	δ_H
1	0	3	3/10
2	2	3	1/2
3	3	3	0

By evolving the couplings from the known values $\alpha_i^{-1}(M_W)$ given in the text, show that the requirement that they coincide at the unification scale $Q = M_X$ leads (independently of the number of fermion generations n_g) to values of M_X and $\sin^2\theta_W$ given by

$$M_X = M_W \exp\left\{\frac{2\pi}{67}[3\alpha^{-1}(M_W) - 8\alpha_3^{-1}(M_W)]\right\} \approx 0.9 \times 10^{15}\ \text{GeV}$$

$$\sin^2\theta_W = \frac{23}{134} + \frac{109}{201}\alpha_3^{-1}(M_W)\alpha(M_W) \approx 0.205.$$

(Assume that $M_W = 80$ GeV.) Show that for three fermion generations these solutions are consistent with $\alpha_G(M_X) = 0.024$.

15.2 Estimate the proton lifetime by using a dimensional argument and assuming that the matrix element for the decay process is dominated by the X boson propagator. Assume the relevant coupling constant is $\alpha_G = 0.024$, the X boson mass is $m_X = 2 \times 10^{14}$ GeV and regulate the dimensions with the proton mass $m_p = 0.938$ GeV.

Appendices

A Fundamental constants

The constants and conversion factors are taken, with approximations, from E. R. Cohen and B. N. Taylor (1987 *Rev Mod Phys* **59** (1121)) and from the Particle Data Group compilation (1992 *Phys Rev* **45D** (No 11, 1 June)). Errors in the constants, often less than a part per million, have been omitted. Symbols are generally in accord with the recommendations of the report *Quantities, Units and Symbols* (1975 The Royal Society).

The permeability of the vacuum μ_0 $(=1/c^2\epsilon_0)$ is $4\pi \times 10^{-7}$ H m exactly and the permittivity of the vacuum is then $8.854\,19 \times 10^{-12}$ F m^{-1}.

The velocity of light is now taken to have the *exact* value $c =$ 299 792 458 m s^{-1} and the metre is defined to be the length of the path travelled by light in a vacuum in 1/299 792 458 s.

Quantity	*Symbol*	*Value*
General		
Gravitational constant	G (or G_N)	6.6726×10^{-11} m^3 kg^{-1} s^{-2}
Velocity of light	c	299 792 458 m s^{-1}
Avogadro's number	N_A	$6.022\,14 \times 10^{23}$ mol^{-1}
Elementary charge	e	$1.602\,18 \times 10^{-19}$ C
Faraday constant	$F = N_A e$	$9.648\,53 \times 10^{4}$ C mol^{-1}
Electron mass	m_e	$9.109\,39 \times 10^{-31}$ kg
Electron charge to mass ratio	$-e/m_e$	$-1.758\,82 \times 10^{11}$ C kg^{-1}
Classical electron radius	$r_e = \mu_0 e^2/4\pi m_e$	$2.817\,94 \times 10^{-15}$ m
Thomson cross-section	$\sigma_T = 8\pi r_e^2/3$	$6.652\,46 \times 10^{-29}$ m^2
Gas constant	R	8.314 51 J mol^{-1} K^{-1}
Boltzmann constant	$k = R/N_A$	$1.380\,66 \times 10^{-23}$ J K^{-1}
Planck constant	h	$6.626\,08 \times 10^{-34}$ J s
Planck constant, reduced	$\hbar$	$1.054\,57 \times 10^{-34}$ J s

Quantity	*Symbol*	*Value*
Compton wavelength		
of electron	$\lambda_C = h/m_e c$	$2.426\,31 \times 10^{-12}$ m
of proton	$\lambda_{C_p} = h/m_p c$	$1.321\,41 \times 10^{-15}$ m
Planck mass	$m_P = (\hbar c/G)^{1/2}$	$2.176\,71 \times 10^{-8}$ kg
Fermi constant	G (or G_F)	1.4355×10^{-62} J m^3
Atomic and nuclear masses		
Atomic mass unit	amu or u	$1.660\,54 \times 10^{-27}$ kg
Atomic mass		
of electron	M_e	$5.485\,80 \times 10^{-4}$ u
of proton	M_p	1.007 276 u
of hydrogen atom	M_H	1.007 826 u
of neutron	M_n	1.008 665 u
Ratio of proton to electron mass	m_p/m_e	1836.15
Mass		
of proton	m_p	$1.672\,62 \times 10^{-27}$ kg
of neutron	m_n	$1.674\,93 \times 10^{-27}$ kg
Neutron–H-atom mass difference	$M_n - M_H$	0.781 MeV/c^2
Spectroscopic constants		
Rydberg constant	$R_\infty = m_e e^4/8h^3\epsilon_0^2 c$	$1.097\,37 \times 10^7$ m^{-1}
Bohr radius	$a_0 = h^2\epsilon_0/\pi m_e e^2$	$5.291\,77 \times 10^{-11}$ m
Fine-structure constant	$\alpha = \mu_0 e^2 c/2h$	$7.297\,35 \times 10^{-3}$
Magnetic quantities		
Bohr magneton	$\mu_B = eh/4\pi m_e$	$9.274\,02 \times 10^{-24}$ J T^{-1}
Nuclear magneton	$\mu_N = eh/4\pi m_p$	$5.050\,79 \times 10^{-27}$ J T^{-1}
Magnetic moment		
of electron	μ_e	$9.284\,77 \times 10^{-24}$ J T^{-1}
of muon	μ_μ	$4.490\,45 \times 10^{-26}$ J T^{-1}
of proton	μ_p	$1.410\,61 \times 10^{-26}$ J T^{-1}
		$2.793\mu_N$
of neutron	μ_n	$-0.966\,24 \times 10^{-26}$ J T^{-1}
		$-1.913\mu_N$
Gyromagnetic ratio of proton (corrected for diagmagnetization of water)	γ_p	$2.675\,22 \times 10^8$ rad s^{-1} T^{-1}
g factors		
of electron	g_l	-1
	g_s	-2.0023
of proton	g_l	1
	g_s	5.586 ($=2\mu_p/\mu_N$)
of neutron	g_l	0
	g_s	-3.826 ($=2\mu_n/\mu_N$)

Quantity	*Symbol*	*Value*
Conversion factors		
1 kg		$5.609\,59 \times 10^{29}$ MeV/c^2
1 MeV/c^2		$1.782\,66 \times 10^{-30}$ kg
1 amu (u)		$\begin{cases} 1.660\,54 \times 10^{-27} \text{ kg} \\ 931.494 \text{ MeV}/c^2 \end{cases}$
1 electron mass (m_e)		0.510 999 MeV/c^2
1 proton mass (m_p)		938.272 MeV/c^2
1 eV		$1.602\,18 \times 10^{-19}$ J
Wavelength of 1 eV/c particle (hc/e)		$1.239\,84 \times 10^{-16}$ m
Width–lifetime product ($\hbar$)		$6.582\,12 \times 10^{-16}$ eV s
$\hbar c$		197.327 MeV fm

B *Cross-section*

If an incident particle actually has to hit a target nucleus in order to initiate a nuclear reaction, it is clear that the probability of it doing so will depend on the projected target area or cross-section πR^2 of the nucleus. This crude picture can be generalized to cover most types of nuclear process but the *cross-section* σ then no longer means the area of a physical object, but rather the area associated with each nucleus through which an incident particle must be considered to pass if it has to cause the specified interaction. It is thus a property of both particles involved in the collision and may depend on the size of each, e.g. on the sum of their radii if the de Broglie wavelength of relative motion is small. If the wavelength is large σ may greatly exceed nuclear sizes, tending to a value of approximately $\pi\lambda\!\!\!^{-2}$ Cross-sections can thus be expected to have a very wide range of values, running from less than the area of a small nucleus, say 10^{-29} m^2, to about the square of the wavelength of a slow neutron, say 10^{-21} m^2. As noted in section 1.5.1 they are usually measured in *barns* (10^{-28} m^2).

The experimentalist uses cross-section as a measure of the yield, or probability, of a particular process, e.g. the elastic scattering X(a, a)Y or the production of particles b in the reaction X(a, b)Y (or in one of the more complex reactions of particle physics). The cross-sections for these two processes may be written σ_{aa}, σ_{ab} and are known as *partial cross-sections.* The sum of all partial cross-sections for a given projectile–target interaction is the *total cross-section* σ_{total} so that

$$\sigma_{total} = \sum_j \sigma_{aj}. \tag{B.1}$$

Consider now a target of area S (figure B.1) in which there are N nuclei X per unit volume. The figure suggests a solid target but it might also be

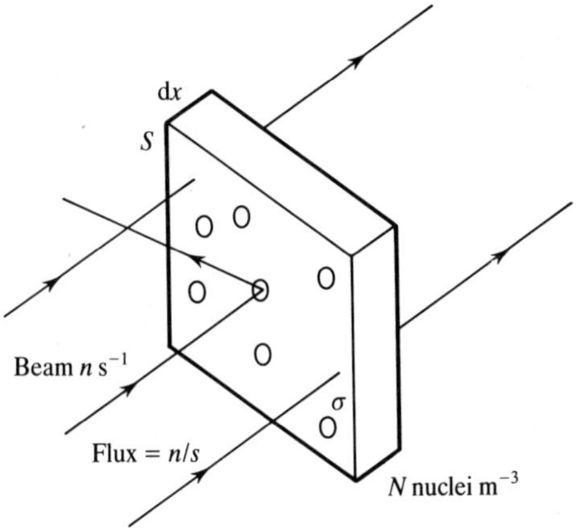

Figure B.1
The concept of cross-section or collision area.

the nuclei of a colliding beam. If the thickness of the target considered is dx the chance of interaction when a projectile enters it is $SN\,\mathrm{d}x\sigma/S = N\sigma\,\mathrm{d}x$. For n projectiles the number of interactions is $nN\sigma\,\mathrm{d}x$ and if these remove particles from the incident beam the *attenuation* in the thickness dx is

$$\mathrm{d}n = -nN\sigma\,\mathrm{d}x. \tag{B.2}$$

For a finite target thickness x this leads to a transmitted beam of

$$n_x = n_0 \exp(-N\sigma x) \tag{B.3}$$

particles (cf. the case of photons, section 2.1.4), where n_0 is the number of particles incident at $x = 0$.

In many nuclear reaction experiments, targets are so thin that the attenuation of the incident beam is small and we are more concerned with the partial cross-sections for specific processes, e.g. the reaction X(a, b)Y. We then write the yield of products b from projectiles a incident on a target of thickness x as

$$n_\mathrm{b} = n_\mathrm{a}(Nx)\sigma_\mathrm{ab} \tag{B.4}$$

in which the quantity Nx is just the number of nuclei X per unit area of the target. This is equal to $N_\mathrm{A}\rho_s/A$ where N_A is Avogadro's number, ρ_s is the mass per unit area of the target and A is the atomic weight in kilograms.

If now we take n_a and n_b to be numbers of particles *per second* the quantity n_a/S is the incident *flux* ϕ_a which can also be expressed as $N_\mathrm{a}v_\mathrm{a}$ where N_a is the *number density* of particles in the assumed parallel beam and v_a is their (uniform) velocity. In terms of the flux the yield of b per unit time can now be written

$$n_\mathrm{b} = \phi_\mathrm{a}(NxS)\sigma_\mathrm{ab} \tag{B.5}$$

in which (NxS) is simply the total number of nuclei exposed to the flux. And if this number is just *one*, n_b becomes the rate, or probability per unit time, under these conditions, for the process X(a, b)Y. We shall call this λ_{ab} so that, from equation (B.5),

$$\lambda_{ab} = \phi_a \sigma_{ab} = N_a v_a \sigma_{ab}. \tag{B.6}$$

If the angular distribution of the particles b about the beam direction is observed experimentally we detect dn_b particles in a small solid angle $d\Omega$ at a polar angle θ with respect to the axis. Usually there is axial symmetry about the beam direction but if not dn_b also depends on the azimuthal angle ϕ. In general, therefore, we write instead of equation (B.5)

$$dn_b = \phi_a(NxS)\frac{d\sigma_{ab}}{d\Omega}\,d\Omega \tag{B.7}$$

where $d\sigma_{ab}/d\Omega$ is the *differential cross-section* for the angles (θ, ϕ), often written $\sigma(\theta, \phi)$. It is measured in submultiples of the barn, e.g. millibarns, per steradian. Differential measurements imply that the incident beam and the detector solid angle are well defined geometrically by stops and counter efficiency factors may be needed in equation (B.7). It may be seen from equation (B.7) that the differential cross-section is just the observed *flow* of particles per unit time and solid angle divided by the incident flux ϕ_a and by the number of target nuclei NxS defined by the beam area. The total cross-section for a given process is related to its differential cross-section by the integral

$$\sigma_{total} = \int^{4\pi} \frac{d\sigma}{d\Omega}\,d\Omega \tag{B.8}$$

which becomes, in the case of axial symmetry,

$$\sigma_{total} = 2\pi \int_0^{\pi} \frac{d\sigma}{d\Omega} \sin\theta\,d\theta. \tag{B.9}$$

The interpretation of the differential cross-section in the partial wave formalism as the square of a scattering amplitude is discussed in section 9.2.1.

In colliding beam installations (section 2.5.4) a useful measure of performance is the *luminosity* $\mathscr{L}$ which is defined by the equation

$$\text{event rate} = \sigma\mathscr{L} \tag{B.10}$$

where σ is the cross-section for the event under consideration at the collision energy. The luminosity conventionally has dimensions $cm^{-2}\,s^{-1}$.

The expression of a cross-section in natural units is discussed in appendix F.

C *Kinematics of non-relativistic collisions*

Kinematic features of collisions, such as angles of deflection, are governed by the laws of conservation of energy and of linear and angular momentum. *Dynamical* features, such as transition probabilities, are determined by the energy available in the collision, by the nature of the forces between the interacting objects and by the internal structure. An understanding of the dynamics of an interaction usually involves a preliminary kinematical analysis and some of the formulae necessary are presented in this appendix.

C.1 *Laboratory system*

Consider the *inelastic reaction* X(a, b)Y, illustrated in figure C.1, in the laboratory system of coordinates and let the energy release in the reaction be Q. Then, using the symbols shown in the figure, we have from the conservation of linear momentum

$$\boldsymbol{p}_{\mathrm{a}} = \boldsymbol{p}_{\mathrm{b}} + \boldsymbol{p}_{\mathrm{Y}} \tag{C.1}$$

and from the conservation of energy

$$T_{\mathrm{a}} + Q = T_{\mathrm{b}} + T_{\mathrm{Y}}. \tag{C.2}$$

We recall that Q is not a classical quantity, but arises because of the small difference of total mass between the initial and final systems, a + X and b + Y. For the mechanical equations, however, it is normally sufficiently

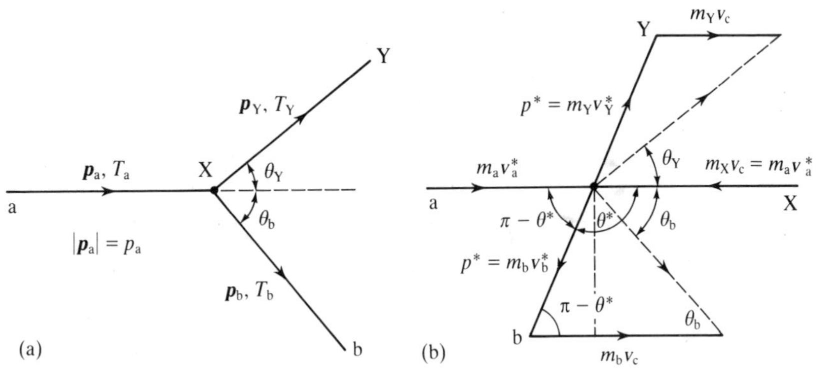

Figure C.1 Kinematics. (a) Inelastic process X(a, b)Y in the *laboratory system* showing angles θ, momenta p and kinetic energies T for the four particles. Particle X is initially at rest. (b) The X(a, b)Y collision viewed in the centre-of-mass system, with particle momenta indicated. Addition of momentum mv_c to the centre-of-mass momenta of particles b, Y as a result of restoration of the velocity of the mass centre v_c leads to the final particle directions shown in part (a).

accurate to assume that

$$m_a + m_X = m_b + m_Y.$$

Suppose that we wish to find the energy T_b of the particle b observed at an angle θ_b with the direction of incidence of a. This is obtained by eliminating from the equations the energy and momentum of Y. From (C.1) we write

$$\boldsymbol{p}_Y = \boldsymbol{p}_a - \boldsymbol{p}_b \tag{C.3}$$

and forming the square of these vectors

$$p_Y^2 = p_a^2 + p_b^2 - 2p_a p_b \cos\theta_b. \tag{C.4}$$

We now convert momenta to kinetic energy using the relation $p^2 = 2mT$ and obtain

$$m_Y T_Y = m_a T_a + m_b T_b - 2(m_a m_b T_a T_b)^{1/2} \cos\theta_b$$

and substituting for T_Y from (C.2) and rearranging

$$(m_b + m_Y)T_b - 2(m_a m_b T_a T_b)^{1/2} \cos\theta_b = (m_Y - m_a)T_a + m_Y Q. \tag{C.5}$$

This equation is homogeneous in the ms which can be absolute or atomic masses or conveniently mass numbers with a slight loss of accuracy. The T_b–T_a relation is given in this form in equation (6.8) of chapter 6.

In the special case of elastic scattering X(a, a)X we set $m_b = m_a$, $m_Y = m_X$, $Q = 0$, $\theta_b = \theta$ and $T_b = T'_a$, the kinetic energy of a after the deflection. Equation (C.5) then yields

$$(m_a + m_X)T'_a - 2m_a(T_a T'_a)^{1/2} \cos\theta = (m_X - m_a)T_a$$

and if we put $n = m_X/m_a$ this can be rewritten

$$2(T_a T'_a)^{1/2} \cos\theta = (1 + n)T'_a + (1 - n)T_a \qquad \text{(C.6)}$$

which relates the final to the initial energy for a scattering angle θ in the laboratory system.

C.2 Centre-of-mass system

In any interaction between particles, the mass centre moves with the same constant velocity before and after the interaction whatever the forces between the particles, assuming no external influences. The mutual forces affect the relative motion only and to learn about the dynamics of the interaction we must 'subtract-off' the irrelevant motion of the mass centre. More formally, we must set up a Galilean transformation from the laboratory frame of reference to the centre-of-mass (c.m.) frame, in which the total resultant linear momentum is zero. Observed angles, cross-sections and energies can then be related to their c.m. counterparts which will be denoted here by an asterisk, e.g. p^*.

In the c.m. system the inelastic reaction X(a, b)Y will appear as in figure C.1(b), which shows zero momentum for both systems a + X and b + Y and just one reaction angle θ^*. The velocity of the centre of mass is $v_c = p_a/(m_a + m_X)$ and the kinetic energy associated with the c.m. motion is $\frac{1}{2}p_a^2/(m_a + m_X) = m_a T_a/(m_a + m_X)$. Subtracting this from the initial laboratory kinetic energy gives the initial c.m. energy or channel energy

$$T^* = \frac{m_X T_a}{m_a + m_X}. \qquad \text{(C.7)}$$

This energy is available for the interaction together with the energy release Q and the total energy of the products b + Y in the c.m. system is $T^* + Q$. If the c.m. momentum of b and Y is p^* we have

$$T^* + Q = T_b^* + T_Y^* = (p^*)^2\left(\frac{1}{2m_b} + \frac{1}{2m_Y}\right)$$

so that

$$(p^*)^2 = \frac{2m_b m_Y}{m_b + m_Y}(T^* + Q). \tag{C.8}$$

Considering now particle b, we find its velocity in the c.m. system to be

$$v_b^* = \frac{p^*}{m_b} = \left[\frac{2m_Y}{m_b(m_b + m_Y)}(T^* + Q)\right]^{1/2} \tag{C.9}$$

and we can also easily show that the c.m. velocity v_c can be put in the form

$$v_c = \left[\frac{2m_a}{m_X(m_a + m_X)}T^*\right]^{1/2}. \tag{C.10}$$

The ratio of these two quantities is conveniently written n_b and is explicitly the positive quantity

$$n_b = \frac{v_b^*}{v_c} = \left[\frac{m_X m_Y}{m_a m_b}\frac{T^* + Q}{T^*}\right]^{1/2} \tag{C.11}$$

in which we have taken $m_a + m_X$ and $m_b + m_Y$ to be equal.

Referring back to figure C.1(b) we can now relate the laboratory and c.m. angles by restoring the velocity of the mass centre to create the laboratory velocity. For particle b

$$\tan\theta_b = \frac{v_b^* \sin\theta^*}{v_c + v_b^* \cos\theta^*} = \frac{\sin\theta^*}{1/n_b + \cos\theta^*} \tag{C.12}$$

and a similar calculation for particle Y gives

$$\tan\theta_Y = \frac{\sin\theta^*}{1/n_Y - \cos\theta^*}. \tag{C.13}$$

For the special case of *elastic scattering* ($X \equiv Y$, $a \equiv b$) we find $n_b = m_X/m_a = n$, say, and $n_Y = 1$ so that

$$\begin{aligned} \tan\theta_b &= \frac{\sin\theta^*}{1/n + \cos\theta^*} \\ \tan\theta_Y &= \frac{\sin\theta^*}{1 - \cos\theta^*} \quad \text{or} \quad \theta_Y = \tfrac{1}{2}(\pi - \theta^*). \end{aligned} \tag{C.14}$$

From the angular relations we may now reduce the transformation of *differential cross-sections* $\sigma(\theta)$ using the relation

$$\sigma(\theta)\sin\theta\,d\theta = \sigma^*(\theta^*)\sin\theta^*\,d\theta^*$$

which states that the same number of events is observed in each coordinate system for corresponding angles and solid angles. For particle b calculation gives

$$\sigma(\theta) = \frac{(1 + 2\cos\theta^*/n_b + 1/n_b^2)^{3/2}}{1 + \cos\theta^*/n_b}\,\sigma^*(\theta^*). \qquad \text{(C.15)}$$

Some of the formulae in this appendix may be expressed more concisely in terms of the *reduced mass* μ which is defined for a pair of interacting particles a, X by the expression $1/\mu_{aX} = 1/m_a + 1/m_X$ or $\mu_{aX} = m_a m_X/(m_a + m_X)$. Using this quantity we find the following:

c.m. momentum $\quad p^*_{aX} = p_a - m_a v_c = \mu_{aX} v_a$

c.m. wavenumber $\quad k^*_{aX} = \dfrac{1}{\lambda\!\!\!^{-}_{aX}} = \dfrac{p^*_{aX}}{\hbar} = \dfrac{\mu_{aX} v_a}{\hbar} \qquad$ (C.16)

c.m. energy $\quad T^*_{aX} = \dfrac{m_X T_a}{m_a + m_X} = \tfrac{1}{2}\mu_{aX} v_a^2.$

The c.m. quantities may thus be calculated by taking a particle with the reduced mass moving with the incident particle velocity towards a fixed target.

D *A particle in a potential well*

The bound states of a particle moving in a spherically symmetrical potential well $V(r)$ are described by solutions of the Schrödinger equation, as shown in standard texts on quantum mechanics.[1,2] For all states of motion except those with zero angular momentum, the orbital motion adds a repulsive centrifugal potential to $V(r)$ so that the motion takes place in an effective potential

$$V_{\mathrm{eff}} = V(r) + \frac{l(l+1)\hbar^2}{2mr^2} \tag{D.1}$$

where m is the mass of the particle.

Solution of the wave equation for discrete eigenfunctions ψ_{nl} is equivalent to fitting appropriate waves into the potential V_{eff} and the wavefunctions and energies are characterized in the first place by the *principal quantum number* n and then by the *orbital angular momentum quantum number* l ($\leqslant (n-1)$), which also determines the *parity* of the motion as $(-1)^l$. Single particle states with $l = 0, 1, 2, 3$ are known as s, p, d, f states. If external fields are applied to the system, energies may depend on the orientation of the angular momentum vector with respect to the axis of quantization and the corresponding eigenfunctions are labelled ψ_{nlm} where $|m|$ ($\leqslant l$) is the *magnetic quantum number*. In the absence of external fields the $(2l+1)$ eigenfunctions for a given l are degenerate.

If $V(r)$ represents a pure Coulomb potential, and the particle is an electron, the problem is that of the hydrogen atom. It is found that in this case there is degeneracy with respect to l, e.g. the energies of the 2s ($n = 2$, $l = 0$) and 2p ($n = 2$, $l = 1$) states are equal. But this degeneracy is removed if the central field departs from the Coulomb shape and in the case of the *screened* Coulomb shape, appropriate to atomic physics, the wavefunctions with low l correspond with states that are more tightly bound, e.g. 2s lies below 2p.

The Coulomb potential describes a long-range force and is not appropriate for the short-range interactions of nuclear physics. For nuclear model calculations (chapter 4) it is often convenient to start with the three-dimensional *oscillator potential*

$$V(r) = -U + \tfrac{1}{2}m\omega^2 r^2 \tag{D.2}$$

where ω is the angular frequency of the particle, e.g. a proton of mass m, in the field of force. Figure D.1 shows this potential for a particular set of parameters, representative of a proton moving in a volume comparable with that of an average nucleus.

The radial eigenfunctions for the oscillator potential are the *associated Laguerre polynomials*, or Hermite polynomials if Cartesian coordinates are used. For a one-dimensional oscillator it is well known that the energy levels, measured from the bottom of the well, are at excitations

$$E_n = (n + \tfrac{1}{2})\hbar\omega \tag{D.3}$$

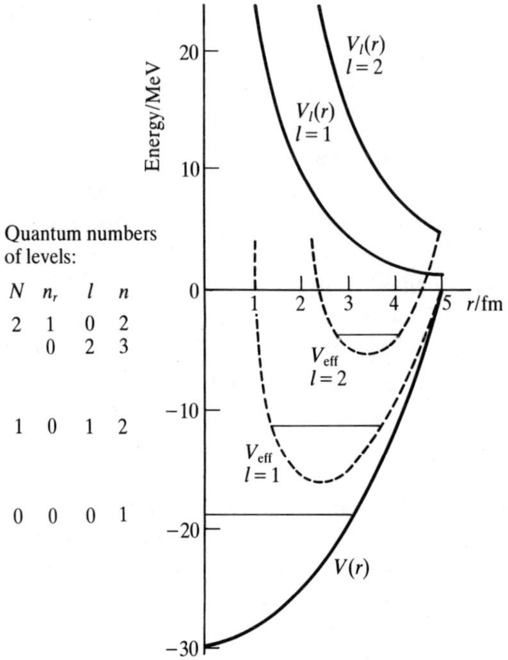

Figure D.1 An oscillator potential drawn with $V(r) = -30 + 1.2r^2$ MeV for $0 < r < R$ where $R = 5$ fm and with $V(r) = 0$ for $r > R$. Centrifugal potentials $V_l(r)$ are drawn for the case $V_l = 20.5l(l+1)/r^2$ MeV corresponding to a proton moving in the well.

and in the three-dimensional case

$$E_{n_1 n_2 n_3} = (n_1 + n_2 + n_3 + \tfrac{3}{2})\hbar\omega = (N + \tfrac{3}{2})\hbar\omega \qquad \text{(D.4)}$$

where $N = n_1 + n_2 + n_3$ ($\geqslant 0$) is the oscillator quantum number. This gives the sequence of equally spaced levels shown in figure D.1. In contrast with the case of the Coulomb potential the single-particle oscillator levels do not close up as the dissociation energy is approached.

For each N, a range of values of the principal quantum number n and of the orbital quantum number l is possible and the algebraic solutions show that these are related by the formula

$$N = 2n - l - 2. \qquad \text{(D.5)}$$

There is thus a degeneracy with respect to l since, for example, for $N = 2$ both s states ($l = 0, n = 2$) and d states ($l = 2, n = 3$) have the same energy. This degeneracy may be removed if the well is distorted from the pure harmonic shape and the level order may then be

$(n, l) \equiv$	(1, 0);	(2, 1);	(2, 0);	(3, 2);	(3, 1);	(4, 3); . . .
	1s	2p	2s	3d	3p	4f
$N =$	0	1	2	2	3	3

It will be noted from figure D.1 that, in further contrast with the levels of the long-range potential, the effect of changes of n and of l on the energy is similar for the oscillator. Moreover, the effect of the well-shape on the level order is opposite to that of the screened Coulomb potential. For the same n, states of high l values are more strongly bound than those of lower l, basically because the potential has no singularity at the origin.

The number of fermions, e.g. electrons, protons or neutrons, that may be accommodated in the states corresponding with the oscillator quantum number N is $(N + 1)(N + 2)$, allowing for two possible spin directions for each spatial state (n, l, m) in accordance with the Pauli principle. If occupation of all the states of a given N is taken to close a *shell*, then these occur at fermion numbers

2, 8, 20, 40, 70, 112.

The oscillator states, reordered by the modification of the well to a Woods–Saxon form and by the addition of a spin–orbit coupling term, provide a set of basic levels for the nuclear-shell model (chapter 4). For these levels, occupation numbers are determined by the *total* angular momentum quantum number j, which takes account of spin direction.

In many accounts of the shell model the principal quantum number n is discarded in favour of the *radial quantum number* n_r ($=n - l - 1$)

which counts the number of radial nodes or changes of sign in the eigenfunctions as r varies from zero to infinity and ignores angular nodes. In terms of n_r equation (D.5) becomes

$$N = 2n_r + l \tag{D.6}$$

and the sequence of levels is written as

$$\begin{array}{lllllll} (n_r, l) \equiv (0, 0); & (0, 1); & (1, 0); & (0, 2); & (1, 1); & (0, 3); \ldots \\ \quad\quad\quad\ 0s & 0p & 1s & 0d & 1p & 0f \end{array}$$

Alternatively, as in chapter 4, we may simply number the levels of a given l serially and list them as

1s   1p   2s   1d   2p   1f

REFERENCES D

1 **Dicke R H and Wittke J P** 1960 *Introduction to Quantum Mechanics* Addison-Wesley

2 **Cassels J M** 1982 *Basic Quantum Mechanics* Macmillan

E *Nuclear effects in spectroscopy*

The broad features of atomic spectroscopy can be understood with the assumptions of a point nucleus of infinite mass and no angular momentum or electromagnetic moments. High resolution spectral data, throughout the electromagnetic spectrum, can only be interpreted if all these assumptions are relaxed and such data are then important for the determination of the corresponding nuclear properties. Many of the so-called *hyperfine structures* arise because of the interaction of nuclear moments with strong internal atomic fields, but external fields can also produce observable effects. Only a very brief account of this very large experimental subject can be given here; it is discussed in detail in references 1 and 2.

E.1 γ ray, X-ray and optical spectra

Because of the smallness of nuclear moments the energy changes due to the coupling of the moments to internal fields are not observable with the usual nuclear detectors. The hyperfine structure of *nuclear* levels can in fact be seen directly by using the high resolution of the *Mössbauer effect* (section 5.1.4) and the number and spacing of the line components (in the γ ray or X-ray energy range) can give information on level spins and also on moments if the internal fields are known. Both magnetic dipole and electric quadrupole interactions may contribute to the level splittings.

The hyperfine interaction is a property of an atom as a whole and may be seen in atomic levels. In the special case of *muonic atoms* the atomic transitions are in the γ ray region. A further important use of muonic transitions arises because muonic orbits are smaller in radius than electronic orbits of the same quantum numbers by a factor $m_e/m_\mu = 1/207$

and level energies are sensitive to the *finite size* of the nuclear charge distribution. Extensive information on the change of mean square charge radius ($\delta\langle r^2\rangle$) between pairs of isotopes has been obtained in this way. This quantity $\delta\langle r^2\rangle$ is also obtainable from the *isotope shifts* of line energies observed in both the X-ray and optical spectrum of ordinary electronic atoms. A powerful and sensitive technique for the optical lines at least is the resonant scattering of laser light of variable frequency by atomic beams. But many years before this technique became available, classical optical spectroscopy had revealed the sharp jump in $\delta\langle r^2\rangle$ at a neutron number of 88–90 which is now known to result from the onset of nuclear deformation (section 4.3.2).

The hyperfine components of a given optical line arising in an atom with nuclear spin may be observed using special high resolution optical techniques, of which the laser method is the latest and most powerful in the cases in which it may be applied. If the internal field can be calculated from atomic wavefunctions the nuclear magnetic moment μ_J (for $J \geqslant \frac{1}{2}$) and electric quadrupole moment Q_J (for $J \geqslant 1$) may be extracted. The *nuclear spin* can in principle be obtained by counting the components of the optical line (if $\boldsymbol{J} \leqslant \boldsymbol{J}_e$, the electronic angular momentum).

Nuclear spins and *nuclear statistics* have been obtained in a number of important cases from the band spectra of homonuclear diatomic molecules. It is found that successive lines of the electronic spectra of such molecules show an alternation in intensity and the ratio of intensities is predicted to be $(J + 1)/J$. If the electronic state which is enhanced can be characterized as of even or odd angular momentum, then the nuclear statistics follows from symmetry arguments.

E.2 Microwave spectra

The microwave region of the electromagnetic spectrum is appropriate for studying rotational transitions of fairly heavy molecules. In these systems hyperfine interactions are chiefly between the nuclear electric quadrupole moment and the molecular field gradient, but the number of hyperfine states depends on the number of orientations possible for the nuclear spin in the internal field. If the hyperfine pattern is observed by *gaseous absorption spectroscopy* both the spin and the quadrupole coupling may be deduced. The magnetic moment is obtainable from Zeeman splittings in an external magnetic field.

The microwave region also embraces the phenomenon of *electron paramagnetic resonance* (EPR) in solids in which ions behave magnetically like single electron spins. In external fields of about 0.5 T absorption of a resonant microwave quantum reverses the direction of the electron spin and $2J + 1$ absorption peaks are found as the field is increased through the hyperfine pattern. The spacing between the peaks is determined by the internal magnetic coupling and if this is known, μ_J may be obtained as well as J. EPR may also be observed with atomic beams by a technique similar to that to be described in the next section, but at higher frequencies.

E.3 Radiofrequency spectra

In atoms in which the magnetic effect of the electronic shells may be disregarded, nuclei will have $2J + 1$ possible orientations with respect to the lines of force of an *external* magnetic field. *Nuclear paramagnetic resonance* (NPR) may be observed when a resonant quantum is absorbed, changing the nuclear orientation. Because of the smallness of the nuclear magneton in comparison with the Bohr magneton, NPR for fields of about 0.5 T lies in the radiofrequency spectrum. The resonant frequency determines the nuclear gyromagnetic ratio μ_J/J and thence the magnetic moment if the spin is known.

Historically NPR, now generally known simply as *nuclear magnetic resonance* (NMR), was observed by Rabi and his collaborators using a material sample in the form of a collision-free neutral atomic or molecular beam. The apparatus was based on that used by Stern and Gerlach to determine atomic moments but it included two inhomogeneous magnetic fields arranged in opposition so that a deflection produced in the first was cancelled by the second. Atoms or molecules with zero electronic angular momentum but with nuclear spin would then pass undeflected through the apparatus overall unless their effective nuclear moment were changed between the deflecting magnets. This, however, could be done by placing there a uniform-field magnet (B_0) and a radiofrequency coil which together defined a set of levels of spacing $(\mu_J/J)B_0$ and caused transitions between them, leading to re-orientation of μ_J and consequent non-cancellation of the first deflection. The resonant signal was an absorption dip at the final detector as the field B_0 was varied for a fixed radiofrequency, say 10 MHz. The method just described was used by Alvarez and Bloch to measure the magnetic moment of the neutron.

A simple and widely used NMR technique is the nuclear induction method of Bloch, Hansen and Packard. In this, the re-orientation of nuclear moments in a macroscopic solid sample in a uniform field with a driving coil is detected by direct pickup into a receiver coil. In an equivalent method, Purcell, Torrey and Pound made the sample, in its uniform field, part of a resonant circuit and observed the drop in transmission of radiofrequency power when the Q value of the circuit was reduced by nuclear absorption.

NMR has been applied to *radioactive nuclei* polarized by low-temperature or nuclear reaction methods. The β or γ emission then has

Table E.1
Determination of nuclear constants by spectroscopic methods

Method	Quantity found	Sensitivity
Optical isotope shift (beams)	$\delta\langle r^2\rangle$	10^{-16} kg
Optical hyperfine splitting	J, a, b	–
Molecular spectra	J, statistics	–
Microwave absorption	J, b	10^{-12} kg
EPR	J, g_J	10^{-15} kg
NMR (beams)	J, a, b	10^{-12} kg
NMR (solids)	J, g_J	10^{-6} kg
Mössbauer effect	B_i, μ_J, b	–
Muonic atoms	$\delta\langle r^2\rangle, a, b$	–

an anisotropic angular distribution, but at the magnetic resonance frequency the anisotropy is reduced or destroyed. Because individual nuclear radiations are detected, this is a technique of great sensitivity.

E.4 Summary and orders of magnitude

In zero field the hyperfine splitting of atomic ground states is about 1800 MHz and in paramagnetic ions in crystals it is about 150 MHz.

Magnetic resonance transitions within multiplets are mainly observed with external fields and the resonant frequencies are then

$$\text{EPR} \qquad \nu_e/B_0 = 2.8 \times 10^4 \text{ MHz T}^{-1}$$

$$\text{NMR} \qquad \nu_p/B_0 = 42.6 \text{ MHz T}^{-1}$$

Both optical and magnetic resonance measurements of hyperfine structures give coupling constants for the magnetic (a) and electrostatic (b) interaction from which nuclear moments may be obtained if internal fields are known. Coupling constants have the form moment × field term.

Table E.1 lists the main quantities determined by the various techniques and their general sensitivity.

REFERENCES E

1 **Segrè E** 1977 *Nuclei and Particles* Benjamin ch. 6

2 **Kuhn H G** 1969 *Atomic Spectra* Longman ch. 6

F *Natural units*

The internationally adopted system of units, *Système International* or SI, is based on the metre as the unit of length, the second as the unit of time and the kilogram as the unit of mass. In fundamental physics, however, it is often much more convenient to work with a system of units, known as *natural units*, in which the speed of light, c, and Planck's constant divided by 2π, $\hbar$, are set equal to 1. Three basic units need to be defined to complete the specification of the system of units and the third is chosen to be the unit of energy, the electronvolt (eV) or its multiples, the mega-electronvolt (MeV = 10^6 eV), the giga-electronvolt (GeV = 10^9 eV) and the tera-electronvolt (TeV = 10^{12} eV). To be definite let us choose the giga-electronvolt as our unit of energy, then

$$1\ \text{GeV} = 1.602 \times 10^{-10}\ \text{J}$$

$$h = 6.626 \times 10^{-34}\ \text{J s}$$

$$(h/2\pi) = 1.055 \times 10^{-34}\ \text{J s} = 6.582 \times 10^{-25}\ \text{GeV s}$$

$$c = 2.998 \times 10^{8}\ \text{m s}^{-1}$$

$$\hbar c = 0.1973\ \text{GeV fm}$$

where the *femtometre* (fm) or *fermi* (F) is 10^{-15} m.

Let us now consider the implications of setting $\hbar = c = 1$. The dimensions of c are

$$[c] = [\text{L}][\text{T}]^{-1}$$

so that, by setting the value of c equal to 1, we are implying that the unit of length is numerically equal to the unit of time and that length and time are equivalent dimensions:

$$[\mathrm{L}] = [\mathrm{T}].$$

This is in accord with the theory of relativity which puts space and time on the same footing: time intervals and distances are different kinds of the same thing and there is no fundamental reason for measuring them in different units. The choice $c = 1$ is a *natural* choice and the number 2.998×10^8 may properly be regarded as a conversion factor which enters into our procedures for calibrating instruments which measure distances and times.

The notion of wave–particle duality, succinctly described by the Einstein and de Broglie relations

$$E = h\nu$$

$$p = h/\lambda$$

implies that, in units in which $h/2\pi = 1$, energy and momentum have dimensions

$$[E] = [\mathrm{T}]^{-1} = [p] = [\mathrm{L}]^{-1}.$$

At a more fundamental level this equivalence arises from the basic commutation relations and the fact that the energy and momentum operators are the generators of translations in space–time. For example, the canonical commutation relations

$$[x_i, p_j] = i\hbar\delta_{ij} \qquad (i, j = 1, 2, 3)$$

show that there is a fundamental connection between momenta and distances and therefore there is no fundamental reason for measuring them in different units. The *natural* way of measuring a momentum is as an inverse length: the number $6.626 \cdots \times 10^{34}$ may properly be regarded as a conversion factor which converts an inverse length into the conventional units for momentum and an inverse time into the conventional units for energy.

The dimensions of $\hbar$ are energy × time so that

$$[\hbar] = [\mathrm{M}][\mathrm{L}]^2[\mathrm{T}]^{-1}.$$

The implication of setting the value of $\hbar$ equal to 1 is that

$$[\mathrm{M}] = [\mathrm{L}]^{-1} = [\mathrm{T}]^{-1}$$

and it is customary in particle physics to choose [M] as the independent dimension.

In units in which $c = 1$ the relativistic relation

$$E^2 = \boldsymbol{p}^2c^2 + m^2c^4$$

reduces to

$$E^2 = \boldsymbol{p}^2 + m^2$$

which implies that energy, momentum and mass have equivalent dimensions. It is customary to refer to momenta in units of 'GeV/c', for example, and to masses in units of 'GeV/c^2', or quite frequently (and loosely) one speaks of mass (m), momentum (mc) and energy (mc^2) all in terms of giga-electronvolts; length and time are measured in units of reciprocal giga-electronvolts. The appropriate conversion factors are

mass	$1\ \text{kg} = 5.607 \times 10^{26}\ \text{GeV}$
length	$1\ \text{m} = 5.068 \times 10^{15}\ \text{GeV}^{-1}$
time	$1\ \text{s} = 1.519 \times 10^{24}\ \text{GeV}^{-1}$.

As an example let us calculate the Compton wavelength of the electron, $ƛ = \hbar/m_e c$, in SI and in natural units. In SI units

$$m_e = 9.109 \times 10^{-31}\ \text{kg}$$

and

$$ƛ = \frac{1.055 \times 10^{-34}}{9.109 \times 10^{-31} \times 2.998 \times 10^8} = 0.386 \times 10^{-12}\ \text{m}.$$

In natural units, with $m_e = 5.11 \times 10^{-4}$ GeV,

$$ƛ = \frac{1}{m_e} = 1.957 \times 10^3\ \text{GeV}^{-1} = \frac{1.957 \times 10^3}{5.068 \times 10^{15}}\ \text{m}$$
$$= 0.386 \times 10^{-12}\ \text{m}.$$

As a further example consider the calculation of a cross-section. A cross-section σ has dimensions

$$[\sigma] = [\text{L}]^2 = [\text{M}]^{-2}$$

so that to convert a cross-section measured in GeV^{-2} to one in millibarns ($1\ \text{mb} = 10^{-31}\ \text{m}^2$) one multiplies by $(1\ \text{GeV})^{-2} = 0.389$ mb. For example, the total cross-section of the annihilation process $e^+e^- \to \mu^+\mu^-$ is

$$\sigma = \frac{4\pi\alpha^2}{3s}$$

where α is the fine-structure constant, with a value of about 1/137, and s is the square of the centre-of-mass energy. At $s = 10\ \text{GeV}^2$, say,

$$\sigma = \frac{4\pi}{30}(1/137)^2\ \text{GeV}^{-2} = 2.232 \times 10^{-5}\ \text{GeV}^{-2}$$

$$= 8.682 \times 10^{-6}\ \text{mb}.$$

Finally, we consider the electric charge e. In SI units e is measured in Coulombs and the fine-structure constant, which measures the strength of the electromagnetic coupling, is given by

$$\alpha = \frac{e^2}{4\pi\epsilon_0\hbar c}$$

$$= \frac{(1.602 \times 10^{-19})^2}{4\pi \times 8.854 \times 10^{-12} \times 1.055 \times 10^{-34} \times 2.998 \times 10^8}$$

$$= 0.730 \times 10^{-2}$$

$$\approx \frac{1}{137}.$$

The permittivity of free space, ϵ_0, and the permeability of free space, μ_0, are related to the speed of light by the equation

$$c = (\epsilon_0\mu_0)^{-1/2}.$$

It should be stressed that ϵ_0 and μ_0 do not describe any physical properties possessed by the vacuum and the product $\epsilon_0\mu_0$ is merely a conversion factor. In Heaviside–Lorentz units, both ϵ_0 and μ_0 are set equal to 1, in keeping with the natural choice $c = 1$, and the fine-structure constant is then given by

$$\alpha = \frac{e^2}{4\pi} \approx \frac{1}{137}.$$

Similar relationships hold for the coupling strengths of other fundamental charges to the appropriate field quanta.

G Clebsch–Gordan coefficients

The vector addition or Clebsch–Gordan coefficients

$$\langle j_1 j_2 m_1 m_2 | jm \rangle = \langle jm | j_1 j_2 m_1 m_2 \rangle$$

are defined in section 8.3. The most commonly used coefficients are given in the following tables. The sign convention is that used by Condon and Shortley (*The Theory of Atomic Spectra* Cambridge University Press 1951). The coefficients given are for the addition of two angular momenta j_1 and j_2, with z components m_1 and m_2, with a resultant total angular momentum j with z component m:

$$\mathbf{j} = \mathbf{j}_1 + \mathbf{j}_2$$

$$m = m_1 + m_2.$$

For each pair of values of j_1 and j_2 the tables are laid out in the following format:

		j	.	.
		m	.	.
m_1	m_2			
.	.			
.	.		coefficients	

(i) $j_1 = \frac{1}{2}, j_2 = \frac{1}{2}$

		j	1	1	0	1
		m	$+1$	0	0	-1
m_1	m_2					
$+\frac{1}{2}$	$+\frac{1}{2}$		1			
$+\frac{1}{2}$	$-\frac{1}{2}$			$\sqrt{\frac{1}{2}}$	$\sqrt{\frac{1}{2}}$	
$-\frac{1}{2}$	$+\frac{1}{2}$			$\sqrt{\frac{1}{2}}$	$-\sqrt{\frac{1}{2}}$	
$-\frac{1}{2}$	$-\frac{1}{2}$					1

(ii) $j_1 = 1, j_2 = \frac{1}{2}$

m_1	m_2	j: $\frac{3}{2}$	$\frac{3}{2}$	$\frac{1}{2}$	$\frac{3}{2}$	$\frac{1}{2}$	$\frac{3}{2}$
		m: $+\frac{3}{2}$	$+\frac{1}{2}$	$+\frac{1}{2}$	$-\frac{1}{2}$	$-\frac{1}{2}$	$-\frac{3}{2}$
$+1$	$+\frac{1}{2}$	1					
$+1$	$-\frac{1}{2}$		$\sqrt{\frac{1}{3}}$	$\sqrt{\frac{2}{3}}$			
0	$+\frac{1}{2}$		$\sqrt{\frac{2}{3}}$	$-\sqrt{\frac{1}{3}}$			
0	$-\frac{1}{2}$				$\sqrt{\frac{2}{3}}$	$\sqrt{\frac{1}{3}}$	
-1	$+\frac{1}{2}$				$\sqrt{\frac{1}{3}}$	$-\sqrt{\frac{2}{3}}$	
-1	$-\frac{1}{2}$						1

(iii) $j_1 = 1, j_2 = 1$

m_1	m_2	j: 2	2	1	2	1	0	2	1	2
		m: $+2$	$+1$	$+1$	0	0	0	-1	-1	-2
$+1$	$+1$	1								
$+1$	0		$\sqrt{\frac{1}{2}}$	$\sqrt{\frac{1}{2}}$						
0	$+1$		$\sqrt{\frac{1}{2}}$	$-\sqrt{\frac{1}{2}}$						
$+1$	-1				$\sqrt{\frac{1}{6}}$	$\sqrt{\frac{1}{2}}$	$\sqrt{\frac{1}{3}}$			
0	0				$\sqrt{\frac{2}{3}}$	0	$-\sqrt{\frac{1}{3}}$			
-1	$+1$				$\sqrt{\frac{1}{6}}$	$-\sqrt{\frac{1}{2}}$	$\sqrt{\frac{1}{3}}$			
0	-1							$\sqrt{\frac{1}{2}}$	$\sqrt{\frac{1}{2}}$	
-1	0							$\sqrt{\frac{1}{2}}$	$-\sqrt{\frac{1}{2}}$	
-1	-1									1

(iv) $j_1 = \frac{3}{2}$, $j_2 = \frac{1}{2}$

	j	2	2	1	2	1	2	1	2
	m	$+2$	$+1$	$+1$	0	0	-1	-1	-2
m_1	m_2								
$+\frac{3}{2}$	$+\frac{1}{2}$	1							
$+\frac{3}{2}$	$-\frac{1}{2}$		$\sqrt{\frac{1}{4}}$	$\sqrt{\frac{3}{4}}$					
$+\frac{1}{2}$	$+\frac{1}{2}$		$\sqrt{\frac{3}{4}}$	$-\sqrt{\frac{1}{4}}$					
$+\frac{1}{2}$	$-\frac{1}{2}$				$\sqrt{\frac{1}{2}}$	$\sqrt{\frac{1}{2}}$			
$-\frac{1}{2}$	$+\frac{1}{2}$				$\sqrt{\frac{1}{2}}$	$-\sqrt{\frac{1}{2}}$			
$-\frac{1}{2}$	$-\frac{1}{2}$						$\sqrt{\frac{3}{4}}$	$\sqrt{\frac{1}{4}}$	
$-\frac{3}{2}$	$+\frac{1}{2}$						$\sqrt{\frac{1}{4}}$	$-\sqrt{\frac{3}{4}}$	
$-\frac{3}{2}$	$-\frac{1}{2}$								1

(v) $j_1 = 2$, $j_2 = \frac{1}{2}$

	j	$\frac{5}{2}$	$\frac{5}{2}$	$\frac{3}{2}$	$\frac{5}{2}$	$\frac{3}{2}$	$\frac{5}{2}$	$\frac{3}{2}$	$\frac{5}{2}$	$\frac{3}{2}$	$\frac{5}{2}$
	m	$+\frac{5}{2}$	$+\frac{3}{2}$	$+\frac{3}{2}$	$+\frac{1}{2}$	$+\frac{1}{2}$	$-\frac{1}{2}$	$-\frac{1}{2}$	$-\frac{3}{2}$	$-\frac{3}{2}$	$-\frac{5}{2}$
m_1	m_2										
$+2$	$+\frac{1}{2}$	1									
$+2$	$-\frac{1}{2}$		$\sqrt{\frac{1}{5}}$	$\sqrt{\frac{4}{5}}$							
$+1$	$+\frac{1}{2}$		$\sqrt{\frac{4}{5}}$	$-\sqrt{\frac{1}{5}}$							
$+1$	$-\frac{1}{2}$				$\sqrt{\frac{2}{5}}$	$\sqrt{\frac{3}{5}}$					
0	$+\frac{1}{2}$				$\sqrt{\frac{3}{5}}$	$-\sqrt{\frac{2}{5}}$					
0	$-\frac{1}{2}$						$\sqrt{\frac{3}{5}}$	$\sqrt{\frac{2}{5}}$			
-1	$+\frac{1}{2}$						$\sqrt{\frac{2}{5}}$	$-\sqrt{\frac{3}{5}}$			
-1	$-\frac{1}{2}$								$\sqrt{\frac{4}{5}}$	$\sqrt{\frac{1}{5}}$	
-2	$+\frac{1}{2}$								$\sqrt{\frac{1}{5}}$	$-\sqrt{\frac{4}{5}}$	
-2	$-\frac{1}{2}$										1

(vi) $j_1 = \frac{3}{2}, j_2 = 1$

m_1	m_2	j: $\frac{5}{2}$ m: $+\frac{5}{2}$	$\frac{5}{2}$ $+\frac{3}{2}$	$\frac{3}{2}$ $+\frac{3}{2}$	$\frac{5}{2}$ $+\frac{1}{2}$	$\frac{3}{2}$ $+\frac{1}{2}$	$\frac{1}{2}$ $+\frac{1}{2}$	$\frac{5}{2}$ $-\frac{1}{2}$	$\frac{3}{2}$ $-\frac{1}{2}$	$\frac{1}{2}$ $-\frac{1}{2}$	$\frac{5}{2}$ $-\frac{3}{2}$	$\frac{3}{2}$ $-\frac{3}{2}$	$\frac{5}{2}$ $-\frac{5}{2}$
$+\frac{3}{2}$	$+1$	1											
$+\frac{3}{2}$	0		$\sqrt{\frac{2}{5}}$	$\sqrt{\frac{3}{5}}$									
$+\frac{1}{2}$	$+1$		$\sqrt{\frac{3}{5}}$	$-\sqrt{\frac{2}{5}}$									
$+\frac{3}{2}$	-1				$\sqrt{\frac{1}{10}}$	$\sqrt{\frac{2}{5}}$	$\sqrt{\frac{1}{2}}$						
$+\frac{1}{2}$	0				$\sqrt{\frac{3}{5}}$	$\sqrt{\frac{1}{15}}$	$-\sqrt{\frac{1}{3}}$						
$-\frac{1}{2}$	$+1$				$\sqrt{\frac{3}{10}}$	$-\sqrt{\frac{8}{15}}$	$\sqrt{\frac{1}{6}}$						
$+\frac{1}{2}$	-1							$\sqrt{\frac{3}{10}}$	$\sqrt{\frac{8}{15}}$	$\sqrt{\frac{1}{6}}$			
$-\frac{1}{2}$	0							$\sqrt{\frac{3}{5}}$	$-\sqrt{\frac{1}{15}}$	$-\sqrt{\frac{1}{3}}$			
$-\frac{3}{2}$	$+1$							$\sqrt{\frac{1}{10}}$	$-\sqrt{\frac{2}{3}}$	$\sqrt{\frac{1}{2}}$			
$-\frac{1}{2}$	-1										$\sqrt{\frac{3}{5}}$	$\sqrt{\frac{2}{5}}$	
$-\frac{3}{2}$	0										$\sqrt{\frac{2}{5}}$	$-\sqrt{\frac{3}{5}}$	
$-\frac{3}{2}$	-1												1

H Evaluation of some rotation matrix elements $d^{(j)}_{m'm}$

An angular momentum state $|jm\rangle$ is transformed under a finite rotation θ about the y or 2 axis into a linear combination of the $2j+1$ states $|jm'\rangle$ with $m' = j, j-1, \ldots, -j+1, -j$. The transformation is conventionally written

$$\exp(-\mathrm{i}\theta J_2)|jm\rangle = \sum_{m'} d^{(j)}_{m'm}(\theta)|jm'\rangle.$$

Then,

$$d^{(j)}_{m'm} = \langle jm'|\exp(-\mathrm{i}\theta J_2)|jm\rangle.$$

The coefficients $d^{(j)}_{m'm}$ are the (m', m)th elements of the matrix $\exp(-\mathrm{i}\theta J_2)$, where J_2 is the operator for the 2-component of angular momentum.

Case 1: $j = \frac{1}{2}$

Written in terms of the Pauli spin matrix,

$$\sigma_2 = \begin{pmatrix} 0 & -\mathrm{i} \\ \mathrm{i} & 0 \end{pmatrix}$$

we have

$$\exp(-\mathrm{i}\theta J_2) = \exp\left[-\mathrm{i}\left(\frac{\theta}{2}\right)\sigma_2\right] = 1 - \mathrm{i}\left(\frac{\theta}{2}\right)\sigma_2 - \left(\frac{\theta}{2}\right)^2\frac{\sigma_2^2}{2!} + \mathrm{i}\left(\frac{\theta}{2}\right)^3\frac{\sigma_2^3}{3!}$$
$$+ \left(\frac{\theta}{2}\right)^4\frac{\sigma_2^4}{4!} - \mathrm{i}\left(\frac{\theta}{2}\right)^5\frac{\sigma_2^5}{5!} - \left(\frac{\theta}{2}\right)^6\frac{\sigma_2^6}{6!} + \cdots.$$

Now $\sigma_2^2 = I$, the unit matrix and, since

$$\sin x = x - \frac{x^3}{3!} + \frac{x^5}{5!} - \cdots$$

and

$$\cos x = 1 - \frac{x^2}{2!} + \frac{x^4}{4!} - \cdots$$

we have

$$\exp\left[-\mathrm{i}\left(\frac{\theta}{2}\right)\sigma_2\right] = I\cos\left(\frac{\theta}{2}\right) - \mathrm{i}\sigma_2\sin\left(\frac{\theta}{2}\right)$$

$$= \begin{pmatrix} \cos\left(\frac{\theta}{2}\right) & -\sin\left(\frac{\theta}{2}\right) \\ \sin\left(\frac{\theta}{2}\right) & \cos\left(\frac{\theta}{2}\right) \end{pmatrix}.$$

Hence,

$$d^{(\frac{1}{2})}_{-\frac{1}{2}\frac{1}{2}} = -d^{(\frac{1}{2})}_{\frac{1}{2}-\frac{1}{2}} = \sin\left(\frac{\theta}{2}\right)$$

$$d^{(\frac{1}{2})}_{\frac{1}{2}\frac{1}{2}} = d^{(\frac{1}{2})}_{-\frac{1}{2}-\frac{1}{2}} = \cos\left(\frac{\theta}{2}\right).$$

Case 2: $j = 1$

From equation (8.21) with $j = 1$ we have

$$J_+ = \begin{pmatrix} 0 & \sqrt{2} & 0 \\ 0 & 0 & \sqrt{2} \\ 0 & 0 & 0 \end{pmatrix} \qquad J_- = \begin{pmatrix} 0 & 0 & 0 \\ \sqrt{2} & 0 & 0 \\ 0 & \sqrt{2} & 0 \end{pmatrix}$$

and

$$J_2^2 = \tfrac{1}{2}\begin{pmatrix} 1 & 0 & -1 \\ 0 & 2 & 0 \\ -1 & 0 & 1 \end{pmatrix}.$$

It is then a simple matter to show that $J_2^{2n+1} = J_2$ and $J_2^{2n} = J_2^2$ $(n = 1, 2, \ldots)$.

On expanding the exponential we have

$$\begin{aligned}
\exp(-\mathrm{i}\theta J_2) &= 1 - \mathrm{i}\theta J_2 - \frac{\theta^2}{2!}J_2^2 + \mathrm{i}\frac{\theta^3}{3!}J_2^3 + \frac{\theta^4}{4!}J_2^4 - \mathrm{i}\frac{\theta^5}{5!}J_2^5 - \frac{\theta^6}{6!}J_2^6 + \cdots \\
&= 1 - \mathrm{i}J_2\left(\theta - \frac{\theta^3}{3!} + \frac{\theta^5}{5!} - \cdots\right) - J_2^2\left(\frac{\theta^2}{2!} - \frac{\theta^4}{4!} + \frac{\theta^6}{6!} - \cdots\right) \\
&= 1 - \mathrm{i}J_2 \sin\theta - J_2^2(1 - \cos\theta) \\
&= \begin{pmatrix} \frac{1}{2}(1+\cos\theta) & -\frac{\sin\theta}{\sqrt{2}} & \frac{1}{2}(1-\cos\theta) \\ \frac{\sin\theta}{\sqrt{2}} & \cos\theta & -\frac{\sin\theta}{\sqrt{2}} \\ \frac{1}{2}(1-\cos\theta) & \frac{\sin\theta}{\sqrt{2}} & \frac{1}{2}(1+\cos\theta) \end{pmatrix}.
\end{aligned}$$

Hence,

$$\begin{aligned}
&d^{(1)}_{01} = -d^{(1)}_{10} = -d^{(1)}_{0-1} = d^{(1)}_{-10} = \frac{\sin\theta}{\sqrt{2}} \\
&d^{(1)}_{11} = d^{(1)}_{-1-1} = \tfrac{1}{2}(1 + \cos\theta) \\
&d^{(1)}_{-11} = d^{(1)}_{1-1} = \tfrac{1}{2}(1 - \cos\theta) \\
&d^{(1)}_{00} = \cos\theta.
\end{aligned}$$

I The Dirac delta function

The Dirac delta function $\delta(x)$ is defined by

$\delta(x) = 0$ for all $x \neq 0$

$\underset{x \to 0}{\text{Lt}}\ \delta(x) \to \infty$ in such a way that $\int \delta(x)\,\mathrm{d}x = 1$ for all ranges of integration which include $x = 0$.

I.1 Properties

(i) It follows from the definition that for any function $f(x)$

$$\int_{x_1}^{x_2} f(x)\delta(x - x_0)\,\mathrm{d}x = \begin{cases} f(x_0) & \text{for } x_1 < x_0 < x_2 \\ 0 & \text{for } x_0 < x_1 \text{ or } x_0 > x_2. \end{cases}$$

A three-dimensional delta function $\delta(\boldsymbol{r})$ may be defined as

$$\delta(\boldsymbol{r}) = \delta(x)\delta(y)\delta(z),$$

and, for any function $f(\boldsymbol{r})$, integration over a volume V gives

$$\int_V f(\boldsymbol{r})\delta(\boldsymbol{r} - \boldsymbol{r}_0)\,\mathrm{d}\boldsymbol{r} = \begin{cases} f(\boldsymbol{r}_0) & \text{if } \boldsymbol{r}_0 \text{ lies inside } V \\ 0 & \text{if } \boldsymbol{r}_0 \text{ lies outside } V. \end{cases}$$

(ii) Suppose we have a delta function $\delta(y)$ where $y = g(x)$, i.e. the argument of the delta function is itself a function. Then, by substitution, we have

$$\int \delta[g(x)]\,\mathrm{d}x = \int \delta(y)\frac{\mathrm{d}y}{|g'(x)|}.$$

The absolute value of $g'(x) = \mathrm{d}y/\mathrm{d}x$ is necessary to ensure that $\mathrm{d}x = \mathrm{d}y/|g'(x)|$ is always positive.

(iii) From (ii) it follows that if x_0 is the solution of $g(x) = 0$, then

$$\int \delta[g(x)]\,\mathrm{d}x = \frac{1}{|g'(x_0)|}.$$

(iv) For any function $f(x)$ which is continuous at $x = x_0$ it follows that

$$\int f(x)\delta[g(x)]\,\mathrm{d}x = \frac{f(x_0)}{|g'(x_0)|}.$$

J U spin multiplets

It is sometimes convenient to plot the SU(3) multiplets in terms of U_3 rather than I_3. This is achieved by rotating the multiplets through 120°, as shown in figure J.1 for the baryon decuplet. The U spin multiplets

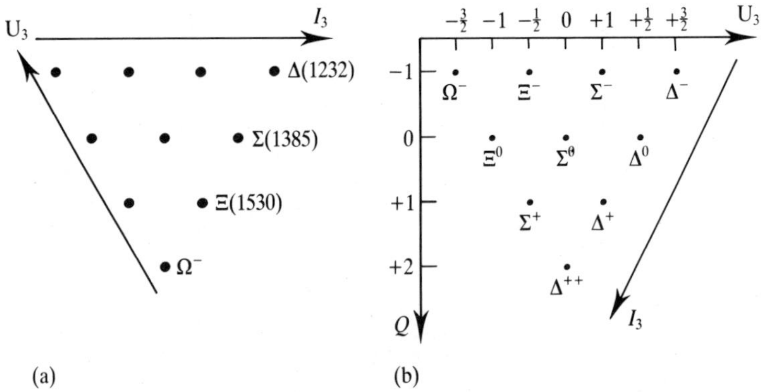

Figure J.1
The $\frac{3}{2}^+$ baryon decuplet plotted (a) in terms of I spin multiplets and (b) in terms of U spin multiplets.

contain particles with the same electric charge: the $\Delta^-(1232)$, $\Sigma^-(1385)$, $\Xi^-(1530)$ and Ω^-, for example, form a U spin quartet with $U = \frac{3}{2}$ and $U_3 = +\frac{3}{2}, +\frac{1}{2}, -\frac{1}{2}$ and $-\frac{3}{2}$ respectively. Each site in the decuplet has multiplicity 1 and hence the rotation is straightforward and leads to no ambiguity in the assignment of particles to U spin multiplets. A slight complication arises in the case of SU(3) octets because the central site is doubly occupied, by an isosinglet (the Λ^0 in the case of the $\frac{1}{2}^+$ baryon octet) and the $I_3 = 0$ member of an isotriplet (the Σ^0 in the $\frac{1}{2}^+$ baryon octet). The particles on the boundary of the multiplet are assigned unambiguously to U spin multiplets. At the centre of the octet we expect a U spin singlet and a member of a U spin triplet with $U_3 = 0$. Let us determine the structure of these two states.

We assume that the $U = 1$ triplet is

$$\begin{array}{cccc} & \Xi^0 & a\Sigma^0 + b\Lambda^0 & \mathrm{n} \\ U_3 & -1 & 0 & +1. \end{array}$$

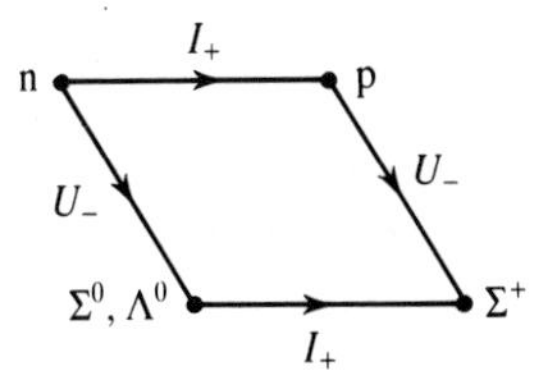

Figure J.2

The $U_3 = 0$ state is a linear combination of the $I_3 = 0$ isotriplet and isosinglet states. With reference to figure J.2 we see that we can effect the transformation $\mathrm{n} \rightarrow \Sigma^+$ in either of two equivalent ways using the step operators I_+ and U_-:

$$\mathrm{n} \xrightarrow{I_+} \mathrm{p} \xrightarrow{U_-} \Sigma^+ \quad \text{or} \quad \mathrm{n} \xrightarrow{U_-} \Sigma, \Lambda \xrightarrow{I_+} \Sigma_+$$

Using the relationships

$$I_+|I, I_3\rangle = \sqrt{[I(I+1) - I_3(I_3+1)]}|I, I_3+1\rangle$$

and

$$U_-|U, U_3\rangle = \sqrt{[U(U+1) - U_3(U_3-1)]}|U, U_3-1\rangle$$

we have

$$I_+|n\rangle = \sqrt{[\tfrac{1}{2}(\tfrac{1}{2}+1) - (-\tfrac{1}{2})(-\tfrac{1}{2}+1)]}|\mathrm{p}\rangle = |\mathrm{p}\rangle$$

and

$$U_-|\mathrm{p}\rangle = \sqrt{[\tfrac{1}{2}(\tfrac{1}{2}+1) - (\tfrac{1}{2})(\tfrac{1}{2}-1)]}|\Sigma^+\rangle = |\Sigma^+\rangle$$

by the first route.

By the second route

$$U_-|\mathrm{n}\rangle = \sqrt{[1(1+1) - 1(1-1)]}|a\Sigma^0 + b\Lambda^0\rangle$$
$$= \sqrt{2}[a|\Sigma^0\rangle + b|\Lambda^0\rangle]$$

and

$$I_+\sqrt{2}[a|\Sigma^0\rangle + b|\Lambda^0\rangle] = \sqrt{2}a\sqrt{[1(1+1) - 0(0+1)]}|\Sigma^+\rangle$$
$$= 2a|\Sigma^+\rangle$$

since $I_+|\Lambda^0\rangle = 0$. Because the two routes are equivalent we have

$$|\Sigma^+\rangle = 2a|\Sigma^+\rangle$$

and therefore

$$a = \tfrac{1}{2}.$$

Normalization of the state requires $a^2 + b^2 = 1$ and hence

$$|b| = \tfrac{1}{2}\sqrt{3}.$$

It is conventional to choose $b = \frac{1}{2}\sqrt{3}$ so the $U = 1$ triplet in the baryon octet is Ξ^0, $\frac{1}{2}(\Sigma^0 + \sqrt{3}\Lambda^0)$, n. The U spin singlet must be orthogonal to the $U_3 = 0$ state and is therefore $\frac{1}{2}(\Sigma^0 - \sqrt{3}\Lambda^0)$. The resultant octet is shown in figure J.3(a). Similar results hold for the meson octets: as an example the 0^- octet is shown in figure J.3(b).*

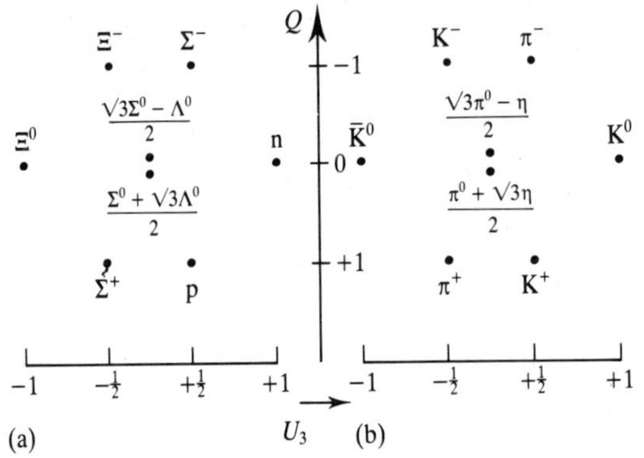

Figure J.3
(a) The $\frac{1}{2}^+$ baryon octet and (b) the 0^- meson octet showing the U spin multiplets consisting of particles with the same electric charge.

The algebra of U spin is identical to that of I spin so that analogous calculations can be performed with U spin multiplets by exploiting the fact that U spin is conserved in strong interactions.

* There is a further complication concerning the mesons which arises from mixing of the octet isosinglet and the unitary singlet states which was discussed in section 10.5.

K The completeness relations for Dirac spinors

The completeness relations for the Dirac spinors (11.52) and (11.54) are

$$\sum_{s=1,2} u^{(s)}(p)\bar{u}^{(s)}(p) = \not{p} + m \tag{K.1}$$

$$\sum_{s=1,2} v^{(s)}(p)\bar{v}^{(s)}(p) = \not{p} - m \tag{K.2}$$

Here, $u^{(s)}$ and $v^{(s)}$ are respectively the positive energy and negative energy spinors. (In section 11.4.5 the negative energy spinors $v^{(1)}$ and $v^{(2)}$ were labelled $u^{(3)}$ and $u^{(4)}$.) We recall that the 'slash' notation means $\not{p} \equiv \gamma^\mu p_\mu$ and that $\bar{u} \equiv u^\dagger\gamma^0$, with $\gamma^0 = \left(\begin{smallmatrix} I & 0 \\ 0 & -I \end{smallmatrix}\right)$, I being the 2 × 2 unit matrix.

We shall prove the completeness relation (K.1) and leave the proof of (K.2) as an exercise for the reader. With the usual definitions $\chi^{(1)} = \left(\begin{smallmatrix} 1 \\ 0 \end{smallmatrix}\right)$ and $\chi^{(2)} = \left(\begin{smallmatrix} 0 \\ 1 \end{smallmatrix}\right)$ the left-hand side of (K.1) is

$$N^2 \sum_{s=1,2} \begin{pmatrix} \chi^{(s)} \\ \dfrac{\boldsymbol{\sigma}\cdot\boldsymbol{p}}{E+m}\chi^{(s)} \end{pmatrix} \begin{pmatrix} \chi^{(s)\dagger} & \chi^{(s)\dagger}\dfrac{\boldsymbol{\sigma}\cdot\boldsymbol{p}}{E+m} \end{pmatrix} \begin{pmatrix} I & 0 \\ 0 & -I \end{pmatrix}$$

$$= N^2 \sum_{s=1,2} \begin{pmatrix} \chi^{(s)} \\ \dfrac{\boldsymbol{\sigma}\cdot\boldsymbol{p}}{E+m}\chi^{(s)} \end{pmatrix} \begin{pmatrix} \chi^{(s)\dagger} & -\chi^{(s)\dagger}\dfrac{\boldsymbol{\sigma}\cdot\boldsymbol{p}}{E+m} \end{pmatrix}$$

$$= N^2 \begin{pmatrix} I & \dfrac{-\boldsymbol{\sigma}\cdot\boldsymbol{p}}{E+m} \\ \dfrac{\boldsymbol{\sigma}\cdot\boldsymbol{p}}{E+m} & \dfrac{-p^2}{(E+m)^2} \end{pmatrix} = \begin{pmatrix} E+m & -\boldsymbol{\sigma}\cdot\boldsymbol{p} \\ \boldsymbol{\sigma}\cdot\boldsymbol{p} & \dfrac{-p^2}{E+m} \end{pmatrix} = \begin{pmatrix} E+m & -\boldsymbol{\sigma}\cdot\boldsymbol{p} \\ \boldsymbol{\sigma}\cdot\boldsymbol{p} & -(E-m) \end{pmatrix}$$

where we have used the covariant normalization, $N = (E + m)^{1/2}$.

For what follows, recall that the matrices β and α_i are given by

$$\beta = \begin{pmatrix} I & 0 \\ 0 & -I \end{pmatrix} \quad \text{and} \quad \alpha_i = \begin{pmatrix} 0 & \sigma_i \\ \sigma_i & 0 \end{pmatrix}$$

where σ_i are the Pauli matrices.

Now, the right-hand side of (K.1) is

$$\begin{aligned} \gamma^\mu p_\mu + m &= \gamma^0 E + \sum_{i=1}^{3} \gamma^i p_i + m \\ &= \beta E - \beta \boldsymbol{\alpha} \cdot \boldsymbol{p} + m \\ &= \begin{pmatrix} E + m & 0 \\ 0 & -E + m \end{pmatrix} - \begin{pmatrix} I & 0 \\ 0 & -I \end{pmatrix} \begin{pmatrix} 0 & \boldsymbol{\sigma} \cdot \boldsymbol{p} \\ \boldsymbol{\sigma} \cdot \boldsymbol{p} & 0 \end{pmatrix} \\ &= \begin{pmatrix} E + m & -\boldsymbol{\sigma} \cdot \boldsymbol{p} \\ \boldsymbol{\sigma} \cdot \boldsymbol{p} & -(E - m) \end{pmatrix} \end{aligned}$$

which completes the proof of (K.1).

L Trace theorems

We first prove some useful properties of γ^5. Recall the definitions of the γ matrices:

$$\gamma^0 = \begin{pmatrix} I & 0 \\ 0 & -I \end{pmatrix} \qquad \gamma^i = \begin{pmatrix} 0 & \sigma_i \\ -\sigma_i & 0 \end{pmatrix} \qquad \text{for } i = 1, 2, 3.$$

The γ matrices satisfy the basic anti-commutation relation

$$\{\gamma^\mu, \gamma^\nu\} = 2g^{\mu\nu}.$$

By definition,

$$\gamma^5 = \mathrm{i}\gamma^0\gamma^1\gamma^2\gamma^3.$$

Property 1 $\quad \gamma^5\gamma^5 = I.$
Proof (independent of representation)

$$\begin{aligned} \gamma^5\gamma^5 &= (\mathrm{i}\gamma^0\gamma^1\gamma^2\gamma^3)(\mathrm{i}\gamma^0\gamma^1\gamma^2\gamma^3) \\ &= -(\gamma^0\gamma^1\gamma^2\gamma^3)(-\gamma^3)(\gamma^2)(-\gamma^1)\gamma^0 \end{aligned}$$

where we have used the basic anti-commutation relation in changing the order of the γ matrices. Now, $(\gamma^i)^2 = -I$ for $i = 1, 2, 3$ and $(\gamma^0)^2 = I$. Therefore

$$\begin{aligned} \gamma^5\gamma^5 &= -\gamma^0\gamma^1\gamma^2\gamma^3\gamma^3\gamma^2\gamma^1\gamma^0 \\ &= -\gamma^0\gamma^1\gamma^2(-I)\gamma^2\gamma^1\gamma^0 \\ &= -\gamma^0\gamma^1(-I)(-I)\gamma^1\gamma^0 \\ &= -\gamma^0(-I)(-I)(-I)\gamma^0 \\ &= I. \end{aligned}$$

Property 2 $\gamma^5\gamma^\mu = -\gamma^\mu\gamma^5$.
Proof Take $\mu = 2$ for example:

$$\gamma^5\gamma^2 = (\mathrm{i}\gamma^0\gamma^1\gamma^2\gamma^3)\gamma^2.$$

On moving γ^2 progressively from the right and using the basic anti-commutation relation we have

$$\begin{aligned}\gamma^5\gamma^2 &= -\mathrm{i}\gamma^0\gamma^1\gamma^2\gamma^2\gamma^3\\ &= \mathrm{i}\gamma^0\gamma^2\gamma^1\gamma^2\gamma^3\\ &= -\mathrm{i}\gamma^2\gamma^0\gamma^1\gamma^2\gamma^3\\ &= -\gamma^2\gamma^5.\end{aligned}$$

Trace theorem (i) The cyclic property

$$\mathrm{Tr}[AB\ldots YZ] = \mathrm{Tr}[ZAB\ldots Y] = \text{etc.}$$

Proof With the usual summation convention

$$\begin{aligned}\mathrm{Tr}[AB\ldots YZ] = (AB\ldots YZ)_{\alpha\alpha} &= A_{\alpha\beta}B_{\beta\gamma}\ldots Y_{\delta\epsilon}Z_{\epsilon\alpha}\\ &= Z_{\epsilon\alpha}A_{\alpha\beta}B_{\beta\gamma}\ldots Y_{\delta\epsilon}\\ &= (ZAB\ldots Y)_{\epsilon\epsilon}\\ &= \mathrm{Tr}[ZAB\ldots Y].\end{aligned}$$

Trace theorem (ii) For arbitrary four-vectors a and b, $\mathrm{Tr}[\not{a}\ \not{b}] = 4a\cdot b$.
Proof

$$\begin{aligned}\not{a}\ \not{b} &= \gamma^\mu a_\mu\gamma^\nu b_\nu\\ &= \gamma^\mu\gamma^\nu a_\mu b_\nu\\ &= (-\gamma^\nu\gamma^\mu + 2g^{\mu\nu})a_\mu b_\nu\\ &= -\not{b}\ \not{a} + 2a\cdot b\end{aligned}$$

where $a\cdot b = a_\mu b_\mu$. Therefore,

$$\mathrm{Tr}[\not{a}\ \not{b} + \not{b}\ \not{a}] = 2\mathrm{Tr}[\not{a}\ \not{b}] = 2\mathrm{Tr}[a\cdot b] = 2a\cdot b\ \mathrm{Tr}(I) = 8a\cdot b$$

since the trace of the 4×4 unit matrix is 4. Hence,

$$\mathrm{Tr}[\not{a}\ \not{b}] = 4a\cdot b.$$

Trace theorem (iii) $\mathrm{Tr}[\gamma^\mu\gamma^\nu] = 4g^{\mu\nu}$.
Proof

$$\gamma^\mu\gamma^\nu + \gamma^\nu\gamma^\mu = 2g^{\mu\nu}.$$

Therefore

$$2\mathrm{Tr}[\gamma^\mu\gamma^\nu] = 2g^{\mu\nu}\,\mathrm{Tr}(I) = 8g^{\mu\nu}$$

as required.

Trace theorem (iv) $\mathrm{Tr}[\gamma^\mu] = 0$.
Proof

$$\begin{aligned}\mathrm{Tr}[\gamma^\mu] &= \mathrm{Tr}[\gamma^\mu\gamma^5\gamma^5] \text{ by property 1}\\ &= -\mathrm{Tr}[\gamma^5\gamma^\mu\gamma^5] \text{ by property 2}\\ &= -\mathrm{Tr}[\gamma^5\gamma^5\gamma^\mu] \text{ by the cyclic property of the trace}\\ &= -\mathrm{Tr}[\gamma^\mu].\end{aligned}$$

Therefore

$$\mathrm{Tr}[\gamma^\mu] = 0.$$

Trace theorem (v) For an *odd* number of γ matrices $\mathrm{Tr}[\gamma^\mu \dots \gamma^\nu] = 0$.
Proof

$$\begin{aligned}\mathrm{Tr}[\gamma^\mu \dots \gamma^\nu] &= \mathrm{Tr}[\gamma^\mu \dots \gamma^\nu\gamma^5\gamma^5] \text{ by property 1}\\ &= -\mathrm{Tr}[\gamma^5\gamma^\mu \dots \gamma^\nu\gamma^5] \text{ by property 2}\\ &= -\mathrm{Tr}[\gamma^5\gamma^5\gamma^\mu \dots \gamma^\nu] \text{ by the cyclic property}\\ &= -\mathrm{Tr}[\gamma^\mu \dots \gamma^\nu].\end{aligned}$$

Therefore

$$\mathrm{Tr}[\gamma^\mu \dots \gamma^\nu] = 0.$$

Trace theorem (vi) $\mathrm{Tr}[\not{a} \dots \not{b}] = 0$ for an odd number of factors.
Proof

$$\begin{aligned}\mathrm{Tr}[\not{a} \dots \not{b}] &= \mathrm{Tr}[\gamma^\mu \dots \gamma^\nu a_\mu \dots b_\nu]\\ &= \mathrm{Tr}[\gamma^\mu \dots \gamma^\nu](a_\mu \dots b_\nu)\\ &= 0 \text{ by theorem (v).}\end{aligned}$$

Trace theorem (vii)

$$\mathrm{Tr}[\not{a}\not{b}\not{c}\not{d}] = 4[(a\cdot b)(c\cdot d) + (a\cdot d)(b\cdot c) - (a\cdot c)(b\cdot d)].$$

Proof Using the result from theorem (ii) $\not{a}\not{b} = -\not{b}\not{a} + 2a\cdot b$, we move $\not{a}$ to the right of $\not{b}$ to obtain

$$\mathrm{Tr}[\not{a}\not{b}\not{c}\not{d}] = 2a\cdot b\,\mathrm{Tr}[\not{c}\not{d}] - \mathrm{Tr}[\not{b}\not{a}\not{c}\not{d}].$$

Repeated application gives

$$\begin{aligned}\mathrm{Tr}[\not{a}\not{b}\not{c}\not{d}] &= 2a\cdot b\,\mathrm{Tr}[\not{c}\not{d}] - 2a\cdot c\,\mathrm{Tr}[\not{b}\not{d}] + \mathrm{Tr}[\not{b}\not{c}\not{a}\not{d}]\\ &= 2a\cdot b\,\mathrm{Tr}[\not{c}\not{d}] - 2a\cdot c\,\mathrm{Tr}[\not{b}\not{d}] + 2a\cdot d\,\mathrm{Tr}[\not{b}\not{c}] - \mathrm{Tr}(\not{b}\not{c}\not{d}\not{a}).\end{aligned}$$

Since, by the cyclic property, $\mathrm{Tr}[\not{b}\not{c}\not{d}\not{a}] = \mathrm{Tr}[\not{a}\not{b}\not{c}\not{d}]$, and $\mathrm{Tr}[\not{c}\not{d}] = 4c\cdot d$ by theorem (ii), we arrive at the desired result

$$\mathrm{Tr}[\not{a}\not{b}\not{c}\not{d}] = 4[(a\cdot b)(c\cdot d) + (a\cdot d)(b\cdot c) - (a\cdot c)(b\cdot d)].$$

M Colour factors

The quantum theory of the interactions between quarks and gluons, QCD, is based on the SU(3) colour group, which, unlike SU(3) flavour, is assumed to be an exact symmetry. The generators of the $SU(3)_c$ group are the eight Gell–Mann matrices, λ_i ($i = 1, \ldots, 8$), introduced in section 10.1.1. In QCD, each quark flavour carries a strong or colour 'charge' which can take on three values, namely, red (R), green (G) and blue (B). These form the fundamental (**3**) representation of the group and are shown in figure M.1 together with the $\bar{\mathbf{3}}$ representation of the anti-colour states $\bar{R}$, $\bar{G}$ and $\bar{B}$. The mediators of the forces between coloured quarks, the gluons, belong to a colour singlet and a colour octet ($\mathbf{3} \otimes \bar{\mathbf{3}} = \mathbf{1} \otimes \mathbf{8}$). The singlet state,

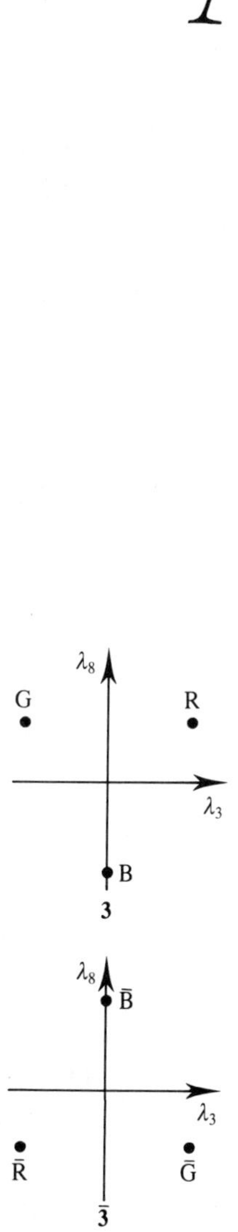

Figure M.1
Weight diagrams for the fundamental **3** and $\bar{\mathbf{3}}$ representations of the $SU(3)_{\text{colour}}$ group.

$$g_0 = \frac{1}{\sqrt{3}}(R\bar{R} + G\bar{G} + B\bar{B})$$

does not carry colour and therefore does not interact with coloured quarks. We consider, therefore, only interactions between the quarks and the octet of gluons:

$$\begin{aligned}
&g_1 = R\bar{G} \qquad g_2 = R\bar{B} \qquad g_3 = G\bar{R} \\
&g_4 = G\bar{B} \qquad g_5 = B\bar{R} \qquad g_6 = B\bar{G} \\
&g_7 = \frac{1}{\sqrt{2}}(R\bar{R} - G\bar{G}) \qquad g_8 = \frac{1}{\sqrt{6}}(R\bar{R} + G\bar{G} - 2B\bar{B}).
\end{aligned} \tag{M.1}$$

These gluon colour wavefunctions are identical to the quark flavour wavefunctions of the octet of pseudoscalar mesons (for example) with the replacement $u \to R$, $d \to G$, $s \to B$, etc. (see section 10.3).

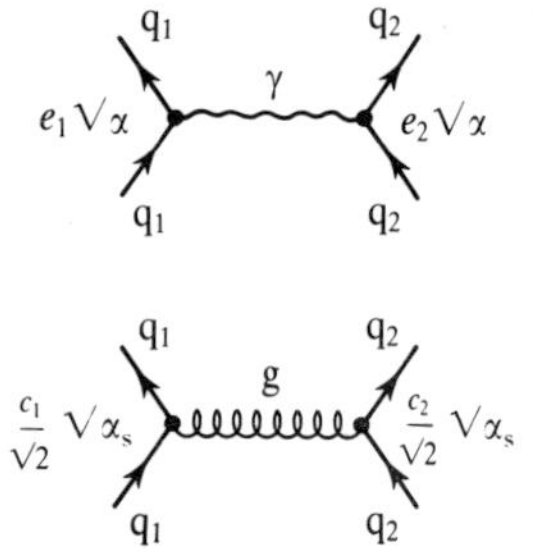

Figure M.2
Feynman diagrams for the electromagnetic interaction between quarks via single photon exchange and the strong interaction between quarks via single gluon exchange.

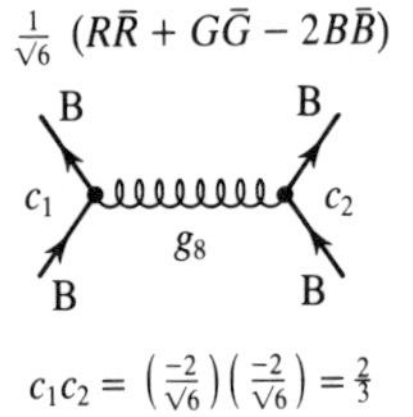

Figure M.3

In QED, the strength of the electromagnetic coupling between two quarks with electric charge e_1 and e_2 (measured in units of e) is $e_1 e_2 \alpha$, where the fine-structure constant $\alpha = e^2/4\pi$. In analogy, the strength of the strong coupling between two quarks is given by $(c_1/\sqrt{2})(c_2/\sqrt{2})\alpha_s$, where c_1 and c_2 are the colour coefficients associated with each vertex (see figure M.2) and $\alpha_s = g_s^2/4\pi$, where g_s is the strong coupling constant. It is unfortunate, but conventional, that the extra factors $1/\sqrt{2}$ are introduced at each vertex. The colour *factor* for the interaction is defined as $\frac{1}{2}c_1c_2$, i.e. the coefficient multiplying α_s in the amplitude for the appropriate Feynman diagram.

Consider first the coupling between a pair of like quarks such as BB → BB as shown in figure M.3. In this case the force can be transmitted only by the exchange of a gluon containing the colour combination $\mathrm{B\bar{B}}$, i.e. g_8, and the colour factor is thus

$$\frac{1}{2}c_1c_2 = \frac{1}{2}\left(\frac{-2}{\sqrt{6}}\right)\left(\frac{-2}{\sqrt{6}}\right) = \frac{1}{3}. \tag{M.2}$$

The interaction between two R quarks, on the other hand, can proceed either by the exchange of gluon g_7 or g_8, as shown in figure M.4. In this case the colour factor is

$$\frac{1}{2}\left(\frac{1}{\sqrt{2}}\right)\left(\frac{1}{\sqrt{2}}\right) + \frac{1}{2}\left(\frac{1}{\sqrt{6}}\right)\left(\frac{1}{\sqrt{6}}\right) = \frac{1}{3}. \tag{M.3}$$

As expected from colour symmetry this is the same as the colour factor for the interaction between B quarks. Similarly, the colour factor for G quarks is

$$\frac{1}{2}\left(\frac{-1}{\sqrt{2}}\right)\left(\frac{-1}{\sqrt{2}}\right) + \frac{1}{2}\left(\frac{1}{\sqrt{6}}\right)\left(\frac{1}{\sqrt{6}}\right) = \frac{1}{3}. \tag{M.4}$$

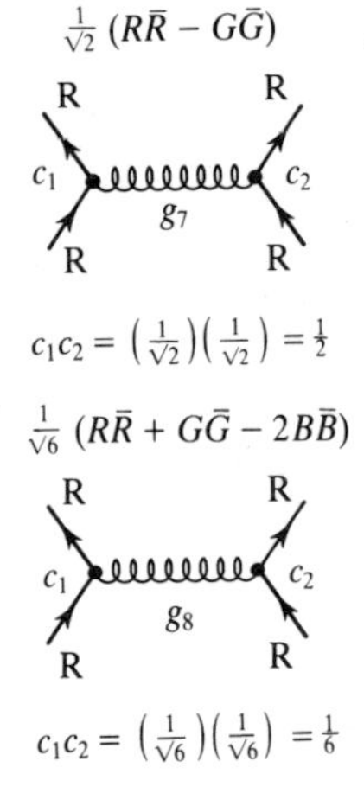

Figure M.4

Let us now determine the colour factors, used in section 10.5, for $q\bar{q}$ and qq pairs relevant to mesons and baryons respectively. In the case of mesons the $q\bar{q}$ pair must be in a colour singlet state with a colour wavefunction

$$(q\bar{q})_{\text{singlet}} = \frac{1}{\sqrt{3}}(R\bar{R} + G\bar{G} + B\bar{B}). \tag{M.5}$$

Since each colour combination appears symmetrically in (M.5) it is sufficient to consider only one, the $\mathrm{B\bar{B}}$ interaction say, which is shown in figure M.5. The minus sign arises in the coefficients c_2 involving antiquarks because, as in QED, quarks and antiquarks have opposite charges. The overall colour factor for the $q\bar{q}$ interaction is then

$$3\left(\frac{1}{2}\right)\left(\frac{1}{\sqrt{3}}\right)\left(\frac{1}{\sqrt{3}}\right)\left(-\frac{2}{3}-1-1\right)=-\frac{4}{3}. \tag{M.6}$$

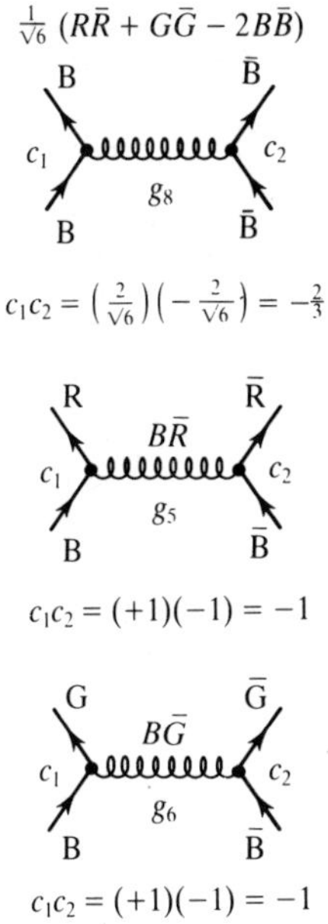

Figure M.5

The first factor of 3 arises from the additional $R\bar{R}$ and $G\bar{G}$ interactions. In contrast to the previous cases considered, the colour factor is negative and indicates that the force is *attractive.*

The calculation of the colour factor for quarks pairs in a baryon is a little more complicated. We need to construct a colour singlet from products of the fundamental **3** representation. We have (see section 10.1.3),

$$\mathbf{3}\otimes\mathbf{3}\otimes\mathbf{3}=\mathbf{3}\otimes(\mathbf{6}\oplus\bar{\mathbf{3}})=(\mathbf{3}\otimes\mathbf{6})\oplus(\mathbf{3}\otimes\bar{\mathbf{3}}).$$

Only the second product contains a singlet: $\mathbf{3}\otimes\bar{\mathbf{3}}=\mathbf{1}\oplus\mathbf{8}$. Thus *each* quark pair in a baryon is in an antisymmetric colour state ($\bar{\mathbf{3}}$) and couples with a third quark (a colour **3** state) to form a colour singlet. The colour wavefunction is then

$$(qqq)_{\text{singlet}}=\frac{1}{\sqrt{6}}\{(RB-BR)G+(BG-GB)R+(GR-RG)B\}. \tag{M.7}$$

We wish to calculate the colour factor for interactions between pairs of quarks and from equation (M.7) we see that this involves interactions between quarks with different colours. The six separate terms in (M.7) give identical results so it is sufficient to consider the first of these, namely the interaction between a red and a blue quark. The relevant diagrams are shown in figure M.6 and correspond to the interactions RB → RB and RB → BR. Taking into account the coefficients in the quark wavefunction we obtain, for the overall contribution from the RB interactions, a colour factor

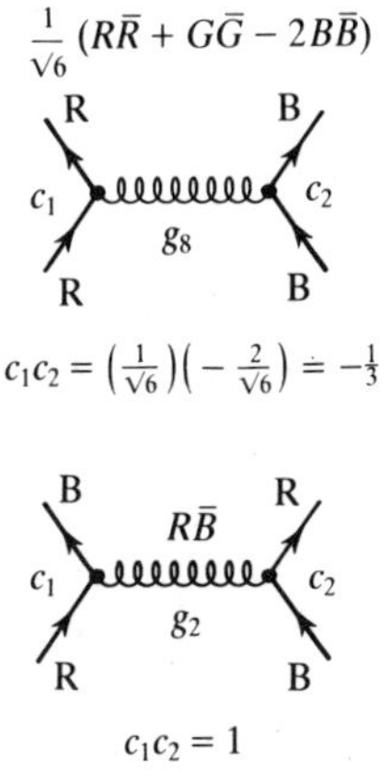

Figure M.6

$$\left(\frac{1}{6}\right)\left(-\frac{1}{6}\right)+\left(-\frac{1}{6}\right)\left(\frac{1}{2}\right)=-\frac{1}{9} \tag{M.8}$$

where the minus sign in the second term arises from the antisymmetry of the wavefunction under quark interchange. Finally, we have to multiply this result by six to obtain a colour factor of $-\frac{2}{3}$ for a pair of quarks in a three-quark colour-singlet baryon.

Solutions to examples

Chapter 1

1.1 $N_t = N_0 \exp(-\lambda t)$

$$\tau = \frac{\int_{N_0}^{0} t \, dN_t}{\int_{N_0}^{0} dN_t} = \frac{\int_0^\infty t \exp(-\lambda t) \, dt}{\int_0^\infty \exp(-\lambda t) \, dt} = \frac{1}{\lambda}.$$

1.2 The chance that an atom shall *not* have undergone change in the time $t = k\Delta$ is

$$(1 - \lambda\Delta)^k = [(1 - \lambda\Delta)^{-1/\lambda\Delta}]^{-\lambda t} = q \text{ say.}$$

Let $\Delta \to 0$ while $k\Delta$ remains finite. The square bracket is then the exponential and $q \to \exp(-\lambda t)$.

1.3 Chemical extraction removes MsTh1 as well as ThX but ThX grows by steady production from RdTh at rate p.

For decay

$$\frac{dN_t}{dt} = -\lambda N_t \qquad N_t = N_0 \exp(-\lambda t).$$

For growth

$$\frac{dN_t}{dt} = p - \lambda N_t \qquad N_t = N_0[1 - \exp(-\lambda t)].$$

N_0 is the equilibrium number of ThX atoms ($= p/\lambda$).

1.4 From equation (1.14)

$$\sigma(\theta) = \frac{1}{n_0}\frac{dY}{d\Omega}\frac{1}{Nx}$$

$$= \frac{2 \times 1.6 \times 10^{-19}}{10^{-6}}\frac{6 \times 10^4 \times 0.1^2}{10^{-4}}\frac{0.1078}{6 \times 10^{23} \times 0.002}$$

$$= 1.72 \times 10^{-28}$$

$$= b^2 \operatorname{cosec}^4\left(\frac{\theta}{2}\right)\Big/ 16$$

from equations (1.15) and (1.11). With given value for θ, $b = 13.1 \times 10^{-15}$ m.

1.5 Let $\gamma = m/M$ where M is the known and m the unknown mass and let the angles for m and M be θ and ϕ. Then by writing down the equations of conservation of energy and momentum it is easy to find that

$$\gamma = \frac{\sin\phi}{\sin(2\theta + \phi)}$$

whence $\gamma = 3.07$ and $A = 12.28$.

1.6 If p is the linear momentum of the proton the angular momentum quantum number is $l = bp/\hbar$ with b given by equation (1.11).

Chapter 2

2.1 Take the origin to be the point at which the particle and electron are separated by a distance b and let s be the distance of the particle from this point at a given instant. The particle–electron separation is then $(s^2 + b^2)^{1/2}$ and we let $\theta = \tan^{-1}(s/b)$. The resolved momentum transfer is

$$q = \frac{1}{4\pi\epsilon_0}\int_{-\infty}^{\infty}\frac{ze^2}{b^2 + s^2}\frac{ds}{v}\frac{b}{(b^2 + s^2)^{1/2}}$$

$$= \frac{1}{4\pi\epsilon_0}\frac{ze^2}{bv}\int_{-\pi/2}^{\pi/2}\cos\theta\, d\theta$$

$$= \frac{1}{4\pi\epsilon_0}\frac{2ze^2}{bv}.$$

The energy transfer is

$$\frac{dE}{dx} = \int \frac{q^2}{2m_e} 2\pi b\, db\, NZ = \frac{1}{(4\pi\epsilon_0)^2}\frac{4\pi z^2 e^4}{m_e v^2} NZ \ln\left(\frac{b_{max}}{b_{min}}\right)$$

which has the form of equation (2.1a) apart from the model-dependent evaluation of the logarithmic term.

2.2 The stopping power s given by equation (2.1a) may be written

$$s \propto \frac{1}{v^2} \ln\left(\frac{2m_e v^2}{I}\right).$$

Setting $\mathrm{d}s/\mathrm{d}v = 0$ gives $2m_e v^2/I = e^1 = 2.7$ say, whence $T_p = \frac{1}{2}m_p v^2 =$ 187 keV for $I = 150$ eV.

2.3 From equation (2.2)

$$R = \frac{m}{z^2} f(v)$$

so that $R_{\mathrm{He}^3}/R_\alpha = 0.75$ and $R_{\mathrm{H}^3}/R_\alpha = 0.75 \times 4 = 3$.

2.4 Taking 1 mass unit as 931 MeV/c^2 the Lorentz factor for the triton is

$$\gamma = \frac{(5000 + 3 \times 931)}{3 \times 931} = 2.79 = \frac{1}{(1 - \beta^2)^{1/2}}$$

whence $\beta = 0.93$ and $\theta = \cos^{-1}(1/\beta n) = 44°$.

2.5 Transform the integration in equation (2.8) to the wavelength variable, integrate between λ_2 and λ_1 and divide by h to get the number of photons per unit distance in the form

$$\frac{\pi e^2}{c\epsilon_0 h}\left(1 - \frac{1}{\beta^2 n^2}\right)\left(\frac{1}{\lambda_1} - \frac{1}{\lambda_2}\right) \text{ photons per metre.}$$

2.6 The X-ray energy must be slightly above an absorption edge in Ti. For Al it will then be considerably above the same edge and for Cu below it. Tables will show that it is the K edge.

2.7 Assume that the density of carbon is 2.27×10^3 kg m^{-3} and that the mass of a carbon atom is $12 \times 1.66 \times 10^{-27}$ kg. The attenuation in 0.01 m is $I/I_0 = \exp(-\mu x) = 0.64$ so that $\mu x = 0.446$ or $\mu = 44.6$ m^{-1}.
From section 2.1.4 $\mu = ZN\sigma$ assuming Z electrons per atom and $N = (2.27 \times 10^3)/(12 \times 1.66 \times 10^{-27})$ atoms m^{-3}. Using the given cross-section $Z = 5.8$.

2.8 From equation (2.14) $\lambda' - \lambda = h/m_e c(1 - \cos\theta) =$ $2.43 \times 10^{-12}(1 - \cos\theta)$ m and with $\cos\theta = 0.71$, $\lambda' = 0.01 + 0.7 \times 10^{-3} =$ 0.0107 nm. The incident energy is $hc/\lambda = 123.9$ keV, the scattered energy is $hc/\lambda' = 115.8$ keV and the electron energy T is therefore 8.1 keV and the electron velocity v_e is $(2T/m_e)^{1/2} = 5.3 \times 10^7$ m s^{-1} neglecting relativistic corrections. The electron momentum is

$$m_e v_e = 9.1 \times 10^{-31} \times 5.3 \times 10^7 \text{ joules m}^{-1}\text{ s}$$

$$= 9.1 \times 5.3 \times 10^{-24} \frac{3 \times 10^8}{1.6 \times 10^{-16}} \text{keV } c^{-1}.$$

2.9 Let the initial and final electron energy be E_1 and E_2 and the initial and final photon energy be $h\nu_1$ and $h\nu_2$. The initial momenta are for the electron $p_1 = (1511^2 - 511^2)^{1/2} = 1422$ keV/c and for the photon 100 keV/c. The equations for conservation of momentum and energy are then

$$1422 - 100 = p_2 + h\nu_2 \text{ keV}/c$$

$$1511 + 100 = E_2 + h\nu_2 \text{ keV}.$$

Eliminate the unwanted E_2 and p_2 by use of $E_2^2 - p_2^2 = m_e^2$. This gives $(1611 - h\nu_2)^2 - (1322 - h\nu_2)^2 = 511^2$ whence $h\nu_2 = 1015$.

2.10 From equation (2.14) $\lambda' = \lambda + h/m_e c$ for $\theta = 90°$ and the energy is

$$\frac{hc}{\lambda'} = \frac{hc}{\lambda + h/m_e c} \rightarrow m_e c^2 \text{ as } \lambda \rightarrow 0.$$

2.11 If θ is the angle which the electron (or positron) makes with the photon direction and p and E are the momentum and energy of each particle then conservation of momentum and energy give, with $c = 1$,

$$h\nu = 2p\cos\theta \qquad (\text{keV}/c \text{ say})$$

$$h\nu = 2E \qquad (\text{keV say})$$

whence $p^2\cos^2\theta = E^2 = p^2 + m_e^2$ which is impossible.

2.12 Let the γ ray energy be E_γ. At threshold the particles are at rest in the centre-of-mass system. Conservation of *four-momentum* gives, for a final system of three electron masses,

$$p_\gamma + p_e = p_{3m}.$$

Taking the scalar product

$$(p_\gamma)^2 + (p_e)^2 + 2\boldsymbol{p}_\gamma \cdot \boldsymbol{p}_e = (p_{3m})^2$$

and inserting values for an electron initially at rest and $c = 1$

$$0 + m_e^2 + 2E_\gamma m_e = 9m_e^2$$

whence $E_\gamma = 4m_e$.

2.13 We assume that the electron energy is very much less than $m_e c^2$. The energy of each annihilation quantum is then $m_e c^2$ and its momentum $m_e c$. Let $p_{\perp r}$ bisect the angle ($\approx \pi$) between the quanta and the result follows.

2.14 Let p and E be the momentum and total energy of the positron and p_1 and p_2 the momenta of the two (collinear) photons. Take $c = 1$ so that the photon energies are also p_1 and p_2. Then by conservation of momentum and energy

$$p = p_1 - p_2$$
$$E + m = p_1 + p_2.$$

Eliminating p_2 and remembering that, for $E \gg m$, $E \approx p$ we find $2p_1 = 2E + m = 2T + 3m$ as required.

2.15 Use equation (2.18) to find the field at the wire. For a field of 2250 keV m^{-1} the same equation indicates a radial distance of 0.145 mm so that the distance to the wire is 0.145 – 0.100 mm = 0.045 mm. This contains nine mean free paths and assuming that each collision leads to ionization the multiplication factor is $2^9 = 512$.

2.16 Counts are lost during a period of 300 × 10 000/60 s during each second. This is 0.05 s so the true rate will be 10 000/0.95 = 10 526.

2.17 From equation (2.14) the maximum loss of energy to an electron is when $\theta = \pi$. We then have $hc/E' - hc/E = 2h/m_e c$ and the high energy Compton edge is at the energy $E - E' = 2E^2/(2E + m_e c^2) = \frac{2}{3}m_e c^2$ for $E = m_e c^2$. This is separated from the photopeak at $E = m_e c^2$ by $\frac{1}{3}m_e c^2 = 170$ keV. The energy of the back-scattered radiation is $E' = \frac{1}{3}m_e c^2 = 170$ keV.

2.18 From equation (2.1a), $\mathrm{d}E/\mathrm{d}x \approx z^2/v^2$ neglecting the logarithmic term. For a non-relativistic particle $T = \frac{1}{2}mv^2$ so that $T\,\mathrm{d}T/\mathrm{d}x \propto mz^2$. For deuterons $m \propto 2$, $z = 1$ and for ^{3}He $m \propto 3$, $z = 2$.

2.19 Express V in terms of r and set $\mathrm{d}V/\mathrm{d}r = 0$.

2.20 Neglecting relativistic corrections $v = (2T/m_p)^{1/2}$ so that $(v/c)^2 = 2T/m_p c^2 = 20/938$ whence $v/c = 0.15$. For uniform acceleration f over a length l we have $l = \frac{1}{2}ft^2$ and $f = Ee/m_p$ where E is the electric field. With the quantities given, $E = 10^7/3$ eV m^{-1} and

$$t^2 = 2l/(Ee/m_p)$$
$$= \frac{2 \times 3}{(10^7 \times 1.6 \times 10^{-19})/(3 \times 1.67 \times 10^{-27})}\ \mathrm{s}^2$$
$$= 1.88 \times 10^{-14}\ \mathrm{s}^2$$

so that $t = 1.4 \times 10^{-7}$ s.

2.21 Let the surface density of charge be σ. Then by Gauss's theorem the electric field near the surface element dS is given by $2E\,\mathrm{d}S = 4\pi\sigma\,\mathrm{d}S/4\pi\epsilon_0$ or $E = \sigma/2\epsilon_0$. The maximum charge carried to the terminal per second is then $\sigma v b$ where v is the speed of the belt and b is its width. Inserting values we get the current as

$$i = 2 \times 8.85 \times 10^{-12} \times 3 \times 10^6 \times 20 \times 0.3 = 319 \times 10^{-6}\ \mathrm{A}.$$

The electrode potential rises at the rate

$$i/C = (319 \times 10^{-6})/(111 \times 10^{-12})\ \mathrm{V\,s^{-1}} = 2.9\ \mathrm{mV\,s^{-1}}.$$

2.22 Since $E = \gamma m$, uniform increments of energy mean that γ increases uniformly with distance along the accelerator, so that

$$\gamma = \gamma_0 + kl \qquad \text{or} \qquad \mathrm{d}l = k^{-1}\,\mathrm{d}\gamma.$$

From the point of view of the electron, a Lorentz transformation gives $\mathrm{d}l_e = \mathrm{d}l/\gamma = \mathrm{d}\gamma/k\gamma$ so that $l_e = k^{-1}\ln(\gamma_f/\gamma_0)$ where γ_f refers to the final energy. Substituting the values given, $l_e = 0.57$ m.

2.23 Since the magnetic force for velocity v is Bev and the electric force is Ee the effective reduction of magnetic field is $\Delta B = E/v$. The deuteron velocity v is given by $v^2 = (2 \times 15 \times 1.6 \times 10^{-13})/(2 \times 1.67 \times 10^{-27})$ whence $v = 3.79 \times 10^7\ \mathrm{m\,s^{-1}}$ and for $E = 6 \times 10^6\ \mathrm{V\,m^{-1}}$, $\Delta B = 0.16$ T. From equation (2.24) the field B is given by

$$B = \frac{mv}{er} = \frac{(2mT)^{1/2}}{er}$$

where T is the kinetic energy and r the orbit radius. Substitution of values gives $B = 1.54$ T and Δr is then given by $r\,\Delta B/B = 0.053$ m.

2.24 Since 10^{10} particles of charge e appear at a point 7×10^6 times per second the current is $i = 10^{10} \times 1.6 \times 10^{-19} \times 7 \times 10^6\ \mathrm{A} = 11.2 \times 10^{-3}$ A.

2.25 In natural units (appendix F) $E^2 - p^2 = E'^2$, where E is the total energy in the laboratory system, p is the beam momentum in the laboratory and E' is the total centre-of-mass energy. If W is the beam energy $E = W + m$ and $p^2 = W^2 - m^2$, where m is the proton mass. Hence $E' = (2mW)^{1/2} = 7.25$ GeV. This is low compared with the collider energy of 56 GeV. The equivalent energy of a fixed target accelerator is $W = E'^2/2m = 1.67$ TeV.

2.26 The transverse momentum imparted to a particle in traversing the length l of separator is $p_T = \int F\,\mathrm{d}t = eEl/\beta c$. Hence

$$\Delta\theta = \frac{\Delta p_T}{p} = \frac{eEl}{pc}\left(\frac{1}{\beta_K} - \frac{1}{\beta_\pi}\right).$$

For a momentum p, $\beta = p/E$, hence $\beta_K^{-1} = 1.0135$ and $\beta_\pi^{-1} = 1.0011$. Thus

$$\Delta\theta = \frac{1 \times 10^{-6} \times 5 \times 5 \times 10^{-6} \times 0.0124}{3 \times 10^3} = 0.1\ \mathrm{mrad}.$$

2.27 Threshold Cherenkov counters discriminate between two particles of the same momentum and different masses simply by whether radiation is emitted or not (choose $1/n$ between β_1 and β_2). We need to compare values of β with values of $1/n$, or equivalently $1/\beta$ with n. We have $\beta = p/E$ or $\beta^{-1} = E/p = (p^2 + m^2)^{1/2}/p = (1 + m^2/p^2)^{1/2}$; hence $\beta^{-1} \approx 1 + \frac{1}{2}m^2/p^2$.

Particle	Mass/GeV	$p/(\text{GeV}/c)$	$\beta^{-1} - 1$	Pressure/atm	$n - 1$
π	0.140	10	9.8×10^{-5}	1	3×10^{-4}
K	0.494	10	1.22×10^{-3}	10	3×10^{-3}
p	0.938	10	4.4×10^{-3}	20	6×10^{-3}

Positive identification may be achieved with three Cherenkov counters with pressures chosen, for example, as shown.

Chapter 3

3.1 The asymmetry energy term arises because of the different internal energy of the two nuclei (Z, N) and $(A/2, A/2)$ each of mass number A. Taking the radius R to be proportional to $A^{1/3}$ we expect the asymmetry energy to be proportional to

$$[Z^{5/3} + N^{5/3} - 2(A/2)^{5/3}]A^{-2/3}$$

and writing $2N = A + (A - 2Z)$, $2Z = A - (A - 2Z)$ this becomes

$$[(1 - D)^{5/3} + (1 + D)^{5/3} - 2]A$$

where $D = (A - 2Z)/A$ is usually considerably less than unity. Making a binomial expansion of the terms in the bracket we find

$$(-\tfrac{5}{3}D + \tfrac{5}{3}\tfrac{2}{3}\tfrac{1}{2}D^2 + \tfrac{5}{3}D + \tfrac{5}{3}\tfrac{2}{3}\tfrac{1}{2}D^2)A$$

to second order and this is proportional to D^2A, i.e. to $(A - 2Z)^2/A$.

3.2 Consider the energy of a thin spherical shell of charge of radius r due to the charge in the enclosed volume $4\pi r^3/3$ and acting from the centre. The total energy is then

$$\frac{1}{4\pi\epsilon_0}\int_0^R \frac{4\pi}{3} r^3\rho\, 4\pi r^2\, dr\rho\, \frac{1}{r}$$

where $\rho = 3Ze/4\pi R^3$ is the charge density. The result follows.

3.3 ^{114}Cd is $^{114}_{48}$Cd, i.e. there are 48 protons and 66 neutrons. Adding the mass excesses for these particles and subtracting that for ^{114}Cd (negative) gives the result for B and B/A follows immediately.

For the separation energies we write

$$^{113}\text{Cd} + \text{n} \rightarrow {}^{114}\text{Cd} + S_\text{n}$$

$$^{113}\text{Ag} + \text{p} \rightarrow {}^{114}\text{Cd} + S_\text{p}$$

and the stated results follow by using the given mass excesses.

3.4 The reaction is

$$\text{X} + \text{d} \rightarrow \text{Y} + \text{p} + Q$$

and we may think of this as the dissociation of a deuteron into a neutron and a proton, costing energy ϵ, followed by the absorption of the neutron by X to form Y, releasing the neutron separation energy for Y. The energy change is therefore $Q = S_\text{n} - \epsilon$ whence $S_\text{n} = Q + \epsilon$.

3.5 Substitute in the formula to get the answer.

3.6 The force between the two magnetic dipoles in the end on position is $(\mu_0/4\pi)(6\mu_1\mu_2/r^4)$ N and if this is a triplet state it is repulsive because of the opposite sign of the two moments. The work is

$$-\int_\infty^r \frac{\mu_0}{4\pi}\frac{6\mu_1\mu_2}{r^4}\,\mathrm{d}r = \frac{\mu_0}{4\pi}\frac{2\mu_1\mu_2}{r^3}\ \text{J}$$

and substitution of values gives the stated answers.

3.7 The normalization constant is given by

$$4\pi\int_0^\infty |\psi|^2 r^2\,\mathrm{d}r = 1$$

and is found to be $C = (\alpha/2\pi)^{1/2}$. The probability of a separation greater than R is

$$4\pi C^2\int_R^\infty \exp(-2\alpha r)\,\mathrm{d}r = \exp(-2\alpha R) = 0.395$$

with the values given.

The average distance of interaction is

$$\langle r\rangle = \frac{\int r|\psi|^2 r^2\,\mathrm{d}r}{\int |\psi|^2 r^2\,\mathrm{d}r} = \frac{1}{2\alpha} = 2.2\ \text{fm}.$$

Chapter 4

4.1 The energy is

$$\frac{1}{4\pi\epsilon_0}\frac{e^2}{r}.$$

4.2 Take $c = 1$ and use the relation $E^2 = p^2 + m^2$. To find p use the uncertainty relation, taking $p = \Delta p = \hbar/\Delta r$. With $\Delta r = r = 7 \times 10^{-15}$ m we obtain

$$p = \frac{1.05 \times 10^{-34}}{7 \times 10^{-15}} \text{ J m}^{-1}\text{ s} = \frac{1.05 \times 10^{-34}}{7 \times 10^{-15}} \frac{3 \times 10^{8}}{1.6 \times 10^{-13}} \frac{\text{MeV}}{c}$$

$$= 28 \frac{\text{MeV}}{c}.$$

We then have for the electron $E^2 = 28^2 + (0.51)^2$ MeV or $E = 28$ MeV and for the proton $E^2 = 28^2 + (938)^2$ MeV or $E = 938.42$ MeV. Subtracting the energy equivalent of the mass in each case gives a kinetic energy of 28 MeV for the electron and 0.42 MeV for the proton.

4.4 In each case a pair is formed in a higher subshell and leaves a hole in a lower subshell. Use figure 4.5.

4.5 From $\boldsymbol{j} = \boldsymbol{l} + \boldsymbol{s}$ we obtain by taking the scalar product of each side with itself

$$j^2 = l^2 + s^2 + 2\boldsymbol{l}\cdot\boldsymbol{s}.$$

Inserting the eigenvalues for j^2, l^2, s^2 operators divided by $\hbar^2$

$$2\boldsymbol{l}\cdot\boldsymbol{s} = j(j+1) - l(l+1) - s(s+1).$$

For $j = l \pm \frac{1}{2}$, $2\boldsymbol{l}\cdot\boldsymbol{s}$ then has the values l and $-(l+1)$ so that the energy difference is proportional to $2l + 1$.

4.6 The first excited state results from completion of the $d_{3/2}$ subshell by removal of an s subshell neutron. The other spins follow the single-particle sequence shown in figure 4.5.

4.7 Use $g_l = 1$ and $g_s = 5.586$ since the nuclei all have an odd proton. The (l, j) values for the three nuclei are obtained from figure 4.5 for $Z = 3$, 19 and 21.

4.8 For the rotation, take $mR^2\omega_r = \hbar$ and $E_r = \hbar\omega_r$ so that $\omega_r \propto 1/mR^2$. For the vibration, the displacement and momentum in the lowest state are related by the uncertainty principle and for $\Delta x = \beta R$ the corresponding momentum is $p = \Delta p \approx \hbar/\Delta x = \hbar/\beta R$. In the vibration the mean potential and kinetic energies are equal and so the total energy E is proportional to the latter, i.e. to $\frac{1}{2}p^2/m = \hbar^2/2m\beta^2R^2$. Writing E equal to $\hbar\omega_v$ we obtain $\omega_v \propto 1/m\beta^2R^2$ and $\omega_v/\omega_r \propto 1/\beta^2$.

4.9 Write equation (4.16) in the form

$$E_r(J) = k[J(J+1) - K^2].$$

Then for the lowest state of the band, $J = K$,

$$E_r(\tfrac{7}{2}) = k[\tfrac{7}{2}\,\tfrac{9}{2} - K^2]$$

and for higher states

$$E_r(\tfrac{9}{2}) = k[\tfrac{9}{2}\,\tfrac{11}{2} - K^2]$$

and so on. Forming the difference $E_r(\frac{9}{2}) - E_r(\frac{7}{2})$, which is given as 120 keV, we find $k = \frac{40}{3}$ and this may be used to find the excitation of the higher states.

4.10 Using equation (4.13) for the 8^+ level we find $\hbar^2/2\mathscr{I} = 6.94$ keV and the 10^+ level is then at 764 keV. The rigid body moment of inertia is given by $2/5mR^2$ where $m = 1.66 \times 10^{-27}A$ kg and $R = 1.25A^{1/3}$ fm. With $A = 234$ we obtain $2\mathscr{I}_{\text{rig}}/\hbar^2 = 269\ \text{MeV}^{-1}$ whereas the observed value of this quantity found above is $144\ \text{MeV}^{-1}$.

4.11 From the discussion of equation (4.5) we expect the radial dependence of V_{so} so be determined by the quantity $(\text{d}\rho/\text{d}r)\boldsymbol{l}\cdot\boldsymbol{s}$ which gives

$$-\frac{\rho_0}{[1 + \exp(r - R)/a]^2}\,\frac{\exp(r - R)/a}{a}\,(\boldsymbol{l}\cdot\boldsymbol{s}).$$

From example 4.5 $\boldsymbol{l}\cdot\boldsymbol{s}$ is positive for $j = l + \frac{1}{2}$ so that V_{so} is negative and increases the (negative) central potential. For $j = l - \frac{1}{2}$ $\boldsymbol{l}\cdot\boldsymbol{s}$ is negative and the central potential is decreased as shown in figure 4.4.

4.12 For 11 protons, figure 4.5 suggests $(\text{d}_{5/2})^3$ or $J^P = \frac{5}{2}^+$. From figure 4.13, however, and $\delta = 0.1$ we note that two of the last three protons will occupy states with $\Lambda = 0$ and $\Omega = \frac{1}{2}$ while the third enters a state with $\Lambda = 1$, $\Omega = \frac{3}{2}$. This indicates $J = \frac{3}{2}$ and since the states derive from $\text{d}_{5/2}$ in the spherical limit, the parity should be even.

Chapter 5

5.1 From equations (3.20) and (3.21) we find, noting that $g_l = 0$ for a neutron,

$$\mu_J = \mu_{\text{n}} = -1.91\mu_{\text{N}} \qquad \text{when } J = l + \tfrac{1}{2}$$

$$\mu_J = 1.91\frac{J}{J+1}\mu_{\text{N}} \qquad \text{when } J = l - \tfrac{1}{2}.$$

The experimental μ_J thus indicates $J = l - \frac{1}{2} = \frac{1}{2}$, $l = 1$. From expressions

(5.7), for an energy of 0.57 MeV,

$$\Gamma(\text{E1}) = 0.45 \text{ eV} \qquad \Gamma(\text{M1}) = 3.9 \times 10^{-3} \text{ eV}$$

$$\Gamma(\text{E2}) = 3.6 \times 10^{-6} \text{ eV}.$$

A transition with a halflife of 130 ps has an equivalent width of 3.5×10^{-6} eV, using $\Gamma\tau = \hbar$, and this agrees with the E2 prediction.

We therefore identify the ground state as $p_{1/2}$ and the excited state must have $J = \frac{3}{2}$ or $\frac{5}{2}$ and odd parity. An $f_{5/2}$ state would agree with the shell-model prediction.

5.2 The transitions are M4 and E3 and there is a 10 keV M1 transition from the first excited state to ground.

The relative intensity is $\Gamma(\text{M4})/\Gamma(\text{E3})$ and using equations (5.4) and (5.6) we obtain a ratio of 3×10^{-9}.

5.3 From the formulae and assuming $R = 1.25A^{1/3} \times 10^{-15}$ m $\Gamma(\text{E3}) = 8.5 \times 10^{-14} E_\gamma^7 A^2$ eV.

5.4 From equation (5.5) the downward B(E2) is one-fifth of the given upward B(E2). Substitution in equation (5.4) then gives $\tau = 5 \times 10^{-13}$ s. For the branching given the actual lifetime is 5×10^{-14} s.

5.5 The counting rate is proportional to $\exp(-x/v\tau)$ where x is the distance travelled by the recoils, of velocity v, and τ is the mean lifetime.

5.6 The detection in coincidence with back-scattered ions means that the Coulomb-excited ^{64}Zn nuclei have the maximum forward velocity. Assuming that the excitation energy is much less than the beam energy, elementary kinematics shows that the velocity of the projected ^{64}Zn nuclei is two-thirds of that of the incident ^{32}S ions and therefore equal to 2×10^7 m s^{-1} for the given energy. If 70 per cent of the recoils survive to a distance of 20 mm the mean life τ is given by $0.7 = \exp(0.02/2 \times 10^7\tau)$, whence $\tau = 2.8 \times 10^{-9}$ s.

5.7 The full recoil shift is $2 \times E_\gamma^2/2mc^2$ where m is the absolute mass of the atom and the source velocity for overlap is given by setting this equal to $E_\gamma v/c$, which is the Doppler shift of γ ray energy for velocity v.

5.8 The splitting is due to the up and down alignment of the nuclear spin and magnetic moment in the internal field B. The energy difference $2\mu B$ is equal to the Doppler shift of the 14.4 keV radiation due to the given source velocity.

5.9 The masses show that ^{74}As may decay to ^{74}Se by electron emission and to ^{74}Ge by positron emission or electron capture. The double β decay $^{74}\text{Ge} \to {}^{74}\text{Se}$ is not possible. Use equations (3.9a) and disregard the atomic electron binding energy term B_e.

5.10 The electron energy is a maximum when the neutrino energy is zero and the energy and momentum equations are then

$$Q = T_e + T_R$$

$$p_e = p_R.$$

Using the relativistic expression for p^2 we have

$$E_e^2 - m_e^2 = E_R^2 - m_R^2.$$

But for each particle $E = T + m$ so that

$$T_e^2 - T_R^2 = 2m_R T_R - 2m_e T_e.$$

Substituting for $T_e + T_R$ from the first equation and rearranging gives the result (masses in energy units).

5.11 For electron capture the neutrino momentum is balanced by the recoil momentum. We use the calculation of example 5.10, but with e replaced by ν, to obtain

$$\frac{T_R}{T_\nu} = \frac{Q_{EC} + 2m_\nu}{Q_{EC} + 2m_R}.$$

We now assume $T_R \ll T_\nu$ and $m_\nu = 0$ and write $T_R \approx Q_{EC}^2/(Q_{EC} + 2m_R)$, whence $T_R = 9.8$ eV, agreeing with the observed value.

5.12 The reaction is $^{34}S + {}^1p \rightarrow {}^{34}Cl + {}^1n + Q$ and a threshold energy occurs because the mass of $^{34}S + p$ is less than that of $^{34}Cl + n$. Only the centre-of-mass energy is available for producing the reaction and at threshold this is $6.45 \times 34/35$ MeV = 6.27 MeV = $-Q$. Correcting for the neutron–proton mass difference gives the Cl–S difference as 5.49 MeV and from equation (3.9a) $Q_{\beta^+} = 5.49 - 1.02 = 4.47$ MeV. Apart from a small recoil correction this is the maximum β^+ particle energy that may be observed, under the assumption that $m_\nu = 0$.

5.13 Use equation (5.27) with $W_0 = (4.47/0.511) + 1 = 9.75$ and $p_0 = (W_0^2 - 1)^{1/2} = 9.7$. Take $p = 1, 2, \ldots, 9, 9.7$ and tabulate $W_0 - W$ where $W^2 = 1 + p^2$. The integral can then be approximated by a summation and is found to be 1954. With the given $t_{1/2}$ we then find $ft_{1/2} = 3068$ s.

5.14 Use equation (5.26), with $t_{1/2} = \ln(2/\lambda)$ and $ft_{1/2} = 3068$ s, to find $G = 1.4 \times 10^{-62}$ J m^3.

5.15 The mean kinetic energy is $\bar{T} = \int T \, d\lambda / \int d\lambda$ between limits (for T) of 0 and T_0.

5.16 At high energies we assume $p_e \approx E_e$ (taking $c = 1$). Using this in equation (5.23) gives the E_0^5 dependence.

5.17 ^{80}Kr, near the middle of the periodic table, is stable against α decay but ^{176}Hf, with a much larger Coulomb energy, is unstable, though α decay is impeded by the barrier.

5.18 The Q value relates to the centre-of-mass system. Allowing for the energy taken by the residual heavy nucleus the α particle energy is $7.83 \times 210/214 = 7.68$ MeV.

Chapter 6

6.1 The reaction is $^{107}Ag + n \rightarrow {}^{108}Ag^*$ (equation (6.13)).

6.2 The second α particle must take the kinetic energy not removed by the first, namely $T_p + Q_{p\alpha} - 9832 = 8515$ keV and it will be emitted opposite to the first in the centre-of-mass system. To find the laboratory angle, substitute known quantities in equation (6.8).

6.3 See appendix C, equation (C.7).
For $^{19}F + p$ the formula gives a centre-of-mass energy of 0.32 MeV to be added to that available from the binding energies. For $^{50}V + n$ the formula may also be applied but the incident energy is too low to affect the quoted excitation.

6.4 From equation (6.20) the required cross-section is $\sigma_{p\alpha} = 4\pi\lambda\!\!\!^{-2}\Gamma_p\Gamma_\alpha/\Gamma^2$ where Γ is the total width and Γ_p and Γ_α are the partial widths for proton and α particle emission. We take these to be the only forms of break-up of the compound nucleus and then $\Gamma_\alpha = \Gamma - \Gamma_p = 41$ keV and $\sigma = 2.09\lambda\!\!\!^{-2}$. The reduced de Broglie wavelength $\lambda\!\!\!^{-}$ $(=1/k)$ is given by $\hbar/p$ where p is the incident momentum in the centre-of-mass system equal to μv_p where $\mu = 19/20$ amu is the reduced mass (appendix C) and v_p is the incident velocity in the laboratory system. With the incident energy given $\lambda\!\!\!^{-2} = 0.26 \times 10^{-28}$ m^2 and $\sigma = 0.55$ b.

6.5 The entropy of a gas may be written

$$\int_{S(0)}^{S(E)} dS = \int_0^E \frac{dE}{T}.$$

Integrating, the left-hand side becomes

$$k\{\ln[\omega(E)] - \ln[\omega(0)]\}$$

and using $dE = 2ak^2T\,dT$ the right-hand side is $2ak^2T$. It follows that

$$\omega(E) = \omega(0)\exp(2akT) = \omega(0)\exp[2(aE)^{1/2}].$$

6.6 From equation (6.18) the total cross-section at resonance is $\sigma_n = 4\pi\lambda\!\!\!^{-2}\Gamma_n/\Gamma$ neglecting the spin factor. If only scattering and capture contribute to the resonance then $\Gamma = \Gamma_n + \Gamma_\gamma$ and the scattering part is $\sigma_n\Gamma_n/\Gamma = \sigma_n^2/4\pi\lambda\!\!\!^{-2}$. For a nucleus as heavy as cadmium the centre-of-mass correction is negligible and we find $4\pi\lambda\!\!\!^{-2} = 1.45 \times 10^{-21}$ m^2 whence $\sigma_{nn} = 3.37$ b.

6.7 The transformation from laboratory to centre-of-mass system is linear in momentum coordinates and the momentum transfer vector is not altered. This may be verified by inspection of figure C.1.

6.8 From example 3.4 we have $Q = S_n - \epsilon = 6.68$ MeV. For $\theta = 90°$ equation (6.8) gives $T_b = 16.41$ MeV directly. For $\theta = 0°$ and $180°$ a quadratic equation must be solved. Use mass numbers in the evaluation.

6.9 The reaction adds another neutron to the nucleus ${}^{131}_{54}Xe$ forming the even–even ($J = 0$) nucleus ${}^{132}_{54}Xe$ in its ground state. From figure 4.5 this, the 78th particle, enters a $d_{3/2}$ state, requiring an angular momentum transfer $l = 2$. The calculation now follows the worked example in section 6.5.2 taking the interaction radius to be just $R = 1.2A^{1/3}$ fm $= 5.1$ fm.

6.10 A full discussion will be found in reference 7, p. 508, of chapter 6 and some results are quoted in section 6.2. Briefly we can make the following comments.

(a) σ_{nn} constant for thermal neutrons; for inelastic scattering there is a threshold and v_b $(= v_{n'})$ changes rapidly in this region while v_a $(= v_n)$ does not. The cross-section $\sigma_{nn'}$ is therefore proportional to the square root of the energy excess above threshold, i.e. to $T_{n'}^{1/2}$.
(b) $\sigma_{n\alpha} \propto 1/v_n$.
(c) Over a small energy range near threshold the barrier factor for the incident particle does not vary rapidly, but the outgoing neutron velocity does and the situation is as for neutron inelastic scattering.
(d) The barrier factor is now important for the outgoing particle and the yield rises above threshold exponentially rather than sharply as in (c).

No account has been taken here of resonance phenomena or of target thickness effects on yields.

6.11 Excluding the asymmetry and pairing terms the semi-empirical mass formula gives

$$-B = -\alpha A + \beta A^{2/3} + \epsilon Z^2/A^{1/3}.$$

If a nucleus A splits into $A_1 + A_2$ the energy released is given by

$$\beta(A^{2/3} - A_1^{2/3} - A_2^{2/3}) + \epsilon\left(\frac{Z^2}{A^{1/3}} - \frac{Z_1^2}{A_1^{1/3}} - \frac{Z_2^2}{A_2^{2/3}}\right).$$

Write $A_2 = A - A_1$ and $Z_2 = Z - Z_1$ and differentiate with respect to A_1. The first term gives a maximum for $A_1 = A/2$ and the second has turning points at $A_1 = A$ and $A_1 = A/2$. Differentiation with respect to Z_1 gives turning points at $Z_1 = Z$ and $Z_1 = Z/2$. Of these possibilities, one describes no fission at all and the other, $A_1 = A_2 = A/2$ and $Z_1 = Z_2 = Z/2$, is the required condition. It may be checked to be a maximum by a second differentiation.

By setting the energy release to zero for the case of equal division and using $\beta = 17.8$ MeV and $\epsilon = 0.71$ MeV we find $Z^2/A \geqslant 17.6$.

6.12 The energies follow directly from the mass differences, using the conversion factor in equation (3.1).

6.13 Using tabulated constants the velocity of the ions is found to be 3.46×10^7 m s^{-1} and the time of flight over 0.3 m is 8.6×10^{-9} s. Generally the time of flight t is proportional to $m^{-1/2}$ where m is the mass of the ion so that $\Delta t/t = \frac{1}{2}\Delta m/m$. For $\Delta m = \pm 0.3$ amu at $m = 16$, $\Delta t = \pm 81$ ps.

Chapter 7

7.1 There are $2I + 1 = 4$ components of I with $I_3 = +\frac{3}{2}, +\frac{1}{2}, -\frac{1}{2}$ and $-\frac{3}{2}$. Using $Q = I_3 + (B + S)/2$ these correspond to charge states $++$, $+$, 0 and $-$ respectively.

7.2 The three charge states correspond to the three possible orientations of the isospin vector. Therefore $I = 1$, with $I_3 = +1$, 0 and -1 corresponding to the Σ^+, Σ^0 and Σ^- respectively. Application of the Gell-Mann–Nishijima formula for any of the charge states gives $S = -1$.

7.4 (a) In the quark model a baryon is a combination of three quarks with charges $+\frac{2}{3}$ or $-\frac{1}{3}$. All possible combinations lead to charges $++$, $+$, 0 and $-$.
(b) Mesons are $q\bar{q}$ combinations with charges $+\frac{2}{3}, -\frac{1}{3}$ and $-\frac{2}{3}, +\frac{1}{3}$. The possible charges are therefore $+$, 0 and $-$.

7.5 (a) The Λ^0 has $S = -1$ and therefore must contain an s quark ($Q = -\frac{1}{3}$). The other quarks necessary to give a neutral baryon are u ($Q = +\frac{2}{3}$) and d ($Q = -\frac{1}{3}$). Hence $\Lambda^0 \equiv$ uds. Note that in the quark *wavefunction*, as opposed to the quark *content*, the u and d quarks must be in an $I = 0$ combination.
(b) The Ξ baryons have $S = -2$ and therefore must contain two s quarks. The third quark is either a u quark corresponding to the Ξ^0 ($Q = 0$, $I_3 = +\frac{1}{2}$) or a d quark corresponding to the Ξ^- ($Q = -1$, $I_3 = -\frac{1}{2}$).
(c) Mesons are $q\bar{q}$ combinations. The K^+ and K^0 with $S = +1$ must contain an $\bar{s}$ quark with $Q = +\frac{1}{3}$. Hence $K^+ \equiv \bar{s}u$ and $K^0 \equiv \bar{s}d$. Similarly $K^- \equiv s\bar{u}$ and $\bar{K}^0 \equiv s\bar{d}$.

7.6 $\Delta E \Delta t \approx \hbar$. Hence the width $\Delta E \approx \hbar/(7.4 \times 10^{-20})$ s. With $\hbar \approx 6.6 \times 10^{-22}$ MeV s we have $\Delta E \approx 9$ keV, typical of an electromagnetic decay.

7.7 $\Delta E \approx mc^2$ and $\Delta t \approx R/c$. $\Delta E \Delta t \approx \hbar = mc^2 R/c$. Hence $R \approx \hbar c/mc^2 \approx 197/140 \approx 1.4$ fm (1.4×10^{-15} m).

7.8

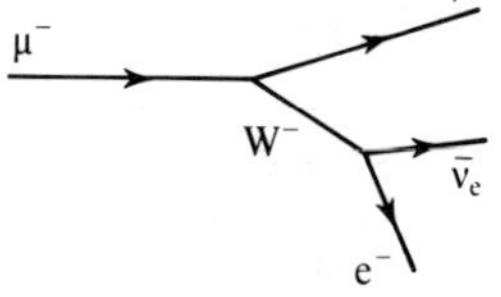

Chapter 8

8.1 The result follows immediately upon integrating the time-dependent Schrödinger equation from t_0 to t to get

$$|\psi(t)\rangle = \exp\left[-\frac{i}{\hbar}H(t - t_0)\right]|\psi(t_0)\rangle.$$

8.2 $D = UD_0U^\dagger$. Then

$$\frac{dD}{dt} = \frac{\partial U}{\partial t} D_0 U^\dagger + U \frac{\partial D_0}{\partial t} U^\dagger + UD_0 \frac{\partial U^\dagger}{\partial t}.$$

With

$$U = \exp\left[-\frac{i}{\hbar} H(t - t_0)\right] \quad \text{and} \quad U^\dagger = \exp\left[+\frac{i}{\hbar} H(t - t_0)\right]$$

we find

$$\frac{dD}{dt} = -\frac{iH}{\hbar} UD_0U^\dagger + U\frac{\partial D_0}{\partial t} U^\dagger + \frac{i}{\hbar} UD_0U^\dagger H = \frac{1}{i\hbar}[H, D] + \frac{\partial D}{\partial t}.$$

8.3 Since, with $\hbar = 1$, $L_z = i\,\partial/\partial\phi$ we have $R(\epsilon) = 1 + \epsilon\,\partial/\partial\phi$. Then, $R(\epsilon)\psi(\phi) = 1 + \epsilon\,\partial\psi(\phi)/\partial\phi = \psi(\phi + \epsilon)$, i.e. $R(\epsilon)$ generates an infinitesimal rotation ϵ about the z axis.

$$R(\theta) = \mathrm{Lt}(1 - i\epsilon L_z)^n = \mathrm{Lt}\left[1 + (-in\epsilon L_z) + \frac{n(n-1)}{2!}(-i\epsilon L_z)^2 + \frac{n(n-1)(n-2)}{3!}(-i\epsilon L_z)^3 + \cdots\right].$$

As $n \to \infty$, $n(n-1) \to n^2$, $n(n-1)(n-2) \to n^3$, etc. and $n\epsilon \to \theta$ as $\epsilon \to 0$. Therefore,

$$R(\theta) = \mathrm{Lt}\left[1 + n(-i\epsilon L_z) + \frac{n^2}{2!}(-i\epsilon L_z)^2 + \frac{n^3}{3!}(-i\epsilon L_z)^3 + \cdots\right]$$
$$= \exp(-i\theta L_z).$$

8.4 Using the matrix elements defined in equation (8.2.1) and the relations $J_x = \frac{1}{2}(J_+ + J_-)$, $J_y = (1/2i)(J_+ - iJ_-)$ we obtain for $j = \frac{1}{2}$

$$J^2 = \frac{3}{4}\begin{pmatrix} 1 & 0 \\ 0 & 1 \end{pmatrix} \quad J_x = \frac{1}{2}\begin{pmatrix} 0 & 1 \\ 1 & 0 \end{pmatrix} \quad J_y = \frac{1}{2}\begin{pmatrix} 0 & -i \\ i & 0 \end{pmatrix} \quad J_z = \frac{1}{2}\begin{pmatrix} 1 & 0 \\ 0 & -1 \end{pmatrix}$$

and for $j = 1$

$$J^2 = 2\begin{pmatrix} 1 & 0 & 0 \\ 0 & 1 & 0 \\ 0 & 0 & 1 \end{pmatrix} \quad J_x = \begin{pmatrix} 0 & \frac{1}{\sqrt{2}} & 0 \\ \frac{1}{\sqrt{2}} & 0 & \frac{1}{\sqrt{2}} \\ 0 & \frac{1}{\sqrt{2}} & 0 \end{pmatrix}$$

$$J_y = \begin{pmatrix} 0 & \frac{-i}{\sqrt{2}} & 0 \\ \frac{i}{\sqrt{2}} & 0 & \frac{-i}{\sqrt{2}} \\ 0 & \frac{i}{\sqrt{2}} & 0 \end{pmatrix} \qquad J_z = \begin{pmatrix} 1 & 0 & 0 \\ 0 & 0 & 0 \\ 0 & 0 & -1 \end{pmatrix}.$$

8.5 We have $J_-|\frac{3}{2}, \frac{3}{2}\rangle = (L_- + S_-)\{|1, 1\rangle|\frac{1}{2}, \frac{1}{2}\rangle\}$. Using equation (8.20) and equivalent expressions for L_- and S_- we find

$$J_-|\tfrac{3}{2}, \tfrac{3}{2}\rangle = \sqrt{(\tfrac{15}{4} - \tfrac{3}{4})}|\tfrac{3}{2}, \tfrac{1}{2}\rangle = \sqrt{3}|\tfrac{3}{2}, \tfrac{1}{2}\rangle$$

$$\begin{aligned}(L_- + S_-)\{|1, 1\rangle|\tfrac{1}{2}, \tfrac{1}{2}\rangle\} &= \sqrt{[1(1+1) - 1(1-1)]}|1, 0\rangle|\tfrac{1}{2}, \tfrac{1}{2}\rangle \\ &\quad + \sqrt{[\tfrac{1}{2}(\tfrac{1}{2}+1) - \tfrac{1}{2}(\tfrac{1}{2}-1)]}|1, 1\rangle|\tfrac{1}{2}, -\tfrac{1}{2}\rangle \\ &= \sqrt{2}|1, 0\rangle|\tfrac{1}{2}, \tfrac{1}{2}\rangle + |1, 1\rangle|\tfrac{1}{2}, -\tfrac{1}{2}\rangle.\end{aligned}$$

Therefore,

$$|\tfrac{3}{2}, \tfrac{1}{2}\rangle = \sqrt{\tfrac{2}{3}}|1, 0\rangle|\tfrac{1}{2}, \tfrac{1}{2}\rangle + \sqrt{\tfrac{1}{3}}|1, 1\rangle|\tfrac{1}{2}, -\tfrac{1}{2}\rangle.$$

The factors $\sqrt{\frac{2}{3}}$ and $\sqrt{\frac{1}{3}}$ are the appropriate Clebsch–Gordan coefficients. Repeated operation of $J_- = L_- + S_-$ yields

$$|\tfrac{3}{2}, -\tfrac{1}{2}\rangle = \sqrt{\tfrac{1}{3}}|1, -1\rangle|\tfrac{1}{2}, \tfrac{1}{2}\rangle + \sqrt{\tfrac{2}{3}}|1, 0\rangle|\tfrac{1}{2}, -\tfrac{1}{2}\rangle$$

$$|\tfrac{3}{2}, -\tfrac{3}{2}\rangle = |1, -1\rangle|\tfrac{1}{2}, -\tfrac{1}{2}\rangle.$$

8.6 See appendix H.

8.7 Under the parity transformation $\theta \to \pi - \theta$ and $\phi \to \pi + \phi$. Then,

$$\exp(im\phi) \to \exp(im\pi)\exp(im\phi) = (-1)^{|m|}\exp(im\phi)$$

and

$$p_l^m(\cos\theta) \to p_l^m[\cos(\pi - \theta)] = p_l^m(-\cos\theta) = (-1)^{l-|m|}p_l^m(\cos\theta).$$

Hence,

$$Y_l^m(\theta, \phi) \to Y_l^m(\pi - \theta, \pi + \phi) = (-1)^l Y_l^m(\theta, \phi)$$

and the parity of the spherical harmonic Y_l^m is $(-1)^l$, independent of m.

8.8 Consider the decay $K^+ \to \pi^+\pi^0$. Since all three particles have spin zero the orbital angular momentum in the final state must be zero to conserve angular momentum. The parity of the final state is therefore $(-1)^0(-1)^2 = +1$. The factor $(-1)^2$ arises from the negative *intrinsic* parities of the pions. For the decay $K^+ \to \pi^+\pi^+\pi^0$ let l be the relative orbital angular momentum of the $\pi^+\pi^+$ pair in their rest frame and let L be the orbital angular momentum between the $\pi^+\pi^+$ pair and the π^-. The total angular momentum in the final state is the resultant of l and L and to obtain zero resultant we must have $l = L$. The parity of the final state is therefore $(-1)^l(-1)^L(-1)^3 = (-1)^{2l}(-1)^3 = -1$, because $2l$ must be even.

Since the final states have opposite parities the decays cannot both conserve parity.

8.9 $$[\tau_1, \tau_2] = \frac{1}{4}\begin{pmatrix} 0 & 1 \\ 1 & 0 \end{pmatrix}\begin{pmatrix} 0 & -i \\ i & 0 \end{pmatrix} - \frac{1}{4}\begin{pmatrix} 0 & -i \\ i & 0 \end{pmatrix}\begin{pmatrix} 0 & 1 \\ 1 & 0 \end{pmatrix} = \frac{i}{2}\begin{pmatrix} 1 & 0 \\ 0 & -1 \end{pmatrix} = i\tau_3, \text{ etc.}$$

$$\tau_+ = \begin{pmatrix} 0 & 1 \\ 0 & 0 \end{pmatrix} \quad \text{and} \quad |n\rangle \equiv \begin{pmatrix} 0 \\ 1 \end{pmatrix}$$

and so

$$\tau_+|n\rangle = \begin{pmatrix} 0 & 1 \\ 0 & 0 \end{pmatrix}\begin{pmatrix} 0 \\ 1 \end{pmatrix} = \begin{pmatrix} 1 \\ 0 \end{pmatrix} \equiv |p\rangle.$$

$$\tau_- = \begin{pmatrix} 0 & 0 \\ 1 & 0 \end{pmatrix} \quad \text{and} \quad |p\rangle \equiv \begin{pmatrix} 1 \\ 0 \end{pmatrix}$$

and so

$$\tau_-|p\rangle = \begin{pmatrix} 0 & 0 \\ 1 & 0 \end{pmatrix}\begin{pmatrix} 1 \\ 0 \end{pmatrix} = \begin{pmatrix} 0 \\ 1 \end{pmatrix} \equiv |n\rangle.$$

8.10 The nucleon has $I = \frac{1}{2}$ and the pion $I = 1$. The Δ^0 has $I_3 = -\frac{1}{2}$. Using Clebsch–Gordan coefficients (appendix G) for $j_1 = 1$ and $j_2 = \frac{1}{2}$ we have

$$\underset{\Delta^0}{|\tfrac{3}{2}, -\tfrac{1}{2}\rangle} = \sqrt{\tfrac{2}{3}}\,\underset{\pi^0}{|1, 0\rangle}\,\underset{n}{|\tfrac{1}{2}, -\tfrac{1}{2}\rangle} + \sqrt{\tfrac{1}{3}}\,\underset{\pi^-}{|1, -1\rangle}\,\underset{p}{|\tfrac{1}{2}, \tfrac{1}{2}\rangle}.$$

The ratio of the amplitudes for the decays $\Delta^0 \to \pi^- p$ and $\Delta^0 \to \pi^0 n$ is just the ratio of the corresponding Clebsch–Gordan coefficients. Hence the branching ratio $(\Delta^0 \to p\pi^-)/(\Delta^0 \to n\pi^0)$ is $(\sqrt{\frac{1}{3}})^2/(\sqrt{\frac{2}{3}})^2 = \frac{1}{2}$. If the Δ had $I = \frac{1}{2}$ we would have

$$\underset{\Delta^0}{|\tfrac{1}{2}, -\tfrac{1}{2}\rangle} = \sqrt{\tfrac{1}{3}}\,\underset{\pi^0}{|1, 0\rangle}\,\underset{n}{|\tfrac{1}{2}, -\tfrac{1}{2}\rangle} - \sqrt{\tfrac{2}{3}}\,\underset{\pi^-}{|1, -1\rangle}\,\underset{p}{|\tfrac{1}{2}, \tfrac{1}{2}\rangle}$$

and in this case the branching ratio is 2.

8.11 In terms of I spin multiplets both reactions are $\bar{K}N \to \pi\Sigma$. In the initial state both I spins are $\frac{1}{2}$ so the resultant I spin is either 0 or 1. In the final state both I spins are 1 so the resultant is 0, 1 or 2. Conservation of I spin rules out any contribution from the $I = 2$ channel, hence only the $I = 0$ and $I = 1$ amplitudes (A_0 and A_1 respectively) contribute. Using Clebsch–Gordan coefficients for $j_1 = \frac{1}{2}$ and $j_2 = \frac{1}{2}$ we have

$$K^-p = \frac{1}{\sqrt{2}}(|1, 0\rangle - |0, 0\rangle)$$

and, using Clebsch–Gordan coefficients for $j_1 = 1$ and $j_2 = 1$ we have

$$\pi^-\Sigma^+ = -\frac{1}{\sqrt{2}}|1, 0\rangle + \frac{1}{\sqrt{3}}|0, 0\rangle$$

$$\pi^+\Sigma^- = \frac{1}{\sqrt{2}}|1, 0\rangle + \frac{1}{\sqrt{3}}|0, 0\rangle.$$

The probability amplitude for the process $K^-p \to \pi^-\Sigma^+$ is

$$\langle\pi^-\Sigma^+|H|K^-p\rangle = \left(-\frac{1}{\sqrt{2}}\langle 1, 0| + \frac{1}{\sqrt{3}}\langle 0, 0|\right)H\frac{1}{\sqrt{2}}\left(|1,0\rangle - |0, 0\rangle\right)$$

$$= -\tfrac{1}{2}\langle 1, 0|H|1, 0\rangle - \frac{1}{\sqrt{6}}\langle 0, 0|H|0, 0\rangle$$

$$= -\left(\tfrac{1}{2}A_1 + \frac{1}{\sqrt{6}}A_0\right).$$

By inspection, the only difference for $K^-p \to \pi^+\Sigma^-$ is in the sign of the $I = 1$ amplitude. Thus

$$\langle\pi^+\Sigma^-|H|K^-p\rangle = \left(\tfrac{1}{2}A_1 - \frac{1}{\sqrt{6}}A_0\right).$$

Hence, the ratio of the cross sections is

$$\left|\frac{\tfrac{1}{2}A_1 + (1/\sqrt{6})A_0}{\tfrac{1}{2}A_1 - (1/\sqrt{6})A_0}\right|^2.$$

8.12 The possible I spins of the initial and final states are $I = \frac{1}{2}$ and $I = \frac{3}{2}$. We have

$$\pi^-p = \sqrt{\tfrac{1}{3}}|\tfrac{3}{2}, -\tfrac{1}{2}\rangle - \sqrt{\tfrac{2}{3}}|\tfrac{1}{2}, -\tfrac{1}{2}\rangle$$

$$\pi^0n = \sqrt{\tfrac{2}{3}}|\tfrac{3}{2}, -\tfrac{1}{2}\rangle + \sqrt{\tfrac{1}{3}}|\tfrac{1}{2}, -\tfrac{1}{2}\rangle.$$

Hence $\langle\pi^-p|H|\pi^-p\rangle = \frac{1}{3}A_3 + \frac{2}{3}A_1$ and

$$\langle\pi^0n|H|\pi^-p\rangle = \frac{\sqrt{2}}{3}A_3 - \frac{\sqrt{2}}{3}A_1,$$

and the ratio of the cross-sections is

$$\frac{\sigma_1}{\sigma_2} = \left|\frac{A_3 + 2A_1}{\sqrt{2}(A_3 - A_1)}\right|^2.$$

Put $A_3 = A_1 e^{i\phi}$ with $\phi = \pm 45°$.

$$\frac{\sigma_1}{\sigma_2} = \frac{1}{2}\left|\frac{e^{i\phi} + 2}{e^{i\phi} - 1}\right|^2 = \frac{1}{2}\frac{(e^{i\phi} + 2)(e^{-i\phi} + 2)}{(e^{i\phi} - 1)(e^{-i\phi} - 1)}$$

$$= \frac{1}{2}\frac{5 + 4\cos\phi}{2 - 2\cos\phi} = 6.68.$$

Note that the ratio is independent of the sign of ϕ.

8.13 For a $\pi^+\pi^-$ system, the charge conjugation operation and the parity operation are equivalent, therefore $C = (-1)^l$. Let L be the relative orbital angular momentum in the $p\bar{p}$ system. The spins of the p and $\bar{p}$ can couple to give a total spin of 0 or 1, hence the total angular momentum in the initial state is $J_i = L, L \pm 1$. Since the pions have zero spin the total angular momentum in the final state is just $J_f = l$. Therefore conservation of angular momentum ($J_i = J_f$) gives $l = L, L \pm 1$. Because of the opposite intrinsic parities of proton and antiproton, conservation of parity rules out $l = L$, therefore the only possibility is $l = L \pm 1$. Hence the possible transitions are $^3S_1 \to P_1$, $^3P_0 \to S_0$, etc. Charge conjugation invariance gives $(-1)^{L+S} = (-1)^l$, where S is the total spin of the $p\bar{p}$ system, and therefore $L + S = l$. Since S can be 0 or 1 this is not as stringent a condition as that arising from conservation of angular momentum and parity. Charge conjugation invariance therefore imposes no further restrictions.

8.14 (a) Since div curl $\boldsymbol{V}$ is identically zero for any vector $\boldsymbol{V}$ it follows from (iv) that

$$\frac{\partial}{\partial t}(\nabla \cdot \boldsymbol{E}) + \nabla \cdot \boldsymbol{j} = \frac{\partial \rho}{\partial t} + \nabla \cdot \boldsymbol{j} = 0.$$

(b) Again, since div curl $\boldsymbol{V} = 0$, (ii) can be satisfied if $\boldsymbol{B}$ is written as the curl of an arbitrary vector field $\boldsymbol{A}$; $\boldsymbol{B} = \nabla \wedge \boldsymbol{A}$. Then, (iii) may be written $\nabla \wedge (\boldsymbol{E} + \partial \boldsymbol{A}/\partial t) = 0$, and, since curl grad $\phi = 0$ for any scalar field ϕ, we can write

$$\boldsymbol{E} + \frac{\partial \boldsymbol{A}}{\partial t} = -\nabla\phi \quad \text{or} \quad \boldsymbol{E} = -\nabla\phi - \frac{\partial \boldsymbol{A}}{\partial t}.$$

Under the gauge transformation $\boldsymbol{A} \to \boldsymbol{A}' = \boldsymbol{A} + \nabla\psi$, $\phi \to \phi' = \phi - \partial\psi/\partial t$ we have

$$\boldsymbol{B} \to \boldsymbol{B}' = \nabla \times (\boldsymbol{A} + \nabla\psi) = \nabla \times \boldsymbol{A} = \boldsymbol{B}$$

$$\boldsymbol{E} \to \boldsymbol{E}' = -\nabla\phi + \frac{\partial}{\partial t}(\nabla\psi) - \frac{\partial \boldsymbol{A}}{\partial t} - \frac{\partial}{\partial t}(\nabla\psi) = -\nabla\phi - \frac{\partial \boldsymbol{A}}{\partial t} = \boldsymbol{E}.$$

(c) On substituting $\boldsymbol{B} = \nabla \wedge \boldsymbol{A}$ and $\boldsymbol{E} = -\nabla\phi - \partial \boldsymbol{A}/\partial t$ into (iv) we obtain

$$\nabla \wedge (\nabla \wedge \boldsymbol{A}) - \frac{\partial}{\partial t}\left(-\nabla\phi - \frac{\partial \boldsymbol{A}}{\partial t}\right) = \boldsymbol{j}.$$

Using the Lorentz gauge $\nabla \cdot \boldsymbol{A} = -\partial\phi/\partial t$, this reduces to the wave equation for $\boldsymbol{A}$; $\nabla^2 \boldsymbol{A} - \partial^2 \boldsymbol{A}/\partial t^2 = -\boldsymbol{j}$. On substituting $\boldsymbol{E} = -\nabla\phi - \partial \boldsymbol{A}/\partial t$ into (i) we have

$$\nabla \cdot \left(-\nabla\phi - \frac{\partial \boldsymbol{A}}{\partial t}\right) = \rho = -\nabla^2\phi - \frac{\partial}{\partial t}(\nabla \cdot \boldsymbol{A}) = -\nabla^2\phi + \frac{\partial^2\phi}{\partial t^2}.$$

Hence,

$$\nabla^2\phi - \frac{\partial^2\phi}{\partial t^2} = -\rho.$$

8.15 (a) Allowed electromagnetic decay.
(b) Allowed weak interaction.
(c) Forbidden by energy conservation: $m_\mu > m_\Sigma - m_\Lambda$.
(d) Forbidden by baryon conservation.
(e) Allowed weak decay.

Chapter 9

9.1 Use invariance of $E^2 - p^2$.

$E^2_{\text{cm}} = (1232)^2 = (T_\pi + m_\pi + m_p)^2 - [(T_\pi + m_\pi)^2 - m_\pi^2]$. $T_\pi \approx 190$ MeV.

9.2 The minimum kinetic energy is the kinetic energy in the laboratory system required to produce K^+p and ϕ *at rest* in the centre-of-mass system. Using the invariance of $E^2 - p^2$ in the laboratory and centre-of-mass systems we have

$$(E_K + m_p)^2 - p_K^2 = (m_K + m_p + m_\phi)^2 = M^2 \text{ say}.$$

$$\text{LHS} = (E_K + m_p)^2 - E_K^2 + m_K^2 = 2E_K m_p + m_p^2 + m_K^2 = M^2.$$

Therefore

$$E_K = \frac{M^2 - m_p^2 - m_K^2}{2m_p} = 2.6037 \text{ GeV}.$$

Kinetic energy $T_K = E_K - m_K = 2.1$ GeV.

9.3 The time-dependent Schrödinger equation and its complex conjugate give

$$\frac{\partial\psi}{\partial t} = \frac{-\hbar}{2im}\nabla^2\psi \quad \text{and} \quad \frac{\partial\psi^*}{\partial t} = \frac{\hbar}{2im}\nabla^2\psi^*.$$

$$\frac{\partial\rho}{\partial t} = \psi\frac{\partial\psi^*}{\partial t} + \psi^*\frac{\partial\psi}{\partial t} = \frac{-\hbar}{2im}(\psi^*\nabla^2\psi - \psi\nabla^2\psi^*)$$

$$= \frac{-\hbar}{2im}\nabla\cdot(\psi^*\nabla\psi - \psi\nabla\psi^*).$$

Hence $\partial\rho/\partial t + \nabla\cdot\boldsymbol{j} = 0$ if we identify $\boldsymbol{j} = \hbar/2im(\psi^*\nabla\psi - \psi\nabla\psi^*)$. Equivalently $\boldsymbol{j} = i\hbar/m\ \mathrm{Re}(\psi\nabla\psi^*)$. For a plane wave $\psi = \exp(ikz)$ and $\nabla\psi^* = -ik\exp(-ikz)$ and $j = \hbar k/m = v$.

9.4 For S wave scattering $d\sigma/d\Omega = \sigma/4\pi$ where $d\Omega = 2\pi\sin\theta\, d\theta$ and θ is the centre-of-mass angle, given in terms of the laboratory recoil angle θ_Y by equation (C.14). From this equation we find $d\sigma = -2\sigma\sin\theta_Y\cos\theta_Y\, d\theta_Y$ and from simple kinematics the recoil energy at angle θ_Y is $T = T_0\cos^2\theta_Y$. It follows that $dT = -2T_0\sin\theta_Y\cos\theta_Y\, d\theta_Y$ so that $d\sigma/dT = \sigma/T_0$ = constant.

9.5 If we write $\chi = ur$ the wave equation (9.4) becomes

$$\frac{\partial^2\chi}{\partial r^2} + k^2\chi = 0$$

where $k^2 = 2mT/\hbar^2$. Inside the well the same wave equation applies but with a wavenumber k' given by $k'^2 = (2m/\hbar^2)(T + U)$. For the S wave, equation (9.14) gives

$$\chi_0 = u_0 r = \frac{\exp(i\delta_0)}{k}\sin(kr + \delta_0)$$

while inside the well a suitable solution is $\chi' = \sin(k'r)$. Continuity of the wavefunctions and their derivatives at the boundary gives

$$\frac{\exp(i\delta_0)}{k}\sin(kR + \delta_0) = \sin(k'R)$$

$$\exp(i\delta_0)\cos(kR + \delta_0) = k'\cos(k'R)$$

whence

$$\tan(kR + \delta_0) = \frac{k}{k'}\tan(k'R).$$

For the S wave $kR \ll 1$ and so an approximate answer is

$$\tan\delta_0 = \frac{k}{k'}\tan(k'R) - \tan(kR).$$

9.6 With $T_l = [\exp(2i\delta_l) - 1]/2i = \exp(i\delta_l)\sin\delta_l$ equation (9.20) becomes

$$f(\theta) = k^{-1}\sum_{l=0}^{\infty}(2l+1)T_l P_l(\cos\theta).$$

With contributions from S ($l = 0$) and P ($l = 1$) waves only,

$$f(\theta) = k^{-1}(T_0 + 3T_1\cos\theta) \qquad (P_0 = 1 \text{ and } P_1 = \cos\theta).$$

Hence

$$\begin{aligned}\frac{d\sigma}{d\Omega} &= |f(\theta)|^2 \\ &= k^{-2}[|T_0|^2 + 6\,\mathrm{Re}(T_0T_1^*)\cos\theta + 9|T_1|^2\cos^2\theta] \\ &= k^{-2}[\sin^2\delta_0 + 6\sin\delta_0\sin\delta_1\cos(\delta_0-\delta_1)\cos\theta \\ &\quad + 9\sin^2\delta_1\cos^2\theta].\end{aligned}$$

A fit to measurements of $d\sigma/d\Omega$ as a function of θ will give the coefficients of 1, $\cos\theta$ and $\cos^2\theta$ in this expression. Knowledge of $\sin^2\delta_0$ gives δ_0 apart from a sign ambiguity. Similarly $\sin^2\delta_1$ gives δ_1. The interference term ($\cos\theta$) should show which sign goes with which but an overall sign ambiguity will remain.

9.7 We write the conservation of momentum in the form $\boldsymbol{p}_n = \boldsymbol{P} - \sum_{i=1}^{n-1}\boldsymbol{p}_i$ where $\boldsymbol{P}$ is the total momentum. From the properties of the δ function

$$\int d^3p_n\,\delta\left[\boldsymbol{p}_n - \left(\boldsymbol{P} - \sum_{i=1}^{n-1}\boldsymbol{p}_i\right)\right] = 1$$

for all integrations which include $\boldsymbol{p}_n = \boldsymbol{P} - \sum_{i=1}^{n-1}\boldsymbol{p}_i$. Then,

$$\begin{aligned}\rho_n(E) &= \frac{d}{dE}\int d^3\boldsymbol{p}_1\cdots d^3\boldsymbol{p}_{n-1}\,d^3\boldsymbol{p}_n\,\delta\left[\boldsymbol{p}_n - \left(\boldsymbol{P} - \sum_{i=1}^{n-1}\boldsymbol{p}_i\right)\right] \\ &= \frac{d}{dE}\prod_{i=1}^{n}\int d^3\boldsymbol{p}_i\,\delta\left(\sum_{i=1}^{n}\boldsymbol{p}_i - \boldsymbol{P}\right).\end{aligned}$$

The conservation of energy implies that $\int\delta(\sum_{i=1}^{n}E_i - E)\,dE = 1$ and clearly

$$\frac{d}{dE}\int\delta\left(\sum_{i=1}^{n}E_i - E\right)dE = \delta\left(\sum_{i=1}^{n}E_i - E\right).$$

Therefore

$$\frac{d}{dE}\prod_{i=1}^{n-1}\int d^3\boldsymbol{p}_i = \prod_{i=1}^{n}\int d^3\boldsymbol{p}_i\,\delta\left(\sum_{i=1}^{n}\boldsymbol{p}_i - \boldsymbol{P}\right)\delta\left(\sum_{i=1}^{n}E_i - E\right).$$

9.8 From the definition, equation (9.60),

$$R_2(E) = \int \frac{d^3p_1\, d^3p_2}{4E_1E_2}\,\delta(\boldsymbol{p}_1 + \boldsymbol{p}_2)\delta(E_1 + E_2 - E).$$

Integration over $\boldsymbol{p}_2$ gives

$$R_2(E) = \int \frac{1}{4E_1E_2(-\boldsymbol{p}_1)}\, d^3p_1\delta[E_1 + E_2(-p_1) - E].$$

Note, after integration over $\boldsymbol{p}_2$ the remaining functions must be evaluated at the value of $\boldsymbol{p}_2$ which makes the argument of the momentum δ function zero, i.e. $\boldsymbol{p}_2 = -\boldsymbol{p}_1$. In spherical polar coordinates $d^3p_1 = p_1^2\, dp_1\, d\Omega_1$, where $d\Omega_1$ is the element of solid angle into which particle 1 is emitted. Assuming that the two particles are distributed isotropically in space, integration over $d\Omega_1$ gives a factor 4π, then

$$R_2(E) = \int \frac{\pi p_1^2\, dp_1}{E_1E_2(-\boldsymbol{p}_1)}\,\delta[E_1 + E_2(-\boldsymbol{p}_1) - E].$$

The remaining δ function is a function of p_1 and the final integration over p_1 can be effected using property (iv) in appendix I. Thus, with $g(p_1) = E_1 + E_2 - E = \sqrt{(p_1^2 + m_1^2)} + \sqrt{(p_1^2 + m_2^2)} - E$ we have $g'(p_1) = p_1/E_1 + p_1/E_2$. Integration over p_1 therefore gives

$$R_2(E) = \frac{\pi p_1^2}{E_1E_2}\left(\frac{p_1}{E_1} + \frac{p_1}{E_2}\right)^{-1} = \frac{\pi p_1}{E}.$$

The solution of $E = (p_1^2 + m_1^2)^{1/2} + (p_1^2 + m_2^2)^{1/2}$, where E is the total energy in the centre-of-mass system, gives p_1.

9.9 By definition,

$$M_{12}^2 = (E_1 + E_2)^2 - (\boldsymbol{p}_1 + \boldsymbol{p}_2)^2.$$

By conservation of energy and momentum this may be written

$$M_{12}^2 = (E - E_3)^2 - p_3^2 = E^2 - 2EE_3 + m_3^2. \tag{1}$$

Therefore $M_{12}\, dM_{12} = (-)E\, dE_3$. Furthermore, $E_3 = (p_3^2 + m_3^2)^{1/2}$ and therefore $dE_3 = p_3\, dp_3/E_3$. Hence

$$\frac{dp_3}{dM_{12}} = \frac{M_{12}E_3}{Ep_3}.$$

Equations (1) may be solved for p_3 and E_3 to give

$$p_3 = \frac{\{[E^2 - (M_{12} - m_3)^2][E^2 - (M_{12} + m_3)^2]\}^{1/2}}{2E}$$

$$E_3 = \frac{E^2 - M_{12}^2 + m_3^2}{2E}$$

Then, using

$$\frac{dR_3}{dM_{12}} = \frac{dR_3}{dp_3}\frac{dp_3}{dM_{12}}$$

with dR_3/dp_3 given by equation (9.64) we obtain the desired solution, equation (9.65).

The dipion invariant mass produced in a $\pi\pi p$ final state with a total centre-of-mass energy 2.0 GeV is shown in the figure.

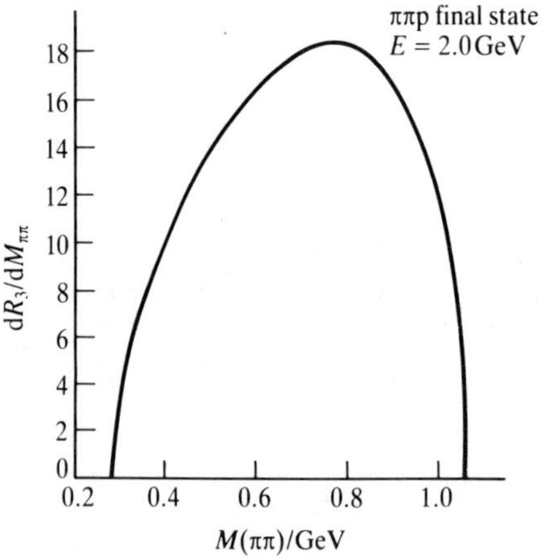

9.10 (a) Conservation of angular momentum requires the relative orbital angular momentum of the two pseudoscalars to be zero in which case the parity of the final state is even.

(b)

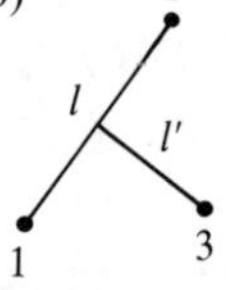

Conservation of angular momentum requires $l = l'$ so the parity of the final state is $(-1)^l(-1)^{l'}(-1)^3 = (-1)^{2l+1} = -1$ since $2l$ is even. Therefore, the decay $0^+ \to 0^-0^-0^-$ is forbidden by parity conservation.

9.11

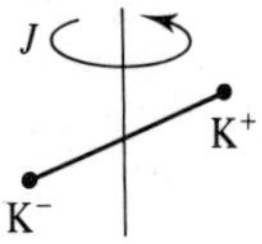

$G = \exp(i\pi I_2)C = C = (-1)^J$ since in the present case C and P are equivalent. Suppression of the 2π decay mode implies $G = (-1)^3$ since the G-parity of n pions is $(-1)^n$. Hence, J must be odd and $J^P = 1^-, 3^- \ldots$.

9.12 The momenta p_0 and p_+ are calculated to be

$$p_0 = \tfrac{1}{2}(m_\phi^2 - 4m_0^2)^{1/2} = 111.3$$

$$p_+ = \tfrac{1}{2}(m_\phi^2 - 4m_+^2)^{1/2} = 128.3$$

using the expression for p_1 in example 9.6. Hence

$$\left(\frac{p_0}{p_+}\right)^3 \approx 0.65 \quad \text{and} \quad \left(\frac{p_0}{p_+}\right)^7 \approx 0.37$$

and $J = 1$ is preferred.

9.13

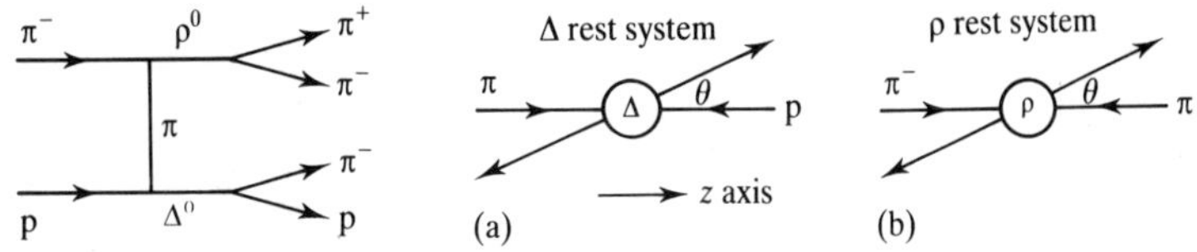

(a) *The decay* $\Delta \to p\pi^-$ Take the z axis as the direction of the exchanged pion in the Δ rest system. Because there can be no component of *orbital* angular momentum in this direction the Δ must be produced in a state with $J_z = \pm\frac{1}{2}$, the possible spin orientations of the proton. The Δ is therefore described by the state vector $|J, J_z\rangle = |\frac{3}{2}, \pm\frac{1}{2}\rangle$. Since these states lead to the same angular distribution it is necessary to consider only one, $|\frac{3}{2}, \frac{1}{2}\rangle$ say. Conservation of angular momentum and parity requires the decay products to be in a state of relative motion with orbital angular momentum $l = 1$ and will therefore be described by spherical harmonics Y_1^m. These must couple with the possible spin states of the decay proton $s_z = +\frac{1}{2}(\uparrow)$ and $s_z = -\frac{1}{2}(\downarrow)$ to conserve angular momentum.

Using the tables of Clebsch–Gordan coefficients (appendix G) for $j_1 = 1$ and $j_2 = \frac{1}{2}$, we obtain

$$|\tfrac{3}{2}, \tfrac{1}{2}\rangle = \sqrt{\tfrac{1}{3}}Y_1^1{\downarrow} + \sqrt{\tfrac{2}{3}}Y_1^0{\uparrow} = \psi.$$

The angular distribution is therefore given by

$$W(\theta) = |\psi|^2 = \frac{1}{8\pi}(1 + 3\cos^2\theta).$$

In arriving at this expression we have used the fact that the spin states are orthogonal.

(b) *The decay* $\rho^0 \to \pi^+\pi^-$ In the ρ rest system we take the quantization axis as the direction of the incident pion. The ρ meson must be produced in an angular momentum state $|1, 0\rangle$ and to conserve angular momentum and parity the decay must be P wave ($l = 1$). In this case $\psi = |1, 0\rangle = Y_1^0$ and the decay angular distribution is

$$W(\theta) = |\psi|^2 = \frac{3}{4\pi}\cos^2\theta.$$

9.14 No matter what the spin-parity the Δ is always produced with $J_z = \pm\frac{1}{2}$ because the only component of angular momentum along the z axis in the initial state is provided by the spin of the proton. To conserve angular momentum and parity the decay must be D wave ($l = 2$). Then, using Clebsch–Gordan coefficients for $j_1 = 2$, $j_2 = \frac{1}{2}$ we have

$$\psi = |\tfrac{3}{2}, \tfrac{1}{2}\rangle = \sqrt{\tfrac{3}{5}}Y_2^1\downarrow - \sqrt{\tfrac{2}{5}}Y_2^0\uparrow$$

$$= -\sqrt{\frac{3}{5}}\sqrt{\left(\frac{15}{8\pi}\right)}\sin\theta\cos\phi\, e^{i\phi}\downarrow - \sqrt{\frac{2}{5}}\sqrt{\left(\frac{5}{16\pi}\right)}(3\cos^2\theta - 1)\uparrow.$$

$$W(\theta, \phi) = |\psi|^2 = \frac{1}{8\pi}(1 + 3\cos^2\theta),$$

i.e. the same as for $J^P = \frac{3}{2}^+$. We conclude that the angular distribution depends on J but not on the parity.

Chapter 10

10.1 $$\exp\left(-\frac{i\alpha}{2}\hat{\boldsymbol{n}}\cdot\boldsymbol{\tau}\right) = 1 - i(\hat{\boldsymbol{n}}\cdot\boldsymbol{\tau})\frac{\alpha}{2} - \frac{(\hat{\boldsymbol{n}}\cdot\boldsymbol{\tau})^2}{2!}\left(\frac{\alpha}{2}\right)^2 + i\frac{(\hat{\boldsymbol{n}}\cdot\boldsymbol{\tau})^3}{3!}\left(\frac{\alpha}{2}\right)^3 + \frac{(\hat{\boldsymbol{n}}\cdot\boldsymbol{\tau})^4}{4!}\left(\frac{\alpha}{2}\right)^4 - \cdots$$

$$= \mathbf{1}\left[1 - \frac{1}{2!}\left(\frac{\alpha}{2}\right)^2 + \frac{1}{4!}\left(\frac{\alpha}{2}\right)^4 - \cdots\right] - i(\hat{\boldsymbol{n}}\cdot\boldsymbol{\tau})\left[\frac{\alpha}{2} - \frac{1}{3!}\left(\frac{\alpha}{2}\right)^3 + \cdots\right]$$

$$= \mathbf{1}\cos\left(\frac{\alpha}{2}\right) - i(\hat{\boldsymbol{n}}\cdot\boldsymbol{\tau})\sin\left(\frac{\alpha}{2}\right).$$

Then,

$$R_2(\alpha) = \mathbf{1}\cos\left(\frac{\alpha}{2}\right) - i\tau_2\sin\left(\frac{\alpha}{2}\right) = \begin{pmatrix} \cos\left(\frac{\alpha}{2}\right) & -\sin\left(\frac{\alpha}{2}\right) \\ \sin\left(\frac{\alpha}{2}\right) & \cos\left(\frac{\alpha}{2}\right) \end{pmatrix}.$$

Hence

$$p' = p\cos\left(\frac{\alpha}{2}\right) - n\sin\left(\frac{\alpha}{2}\right)$$

$$n' = p\sin\left(\frac{\alpha}{2}\right) + n\cos\left(\frac{\alpha}{2}\right).$$

If we operate on these equations with the charge conjugation operator C, and rearrange (since the antineutron has $I_3 = +\frac{1}{2}$ and the antiproton

$I_3 = -\frac{1}{2}$) we obtain

$$\bar{n}' = \bar{n}\cos\left(\frac{\alpha}{2}\right) + \bar{p}\sin\left(\frac{\alpha}{2}\right)$$

$$\bar{p}' = -\bar{n}\sin\left(\frac{\alpha}{2}\right) + \bar{p}\cos\left(\frac{\alpha}{2}\right),$$

i.e.

$$\begin{pmatrix}\bar{n}' \\ \bar{p}'\end{pmatrix} = \begin{pmatrix}\cos\left(\frac{\alpha}{2}\right) & \sin\left(\frac{\alpha}{2}\right) \\ -\sin\left(\frac{\alpha}{2}\right) & \cos\left(\frac{\alpha}{2}\right)\end{pmatrix}\begin{pmatrix}\bar{n} \\ \bar{p}\end{pmatrix},$$

and the transformation matrix is not equal to $R_2(\alpha)$. However, if we define the $\bar{2}$ doublet as $\binom{-\bar{n}}{\bar{p}}$ we have

$$-\bar{n}' = -\bar{n}\cos\left(\frac{\alpha}{2}\right) - \bar{p}\sin\left(\frac{\alpha}{2}\right)$$

$$\bar{p}' = -\bar{n}\sin\left(\frac{\alpha}{2}\right) + \bar{p}\cos\left(\frac{\alpha}{2}\right),$$

i.e.

$$\begin{pmatrix}-\bar{n}' \\ \bar{p}'\end{pmatrix} = \begin{pmatrix}\cos\left(\frac{\alpha}{2}\right) & -\sin\left(\frac{\alpha}{2}\right) \\ \sin\left(\frac{\alpha}{2}\right) & \cos\left(\frac{\alpha}{2}\right)\end{pmatrix}\begin{pmatrix}-\bar{n} \\ \bar{p}\end{pmatrix},$$

and the 2 and $\bar{2}$ transform identically.

10.2 Using tables of Clebsch–Gordan coefficients for $\frac{1}{2} \times \frac{1}{2}$ (appendix G) we obtain

	Triplet ($I = 1$)		Singlet ($I = 0$)
$I_3 = +1$	$-p\bar{n}$		
$I_3 = 0$	$\frac{1}{\sqrt{2}}(p\bar{p} - n\bar{n})$	$I_3 = 0$	$\frac{1}{\sqrt{2}}(p\bar{p} + n\bar{n})$
$I_3 = -1$	$n\bar{p}$		

By definition $G = C\exp(-i\tau_2\pi)$ and $\exp(-i\tau_2\pi)|I, I_3\rangle = (-1)^{I-I_3}|I, -I_3\rangle$ (see section 8.11).

Hence, for the triplet states

$$\begin{array}{ccccc} -p\bar{n} & \xrightarrow{R_2(\pi)} & n\bar{p} & \xrightarrow{C} & p\bar{n} \\ (p\bar{p} - n\bar{n}) & \longrightarrow & (-p\bar{p} + n\bar{n}) & \longrightarrow & -(p\bar{p} - n\bar{n}) \\ n\bar{p} & \longrightarrow & -p\bar{n} & \longrightarrow & -n\bar{p}, \end{array}$$

i.e. the C-parity of the triplet states is -1.

For the singlet state

$$(p\bar{p} + n\bar{n}) \xrightarrow{R2(\pi)} (p\bar{p} + n\bar{n}) \xrightarrow{C} (p\bar{p} + n\bar{n})$$

and the G-parity of the singlet state is $+1$. For $l = 0$ and $s = 0$ the spin-parities of these states must be 0^- where the negative intrinsic parity arises because the parities of fermion and antifermion are opposite.

For the triplet states $I^G J^P = 1^- 0^-$ corresponding to the π^+, π^0 and π^- and for the singlet state $I^G J^P = 0^+ 0^-$ corresponding to the η^0.

10.3 The matrix representations of the SU(3) operators are readily obtained from the definitions (10.7) and the Gell-Mann matrices (10.3). The only non-zero elements are given below.

$$I_+(12) = 1 \quad I_-(21) = 1 \quad I_3(11) = \tfrac{1}{2} \quad I_3(22) = -\tfrac{1}{2}$$

$$V_+(13) = 1 \quad V_-(31) = 1 \quad U_+(23) = 1 \quad U_-(32) = 1$$

$$Y(11) = \tfrac{1}{3} \quad Y(22) = \tfrac{1}{3} \quad Y(33) = -\tfrac{2}{3}.$$

The commutation relations are readily verified by matrix multiplication.

The properties of the step operators follow from the appropriate commutation relations. Thus, for example, we have

$$[Y, U_\pm] = \pm U_\pm \qquad \text{therefore } YU_\pm = U_\pm Y \pm U_\pm.$$

Let $|y\rangle$ be an eigenstate of Y with eigenvalue y. Then

$$YU_\pm|y\rangle = (U_\pm Y \pm U_\pm)|y\rangle = U_\pm(Y \pm 1)|y\rangle = (y \pm 1)U_\pm|y\rangle,$$

i.e. the state $U_\pm|y\rangle$ is an eigenstate of Y with eigenvalue $y \pm 1$. Similarly, if $|i_3\rangle$ is an eigenstate of I_3 with eigenvalue i_3, we have, from the commutation relation $[I_3, U_\pm] = \mp\tfrac{1}{2}U_\pm$

$$I_3 U_\pm|i_3\rangle = (U_\pm I_3 \mp \tfrac{1}{2}U_\pm)|i_3\rangle = U_\pm(I_3 \mp \tfrac{1}{2})|i_3\rangle = (i_3 \mp \tfrac{1}{2})U_\pm|i_3\rangle.$$

Thus, the state $U_\pm|i_3\rangle$ is an eigenstate of I_3 with eigenvalue $i_3 \mp \tfrac{1}{2}$.

The results for $V_\pm$ follow in a similar way.

10.4 $V_-|u\rangle = V_-|\tfrac{1}{2}, \tfrac{1}{2}\rangle = \sqrt{[\tfrac{1}{2}(\tfrac{1}{2} + 1) - \tfrac{1}{2}(\tfrac{1}{2} - 1)]}|\tfrac{1}{2}, -\tfrac{1}{2}\rangle = |\tfrac{1}{2}, -\tfrac{1}{2}\rangle = |s\rangle.$

$U_+|s\rangle = U_+|\tfrac{1}{2}, -\tfrac{1}{2}\rangle = \sqrt{[\tfrac{1}{2}(\tfrac{1}{2} + 1) + \tfrac{1}{2}(-\tfrac{1}{2} + 1)]}|\tfrac{1}{2}, \tfrac{1}{2}\rangle = |\tfrac{1}{2}, \tfrac{1}{2}\rangle = |d\rangle.$

10.5 In the sextet the $I_3 = +1$ state in the I spin triplet $\{\mathbf{6}, |1, 1\rangle\}$ is uniquely $|uu\rangle$. All the other states in the sextet can be generated from this state using appropriate shift operators.

Thus

$$\{\mathbf{6}, |1, 0\rangle\} = I_-|uu\rangle = \frac{1}{\sqrt{2}}\{|ud\rangle + |du\rangle\}$$

$$\{\mathbf{6}, |1, -1\rangle\} = I_-\{\mathbf{6}, |1, 0\rangle\} = |dd\rangle.$$

Furthermore,

$$\{\mathbf{6}, |\tfrac{1}{2}, \tfrac{1}{2}\rangle\} = V_-|uu\rangle = \frac{1}{\sqrt{2}}\{|us\rangle + |su\rangle\}$$

$$\{\mathbf{6}, |\tfrac{1}{2}, -\tfrac{1}{2}\rangle\} = U_-|dd\rangle = \frac{1}{\sqrt{2}}\{|ds\rangle + |sd\rangle\}.$$

The I spin singlet in the sextet is unique and is $\{\mathbf{6}, |0, 0\rangle\} = |ss\rangle$.

The states in the $\bar{\mathbf{3}}$ have the same quark content as the states $\{\mathbf{6}, |1, 0\rangle\}$ and $\{\mathbf{6}, |\tfrac{1}{2}, \pm\tfrac{1}{2}\rangle\}$ but their wavefunctions must be orthogonal to the corresponding wavefunctions in the $\mathbf{6}$ representation. Thus

$$\{\bar{\mathbf{3}}, |0, 0\rangle\} = \frac{1}{\sqrt{2}}\{|ud\rangle - |du\rangle\}$$

$$\{\bar{\mathbf{3}}, |\tfrac{1}{2}, \tfrac{1}{2}\rangle\} = \frac{1}{\sqrt{2}}\{|us\rangle - |su\rangle\}$$

$$\{\bar{\mathbf{3}}, |\tfrac{1}{2}, -\tfrac{1}{2}\rangle\} = \frac{1}{\sqrt{2}}\{|ds\rangle - |sd\rangle\}.$$

10.6 (i) The decuplet states arise from the product $\mathbf{6} \otimes \mathbf{3}$. Hence to the *ud* and *uu* states in the sextet add a u and d quark respectively to obtain, after normalization,

$$\Delta^+ = \frac{1}{\sqrt{3}}[uud + (ud + du)u].$$

The antisymmetric octet states arise from the product $\bar{\mathbf{3}} \otimes \mathbf{3}$. Hence to the $\bar{\mathbf{3}}$ *ud* state add a u quark to obtain

$$p_{\mathrm{M_A}} = \frac{1}{\sqrt{2}}(ud - du)u.$$

The symmetric octet states arise from the product $\mathbf{6} \otimes \mathbf{3}$. Therefore add a u quark to the *ud* sextet state and a d quark to the *uu* state to obtain

$$8_{\mathrm{M_S}} = \alpha(ud + du)u + \beta uud.$$

This state must be orthogonal to the $\mathbf{10}$ state (Δ^+) so after normalization we obtain

$$p_{\mathrm{M_S}} = \frac{1}{\sqrt{6}}[(ud + du)u - 2uud].$$

(ii) For the decuplet states add a u to *ds*, a d to *us* and an s to *ud* in the sextet to obtain the symmetric state

$$\Sigma^0(1385) = \frac{1}{\sqrt{6}}[(sd + ds)u + (su + us)d + (du + ud)s].$$

The $I = 1$ octet states are obtained from p_{M_A} and p_{M_S} by successive application of U_- and I_-. After normalization we obtain

$$\Sigma^0_{M_A} = \tfrac{1}{2}[(sd - ds)u + (su - us)d]$$

$$\Sigma^0_{M_S} = \frac{1}{\sqrt{12}}[(sd + ds)u + (su + us)d - 2(du + ud)s].$$

The $I = 0$ states must be orthogonal to $\Sigma^0(1385)$ and $\Sigma^0_{M_A}$ and $\Sigma^0_{M_S}$ respectively. Hence

$$\Lambda^0_{M_S} = \tfrac{1}{2}[(sd + ds)u - (su + us)d]$$

$$\Lambda^0_{M_A} = \frac{1}{\sqrt{12}}[(sd - ds)u + (us - su)d - 2(du - ud)s].$$

(iii) The unitary singlet state must contain the u and d quarks in an $I = 0$ combination and contain u, d and s on an equal footing.

Hence

$$\mathbf{1}_A = \frac{1}{\sqrt{6}}[(ud - du)s + (ds - sd)u + (su - us)d]$$

which is antisymmetric under interchange of any two quarks.

10.7 The coupling of two spin $\frac{1}{2}$ doublets results in a triplet and a singlet, $\mathbf{2} \otimes \mathbf{2} = \mathbf{3}_S \oplus \mathbf{1}_A$, and the wavefunctions are

	m_s	$\chi(s, m_s)$
$\mathbf{3}_S$	$+1$	$\uparrow\uparrow$
	0	$\frac{1}{\sqrt{2}}(\uparrow\downarrow + \downarrow\uparrow)$
	-1	$\downarrow\downarrow$
$\mathbf{1}_A$	0	$\frac{1}{\sqrt{2}}(\uparrow\downarrow - \downarrow\uparrow)$.

Adding a doublet to the $s = 1$ triplet gives a symmetric quartet

$$\mathbf{4}_S \begin{cases} m_s & \chi(s, m_s) \\ +\frac{3}{2} & (\uparrow\uparrow)\uparrow \\ +\frac{1}{2} & \frac{1}{\sqrt{3}}[(\uparrow\downarrow + \downarrow\uparrow)\uparrow + (\uparrow\uparrow)\downarrow] \\ -\frac{1}{2} & \frac{1}{\sqrt{3}}[(\uparrow\downarrow + \downarrow\uparrow)\downarrow + (\downarrow\downarrow)\uparrow] \\ -\frac{3}{2} & (\downarrow\downarrow)\downarrow \end{cases}$$

and a mixed-symmetry doublet $\mathbf{2}_{M_S}$

$$\mathbf{2}_{M_S} \begin{cases} m_s & \chi(s, m_s) \\ +\frac{1}{2} & \frac{1}{\sqrt{6}}[(\uparrow\downarrow + \downarrow\uparrow)\uparrow - 2(\uparrow\uparrow)\downarrow] \\ -\frac{1}{2} & \frac{1}{\sqrt{6}}[(\uparrow\downarrow + \downarrow\uparrow)\downarrow - 2(\downarrow\downarrow)\uparrow]. \end{cases}$$

These two states are obtained by assuming they have the same form as, but are orthogonal to, the corresponding states in the $\mathbf{4}_S$. Note the symmetry with respect to interchange of the first two spins.

The $\mathbf{2}_{M_A}$ states are obtained simply by adding a doublet to the $\mathbf{1}_A$ state. Thus

$$\mathbf{2}_{M_A} \begin{cases} m_s & \chi(s, m_s) \\ +\frac{1}{2} & \frac{1}{\sqrt{2}}[(\uparrow\downarrow - \downarrow\uparrow)\uparrow] \\ -\frac{1}{2} & \frac{1}{\sqrt{2}}[(\uparrow\downarrow - \downarrow\uparrow)\downarrow]. \end{cases}$$

Note that this procedure is the same as that used in the *ud* sector in example 10.6 with the replacement u → ↑ and d → ↓.

10.8 The Δ^-, $\Sigma^-(1385)$, $\Xi^-(1530)$ and Ω^- have $U = \frac{3}{2}$ and $U_3 = +\frac{3}{2}, +\frac{1}{2}, -\frac{1}{2}$ and $-\frac{3}{2}$ respectively. The U spin scalar part of the mass-splitting operator has the same expectation value for all states in the multiplet, while the U spin vector part gives a splitting which is proportional to U_3 and therefore gives rise to equal mass splitting between the states: $m_\Sigma - m_\Delta \approx m_\Xi - m_\Sigma \approx m_\Omega - m_\Xi$.

10.9 From (10.24) we have

$$\langle n|H|n\rangle = m_0 + m_S + m_V \qquad (U_3 = +1)$$

$$\langle \tfrac{1}{2}\Sigma^0 + \tfrac{1}{2}\sqrt{3}\Lambda^0|H|\tfrac{1}{2}\Sigma^0 + \tfrac{1}{2}\sqrt{3}\Lambda^0\rangle = m_0 + m_S \qquad (U_3 = 0)$$

$$\langle \Xi^0|H|\Xi^0\rangle = m_0 + m_S - m_V \qquad (U_3 = -1).$$

Since the strong interactions conserve isospin H has no off-diagonal elements between the states Σ^0 and Λ^0. Thus,

$$\tfrac{1}{4}\langle \Sigma^0|H|\Sigma^0\rangle + \tfrac{3}{4}\langle \Lambda^0|H|\Lambda^0\rangle = m_0 + m_S.$$

On combining these equations we obtain

$$\tfrac{1}{2}\langle n|H|n\rangle + \tfrac{1}{2}\langle \Xi^0|H|\Xi^0\rangle = \tfrac{1}{4}\langle \Sigma^0|H|\Sigma^0\rangle + \tfrac{3}{4}\langle \Lambda^0|H|\Lambda^0\rangle,$$

i.e.

$$\tfrac{1}{2}m_n + \tfrac{1}{2}m_{\Xi^0} = \tfrac{1}{4}m_{\Sigma^0} + \tfrac{3}{4}m_{\Lambda^0}.$$

10.10 Since the initial states have $U = \frac{3}{2}$ the triplet and doublet in the final state must couple to give $U = \frac{3}{2}$ if U spin is conserved. All the decay amplitudes are therefore proportional to a single amplitude $A_{3/2}$ with the proportionality factor given by the appropriate Clebsch–Gordan coefficient.

$$\langle \Delta^-|A|n\pi^-\rangle = A_{3/2} \qquad \langle \Sigma^-(1385)|A|nK^-\rangle = \sqrt{\tfrac{1}{3}}A_{3/2}$$

$$\langle \Sigma^-(1385)|A|\Sigma^0\pi^-\rangle = \tfrac{1}{2}\sqrt{\tfrac{2}{3}}A_{3/2} \qquad \langle \Sigma^-(1385)|A|\Lambda^0\pi^-\rangle = \frac{\sqrt{3}}{2}\sqrt{\tfrac{2}{3}}A_{3/2}$$

$$\langle \Xi^-(1530)|A|\Xi^0\pi^-\rangle = \sqrt{\tfrac{1}{3}}A_{3/2} \qquad \langle \Xi^-(1530)|A|\Sigma^0K^-\rangle = \tfrac{1}{2}\sqrt{\tfrac{2}{3}}A_{3/2}$$

$$\langle \Xi^-(1530)|A|\Lambda^0K^-\rangle = \frac{\sqrt{3}}{2}\sqrt{\tfrac{2}{3}}A_{3/2} \qquad \langle \Omega^-|A|\Xi^0K^-\rangle = A_{3/2}.$$

10.11 The $U = 1$, $U_3 = 0$ state in the pseudoscalar octet is $|\frac{1}{2}\pi^0 + \frac{1}{2}\sqrt{3}\eta^0\rangle$. U spin conservation implies that the transition matrix element

$$\langle \tfrac{1}{2}\pi^0 + \tfrac{1}{2}\sqrt{3}\eta^0|A|\gamma\gamma\rangle = 0$$

therefore

$$\langle \pi^0|A|\gamma\gamma\rangle = -\sqrt{3}\langle \eta^0|A|\gamma\gamma\rangle.$$

10.12 The π^- and K^- belong to a U spin doublet ($U = \frac{1}{2}$) and the proton is a member of a U spin doublet. The possible values of the U spin in the initial states are therefore $U = 0$ or 1. The π^+ and K^+ belong to a U spin doublet while the $\Sigma^-(1385)$, Δ^- and $\Xi^-(1530)$ belong to a $U = \frac{3}{2}$ quartet. The possible values of the U spin in the final states are therefore $U = 1$ or 2. U spin conservation implies that only the $U = 1$ amplitude, A_1, contributes. Using tables of Clebsch–Gordan coefficients we obtain the amplitudes $-\frac{1}{2}A_1$, $\frac{1}{2}\sqrt{3}A_1$, $-\frac{1}{2}A_1$ and $\frac{1}{2}A_1$ respectively.

10.13 With respect to the η', η basis the mass matrix is diagonal,

$$H\begin{pmatrix}\eta'\\ \eta\end{pmatrix} = \begin{pmatrix} m_{\eta'}^2 & 0 \\ 0 & m_\eta^2 \end{pmatrix}\begin{pmatrix}\eta'\\ \eta\end{pmatrix}.$$

With the base states transforming as

$$\begin{pmatrix}\eta' \\ \eta\end{pmatrix} = R\begin{pmatrix}\eta_1 \\ \eta_8\end{pmatrix}$$

the mass matrix transforms as

$$\begin{pmatrix}m_{\eta'}^2 & 0 \\ 0 & m_\eta^2\end{pmatrix} = R^\dagger\begin{pmatrix}M_{11}^2 & M_{18}^2 \\ M_{18}^2 & M_{88}^2\end{pmatrix}R \qquad (1)$$

where R is the rotation matrix

$$R = \begin{pmatrix}\cos\theta & \sin\theta \\ -\sin\theta & \cos\theta\end{pmatrix}.$$

From (1) we obtain

$$m_{\eta'}^2 = M_{11}^2\cos^2\theta + M_{88}^2\sin^2\theta - 2M_{18}^2\sin\theta\cos\theta$$

$$m_\eta^2 = M_{11}^2\sin^2\theta + M_{88}^2\cos^2\theta + 2M_{18}^2\sin\theta\cos\theta$$

$$0 = (M_{11}^2 - M_{88}^2)\sin\theta\cos\theta + M_{18}^2(\cos^2\theta - \sin^2\theta).$$

On eliminating M_{11}^2 and M_{18}^2 from these equations we obtain

$$\tan^2\theta = \frac{M_{88}^2 - m_\eta^2}{m_{\eta'}^2 - M_{88}^2}.$$

10.14 To predict the meson masses we use the quark wavefunctions to determine the weights of the constituent quarks in the meson and the value of $\boldsymbol{s}_1\cdot\boldsymbol{s}_2$ using $J^2 = (\boldsymbol{s}_1 + \boldsymbol{s}_2)^2 = s_1^2 + s_2^2 + 2\boldsymbol{s}_1\cdot\boldsymbol{s}_2$. For pseudoscalar mesons ($J = 0$) $\boldsymbol{s}_1\cdot\boldsymbol{s}_2 = -\frac{3}{4}$ and for vector mesons ($J = 1$) $\boldsymbol{s}_1\cdot\boldsymbol{s}_2 = \frac{1}{4}$. Using equation (10.38) we obtain the values in the table overleaf.

10.15 The wavefunction is

$$|\Lambda^0\uparrow\rangle = \frac{1}{\sqrt{2}}(\Lambda^0_{M_S}\chi_{M_S} + \Lambda^0_{M_A}\chi_{M_A}).$$

Using the results of examples 10.6 and 10.7 we have explicitly

$$\begin{aligned}|\Lambda^0\uparrow\rangle &= \tfrac{1}{2}\sqrt{(\tfrac{1}{12})}\,(sdu + dsu - sud - usd)(\uparrow\downarrow\uparrow + \downarrow\uparrow\uparrow - 2\uparrow\uparrow\downarrow) \\ &\quad + \tfrac{1}{2}\sqrt{(\tfrac{1}{12})}(sdu - dsu + usd - sud - 2dus + 2uds)(\uparrow\downarrow\uparrow - \downarrow\uparrow\uparrow) \\ &= \sqrt{(\tfrac{1}{12})}(s\uparrow d\downarrow u\uparrow - s\uparrow d\uparrow u\downarrow + d\downarrow s\uparrow u\uparrow - d\uparrow s\uparrow u\downarrow \\ &\quad - s\uparrow u\downarrow d\uparrow + s\uparrow u\uparrow d\downarrow - u\downarrow s\uparrow d\uparrow + u\uparrow s\uparrow d\downarrow \\ &\quad - d\uparrow u\downarrow s\uparrow + d\downarrow u\uparrow s\uparrow + u\uparrow d\downarrow s\uparrow - u\downarrow d\uparrow s\uparrow).\end{aligned}$$

Meson	Wavefunction	Predicted mass/(GeV/c^2)	Measured mass/(GeV/c^2)
π	$-u\bar{d}$	$2m_u - \frac{3a}{4m_u^2} = 0.140$	0.140
K	$u\bar{s}$	$m_u + m_s - \frac{3a}{4m_u m_s} = 0.485$	0.494
η	$\frac{1}{\sqrt{6}}(u\bar{u} + d\bar{d} - 2s\bar{s})$	$\frac{2}{3}m_u + \frac{4}{3}m_s - \frac{a}{4m_u^2} - \frac{a}{2m_s^2} = 0.559$	0.549
ρ, ω	$\frac{1}{\sqrt{2}}(u\bar{u} \mp d\bar{d})$	$2m_u + \frac{a}{4m_u^2} = 0.780$	0.768, 0.782
K*(892)	$u\bar{s}$	$m_u + m_s + \frac{a}{4m_u m_s} = 0.896$	0.892
φ	$s\bar{s}$	$2m_s + \frac{a}{4m_s^2} = 1.032$	1.019

The magnetic moment of the Λ^0 is therefore

$$\mu_\Lambda = \sum_q \langle \Lambda^0\uparrow|\mu_q|\Lambda^0\uparrow\rangle$$

$$= \frac{1}{12}(\mu_s - \mu_d + \mu_u + \mu_s + \mu_d - \mu_u - \cdots)$$

$$= \mu_s.$$

10.16 On making the suggested substitution the integral becomes

$$\frac{3\pi\lambda\!\!\!^{-2}}{2}\int_{\pi/2}^{3\pi/2}\left(\frac{\Gamma_e}{\Gamma}\right)^2 \Gamma\, d\theta = \frac{3\pi^2}{2}\lambda\!\!\!^{-2}\left(\frac{\Gamma_e}{\Gamma}\right)^2 \Gamma.$$

On substituting $\lambda\!\!\!^- = \hbar/p = \hbar c/cp = 197/1500$, $\Gamma_e/\Gamma = 0.07$ and $\int \sigma(E)\, dE = 870$ nb MeV we obtain $\Gamma = 0.07$ MeV.

Chapter 11

11.1 $$\langle\lambda\rangle = \int \psi^*(\boldsymbol{r})(\boldsymbol{s}\cdot\hat{\boldsymbol{p}})\psi(\boldsymbol{r})\, d\tau \xrightarrow{P} \int \psi^*(-\boldsymbol{r})(-\boldsymbol{s}\cdot\hat{\boldsymbol{p}})\psi(-\boldsymbol{r})\, d\tau.$$

If $\psi(\boldsymbol{r})$ is an eigenstate of parity $\psi(-\boldsymbol{r}) = \pm\psi(\boldsymbol{r})$. Hence

$$\langle\lambda\rangle = -\int \psi^*(\boldsymbol{r})(\boldsymbol{s}\cdot\hat{\boldsymbol{p}})\psi(\boldsymbol{r})\, d\tau = -\langle\lambda\rangle.$$

Therefore $\langle\lambda\rangle$ must be zero in a parity-conserving interaction.

11.2 In centre-of-mass system $E_\nu = cp_\nu = cp_{S_m^*}$ (by momentum conservation). For non-relativistic recoil

$$E_{S_m^*} = \frac{p_{S_m^*}^2}{2M} = \frac{E_\nu^2}{2Mc^2} = \frac{Mv^2}{2}.$$

Therefore $v/c = E_\nu/Mc^2$. The energy of the γ ray is given by

$$E_\gamma = E_0\left(1 + \frac{v}{c}\cos\theta\right) - \frac{E_0^2}{2Mc^2}$$

where the first term is the Doppler-shifted energy and the second is the recoil energy loss. On absorption, there is a further recoil loss of $E_0^2/2Mc^2$; therefore, the energy available for excitation is

$$E_\gamma = E_0\left(1 + \frac{v}{c}\cos\theta\right) - \frac{E_0^2}{Mc^2}.$$

The resonance condition is $E_\gamma = E_0$, and hence $E_\nu \cos\theta = E_0$.

11.3 Take the quantization axis as the Λ spin direction, i.e. Λ in state $|\frac{1}{2}, \frac{1}{2}\rangle$. The final state wavefunction is therefore

$$\begin{aligned}\psi(\theta, \phi) &= SY_0^0\uparrow + P(\sqrt{\tfrac{2}{3}}Y_1^1\downarrow - \sqrt{\tfrac{1}{3}}Y_1^0\uparrow)\\ &= (SY_0^0 - \sqrt{\tfrac{1}{3}}PY_1^0)\uparrow + \sqrt{\tfrac{2}{3}}PY_1^1\downarrow.\end{aligned}$$

The factors $\sqrt{\frac{2}{3}}$ and $\sqrt{\frac{1}{3}}$ are Clebsch–Gordan coefficients. The angular distribution is therefore

$$\begin{aligned}W(\theta, \phi) = |\psi(\theta, \phi)|^2 &= |S|^2|Y_0^0|^2 + \tfrac{1}{3}|P|^2|Y_1^0|^2\\ &\quad - 2\sqrt{\tfrac{1}{3}}\,\mathrm{Re}\,S^*P + \tfrac{2}{3}|P|^2|Y_1^1|^2\end{aligned}$$

where we have used the fact that the spin states $\uparrow$ and $\downarrow$ are orthogonal. Substituting

$$Y_0^0 = \left(\frac{1}{4\pi}\right)^{1/2}, \qquad Y_1^0 = \left(\frac{3}{4\pi}\right)^{1/2}\cos\theta$$

and

$$Y_1^1 = -\left(\frac{3}{8\pi}\right)^{1/2}\sin\theta\, e^{i\phi}$$

gives

$$W(\theta) = \tfrac{1}{4}[|S|^2 + |P|^2]\left(1 - \frac{2\,\mathrm{Re}\,S^*P}{|S|^2 + |P|^2}\cos\theta\right).$$

11.4 Multiply the Klein–Gordon equation by $-i\phi^*$ and its complex conjugate by $-\mathrm{i}\phi$ and subtract to obtain

$$-\mathrm{i}(\phi^*\nabla^2\phi - \phi\nabla^2\phi^*) = -\mathrm{i}\left(\phi^*\frac{\partial^2\phi}{\partial t^2} - \phi\frac{\partial^2\phi^*}{\partial t^2}\right).$$

Therefore,

$$-\mathrm{i}\boldsymbol{\nabla}\cdot(\phi^*\nabla\phi - \phi\nabla\phi^*) = -\mathrm{i}\frac{\partial}{\partial t}\left(\phi^*\frac{\partial\phi}{\partial t} - \phi\frac{\partial\phi^*}{\partial t}\right).$$

Divide both sides by i^2 to obtain

$$\frac{\partial}{\partial t}\left[\mathrm{i}\left(\phi^*\frac{\partial\phi}{\partial t} - \phi\frac{\partial\phi^*}{\partial t}\right)\right] + \boldsymbol{\nabla}\cdot\left[\frac{1}{\mathrm{i}}(\phi^*\nabla\phi - \phi\nabla\phi^*)\right] = 0.$$

With $\hbar = 1$, $\phi = N\exp[\mathrm{i}(\boldsymbol{p}\cdot\boldsymbol{x} - Et)]$ is a plane wave solution to the Klein–Gordon equation. Substitution of ϕ and ϕ^* gives $\rho = 2|N|^2E$ and $\boldsymbol{j} = 2|N|^2\boldsymbol{p}$.

11.5 $$\alpha_i = \begin{pmatrix} 0 & \sigma_i \\ \sigma_i & 0 \end{pmatrix} \quad \text{and} \quad \beta = \begin{pmatrix} I & 0 \\ 0 & -I \end{pmatrix}.$$

$$\alpha_i\alpha_j = \begin{pmatrix} \sigma_i\sigma_j & 0 \\ 0 & \sigma_i\sigma_j \end{pmatrix} \quad \text{and} \quad \alpha_j\alpha_i = \begin{pmatrix} \sigma_j\sigma_i & 0 \\ 0 & \sigma_j\sigma_i \end{pmatrix}.$$

Therefore,

$$\alpha_i\alpha_j + \alpha_j\alpha_i = \{\alpha_i, \alpha_j\} = \begin{pmatrix} \sigma_i\sigma_j + \sigma_j\sigma_i & 0 \\ 0 & \sigma_i\sigma_j + \sigma_j\sigma_i \end{pmatrix} = 2\delta_{ij}I$$

since $\sigma_i^2 = I$ and $\sigma_i\sigma_j = -\sigma_j\sigma_i$ $(i \neq j)$.

$$\alpha_i\beta = \begin{pmatrix} 0 & -\sigma_i \\ \sigma_i & 0 \end{pmatrix} \quad \text{and} \quad \beta\alpha_i = \begin{pmatrix} 0 & \sigma_i \\ -\sigma_i & 0 \end{pmatrix}.$$

Therefore,

$$\{\alpha_i, \beta\} = 0.$$

11.6 $$\{\gamma^\mu, \gamma^\nu\} = \beta\alpha_\mu\beta\alpha_\nu + \beta\alpha_\nu\beta\alpha_\mu = -\beta^2\{\alpha_\mu, \alpha_\nu\} = -2\delta_{\mu\nu}I = 2g^{\mu\nu}I \qquad (\mu, \nu \neq 0).$$

$$\{\gamma^0, \gamma^0\} = 2\beta^2 = 2I = 2g^{00}I.$$

$$\{\gamma^0, \gamma^k\} = \{\beta, \beta\alpha_k\} = \beta^2\alpha_k + \beta\alpha_k\beta = \beta^2\alpha_k - \beta^2\alpha_k = 0.$$

Therefore,

$$\gamma^\mu\gamma^\nu + \gamma^\nu\gamma^\mu = 2g^{\mu\nu}I \qquad (\mu, \nu = 0, 1, 2, 3).$$

$$\gamma^0 = \begin{pmatrix} I & 0 \\ 0 & -I \end{pmatrix} \qquad (\gamma^0)^\dagger = \begin{pmatrix} I & 0 \\ 0 & -I \end{pmatrix} = \gamma^0$$

$$\gamma^k = \begin{pmatrix} 0 & \sigma_k \\ -\sigma_k & 0 \end{pmatrix} \qquad (\gamma^k)^\dagger = \begin{pmatrix} 0 & -\sigma_k \\ \sigma_k & 0 \end{pmatrix} = -\gamma^k.$$

$$(\gamma^5)^2 = \mathrm{i}^2\gamma^0\gamma^1\gamma^2\gamma^3\gamma^0\gamma^1\gamma^2\gamma^3.$$

The required result is most easily arrived at by moving the first γ^0 to the right (using $\gamma^0\gamma^\mu = -\gamma^\mu\gamma^0$, $\mu \neq 0$) until we have

$$\begin{aligned}(\gamma^5)^2 &= \mathrm{i}^2(-1)^3\gamma^1\gamma^2\gamma^3(\gamma^0)^2\gamma^1\gamma^2\gamma^3 \\ &= \mathrm{i}^2(-1)^3\gamma^1\gamma^2\gamma^3\gamma^1\gamma^2\gamma^3 I \qquad ((\gamma^0)^2 = I).\end{aligned}$$

Repeat for γ^1,

$$(\gamma^5)^2 = \mathrm{i}^2(-1)^5\gamma^2\gamma^3\gamma^2\gamma^3 I(-I) \qquad ((\gamma^1)^2 = -I).$$

Move γ^2,

$$\begin{aligned}(\gamma^5)^2 &= \mathrm{i}^2(-1)^6\gamma^3\gamma^3 I(-I)(-I) \qquad ((\gamma^2)^2 = -I) \\ &= \mathrm{i}^2(-1)^9 I \qquad ((\gamma^3)^2 = -I) \\ &= I.\end{aligned}$$

Again, $\gamma^5 = \mathrm{i}\gamma^0\gamma^1\gamma^2\gamma^3$ and therefore $(\gamma^5)^\dagger = -\mathrm{i}(-\gamma^3)(-\gamma^2)(-\gamma^1)\gamma^0$, where we have used $(\gamma^0)^\dagger = \gamma^0$ and $(\gamma^k)^\dagger = -\gamma^k$. Therefore

$$(\gamma^5)^\dagger = \mathrm{i}\gamma^3\gamma^2\gamma^1\gamma^0 = \mathrm{i}\gamma^0\gamma^1\gamma^2\gamma^3 = \gamma^5 \qquad \text{(six sign changes)}.$$

Consider $\gamma^\mu\gamma^5$. Moving γ^μ to the right involves three sign changes; γ^μ encounters itself (no sign change) and the three other γ^ν, $\nu \neq \mu$. Therefore, $\gamma^\mu\gamma^5 = -\gamma^5\gamma^\mu$.

11.7 Multiply the Dirac equation from the left by β to obtain

$$\left(\mathrm{i}\beta\frac{\partial}{\partial t} + \mathrm{i}\beta\boldsymbol{\alpha}\cdot\boldsymbol{\nabla} - \beta^2 m\right)\psi = 0.$$

With $\beta^2 = I$, $\partial_\mu = (\partial/\partial t, \boldsymbol{\nabla})$ and $\gamma^\mu = (\beta, \beta\boldsymbol{\alpha})$ this becomes

$$(\mathrm{i}\gamma^\mu\partial_\mu - m)\psi = 0.$$

11.8 (a) The Hermitian conjugate equation is

$$-\mathrm{i}\frac{\partial\psi^\dagger}{\partial t}\gamma^0 - \mathrm{i}\frac{\partial\psi^\dagger}{\partial x^k}(-\gamma^k) - m\psi^\dagger = 0.$$

Multiply from the right by γ^0 to give

$$-\mathrm{i}\frac{\partial\psi^\dagger}{\partial t}\gamma^0\gamma^0 - \mathrm{i}\frac{\partial\psi^\dagger}{\partial x^k}\gamma^0\gamma^k - m\psi^\dagger\gamma^0 = 0$$

where we have used $\gamma^k\gamma^0 = -\gamma^0\gamma^k$. With $\bar{\psi} = \psi^\dagger\gamma^0$ this becomes

$$\mathrm{i}\partial_\mu\bar{\psi}\gamma^\mu + m\bar{\psi} = 0$$

the adjoint equation.

(b) Multiply the Dirac equation from the left by $\bar{\psi}$ to obtain

$$\mathrm{i}\bar{\psi}\gamma^\mu\partial_\mu\psi - m\bar{\psi}\psi = 0.$$

Multiply the adjoint equation from the right by ψ to get

$$\mathrm{i}\partial_\mu\bar{\psi}\gamma^\mu\psi + m\bar{\psi}\psi = 0.$$

Add these to give

$$\bar{\psi}\gamma^\mu\partial_\mu\psi + (\partial_\mu\bar{\psi})\gamma^\mu\psi = 0,$$

i.e.

$$\partial_\mu(\bar{\psi}\gamma^\mu\psi) = 0.$$

11.9 Using $\sigma_1\sigma_2 = \mathrm{i}\sigma_3$, $\sigma_2\sigma_1 = -\mathrm{i}\sigma_3$, etc., and $\sigma_i^2 = 1$ $(i = 1, 3)$, we have

$$\begin{aligned}(\boldsymbol{\sigma}\cdot\boldsymbol{a})(\boldsymbol{\sigma}\cdot\boldsymbol{b}) &= (\sigma_1 a_1 + \sigma_2 a_2 + \sigma_3 a_3)(\sigma_1 b_1 + \sigma_2 b_2 + \sigma_3 b_3)\\ &= \sigma_1^2(a_1 b_1) + \sigma_2^2(a_2 b_2) + \sigma_3^2(a_3 b_3)\\ &\quad + \sigma_1\sigma_2(a_1 b_2) + \sigma_2\sigma_1(a_2 b_1) + \sigma_1\sigma_3(a_1 b_3)\\ &\quad + \sigma_3\sigma_1(a_3 b_1) + \sigma_2\sigma_3(a_2 b_3) + \sigma_3\sigma_2(a_3 b_2)\\ &= \boldsymbol{a}\cdot\boldsymbol{b} + \sigma_1\sigma_2(a_1 b_2 - a_2 b_1) + \sigma_1\sigma_3(a_1 b_3 - a_3 b_1)\\ &\quad + \sigma_2\sigma_3(a_2 b_3 - a_3 b_2)\\ &= \boldsymbol{a}\cdot\boldsymbol{b} + \mathrm{i}\sigma_3(\boldsymbol{a}\times\boldsymbol{b})_3 + \mathrm{i}\sigma_2(\boldsymbol{a}\times\boldsymbol{b})_2 + \mathrm{i}\sigma_1(\boldsymbol{a}\times\boldsymbol{b})_1\\ &= \boldsymbol{a}\cdot\boldsymbol{b} + \mathrm{i}\boldsymbol{\sigma}\cdot(\boldsymbol{a}\times\boldsymbol{b}).\end{aligned}$$

11.10 In appendix F it is shown that in natural units 1 GeV = 1.602×10^{-10} J and 1 m = 5.068×10^{15} GeV^{-1}. Therefore,

$$\begin{aligned}G_\mathrm{F} = 1.4355 \times 10^{-62}\ \mathrm{J\,m^3} &= 1.4355 \times 10^{-62} \times 0.6242 \times 10^{10}\\ &\quad\times 1.3017 \times 10^{47}\\ &= 1.1664 \times 10^{-5}\ \mathrm{GeV^{-2}}\\ &\approx \frac{10^{-5}}{m_\mathrm{p}^2}\ (= 1.1366 \times 10^{-5}\ \mathrm{GeV^{-2}}).\end{aligned}$$

11.11 Spin 'up' and spin 'down' solutions are respectively

$$u^{(1)} = N\begin{pmatrix} 1 \\ 0 \\ \dfrac{p}{E+m} \\ 0 \end{pmatrix} \qquad u^{(2)} = N\begin{pmatrix} 0 \\ 1 \\ 0 \\ \dfrac{-p}{E+m} \end{pmatrix}.$$

Using equation (11.65) we have

$$\tfrac{1}{2}(1-\gamma^5) = \frac{1}{2}\begin{pmatrix} 1 & 0 & -1 & 0 \\ 0 & 1 & 0 & -1 \\ -1 & 0 & 1 & 0 \\ 0 & -1 & 0 & 1 \end{pmatrix}$$

and

$$v^{(1)} = \tfrac{1}{2}(1-\gamma^5)u^{(1)} = \frac{N}{2(E+m)}\begin{pmatrix} E+m-p \\ 0 \\ -(E+m-p) \\ 0 \end{pmatrix}$$

$$v^{(2)} = \tfrac{1}{2}(1-\gamma^5)u^{(2)} = \frac{N}{2(E+m)}\begin{pmatrix} 0 \\ E+m+p \\ 0 \\ -(E+m+p) \end{pmatrix}.$$

Hence the probability of spin up is $v^{(1)\dagger}v^{(1)} \propto (E+m-p)^2$, the probability of spin down is $v^{(2)\dagger}v^{(2)} \propto (E+m+p)^2$ and the longitudinal polarization is

$$\frac{(E+m-p)^2 - (E+m+p)^2}{(E+m-p)^2 + (E+m+p)^2} = -\frac{p}{E}\left(= -\frac{v}{c}\right).$$

11.12 Scalar current:

$$\begin{aligned} \bar{\psi}_e I(1-\gamma^5)\psi_\nu &= \psi_e^\dagger \gamma^0 I(1-\gamma^5)\psi_\nu \\ &= \psi_e^\dagger(1+\gamma^5)\gamma^0\psi_\nu \qquad (\text{since } \gamma^0\gamma^5 = -\gamma^5\gamma^0) \\ &= [(1+\gamma^5)\psi_e]^\dagger\gamma^0\psi_\nu \quad (\text{since } (\gamma^5)^\dagger = \gamma^5) \\ &= (1+\gamma^5)\bar{\psi}_e\psi_\nu, \end{aligned}$$

i.e. a scalar current would produce mainly right-handed electrons (fully polarized in the limit $m_e \to 0$ but with average helicity $+v/c$ in general, cf. example 11.11).

Vector current:

$$\begin{aligned}\bar{\psi}_e\gamma^\lambda(1-\gamma^5)\psi_\nu &= \psi_e^\dagger\gamma^0\gamma^\lambda(1-\gamma^5)\psi_\nu\\ &= \psi_e^\dagger\gamma^0(1+\gamma^5)\gamma^\lambda\psi_\nu\\ &= \psi_e^\dagger(1-\gamma^5)\gamma^0\gamma^\lambda\psi_\nu\\ &= [(1-\gamma^5)\psi_e]^\dagger\gamma^0\gamma^\lambda\psi_\nu\\ &= (1-\gamma^5)\bar{\psi}_e\gamma^\lambda\psi_\nu,\end{aligned}$$

i.e. mainly left-handed electrons from a vector current. In general, the handedness depends on the number of γ matrices in O_i – an even number gives right-handed electrons; an odd number left-handed electrons. The S, V, T, A and P operators contain respectively 0, 1, 2, 3 and 4 γ matrices.

11.13 With $c = 1$, the total energy

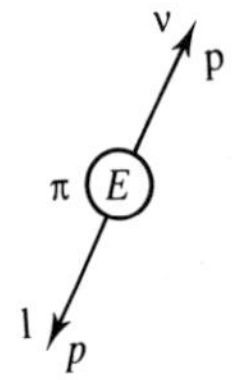

$$E = M = p + \sqrt{(p^2 + m^2)} \tag{1}$$

where M is the pion mass, m is the lepton mass and $m_\nu = 0$. Hence $p = (M^2 - m^2)/2M$.

The lepton energy is $E_l = M - p = (M^2 + m^2)/M$. From equation (1) $\mathrm{d}p/\mathrm{d}E = E_l/M$ and therefore the phase-space factor is

$$p^2\frac{\mathrm{d}p}{\mathrm{d}E} = \left(\frac{M^2 - m^2}{2M}\right)^2 \frac{M^2 + m^2}{M^2}.$$

The V–A factor is $(1 - v/c) = 1 - p/E_l = m^2/(M^2 + m^2)$ and therefore the phase space factor × (V–A) factor is $m^2(M^2 - m^2)/4M^4$. Hence,

$$\frac{\Gamma(\pi \to e\nu)}{\Gamma(\pi \to \mu\nu)} = \frac{m_e^2(M^2 - m_e^2)^2}{m_\mu^2(M^2 - m_\mu^2)^2} = 1.28 \times 10^{-4}.$$

11.14 Neutron decay at the quark level $d \to ue^-\bar{\nu}_e$ has a Cabibbo factor $\cos\theta_C$ while Λ decay, $s \to ue^-\bar{\nu}_e$ has a Cabibbo factor $\sin\theta_C$.

$$\Gamma(n \to pe^-\bar{\nu}_e) = \frac{f_n}{\tau_n} \propto \frac{\cos^2\theta_C(E_n)^5}{30}$$

$$\Gamma(\Lambda \to pe^-\bar{\nu}_e) = \frac{f_\Lambda}{\tau_\Lambda} \propto \frac{\sin^2\theta_C(E_\Lambda)^5}{30}.$$

Hence,

$$\tan^2\theta_C\frac{f_\Lambda\tau_n}{f_n\tau_\Lambda}\left(\frac{E_n}{E_\Lambda}\right)^5 = 0.060$$

and $\theta_C = 13.8°$.

11.15 From section 11.13.5 we obtain

$$\langle\pi^+\pi^-|H|K_L^0\rangle = \text{constant} \times \epsilon(\text{Re}\,A_2\,e^{i\delta_2} + \sqrt{2}A_0\,e^{i\delta_0}) + \text{Im}\,A_2\,e^{i\delta_2}$$

$$\langle\pi^+\pi^-|H|K_S^0\rangle = \text{constant} \times (\text{Re}\,A_2\,e^{i\delta_2} + \sqrt{2}A_0\,e^{i\delta_0} + \epsilon\,\text{Im}\,A_2\,e^{i\delta_2})$$

$$\langle\pi^0\pi^0|H|K_L^0\rangle = \text{constant} \times \epsilon(\sqrt{2}\,\text{Re}\,A_2\,e^{i\delta_2} - A_0\,e^{i\delta_0}) + \sqrt{2}\,\text{Im}\,A_2\,e^{i\delta_2}$$

$$\langle\pi^0\pi^0|H|K_S^0\rangle = \text{constant} \times (\sqrt{2}\,\text{Re}\,A_2\,e^{i\delta_2} - A_0\,e^{i\delta_0} + \epsilon\sqrt{2}\,\text{Im}\,A_2\,e^{i\delta_2})$$

where the constant is $2 \times 3^{-1/2}[2(1 + |\epsilon|^2)]^{-1/2}$. Hence,

$$\begin{aligned}
\eta_{+-} &= \frac{\epsilon\,\text{Re}\,A_2\,e^{i\delta_2} + \epsilon\sqrt{2}A_0\,e^{i\delta_0} + \text{Im}\,A_2\,e^{i\delta_2}}{\text{Re}\,A_2\,e^{i\delta_2} + \sqrt{2}A_0\,e^{i\delta_0} + \epsilon\,\text{Im}\,A_2\,e^{i\delta_2}} \\
&\approx \frac{\epsilon + (1/\sqrt{2})(\text{Im}\,A_2/A_0)\exp[i(\delta_2 - \delta_0)]}{1 + (1/\sqrt{2})(\text{Re}\,A_2/A_0)\exp[i(\delta_2 - \delta_0)]} \\
&\approx \left\{\epsilon + \frac{1}{\sqrt{2}}\frac{\text{Im}\,A_2}{A_0}\exp[i(\delta_2 - \delta_0)]\right\} \\
&\quad \times \left\{1 - \frac{1}{\sqrt{2}}\frac{\text{Re}\,A_2}{A_0}\exp[i(\delta_2 - \delta_0)]\right\} \\
&\approx \epsilon + \frac{1}{\sqrt{2}}\frac{\text{Im}\,A_2}{A_0}\exp[i(\delta_2 - \delta_0)] = \epsilon + \epsilon'.
\end{aligned}$$

Similarly,

$$\eta_{00} \approx \epsilon - \sqrt{2}\frac{\text{Im}\,A_2}{A_0}\exp[i(\delta_2 - \delta_0)] = \epsilon - 2\epsilon'.$$

Chapter 12

12.1 We have $p' = k - k' + p$ and $q = (k - k')$. Then

$$q^2 = (k - k')^2 = k^2 + k'^2 - 2k\cdot k' \approx -2k\cdot k'.$$

Further,

$$k'\cdot p' = k'\cdot(k - k' + p) = k'\cdot k - k'^2 + k'\cdot p \approx -\tfrac{1}{2}q^2 + k'\cdot p$$

and

$$k\cdot p' = k\cdot(k - k' + p) = k^2 - k\cdot k' + k\cdot p \approx \tfrac{1}{2}q^2 + k\cdot p.$$

Then,

$$(k'\cdot p')(k\cdot p) + (k'\cdot p)(k\cdot p') = -\tfrac{1}{2}q^2(k\cdot p - k'\cdot p) + 2(k'\cdot p)(k\cdot p).$$

Furthermore, $-M^2 k\cdot k' \approx \frac{1}{2}q^2 M^2$ and equation (12.18) follows.

12.2 From equation (12.18)

$$\overline{|\mathcal{M}|^2} \approx -\tfrac{1}{2}q^2(k\cdot p - k'\cdot p) + 2(k'\cdot p)(k\cdot p) + \tfrac{1}{2}M^2q^2.$$

With reference to figure 12.5, $k\cdot p = EM$ and $k'\cdot p = E'M$, so that

$$\overline{|\mathcal{M}|^2} \approx 2EE'M^2\left[1 + \frac{q^2}{4EE'} - \frac{q^2}{2M^2}\frac{M(E-E')}{2EE'}\right].$$

Now,

$$q^2 = (k-k')^2 \approx -2k\cdot k' = -2EE' + 2k\cdot k' \cos\theta$$

$$\approx -2EE'(1-\cos\theta) = -4EE'\sin^2\left(\frac{\theta}{2}\right).$$

Furthermore, $q + p = p'$, so $q^2 = -2q\cdot p = -2\nu M = -2(E-E')M$. Hence

$$\overline{|\mathcal{M}|^2} = \frac{8e^4}{q^4}2EE'M^2\left[\cos^2\left(\frac{\theta}{2}\right) - \frac{q^2}{2M^2}\sin^2\left(\frac{\theta}{2}\right)\right].$$

12.3 For normalization, $\int_0^\infty \rho_0 \exp(-mr)4\pi r^2\,\mathrm{d}r = 1$ and $\rho_0 = m^3/8\pi$.

$$F(q) = \int \rho(r)\exp(iqr\cos\theta)r^2\,\mathrm{d}r\,\mathrm{d}\phi\,\mathrm{d}(\cos\theta)$$

$$= \frac{2\pi}{iq}\int_0^\infty \rho(r)[\exp(iqr) - \exp(-iqr)]r\,\mathrm{d}r$$

$$= \frac{m^3}{4iq}\int_0^\infty r\{\exp[-(m-iq)r] - \exp[-(m+iq)r]\}\,\mathrm{d}r$$

$$= \frac{m^4}{(m^2+q^2)^2}$$

$$= \left(1 + \frac{q^2}{m^2}\right)^{-2}.$$

Note that here, q is an ordinary vector momentum. The Fourier transformation interpretation of the form factor is strictly valid only for a *static* charge distribution. To use this interpretation for $G(q^2)$, where q^2 is a four-momentum squared, the photon must be soft ($\nu \approx 0$) so that no energy is transferred to the proton. In this limit $q^2 = -|q|^2$ and the above result is identical to the dipole formula given in section 12.3.

$$\langle r^2\rangle = \int_0^\infty \rho(r)r^2 4\pi r^2\,\mathrm{d}r = \frac{m^3}{2}\int_0^\infty r^4\exp(-mr)\,\mathrm{d}r = \frac{m^3}{2}\frac{4!}{m^5} = \frac{12}{m^2}.$$

With $m^2 = 0.71\ \text{GeV}^2$,

$$r_{\text{rms}} = \sqrt{12/0.84}\ \text{GeV}^{-1} = \sqrt{12/(0.84 \times 5.1)}\ \text{fm} = 0.81\ \text{fm}.$$

12.4 For small $|\boldsymbol{q}|$,

$$F(\boldsymbol{q}) = \int_0^\infty r^2\, dr \int_0^{2\pi} d\phi \int_{-1}^{+1} d(\cos\theta)\left(1 - \frac{q^2r^2}{2}\cos^2\theta\right)\rho(r)$$

since $\boldsymbol{q}\cdot\boldsymbol{r} = qr\cos\theta$ is an odd function of $\cos\theta$. Hence,

$$F(q) = \int_0^\infty 4\pi r^2\left(1 - \frac{q^2r^2}{6}\right)\rho(r)\, dr$$

$$= \int_0^\infty \left(1 - \frac{q^2r^2}{6}\right)\rho(r)\, d\tau$$

$$= 1 - \frac{q^2}{6}\langle r^2\rangle$$

since $\rho(r)$ is normalized to unity. Therefore, $\partial F(q)/\partial q^2 = -\frac{1}{6}\langle r^2\rangle$. With $F = m^4(m^2 + q^2)^{-2}$,

$$\left.\frac{\partial F(q)}{\partial q^2}\right|_{q^2=0} = \left.\frac{-2m^4}{(m^2 + q^2)^3}\right|_{q^2=0} = -\frac{2}{m^2}$$

and $\langle r^2\rangle = 12/m^2$ as in example 12.3.

12.5 We have $(xp + q)^2 = m^2 \approx 0$. Then, $x^2p^2 + 2xp\cdot q + q^2 = 0$, and $x = -q^2/2p\cdot q$ (since $p^2 = 0$) so $x = Q^2/2p\cdot q$. Since $p\cdot q$ is an invariant it can be evaluated in any frame, in particular the lab frame where $p = (M, 0, 0, 0)$ and $q = (\nu, \boldsymbol{q})$, ν being the energy transfer, $E - E'$. Then $p\cdot q = M\nu$ and the result follows.

The parton mass $m = (x^2E^2 - x^2P^2)^{1/2} = xM$ and hence $\nu = Q^2/2xM = Q^2/2m$.

12.6 In the lab system $p = (M, 0)$, $q = (\nu, q)$ and $k = (E_{\text{lab}}, \boldsymbol{k})$. Then $p\cdot q = M\nu$ and $p\cdot k = ME_{\text{lab}}$. Hence $y = (p\cdot q)/(p\cdot k) = \nu/E_{\text{lab}}$. With $q = p' - p$, $y = p\cdot(p' - p)/(p\cdot k) = (p\cdot p')/(p\cdot k)$. Neglecting particle masses, we have

$$p\cdot p' = \omega E' - \boldsymbol{p}\cdot\boldsymbol{p}' \approx \omega E'(1 - \cos\theta) \approx \frac{s}{4}(1 - \cos\theta).$$

$$s = (p + k)^2 = p^2 + 2p\cdot k + k^2 \approx 2p\cdot k.$$

Hence, $y = \frac{1}{2}(1 - \cos\theta)$ and $1 - y = \frac{1}{2}(1 + \cos\theta)$. We have $d\Omega = \sin\theta\, d\theta\, d\phi = -2\pi d(\cos\theta) = 4\pi\, dy$.

Chapter 13

13.1 We have

$$\frac{df}{dx} = \frac{\partial f}{\partial x} + y'\frac{\partial f}{\partial y} + y''\frac{\partial f}{\partial y'} = y'\frac{\partial f}{\partial y} + y''\frac{\partial f}{\partial y'}$$

since $\partial f/\partial x = 0$. On multiplying the Euler equation by y' and adding and subtracting $y''\,\partial f/\partial y'$ we obtain

$$y'\frac{\partial f}{\partial y} + y''\frac{\partial f}{\partial y'} - \left(y'\frac{d}{dx}\frac{\partial f}{\partial y'} + y''\frac{\partial f}{\partial y'}\right) = 0,$$

i.e.

$$\frac{df}{dx} - \frac{d}{dx}\left(y'\frac{\partial f}{\partial y'}\right) = 0$$

or

$$\frac{d}{dx}\left(f - y'\frac{\partial f}{\partial y'}\right) = 0.$$

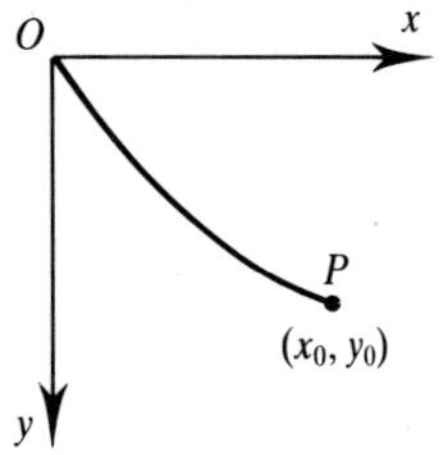

13.2 Choose a coordinate system in which y is measured vertically downward. The total time taken in sliding from O to P is $t = \int_O^P ds/v$ where the element of path is $ds = \sqrt{(dx^2 + dy^2)} = \sqrt{(1 + y'^2)}\,dx$ and $v = \sqrt{(2gy)}$. Hence

$$t = \frac{1}{\sqrt{(2g)}}\int_O^{x_0} \sqrt{\left(\frac{1 + y'^2}{y}\right)}\,dx.$$

This is a case where the function $f(y, y') = \sqrt{[(1 + y'^2)/y]}$ does not depend explicitly on x. Using the result of example 13.1 we have $f - y'(\partial f/\partial y') = \text{constant}$, and therefore

$$y(1 + y'^2) = c.$$

If we make the substitution $y' = \cot\phi$ then

$$y = c(1 + y'^2)^{-1} = c\sin^2\phi = \frac{c}{2}[1 - \cos(2\phi)]$$

and

$$\frac{dx}{d\phi} = \frac{1}{y'}\frac{dy}{d\phi} = c\tan\phi\sin(2\phi) = c[1 - \cos(2\phi)].$$

On integration $x = (c/2)[2\phi - \sin(2\phi)]$. Defining $c = 2a$ and $\theta = 2\phi$ we obtain the parametric equations of an inverted cycloid (the curve traced out by a point on the rim of a wheel rolling along the x axis).

$$x = a(\theta - \sin\theta)$$

$$y = a(1 - \cos\theta).$$

13.3 $\Lambda^{\mu}_{\mu'}\Lambda^{\mu'}_{\nu} = \dfrac{\partial x^{\mu}}{\partial x^{\mu'}}\dfrac{\partial x^{\mu'}}{\partial x^{\nu}} = \dfrac{\partial x^{\mu}}{\partial x^{\nu}} = \delta^{\mu}_{\nu}$,

i.e. $\Lambda^{\mu}_{\mu'} = (\Lambda^{\mu'}_{\mu})^{-1}$.

$$\partial_{\mu'}\phi = \frac{\partial\phi}{\partial x^{\mu'}} = \frac{\partial x^{\mu}}{\partial x^{\mu'}}\frac{\partial\phi}{\partial x^{\mu}} = \Lambda^{\mu}_{\mu'}\partial_{\mu}\phi,$$

i.e. $\partial_{\mu}\phi$ transforms as a covariant four-vector.

13.4 Since $F^{\mu\nu} = \partial^{\mu}A^{\nu} - \partial^{\nu}A^{\mu}$ the diagonal elements are zero and $F^{\mu\nu} = -F^{\nu\mu}$, i.e. $F^{\mu\nu}$ is antisymmetric. For $i = 1, 2, 3$

$$F^{0i} = \partial^{0}A^{i} - \partial^{i}A^{0} = \frac{\partial A^{i}}{\partial t} - \frac{\partial\phi}{\partial x_i} = -E^{i}.$$

$$F^{12} = \partial^{1}A^{2} - \partial^{2}A^{1} = -\frac{\partial A^{2}}{\partial x_1} + \frac{\partial A^{1}}{\partial x_2} = -B^{3}$$

$$F^{13} = \partial^{1}A^{3} - \partial^{3}A^{1} = -\frac{\partial A^{3}}{\partial x_1} + \frac{\partial A^{1}}{\partial x_3} = B^{2}$$

$$F^{23} = \partial^{2}A^{3} - \partial^{3}A^{2} = -\frac{\partial A^{3}}{\partial x_2} + \frac{\partial A^{2}}{\partial x_3} = -B^{1}.$$

Therefore

$$F^{\mu\nu} = \begin{pmatrix} 0 & -E^{1} & -E^{2} & -E^{3} \\ E^{1} & 0 & -B^{3} & B^{2} \\ E^{2} & B^{3} & 0 & -B^{1} \\ E^{3} & -B^{2} & B^{1} & 0 \end{pmatrix}.$$

13.5
$$\begin{aligned}\partial_{\alpha}F_{\beta\gamma} + \partial_{\beta}F_{\gamma\alpha} + \partial_{\gamma}F_{\alpha\beta} &= \partial_{\alpha}(\partial_{\beta}A_{\gamma} - \partial_{\gamma}A_{\beta}) + \partial_{\beta}(\partial_{\gamma}A_{\alpha} - \partial_{\alpha}A_{\gamma}) \\ &\quad + \partial_{\gamma}(\partial_{\alpha}A_{\beta} - \partial_{\beta}A_{\alpha}) \\ &= (\partial_{\alpha}\partial_{\beta}A_{\gamma} - \partial_{\beta}\partial_{\alpha}A_{\gamma}) + (\partial_{\beta}\partial_{\gamma}A_{\alpha} - \partial_{\gamma}\partial_{\beta}A_{\alpha}) \\ &\quad + (\partial_{\gamma}\partial_{\alpha}A_{\beta} - \partial_{\alpha}\partial_{\gamma}A_{\beta}).\end{aligned}$$

The second-order mixed partial derivatives are equal, i.e.

$$\partial_{\alpha}\partial_{\beta}A_{\gamma} - \partial_{\beta}\partial_{\alpha}A_{\gamma} \equiv \frac{\partial^{2}A_{\gamma}}{\partial x^{\alpha}\,\partial x^{\beta}} - \frac{\partial^{2}A_{\gamma}}{\partial x^{\beta}\,\partial x^{\alpha}} = 0.$$

Therefore

$$\partial_{\alpha}F_{\beta\gamma} + \partial_{\beta}F_{\gamma\alpha} + \partial_{\gamma}F_{\alpha\beta} = 0.$$

This identity represents a whole series of equations. For example, with

$\alpha = 0$, $\beta = 1$ and $\gamma = 2$ we have

$$\partial_0 F_{12} + \partial_1 F_{20} + \partial_2 F_{01} = 0 = -\frac{\partial B_3}{\partial t} - \frac{\partial E_2}{\partial x^1} + \frac{\partial E_1}{\partial x^2},$$

i.e.

$$(\nabla \wedge \boldsymbol{E})_3 = -\left(\frac{\partial \boldsymbol{B}}{\partial t}\right)_3.$$

Similarly with $\alpha = 0$, $\beta = 2$ and $\gamma = 3$ we obtain $(\nabla \wedge \boldsymbol{E})_1 = -(\partial \boldsymbol{B}/\partial t)_1$ and with $\alpha = 0$, $\beta = 1$ and $\gamma = 3$, $(\nabla \wedge \boldsymbol{E})_2 = -(\partial \boldsymbol{B}/\partial t)_2$. Thus, if one of the indices is zero and the other two are any two of 1, 2, 3 we obtain $\nabla \wedge \boldsymbol{E} + \partial \boldsymbol{B}/\partial t = 0$. Note that here we have used the expression for $F_{\mu\nu}$, see example 13.8. With $\alpha = 1$, $\beta = 2$ and $\gamma = 3$ we have

$$\partial_1 F_{23} + \partial_2 F_{31} + \partial_3 F_{12} = -\left(\frac{\partial B_1}{\partial x^1} + \frac{\partial B_2}{\partial x^2} + \frac{\partial B_3}{\partial x^3}\right) = 0.$$

i.e.

$$\nabla \cdot \boldsymbol{B} = 0.$$

13.6 For $\nu = 0$

$$\partial_0 F^{00} + \partial_1 F^{10} + \partial_2 F^{20} + \partial_3 F^{30} = j^0 = \rho,$$

i.e.

$$\frac{\partial E^1}{\partial x^1} + \frac{\partial E^2}{\partial x^2} + \frac{\partial E^3}{\partial x^3} = \nabla \cdot \boldsymbol{E} = \rho.$$

For $\nu = 1$

$$\partial_0 F^{01} + \partial_1 F^{11} + \partial_2 F^{21} + \partial_3 F^{31} = j^1,$$

i.e.

$$\frac{-\partial E^1}{\partial t} + \frac{\partial B^3}{\partial x^2} - \frac{\partial B^2}{\partial x^3} = j^1 \text{ or } (\nabla \wedge \boldsymbol{B})_1 = j^1 + \frac{\partial E^1}{\partial t}.$$

Similarly for $\nu = 2$ we obtain $(\nabla \wedge \boldsymbol{B})_2 = j^2 + \partial E^2/\partial t$, etc. Therefore

$$\nabla \wedge \boldsymbol{B} = \boldsymbol{j} + \frac{\partial E}{\partial t}.$$

13.7 $j^\nu = \partial_\mu F^{\mu\nu}$. Therefore $\partial_\nu j^\nu = \partial_\nu \partial_\mu F^{\mu\nu} = -\partial_\nu \partial_\mu F^{\nu\mu}$ because of the antisymmetry of $F^{\mu\nu}$. On interchanging the dummy indices we have $\partial_\nu j^\nu = -\partial_\mu \partial_\nu F^{\mu\nu}$. Therefore $\partial_\nu j^\nu = \frac{1}{2}(\partial_\nu \partial_\mu - \partial_\mu \partial_\nu) F^{\mu\nu} = 0$.

13.8 The covariant form of the field-strength tensor is readily derived from the definition $F_{\mu\nu} = \partial_\mu A_\nu - \partial_\nu A_\mu$. Recalling that $\partial_\mu \equiv (\partial/\partial t, \nabla)$ and

$A_\mu \equiv (\phi, -\boldsymbol{A})$ we find

$$F_{\mu\nu} = \begin{pmatrix} 0 & E_1 & E_2 & E_3 \\ -E_1 & 0 & -B_3 & B_2 \\ -E_2 & B_3 & 0 & -B_1 \\ -E_3 & -B_2 & B_1 & 0 \end{pmatrix}.$$

Using the values of $F^{\mu\nu}$ from example 13.4 we find on matrix multiplication that $-\frac{1}{4}F_{\mu\nu}F^{\mu\nu} = \frac{1}{2}(\boldsymbol{E}^2 - \boldsymbol{B}^2)$.

13.9 In section 13.3.3 we found that with $\mathscr{L} = -\frac{1}{4}F_{\mu\nu}F^{\mu\nu}$, $\partial\mathscr{L}/[\partial(\partial_\nu A_\mu)] = -F^{\nu\mu}$. Hence for $\nu = \mu = 0$ we have $\pi^0 = \partial\mathscr{L}/[\partial(\partial_0 A_0)] = -F^{00} = 0$, and for $\nu = 0$, $\mu = 1, 2, 3$, $\pi^\mu = -F^{0\mu} = E^\mu$. Therefore the Hamiltonian

$$H = \int \pi^\mu \partial_0 A_\mu \, d\tau - L = \int \left(-E^1 \frac{\partial A_1}{\partial t} - E^2 \frac{\partial A_2}{\partial t} - E^3 \frac{\partial A_3}{\partial t} \right) d\tau - L.$$

Since $-\partial\boldsymbol{A}/\partial t = \boldsymbol{E} + \nabla\phi$ we have $H = \int (\boldsymbol{E}^2 + \boldsymbol{E}\cdot\nabla\phi)\, d\tau - L$. Since $\nabla\cdot\boldsymbol{E} = 0$ the second term in the integral may be written

$$\int (\boldsymbol{E}\cdot\nabla\phi)\, d\tau = \int (\nabla\cdot\phi\boldsymbol{E})\, d\tau = \int \phi\boldsymbol{E}\cdot d\boldsymbol{\Sigma}$$

where Σ is the surface bounding the volume τ. Since both ϕ and E are identically zero at infinity the integral over all space is zero. Therefore $H = \int \frac{1}{2}(\boldsymbol{E}^2 + \boldsymbol{B}^2)\, d\tau$.

13.10 With $\mathscr{L} = -\frac{1}{4}F_{\mu\nu}F^{\mu\nu} + \frac{1}{2}m^2 A^\nu A_\nu$ we have

$$\frac{\partial\mathscr{L}}{\partial(\partial_\mu A_\nu)} = -F^{\mu\nu} \quad \text{and} \quad \frac{\partial\mathscr{L}}{\partial A_\nu} = m^2 A^\nu$$

and the Euler–Lagrange equation yields

$$\partial_\mu F^{\mu\nu} + m^2 A^\nu = 0.$$

13.11 $\mathscr{L} = \frac{i}{2}[\bar{\psi}\gamma^\mu(\partial_\mu\psi) - (\partial_\mu\bar{\psi})\gamma^\mu\psi] - m\bar{\psi}\psi.$

Then,

$$\frac{\partial\mathscr{L}}{\partial(\partial_\mu\bar{\psi})} = \frac{-i}{2}\gamma^\mu\psi \quad \text{and} \quad \frac{\partial\mathscr{L}}{\partial\bar{\psi}} = \frac{i}{2}\gamma^\mu(\partial_\mu\psi) - m\psi$$

and the Euler–Lagrange equation yields $i\gamma^\mu\partial_\mu\psi - m\psi = 0$, the Dirac equation. Further,

$$\frac{\partial\mathscr{L}}{\partial(\partial_\mu\psi)} = \frac{i}{2}\bar{\psi}\gamma^\mu \quad \text{and} \quad \frac{\partial\mathscr{L}}{\partial\psi} = \frac{-i}{2}(\partial_\mu\bar{\psi})\gamma^\mu - m\bar{\psi}$$

and the Euler–Lagrange equation yields $i\partial_\mu\bar{\psi}\gamma^\mu + m\bar{\psi} = 0$, the adjoint equation.

13.12 Using the procedure and notation of section 13.6.3 we find for the leptons ν_μ and μ^-

$$j_\mu^+ = \bar{\nu}_L\gamma_\mu\mu_L \qquad j_\mu^- = \bar{\mu}_L\gamma_\mu\nu_L$$

$$j_\mu^3 = \tfrac{1}{2}\bar{\nu}_L\gamma_\mu\nu_L - \tfrac{1}{2}\bar{\mu}_L\gamma_\mu\mu_L$$

$$j_\mu^Y = -2(\bar{\mu}_R\gamma_\mu\mu_R) - 1(\bar{\nu}_L\gamma_\mu\nu_L + \bar{\mu}_L\gamma_\mu\mu_L)$$

and for the quarks c, s′

$$j_\mu^+ = \bar{c}_L\gamma_\mu s'_L \qquad j_\mu^- = \bar{s}'_L\gamma_\mu c_L$$

$$j_\mu^3 = \tfrac{1}{2}\bar{c}_L\gamma_\mu c_L - \tfrac{1}{2}\bar{s}'_L\gamma_\mu s_L$$

$$j_\mu^Y = \tfrac{1}{3}(\bar{c}_L\gamma_\mu c_L + \bar{s}'_L\gamma_\mu s_L) + \tfrac{4}{3}(\bar{c}_R\gamma_\mu c_R) - \tfrac{2}{3}(\bar{s}'_R\gamma_\mu s_R).$$

13.13 In the standard model the fermion couplings to the Z^0 are $c_V^f = I_3^f - 2Q^f \sin^2\theta_W$ and $c_A^f = I_3^f$, and therefore

$$2[(c_V^f)^2 + (c_A^f)^2] = 4(I_3^f)^2 - 8I_3^fQ^f \sin^2\theta_W + 8(Q^f)^2 \sin^4\theta_W$$

$$= 1 - 4|Q^f| \sin^2\theta_W + 8(Q^f)^2 \sin^4\theta_W.$$

With $G = 1.17 \times 10^{-5}\ \text{GeV}^{-2}$, $M_Z = 91.2$ GeV and $\sin^2\theta_W = 0.23$ we have

$$\Gamma_{Z^0} = \frac{G}{\sqrt{2}}\frac{M_Z^3}{12\pi} \approx 0.17\ \text{GeV}.$$

Thus, for the lightest fermion family we have

$$\Gamma(Z \to \nu_e\bar{\nu}_e) = \Gamma_{Z^0} = 0.17\ \text{GeV}$$

$$\Gamma(Z \to e^-e^+) = \Gamma_{Z^0}(1 - 4\sin^2\theta_W + 8\sin^4\theta_W) = 0.08\ \text{GeV}$$

$$\Gamma(Z \to u\bar{u}) = 3\Gamma_{Z^0}(1 - \tfrac{8}{3}\sin^2\theta_W + \tfrac{32}{9}\sin^4\theta_W) = 0.28\ \text{GeV}$$

$$\Gamma(Z \to d\bar{d}) = 3\Gamma_{Z^0}(1 - \tfrac{4}{3}\sin^2\theta_W + \tfrac{8}{9}\sin^4\theta_W) = 0.37\ \text{GeV}.$$

Thus, for the first family the total width is

$$\Gamma_Z \approx 8\Gamma_{Z^0}(1 - 2\sin^2\theta_W + \tfrac{8}{3}\sin^4\theta_W) = 0.9\ \text{GeV}.$$

Consequently, for three-fermion families the total width of the Z^0 is

$$\Gamma_Z^{TOT} = 3\Gamma_Z = 2.7\ \text{GeV}.$$

Chapter 14

14.1 On integrating the differential cross-sections over y between 0 and 1 we obtain

$$\frac{\sigma^{\rm NC}(\nu)}{\sigma^{\rm CC}(\nu)} = g_{\rm L}^2 + \tfrac{1}{3}g_{\rm R}^2 \quad \text{and} \quad \frac{\sigma^{\rm NC}(\bar{\nu})}{\sigma^{\rm CC}(\bar{\nu})} = g_{\rm L}^2 + 3g_{\rm R}^2.$$

From table 13.3 we have, using $g_{\rm L} = \frac{1}{2}(c_{\rm V} + c_{\rm A})$, $g_{\rm R} = \frac{1}{2}(c_{\rm V} - c_{\rm A})$,

	$g_{\rm L}$	$g_{\rm R}$
u	$\frac{1}{2} - \frac{2}{3}\sin^2\theta_{\rm W}$	$-\frac{2}{3}\sin^2\theta_{\rm W}$
d	$-\frac{1}{2} + \frac{1}{3}\sin^2\theta_{\rm W}$	$\frac{1}{3}\sin^2\theta_{\rm W}$

Hence

$$\frac{\sigma^{\rm NC}(\nu)}{\sigma^{\rm CC}(\nu)} = (\tfrac{1}{2} - \tfrac{2}{3}\sin^2\theta_{\rm W})^2 + (-\tfrac{1}{2} + \tfrac{1}{3}\sin^2\theta_{\rm W})^2$$
$$+ \tfrac{1}{3}(\tfrac{4}{9}\sin^4\theta_{\rm W} + \tfrac{1}{9}\sin^4\theta_{\rm W})$$
$$= \tfrac{1}{2} - \sin^2\theta_{\rm W} + \tfrac{20}{27}\sin^4\theta_{\rm W}$$

$$\frac{\sigma^{\rm NC}(\bar{\nu})}{\sigma^{\rm CC}(\bar{\nu})} = (\tfrac{1}{2} - \tfrac{2}{3}\sin^2\theta_{\rm W})^2 + (-\tfrac{1}{2} + \tfrac{1}{3}\sin^2\theta_{\rm W}) + \tfrac{5}{3}\sin^4\theta_{\rm W}$$
$$= \tfrac{1}{2} - \sin^2\theta_{\rm W} + \tfrac{20}{9}\sin^4\theta_{\rm W}.$$

14.2 A nucleus ${}^{A}_{N}Z$ contains $2Z + N$ u quarks and $Z + 2N$ d quarks and has weak charge $\sum_q c_{\rm V}^q$. We have

$$c_{\rm V}^q = g_{\rm L}^q + g_{\rm R}^q = \tfrac{1}{2}(c_{\rm V}^{q_{\rm L}} + c_{\rm A}^{q_{\rm L}}) + \tfrac{1}{2}(c_{\rm V}^{q_{\rm R}} - c_{\rm A}^{q_{\rm R}}).$$

Hence, from table 13.3,

$$c_{\rm V}^{\rm u} = \tfrac{1}{2} - \tfrac{4}{3}\sin^2\theta_{\rm W} \quad \text{and} \quad c_{\rm V}^{\rm d} = -\tfrac{1}{2} + \tfrac{2}{3}\sin^2\theta_{\rm W}.$$

Therefore

$$\sum_q c_{\rm V}^q = (2Z + N)(\tfrac{1}{2} - \tfrac{4}{3}\sin^2\theta_{\rm W}) + (Z + 2N)(-\tfrac{1}{2} + \tfrac{2}{3}\sin^2\theta_{\rm W})$$
$$= \tfrac{1}{2}[-N + (1 - 4\sin^2\theta_{\rm W})Z].$$

Due to a 'conspiracy' in the quark vector coupling constants the term multiplying the proton contribution is very small ($\sin^2\theta_{\rm W} \approx \frac{1}{4}$) and therefore the technique is not very sensitive to the value of $\sin^2\theta_{\rm W}$.

14.3 Substituting the numerical values of G and $M_{\rm W}$ gives $\Gamma_{\rm W}^0 = 0.23$ GeV. Therefore, assuming universality, the leptonic width for N_ν light neutrino species is $0.23N_\nu$. Summing over quark generations we have a total hadronic width

$$\Gamma_{\rm had} = 3\Gamma_{\rm W}^0 \sum_{qq'} |V_{qq'}|^2 = 3\Gamma_{\rm W}^0 \sum_q 1 = 3N_\nu \Gamma_{\rm W}^0 = 0.69N_\nu.$$

The total width is therefore $\Gamma_{\rm W} = 0.92N_\nu = 2.8$ GeV and $N_\nu = 3$.

14.4 The eigenvalues λ are obtained by solving the determinantal equation

$$\begin{vmatrix} M - \mathrm{i}\Gamma/2 - \lambda & M_{12} - \mathrm{i}\Gamma_{12}/2 \\ M_{12}^* - \mathrm{i}\Gamma_{12}^*/2 & M - \mathrm{i}\Gamma/2 - \lambda \end{vmatrix} = 0,$$

i.e. $(M - \mathrm{i}\Gamma/2 - \lambda)^2 - F^2 = 0$ with $F = \sqrt{[(M_{12} - \mathrm{i}\Gamma_{12}/2)(M_{12}^* - \mathrm{i}\Gamma_{12}^*/2)]}$. Therefore $(M - \mathrm{i}\Gamma/2 - \lambda - F)(M - \mathrm{i}\Gamma/2 - \lambda + F) = 0$. Writing the eigenvalues as $\lambda_j = M_j - \mathrm{i}\Gamma_j/2$ $(j = 1, 2)$ and equating real and imaginary parts we obtain

$$M_1 = M + \mathrm{Re}\, F \qquad M_2 = M - \mathrm{Re}\, F$$

$$\Gamma_1 = \Gamma - 2\, \mathrm{Im}\, F \qquad \Gamma_2 = \Gamma + 2\, \mathrm{Im}\, F.$$

Writing the eigenvectors $|B_1\rangle$ and $|B_2\rangle$ in the B^0–$\bar{B}^0$ basis as $a_1^j|B^0\rangle + a_2^j|\bar{B}^0\rangle$ and solving the equations

$$\begin{pmatrix} M - \mathrm{i}\Gamma/2 & M_{12} - \mathrm{i}\Gamma_{12}/2 \\ M_{12}^* - \mathrm{i}\Gamma_{12}^*/2 & M - \mathrm{i}\Gamma/2 \end{pmatrix} \begin{pmatrix} a_1^j \\ a_2^j \end{pmatrix} = \left(M_j - \frac{\mathrm{i}\Gamma_j}{2} \right) \begin{pmatrix} a_1^j \\ a_2^j \end{pmatrix}$$

for $j = 1, 2$, we obtain

$$\frac{a_2}{a_1} = \sqrt{\left(\frac{M_{12}^* - \mathrm{i}\Gamma_{12}^*/2}{M_{12} - \mathrm{i}\Gamma_{12}/2} \right)} = \eta = \frac{1 - \epsilon}{1 + \epsilon} \text{ for } j = 1.$$

On setting $a_2 = 1 - \varepsilon$ and $a_1 = 1 + \varepsilon$ and normalizing we obtain

$$|B_1\rangle = \frac{(1 + \epsilon_1)|B_0\rangle + (1 - \varepsilon)|\bar{B}^0\rangle}{\sqrt{[2(1 + |\epsilon|^2)]}}.$$

Similarly, for $j = 2$ we obtain $a_2/a_1 = -\eta = -(1 - \epsilon)/(1 + \epsilon)$ and

$$|B_2\rangle = \frac{(1 + \epsilon)|B^0\rangle - (1 - \epsilon)|\bar{B}^0\rangle}{\sqrt{[2(1 + |\epsilon|^2)]}}.$$

14.5 $$|\psi(t)\rangle = \frac{\sqrt{(1 + |\epsilon|^2)}}{\sqrt{2}(1 + \epsilon)} \left\{ |B_1(0)\rangle \exp\left[-\mathrm{i}\left(M_1 - \frac{\mathrm{i}\Gamma_1}{2} \right) t \right] \right.$$

$$\left. + |B_2(0)\rangle \exp\left[-\mathrm{i}\left(M_2 - \frac{\mathrm{i}\Gamma_2}{2} \right) t \right] \right\}.$$

Using the results of example 14.4 we transform to the B^0–$\bar{B}^0$ basis and obtain

$$|\psi(t)\rangle = \tfrac{1}{2}[\exp(-\mathrm{i}M_1 t)\exp(-\tfrac{1}{2}\Gamma_1 t) + \exp(-\mathrm{i}M_2 t)\exp(-\tfrac{1}{2}\Gamma_2 t)]|B^0\rangle$$
$$+\frac{1-\epsilon}{1+\epsilon}\tfrac{1}{2}[\exp(-\mathrm{i}M_1 t)\exp(-\tfrac{1}{2}\Gamma_1 t) - \exp(-\mathrm{i}M_2 t)\exp(-\tfrac{1}{2}\Gamma_2 t)]|\bar{B}^0\rangle.$$

Hence,

$$A(B^0 \to B^0) = \langle B^0 | \psi(t)\rangle$$
$$= \tfrac{1}{2}[\exp(-\mathrm{i}M_1 t)\exp(-\tfrac{1}{2}\Gamma_1 t) + \exp(-\mathrm{i}M_2 t)\exp(-\tfrac{1}{2}\Gamma_2 t)]$$
$$A(B^0 \to \bar{B}^0) = \langle \bar{B}^0 | \psi(t)\rangle$$
$$= \frac{1-\epsilon}{1+\epsilon}\tfrac{1}{2}[\exp(-\mathrm{i}M_1 t)\exp(-\tfrac{1}{2}\Gamma_1 t) - \exp(-\mathrm{i}M_2 t)\exp(-\tfrac{1}{2}\Gamma_2 t)].$$

Putting $\epsilon = 0$ we have

$$r = \frac{\int_0^\infty |A(B^0 \to \bar{B}^0)|^2\,\mathrm{d}t}{\int_0^\infty |A(B^0 \to B^0)|^2\,\mathrm{d}t}$$
$$= \frac{\int_0^\infty [\exp(-\Gamma_1 t) + \exp(-\Gamma_2 t) - 2\exp(-\Gamma t)\cos(\Delta m t)]\,\mathrm{d}t}{\int_0^\infty [\exp(-\Gamma_1 t) + \exp(-\Gamma_2 t) + 2\exp(-\Gamma t)\cos(\Delta m t)]\,\mathrm{d}t}.$$

On integrating we obtain

$$r = \frac{1/(\Gamma_1\Gamma_2) - 1/[\Gamma^2 + (\Delta m)^2]}{1/(\Gamma_1\Gamma_2) + 1/[\Gamma^2 + (\Delta m)^2]}.$$

Using the identities $\Gamma_1 + \Gamma_2 = 2\Gamma$ and $\Gamma_1 - \Gamma_2 = \Delta\Gamma$ we obtain $\Gamma_1\Gamma_2 = \Gamma^2 - \frac{1}{4}(\Delta\Gamma)^2$ and hence

$$r = \frac{(\Delta m)^2 + \frac{1}{4}(\Delta\Gamma)^2}{(\Delta m)^2 + 2\Gamma^2 - \frac{1}{4}(\Delta\Gamma)^2}.$$

14.6

$$E = \sqrt{(p_\mathrm{T}^2 + m^2)}\cosh y = \sqrt{(p_\mathrm{T}^2 + m^2)}\,\frac{\exp y + \exp(-y)}{2}$$
$$p_z = \sqrt{(p_\mathrm{T}^2 + m^2)}\sinh y = \sqrt{(p_\mathrm{T}^2 + m^2)}\,\frac{\exp y - \exp(-y)}{2}.$$

Adding and subtracting we have

$$E + p_z = \sqrt{(p_\mathrm{T}^2 + m^2)}\exp y$$
$$E - p_z = \sqrt{(p_\mathrm{T}^2 + m^2)}\exp(-y).$$

Therefore $(E + p_z)/(E - p_z) = \exp(2y)$ and $y = \frac{1}{2}\ln[(E + p_z)/(E - p_z)]$. Under a Lorentz transformation to a reference frame moving with velocity β along the z axis we have

$$\begin{pmatrix} E' \\ p'_x \\ p'_y \\ p'_z \end{pmatrix} = \begin{pmatrix} \gamma & 0 & 0 & -\beta\gamma \\ 0 & 1 & 0 & 0 \\ 0 & 0 & 1 & 0 \\ -\beta\gamma & 0 & 0 & \gamma \end{pmatrix} \begin{pmatrix} E \\ p_x \\ p_y \\ p_z \end{pmatrix},$$

i.e. $E' = \gamma E - \beta\gamma p_z$ and $p'_z = -\beta\gamma E + \gamma p_z$ and

$$y' = \tfrac{1}{2}\ln\left[\frac{(E + p_z)(\gamma - \beta\gamma)}{(E - p_z)(\gamma + \beta\gamma)}\right]$$

$$= \tfrac{1}{2}\ln\left(\frac{E + p_z}{E - p_z}\right) + \tfrac{1}{2}\ln\left(\frac{1 - \beta}{1 + \beta}\right)$$

$$= y + \tfrac{1}{2}\ln\left(\frac{1 - \beta}{1 + \beta}\right).$$

Chapter 15

15.1 Setting $\sin^2\theta_W = x$, $n_g = n$ and substituting the values of n_b and δ_H we obtain

$$\alpha_1^{-1}(M_W) = \alpha_G^{-1}(M_X) - \frac{40n + 3}{60\pi}\ln\left(\frac{M_W}{M_X}\right) = \frac{3}{5}\frac{1 - x}{\alpha(M_W)} \tag{1}$$

$$\alpha_2^{-1}(M_W) = \alpha_G^{-1}(M_X) + \frac{44 - 8n - 1}{12\pi}\ln\left(\frac{M_W}{M_X}\right) = \frac{x}{\alpha(M_W)}. \tag{2}$$

$$\alpha_G^{-1}(M_X) + \frac{33 - 4n}{6\pi}\ln\left(\frac{M_W}{M_X}\right) = \alpha_3^{-1}(M_W). \tag{3}$$

We eliminate x by multiplying equation (2) by $\frac{3}{5}$ and adding to equation (1):

$$8\alpha_G^{-1}(M_X) + \frac{63 - 32n}{6\pi}\ln\left(\frac{M_W}{M_X}\right) = \frac{3}{\alpha(M_W)}. \tag{4}$$

On subtracting equation (4) from 8 × equation (3) we obtain

$$\ln\left(\frac{M_W}{M_X}\right) = \frac{2\pi}{67}[8\alpha_3^{-1}(M_W) - 3\alpha^{-1}(M_W)]. \tag{5}$$

Hence,

$$\ln\left(\frac{M_X}{M_W}\right) = \frac{2\pi}{67}[3\alpha^{-1}(M_W) - 8\alpha_3^{-1}(M_W)]$$

and

$$M_X = M_W \exp\left\{\frac{2\pi}{67}[3\alpha^{-1}(M_W) - 8\alpha_3^{-1}(M_W)]\right\} \approx 0.9 \times 10^{15}\ \text{GeV}.$$

From equations (2) and (3), using $\ln(M_W/M_X)$ from equation (5), we obtain

$$\sin^2\theta_W = x = \frac{23}{134} + \frac{109}{201}\alpha_3^{-1}(M_W)\alpha(M_W) = 0.205.$$

Note that these results are independent of the value of n.

For $n = 3$ we have from equation (3)

$$\alpha_G^{-1}(M_X) = \alpha_3^{-1}(M_W) + \frac{21}{6\pi}\ln\left(\frac{M_X}{M_W}\right) = 41.4$$

$$\alpha_G(M_X) = 0.024.$$

15.2 The partial width for the decay must have dimensions of mass. Then, assuming dominance of the propagator $(q^2 + m_W^2)^{-1}$ in the matrix element and regulating the dimensions with the proton mass we have, since $m_W^2 \gg q^2 \approx 1\ \text{GeV}^2$,

$$\Gamma \approx \frac{\alpha_G^2(m_p)^N}{(q^2 + m_W^2)^2} \approx \frac{\alpha_G^2(m_p)^N}{m_W^4}.$$

Therefore $N = 5$.

$$\tau_p \approx \frac{1}{\Gamma} = \frac{m_W^4}{\alpha_G^2 m_p^5} = \frac{16 \times 10^{56}}{5.8 \times 10^{-4} \times 0.726} = 3.8 \times 10^{60}\ \text{GeV}^{-1}.$$

Using the conversion factor in appendix F we obtain

$$\tau_p \approx \frac{3.8 \times 10^{60}}{1.519 \times 10^{24}}\ \text{s} \approx 0.8 \times 10^{29}\ \text{a}.$$

Index